STUDENT SOLUTIONS MANUAL

Lea Rosenberry

INTRODUCTORY and INTERMEDIATE ALGEBRA

for College Students

Robert Blitzer

Prentice
Hall

Upper Saddle River, NJ 07458

Executive Editor: Karin E. Wagner
Editorial Assistant: Heather Balderson
Assistant Managing Editor: John Matthews
Production Editor: Wendy A. Perez
Supplement Cover Manager: Paul Gourhan
Supplement Cover Designer: Joanne Alexandris
Manufacturing Buyer: Ilene Kahn

© 2002 by Pearson Education, Inc.
Pearson Education, Inc.
Upper Saddle River, NJ 07458

The author and publisher of this book have used their best efforts in preparing this book. These efforts include the development, research, and testing of the theories and programs to determine their effectiveness. The author and publisher make no warranty of any kind, expressed or implied, with regard to these programs or the documentation contained in this book. The author and publisher shall not be liable in any event for incidental or consequential damages in connection with, or arising out of, the furnishing, performance, or use of these programs.

Printed in the United States of America

10 9 8 7 6 5 4

ISBN 0-13-034327-7

Pearson Education Ltd., *London*
Pearson Education Australia Pty. Ltd., *Sydney*
Pearson Education Singapore, Pte. Ltd.
Pearson Education North Asia Ltd., *Hong Kong*
Pearson Education Canada, Inc., *Toronto*
Pearson Educacíon de Mexico, S.A. de C.V.
Pearson Education—Japan, *Tokyo*
Pearson Education Malaysia, Pte. Ltd.
Pearson Education, *Upper Saddle River, New Jersey*

Table of Contents

THE REAL NUMBER SYSTEM

Fractions

1.1 CHECK POINTS

CHECK POINT 1

a. $\dfrac{10}{15} = \dfrac{\cancel{5} \cdot 2}{\cancel{5} \cdot 3} = \dfrac{2}{3}$

b. $\dfrac{42}{24} = \dfrac{\cancel{6} \cdot 7}{\cancel{6} \cdot 4} = \dfrac{7}{4}$

c. Because 13 and 15 share no common factor (other than 1), $\frac{13}{15}$ is already reduced to lowest terms.

d. $\dfrac{9}{45} = \dfrac{\cancel{9} \cdot 1}{\cancel{9} \cdot 5} = \dfrac{1}{5}$

CHECK POINT 2

a. $\dfrac{4}{11} \cdot \dfrac{2}{3} = \dfrac{4 \cdot 2}{11 \cdot 3} = \dfrac{8}{33}$

b. $6 \cdot \dfrac{3}{5} = \dfrac{6}{1} \cdot \dfrac{3}{5} = \dfrac{18}{5}$

c. $\dfrac{3}{7} \cdot \dfrac{2}{3} = \dfrac{\cancel{3} \cdot 2}{7 \cdot \cancel{3}} = \dfrac{2}{7}$

CHECK POINT 3

a. $\dfrac{5}{4} \div \dfrac{3}{8} = \dfrac{5}{4} \cdot \dfrac{8}{3} = \dfrac{5 \cdot 8}{4 \cdot 3} = \dfrac{40}{12}$

$= \dfrac{\cancel{4} \cdot 10}{\cancel{4} \cdot 3} = \dfrac{10}{3}$

b. $\dfrac{2}{3} \div 3 = \dfrac{2}{3} \cdot \dfrac{1}{3} = \dfrac{2}{9}$

CHECK POINT 4

a. $\dfrac{2}{11} + \dfrac{3}{11} = \dfrac{2+3}{11} = \dfrac{5}{11}$

b. $\dfrac{5}{6} - \dfrac{1}{6} = \dfrac{5-1}{6} = \dfrac{4}{6} = \dfrac{\cancel{2} \cdot 2}{\cancel{2} \cdot 3} = \dfrac{2}{3}$

CHECK POINT 5

$\dfrac{2}{3} = \dfrac{2}{3} \cdot \dfrac{7}{7} = \dfrac{14}{21}$

CHECK POINT 6

a. $\dfrac{1}{2} + \dfrac{3}{5}$

The least common denominator for the denominators 2 and 5 is 10.

$$\dfrac{1}{2} + \dfrac{3}{5} = \dfrac{1}{2} \cdot \dfrac{5}{5} + \dfrac{3}{5} \cdot \dfrac{2}{2}$$
$$= \dfrac{5}{10} + \dfrac{6}{10} = \dfrac{11}{10}$$

b. $\dfrac{4}{3} - \dfrac{3}{4}$

The least common denominator is 12.

$$\dfrac{4}{3} - \dfrac{3}{4} = \dfrac{4}{3} \cdot \dfrac{4}{4} - \dfrac{3}{4} \cdot \dfrac{3}{3}$$
$$= \dfrac{16}{12} - \dfrac{9}{12} = \dfrac{7}{12}$$

c. $\dfrac{13}{18} - \dfrac{2}{9}$

The least common denominator is 18. The first fraction already has this denominator, so only the second one needs to be rewritten.

$$\dfrac{13}{18} - \dfrac{2}{9} = \dfrac{13}{18} - \dfrac{2}{9} \cdot \dfrac{2}{2}$$
$$= \dfrac{13}{18} - \dfrac{4}{18}$$
$$= \dfrac{9}{18} = \dfrac{\cancel{9} \cdot 1}{\cancel{9} \cdot 2} = \dfrac{1}{2}$$

CHECK POINT 7

First, add the fractions for all of the activities other than going to class. The least common denominator for all of these fractions is 24.

$$\frac{1}{3} + \frac{7}{24} + \frac{1}{24} + \frac{1}{8}$$
$$= \frac{1}{3} \cdot \frac{8}{8} + \frac{7}{24} + \frac{1}{12} \cdot \frac{2}{2} + \frac{1}{8} \cdot \frac{3}{3}$$
$$= \frac{8}{24} + \frac{7}{24} + \frac{2}{24} + \frac{3}{24}$$
$$= \frac{20}{24} = \frac{\cancel{4} \cdot 5}{\cancel{4} \cdot 6} = \frac{5}{6}$$

The fractions representing all activities must add up to 1, so the fraction of the student's time spent in class can be found by subtracting $\frac{5}{6}$ from 1.

$$1 - \frac{5}{6} = \frac{6}{6} - \frac{5}{6} = \frac{1}{6}$$

Thus, the student spends $\frac{1}{6}$ of her time on weekdays attending class.

EXERCISE SET 1.1

1. $\dfrac{10}{16} = \dfrac{\cancel{2} \cdot 5}{\cancel{2} \cdot 8} = \dfrac{5}{8}$

3. $\dfrac{15}{18} = \dfrac{\cancel{3} \cdot 5}{\cancel{3} \cdot 6} = \dfrac{5}{6}$

5. $\dfrac{35}{50} = \dfrac{\cancel{5} \cdot 7}{\cancel{5} \cdot 10} = \dfrac{7}{10}$

7. $\dfrac{32}{80} = \dfrac{\cancel{16} \cdot 2}{\cancel{16} \cdot 5} = \dfrac{2}{5}$

9. $\dfrac{44}{50} = \dfrac{\cancel{2} \cdot 22}{\cancel{2} \cdot 25} = \dfrac{22}{25}$

11. $\dfrac{120}{86} = \dfrac{\cancel{2} \cdot 60}{\cancel{2} \cdot 43} = \dfrac{60}{43}$

13. $\dfrac{2}{5} \cdot \dfrac{1}{3} = \dfrac{2 \cdot 1}{5 \cdot 3} = \dfrac{2}{15}$

15. $\dfrac{3}{8} \cdot \dfrac{7}{11} = \dfrac{3 \cdot 7}{8 \cdot 11} = \dfrac{21}{88}$

17. $9 \cdot \dfrac{4}{7} = \dfrac{9}{1} \cdot \dfrac{4}{7} = \dfrac{9 \cdot 4}{1 \cdot 7} = \dfrac{36}{7}$

19. $\dfrac{1}{10} \cdot \dfrac{5}{6} = \dfrac{1 \cdot 5}{10 \cdot 6} = \dfrac{5}{60} = \dfrac{5 \cdot 1}{5 \cdot 12} = \dfrac{1}{12}$

21. $\dfrac{5}{4} \cdot \dfrac{6}{7} = \dfrac{5 \cdot 6}{4 \cdot 7} = \dfrac{30}{28} = \dfrac{2 \cdot 15}{2 \cdot 14} = \dfrac{15}{14}$

23. $\dfrac{5}{4} \div \dfrac{4}{3} = \dfrac{5}{4} \cdot \dfrac{3}{4} = \dfrac{5 \cdot 3}{4 \cdot 4} = \dfrac{15}{16}$

25. $\dfrac{18}{5} \div 2 = \dfrac{18}{5} \cdot \dfrac{1}{2} = \dfrac{18 \cdot 1}{5 \cdot 2} = \dfrac{18}{10}$
$$= \dfrac{\cancel{2} \cdot 9}{\cancel{2} \cdot 5} = \dfrac{9}{5}$$

27. $2 \div \dfrac{18}{5} = \dfrac{2}{1} \cdot \dfrac{5}{18} = \dfrac{2 \cdot 5}{1 \cdot 18} = \dfrac{10}{18}$
$$= \dfrac{\cancel{2} \cdot 5}{\cancel{2} \cdot 9} = \dfrac{5}{9}$$

29. $\dfrac{3}{4} \div \dfrac{1}{4} = \dfrac{3}{4} \cdot \dfrac{4}{1} = \dfrac{3 \cdot 4}{4 \cdot 1} = \dfrac{12}{4} = 3$

31. $\dfrac{7}{6} \div \dfrac{5}{3} = \dfrac{7}{6} \cdot \dfrac{3}{5} = \dfrac{7 \cdot 3}{6 \cdot 5} = \dfrac{21}{30}$
$$= \dfrac{\cancel{3} \cdot 7}{\cancel{3} \cdot 10} = \dfrac{7}{10}$$

33. $\dfrac{1}{14} \div \dfrac{1}{7} = \dfrac{1}{14} \cdot \dfrac{7}{1} = \dfrac{1 \cdot 7}{14 \cdot 1} = \dfrac{7}{14}$
$$= \dfrac{\cancel{7} \cdot 1}{\cancel{7} \cdot 2} = \dfrac{1}{2}$$

35. $\dfrac{2}{11} + \dfrac{4}{11} = \dfrac{2+4}{11} = \dfrac{6}{11}$

37. $\dfrac{7}{12} + \dfrac{1}{12} = \dfrac{8}{12} = \dfrac{\cancel{4} \cdot 2}{\cancel{4} \cdot 3} = \dfrac{2}{3}$

39. $\dfrac{5}{8} + \dfrac{5}{8} = \dfrac{10}{8} = \dfrac{\cancel{2} \cdot 5}{\cancel{2} \cdot 4} = \dfrac{5}{4}$

41. $\dfrac{7}{12} - \dfrac{5}{12} = \dfrac{2}{12} = \dfrac{1}{6}$

43. $\dfrac{16}{7} - \dfrac{2}{7} = \dfrac{14}{7} = 2$

45. $\dfrac{1}{2} + \dfrac{1}{5} = \dfrac{1}{2} \cdot \dfrac{5}{5} + \dfrac{1}{5} \cdot \dfrac{2}{2}$

$\qquad = \dfrac{5}{10} + \dfrac{2}{10}$

$\qquad = \dfrac{5+2}{10} = \dfrac{7}{10}$

47. $\dfrac{3}{4} + \dfrac{3}{20} = \dfrac{3}{4} \cdot \dfrac{5}{5} + \dfrac{3}{20}$

$\qquad = \dfrac{15}{20} + \dfrac{3}{20}$

$\qquad = \dfrac{18}{20} = \dfrac{9}{10}$

49. $\dfrac{3}{8} + \dfrac{5}{12} = \dfrac{3}{8} \cdot \dfrac{3}{3} + \dfrac{5}{12} \cdot \dfrac{2}{2}$

$\qquad = \dfrac{9}{24} + \dfrac{10}{24} = \dfrac{19}{24}$

51. $\dfrac{11}{18} - \dfrac{2}{9} = \dfrac{11}{18} - \dfrac{2}{9} \cdot \dfrac{2}{2} = \dfrac{11}{18} - \dfrac{4}{18} = \dfrac{7}{18}$

53. $\dfrac{4}{3} - \dfrac{3}{4} = \dfrac{4}{3} \cdot \dfrac{4}{4} - \dfrac{3}{4} \cdot \dfrac{3}{3}$

$\qquad = \dfrac{16}{12} - \dfrac{9}{12} = \dfrac{7}{12}$

55. $\dfrac{7}{10} - \dfrac{3}{16} = \dfrac{7}{10} \cdot \dfrac{8}{8} - \dfrac{3}{16} \cdot \dfrac{5}{5}$

$\qquad = \dfrac{56}{80} - \dfrac{15}{80} = \dfrac{41}{80}$

57. $\dfrac{13}{4} + \dfrac{13}{9} = \dfrac{13}{4} \cdot \dfrac{9}{9} + \dfrac{13}{9} \cdot \dfrac{4}{4}$

$\qquad = \dfrac{117}{36} + \dfrac{52}{36} = \dfrac{169}{36}$

$\dfrac{13}{4} \times \dfrac{13}{9} = \dfrac{13}{4} \cdot \dfrac{13}{9} = \dfrac{169}{36}$

59. $\dfrac{512}{800} = \dfrac{\cancel{32} \cdot 16}{\cancel{32} \cdot 25} = \dfrac{16}{25}$

$\dfrac{16}{25}$ of the white adults thought that racism is a big problem.

61. $300 - 186 = 114$

114 black teenagers replied that racism is *not* a big problem.

$$\dfrac{114}{300} = \dfrac{\cancel{6} \cdot 19}{\cancel{6} \cdot 50} = \dfrac{19}{50}$$

$\dfrac{19}{50}$ of the black teenagers thought that racism is *not* a problem.

63. The word *of* indicates multiplication.

$$\dfrac{19}{20} \cdot 300 = \dfrac{19}{20} \cdot \dfrac{300}{1} = \dfrac{5700}{20} = 285$$

Of the 300 black teenagers surveyed, 285 planned to go to college.

65. $\dfrac{1}{2} \cdot \dfrac{3}{4} = \dfrac{3}{8}$

To make half a recipe, $\dfrac{3}{8}$ cup of sugar is needed.

67. $1 - \dfrac{5}{12} - \dfrac{1}{4} = \dfrac{1}{1} \cdot \dfrac{12}{12} - \dfrac{5}{12} - \dfrac{1}{4} \cdot \dfrac{3}{3}$

$\qquad = \dfrac{12}{12} - \dfrac{5}{12} - \dfrac{3}{12}$

$\qquad = \dfrac{12 - 5 - 3}{12} = \dfrac{4}{12} = \dfrac{1}{3}$

$\dfrac{1}{3}$ of the business is owned by the third person.

69. 40 hours at \$12 an hour:

$$40 \cdot \$12 = \$480$$

"Time and a half":

$$\dfrac{3}{2} \cdot 12 = \dfrac{3}{2} \cdot \dfrac{12}{1} = \dfrac{36}{2} = 18$$

6 hours at \$18 an hour:

$$6 \cdot \$18 = \$108$$
$$\$480 + \$108 = \$588$$

The student's total pay before taxes was \$588.

For Exercises 71–75, answers may vary.

77. Statements a, b, and c are false. The methods illustrated are incorrect. The only true statement is d.

79. There are 4 measures:

The first measure contains two quarter-notes and two eighth-notes. Draw a vertical line after the fourth note, which corresponds to the end of the word *that*.
The second measure contains three quarter-notes. Draw a vertical line after the seventh note in the excerpt, which corresponds to the syllable *gled*.
The third measure contains one quarter-note and four eighth-notes. Draw a line after the twelfth note in the excerpt, which corresponds to the end of the word *yet*.
The fourth measure contains two quarter-notes and two eighth-notes. Draw a vertical line at the end of the excerpt.

81. $\dfrac{5}{24} + \dfrac{7}{30} = \dfrac{53}{120}$

83. $\dfrac{7}{24} - \dfrac{1}{15} = \dfrac{9}{40}$

The Real Numbers

1.2 CHECK POINTS

CHECK POINT 1

a. A debt of $500 can be expressed by the negative integer -500.

b. The elevation of Death Valley, 282 feet below sea level, can be expressed by the negative integer -282.

CHECK POINT 2

CHECK POINT 3

CHECK POINT 4

a.
$$\begin{array}{r} 0.375 \\ 8\overline{)3.000} \\ \underline{24} \\ 60 \\ \underline{56} \\ 40 \\ \underline{40} \\ 0 \end{array}$$

$\dfrac{3}{8} = 0.375$

b.
$$\begin{array}{r} 0.4545\ldots \\ 11\overline{)5.0000\ldots} \\ \underline{44} \\ 60 \\ \underline{55} \\ 50 \\ \underline{44} \\ 60 \\ \underline{55} \\ 50 \\ \vdots \end{array}$$

$\dfrac{5}{11} = 0.\overline{45}$

CHECK POINT 5

$$\left\{-9, -1.3, 0, 0.\overline{3}, \frac{\pi}{2}, \sqrt{9}, \sqrt{10}\right\}$$

a. Natural numbers: The only natural number in the set is $\sqrt{9} = 3$.

b. Whole numbers: $0, \sqrt{9}$

c. Integers: $-9, 0, \sqrt{9}$

d. Rational numbers: $-9, -1.3, 0, 0.\overline{3}, \sqrt{9}$

e. Irrational number: $\frac{\pi}{2}, \sqrt{10}$

f. Real numbers: $\left\{-9, -1.3, 0, 0.\overline{3}, \frac{\pi}{2}, \sqrt{9}, \sqrt{10}\right\}$

(all numbers in the given set)

CHECK POINT 6

a. $14 > 5$ because 14 is to the right of 5 on the number line.

b. $-5.4 < 2.3$ because -5.4 is to the left of 2.3 on the number line.

c. $-19 < -6$ because -19 is to the left of -6 on the number line.

d. To compare $\frac{1}{4}$ and $\frac{1}{2}$, use a common denominator: $\frac{1}{2} = \frac{2}{4}$. Since $\frac{1}{4}$ is to the left of $\frac{2}{4}$ on the number line, $\frac{1}{4} < \frac{1}{2}$.

CHECK POINT 7

a. $-2 \le 3$ is true because $-2 < 3$ is true.

b. $-2 \ge -2$ is true because $-2 = -2$ is true.

c. $-4 \ge 1$ is false because neither $-4 > 1$ nor $-4 = 1$ is true.

CHECK POINT 8

a. $|-4| = 4$ because -4 is 4 units from 0.

b. $|6| = 6$ because 6 is 6 units from 0.

c. $|-\sqrt{2}| = \sqrt{2}$ because $-\sqrt{2}$ is $\sqrt{2}$ units from 0.

EXERCISE SET 1.2

1. -20 **3.** 8

5. -3000 **7.** -4 billion

9.

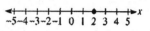

11.

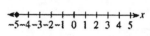

13.

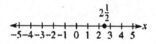

15.

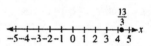

17.

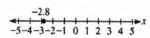

19.

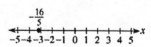

21.

$$\begin{array}{r} 0.75 \\ 4\overline{)3.00} \\ \underline{2\,8} \\ 20 \\ \underline{20} \\ 0 \end{array}$$

$$\frac{3}{4} = 0.75$$

23.
$$\begin{array}{r} 0.35 \\ 20\overline{)7.00} \\ \underline{6\,0} \\ 100 \\ \underline{100} \\ 0 \end{array}$$

$$\frac{7}{20} = 0.35$$

25.
$$\begin{array}{r} 0.875 \\ 8\overline{)7.000} \\ \underline{64} \\ 60 \\ \underline{56} \\ 40 \\ \underline{40} \\ 0 \end{array}$$

$$\frac{7}{8} = 0.875$$

27.
$$\begin{array}{r} 0.818\ldots \\ 11\overline{)9.000\ldots} \\ \underline{8\,8} \\ 20 \\ \underline{11} \\ 90 \\ \underline{88} \\ 20 \\ \vdots \end{array}$$

$$\frac{9}{11} = 0.\overline{81}$$

29.
$$\begin{array}{r} 0.5 \\ 2\overline{)1.0} \\ \underline{10} \\ 0 \end{array}$$

$$-\frac{1}{2} = -0.5$$

31.
$$\begin{array}{r} 0.833\ldots \\ 6\overline{)5.000\ldots} \\ \underline{48} \\ 20 \\ \underline{18} \\ 20 \\ \underline{18} \\ 20 \\ \vdots \end{array}$$

$$\frac{5}{6} = 0.8\overline{3}$$

33. **a.** $\sqrt{100}\ (= 10)$
b. $0, \sqrt{100}$
c. $-9, 0, \sqrt{100}$
d. $-9, -\dfrac{4}{5}, 0, 0.25, 9.2, \sqrt{100}$

e. $\sqrt{3}$
f. All numbers in the given set

35. **a.** $\sqrt{64}\ (= 8)$
b. $0, \sqrt{64}$
c. $-11, 0, \sqrt{64}$
d. $-11, -\dfrac{5}{6}, 0, 0.75, \sqrt{64}$

e. $\sqrt{5}, \pi$
f. All numbers in the given set

37. The only whole number that is not a natural number is 0.

In Exercises 39–43, examples may vary.

39. One rational number that is not an integer is $\frac{1}{2}$.

41. One number that is an integer, a whole number, and a natural number is 5.

43. One number that is an irrational number and a real number is $\sqrt{2}$.

45. $\frac{1}{2} < 2$; $\frac{1}{2}$ is to the left of 2 on the number line, so $\frac{1}{2}$ is less than 2.

47. $3 > -\frac{5}{2}$; 3 is to the right of $-\frac{5}{2} = -2\frac{1}{2}$, so 3 is greater than $-\frac{5}{2}$.

49. $-4 > -6$; -4 is to the right of -6, so -4 is greater than -6.

51. $-2.5 < 1.5$; -2.5 is to the left of 1.5, so $-2.5 < 1.5$.

53. $-\frac{3}{4} > -\frac{5}{4}$; $-\frac{3}{4}$ is to the right of $-\frac{5}{4}$, so $-\frac{3}{4} > -\frac{5}{4}$.

55. $-4.5 < 3$; -4.5 is to the left of 3, so $-4.5 < 3$.

57. $\sqrt{2} < 1.5$; $\sqrt{2} \approx 1.414$, so $\sqrt{2}$ is to the left of 1.5 and $\sqrt{2} < 1.5$.

59. $0.\overline{3} > 0.3$; $0.\overline{3} = 0.333\ldots$, while $0.3 = 0.3000$, so $0.\overline{3}$ is to the right of 0.3 and $0.\overline{3} > 0.3$.

61. $-\pi > -3.5$; $-\pi \approx -3.14$, so -3.14 is to the right of -3.5 and $-3.14 > -3.5$.

63. $-5 \geq -13$ is true because $-5 > -13$ is true.

65. $-9 \geq -9$ is true because $-9 = -9$ is true.

67. $0 \geq -6$ is true because $0 > -6$ is true.

69. $-17 \geq 6$ is false because neither $-17 > 6$ nor $-17 = 6$ is true.

71. $|6| = 6$ because the distance between 6 and 0 on the number line is 6 units.

73. $|-7| = 7$ because the distance between -7 and 0 on the number line is 7 units.

75. $\left|\frac{2}{3}\right| = \frac{2}{3}$ because the distance between $\frac{2}{3}$ and 0 on the number line is $\frac{2}{3}$ unit.

77. $|-\sqrt{13}| = \sqrt{13}$ because the distance between $-\sqrt{13}$ and 0 on the number line is $\sqrt{13}$ units.

79. -3

81. The years for which

money collected < money spent

are 1996, and 1997. There was a budget deficit in these years.

For Exercises 83–93, answers may vary.

95. Statement c is true since some rational numbers are negative and also 0 is a rational number that is not positive.

97. Since $\sqrt{36} = 6$ and $\sqrt{49} = 7$, $-\sqrt{47}$ is between -7 and -6.

99. $\sqrt{3} \approx 1.732$

$\sqrt{3}$ should be graphed between 1 and 2.

101. $1 - \sqrt{2} \approx -0.414$
$1 - \sqrt{2}$ should be graphed between -1 and 0.

Ordered Pairs and Graphs

1.3 CHECK POINTS

CHECK POINT 1

$A(-2, 4)$: 2 units left, 4 units up (in quadrant II)
$B(4, -2)$: 4 units right, 2 units down (in quadrant IV)
$C(-3, 0)$: 3 units left, 0 units up or down (on the x-axis)
$D(0, -3)$: 0 units right or left, 3 units down (on the y-axis)

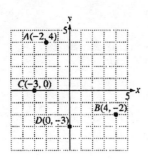

CHECK POINT 2

Point	Position	Coordinates
E	4 units left, 2 units down	$(-4, -2)$
F	2 units left, 0 units up or down	$(-2, 0)$
G	6 units right, 0 units up or down	$(6, 0)$

CHECK POINT 3

The coordinates of point B are $(8, 200)$. This means that after 8 seconds, the watermelon is 200 feet above the ground.

CHECK POINT 4

The coordinates of point D are approximately $(8.8, 0)$. This means that after 8.8 seconds, the watermelon is 0 feet above the ground. Equivalently, the watermelon splatters after 8.8 seconds.

CHECK POINT 5

According to the graph, the minimum average age at which U.S. women marry for the first time is 20 years old. This occurred in 1950, 1960, and 1970.

CHECK POINT 6

a. Approximately 14% of the teenagers named Levi's as one of the "coolest."

b. The brands rated "coolest" by more than 15% of the teenagers were Tommy Hilfiger, Calvin Klein, and Nike.

CHECK POINT 7

a. The sector labeled "Black" indicates that in 2050, 13.6% of the U.S. population will be black.

b. To estimate the number of Asian Americans in 2050, round 8.2% to 8% = 0.08, and multiply:

$$0.08(400,000,000) = 32,000,000.$$

In 2050, the population of Asian Americans is expected to be about 32,000,000.

EXERCISE SET 1.3

1. Quadrant I

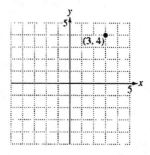

3. Quadrant II

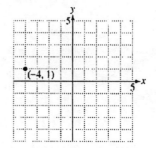

5. Quadrant III

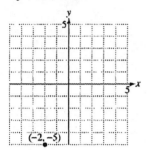

13.

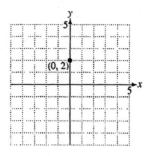

7. Quadrant IV

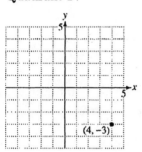

15.

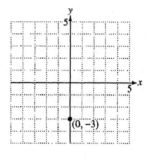

9.

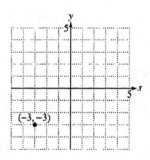

17.

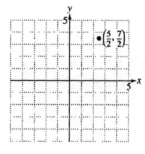

11.

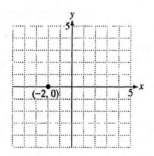

19.

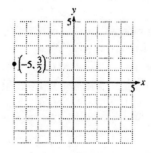

21.

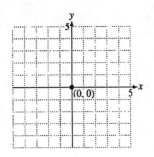

23.

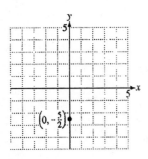

25. $A(5, 2)$

27. $C(-6, 5)$

29. $E(-2, -3)$

31. $G(5, -3)$

33. The coordinates of point A are $(2, 7)$. When the football is 2 yards from the quarterback, its height is 7 feet.

35. The coordinates of point C are approximately $(3, 9.25)$.

37. The football's maximum height is 12 feet. It reaches this height when it is 15 yards from the quarterback.

39. The coordinates of point A are approximately $(1970, 61)$.
In 1970, there were approximately 61 million people under 16 in the United States.

41. The coordinates of point C are approximately $(1990, 60)$.

In 1990, there were approximately 60 million people under 16 in the United States.

43. The unemployment rate in 1970 was approximately 5%.

45. The unemployment rate reached a maximum in 1982. The rate in that year was approximately 9.9%.

47. Approximately 33% of vacations include shopping.

49. Shopping, outdoor recreation, and historical places and museums are included on more than 15% of vacations.

51. Life expectancy for men born in 1900 was approximately 48 years.

53. Women born in 1996 can expect to live approximately $(79 - 65 = 14)$ more years than men born in 1950.

55. Approximately $470 was spent buying sports gear for scuba diving.

57. Approximately $50 - $30 = $20 more is spent buying sports gear for table tennis than for croquet.

59. The number of Protestants was approximately 60% of 272 million, which is about 160 million or 160,000,000.

61. The number of hate-crime incidents motivated by race was approximately 60% of $10,000 or $6000.

For Exercises 63–71, answers may vary.

73. Statement c is false.

Review Exercises

75. $\dfrac{3}{4} + \dfrac{2}{5} = \dfrac{3}{4} \cdot \dfrac{5}{5} + \dfrac{2}{5} \cdot \dfrac{4}{4}$

$\qquad = \dfrac{15}{20} + \dfrac{8}{20} = \dfrac{23}{20}$

76. $-\frac{1}{4} < 0$; $-\frac{1}{4}$ is to the left of 0 on the number line.

77. $|-5.83| = 5.83$ because the distance between -5.83 and 0 on the number line is 5.83 units.

Basic Rules of Algebra

1.4 CHECK POINTS

CHECK POINT 1

$2.35x + 179.5$ when $x = 20$

$$2.35x + 179.5 = 2.35(20) + 179.5$$
$$= 47 + 179.5$$
$$= 226.5$$

This means that in 1980 (20 years after 1960), the population of the United States was 226.5 million.

CHECK POINT 2

$6x + 2x + 11$

a. Because terms are separated by addition, the expression contains 3 terms.

b. The coefficient of the first term, $6x$, is 6.

c. The constant term is 11.

d. The like terms are $6x$ and $2x$.

CHECK POINT 3

a. $x + 14 = 14 + x$

b. $7y = y7$

CHECK POINT 4

a. Change the order of the terms being added:

$$5x + 17 = 17 + 5x.$$

b. Change the order of the factors being multiplied:

$$5x + 17 = x5 + 17.$$

CHECK POINT 5

a. $8 + (12 + x) = (8 + 12) + x$
$\qquad\qquad\quad = 20 + x$

b. $6(5x) = (6 \cdot 5)x$
$\qquad\quad = 30x$

CHECK POINT 6

$8 + (x + 4) = 8 + (4 + x)$
$\qquad\qquad = (8 + 4) + x$
$\qquad\qquad = 12 + x$

CHECK POINT 7

$5(x + 3) = 5x + 5 \cdot 3$
$\qquad\quad = 5x + 15$

CHECK POINT 8

$6(4y + 7) = 6 \cdot 4y + 6 \cdot 7$
$\qquad\qquad = 24y + 42$

CHECK POINT 9

a. $7x + 3x = (7 + 3)x$
$\qquad\qquad = 10x$

b. $9a - 4a = (9 - 4)a$
$\qquad\qquad = 5a$

CHECK POINT 10

a. $8x + 7x + 10x + 3 = (8x + 10x) + (7 + 3)$
$$= 18x + 10$$

b. $9x + 6y - 5x - 2y = (9x - 5x) + (6y - 2y)$
$$= 4x + 4y$$

CHECK POINT 11

$7(2x - 3) - 11x = 7 \cdot 2x - 7 \cdot 3 - 11x$
$$= 14x - 21 - 11x$$
$$= (14x - 11x) - 21$$
$$= 3x - 21$$

CHECK POINT 12

$7(4x + 3y) + 2(5x - y)$
$$= 7 \cdot 4x + 7 \cdot 3y + 2 \cdot 5x - 2 \cdot y$$
$$= 28x + 21y + 10x - 2y$$
$$= (28x + 10x) + (21y - 2y)$$
$$= 38x + 19y$$

CHECK POINT 13

Using $0.6(220 - a)$:   Using $132 - 0.6a$:
$0.6(220 - 40)$ $132 - 0.6(40)$
$\quad = 0.6(180)$ $\quad = 132 - 24$
$\quad = 108$ $\quad = 108$

Both forms of the algebraic expression indicate that the optimum heart rate for a 40-year-old runner is 108 beats per minute.

EXERCISE SET 1.4

1. $x + 13$; $x = 5$
$$x + 13 = 5 + 13 = 18$$

3. $7x$; $x = 10$
$$7x = 7(10) = 70$$

5. $5x + 7$; $x = 4$
$$5x + 7 = 5(4) + 7$$
$$= 20 + 7 = 27$$

7. $4(x + 3)$; $x = 2$
$$4(x + 3) = 4(2 + 3)$$
$$= 4(5) = 20$$

9. $\frac{5}{9}(F - 32)$; $F = 77$
$$\frac{5}{9}(F - 32) = \frac{5}{9}(77 - 32)$$
$$= \frac{5}{9}(45) = 25$$

11. $3x + 5$
   a. 2 terms
   b. 3
   c. 5
   d. No like terms

13. $x + 2 + 5x$
   a. 3 terms
   b. 1
   c. 2
   d. x and $5x$ are like terms.

15. $4y + 1 + 3$
   a. 3 terms
   b. 4
   c. 1
   d. No like terms

17. $y + 4 = 4 + y$

19. $5 + 3x = 3x + 5$

21. $4x + 5y = 5y + 4x$

23. $5(x + 3) = 5(3 + x)$

25. $9x = x \cdot 9$ or $x9$

27. $x + y6 = x + 6y$

29. $7x + 23 = x7 + 23$

31. $5(x + 3) = (x + 3)5$

33. $7 + (5 + x) = (7 + 5) + x = 12 + x$

35. $7(4x) = (7 \cdot 4)x = 28x$

37. $3(x + 5) = 3(x) + 3(5) = 3x + 15$

39. $8(2x + 3) = 8(2x) + 8(3) = 16x + 24$

41. $\frac{1}{3}(12 + 6r) = \frac{1}{3}(12) + \frac{1}{3}(6r) = 4 + 2r$

43. $5(x + y) = 5x + 5y$

45. $3(x - 2) = 3(x) - 3(2) = 3x - 6$

47. $2(4x - 5) = 2(4x) - 2(5) = 8x - 10$

49. $\frac{1}{2}(5x - 12) = \frac{1}{2}(5x) + \frac{1}{2}(-12) = \frac{5}{2}x - 6$

51. $(2x + 7)4 = 2x(4) + 7(4) = 8x + 28$

53. $6(x + 3 + 2y) = 6(x) + 6(3) + 6(2y)$
$$= 6x + 18 + 12y$$

55. $5(3x - 2 + 4y) = 5(3x) - 5(2) + 5(4y)$
$$= 15x - 10 + 20y$$

57. $7x + 10x = (7 + 10)x = 17x$

59. $11a - 3a = (11 - 3)aa = 8a$

61. $3 + (x + 11) = (3 + 11) + x = 14 + x$

63. $5y - 3 + 6y = (5y + 6y) - 3 = 11y - 3$

65. $2x + 5 + 7x - 4 = (2x + 7x) + (5 - 4)$
$$= 9x + 1$$

67. $11a + 12 - 3a - 2 = (11a - 3a) + (12 - 2)$
$$= 8a + 10$$

69. $5(3x + 2) - 4 = 15x + 10 - 4 = 15x + 6$

71. $12 + 5(3x - 2) = 12 + 15x - 10$
$$= 15x + (12 - 10)$$
$$= 15x + 2$$

73. $7(3a + 2b) + 5(4a - 2b)$
$$= 21a + 14b + 20a - 10b$$
$$= 21a + 20a + 14b - 10b$$
$$= 41a + 4b$$

75. $15x; \; x = 20$

$15x = 15(20) = 300$

This means that you can stay in the sun for 300 minutes (or 5 hours) without burning with a number 15 lotion.

77. $1527x + 31,290; \; x = 2000 - 1990 = 10$

$1527x + 31,290 = 1527(10) + 31,290$
$$= 15,270 + 31,290$$
$$= 46,560$$

This means that the average yearly earnings for elementary and secondary teachers in the United States in 2000 was $46,560.

79. $\dfrac{DA + D}{24} = \dfrac{200(12) + 200}{24}$
$$= \dfrac{2400 + 200}{24}$$
$$= 108.\overline{3} \text{ mg}$$

$\dfrac{D(A + 1)}{24} = \dfrac{200(12 + 1)}{24}$
$$= \dfrac{200(13)}{24} = \dfrac{2600}{24}$$
$$= 108.\overline{3} \text{ mg}$$

The proper dose of a 12-year-old is approximately 108 milligrams.

For Exercises 81–91, answers may vary.

93. The only correct statement is c, which is an example of the distributive property.

95. $\dfrac{0.5x + 5000}{x}$

a. $x = 100$

$\dfrac{0.5x + 5000}{x} = \dfrac{0.5(100) + 5000}{100}$
$$= \dfrac{50 + 5000}{100}$$
$$= \dfrac{5050}{100} = 50.5$$

The average cost per clock for 100 clocks is $50.50.

$x = 1000$

$$\frac{0.5x + 5000}{x} = \frac{0.5(1000) + 5000}{1000}$$

$$= \frac{500 + 5000}{1000}$$

$$= \frac{5500}{1000}$$

$$= 5.5$$

The average cost per clock for 1000 clocks is $5.50.

$x = 10{,}000$

$$\frac{0.5x + 5000}{x} = \frac{0.5(10{,}000) + 5000}{10{,}000}$$

$$= \frac{5000 + 5000}{10{,}000}$$

$$= \frac{10{,}000}{10{,}000}$$

$$= 1$$

The average cost per clock for 10,000 clocks is $1.

b. $x = 2000$

$$\frac{0.5x + 5000}{x} = \frac{0.5(2000) + 5000}{2000}$$

$$= \frac{1000 + 5000}{2000} = \frac{6000}{2000}$$

$$= 3$$

The average cost per clock to manufacture 2000 clocks is $3. Since the clocks cannot be sold for more than $1.50, the business cannot make a profit so doesn't have a promising future.

Review Exercises

96.

$$
\begin{array}{r}
0.44\ldots \\
9)\overline{4.00\ldots} \\
\underline{3\,6} \\
40 \\
\underline{36} \\
40 \\
\vdots
\end{array}
$$

$$\frac{4}{9} = 0.\overline{4}$$

97.

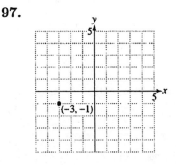

98. $\dfrac{3}{7} \div \dfrac{15}{7} = \dfrac{3}{7} \cdot \dfrac{7}{15} = \dfrac{21}{105} = \dfrac{1 \cdot \cancel{21}}{5 \cdot \cancel{21}} = \dfrac{1}{5}$

Addition of Real Numbers

1.5 CHECK POINTS

CHECK POINT 1

$4 + (-7)$

Step 1 Start at 4.

Step 2 Because -7 is a negative number, move 7 units to the left.

Step 3 Finish at -3, which represents the sum of 4 and -7. Thus, $4 + (-7) = -3$.

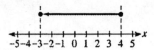

CHECK POINT 2

a. $-1 + (-3)$

Start at -1. Move 3 units to the left because -3 is negative. Finish at -4. Thus, $-1 + (-3) = -4$.

b. $-5 + 3$

Start -5. Move 3 units to the right because 3 is positive. Finish at -2. Thus, $-5 + 3 = -2$.

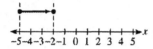

CHECK POINT 3

a. $-10 + (-25)$

To add -10 and -25, first add their absolute values: $10 + 25 = 35$. The common sign is $-$, so this is the sign of the sum. Thus,
$$-10 + (-25) = -35.$$

b. $-0.3 + (-1.2)$

Add the absolute values: $0.3 + 1.2 = 1.5$. The common sign is $-$. Thus,
$$-0.3 + (-1.2) = -1.5$$

c. $-\dfrac{2}{3} + \left(-\dfrac{1}{6}\right)$

Add the absolute values using 6 as the common denominator:
$$\frac{2}{3} + \frac{1}{6} = \frac{4}{6} + \frac{1}{6} = \frac{5}{6}.$$
The common sign is $-$. Thus,
$$-\frac{2}{3} + \left(-\frac{1}{6}\right) = -\frac{5}{6}.$$

CHECK POINT 4

a. $-15 + 2$

To add -15 and 2, first subtract the absolute values: $15 - 2 = 13$. Use the sign of the number with the greater absolute value. This is -15, so the sign of the sum will be negative. Thus,
$$-15 + 2 = -13.$$

b. $-0.4 + 1.6$

Subtract the absolute values: $1.6 - 0.4 = 1.2$. Since 1.6 has the greater absolute value, the sign of the sum will be positive:
$$-0.4 + 1.6 = 1.2$$

c. $-\dfrac{2}{3} + \dfrac{1}{6}$

Subtract the absolute values using 6 as the common denominator:
$$\frac{2}{3} - \frac{1}{6} = \frac{4}{6} - \frac{1}{6} = \frac{3}{6} = \frac{1}{2}.$$
Since $\frac{2}{3}$ has the greater absolute value, the sign of the sum will be negative. Thus,
$$-\frac{2}{3} + \frac{1}{6} = -\frac{1}{2}.$$

CHECK POINT 5

a. $-20x + 3x = (-20 + 3)x$
$$= -17x$$

b. $3y + (-10z) + (-10y) + 16z$
$$= 3y + (-10y) + (-10z) + 16z$$
$$= [3 + (-10)]y + [(-10) + 16]z$$
$$= -7y + 6z$$

c. $4(10 - 8x) + 4(4x - 5)$
$$= 4 \cdot 10 + 4(-8z) + 4 \cdot 3z + 4(-5)$$
$$= 40 - 32z + 12z - 20$$
$$= (40 - 20) + (-32 + 12)z$$
$$= 20 - 20z$$

CHECK POINT 6

Represent the amounts the water level rose by positive integers and the amounts it fell by negative numbers.

$$2 + (-4) + 1 + (-5) + 3$$
$$= (2 + 1 + 3) + [(-4) + (-5)]$$
$$= 6 + (-9) = -3$$

The water level fell 3 feet at the end of 5 months.

EXERCISE SET 1.5

1. $3 + (-7) = -4$

Start at 3. Move 7 units to the left because -7 is negative. Finish at -4.

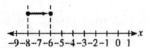

3. $-4 + (-5) = -9$

Start at -4. Move 5 units to the left because -5 is negative. Finish at -9.

5. $-8 + 2 = -6$

Start at -8. Move 2 units to the right because 2 is positive. Finish at -6.

7. $2 + (-2) = 0$

Start at 2. Move 2 units to the left because 2 is negative. Finish at 0.

9. $-4 + 0 = -4$

11. $9 + (-9) = 0$

13. $-9 + (-9) = 18$

15. $-7 + (-5) = -12$

17. $-0.4 + (-0.9) = -1.3$

19. $-\dfrac{7}{10} + \left(-\dfrac{3}{10}\right) = -\dfrac{10}{10} = -1$

21. $-9 + 4 = -5$

23. $12 + (-8) = 4$

25. $6 + (-9) = -3$

27. $-3.6 + 2.1 = -1.5$

29. $-3.6 + (-2.1) = -5.7$

31. $\dfrac{9}{10} + \left(-\dfrac{3}{5}\right) = \dfrac{9}{10} + \left(-\dfrac{6}{10}\right) = \dfrac{3}{10}$

33. $-\dfrac{5}{8} + \dfrac{3}{4} = -\dfrac{5}{8} + \dfrac{6}{8} = \dfrac{1}{8}$

35. $-\dfrac{3}{7} + \left(-\dfrac{4}{5}\right) = -\dfrac{15}{35} + \left(-\dfrac{28}{35}\right) = -\dfrac{43}{35}$

37. $4 + (-7) + (-5) = [4 + (-7)] + (-5)$
$$= -3 + (-5) = -8$$

39. $85 + (-15) + (-20) + 12$
$$= [85 + (-15)] + (-20) + 12$$
$$= 70 + (-20) + 12$$
$$= [70 + (-20) + 12$$
$$= 50 + 12 = 62$$

41. $17 + (-4) + 2 + 3 + (-10)$
$$= 13 + 2 + 3 + (-10)$$
$$= 15 + 3 + (-10)$$
$$= 18 + (-10) = 8$$

43. $-45 + \left(-\dfrac{3}{7}\right) + 25 + \left(-\dfrac{4}{7}\right)$

$\quad = (-45 + 25) + \left[-\dfrac{3}{7} + \left(-\dfrac{4}{7}\right)\right]$

$\quad = -20 + \left(-\dfrac{7}{7}\right)$

$\quad = -20 + (-1) = -21$

45. $3.5 + (-45) + (-8.4) + 72$

$\quad = [3.5 + (-8.4)] + (-45 + 72)$

$\quad = -4.9 + 27 = 22.1$

47. $-8x + 5x = (-8 + 5)x = -3x$

49. $15y + (-2y) = [15 + (-12)]y = 3y$

51. $-7a + (-10a) = [-7 + (-10)a] = -17a$

53. $-4 + 7x + 5 + (-13x)$

$\quad = -4 + 5 + 7x + (-13x)$

$\quad = (-4 + 5) + [7 + (-13)]x$

$\quad = 1 - 6x$

55. $7b + 2 + (-b) + (-6)$

$\quad = 7b + (-b) + 2 + (-6)$

$\quad = [7 + (-1)]b + [2 + (-6)]$

$\quad = 6b - 4 \text{ or } -4 + 6b$

57. $7x + (-5y) + (-9x) + 2y$

$\quad = 7x + (-9x) + (-5y) + 2y$

$\quad = [7 + (-9)]x + (-5 + 2)y$

$\quad = -2x - 3y$

59. $4(5x - 3) + 6$

$\quad = 4 \cdot 5x + 4(-3) + 6$

$\quad = 20x - 12 + 6$

$\quad = 20x - 6$

61. $8(3 - 4y) + 35y$

$\quad = 8 \cdot 3 + 8(-4y) + 35y$

$\quad = 24 - 32y + 35y$

$\quad = 24 + (-32 + 35)y$

$\quad = 24 + 3y$

63. $6(2 - 9a) + 7(3a + 5)$

$\quad = 6 \cdot 2 + 6(-9a) + 7 \cdot 3a + 7 \cdot 5$

$\quad = 12 - 54a + 21a + 35$

$\quad = (12 + 35) + (-54 + 21a)$

$\quad = 47 - 33a$

65. $-56 + 100 = 44$

The high temperature was 44°F.

67. $-1312 + 712 = -600$

The elevation of the person is 600 feet below sea level.

69. Temperature at 8:00 A.M. + rise 15°F by noon + fall 5°F by 4 P.M.

$\quad = -7 + 15 - 5 = 3$

The temperature at 4:00 P.M. was 3°F.

71. Start at 27-yard line + 4-yard gain + 2-yard loss + 8-yard gain + 12-yard loss

$\quad = 27 + 4 - 2 + 8 - 12 = 39 - 14 = 25$

The location of the football at the end of the fourth play is at the 25-yard line.

73. $1274 - 82 + 428 + 818 + 570 + 676 + 716 = 4400$

In the 2000 Olympics, 4400 women participated.

For Exercises 75–81, answers may vary.

83. Statement d is true. (Statement a is sometimes true, but is not considered true because it is not always true.)

85. $\underline{\quad} + 11x + (-3y) + 3x = \underline{\quad} + 14x + (-3y)$

$\quad 7(2x - 3y) = 14x - 2y$

Comparing these expressions gives

$\quad \underline{\quad} + (-3y) = -21y.$

Since $(-18y) + (-3y) = -21y$, the missing term is $-18y$.

87. Answers will vary according to the exercises chosen.

89. $3\sqrt{5} - 2\sqrt{7} - \sqrt{11} + 4\sqrt{3} \approx 5.0283$

Review Exercises

90. $-19 \geq -18$ is true because $-19 > -18$ is true.

91. a. $\sqrt{4} \ (= 2)$
   b. $0, \sqrt{4}$
   c. $-6, 0, \sqrt{4}$
   d. $-6, 0, 0.\overline{7}, \sqrt{4}$
   e. $-\pi, \sqrt{3}$
   f. All numbers in given set

92.   Quadrant IV

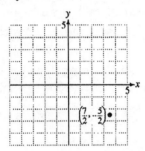

Subtraction of Real Numbers

1.6 CHECK POINTS

CHECK POINT 1

a. $3 - 11 = 3 + (-11) = -8$

b. $4 - (-5) = 4 + 5 = 9$

c. $-7 - (-2) = -7 + 2 = -5$

CHECK POINT 2

a. $-3.4 - (-12.6) = -3.4 + 12.6$
$$= 9.2$$

b. $-\dfrac{3}{5} - \dfrac{1}{3} = -\dfrac{3}{5} + \left(-\dfrac{1}{3}\right)$
$$= -\dfrac{9}{15} + \left(-\dfrac{5}{15}\right)$$
$$= -\dfrac{14}{15}$$

c. $5\pi - (-2\pi) = 5\pi + 2\pi = 7\pi$

CHECK POINT 3

$10 - (-12) - 4 - (-3) - 6$
$= 10 + 12 + (-4) + 3 + (-6)$
$= (10 + 12 + 3) + [(-4) + (-6)]$
$= 25 + (-10)$
$= 15$

CHECK POINT 4

$-6 + 4a - 7ab = -6 + 4a + (-7ab)$

Because terms are separated by addition, the three terms are $-6, 4a,$ and $-7ab$.

CHECK POINT 5

a. $4 + 2x - 9x = 4 + 2x + (-9x)$
$$= 4 + [2 + (-9)]x$$
$$= 4 + (-7x)$$
$$= 4 - 7x$$

b. $-3x - 10y - 6x + 14y$
$= -3x + (-10y) + (-6x) + 14y$
$= [(-3x) + (-6x)] + [(-10y) + 14y]$
$= [-3 + (-6)]x + (-10 + 14)$
$= -9x + 4y$

CHECK POINT 6

$8848 - (-10{,}915) = 8848 + 10{,}915$
$$= 19{,}763$$

The difference between the elevations is 19,763 meters.

EXERCISE SET 1.6

1. a. -12
  b. $5 - 12 = 5 + (-12)$

3. a. 7
  b. $5 - (-7) = 5 + 7$

5. $13 - 8 = 13 + (-8) = 5$

7. $8 - 15 = 8 + (-15) = -7$

9. $4 - (-10) = 4 + 10 = 14$

11. $-6 - (-17) = -6 + 17 = 11$

13. $-12 - (-3) = -12 + 3 = -9$

15. $-11 - 17 = -11 + (-17) = -28$

17. $-25 - (-25) = -25 + 25 = 0$

19. $13 - 13 = 13 + (-13) = 0$

21. $7 - (-7) = 7 + 7 = 14$

23. $0 - 8 = 0 + (-8) = -8$

25. $0 - (-3) = 0 + 3 = 3$

27. $\dfrac{3}{7} - \dfrac{5}{7} = \dfrac{3}{7} + \left(-\dfrac{5}{7}\right) = -\dfrac{2}{7}$

29. $\dfrac{1}{5} - \left(-\dfrac{3}{5}\right) = \dfrac{1}{5} + \dfrac{3}{5} = \dfrac{4}{5}$

31. $-\dfrac{4}{5} - \dfrac{1}{5} = -\dfrac{4}{5} + \left(-\dfrac{1}{5}\right) = -\dfrac{5}{5} = -1$

33. $-\dfrac{4}{5} - \left(-\dfrac{1}{5}\right) = -\dfrac{4}{5} + \dfrac{1}{5} = -\dfrac{3}{5}$

35. $\dfrac{1}{2} - \left(-\dfrac{1}{4}\right) = \dfrac{1}{2} + \dfrac{1}{4} = \dfrac{2}{4} + \dfrac{1}{4} = \dfrac{3}{4}$

37. $\dfrac{1}{2} - \dfrac{1}{4} = \dfrac{1}{2} + \left(-\dfrac{1}{4}\right) = \dfrac{2}{4} + \left(-\dfrac{1}{4}\right) = \dfrac{1}{4}$

39. $9.8 - 2.2 = 9.8 + (-2.2) = 7.6$

41. $-3.1 - (-1.1) = -3.1 + 1.1 = -2$

43. $1.3 - (-1.3) = 1.3 + 1.3 = 2.6$

45. $-2.06 - (-2.06) = -2.06 + 2.06 = 0$

47. $5\pi - 2\pi = 5\pi + (-2\pi) = 3\pi$

49. $3\pi - (-10) = 3\pi + 10\pi = 13\pi$

51. $13 - 2 - (-8) = 13 + (-2) + 8$
$$= (13 + 8) + (-2)$$
$$= 21 + (-2)$$
$$= 19$$

53. $9 - 8 + 3 - 7 = 9 + (-8) + 3 + (-7)$
$$= (9 + 3) + [(-8) + (-7)]$$
$$= 12 + (-15)$$
$$= -3$$

55. $-6 - 2 + 3 - 10$
$$= -6 + (-2) + 3 + (-10)$$
$$= [(-6) + (-2) + (-10)] + 3$$
$$= -18 + 3$$
$$= -15$$

57. $-10 - (-5) + 7 - 2$
$$= -10 + 5 + 7 + (-2)$$
$$= [(-10) + (-2)] + (5 + 7)$$
$$= -12 + 12 = 0$$

59. $-23 - 11 - (-7) + (-25)$
$$= (-23) + (-11) + 7 + (-25)$$
$$= [(-23) + (-11) + (-25)] + 7$$
$$= -59 + 7$$
$$= -52$$

61. $-823 - 146 - 50 - (-832)$
$$= -823 + (-146) + (-50) + 832$$
$$= [(-823) + (-146) + (-50)] + 832$$
$$= -1019 + 832$$
$$= -187$$

63. $1 - \dfrac{2}{3} - \left(-\dfrac{5}{6}\right) = 1 + \left(-\dfrac{2}{3}\right) + \dfrac{5}{6}$

$\qquad = \left(1 + \dfrac{5}{6}\right) + \left(-\dfrac{2}{3}\right)$

$\qquad = \left(\dfrac{6}{6} + \dfrac{5}{6}\right) + \left(-\dfrac{2}{3}\right)$

$\qquad = \dfrac{11}{6} + \left(-\dfrac{2}{3} \cdot \dfrac{2}{2}\right)$

$\qquad = \dfrac{11}{6} + \left(-\dfrac{4}{6}\right) = \dfrac{7}{6}$

65. $-0.16 - 5.2 - (-0.87)$

$\qquad = -0.16 + (-5.2) + 0.87$

$\qquad = [(-0.16) + (-5.2)] + 0.87$

$\qquad = -5.36 + 0.87$

$\qquad = -4.49$

67. $-\dfrac{3}{4} - \dfrac{1}{4} - \left(-\dfrac{5}{8}\right) = -\dfrac{3}{4} + \left(-\dfrac{1}{4}\right) + \dfrac{5}{8}$

$\qquad = -\dfrac{4}{4} + \dfrac{5}{8}$

$\qquad = -1 + \dfrac{5}{8}$

$\qquad = -\dfrac{8}{8} + \dfrac{5}{8} = -\dfrac{3}{8}$

69. $-3x - 8y = -3x + (-8y)$

The terms are $-3x$ and $-8y$.

71. $12x - 5xy - 4 = 12x + (-5xy) + (-4)$

The terms are $12x$, $-5xy$, and -4.

73. $3x - 9x = 3x + (-9x)$

$\qquad = [3 + (-9)]x$

$\qquad = -6x$

75. $4 + 7y - 17y = 4 + 7y + (-17y)$

$\qquad = 4 + [7 + (-17)]y$

$\qquad = 4 - 10y$

77. $2a + 5 - 9a = 2a + 5 + (-9a)$

$\qquad = 2a + (-9a) + 5$

$\qquad = [2 + (-9)]a + 5$

$\qquad = -7a + 5 \quad \text{or} \quad 5 - 7a$

79. $4 - 6b - 8 - 3b$

$\qquad = 4 + (-6b) + (-8) + (-3b)$

$\qquad = 4 + (-8) + (-6b) + (-3b)$

$\qquad = 4 + (-8) + [-6 + (-3)]b$

$\qquad = -4 - 9b$

81. $13 - (-7x) + 4x - (-11)$

$\qquad = 13 + 7x + 4x + 11$

$\qquad = 13 + 11 + 7x + 4x$

$\qquad = 24 + 11x$

83. $-5x - 10y - 3x + 13y$

$\qquad = -5x + (-10y) + (-3x) + 13y$

$\qquad = -5x + (-3x) + (-10y) + 13y$

$\qquad = [-5 + (-3)]x + (-10 + 13)y$

$\qquad = -8x + 3y \quad \text{or} \quad 3y - 8x$

85. Elevation of Mount Kilimanjaro
$\quad$ − elevation of Qattara Depression
$\quad = 19,321 - (-436) = 19,757$

The difference in elevation between the two geographic locations is 19,757 feet.

87. 14 billion $- \$6$ billion $= \$8$ billion

The difference between veterinary costs for dogs and cats in 2000 was about $8 billion.

89. $2 - (-19) = 2 + 19 = 21$

The difference between the average daily low temperatures for March and February is 21°F.

91. $-19 - (-22) = -19 + 22 = 3$

February's average low temperature is 3°F warmer than January's.

93. The maximum point on the graph is $(3, 0.05)$. This means that the drug's maximum concentration is 0.05 milligrams per 100 milliliters and this occurs 3 hours after the injection.

95. $0.045 - 0.03 = 0.045 + (-0.03) = 0.015$

The difference in concentrations between 4 hours and 1 hour after injection is 0.015.

97. The drug's concentration is increasing between 0 and 3 hours after the injection (from the time of the injection to three hours later).

99. $520 - (-112) = 520 + 112 = 632$

The difference in growth between systems and analysts and farmers is 632 thousand or 632,000 jobs.

For Exercises 101–105, answers will vary.

107. Consider dates B.C. as negative numbers and dates A.D. as positive numbers.

$$500 - (-212) = 500 + 212 = 712$$

Because there was no year 0, the number of elapsed years is $712 - 1 = 711$.

109. Student answers will vary according to the exercises chosen.

111. $4\sqrt{2} - (-3\sqrt{5}) - (-\sqrt{7}) + \sqrt{3}$
$= 4\sqrt{2} + 3\sqrt{5} + \sqrt{7} + \sqrt{3}$
≈ 16.7429

Review Exercises

113.

114. $10(a + 4) = 10(4 + a)$

115. Examples will vary. One integer that is not a natural number is -7.

Multiplication and Division of Real Numbers

1.7 CHECK POINTS

CHECK POINT 1

a. $8(-5)$

Multiply the absolute values: $8 \cdot 5 = 40$. Because the numbers have opposite signs, the product is negative. Thus,

$$8(-5) = -40.$$

b. $-\dfrac{1}{3} \cdot \dfrac{4}{7} = -\dfrac{1 \cdot 4}{3 \cdot 7} = -\dfrac{4}{21}$

c. $(-12)(-3)$

Multiply the absolute values: $12 \cdot 3 = 36$. Because the numbers have the same sign, the product is positive. Thus,

$$(-12)(-3) = 36.$$

d. $(-1.1)(-5) = 5.5$

e. $(-543)(0)$

The product of 0 and any number is 0. Thus,

$$(-543)(0) = 0.$$

CHECK POINT 2

a. $(-2)(3)(-1)(4)$

There is an even number of negative factors (two), so the product is positive.

$$(-2)(3)(-1)(4) = 24$$

b. $(-1)(-3)(2)(-1)(5)$

There is an odd number of negative factors (three), so the product is negative.

$$(-1)(-3)(2)(-1)(5) = -30$$

CHECK POINT 3

a. The multiplicative inverse of 7 is $\frac{1}{7}$
because $7 \cdot \frac{1}{7} = 1$.

b. The multiplicative inverse of $\frac{1}{8}$ is 8
because $\frac{1}{8} \cdot 8 = 1$.

c. The multiplicative inverse of -6 is $-\frac{1}{6}$
because $(-6)\left(-\frac{1}{6}\right) = 1$.

d. The multiplicative inverse of $-\frac{7}{13}$ is $-\frac{13}{7}$
because $\left(-\frac{7}{13}\right)\left(-\frac{13}{7}\right) = 1$.

CHECK POINT 4

a. $-28 \div 7 = -28 \cdot \dfrac{1}{7} = -4$

b. $\dfrac{-16}{-2} = -16 \cdot \left(-\dfrac{1}{2}\right) = 8$

CHECK POINT 5

a. $\dfrac{-32}{-4}$

Divide the absolute values: $\frac{32}{4} = 8$.
The quotient will be positive because the
two numbers have the same sign.

$$\frac{-32}{-4} = 8$$

b. $-\dfrac{2}{3} \div \dfrac{5}{4}$

Divide the absolute values:

$$-\frac{2}{3} \div \frac{5}{4} = \frac{2}{3} \cdot \frac{4}{5} = \frac{8}{15}.$$

The quotient will be negative because the
two numbers have opposite signs. Thus,

$$-\frac{2}{3} \div \frac{5}{4} = -\frac{8}{15}.$$

c. $\dfrac{21.9}{-3}$

Divide the absolute values: $\frac{21.9}{3} = 7.3$.
The quotient will be negative because the
two numbers have opposite signs. Thus,

$$\frac{21.9}{-3} = -7.3.$$

d. $\dfrac{0}{-5}$

Any nonzero number divided into 0 is 0.

$$\frac{0}{-5} = 0$$

CHECK POINT 6

a. $-4(5x) = (-4 \cdot 5)x = -20x$

b. $9x + x = (9 + 1)x = 10x$

c. $13b - 14b = (13 - 14)b = -1b = -b$

d. $-7(3x - 4) = -7(3x) - 7(-4)$
$\qquad\qquad = -21x + 28$

e. $-(7y - 6) = -7y + 6$

Remove parentheses by changing the sign
of every term inside parentheses.

CHECK POINT 7

$4(3y - 7) - (13y - 2)$
$\quad = 4 \cdot 3y - 4 \cdot 7 - (13y - 2)$
$\quad = 12y - 28 - 13y + 2$
$\quad = (12y - 13y) + (-28 + 2)$
$\quad = -y - 26$

CHECK POINT 8
$\dfrac{30x + 300,000}{x}$

a. $x = 1000$

$\dfrac{30x + 300,000}{x} = \dfrac{30(1000) + 300,000}{1000}$
$\qquad\qquad = \dfrac{330,000}{1000} = 330$

To manufacture 1000 pairs of running shoes per week, the average cost per pair is $330.

b. $x = 10,000$

$$\frac{30x + 300,000}{10,000} = \frac{30(10,000) + 300,000}{10,000}$$

$$= \frac{300,000 + 300,000}{10,000}$$

$$= \frac{600,000}{10,000} = 60$$

To manufacture 10,000 pairs of running shoes per week, the average cost per pair is $60.

c. $x = 100,000$

$$\frac{30x + 300,000}{x} = \frac{30(100,000) + 300,000}{100,000}$$

$$= \frac{3,000,000 + 300,000}{100,000}$$

$$= \frac{3,300,000}{100,000}$$

$$= 33$$

To manufacture 100,000 pairs of running shoes per week, the average cost per pair is $33.

EXERCISE SET 1.7

1. $6(-9) = -(6 \cdot 9) = -54$

3. $(-7)(-3) = +(7 \cdot 3) = 21$

5. $(-2)(6) = -12$

7. $(-13)(-1) = 13$

9. $0(-5) = 0$

11. $\frac{1}{2}(-14) = -7$

13. $\left(-\frac{3}{4}\right)(-20) = \frac{3 \cdot 20}{4 \cdot 1} = 15$

15. $-\frac{3}{5} \cdot \left(-\frac{4}{7}\right) = \frac{3 \cdot 4}{5 \cdot 7} = \frac{12}{35}$

17. $-\frac{7}{9} \cdot \frac{2}{3} = -\frac{7 \cdot 2}{9 \cdot 3} = -\frac{14}{27}$

19. $3(-1.2) = -3.6$

21. $-0.2(-0.6) = 0.12$

23. $(-5)(-2)(3) = 30$

25. $(-4)(-3)(-1)(6) = -72$

27. $-2(-3)(-4)(-1) = 24$

29. $(-3)(-3)(-3) = -27$

31. $5(-3)(-1)(2)(3) = 90$

33. $(-8)(-4)(0)(-17)(-6) = 0$

35. The multiplicative inverse of 4 is $\frac{1}{4}$.

37. The multiplicative inverse of $\frac{1}{5}$ is 5.

39. The multiplicative inverse of -10 is $-\frac{1}{10}$.

41. The multiplicative inverse of $-\frac{2}{5}$ is $-\frac{5}{2}$.

43. a. $-32 \div 4 = -32 \cdot \frac{1}{4}$

   b. $-32 \cdot \frac{1}{4} = -8$

45. a. $\frac{-60}{-5} = -60 \cdot \left(-\frac{1}{5}\right)$

   b. $-60 \cdot \left(-\frac{1}{5}\right) = 12$

47. $\frac{12}{-4} = 12 \cdot \left(-\frac{1}{4}\right) = -3$

49. $\frac{-21}{3} = -21 \cdot \frac{1}{3} = -7$

51. $\frac{-90}{-3} = -90 \cdot \left(-\frac{1}{3}\right) = 30$

53. $\frac{0}{-7} = 0$

55. $\dfrac{-7}{0}$ is undefined.

57. $-15 \div 3 = -15 \cdot \dfrac{1}{3} = -5$

59. $120 \div (-10) = 120 \cdot \left(-\dfrac{1}{10}\right) = -12$

61. $(-180) \div (-30) = -180 \cdot \left(-\dfrac{1}{30}\right) = 6$

63. $0 \div (-4) = 0$

65. $-4 \div 0$ is undefined.

67. $\dfrac{-12.9}{3} = -12.9 \cdot \dfrac{1}{3} = -4.3$

69. $-\dfrac{1}{2} \div \left(-\dfrac{3}{5}\right) = -\dfrac{1}{2} \cdot \left(-\dfrac{5}{3}\right) = \dfrac{5}{6}$

71. $-\dfrac{14}{9} \div \dfrac{7}{8} = -\dfrac{14}{9} \cdot \dfrac{8}{7} = -\dfrac{112}{63}$
$= -\dfrac{\cancel{7} \cdot 16}{\cancel{7} \cdot 9} = -\dfrac{16}{9}$

73. $\dfrac{1}{3} \div \left(-\dfrac{1}{3}\right) = \dfrac{1}{3} \cdot (-3) = -1$

75. $6 \div \left(-\dfrac{2}{5}\right) = 6 \cdot \left(-\dfrac{5}{2}\right) = -\dfrac{30}{2} = -15$

77. $-5(2x) = (-5 \cdot 2)x = -10x$

79. $-4\left(-\dfrac{3}{4}y\right) = \left[-4 \cdot \left(-\dfrac{3}{4}\right)\right]y = 3y$

81. $8x + x = 8x + 1x = (8+1)x = 9x$

83. $-5x + x = -5x + 1x = (-5+1)x = -4x$

85. $6b - 7b = (6-7)b = -1b = -b$

87. $-y + 4y = -1y + 4y = (-1+4)y = 3y$

89. $-4(2x - 3) = -4(2x) - 4(-3) = -8x + 12$

91. $-3(-2x + 4) = -3(-2x) - 3(4)$
$= 6x - 12$

93. $-(2y - 5) = -2y + 5$

95. $4(2y - 3) - (7y + 2)$
$= 4(2y) + 4(-3) - 7y - 2$
$= 8y - 12 + 7y - 2$
$= 8y - 7y - 12 - 2$
$= y - 14$

97. There were about 233 thousand or 233,000 liposuctions in the United States in 2000.

99. a. From the graph, a reasonable estimate is 11 words.

    b. $\dfrac{5x + 30}{x}; x = 5$

$$\dfrac{5x + 30}{x} = \dfrac{5(5) + 30}{5}$$
$$= \dfrac{25 + 30}{5}$$
$$= \dfrac{55}{5} = 11$$

According to the model, 11 Latin words will be remembered after 5 days. This is the same as the estimate from part (a).

101. a. $\dfrac{200x}{100 - x}; x = 50$

$$\dfrac{200x}{100 - x} = \dfrac{200(50)}{100 - 50}$$
$$= \dfrac{10,000}{50} = 200$$

The cost for removing 50% of the containments is 200($10,000) = $2,000,000.

    b. $\dfrac{200x}{100 - x}; x = 80$

$$\dfrac{200x}{100 - x} = \dfrac{200(80)}{100 - 80}$$
$$= \dfrac{16,000}{20} = 800$$

The cost for removing 80% of the contaminants is 800($10,000) = $8,000,000.

c. As the percentage of contaminant removed increases, the cost of the cleanup rises very rapidly.

For Exercises 103–109, answers may vary.

111. Statement b is true.

113. $5x$

115. Student solutions will vary according to the exercises chosen.

117. $0.3(4.7x - 5.9) - 0.07(3.8x - 61)$
$$= 0.3(4.7x) + 0.3(-5.9) - (0.07)(3.8x)$$
$$- (0.07)(-61)$$
$$= 1.41x - 1.77 - 0.266x + 4.27$$
$$= [1.41x + (-0.266x)] + (-1.77 + 4.27)$$
$$= 1.144x + 2.5$$

Review Exercises

119. $-6 + (-3) = -9$

120. $-6 - (-3) = -6 + 3 = -3$

121. $-6 \div (-3) = -6 \left(-\dfrac{1}{3}\right) = 2$

Exponents, Order of Operations, and Mathematical Models

1.8 CHECK POINTS

CHECK POINT 1

a. $6^2 = 6 \cdot 6 = 36$

b. $(-4)^3 = (-4)(-4)(-4) = -64$

c. $(-1)^4 = (-1)(-1)(-1)(-1) = 1$

d. $-1^4 = -1 \cdot 1 \cdot 1 \cdot 1 = -1$

CHECK POINT 2

a. $16x^2 + 5x^2 = (16 + 5)x^2 = 21x^2$

b. $7x^3 + x^3 = 7x^3 + 1x^3 = (7 + 1)x^3 = 8x^3$

c. $10x^2 + 8x^3$ cannot be simplified because $10x^2$ and $8x^3$ are not like terms.

CHECK POINT 3

$$20 + 4 \cdot 3 - 17 = 20 + 12 - 17$$
$$= 32 - 17$$
$$= 15$$

CHECK POINT 4

$$7^2 - 48 \div 4^2 \cdot 5 - 2 = 49 - 48 \div 16 \cdot 5 - 2$$
$$= 49 - 3 \cdot 5 - 2$$
$$= 49 - 15 - 2$$
$$= 34 - 2$$
$$= 32$$

CHECK POINT 5

a. $(3 \cdot 2)^2 = 6^2 = 36$

b. $3 \cdot 2^2 = 3 \cdot 4 = 12$

CHECK POINT 6

$$(-8)^2 - (10 - 13)^2(-2) = (-8)^2 - (-3)^2(-2)$$
$$= 64 - 9(-2)$$
$$= 64 - (-18)$$
$$= 64 + 18$$
$$= 82$$

CHECK POINT 7

$$4[3(6 - 11) + 5] = 4[3(-5) + 5]$$
$$= 4[-15 + 5]$$
$$= 4[-10]$$
$$= -40$$

CHECK POINT 8

$$25 \div 5 + 3[4 + 2(7 - 9)^3]$$
$$= 25 \div 5 + 3[4 + 2(-2)^3]$$
$$= 25 \div 5 + 3[4 + 2(-8)]$$
$$= 25 \div 5 + 3[4 + (-16)]$$
$$= 25 \div 5 + 3[-12]$$
$$= 25 \div 5 + (-36)$$
$$= 5 + (-36)$$
$$= -31$$

CHECK POINT 9

$$\frac{5(4-9)+10\cdot 3}{2^3-1} = \frac{5(-5)+10\cdot 3}{8-1}$$
$$= \frac{-25+30}{8-1}$$
$$= \frac{5}{7}$$

CHECK POINT 10

Evaluate $-x^2-4x$ for $x=-5$.

$$-x^2-4x = -(-5)^2-4(-5)$$
$$= -25-4(-5)$$
$$= -25+20$$
$$= -5$$

CHECK POINT 11

$$14x^2+5-[7(x^2-2)+4]$$
$$= 14x^2+5-[7x^2-14+4]$$
$$= 14x^2+5-[7x^2-10]$$
$$= 14x^2+5-7x^2+10$$
$$= (14x^2-7x^2)+5+10$$
$$= 7x^2+15$$

CHECK POINT 12

$$N=0.4x^2-36x+1000;\ x=40$$

$$N = 0.4x^2-36x+1000$$
$$= 0.4(40)^2-36(40)+1000$$
$$= 0.4(1600)-1440+1000$$
$$= 640-1440+1000$$
$$= 200$$

For 40-year-old drivers, there are 200 accidents per 50 million miles driven.

CHECK POINT 13

$$C=\frac{5}{9}(F-32);\ F=86$$

$$C = \frac{5}{9}(F-32)$$
$$= \frac{5}{9}(86-32)$$
$$= \frac{5}{9}(54)$$
$$= 30$$

$86°F$ is equivalent to $30°C$.

EXERCISE SET 1.8

1. $9^2 = 9\cdot 9 = 81$

3. $4^3 = 4\cdot 4\cdot 4 = 64$

5. $(-4)^2 = (-4)(-4) = 16$

7. $(-4)^3 = (-4)(-4)(-4) = -64$

9. $(-5)^4 = (-5)(-5)(-5)(-5) = 625$

11. $-5^4 = -5\cdot 5\cdot 5\cdot 5 = -625$

13. $-10^2 = -10\cdot 10 = -100$

15. $6x^2+11x^2 = (6+11)x^2 = 17x^2$

17. $9x^3+4x^3 = (9+4)x^3 = 13x^3$

19. $7x^4+x^4 = 7x^4+1x^4 = (7+1)x^4 = 8x^4$

21. $16x^2-17x^2 = 16x^2+(-17x^2)$
$$= [16+(-17)]x^2$$
$$= -1x^2 = -x^2$$

23. $17x^3-16x^3 = 17x^3+(-16x^3)$
$$= 1x^3 = x^3$$

25. $2x^2+2x^3$ cannot be simplified. The terms $2x^2$ and $2x^3$ are not like terms because they have different variable factors, namely, x^2 and x^3.

27. $6x^2 - 6x^2 = 6x^2 + (-6x^2) = [6 + (-6)]x^2$
$$= 0x^2 = 0$$

29. $7 + 6 \cdot 3 = 7 + 18 = 25$

31. $45 \div 5 \cdot 3 = 9 \cdot 3 = 27$

33. $6 \cdot 8 \div 4 = 48 \div 4 = 12$

35. $14 - 2 \cdot 6 + 3 = 14 - 12 + 3$
$$= 2 + 3 = 5$$

37. $8^2 - 16 \div 2^2 \cdot 4 - 3 = 64 - 16 \div 4 \cdot 4 - 3$
$$= 64 - 4 \cdot 4 - 3$$
$$= 64 - 16 - 3$$
$$= 48 - 3 = 45$$

39. $3(-2)^2 - 4(-3)^2 = 3 \cdot 4 - 4 \cdot 9$
$$= 12 - 36$$
$$= 12 + (-36)$$
$$= -24$$

41. $(4 \cdot 5)^2 - 4 \cdot 5^2 = 20^2 - 4 \cdot 25$
$$= 400 - 100$$
$$= 300$$

43. $(2-6)^2 - (3-7)^2 = (-4)^2 - (-4)^2$
$$= 16 - 16 = 0$$

45. $6(3-5)^3 - 2(1-3)^3 = 6(-2)^3 - 2(-2)^3$
$$= 6(-8) - 2(-8)$$
$$= -48 + 16$$
$$= -32$$

47. $[2(6-2)]^2 = (2 \cdot 4)^2 = 8^2 = 64$

49. $2[5 + 2(9-4)] = 2[5 + 2(5)]$
$$= 2(5 + 10)$$
$$= 2 \cdot 15 = 30$$

51. $[7 + 3(2^3 - 1)] \div 21 = [7 + 3(8-1)] \div 21$
$$= (7 + 3 \cdot 7) \div 21$$
$$= (7 + 21) \div 21$$
$$= 28 \div 21$$
$$= \frac{28}{21} = \frac{\not{7} \cdot 4}{\not{7} \cdot 3} = \frac{4}{3}$$

53. $\dfrac{10 + 8}{5^2 - 4^2} = \dfrac{18}{25 - 16} = \dfrac{18}{9} = 2$

55. $\dfrac{37 + 15 \div (-3)}{2^4} = \dfrac{37 + (-5)}{16}$
$$= \frac{32}{16} = 2$$

57. $\dfrac{(-11)(-4) + 2(-7)}{7 - (-3)} = \dfrac{44 + (-14)}{7 + 3}$
$$= \frac{30}{10} = 3$$

59. $4|10 - (8-20)| = 4|10 - (-12)|$
$$= 4|22|$$
$$= 4 \cdot 22 = 88$$

61. $8(-10) + |4(-5)| = -80 + |-20|$
$$= -80 + 20$$
$$= -60$$

63. $-2^2 + 4[16 + (3-5)]$
$$= -4 + 4[16 + (-2)]$$
$$= -4 + 4(-8)$$
$$= -4 - 32 = -36$$

65. $24 \div \dfrac{3^2}{8-5} - (-6) = 24 \div \dfrac{9}{3} - (-6)$
$$= 24 \div 3 - (-6)$$
$$= 8 + 6 = 14$$

67. $x^2 + 5x; x = 3$
$$x^2 + 5x = 3^2 + 5 \cdot 3$$
$$= 9 + 5 \cdot 3$$
$$= 9 + 15 = 24$$

69. $3x^2 - 8x; x = -2$
$$3x^2 - 8x = 3(-2)^2 - 8(-2)$$
$$= 3 \cdot 4 - 8(-2)$$
$$= 12 + 16 = 28$$

71. $-x^2 - 10x; x = -1$
$$-x^2 - 10x = -(-1)^2 - 10(-1)$$
$$= -1 + 10 = 9$$

73. $\dfrac{6y - 4y^2}{y^2 - 15}$; $y = 5$

$$\dfrac{6y - 4y^2}{y^2 - 15} = \dfrac{6(5) - 4(5^2)}{5^2 - 15}$$

$$= \dfrac{6(5) - 4(25)}{25 - 15}$$

$$= \dfrac{30 - 100}{25 - 15}$$

$$= \dfrac{-70}{10} = -7$$

75. $3[5(x - 2) + 1] = 3(5x - 10 + 1)$
$$= 3(5x - 9)$$
$$= 15x - 27$$

77. $3[6 - (y + 1)] = 3(6 - y - 1)$
$$= 3(5 - y)$$
$$= 15 - 3y$$

79. $7 - 4[3 - (4y - 5)]$
$$= 7 - 4(3 - 4y + 5)$$
$$= 7 - 12 + 16y - 20$$
$$= -25 + 16y \quad \text{or} \quad 16y - 25$$

81. $2(3x^2 - 5) - [4(2x^2 - 1) + 3]$
$$= 6x^2 - 10 - (8x^2 - 4 + 3)$$
$$= 6x^2 - 10 - (8x^2 - 1)$$
$$= 6x^2 - 10 - 8x^2 - 1$$
$$= -2x^2 - 9$$

83. $W = 1.5x + 7$; $x = 4$

$$W = 1.5x + 7 = 1.5(4) + 7 = 13$$

On the average, a four-month-old infant girl weighs 13 pounds. This corresponds to the point $(4, 13)$ on the graph.

85. $R = 165 - 0.75A$; $A = 40$

$$R = 165 - 0.75A = 165 - 0.75(40)$$
$$= 165 - 30 = 135$$

The desirable heart rate during exercise for a 40-year-old man is 135 beats per minute. This corresponds to the point $(40, 135)$ on the graph.

87. Since $2000 - 1996 = 4$, the year 2000 corresponds to $x = 4$.

$$N = 0.4x^2 + 0.5; \; x = 4$$

$$N = 0.4x^2 + 0.5 = 0.4(4^2) + 0.5$$
$$= 0.4(16) + 0.5$$
$$= 6.4 + 0.5$$
$$= 6.9$$

According to the formula, 6.9 million people in the United States used cable TV modems in 2000. This is quite close to the 7 million shown by the bar graph.

89. Since $2000 - 1995 = 5$, the year 2005 corresponds to $x = 5$.

$$N = 1.2x^2 + 15.2x + 181.4; \; x = 5$$

$$N = 1.2x^2 + 15.2x + 181.4$$
$$= 1.2(5^2) + 15.2(5) + 181.4$$
$$= 1.2(25) + 15.2(5) + 181.4$$
$$= 30 + 76 + 181.4$$
$$= 287.4$$

According to the formula, the cost of Medicare in 2000 was $287.4 billion. This is a very good estimate for the cost shown by the bar graph.

91. $C = \dfrac{5}{9}(F - 32)$; $F = 68$

$$C = \dfrac{5}{9}(F - 32) = \dfrac{5}{9}(68 - 32)$$

$$= \dfrac{5}{9}(36)$$

$$= \dfrac{5}{9} \cdot \dfrac{36}{1}$$

$$= \dfrac{180}{9} = 20$$

$68°\text{F} = 20°\text{C}$

93. $C = \dfrac{5}{9}(F - 32); \; F = -22$

$$C = \frac{5}{9}(F - 32) = \frac{5}{9}(-22 - 32)$$

$$= \frac{5}{9}(-54)$$

$$= \frac{5}{9} \cdot \frac{54}{1}$$

$$= -\frac{270}{9} = -30$$

$$-22°\text{F} = -30°\text{C}$$

For Exercises 95–99, answers may vary.

101. $\dfrac{1}{4} - 6(2 + 8) \div \left(-\dfrac{1}{3}\right)\left(-\dfrac{1}{9}\right)$

$$= \frac{1}{4} - 6(10) \div \left(-\frac{1}{3}\right)\left(-\frac{1}{9}\right)$$

$$= \frac{1}{4} - 60 \div \left(-\frac{1}{3}\right)\left(-\frac{1}{9}\right)$$

$$= \frac{1}{4} - 60 \div (-3)\left(-\frac{1}{9}\right)$$

$$= \frac{1}{4} + 180\left(-\frac{1}{9}\right)$$

$$= \frac{1}{4} - 20$$

$$= \frac{1}{4} - \frac{80}{4} = -\frac{79}{4}$$

103. $\left(2 \cdot 5 - \dfrac{1}{2} \cdot 10\right) \cdot 9 = (10 - 5) \cdot 9$

$$= 5 \cdot 9 = 45$$

105. Since $1999 - 1990 = 8$, the year 1999 corresponds to $x = 9$.

$$N = -1.65x^2 + 51.8x + 111.44; \; x = 9$$

$$N = -1.65(9^2) + 51.8(9) + 111.44$$
$$= 443.99$$

According to the formula, the cumulative number of AIDS deaths in 1999 was 443.99 thousand or 443,990.

Review Exercises

107. $-8 - 2 - (-5) + 11$
$$= -8 + (-2) + 5 + 11$$
$$= [(-8) + (-2)] + (5 + 11)$$
$$= -10 + 16 = 6$$

108. $-4(-1)(-3)(2) = -24$

109. Any rational number is a real number that is not an irrational number. One example is $-\dfrac{3}{4}$.

Chapter 1 Review Exercises

1. $\dfrac{15}{33} = \dfrac{\cancel{3} \cdot 5}{\cancel{3} \cdot 11} = \dfrac{5}{11}$

2. $\dfrac{40}{75} = \dfrac{\cancel{5} \cdot 8}{\cancel{5} \cdot 15} = \dfrac{8}{15}$

3. $\dfrac{3}{5} \cdot \dfrac{7}{10} = \dfrac{3 \cdot 7}{5 \cdot 10} = \dfrac{21}{50}$

4. $\dfrac{4}{5} \div \dfrac{3}{10} = \dfrac{4}{5} \cdot \dfrac{10}{3} = \dfrac{40}{15}$

$$= \frac{\cancel{5} \cdot 8}{\cancel{5} \cdot 3} = \frac{8}{3}$$

5. $\dfrac{2}{9} + \dfrac{4}{9} = \dfrac{2 + 4}{9} = \dfrac{6}{9} = \dfrac{2}{3}$

6. $\dfrac{5}{6} + \dfrac{7}{9} = \dfrac{5}{6} \cdot \dfrac{3}{3} + \dfrac{7}{9} \cdot \dfrac{2}{2}$

$$= \frac{15}{18} + \frac{14}{18} = \frac{29}{18}$$

7. $\dfrac{3}{4} - \dfrac{2}{15} = \dfrac{3}{4} \cdot \dfrac{15}{15} - \dfrac{2}{15} \cdot \dfrac{4}{4}$

$$= \frac{45}{60} - \frac{8}{60} = \frac{37}{60}$$

8. $1 - \dfrac{1}{4} - \dfrac{1}{3} = \dfrac{12}{12} - \dfrac{3}{12} - \dfrac{4}{12} = \dfrac{5}{12}$

At the end of the second day, $\dfrac{5}{12}$ of the tank is filled.

9.

$$-2.5$$
number line with $-5\,-4\,-3\,-2\,-1\;0\;1\;2\;3\;4\;5$ and point plotted at -2.5, labeled x

10.

$$4\tfrac{3}{4}$$
number line with $-5\,-4\,-3\,-2\,-1\;0\;1\;2\;3\;4\;5$ and point plotted at $4\tfrac{3}{4}$, labeled x

11.

$$
\begin{array}{r}
0.625 \\
8\overline{)5.000} \\
\underline{4\,8} \\
20 \\
\underline{16} \\
40 \\
\underline{40} \\
0
\end{array}
$$

$$\frac{5}{8} = 0.625$$

12.

$$
\begin{array}{r}
0.2727\ldots \\
11\overline{)3.0000\ldots} \\
\underline{2\,2} \\
80 \\
\underline{77} \\
30 \\
\underline{27} \\
30 \\
\underline{22} \\
8 \\
\vdots
\end{array}
$$

$$\frac{3}{11} = 0.\overline{27}$$

13.
a. $\sqrt{81}\ (=9)$
b. $0, \sqrt{81}$
c. $-17, 0, \sqrt{81}$
d. $-17, -\dfrac{9}{13}, 0, 0.75, \sqrt{81}$
e. $\sqrt{2}, \pi$
f. All numbers in given set.

In Exercises 14–16, examples may vary.

14. One integer that is not a natural number is -7.

15. One rational number that is not an integer is $\frac{3}{4}$.

16. One real number that is not a rational number is π.

17. $-93 < 17$; -93 is to the left of 17, so -93 is less than 17.

18. $-2 > -200$; -2 is to the right of -200, so -2 is greater than -200.

19. $0 > -\frac{1}{3}$; 0 is to the right of $-\frac{1}{3}$ so $0 > -\frac{1}{3}$.

20. $-\frac{1}{4} < -\frac{1}{5}$; $-\frac{1}{4} = -0.25$ is to the left of $-\frac{1}{5} = -0.2$, so $-\frac{1}{4} < -\frac{1}{5}$.

21. $-13 \geq -11$ is false because neither $-13 > -11$ nor $-13 = -11$ is true.

22. $-126 \leq -126$ is true because $-126 = -126$.

23. $|-58| = 58$ because the distance between -58 and 0 on the number line is 58.

24. $|2.75| = 2.75$ because the distance between 2.75 and 0 on the number line is 2.75.

25. Quadrant IV

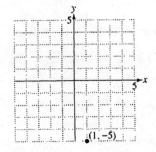

26.   Quadrant IV

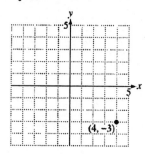

27.   Quadrant I

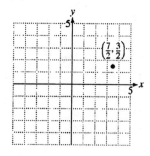

28.   Quadrant II

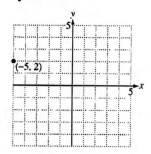

29. $A(5,6)$
$B(-2,0)$
$C(-5,2)$
$D(-4,-2)$
$E(0,-5)$
$F(3,-1)$

30. The number of murders per 100,000 people in 2000 was approximately 7.

31. The murder rate reached a maximum in 1980. There were approximately 10 murders per 100,000 people that year.

32. Approximately 90% of households in the United States have VCRs.

33. According to the graph, fewer than 40% of people in the United States use a camcorder or satellite dish.

34. 45% of 24 million $= 0.45\,(24\text{ million})$
$= 10.8$ million

There are about 10.8 million female runners in the United States.

35. $7x + 3$; $x = 10$
$$7x + 3 = 7(10) + 3 = 70 + 3 = 73$$

36. $5(x - 4)$; $x = 12$
$$5(x - 4) = 5(12 - 4) = 5 \cdot 8 = 40$$

37. $7 + 13y = 13y + 7$

38. $9(x + 7) = (x + 7)9$

39. $6 + (4 + y) = (6 + 4) + y = 10 + y$

40. $7(10x) = (7 \cdot 10)x = 70x$

41. $6(4x - 2 + 5y) = 6(4x) + 6(-2) + 6(5y)$
$$= 24x - 12 + 30y$$

42. $4a + 9 + 3a - 7 = 4a + 3a + 9 - 7$
$$= (4 + 3)a + (9 - 7)$$
$$= 7a + 2$$

43. $6(3x + 4) + 5(2x - 1)$
$$= 6(3x) + 6(4) + 5(2x) + 5(-1)$$
$$= 18x + 24 + 10x - 5$$
$$= 18x + 10x + 24 - 5$$
$$= (18 + 10)x + [24 + (-5)]$$
$$= 28x + 19$$

44. $x - 0.25x$; $x = 2400$
$$x - 0.25x = 2400 - 0.25(2400)$$
$$= 2400 - 600 = 1800$$

This means that a computer with a regular price of \$2400 will have a sale price of \$1800.

45. $-6 + 8 = 2$

Start at -6. Move 8 units to the right because 8 is positive. Finish at 2.

46. $8 + (-11) = -3$

47. $-\dfrac{3}{4} + \dfrac{1}{5} = -\dfrac{3}{4} \cdot \dfrac{5}{5} + \dfrac{1}{5} \cdot \dfrac{4}{4}$

$\qquad = -\dfrac{15}{20} + \dfrac{4}{20} = -\dfrac{11}{20}$

48. $7 + (-5) + (-13) + 4$
$\quad = [7 + (-5)] + (-13) + 4$
$\quad = 2 + (-13) + 4$
$\quad = [2 + (-13)] + 4$
$\quad = -11 + 4 = -7$

49. $8x + (-6y) + (-12x) + 11y$
$\quad = 8x + (-12x) + (-6y) + 11y$
$\quad = [8 + (-12)]x + (-6 + 11)y$
$\quad = -4x + 5y \text{ or } 5y - 4x$

50. $10(4 - 3y) + 28y$
$\quad = 10(4) + 10(-3y) + 28y$
$\quad = 40 - 30y + 28y$
$\quad = 40 + (-30 + 28)y$
$\quad = 40 - 2y$

51. $-1312 + 512 = -800$

The person's elevation is 800 feet below sea level.

52. $25 - 3 + 2 + 1 - 4 + 2$
$\quad = 25 + (-3) + 2 + 1 + (-4) + 2$
$\quad = 23$

The reservoir's water level at the end of five months is 23 feet.

53. $9 - 13 = 9 + (-13)$

54. $-9 - (-13) = -9 + 13 = 4$

55. $-\dfrac{7}{10} - \dfrac{1}{2} = -\dfrac{7}{10} - \dfrac{1}{2} \cdot \dfrac{5}{5}$

$\qquad = -\dfrac{7}{10} - \dfrac{5}{10}$

$\qquad = -\dfrac{12}{10} = -\dfrac{6}{5}$

56. $-3.6 - (-2.1) = -3.6 + 2.1 = -1.5$

57. $-7 - (-5) + 11 - 16 = -7 + 5 + 11 + (-16)$
$\qquad\qquad\qquad\qquad = -2 + 11 + (-16)$
$\qquad\qquad\qquad\qquad = 9 + (-16) = -7$

58. $-25 - 4 - (-10) + 16$
$\quad = -25 - 4 + 10 + 16$
$\quad = (-25) + (-4) + 10 + 16$
$\quad = -29 + 10 + 16$
$\quad = (-29) + 10 + 16$
$\quad = -19 + 16$
$\quad = (-19) + 16 = -3$

59. $3 - 6a - 8 - 2a = 3 - 8 - 6a - 2a$
$\qquad\qquad\qquad = [3 + (-8)] + [-6a - 2a]$
$\qquad\qquad\qquad = -5 + (-6 - 2)a$
$\qquad\qquad\qquad = -5 - 8a$

60. $26{,}500 - (-650) = 26{,}500 + 650$
$\qquad\qquad\qquad = 27{,}150$

The difference in elevation is 27,150 feet.

61. $(-7)(-12) = 84$

62. $\dfrac{3}{5}\left(-\dfrac{5}{11}\right) = -\dfrac{3 \cdot \cancel{5}}{\cancel{5} \cdot 11} = -\dfrac{3}{11}$

63. $5(-3)(-2)(-4) = -120$

64. $\dfrac{45}{-5} = 45\left(-\dfrac{1}{5}\right) = -9$

65. $-17 \div 0$ is undefined.

66. $-\dfrac{4}{5} \div \left(-\dfrac{2}{5}\right) = -\dfrac{4}{5}\left(-\dfrac{5}{2}\right) = \dfrac{20}{10} = 2$

67. $-4\left(-\dfrac{3}{4}x\right) = \left[-4\left(-\dfrac{3}{4}\right)\right]x = 3x$

68. $-3(2x - 1) - (4 - 5x)$

$\quad = -3(2x) + (-3)(-1) - 4 + 5x$

$\quad = -6x + 3 - 4 + 5x$

$\quad = -6x + 5x + 3 - 4$

$\quad = (-6 + 5)x + [3 + (-4)]$

$\quad = -1x - 1 = -x - 1$

69. $(-6)^2 = (-6)(-6) = 36$

70. $-6^2 = -6 \cdot 6 = -36$

71. $(-2)^5 = (-2)(-2)(-2)(-2)(-2) = -32$

72. $4x^3 + 2x^3 = (4 + 2)x^3 = 6x^3$

73. $4x^3 + 4x^2$ cannot be simplified. The terms $4x^3 + 4x^2$ are not like terms because they have different variable factors, x^3 and x^2.

74. $-40 \div 5 \cdot 2 = -8 \cdot 2 = -16$

75. $-6 + (-2) \cdot 5 = -6 + (-10) = -16$

76. $6 - 4(-3 + 2) = 6 - 4(-1) = 6 + 4 = 10$

77. $28 \div (2 - 4^2) = 28 \div (2 - 16)$

$\quad = 28 \div [2 + (-16)]$

$\quad = 28 \div (-14) = -2$

78. $36 - 24 \div 4 \cdot 3 - 1 = 36 - 6 \cdot 3 - 1$

$\quad = 36 - 18 - 1$

$\quad = 18 - 1 = 17$

79. $-8[-4 - 5(-3)] = -8(-4 + 15)$

$\quad = -8(11) = -88$

80. $\dfrac{6(-10 + 3)}{2(-15) - 9(-3)} = \dfrac{6(-7)}{-30 + 27}$

$\quad = \dfrac{-42}{-3} = 14$

81. $x^2 - 2x + 3; \; x = -1$

$\quad x^2 - 2x + 3 = (-1)^2 - 2(-1) + 3$

$\quad = 1 + 2 + 3 = 6$

82. $-x^2 - 7x; \; x = -2$

$\quad -x^2 - 7x = -(-2)^2 - 7(-2)$

$\quad = -4 + 14 = 10$

83. $4[7(a - 1) + 2] = 4(7a - 7 + 2)$

$\quad = 4(7a - 5)$

$\quad = 4(7a) + 4(-5)$

$\quad = 28a - 20$

84. $-6[4 - (y + 2)] = -6(4 - y - 2)$

$\quad = -6(2 - y)$

$\quad = -6(2) + (-6)(-y)$

$\quad = -12 + 6y \quad \text{or} \quad 6y - 12$

85. Since $2004 - 1984 = 20$, the year 2004 corresponds to $x = 20$.

$\quad N = 0.07x + 4.1; \; x = 20$

$\quad N = 0.07x + 4.1 = 0.07(20) + 4.1$

$\quad = 1.4 + 4.1$

$\quad = 5.5$

According to the formula, 5.5 women will be enrolled in U.S. colleges in 2004. This is close to the enrollment shown in the line graph, which is about 5.3 million.

86. $N = 0.01x + 3.9; \; x = 20$

$\quad N = 0.01x + 3.9 = 0.01(20) + 3.9$

$\quad = 0.2 + 3.9$

$\quad = 4.1$

According to the formula, 4.1 million men will be enrolled in U.S. colleges in 2004. The line graph also shows about 4.1 million.

87. Since $1990 - 1980 = 10$, the year 1990 corresponds to $x = 10$.

$\quad N = 2x^2 + 22x + 320; \; x = 10$

$\quad N = 2x^2 + 22x + 320$

$\quad = 2(10^2) + 22(10) + 320$

$\quad = 200 + 220 + 320$

$\quad = 740$

According to the formula, the U.S. prison population in 1990 was 740 thousand or 740,000. This is very close to the number shown in the line graph.

88. The prison population is growing at an increasing rate.

Chapter 1 Test

1. $1.4 - (-2.6) = 1.4 + 2.6 = 4$

2. $-9 + 3 + (-11) + 6 = (-9 + 3) + (-11) + 6$
$$= -6 + (-11) + 6$$
$$= -17 + 6 = -11$$

3. $3(-17) = -51$

4. $\left(-\dfrac{3}{7}\right) \div \left(-\dfrac{15}{7}\right) = \left(-\dfrac{3}{7}\right)\left(-\dfrac{7}{15}\right) = \dfrac{21}{105}$
$$= \dfrac{2\!\!\!/1 \cdot 1}{2\!\!\!/1 \cdot 5} = \dfrac{1}{5}$$

5. $-50 \div 10 = -50\left(\dfrac{1}{10}\right) = -5$

6. $-6 - (5 - 12) = -6 - (-7) = -6 + 7 = 1$

7. $(-3)(-4) \div (7 - 10)$
$$= (-3)(-4) \div [7 + (-10)]$$
$$= (-3)(-4) \div (-3)$$
$$= 12 \div (-3) = -4$$

8. $(6 - 8)^2(5 - 7)^3 = (-2)^2(-2)^3$
$$= 4(-8) = -32$$

9. $\dfrac{3(-2) - 2(2)}{-2(8 - 3)} = \dfrac{-6 - 4}{-2(5)}$
$$= \dfrac{-6 + (-4)}{-2(5)}$$
$$= \dfrac{-10}{-10} = 1$$

10. $11x - (7x - 4) = 11x - 7x + 4$
$$= 11x + (-7x) + 4$$
$$= [11 + (-7)]x + 4$$
$$= 4x + 4$$

11. $5(3x - 4y) - (2x - y)$
$$= 5(3x) + 5(-4y) - 2x + y$$
$$= 15x - 20y - 2x + y$$
$$= 15x - 2x - 20y + y$$
$$= 13x - 19y$$

12. $6 - 2[3(x + 1) - 5] = 6 - 2[3x + 3 - 5]$
$$= 6 - 2(3x - 2)$$
$$= 6 - 6x + 4$$
$$= 10 - 6x$$

13. Rational numbers can be written as the quotient of two integers.
$$-7 = -\dfrac{7}{1}, -\dfrac{4}{5} = \dfrac{-4}{5}, 0 = \dfrac{0}{1}, 0.25 = \dfrac{1}{4},$$
$$\sqrt{4} = 2 = \dfrac{2}{1}, \text{ and } \dfrac{22}{7} = \dfrac{22}{7}.$$
Therefore, $-7, -\dfrac{4}{5}, 0, 0.25, \sqrt{4},$ and, $\dfrac{22}{7}$ are the rational numbers of the set.

14. $-1 > -100$; -1 is to the right of -100 on the number line, so -1 is greater than -100.

15. $|-12.8| = 12.8$ because the distance between 12.8 and 0 on the number line is 12.8.

16. Quadrant II

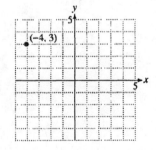

17. The coordinates of point A are $(-5, -2)$.

18. $5(x - 7)$; $x = 4$

$$5(x - 7) = 5(4 - 7) = 5(-3) = -15$$

19. $x^2 - 5x$; $x = -10$

$$x^2 - 5x = (-10)^2 - 5(-10)$$
$$= 100 + 50 = 150$$

20. $2(x + 3) = 2(3 + x)$

21. $-6(4x) = (-6 \cdot 4)x = -24x$

22. $7(5x - 1 + 2y) = 7(5x) + 7(-1) + 7(2y)$
$$= 35x - 7 + 14y$$

23. The coordinates of point A are $(30, 200)$. This means that 30 years after the elk were introduced into the habitat, the elk population was 200.

24. The point $(0, 50)$ indicates that 50 elk were introduced into the habitat.

25. According to the bar graph, approximately 9.7 million U.S. households will be investing online in 2003.

26. A good estimate is 37% of $17 = 0.37(17)$
$$= 6.29 \approx 6.3.$$

There are approximately 6.3 million acres of impaired lakes in the United States.

27. $T = 3(A - 20)^2 \div 50 + 10$; $A = 30$

$$T = 3(A - 20)^2 \div 50 + 10$$
$$= 3(30 - 20)^2 \div 50 + 10$$
$$= 3(10^2) \div 50 + 10$$
$$= 300 \div 50 + 10$$
$$= 6 + 10 = 16$$

According to the formula, it takes a 30-year-old runner 16 seconds to run the 100-yard dash.

28. According to the line graph, the average mortgage loan in 1990 was about $95 thousand or $95,000.

29. Since $1990 - 1980 = 10$, the year 1990 corresponds to $x = 10$.

$$N = 3.5x + 58; \ x = 10$$

$$N = 3.5x + 58 = 3.5(10) + 58$$
$$= 35 + 58 = 93$$

According to the formula, the average mortgage loan in 1990 was $93 thousand or $93,000.

30. $16,200 - (-830) = 17,030$

The difference in elevations is 17,030 feet.

Chapter 2

LINEAR EQUATIONS AND INEQUALITIES IN ONE VARIABLE

The Addition Property of Equality

2.1 CHECK POINTS

CHECK POINT 1

$$5x - 3 = 17$$

a. Substitute 3 for x.

$$5x - 3 = 17$$
$$5(3) - 3 \overset{?}{=} 17$$
$$15 - 3 \overset{?}{=} 17$$
$$12 = 17 \text{ false}$$

3 is not a solution to the given equation.

b. Substitute 4 for x.

$$5x - 3 = 17$$
$$5(4) - 3 \overset{?}{=} 17$$
$$20 - 3 \overset{?}{=} 17$$
$$17 = 17 \text{ true}$$

4 is a solution to the given equation.

CHECK POINT 2

$$x - 5 = 12$$
$$x - 5 + 5 = 12 + 5$$
$$x = 17$$

Check

$$x - 5 = 12$$
$$17 - 5 = 12$$
$$12 = 12 \text{ true}$$

Because the check results in a true statement, the solution to the given equation is 17.

CHECK POINT 3

$$x + 2.8 = 5.09$$
$$x + 2.8 - 2.8 = 5.09 - 2.8$$
$$x = 2.29$$

Check:

$$x + 2.8 = 5.09$$
$$2.29 + 2.8 \overset{?}{=} 5.09$$
$$5.09 = 5.09 \text{ true}$$

The solution is 2.29.

CHECK POINT 4

$$-\frac{1}{2} = x - \frac{3}{4}$$
$$-\frac{1}{2} + \frac{3}{4} = x - \frac{3}{4} + \frac{3}{4}$$
$$-\frac{2}{4} + \frac{3}{4} = x$$
$$\frac{1}{4} = x$$

Check:

$$-\frac{1}{2} = x - \frac{3}{4}$$
$$-\frac{1}{2} \overset{?}{=} \frac{1}{4} - \frac{3}{4}$$
$$-\frac{1}{2} \overset{?}{=} -\frac{2}{4}$$
$$-\frac{1}{2} = -\frac{1}{2} \text{ true}$$

The solution is $\frac{1}{4}$.

CHECK POINT 5

$$8y + 7 - 7y - 10 = 6 + 4$$
$$y - 3 = 10$$
$$y - 3 + 3 = 10 + 3$$
$$y = 13$$

Check:

$$8y + 7 - 7y - 10 = 6 + 4$$
$$8(13) + 7 - 7(13) - 10 \stackrel{?}{=} 6 + 4$$
$$104 + 7 - 91 - 10 \stackrel{?}{=} 6 + 4$$
$$111 - 101 \stackrel{?}{=} 10$$
$$10 = 10 \text{ true}$$

The solution is 13.

CHECK POINT 6

$$7x = 12 + 6x$$
$$7x - 6x = 12 + 6x - 6x$$
$$x = 12$$

Check:

$$7x = 12 + 6x$$
$$7(12) \stackrel{?}{=} 12 + 6(12)$$
$$84 \stackrel{?}{=} 12 + 72$$
$$84 = 84 \text{ true}$$

The solution is 12.

CHECK POINT 7

$$3x - 6 = 2x + 5$$
$$3x - 2x - 6 = 2x - 2x + 5$$
$$x - 6 = 5$$
$$x - 6 + 6 = 5 + 6$$
$$x = 11$$

Check:

$$3x - 6 = 2x + 5$$
$$3(11) - 6 \stackrel{?}{=} 2(11) + 5$$
$$33 - 6 \stackrel{?}{=} 22 + 5$$
$$27 = 27 \text{ true}$$

The solution is 11.

CHECK POINT 8

Substitute 50 for A in the given formula, and find the corresponding value of V.

$$V + 900 = 60A$$
$$V + 900 = 60(50)$$
$$V + 900 = 3000$$
$$V + 900 - 900 = 3000 - 900$$
$$V = 2100$$

According to the formula, the vocabulary of a 50-month-old child is 2100 words.

EXERCISE SET 2.1

1.
$$x - 7 = 13$$
$$x - 7 + 7 = 13 + 7$$
$$x + 0 = 20$$
$$x = 20$$

Check:

$$x - 7 \stackrel{?}{=} 13$$
$$20 - 7 = 13$$
$$13 = 13$$

The solution is 20.

3. $z + 5 = -12$
$$z + 5 = -12 - 5$$
$$z = -17$$

Check:

$$z + 5 \stackrel{?}{=} -12$$
$$-17 + 5 \stackrel{?}{=} -12$$
$$-12 = -12$$

The solution is -17.

5.
$$-3 = x + 14$$
$$-3 = x + 14 - 14$$
$$-17 = x$$

Check:

$$-3 \stackrel{?}{=} -17 + 14$$
$$-3 = -3$$

The solution is -17.

7.
$$-18 = y - 5$$
$$-18 + 5 = y - 5 + 5$$
$$-13 = y$$

Check:

$$-18 \overset{?}{=} -13 - 5$$
$$-18 = -18$$

The solution is -13.

9. $7 + z = 13$
$$z = 13 - 7$$
$$z = 6$$

Check:

$$7 + 6 \overset{?}{=} 13$$
$$13 = 13$$

The solution is 6.

11. $-3 + y = -17$
$$y = -17 + 3$$
$$y = -14$$

Check:

$$-3 - 14 \overset{?}{=} -17$$
$$-17 = -17$$

The solution is -14.

13. $x + \dfrac{1}{3} = \dfrac{7}{3}$
$$x = \frac{7}{3} - \frac{1}{3}$$
$$x = 2$$

Check:

$$2 + \frac{1}{3} \overset{?}{=} \frac{7}{3}$$
$$\frac{6}{3} + \frac{1}{3} = \frac{7}{3}$$
$$\frac{7}{3} = \frac{7}{3}$$

The solution is 2.

15. $t + \dfrac{5}{6} = -\dfrac{7}{12}$
$$t = -\frac{7}{12} - \frac{5}{6}$$
$$t = -\frac{7}{12} - \frac{10}{12} = -\frac{17}{12}$$

Check:

$$-\frac{17}{12} + \frac{5}{6} \overset{?}{=} -\frac{7}{12}$$
$$-\frac{17}{12} + \frac{10}{12} \overset{?}{=} -\frac{7}{12}$$
$$-\frac{7}{12} = -\frac{7}{12}$$

The solution is $-\frac{17}{12}$.

17. $x - \dfrac{3}{4} = \dfrac{9}{2}$
$$x - \frac{3}{4} + \frac{3}{4} = \frac{9}{2} + \frac{3}{4}$$
$$x = \frac{21}{4}$$

Check:

$$\frac{21}{4} - \frac{3}{4} \overset{?}{=} \frac{9}{2}$$
$$\frac{18}{4} \overset{?}{=} \frac{9}{2}$$
$$\frac{9}{2} = \frac{9}{2}$$

The solution is $\frac{21}{4}$.

19. $-\dfrac{1}{5} + y = -\dfrac{3}{4}$
$$y = -\frac{3}{4} + \frac{1}{5}$$
$$y = -\frac{15}{20} + \frac{4}{20} = -\frac{11}{20}$$

Check:

$$-\frac{1}{5} - \frac{11}{20} \overset{?}{=} -\frac{3}{4}$$

$$-\frac{4}{20} - \frac{11}{20} \overset{?}{=} -\frac{3}{4}$$

$$-\frac{15}{20} \overset{?}{=} -\frac{3}{4}$$

$$-\frac{3}{4} = -\frac{3}{4}$$

The solution is $-\frac{11}{20}$.

21. $\quad 3.2 + x = 7.5$

$3.2 + x - 3.2 = 7.5 - 3.2$

$\quad\quad\quad x = 4.3$

Check:

$3.2 + 4.3 \overset{?}{=} 7.5$

$\quad 7.5 = 7.5$

The solution is 4.3.

23. $\quad x + \frac{3}{4} = -\frac{9}{2}$

$x + \frac{3}{4} - \frac{3}{4} = -\frac{9}{2} - \frac{3}{4}$

$\quad\quad\quad x = -\frac{21}{4}$

Check:

$$-\frac{21}{4} + \frac{3}{4} \overset{?}{=} -\frac{9}{2}$$

$$-\frac{18}{4} = -\frac{9}{2}$$

$$-\frac{9}{2} = -\frac{9}{2}$$

The solution is $-\frac{21}{4}$.

25. $\quad 5 = -13 + y$

$5 + 13 = y$

$\quad 18 = y$

Check:

$5 \overset{?}{=} -13 + 18$

$5 = 5$

The solution is 18.

27. $\quad -\frac{3}{5} = -\frac{3}{2} + s$

$-\frac{3}{5} + \frac{3}{2} = s$

$-\frac{6}{10} + \frac{15}{10} = s$

$\frac{9}{10} = s$

Check:

$$-\frac{3}{5} = -\frac{3}{2} + \frac{9}{10}$$

$$-\frac{6}{10} = -\frac{15}{10} + \frac{9}{10}$$

$$-\frac{6}{10} = -\frac{6}{10}$$

The solution is $\frac{9}{10}$.

29. $830 + y = 520$

$\quad y = 520 - 830$

$\quad y = -310$

Check:

$830 - 310 \overset{?}{=} 520$

$\quad 520 = 520$

The solution is -310.

31. $r + 3.7 = 8$

$\quad r = 8 - 3.7$

$\quad r = 4.3$

Check:

$4.3 + 3.7 \overset{?}{=} 8$

$\quad 8 = 8$

The solution is 4.3.

33. $-3.7 + m = -3.7$

$\quad m = -3.7 + 3.7$

$\quad m = 0$

Check:

$-3.7 + 0 \overset{?}{=} -3.7$

$\quad -3.7 = -3.7$

The solution is 0.

35. $6y + 3 - 5y = 14$

$$y + 3 = 14$$
$$y = 14 - 3$$
$$y = 11$$

Check:

$$6(11) + 3 - 5(11) \overset{?}{=} 14$$
$$66 + 3 - 55 \overset{?}{=} 14$$
$$14 = 14$$

The solution is 11.

37. $7 - 5x + 8 + 2x + 4x - 3 = 2 + 3 \cdot 5$

$$x + 12 = 2 + 15$$
$$x = 17 - 12$$
$$x = 5$$

Check:

$$7 - 5(5) + 8 + 2(5) + 4(5) - 3 \overset{?}{=} 2 + 3 \cdot 5$$
$$7 - 25 + 8 + 10 + 20 - 3 \overset{?}{=} 2 + 15$$
$$45 - 18 \overset{?}{=} 17$$
$$17 = 17$$

The solution is 5.

39. $\qquad 7y + 4 = 6y - 9$

$$7y - 6y + 4 = -9$$
$$y = -9 - 4$$
$$y = -13$$

Check:

$$7(-13) + 4 \overset{?}{=} 6(-13) - 9$$
$$-91 + 4 \overset{?}{=} -78 - 9$$
$$-87 = -87$$

The solution is -13.

41. $18 - 7x = 12 - 6x$

$$18 = 12 + x$$
$$6 = x$$

Check:

$$18 - 7(6) \overset{?}{=} 12 - 6(6)$$
$$18 - 42 \overset{?}{=} 12 - 36$$
$$-24 = -24$$

The solution is 6.

43. Since $2005 - 1995 = 10$, the year 2005 corresponds to $x = 10$.

$$D - 15x = 62; \; x = 10$$

$$D - 15x = 62$$
$$D - 15(10) = 62$$
$$D - 150 = 62$$
$$D = 62 + 150$$
$$D = 212$$

According to the formula, about \$212 billion will be spend on prescription drugs in the United States in 2005.

45. $C + M = S; \; S = 1850, M = 150$

$$C + M - S$$
$$C + 150 = 1850$$
$$C = 1850 - 150$$
$$C = 1700$$

The cost of the computer is \$1700.

47. $d + 525{,}000 = 5000c; \; c = 210$

$$d + 525{,}000 = 5000c$$
$$d + 525{,}000 = 5000(210)$$
$$d + 525{,}000 = 1{,}050{,}000$$
$$d = 1{,}050{,}000 - 525{,}000$$
$$d = 525{,}000$$

According to the formula, 525,000 deaths per year from heart disease can be expected at this cholesterol level.

For Exercises 49–53, answers may vary.

55. $|x| + 4 = 10$

$$|x| = 10 - 4$$
$$|x| = 6$$

There are two numbers whose absolute value (distance from 0) is 6: -6 and 6. Therefore, the equation has two solutions, -6 and 6.

57.
$$6.9825 = 4.2296 + y$$
$$6.9825 - 4.2296 = y$$
$$2.7529 = y$$

The solution is 2.7529.

Review Exercises

58. Quadrant II

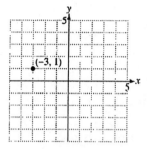

59.
$$-16 - 8 \div 4 \cdot (-2) = -16 - 2(-2)$$
$$= -16 + 4$$
$$= -12$$

60.
$$3[7x - 2(5x - 1)] = 3(7x - 10x + 2)$$
$$= 3(-3x + 2)$$
$$= -9x + 6 \text{ or } 6 - 9x$$

The Multiplication Property of Equality

2.2 CHECK POINTS

CHECK POINT 1
$$\frac{x}{3} = 12$$
$$3 \cdot \frac{x}{3} = 3 \cdot 12$$
$$1x = 36$$
$$x = 36$$

The solution is 36.

CHECK POINT 2

a.
$$4x = 84$$
$$\frac{4x}{4} = \frac{84}{4}$$
$$x = 21$$

The solution is 21.

b.
$$-11y = 44$$
$$\frac{-11y}{-11} = \frac{44}{-11}$$
$$y = -4$$

The solution is -4.

c.
$$-15.5 = 5z$$
$$\frac{-15.5}{5} = \frac{5z}{5}$$
$$-3.1 = z$$

The solution is -3.1.

CHECK POINT 3

a.
$$\frac{2}{3}y = 16$$
$$\frac{3}{2}\left(\frac{2}{3}y\right) = \frac{3}{2} \cdot 16$$
$$1y = 24$$
$$y = 24$$

The solution is 24.

b.
$$28 = -\frac{7}{4}x$$
$$-\frac{4}{7}(28) = -\frac{4}{7}\left(-\frac{7}{4}x\right)$$
$$-16 = 1x$$
$$-16 = x$$

The solution is -16.

CHECK POINT 4

a.
$$-x = 5$$
$$-1x = 5$$
$$(-1)(-1x) = (-1)(5)$$
$$1x = -5$$
$$x = -5$$

The solution is −5.

b.
$$-x = -3$$
$$-1x = -3$$
$$(-1)(-1x) = (-1)(-3)$$
$$1x = 3$$
$$x = 3$$

The solution is 3.

CHECK POINT 5

$$4x + 3 = 27$$
$$4x + 3 - 3 = 27 - 3$$
$$4x = 24$$
$$\frac{4x}{4} = \frac{24}{4}$$
$$x = 6$$

The solution is 6.

CHECK POINT 6

$$-4y - 15 = 25$$
$$-4y - 15 + 15 = 25 + 15$$
$$-4y = 40$$
$$\frac{-4y}{-4} = \frac{40}{-4}$$
$$y = -10$$

The solution is −10.

CHECK POINT 7

$$2x - 15 = -4x + 21$$
$$2x + 4x - 15 = -4x + 4x + 21$$
$$6x - 15 = 21$$
$$6x - 15 + 15 = 21 + 15$$
$$6x = 36$$
$$\frac{6x}{6} = \frac{36}{6}$$
$$x = 6$$

The solution is 6.

CHECK POINT 8

$$D = 0.2F - 1$$

Substitute 19 for D and solve for F.

$$D = 0.2F - 1$$
$$19 = 0.2F - 1$$
$$19 + 1 = 0.2F - 1 + 1$$
$$20 = 0.2F$$
$$\frac{20}{0.2} = \frac{0.2F}{0.2}$$
$$100 = F$$

The daily fat intake is 100 grams.

EXERCISE SET 2.2

1.
$$\frac{x}{3} = 4$$
$$3 \cdot \frac{x}{3} = 3 \cdot 4$$
$$1x = 12$$
$$x = 12$$

Check:
$$\frac{12}{3} \overset{?}{=} 4$$
$$4 = 4$$

The solution is 12.

3. $\dfrac{x}{-5} = 11$

$-5 \cdot \dfrac{x}{-5} = -5(11)$

$1x = -55$

$x = -55$

Check:

$\dfrac{-55}{-5} \overset{?}{=} 11$

$11 = 11$

The solution is -55.

5. $5y = 45$

$\dfrac{5y}{5} = \dfrac{45}{5}$

$y = 9$

Check:

$5(9) \overset{?}{=} 45$

$45 = 45$

The solution is 9.

7. $-7y = 56$

$\dfrac{-7y}{-7} = \dfrac{56}{-7}$

$y = -8$

Check:

$-7(-8) \overset{?}{=} 56$

$56 = 56$

The solution is -8.

9. $-24 = 8z$

$\dfrac{-24}{8} = \dfrac{8z}{8}$

$-3 = z$

Check:

$-24 \overset{?}{=} 8(-3)$

$-24 = -24$

The solution is -3.

11. $-15 = -3z$

$\dfrac{-15}{-3} = \dfrac{-3z}{-3}$

$5 = z$

Check:

$-15 \overset{?}{=} -3(5)$

$-15 = -15$

The solution is 5.

13. $-8x = 2$

$\dfrac{-8x}{-8} = \dfrac{2}{-8}$

$x = -\dfrac{2}{8} = -\dfrac{1}{4}$

Check:

$-8\left(-\dfrac{1}{4}\right) \overset{?}{=} 2$

$2 = 2$

The solution is $-\frac{1}{4}$.

15. $7y = 0$

$\dfrac{7y}{7} = \dfrac{0}{7}$

$y = 0$

Check:

$7(0) \overset{?}{=} 0$

$0 = 0$

The solution is 0.

17. $\dfrac{2}{3}y = 8$

$\dfrac{3}{2}\left(\dfrac{2}{3}y\right) = \dfrac{3}{2}(8)$

$1y = \dfrac{3}{2} \cdot \dfrac{8}{1} = \dfrac{24}{2}$

$y = 12$

Check:

$$\frac{2}{3}(12) \stackrel{?}{=} 8$$

$$\frac{2}{3} \cdot \frac{12}{1} \stackrel{?}{=} 8$$

$$\frac{24}{3} \stackrel{?}{=} 8$$

$$3 = 3$$

The solution is 12.

19. $$21 = -\frac{7}{2}x$$

$$-\frac{2}{7}(21) = -\frac{2}{7}\left(-\frac{7}{2}x\right)$$

$$-\frac{42}{7} = 1x$$

$$-6 = x$$

Check:

$$21 \stackrel{?}{=} -\frac{7}{2}(-6)$$

$$21 \stackrel{?}{=} \frac{42}{2}$$

$$21 = 21$$

The solution is -6.

21. $$-x = 7$$

$$-1x = 7$$

$$-1(-1x) = -1(7)$$

$$x = -7$$

Check:

$$-(-7) \stackrel{?}{=} 7$$

$$7 = 7$$

The solution is -7.

23. $$-15 = -y$$

$$15 = y$$

Check:

$$-15 = -15$$

The solution is 15.

25. $$-\frac{x}{5} = -10$$

$$5\left(-\frac{x}{5}\right) = 5(-10)$$

$$-x = -50$$

$$x = 50$$

Check:

$$-\frac{50}{5} \stackrel{?}{=} -10$$

$$-10 = -10$$

The solution is 50.

27. $$2x - 8x = 24$$

$$2x + (-8x) = 24$$

$$-6x = 24$$

$$\frac{-6x}{-6} = \frac{24}{-6}$$

$$x = -4$$

Check:

$$2(-4) - 8(-4) \stackrel{?}{=} 24$$

$$-8 - (-32) \stackrel{?}{=} 24$$

$$-8 + 32 \stackrel{?}{=} 24$$

$$24 = 24$$

The solution is -4.

29. $$2x + 1 = 1$$

$$2x + 1 - 1 = 11 - 1$$

$$2x = 10$$

$$\frac{2x}{2} = \frac{10}{2}$$

$$x = 5$$

Check:

$$2(5) + 1 \stackrel{?}{=} 11$$

$$10 + 1 \stackrel{?}{=} 11$$

$$11 = 11$$

The solution is 5.

31.
$$2x - 3 = 9$$
$$2x - 3 + 3 = 9 + 3$$
$$2x = 12$$
$$\frac{2x}{2} = \frac{12}{2}$$
$$x = 6$$

Check:

$$2(6) - 3 \stackrel{?}{=} 9$$
$$12 - 3 \stackrel{?}{=} 9$$
$$9 = 9$$

The solution is 6.

33.
$$-2y + 5 = 7$$
$$-2y + 5 - 5 = 7 - 5$$
$$-2y = 2$$
$$\frac{-2y}{-2} = \frac{2}{-2}$$
$$y = -1$$

Check:

$$-2(-1) + 5 \stackrel{?}{=} 7$$
$$2 + 5 \stackrel{?}{=} 7$$
$$7 = 7$$

The solution is -1.

35.
$$-3y - 7 = -1$$
$$-3y - 7 + 7 = -1 + 7$$
$$-3y = 6$$
$$\frac{-3y}{-3} = \frac{6}{-3}$$
$$y = -2$$

Check:

$$-3(-2) - 7 \stackrel{?}{=} -1$$
$$6 - 7 \stackrel{?}{=} -1$$
$$-1 = -1$$

The solution is -2.

37.
$$12 = 4z + 3$$
$$12 - 3 = 4z + 3 - 3$$
$$9 = 4z$$
$$\frac{9}{4} = \frac{4z}{4}$$
$$\frac{9}{4} = z$$

Check:

$$12 \stackrel{?}{=} 4\left(\frac{9}{4}\right) + 3$$
$$12 \stackrel{?}{=} 9 + 3$$
$$12 = 12$$

The solution is $\frac{9}{4}$.

39.
$$-x - 3 = 3$$
$$-x - 3 + 3 = 3 + 3$$
$$-x = 6$$
$$x = -6$$

Check:

$$-(-6) - 3 \stackrel{?}{=} 3$$
$$6 - 3 \stackrel{?}{=} 3$$
$$3 = 3$$

The solution is -6.

41.
$$6y = 2y - 12$$
$$6y + 12 = 2y - 12 + 12$$
$$6y + 12 = 2y$$
$$6y + 12 - 6y = 2y - 6y$$
$$12 = -4y$$
$$\frac{12}{-4} = \frac{-4y}{-4}$$
$$-3 = y$$

Check:

$$6(-3) \stackrel{?}{=} 2(-3) - 12$$
$$-18 \stackrel{?}{=} -6 - 12$$
$$-18 = -18$$

The solution is -3.

43.
$$3z = -2z - 15$$
$$3z + 2z = -2z - 15 + 2z$$
$$5z = -15$$
$$\frac{5z}{5} = \frac{-15}{5}$$
$$z = -3$$

Check:
$$3(-3) \stackrel{?}{=} -2(-3) - 15$$
$$-9 \stackrel{?}{=} 6 - 15$$
$$-9 = -9$$

The solution is -3.

45.
$$-5x = -2x - 12$$
$$-5x + 2x = -2x - 12 + 2x$$
$$-3x = -12$$
$$\frac{-3x}{-3} = \frac{-12}{-3}$$
$$x = 4$$

Check:
$$-5(4) \stackrel{?}{=} -2(4) - 12$$
$$-20 \stackrel{?}{=} -8 - 12$$
$$-20 = -20$$

The solution is 4.

47.
$$8y + 4 = 2y - 5$$
$$8y + 4 - 2y = 2y - 5 - 2y$$
$$6y + 4 = -5$$
$$6y + 4 - 4 = -5 - 4$$
$$6y = -9$$
$$\frac{6y}{6} = \frac{-9}{6}$$
$$y = -\frac{3}{2}$$

Check:
$$8\left(-\frac{3}{2}\right) + 4 \stackrel{?}{=} 2\left(-\frac{3}{2}\right) - 5$$
$$-12 + 4 \stackrel{?}{=} -3 - 5$$
$$-8 = -8$$

The solution is $-\frac{3}{2}$.

49.
$$6z - 5 = z + 5$$
$$6z - 5 - z = z + 5 - z$$
$$5z - 5 = 5$$
$$5z - 5 + 5 = 5 + 5$$
$$5z = 10$$
$$\frac{5z}{5} = \frac{10}{5}$$
$$z = 2$$

Check:
$$6(2) - 5 \stackrel{?}{=} 2 + 5$$
$$12 - 5 \stackrel{?}{=} 2 + 5$$
$$7 = 7$$

The solution is 2.

51.
$$6x + 14 = 2x - 2$$
$$6x - 2x + 14 = -2$$
$$4x = -2 - 14$$
$$4x = -16$$
$$x = -4$$

Check:
$$6(-4) + 14 \stackrel{?}{=} 2(-4) - 2$$
$$-24 + 14 \stackrel{?}{=} -8 - 2$$
$$-10 = -10$$

The solution is -4.

53.
$$-3y - 1 = 5 - 2y$$
$$-3y + 2y - 1 = 5$$
$$-y = 5 + 1$$
$$-y = 6$$
$$y = -6$$

Check:
$$-3(-6) - 1 \stackrel{?}{=} 5 - 2(-6)$$
$$18 - 1 \stackrel{?}{=} 5 + 12$$
$$17 = 17$$

The solution is -6.

55. $M = \dfrac{n}{5}$; $M = 2$

$$M = \dfrac{n}{5}$$

$$2 = \dfrac{n}{5}$$

$$5(2) = 5\left(\dfrac{n}{5}\right)$$

$$10 = n$$

If you are 2 miles away from the lightening flash, it will take 10 seconds for the sound of thunder to reach you.

57. $M = \dfrac{A}{740}$; $M = 2.03$

$$M = \dfrac{A}{740}$$

$$2.03 = \dfrac{A}{740}$$

$$740(2.03) = 740\left(\dfrac{A}{740}\right)$$

$$1502.2 = A$$

The speed is 1502.2 miles per hour.

59. $P = -0.5d + 100$; $P = 70$

$$P = -0.5d + 100$$

$$70 = -0.5d + 100$$

$$70 - 100 = -0.5d + 100 - 100$$

$$-30 = -0.5d$$

$$\dfrac{-30}{-0.5} = \dfrac{-0.5d}{-0.5}$$

$$60 = d$$

The parallel distance of separation is 60 yards.

For Exercises 61–63, answers may vary.

65. Statement d is true since the solution to $6x = 0$ is 0, which is not a natural number.

67. This would require either using a huge number of searchers, who may not be available, or covering a smaller area and possibly missing the area where the hikers are located.

69.
$$-72.8y - 14.6 = -455.43 - 4.98y$$
$$-72.8y - 14.6 + 4.98y = -455.43 - 4.98y + 4.98y$$
$$-67.82y - 14.6 = -455.43$$
$$-67.82y - 14.6 + 14.6 = -455.43 + 14.6$$
$$-67.82y = -440.83$$
$$\dfrac{-67.82y}{-67.82} = \dfrac{-440.83}{-67.82}$$
$$y = 6.5$$

The solution is 6.5.

Review Exercises

70. $(-10)^2 = (-10)(-10) = 100$

71. $-10^2 = -10 \cdot 10 = -100$

72. $x^3 - 4x$; $x = -1$

$$x^3 - 4x = (-1)^3 - 4(-1) = -1 + 4 = 3$$

Solving Linear Equations

2.3 CHECK POINTS

CHECK POINT 1

$$-7x + 25 + 3x = 16 - 2x - 3$$
$$-4x + 25 = 13 - 2x$$
$$-4x + 2x + 25 = 13 - 2x + 2x$$
$$-2x + 25 = 13$$
$$-2x + 25 - 25 = 13 - 25$$
$$-2x = -12$$
$$\dfrac{-2x}{-2} = \dfrac{-12}{-2}$$
$$x = 6$$

Check:

$$-7x + 25 + 3x = 16 - 2x - 3$$
$$-7(6) + 25 + 3(6) \stackrel{?}{=} 16 - 2(6) - 3$$
$$-42 + 25 + 18 \stackrel{?}{=} 16 - 12 - 3$$
$$-17 + 18 \stackrel{?}{=} 4 - 3$$
$$1 = 1 \text{ true}$$

The solution is 6.

CHECK POINT 2

$$8x = 2(x + 6)$$
$$8x = 2x + 12$$
$$8x - 2x = 2x + 12 - 2x$$
$$6x = 12$$
$$\frac{6x}{6} = \frac{12}{6}$$
$$x = 2$$

Check:

$$8x = 2(x + 6)$$
$$8(2) \stackrel{?}{=} 2(2 + 6)$$
$$16 \stackrel{?}{=} 2(8)$$
$$16 = 16 \text{ true}$$

The solution is 2.

CHECK POINT 3

$$4(2x + 1) - 29 = 3(2x - 5)$$
$$8x + 4 - 29 = 6x - 15$$
$$8x - 25 = 6x - 15$$
$$8x - 6x - 25 = 6x - 15 - 6x$$
$$2x - 25 = -15$$
$$2x - 25 + 25 = -15 + 25$$
$$2x = 10$$
$$\frac{2x}{2} = \frac{10}{2}$$
$$x = 5$$

Check:

$$4(2x + 1) - 29 = 3(2x - 5)$$
$$4(2 \cdot 5 + 1) - 29 \stackrel{?}{=} 3(2 \cdot 5 - 5)$$
$$4(10 + 1) - 29 \stackrel{?}{=} 3(10 - 5)$$
$$4(11) - 29 \stackrel{?}{=} 3(5)$$
$$44 - 29 = 15$$
$$15 = 15$$

The solution is 5.

CHECK POINT 4

$$\frac{x}{4} = \frac{2x}{3} + \frac{5}{6}$$

Multiply both sides of the equation by the least common denominator, which is 12.

$$12 \cdot \frac{x}{4} = 12 \left(\frac{2x}{3} + \frac{5}{6} \right)$$
$$12 \cdot \frac{x}{4} = 12 \cdot \frac{2x}{3} + 12 \cdot \frac{5}{6}$$
$$3x = 8x + 10$$
$$3x - 8x = 8x + 10 - 8x$$
$$-5x = 10$$
$$\frac{-5x}{-5} = \frac{10}{-5}$$
$$x = -2$$

Check:

$$\frac{x}{4} = \frac{2x}{3} + \frac{5}{6}$$
$$\frac{-2}{4} \stackrel{?}{=} \frac{2(-2)}{3} + \frac{5}{6}$$
$$-\frac{1}{2} \stackrel{?}{=} -\frac{4}{3} + \frac{5}{6}$$
$$-\frac{1}{2} \stackrel{?}{=} -\frac{8}{6} + \frac{5}{6}$$
$$-\frac{1}{2} \stackrel{?}{=} -\frac{3}{6}$$
$$-\frac{1}{2} = -\frac{1}{2} \text{ true}$$

The solution is -2.

CHECK POINT 5

$$3x + 7 = 3(x + 1)$$
$$3x + 7 = 3x + 3$$
$$3x + 7 - 3x = 3x + 3 - 3x$$
$$7 = 3$$

The original equation is equivalent to the false statement $7 = 3$, which is false for every value of x. The equation is inconsistent and has no solution.

CHECK POINT 6

$$3(x - 1) + 9 = 8x + 6 - 5x$$
$$3x - 3 + 9 = 8x + 6 - 5x$$
$$3x + 6 = 3x + 6$$
$$3x + 6 - 3x = 3x + 6 - 3x$$
$$6 = 6$$

The original equation is equivalent to the true statement $6 = 6$, which is true for every value of x. The equation is an identity and all real numbers are solutions.

CHECK POINT 7

$$\frac{W}{2} - 3H = 53$$

Substitute 3 for H since a man who is 5 feet, 3 inches tall is 3 inches over 5 feet.

$$\frac{W}{2} - 3(3) = 53$$
$$\frac{W}{2} - 9 = 53$$
$$2\left(\frac{W}{2} - 9\right) = 2 \cdot 53$$
$$W - 18 = 106$$
$$W - 18 + 18 = 106 + 18$$
$$W = 124$$

The recommended weight for a man who is 5 feet, 3 inches tall is 124 pounds.

EXERCISE SET 2.3

For Exercises 1–45, students should check the proposed solutions. The checks will not be shown here.

1.
$$5x + 3x - 4x = 10 + 2$$
$$8x - 4x = 12$$
$$4x = 12$$
$$\frac{4x}{4} = \frac{12}{4}$$
$$x = 3$$

The solution is 3.

3.
$$3x - 7x + 30 = 10 - 2x$$
$$-4x + 30 = 10 - 2x$$
$$-4x + 30 = 10 - 2x - 10$$
$$-4x + 20 = -2x$$
$$-4x + 20 + 4x = -2x + 4x$$
$$20 = 2x$$
$$10 = x$$

The solution is 10.

5.
$$3x + 6 - x = 8 + 3x - 6$$
$$2x + 6 = 2 + 3x$$
$$2x + 6 = 2 + 3x - 2$$
$$2x + 4 = 3x$$
$$2x + 4 - 2x = 3x - 2x$$
$$4 = x$$

The solution is 4.

7.
$$3(x - 2) = 12$$
$$3x - 6 = 12$$
$$3x - 6 + 6 = 12 + 6$$
$$3x = 18$$
$$x = 6$$

The solution is 6.

9.
$$7(2x - 1) = 21$$
$$14x - 7 = 21$$
$$14x - 7 + 7 = 21 + 7$$
$$14x = 28$$
$$\frac{14x}{14} = \frac{28}{14}$$
$$x = 2$$

The solution is 2.

11.
$$25 = 5(3y + 4)$$
$$25 = 15y + 20$$
$$25 - 20 = 15y + 20 - 20$$
$$5 = 15y$$
$$\frac{5}{15} = \frac{15y}{15}$$
$$\frac{1}{3} = y$$

The solution is $\frac{1}{3}$.

13.
$$2(4z + 3) - 8 = 46$$
$$8z + 6 - 8 = 46$$
$$8z - 2 = 46$$
$$8z - 2 + 2 = 46 + 2$$
$$8z = 48$$
$$\frac{8z}{8} = \frac{48}{8}$$
$$z = 6$$

The solution is 6.

15.
$$6x - (3x + 10) = 14$$
$$6x - 3x - 10 = 14$$
$$3x - 10 = 14$$
$$3x - 10 + 10 = 14 + 10$$
$$3x = 24$$
$$\frac{3x}{3} = \frac{24}{3}$$
$$x = 8$$

The solution is 8.

17.
$$14(y - 2) = 10(y + 4)$$
$$14y - 28 = 10y + 40$$
$$14y - 28 - 10y = 10y + 40 - 10y$$
$$4y - 28 = 40$$
$$4y - 28 + 28 = 40 + 28$$
$$4y = 68$$
$$\frac{4y}{y} = \frac{68}{4}$$
$$y = 17$$

The solution is 17.

19.
$$3(5 - x) = 4(2x + 1)$$
$$15 - 3x = 8x + 4$$
$$15 - 3x - 8x = 8x + 4 - 8x$$
$$15 - 11x = 4$$
$$15 - 11x - 15 = 4 - 15$$
$$-11x = -11$$
$$\frac{-11x}{-11} = \frac{-11}{-11}$$
$$x = 1$$

The solution is 1.

21.
$$8(y + 2) = 2(3y + 4)$$
$$8y + 16 = 6y + 8$$
$$8y + 16 - 16 = 6y + 8 - 16$$
$$8y = 6y - 8$$
$$8y - 6y = 6y - 8 - 6y$$
$$2y = -8$$
$$y = -4$$

The solution is -4.

23.
$$3(x + 1) = 7(x - 2) - 3$$
$$3x + 3 = 7x - 14 - 3$$
$$3x + 3 = 7x - 17$$
$$3x + 3 - 3 = 7x - 17 - 3$$
$$3x = 7x - 20$$
$$3x - 7x = 7x - 20 - 7x$$
$$-4x = -20$$
$$\frac{-4x}{-4} = \frac{-20}{-4}$$
$$x = 5$$

The solution is 5.

25.
$$5(2x - 8) - 2 = 5(x - 3) + 3$$
$$10x - 40 - 2 = 5x - 15 + 3$$
$$10x - 42 = 5x - 12$$
$$10x - 42 + 42 = 5x - 12 + 42$$
$$10x = 5x + 30$$
$$10x = 5x + 30 - 5x$$
$$5x = 30$$
$$\frac{5x}{5} = \frac{30}{5}$$
$$x = 6$$

The solution is 6.

27.
$$6 = -4(1 - x) + 3(x + 1)$$
$$6 = -4 + 4x + 3x + 3$$
$$6 = -1 + 7x$$
$$6 + 1 = -1 + 7x + 1$$
$$7 = 7x$$
$$\frac{7}{7} = \frac{7x}{7}$$
$$1 = x$$

The solution is 1.

29.
$$10(z + 4) - 4(z - 2) = 3(z - 1) + 2(z - 3)$$
$$10z + 40 - 4z + 8 = 3z - 3 + 2z - 6$$
$$6z + 48 = 5z - 9$$
$$6z + 48 - 48 = 5z - 9 - 48$$
$$6z - 5z = 5z - 57 - 5z$$
$$z = -57$$

The solution is -57.

31. $\dfrac{x}{5} - 4 = -6$

To clear the equation of fractions, multiply both sides by the least common denominator (LCD), which is 5.

$$5\left(\frac{x}{5} - 4\right) = 5(-6)$$
$$5 \cdot \frac{x}{5} = 5 \cdot 4 = -30$$
$$x - 20 = -30$$
$$x - 20 + 20 = -30 + 20$$
$$x = -10$$

The solution is -10.

33. $\dfrac{2x}{3} - 5 = 7$

LCD = 3

$$3\left(\frac{2x}{3} - 5\right) = 3(7)$$
$$3 \cdot \frac{2x}{3} - 3 \cdot 5 = 21$$
$$2x - 15 = 21$$
$$2x - 15 + 15 = 21 + 15$$
$$2x = 36$$
$$\frac{2x}{2} = \frac{36}{2}$$
$$x = 18$$

The solution is 18.

35. $\dfrac{2y}{3} - \dfrac{3}{4} = \dfrac{5}{12}$

LCD = 12

$$12\left(\frac{2y}{3} - \frac{3}{4}\right) = 12\left(\frac{5}{12}\right)$$
$$12\left(\frac{2y}{3}\right) - 12\left(\frac{3}{4}\right) = 5$$
$$8y - 9 = 5$$
$$8y - 9 + 9 = 5 + 9$$
$$8y = 14$$
$$\frac{8y}{8} = \frac{14}{8}$$
$$y = \frac{14}{8} = \frac{7}{4}$$

The solution is $\frac{7}{4}$.

37. $\dfrac{x}{3} + \dfrac{x}{2} = \dfrac{5}{6}$

LCD = 6

$$6\left(\frac{x}{3} + \frac{x}{2}\right) = 6\left(\frac{5}{6}\right)$$
$$2x + 3x = 5$$
$$5x = 5$$
$$\frac{5x}{5} = \frac{5}{5}$$
$$x = 1$$

The solution is 1.

39. $20 - \dfrac{z}{3} = \dfrac{z}{2}$

$LCD = 6$

$$6\left(20 - \frac{z}{3}\right) = 6\left(\frac{z}{2}\right)$$
$$120 - 2z = 3z$$
$$120 - 2z + 2z = 3z + 2z$$
$$120 = 5z$$
$$\frac{120}{5} = \frac{5z}{5}$$
$$24 = z$$

The solution is 24.

41. $\dfrac{y}{3} + \dfrac{2}{5} = \dfrac{y}{5} - \dfrac{2}{5}$

$LCD = 15$

$$15\left(\frac{y}{3} + \frac{2}{5}\right) = 15\left(\frac{y}{5} + \frac{2}{5}\right)$$
$$15\left(\frac{y}{3}\right) + 15\left(\frac{2}{5}\right) = 15\left(\frac{y}{5}\right) + 15\left(-\frac{2}{5}\right)$$
$$5y + 6 = 3y - 6$$
$$5y + 6 - 3y = 3y - 6 - 3y$$
$$2y + 6 = -6$$
$$2y + 6 - 6 = -6 - 6$$
$$2y = -12$$
$$\frac{2y}{2} = \frac{-12}{2}$$
$$y = -6$$

The solution is -6.

43. $\dfrac{3x}{4} - 3 = \dfrac{x}{2} + 2$

$LCD = 8$

$$8\left(\frac{3x}{4} - 3\right) = 8\left(\frac{x}{2} + 2\right)$$
$$8\left(\frac{3x}{4}\right) - 8 \cdot 3 = 8\left(\frac{x}{2}\right) + 8 \cdot 2$$
$$6x - 24 = 4x + 16$$
$$6x - 24 - 4x = 4x + 16 - 4x$$
$$2x - 24 = 16$$
$$2x - 24 + 24 = 16 + 24$$
$$2x = 40$$
$$\frac{2x}{x} = \frac{40}{2}$$
$$x = 20$$

The solution is 20.

45. $\dfrac{3x}{5} - x = \dfrac{x}{10} - \dfrac{5}{2}$

$LCD = 10$

$$10\left(\frac{3x}{5} - x\right) = 10\left(\frac{x}{10} - \frac{5}{2}\right)$$
$$6x - 10x = x - 25$$
$$6x - 10x - x = x - 25 - x$$
$$-5x = -25$$
$$\frac{-5x}{-5} = \frac{-25}{-5}$$
$$x = 5$$

The solution is 5.

47.
$$3x - 7 = 3(x + 1)$$
$$3x - 7 = 3x + 3$$
$$3x - 7 - 3x = 3x + 3 - 3x$$
$$-7 = 3$$

The original equation is equivalent to the false statement $-7 = 3$, so the equation is inconsistent and has no solution.

49.
$$2(x+4) = 4x + 5 - 2x + 3$$
$$2x + 8 = 2x + 8$$
$$2x - 8 - 2x = 2x + 8 - 2x$$
$$8 = 8$$

The original equation is equivalent to the true statement $8 = 8$, so the equation is an identity and all real numbers are solutions.

51.
$$4x + 1 - 5x = 5 - (x + 4)$$
$$-x + 1 = 5 - x - 4$$
$$-x + 1 = 1 - x$$
$$-x + 1 + x = 1 - x + x$$
$$1 = 1$$

Since $1 = 1$ is a true statement, the original equation is an identity and all real numbers are solutions.

53.
$$4(x + 2) + 1 = 7x - 3(x - 2)$$
$$4x + 8 + 1 = 7x - 3x + 6$$
$$4x + 9 = 4x + 6$$
$$4x + 9 - 4x = 4x + 6 - 4x$$
$$9 = 6$$

Since $9 = 6$ is a false statement, the original equation is inconsistent and has no solution.

55. $\dfrac{x}{3} + 2 = \dfrac{x}{3}$

Multiply by the LCD, which is 6.
$$6\left(\frac{x}{3} + 2\right) = 6\left(\frac{x}{3}\right)$$
$$2x + 12 = 2x$$
$$2x + 12 - 2x = 2x - 2x$$
$$12 = 0$$

Since $12 = 0$ is a false statement, the original equation has no solution.

57.
$$3 - x = 2x + 3$$
$$3 - x - 3 = 2x + 3 - 3$$
$$-x = 2x$$
$$-x - 2x = 2x - 2x$$
$$-3x = 0$$
$$\frac{-3x}{-3} = \frac{0}{-3}$$
$$x = 0$$

The solution is 0.

59. $F = 10(x - 65) + 50;\ F = 250$
$$F = 10(x - 65) + 50$$
$$250 = 10(x - 65) + 50$$
$$250 - 50 = 10(x - 65) + 50 - 50$$
$$200 = 10x - 650$$
$$200 + 650 = 10x - 650 + 650$$
$$850 = 10x$$
$$\frac{850}{10} = \frac{10x}{10}$$
$$85 = x$$

A person receiving a \$250 fine was driving 85 miles per hour.

61. $\dfrac{c}{2} + 80 = 2F;\ F = 70$
$$\frac{c}{2} + 80 = 2F$$
$$\frac{c}{2} + 80 = 2(70)$$
$$\frac{c}{2} + 80 = 140$$
$$\frac{c}{2} + 80 - 80 = 140 - 80$$
$$\frac{c}{2} = 60$$
$$2\left(\frac{c}{2}\right) = 2(60)$$
$$c = 120$$

At 70°F, there are 120 cricket chirps per minute.

63. $p = 15 + \dfrac{5d}{11}$; $p = 201$

$$201 = 15 + \frac{5d}{11}$$

$$201 - 15 = 15 + \frac{5d}{11} - 15$$

$$186 = \frac{5d}{11}$$

$$11(186) = 11\left(\frac{5d}{11}\right)$$

$$2046 = 5d$$

$$\frac{2046}{5} = d$$

$$409.2 = d$$

He descended to a depth of 409.2 feet below the surface.

For Exercises 65–67, answers may vary.

69. Statement c is true. The solution to the linear equation is -3. When -3 is substituted into $y^2 + 2y - 3$, the result is 0.

71. $\dfrac{2x-3}{9} + \dfrac{x-3}{2} = \dfrac{x+5}{6} - 1$

LCD = 18

$$18\left(\frac{2x-3}{9} + \frac{x-3}{2}\right) = 18\left(\frac{x+5}{6} - 1\right)$$

$$18\left(\frac{2x-3}{9}\right) + 18\left(\frac{x-3}{2}\right) = 18\left(\frac{x+5}{6}\right)$$
$$- 18 \cdot 1$$

$$2(2x-3) + 9(x-3) = 3(x+5) - 18$$

$$4x - 6 + 9x - 27 = 3x + 15 - 18$$

$$13x - 33 = 3x - 3$$

$$13x - 33 - 3x = 3x - 3 - 3x$$

$$10x - 33 = -3$$

$$10x - 33 + 33 = -3 + 33$$

$$10x = 30$$

$$\frac{10x}{10} = \frac{30}{10}$$

$$x = 3$$

Check:

$$\frac{2(3)-3}{9} + \frac{3-3}{2} \overset{?}{=} \frac{3+5}{6} - 1$$

$$\frac{6-3}{9} + \frac{0}{2} \overset{?}{=} \frac{8}{6} - 1$$

$$\frac{3}{9} + 0 \overset{?}{=} \frac{4}{3} - 1$$

$$\frac{1}{3} = \frac{1}{3}$$

The solution is 3.

73.
$$2.24y - 9.28 = 5.74y + 5.42$$
$$2.24y - 9.28 - 5.74y = 5.74y + 5.42$$
$$- 5.74y$$
$$-3.5y - 9.28 = 5.42$$
$$-3.5y - 9.28 + 9.28 = 5.42 + 9.28$$
$$-3.5y = 14.7$$
$$\frac{-3.5y}{-3.5} = \frac{14.7}{-3.5}$$
$$y = -4.2$$

The solution is -4.2.

Review Exercises

75. $-24 < -20$; -24 is to the left of -20 on the number line, so -24 is less than -20.

76. $-\frac{1}{3} < -\frac{1}{5}$; $-\frac{1}{3}$ is to the left of $-\frac{1}{5}$ on the number line, so $-\frac{1}{3}$ is less than $-\frac{1}{5}$.
To compare these numbers, write them with a common denominator:
$$-\frac{1}{3} = -\frac{5}{15}, -\frac{1}{5} = -\frac{3}{15}.$$

77. $-9 - 11 + 7 - (-3)$
$$= (-9) + (-11) + 7 + 3$$
$$= (7 + 3) + [(-9) + (-11)]$$
$$= 10 + (-20)$$
$$= -10$$

Formulas and Percents

2.4 CHECK POINTS

CHECK POINT 1

Solve $A = lw$ for l.

$$A = lw$$
$$\frac{A}{w} = \frac{lw}{w}$$
$$\frac{A}{w} = l \quad \text{or} \quad l = \frac{A}{w}$$

CHECK POINT 2

Solve $2l + 2w = P$ for l.

$$2l + 2w = P$$
$$2l + 2w - 2w = P - 2w$$
$$2l = P - 2w$$
$$\frac{2l}{l} = \frac{P - 2w}{2}$$
$$l = \frac{P - 2w}{2}$$

CHECK POINT 3

Solve $T = D + pm$ for m.

$$T = D + pm$$
$$T - D = D - D + pm$$
$$T - D = pm$$
$$\frac{T - D}{p} = \frac{pm}{p}$$
$$\frac{T - D}{p} = m \quad \text{or} \quad m = \frac{T - D}{p}$$

CHECK POINT 4

Solve $\dfrac{x}{3} - 4y = 5$ for x.

$$\frac{x}{3} - 4y = 5$$
$$3\left(\frac{x}{3} - 4y\right) = 3 \cdot 5$$
$$3 \cdot \frac{x}{3} - 3 \cdot 4y = 3 \cdot 5$$
$$x - 12 = 15$$
$$x - 12y + 12y = 15 + 12y$$
$$x = 15 + 12y$$

CHECK POINT 5

To express a decimal number as a percent, move the decimal point two places to the right and attach a percent sign.

$$0.023 = 2.3\%$$

CHECK POINT 6

To express a percent as a decimal number, move the decimal point two places to the left and remove the percent sign.

a. $67\% = 0.67$

b. $250\% = 2.5$

CHECK POINT 7

What is 9% of 50?
Use the percent formula $A = PB$ with $P = 9\% = 0.09$ and $B = 50$ to find the quantity A.

$$A = PB$$
$$A = 0.09 \cdot 50$$
$$A = 4.5$$

9% of 50 is 4.5.

CHECK POINT 8

9 is 60% of what?
Use the formula $A = PB$ with $A = 9$ and $P = 60\% = 0.6$ to find the quantity B.

$$A = PB$$
$$9 = 0.6 \cdot B$$
$$\frac{9}{0.6} = \frac{0.6B}{0.6}$$
$$15 = B$$

9 is 60% of 15.

CHECK POINT 9

18 is what percent of 50?
Use the percent formula $A = PB$ with $A = 18$ and $B = 50$ to find the quantity P.

$$A = PB$$
$$18 = P \cdot 50$$
$$\frac{18}{50} = \frac{P \cdot 50}{50}$$
$$0.36 = P$$

$0.36 = 36\%$, so 18 is 36% of 50.

CHECK POINT 10

The question is, "3.44 is what percent of 4.30?" Use the percent formula with $A = 3.44$ and $B = 4.30$ to find the quantity P.

$$A = PB$$
$$3.44 = P \cdot 4.30$$
$$\frac{3.44}{4.30} = \frac{P \cdot 3.40}{4.30}$$
$$0.8 = P$$

$0.8 = 80\%$, so 80% of the fuel cost is for taxes.

EXERCISE SET 2.4

1. $d = rt$ for r

$$\frac{d}{t} = \frac{rt}{t}$$
$$\frac{d}{t} = r \quad \text{or} \quad r = \frac{d}{t}$$

This is the distance formula:

$$\text{distance} = \text{rate} \cdot \text{time}.$$

3. $I = Prt$ for P

$$\frac{I}{rt} = \frac{Prt}{rt}$$
$$\frac{I}{rt} = P \quad \text{or} \quad P = \frac{I}{rt}$$

This is the formula for simple interest:

$$\text{interest} = \text{principal} \cdot \text{rate} \cdot \text{time}.$$

5. $C = 2\pi r$ for r

$$\frac{C}{2\pi} = \frac{2\pi C}{2\pi}$$
$$\frac{C}{2\pi} = r \quad \text{or} \quad r = \frac{C}{2\pi}$$

This is the formula for finding the circumference of a circle if you know its radius.

7. $E = mc^2$

$$\frac{E}{c^2} = \frac{mc^2}{c^2}$$
$$\frac{E}{c^2} = m \quad \text{or} \quad m = \frac{E}{c^2}$$

This is Einstein's formula relating energy, mass, and the speed of light.

9. $y = mx + b$ for m

$$y - b = mx$$
$$\frac{y - b}{x} = \frac{mx}{x}$$
$$\frac{y - b}{x} = m \quad \text{or} \quad m = \frac{y - b}{x}$$

This is the slope-intercept formula for the equation of a line. (This formula will be discussed later in the textbook.)

11. $T = D + pm$ for p

$$T - D = D + pm - D$$
$$T - D = pm$$
$$\frac{T - D}{m} = \frac{pm}{m}$$
$$\frac{T - D}{m} = p \quad \text{or} \quad p = \frac{T - D}{m}$$

13. $A = \frac{1}{2}bh$ for b

$$2A = 2\left(\frac{1}{2}bh\right)$$
$$2A = bh$$
$$\frac{2A}{h} = \frac{bh}{h}$$
$$\frac{2A}{h} = b \quad \text{or} \quad b = \frac{2A}{h}$$

This is the formula for the area of a triangle:
$$\text{area} = \frac{1}{2} \cdot \text{base} \cdot \text{height}.$$

15. $M = \frac{n}{5}$ for n

$$5M = 5\left(\frac{n}{5}\right)$$
$$5M = n \quad \text{or} \quad n = 5M$$

17. $\frac{c}{2} + 80 = 2F$ for c

$$\frac{c}{2} + 80 - 80 = 2F - 80$$
$$\frac{c}{2} = 2F - 80$$
$$2\left(\frac{c}{2}\right) = 2(2F - 80)$$
$$c = 4F - 160$$

19. $A = \frac{1}{2}(a + b)$ for a

$$2A = 2\left[\frac{1}{2}(a + b)\right]$$
$$2A = a + b$$
$$2A - a = a + b - a$$
$$2A - b = a \quad \text{or} \quad a = 2A - b$$

This is the formula for finding the average of two numbers.

21. $S = P + Prt$ for r

$$S - P = P + Prt - P$$
$$S - P = Prt$$
$$\frac{S - P}{Pt} = \frac{Prt}{Pt}$$
$$\frac{S - P}{Pt} = r \quad \text{or} \quad r = \frac{S - P}{Pt}$$

23. $A = \frac{1}{2}h(a + b)$ for b

$$2A = 2\left[\frac{1}{2}h(a + b)\right]$$
$$2A = h(a + b)$$
$$2A = ha + hb$$
$$2A - ha = ha + hb - ha$$
$$2A - ha = hb$$
$$\frac{2A - ha}{h} = \frac{hb}{h}$$
$$\frac{2A - ha}{h} = b \text{ or } b = \frac{2A - ha}{h} \text{ or } \frac{2A}{h} - a$$

This is the formula for the area of a trapezoid.

25. $Ax + By = C$ for x

$$Ax + By - By = C - By$$
$$Ax = C - By$$
$$\frac{Ax}{A} = \frac{C - By}{A}$$
$$x = \frac{C - By}{A}$$

This is the standard form on the equation of a line. (This formula will be discussed later in the textbook.)

27. To change a decimal number to a percent, move the decimal point two places to the right and add a percent sign.

$$0.59 = 59\%$$

29. $0.003 = 0.3\%$

31. $2.87 = 287\%$

33. $100 = 10,000\%$

35. To change a percent to a decimal number, move the decimal point two places to the left and remove the percent sign.

$$72\% = 0.72$$

37. $43.6\% = 0.436$

39. $130\% = 1.3$

41. $2\% = 0.02$

43. $62.5\% = 0.625$

45. $A = PB$; $P = 3\% = 0.03, B = 200$

$$A = PB$$
$$A = 0.03 \cdot 200$$
$$A = 6$$

3% of 200 is 6.

47. $A = PB$; $P = 18\% = 0.18, B = 40$

$$A = PB$$
$$A = 0.18 \cdot 40$$
$$A = 7.2$$

18% of 40 is 7.2.

49. $A = PB$; $A = 3, P = 60\% = 0.6$

$$A = PB$$
$$3 = 0.6 \cdot B$$
$$\frac{3}{0.6} = \frac{0.6B}{0.6}$$
$$5 = B$$

3 is 60% of 5.

51. $A = PB$; $A = 40.8, P = 24\% = 0.24$

$$A = PB$$
$$40.8 = 0.24 \cdot B$$
$$\frac{40.8}{0.24} = \frac{0.24B}{0.24}$$
$$170 = B$$

24% of 170 is 40.8.

53. $A = PB$; $A = 3, B = 15$

$$A = PB$$
$$3 = P \cdot 15$$
$$\frac{3}{15} = \frac{P \cdot 15}{15}$$
$$0.2 = P$$

$0.2 = 20\%$
3 is 20% of 15.

55. $A = PB$; $A = 0.3, B = 2.5$

$$A = PB$$
$$0.3 = P \cdot 2.5$$
$$\frac{0.3}{2.5} = \frac{P \cdot 2.5}{2.5}$$
$$0.12 = P$$

$0.12 = 12\%$
0.3 is 12% of 2.5.

57. $A = \dfrac{x+y+z}{3}$

a. $A = \dfrac{x+y+z}{3}$ for z

$$3A = 3\left(\dfrac{x+y+z}{3}\right)$$

$$3A = x+y+z$$
$$3A - x - y = x+y+z-x-y$$
$$3A - x - y = z$$

b. $z = 3A - x - y$; $A = 90, x = 86, y = 88$

$$z = 3A - x - y$$
$$z = 3(90) - 86 - 88$$
$$z = 96$$

You need to get 96% on the third exam to have an average of 90%.

59. $d = rt$

a. $d = rt$ for t

$$\dfrac{d}{r} = \dfrac{rt}{r}$$

$$\dfrac{d}{r} = t$$

b. $t = \dfrac{d}{r}$; $d = 100, r = 40$

$$t = \dfrac{100}{40} = 2.5$$

You would travel for 2.5 (or $2\frac{1}{2}$) hours.

61. 23¢ is $\frac{23}{100} = 23\%$ of a dollar, so 23% of the cost of prescription drugs goes to the pharmacy.

63. The total number of executions was 418 + 214 = 632. The percent of total executions that took place in Texas was

$$\dfrac{214}{632} \approx 0.34 = 34\%.$$

65. This question is equivalent to, "122 is 34% of what number?"

$A = PB$; $A = 122, P = 0.34$

$$A = PB$$
$$122 = 0.34 \cdot B$$
$$\dfrac{122}{0.34} = \dfrac{0.34 \cdot B}{0.34}$$
$$359 \approx B$$

There were about 359 women in the poll.

67. $A = PB$; $A = 7500, B = 60{,}000$

$$A = PB$$
$$7500 = P \cdot 60{,}000$$
$$\dfrac{7500}{60{,}000} = \dfrac{P \cdot 60{,}000}{60{,}000}$$
$$0.125 = P$$

$0.125 = 12.5\%$
The charity has raised 12.5% of its goal.

69. $A = PB$; $P = 15\% = 0.15, B = 60$

$$A = PB$$
$$A = 0.15 \cdot 60$$
$$A = 9$$

The tip was $9.

71. a. The sales tax is 6% of $16,800.

$$0.06(16{,}800) = 1008$$

The sales tax due on the car is $1008.

b. The total cost is the sum of the price of the car and the sales tax.

$$\$16{,}800 + \$1008 = \$17{,}808$$

The car's total cost is $17,808.

73. a. The discount amount is 12% of $860.

$$0.12(860) = 103.20$$

The discount amount is $103.20.

b. The sale price is the regular price minus the discount amount.

$$\$860 - \$103.20 = \$756.80$$

The sale price is $756.80.

For Exercises 75–77, answers may vary.

81. Statement d is true.

83. $v = -32t + 64$; $v = 16$

$$16 = -32t + 64$$
$$-48 = 32t$$
$$\frac{-48}{-32} = \frac{-32t}{-32}$$
$$1.5 = t$$

$h = -16t^2 + 64t$; $t = 1.5$

$$h = -16(1.5^2) + 64(1.5)$$
$$h = 60$$

When the velocity is 16 feet per second, the time is 1.5 seconds and the height is 60 feet.

Review Exercises

84.
$$5x + 20 = 8x - 16$$
$$5x + 20 - 8x = 8x - 16 - 8x$$
$$-3x + 20 = -16$$
$$-3x + 20 - 20 = -16 - 20$$
$$-3x = -36$$
$$\frac{-3x}{-3} = \frac{-36}{-3}$$
$$x = 12$$

Check:
$$5(12) + 20 \overset{?}{=} 8(12) - 16$$
$$60 + 20 = 96 - 16$$
$$80 = 80$$

The solution is 12.

85.
$$5(2y - 3) - 1 = 4(6 + 2y)$$
$$10y - 15 - 1 = 24 + 8y$$
$$10y - 16 = 24 + 8y$$
$$10y - 16 - 8y = 24 + 8y - 8y$$
$$2y - 16 = 24$$
$$2y - 16 + 16 = 24 + 16$$
$$2y = 40$$
$$\frac{2y}{2} = \frac{40}{2}$$
$$y = 20$$

Check:
$$5(2 \cdot 20 - 3) - 1 \overset{?}{=} 4(6 + 2 \cdot 20)$$
$$5(40 - 3) - 1 \overset{?}{=} 4(6 + 40)$$
$$5(37) - 1 \overset{?}{=} 4(46)$$
$$185 - 1 \overset{?}{=} 184$$
$$184 = 184$$

86. $x - 0.3x = 1x - 0.3x = (1 - 0.3)x = 0.7x$

An Introduction to Problem Solving

2.5 CHECK POINTS

CHECK POINT 1

a. The algebraic expression for "four times a number, increased by 6" is $4x + 6$.

b. The algebraic expression for the quotient of a number decreased by 4 and 9" is $\frac{x-4}{9}$.

CHECK POINT 2

Step 1 Let x = the number.

Step 2 There are no other unknown
quantities.

Step 3 Write an equation that describes
the situation.

$$6x - 4 = 68$$

Step 4 Solve the equation and answer
the question.

$$6x - 4 = 68$$
$$6x - 4 + 4 = 68 + 4$$
$$6x = 72$$
$$\frac{6x}{6} = \frac{72}{6}$$
$$x = 12$$

The number is 12.

Step 5 Check the proposed solution is
the original wording of the
problem. The proposed num-
ber is 12. Six times 12 is $6 \cdot 12$
or 72. Four subtracted from 72
is $72 - 4$ or 68, so the proposed
solution checks.

CHECK POINT 3

Step 1 Let x = the number (in millions)
of *Saturday Night Fever*
albums sold.

Step 2 Let $x + 5$ = the number (in
millions) of *Jagged
Little Pill* albums
sold.

Step 3 Combined, the two albums sold
27 million copies, so

$$x + (x + 5) = 27.$$

Step 4

$$x + x + 5 = 27$$
$$2x + 5 = 27$$
$$2x = 22$$
$$x = 11$$
$$x + 5 = 16$$

Jagged Little Pill sold 16 million albums
and *Saturday Night Fever* sold 11 million
albums.

Step 5 The total number of albums sold was
16 million + 11 million = 27 million.

CHECK POINT 4

Let $\quad x$ = the page number of the
page on the left.
Then $x + 1$ = the page number of the
page on the right.

$$x + (x + 1) = 193$$
$$2x + 1 = 193$$
$$2x = 192$$
$$x = 96$$
$$x + 1 = 97$$

The page numbers are 96 and 97.

CHECK POINT 5

Let x = the number of eighths of a
mile.

$$2 + 0.25x = 10$$
$$0.25x = 10$$
$$\frac{0.25x}{0.25} = \frac{8}{0.25}$$
$$x = 32$$

You can go 32 eighths of a mile for \$10.
Since $32 \cdot \frac{1}{8} = 4$, this is 4 miles.

CHECK POINT 6

Let x = the width.
Then $3x$ = the length.

Use the formula for the perimeter of a rectangle to write the equation.

$$2l + 2w = P$$
$$2(3x) + 2x = 320$$
$$6x + 2x = 320$$
$$8x = 320$$
$$\frac{8x}{8} = \frac{320}{8}$$
$$x = 40$$

Width = $x = 40$
Length = $3x = 3(40) = 120$
The dimensions of the swimming pool are 120 feet by 40 feet.

CHECK POINT 7

Let x = the price of the exercise machine before the reduction.

$$x - 0.4x = 564$$
$$1x - 0.4x = 564$$
$$0.6x = 564$$
$$\frac{0.6x}{0.6} = \frac{564}{0.6}$$
$$x = 940$$

The exercise machine's price before the reduction was $940.

EXERCISE SET 2.5

1. $x + 9$ **3.** $20 - x$ **5.** $8 - 5x$

7. $\dfrac{15}{x}$ **9.** $2x + 20$ **11.** $7x - 30$

13. $4(x + 12)$

15. $x + 40 = 450$
$x + 40 - 40 = 450 - 40$
$x = 410$

The number is 410.

17. $x - 13 = 123$
$x - 13 + 13 = 123 + 13$
$x = 136$

The number is 136.

19. $7x = 91$
$\dfrac{7x}{7} = \dfrac{91}{7}$
$x = 13$

The number is 13.

21. $\dfrac{x}{18} = 6$
$18\left(\dfrac{x}{18}\right) = 18(6)$
$x = 108$

The number is 108.

23. $4 + 2x = 36$
$2x = 32$
$x = 16$

The number is 16.

25. $5x - 7 = 123$
$5x = 130$
$x = 26$

The number is 26.

27.
$$x + 5 = 2x$$
$$x + 5 - x = 2x - x$$
$$5 = x$$

The number is 5.

29. $2(x + 4) = 36$
$$2x + 8 = 36$$
$$2x = 28$$
$$x = 14$$

The number is 14.

31. $9x = 30 + 3x$
$$6x = 30$$
$$x = 5$$

The number is 5.

33. $\dfrac{3x}{5} + 4 = 34$
$$\dfrac{3x}{5} = 30$$
$$3x = 150$$
$$x = 50$$

The number is 50.

35. *Step 1*   Let $x =$ the cost to make *Waterworld* (in millions of dollars).

Step 2 $x + 40 =$ the cost to make *Titanic*.

Step 3   The combined cost was $360 million, so the equation is
$$x + (x + 40) = 360.$$

Step 4 $x + x + 40 = 360$
$$2x + 40 = 360$$
$$2x = 320$$
$$x = 160$$

It would cost $160 million to make *Waterworld* and $160 million + $40 million = $200 million to make *Titanic*.

37. *Step 1* Let $x =$ the number of hours that the average motorist in Miami spends stuck in traffic in one year.

Step 2 $2x - 32 =$ the number of hours that the average motorist in Los Angeles spends stuck in traffic in one year

Step 3   The total for the two cities is 139 hours, so the equation is
$$x + (2x - 32) = 139.$$

Step 4 $x + 2x - 32 = 139$
$$3x - 32 = 139$$
$$3x - 32 + 32 = 139 + 32$$
$$3x = 171$$
$$\dfrac{3x}{3} = \dfrac{171}{3}$$
$$x = 57$$

Step 5   In Miami, the average motorist spends 57 hours stuck in traffic. In Los Angeles, the average motorist spends $2(57) - 32 = 82$ hours stuck in traffic in one year.

In Exercises 39–41, the five-step problem in this section of the textbook and illustrated in the solutions for Exercises 35 and 37 should be used. This strategy is used in the following solutions, although the steps are not listed.

39. Let $x =$ the smaller page number. Then $x + 1 =$ the larger page number.
$$x + (x + 1) = 629$$
$$2x + 1 = 629$$
$$2x = 628$$
$$x = 314$$

The smaller page number is 314. The larger page number is $314 + 1 = 315$. The page numbers are 314 and 315.

41. Let x = the losing score.
Then $x + 1$ = the winning score.

$$x + (x + 1) = 39$$
$$2x + 1 = 39$$
$$2x = 38$$
$$x = 19$$

The losing score was 19. The winning score was $19 + 1 = 20$. The sum of the scores was $19 + 20 = 39$.

43. Two even integers differ by 2.
Let x = the smaller integer.
Then $x + 2$ = the larger integer.

$$x + (x + 2) = 66$$
$$2x + 2 = 66$$
$$2x = 34$$
$$x = 32$$

The smaller integer is 32. The larger integer is $32 + 2 = 34$. Their sum is $32 + 34 = 66$.

45. Let x = the number of miles you can travel in one week for \$320.

$$200 + 0.15x = 320$$
$$200 + 0.15x - 200 = 320 - 200$$
$$0.15x = 120$$
$$\frac{0.15x}{0.15} = \frac{120}{0.15}$$
$$x = 800$$

You can travel 800 miles in one week for \$320. This checks because \$200 + 0.15(\$800) = \$320.

47. Let x = the number of months it will take for a baby girl to weigh 16 pounds.

$$7 + 1.5x = 16$$
$$7 + 1.5x - 7 = 16 - 7$$
$$1.5x = 9$$
$$\frac{1.5x}{1.5} = \frac{9}{1.5}$$
$$x = 6$$

The average baby girl weighs 16 pounds after 6 months.

49. Let x = the width of the field (in yards).
Then $4w$ = the width.
The perimeter of a rectangle is twice the length plus twice the width, so

$$2w + 2(4w) = 500.$$

Solve this equation.

$$2w + 8w = 500$$
$$10w = 500$$
$$w = 50$$

The width is 50 yards and the length is $4(50) = 200$ yards. This checks because $2(50) + 2(200) = 500$.

51. Let w = the width of a football field (in feet).
Then $w + 200$ = the length.

$$2w + 2(w + 200) = 1040$$
$$2w + 2w + 400 = 1040$$
$$4w + 400 = 1040$$
$$4w = 640$$
$$w = 160$$

The width 160 feet and the length is $160 + 200 = 360$ feet. This checks because $2(160) + 2(200) = 720$.

53. As shown in the diagram, let $x = $ the height and $3x = $ the length. To construct the bookcase, 3 heights and 4 lengths are needed. Since 60 feet of lumber is available,

$$3x + 4(3x) = 60.$$

Solve this equation.

$$3x + 12x = 60$$
$$15x = 60$$
$$x = 4$$

If $x = 4, 3x = 3 \cdot 4 = 12.$
The bookcase is 12 feet long and 4 feet high.

55. Let $x = $ the price before the reduction.

$$x - 0.20x = 320$$
$$1x - 0.20x = 320$$
$$0.80x = 320$$
$$\frac{0.80x}{0.80} = \frac{320}{0.80}$$
$$x = 400$$

The price before the reduction was $400.

57. Let $x = $ the price before the reduction.

$$x - \frac{1}{4}x = 21$$
$$\frac{3}{4}x = 21$$
$$\frac{4}{3}\left(\frac{3}{4}x\right) = \frac{4}{3}(21)$$
$$1x = 28$$
$$x = 28$$

The price before the reduction was $28.

59. Let $x = $ the price of the car without tax.

$$x + 0.06x = 15,370$$
$$1x + 0.06x = 15,370$$
$$1.06x = 15,370$$
$$\frac{1.06x}{1.06} = \frac{15,370}{1.06}$$
$$x = 14,500$$

The price of the car without sales tax was $14,500.

61. Let $x = $ the number of hours of labor.

$$63 + 35x = 448$$
$$63 + 35x - 63 = 448 - 63$$
$$35x = 385$$
$$\frac{35x}{35} = \frac{385}{35}$$
$$x = 11$$

It took 11 hours of labor to repair the car.

For Exercises 63–65, answers may vary.

67. Statement a should be translated as $x - 10 = 160.$
Statement b should be translated as $5x + 4 = 6x - 1.$
Statement c should be translated as $7 = x + 3.$
Since none of these statements was translated correctly, the correct response is d.

69. Let $x = $ the number of additional minutes (after the first).

$$0.55 + 0.40x = 6.95$$
$$0.55 + 0.40x - 0.55 = 6.95 - 0.55$$
$$0.40x = 6.40$$
$$\frac{0.40x}{0.40} = \frac{6.40}{0.40}$$
$$x = 16$$

Since there were 16 additional minutes after the first, the length of the call was 17 minutes.

71. Let $x =$ weight of unpeeled banana.

Then $\dfrac{1}{8}x =$ weight of banana peel

and $\dfrac{7}{8}x =$ weight of peeled banana.

The information in the cartoon translates into the equation

$$x = \frac{7}{8}x + \frac{7}{8}.$$

To solve this equation, first eliminate fractions by multiplying both sides by the LCD, which is 8.

$$8x = 8\left(\frac{7}{8}x + \frac{7}{8}\right)$$

$$8x = 8\left(\frac{7}{8}x\right) + 8\left(\frac{7}{8}\right)$$

$$8x = 7x + 7$$
$$8x - 7x = 7x + 7 - 7x$$
$$x = 7$$

The unpeeled banana weighs 7 ounces.

Review Exercises

72. $\dfrac{4}{5}x = -16$

$$\frac{5}{4}\left(\frac{4}{5}x\right) = \frac{5}{4}(-16)$$

$$x = -20$$

Check:

$$\frac{4}{5}(-20) \overset{?}{=} -16$$

$$\frac{4}{5} \cdot \frac{-20}{1} \overset{?}{=} -16$$

$$\frac{-80}{5} \overset{?}{=} -16$$

$$-16 = -16$$

The solution is -20.

73. $6(y - 1) + 7 = 9y - y + 1$
$$6y - 6 + 7 = 9y - y + 1$$
$$6y + 1 = 8y + 1$$
$$6y + 1 - 1 = 8y + 1 - 1$$
$$6y = 8y$$
$$6y - 8y = 8y - 8y$$
$$-2y = 0$$
$$\frac{-2y}{-2} = \frac{0}{-2}$$
$$y = 0$$

Check:

$$6(0 - 1) + 7 \overset{?}{=} 9(0) - 0 + 1$$
$$6(-10 + 7 \overset{?}{=} 0 - 0 \mid 1$$
$$-6 + 7 \overset{?}{=} 1$$
$$1 = 1$$

The solution is 0.

74. $V = \dfrac{1}{3}lwh$ for w

$$V = \frac{1}{3}lwh$$

$$3V = 3\left(\frac{1}{3}lwh\right)$$

$$3V = lwh$$
$$\frac{3V}{lh} = \frac{lwh}{lh}$$
$$\frac{3V}{lh} = w \quad \text{or} \quad w = \frac{3V}{lh}$$

Problem Solving in Geometry

2.6 CHECK POINTS

CHECK POINT 1

$$A = \frac{1}{2}bh$$

$$24 = \frac{1}{2}(4)h$$

$$24 = 2h$$

$$\frac{24}{2} = \frac{2h}{2}$$

$$12 = h$$

The height of the sail is 12 feet.

CHECK POINT 2

The radius is half the diameter, so $r = \frac{40}{2} = 20$ feet.

$$A = \pi r^2 \qquad\qquad C = 2\pi r$$
$$A = \pi(20)^2 \qquad\quad C = 2\pi(20)$$
$$A = 400\pi \qquad\qquad C = 40\pi$$

The area of the landing pad is 400π square feet and the circumference is 40π feet. Using 3.14 as an approximation for π, the area is approximately 1256 square feet and the circumference is approximately 126 feet.

CHECK POINT 3

The radius of the large pizza is $\frac{1}{2} \cdot 18$ inches $= 9$ inches, and the radius of the small pizza is $\frac{1}{2} \cdot 14$ inches $= 7$ inches. Find the area of the surface of each pizza.

Large pizza:

$$A = \pi r^2 = \pi(9 \text{ in.})^2$$
$$= 81\pi \text{ in.}^2$$
$$\approx 254 \text{ in.}^2$$

Medium pizza:

$$A = \pi r^2 = \pi(7 \text{ in.})^2$$
$$= 49 \text{ in.}^2$$
$$\approx 154 \text{ in.}^2$$

Now find the price per square inch for each pizza.

Price per square inch for large pizza

$$= \frac{\$20.00}{81\pi \text{ in.}^2} \approx \frac{\$20}{254 \text{ in.}^2} \approx \frac{\$0.08}{\text{in.}^2}$$

Price per square inch for medium pizza

$$= \frac{\$14.00}{49\pi \text{ in.}^2} \approx \frac{\$14.00}{154 \text{ in.}^2} \approx \frac{\$0.09}{\text{in.}^2}$$

The large pizza is the better buy.

CHECK POINT 4

Use the formula for the volume of a cylinder:

$$V = \pi r^2 h.$$

Smaller cylinder: $r = 3$ in., $h = 5$ in.

$$V_{\text{Smaller}} = \pi(3)^2(5)$$
$$= \pi(9)(5)$$
$$= 45\pi$$

The volume of the smaller cylinder is 45π in.^{3}.

Large cylinder: $r = 3$ in., $h = 2(5 \text{ in.}) = 10$ in.

$$V_{\text{Larger}} = \pi(3)^2(10)$$
$$= \pi(9)(10)$$
$$= 90\pi$$

The volume of the larger cylinder is 90π in.^{3}.

Write a ratio to compare the two volumes:

$$\frac{V_{\text{Larger}}}{V_{\text{Smaller}}} = \frac{90\pi}{45\pi} = \frac{2}{1}.$$

Thus, the volume of the larger cylinder is 2 times the volume of the smaller cylinder.

CHECK POINT 5

Use the formula for the volume of a sphere with $r = 4.5$ in.

$$V = \frac{4}{3}\pi r^3$$
$$V = \frac{4}{3}\pi (4.5 \text{ in.})^3$$
$$= \frac{4}{3}\pi (91.125 \text{ in.}^3)$$
$$\approx 382 \text{ in.}^3$$

Since the volume of the sphere is 382 cubic inches, 350 cubic inches of air will not fill it completely. About 32 more cubic inches of air are needed.

CHECK POINT 6

Let x = the measure of the second angle.
Then $3x$ = the measure of the first angle;
$x - 20$ = the measure of the third angle.

$$3x + x + (x - 20) = 180$$
$$5x - 20 = 180$$
$$5x = 200$$
$$x = 40$$

Measure of first angle $= 3x = 3 \cdot 40° = 120°$
Measure of second angle $= x = 40°$
Measure of third angle $= x - 2 = 20°$
The angles measure $120°, 40°$, and $20°$.
Check: The sum of the measure of the angles of this triangle is $120° + 40° + 20° = 180°$.

CHECK POINT 7

Let x = the measure of the angle.
Then $90 - x$ = the measure of its complement.

$$x = 2(90 - x)$$
$$x = 180 - 2x$$
$$3x = 180$$
$$x = 60$$

The angle's measure is $60°$.
Check: The measure of the complement is $90° - 60° = 30°$. The angle's measure, $60°$, is twice $30°$.

EXERCISE SET 2.6

1. Use the formulas for the perimeter and area of a rectangle. The length is 6 m and the width is 3 m.

$$P = 2l + 2w$$
$$P = 2(6) + 2(3)$$
$$P = 12 + 6 = 18$$

The perimeter is 18 m.

$$A = lw$$
$$A = 6 \cdot 3 = 18$$

The area is 18 m².

3. Use the formula for the area of a triangle. The base is 14 in. and the height is 8 in. The lengths of the other two sides are not used in calculating the area.

$$A = \frac{1}{2}bh$$
$$A = \frac{1}{2}(14)(8) = 56$$

The area is 56 in.².

5. Use the formula for the area of a trapezoid. The bases are 16 m and 10 m and the height is 7 m. The lengths of the other two sides of the trapezoid are not used in calculating the area.

$$A = \frac{1}{2}h(a+b)$$

$$A = \frac{1}{2}(7)(16+10)$$

$$= \frac{1}{2} \cdot 7 \cdot 26 = 91$$

The area is 91 m².

7. $A = lw; A = 1250, w = 25$

$$A = lw$$
$$1250 = l \cdot 25$$
$$50 = l$$

The length of the swimming pool is 50 ft.

9. $A = \frac{1}{2}bh; A = 20, b = 5$

$$A = \frac{1}{2}bh$$

$$20 = \frac{1}{2} \cdot 5 \cdot h$$

$$20 = \frac{5}{2}h$$

$$\frac{2}{5}(20) = \frac{2}{5}\left(\frac{5}{2}h\right)$$

$$8 = h$$

The height of the triangle is 8 ft.

11. $P = 2l + 2w; P = 188, w = 44$

$$188 = 2l + 2(44)$$
$$188 = 2l + 88$$
$$100 = 2l$$
$$50 = l$$

The length of the rectangle is 50 cm.

13. Use the formulas for the area and circumference of a circle. The radius is 4 cm.

$$A = \pi r^2$$
$$A = \pi(4)^2$$
$$A = 16\pi \approx 50$$

The area is 16π cm² or approximately 50 cm².

$$C = 2\pi r$$
$$C = 2\pi(4)$$
$$C = 8\pi \approx 25$$

The circumference is 8π cm or approximately 25 cm.

15. Since the diameter is 12 yd, the radius is $\frac{12}{2} = 6$ yd.

$$A = \pi r^2$$
$$A = \pi(6)^2$$
$$A = 36\pi \approx 113$$

The area is 36π yd² or approximately 113 yd².

$$C = 2\pi r$$
$$C = 2\pi \cdot 6$$
$$C = 12\pi \approx 38$$

The circumference is 12π yd or approximately 38 yd.

17. $C = 2\pi r; C = 14\pi$

$$C = 2\pi r$$
$$14\pi = 2\pi r$$
$$\frac{14\pi}{2\pi} = \frac{2\pi r}{2\pi}$$
$$7 = r$$

The radius is 7 in. and the diameter is 2(7 in.) = 14 in.

19. Use the formula for the volume of a rectangular solid. The length and width are each 3 in. and the height is 4 in.

$$V = lwh$$
$$V = 3 \cdot 3 \cdot 4 = 36$$

The volume is 36 in.³.

21. Use the formula for the volume of a cylinder. The radius is 5 cm and the height is 6 cm.

$$V = \pi r^2 h$$
$$V = \pi(5)^2 \cdot 6$$
$$V = 150\pi \approx 471$$

The volume is 150π cm³ or approximately 471 cm³.

23. Use the formula for the volume of a sphere. The diameter is 18 cm, so the radius is 9 cm.

$$V = \frac{4}{3}\pi r^3$$
$$V = \frac{4}{3}\pi(9)^3$$
$$V = 972\pi \approx 3052$$

The volume is 972π cm³ or approximately 3052 cm³.

25. Use the formula for the volume of a cone. The radius is 4 m and the height is 9 m.

$$V = \frac{1}{3}\pi r^2 h$$
$$V = \frac{1}{3}\pi(4)^2 \cdot 9$$
$$V = 48\pi \approx 151$$

The volume is 48π m³ or approximately 151 m³.

27. $V = \pi r^2 h$ for h

$$V = \pi r^2 h$$
$$\frac{V}{\pi r^2} = \frac{\pi r^2 h}{\pi r^2}$$
$$\frac{V}{\pi r^2} = h$$

29. Smaller cylinder: $r = 3$ in., $h = 4$ in.

$$V = \pi r^2 h$$
$$V = \pi(3)^2 \cdot 4$$
$$V = 36\pi$$

The volume of the smaller cylinder is 36π in.³.

Larger cylinder: $r = 3(3 \text{ in.}) = 9$ in., $h = 4$ in.

$$V = \pi r^2 h$$
$$V = \pi(9)^2 \cdot 4$$
$$V = 324\pi$$

The volume of the larger cylinder is 324π. The ratio of the volumes of the two cylinders is

$$\frac{V_{\text{larger}}}{V_{\text{smaller}}} = \frac{324\pi}{36\pi} = \frac{9}{1}.$$

so the volume of the larger cylinder is 9 times the volume of the smaller cylinder.

31. The sum of the measures of the three angles of any triangle is 180°, so

$$x + x + (x + 30) = 180.$$

Solve this equation.

$$3x + 30 = 180$$
$$3x = 150$$
$$x = 50$$

If $x = 50, x + 30 = 80$, so the three angle measures are $50°, 50°$, and $80°$. This solution checks because $50° + 50° + 80° = 180°$.

33. $4x + (3x + 4) + (2x + 5) = 180$
$$9x + 9 = 180$$
$$9x = 171$$
$$x = 19$$

If $x = 19$, then $4x = 76, 3x + 4 = 61$, and $2x + 5 = 43$. Therefore, the angle measures are $76°, 61°$, and $43°$. This solution checks because $76° + 61° + 43° = 180°$.

35. Let $x =$ the measure of the smallest angle. Then $2x =$ the measure of the second angle; $x + 20 =$ the measure of the third angle.

$$x + 2x + (x + 20) = 180$$
$$4x + 20 = 180$$
$$4x = 160$$
$$x = 40$$

Measure of smallest angle $= x = 40°$
Measure of second angle $= 2x = 80°$
Measure of third angle $= x + 20 = 60°$

37. If the measure of an angle is $48°$, the measure of its complement is $90° - 48° = 42°$.

39. If the measure of an angle is $89°$, the measure of its complement is 1.

41. If the measure of an angle is $111°$, the measure of its supplement is $180° - 111° = 69°$.

43. If the measure of an angle is $90°$, the measure of its supplement is $180° - 90° = 90°$.

45. *Step 1* Let $x =$ the measure of the angle.

Step 2 Then $90 - x =$ the measure of its complement.

Step 3 The angle's measure is $60°$ more than that of its complement, so the equation is

$$x = (90 - x) + 60.$$

Step 4 Solve this equation.

$$x = 90 - x + 60$$
$$x = 150 - x$$
$$2x = 150$$
$$x = 75$$

The measure of the angle is $75°$.

Step 5 The complement of the angle is $90° - 75° = 15°$, and $75°$ is $60°$ more than $15°$.

47. Let $x =$ the measure of the angle. Then $180 - x =$ the measure of its supplement.

$$x = 3(180 - x)$$
$$x = 540 - 3x$$
$$4x = 540$$
$$x = 135$$

The measure of the angle is $135°$. The measure of its supplement is $180° - 135° = 45°$, and $135° = 3(45°)$, so the proposed solution checks.

49. Let $x =$ the measure of the angle. Then $180 - x =$ the measure of its supplement; $90 - x =$ the measure of its complement.

$$180 - x = 3(90 - x) + 10$$
$$180 - x = 270 - 3x + 10$$
$$180 - x = 280 - 3x$$
$$180 + 2x = 280$$
$$2x = 100$$
$$x = 50$$

The measure of the angle is $50°$. The measure of its supplement is $130°$ and the measure of its complement is $40°$. Since $130° = 3(40°) + 10°$, the proposed solution checks.

51. The area of the office is $(20 \text{ ft})(16 \text{ ft}) = 320 \text{ ft}^2$. Use a proportion to find how much of the yearly electric bill is deductible.

Let $x =$ the amount of the electric bill that is deductible.

$$\frac{320}{2200} = \frac{x}{4800}$$
$$2200x = (320)(4800)$$
$$2200x = 1{,}536{,}000$$
$$\frac{2200x}{2200} = \frac{1{,}536{,}000}{2200}$$
$$x \approx 698.18$$

$698.18 of the yearly electric bill is deductible.

53. The radius of the large pizza is $\frac{1}{2} \cdot 14$ inches $= 7$ inches, and the radius of the medium pizza is $\frac{1}{2} \cdot 7$ inches $= 3.5$ inches.

Large pizza:

$$A = \pi r^2 = \pi(7 \text{ in.})^2$$
$$= 49\pi \text{ in.}^2 \approx 154 \text{ in.}^2$$

Medium pizza:

$$A = \pi r^2 = \pi(3.5 \text{ in.})^2$$
$$= 12.25 \text{ in.}^2 \approx 38.465 \text{ in.}^2$$

For each pizza, find the price per square inch by dividing the price by the area:

Price per square inch for large pizza

$$= \frac{\$12.00}{154 \text{ in.}^2} \approx \frac{\$0.08}{\text{in.}^2}$$

Price per square inch for medium pizza

$$= \frac{\$5.00}{38.465 \text{ in.}^2} \approx \frac{\$0.13}{\text{in.}^2}$$

The large pizza is the better buy.

55. The area of the larger circle is

$$A = \pi r^2 = \pi \cdot 50^2 = 2500\pi \text{ ft}^2.$$

The area of the smaller circle is

$$A = \pi r^2 = \pi \cdot 40^2 = 1600\pi \text{ ft}^2.$$

The area of the circular road is the difference between the area of the outer circle and the area of the smaller circle:

$$A = 2500\pi \text{ ft}^2 - 1600\pi \text{ ft}^2 = 900\pi \text{ ft}^2$$

The cost to pave the circular road is $0.08(900\pi) \approx $2260.80.

57. The perimeter of the bottom of two sides of the rectangular portion of the window is $3 \text{ ft} + 6 \text{ ft} + 6 \text{ ft} = 15 \text{ ft}$. The radius of the semicircle is $\frac{1}{2} \cdot 3 \text{ ft} = 1.5 \text{ ft}$, so the circumference of the semicircular portion of the window is $\frac{1}{2} \cdot 2\pi r \approx 3.14(1.5) = 4.7 \text{ ft}$. Therefore, approximately $15 \text{ ft} + 4.7 \text{ ft} = 19.7 \text{ ft}$ of stripping would be needed to frame the window.

59. First, find the volume of water when the reservoir was full:

$$V = lwh$$
$$V = 50 \cdot 30 \cdot 20 = 30{,}000.$$

The volume was $30{,}000 \text{ yd}^3$. Now find the volume when the height of the water was 6 yards:

$$V = 50 \cdot 30 \cdot 6 = 9000.$$

The volume was 9000 yd^3. The amount of water used in the three-month period was

$$30{,}000 \text{ yd}^3 - 9000 \text{ yd}^3 = 21{,}000 \text{ yd}^3.$$

61. For the first can, the diameter is 6 in. so the radius is 3 in. Find the volume of this can.

$$V = \pi r^2 h$$
$$V = \pi(3)^2 \cdot 5$$
$$= 45\pi \approx 141.3$$

The volume is about 141.3 in.^{3}. For the second can, the diameter is 5 in., so the radius is 2.5 in. Find the volume of this can.

$$V = \pi r^2 h$$
$$V = \pi(2.5)^2 \cdot 6$$
$$= 37.5\pi \approx 117.75$$

The volume of the second can is 117.75 in.^{2}.

The first can (the one with a diameter of 6 in. and a height of 5 in.) contains more soup, so it is the better buy.

63. Find the volume of a cylinder with radius 3 feet and height 2 feet 4 inches or $2\frac{1}{3}$ feet or $\frac{7}{3}$ feet:

$$V = \pi r^2 h$$
$$V = \pi(3)^2 \left(\frac{7}{3}\right)$$
$$V = \pi \cdot 9 \cdot \frac{7}{3}$$
$$V = 21\pi \approx 65.94$$

The volume of the tank is about 65.94 ft^3, so it is a little over one cubic foot too small to hold 500 gallons of water. Yes, you should be able to win your case.

For Exercises 65–73, answers may vary.

75. Area of smaller deck $= (8 \text{ ft})(10 \text{ ft})$
$$= 80 \text{ ft}^2$$
Area of larger deck $= (12 \text{ ft})(15 \text{ ft})$
$$= 180 \text{ ft}^2$$
Find the ratio of the areas:

$$\frac{A_{\text{larger}}}{A_{\text{smaller}}} = \frac{180 \text{ ft}^2}{80 \text{ ft}^2} = \frac{2.25}{1} \text{ or } 2.25{:}1$$

The cost will increase 2.25 times.

77. Let $x =$ the radius of the original sphere. Then $2x =$ the radius of the larger sphere.

Find the ratio of the volumes of the two spheres:

$$\frac{A_{\text{larger}}}{A_{\text{original}}} = \frac{\frac{4}{3}\pi(2x)^3}{\frac{4}{3}\pi x^3} = \frac{8x^3}{x^3} = \frac{8}{1} \text{ or } 8{:}1$$

If the radius of a sphere is doubled, the volume increases 8 times.

79. The angles marked $(2x)°$ and $(2x+40)°$ in the figure are supplementary, so

$$2x + (2x + 40) = 180.$$

Solve this equation.

$$2x + 2x + 40 = 180$$
$$4x + 40 = 180$$
$$4x = 140$$
$$x = 35$$

The angle of inclination is 35°.

Review Exercises

80. $P = 2s + b$ for s
$$P - b = 2s$$
$$\frac{P-b}{2} = \frac{2s}{2}$$
$$\frac{P-b}{2} = s \quad \text{or} \quad s = \frac{P-b}{2}$$

81. $\dfrac{x}{2} + 7 = 13 - \dfrac{x}{4}$

Multiply both sides by the LCD, which is 4.

$$4\left(\frac{x}{2} + 7\right) = 4\left(13 - \frac{x}{4}\right)$$
$$2x + 28 = 52 - x$$
$$2x + 28 + x = 52 - x + x$$
$$3x + 28 = 52$$
$$3x + 28 - 28 = 52 - 28$$
$$3x = 24$$
$$\frac{3x}{3} = \frac{24}{3}$$
$$x = 8$$

82. $[3(12 \div 2^2 - 3)^2]^2 = [3(12 \div 4 - 3)^2]^2$
$$= [3(3 - 3)^2]^2$$
$$= (3 \cdot 0^2)^2$$
$$= 0^2 = 0$$

Solving Linear Inequalities

2.7 CHECK POINTS

CHECK POINT 1

a. $x < 4$

The solutions of $x < 4$ are all real numbers less than 4. Shade all points to the left of 4 and use an open dot at 4 to show that 4 is not a solution.

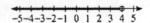

$-5\ -4\ -3\ -2\ -1\ \ 0\ \ 1\ \ 2\ \ 3\ \ 4\ \ 5$

b. $x \geq -2$

The solutions of $x \geq -2$ are all real numbers greater than or equal to -2. Shade all points to the right of -2 and the point -2 itself. Use a closed dot at -2 to show that -2 is a solution.

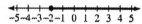

c. $-4 \leq x < 1$

The solutions of $-4 \leq x < 1$ are all real numbers between -4 and 1, including -4 but not including 1. Use a closed dot at -4 and an open dot at 1.

CHECK POINT 2

$$x + 6 < 9$$
$$x + 6 = 6 < 9 - 6$$
$$x < 3$$

The solution set is written is set-builder notation as $\{x|x < 3\}$.

CHECK POINT 3

$$8x - 2 \geq 7x - 4$$
$$8 - 7x - 2 \geq 7x - 7x - 4$$
$$x - 2 \geq -4$$
$$x - 2 + 2 \geq -4 + 2$$
$$x \geq -2$$

Solution set: $\{x|x \geq -2\}$

CHECK POINT 4

a.
$$\frac{1}{4}x < 2$$
$$4 \cdot \frac{1}{4}x < 4 \cdot 2$$
$$x < 8$$

Solution set: $\{x|x < 8\}$

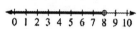

b. $-6x < 18$
$$\frac{-6x}{-6} > \frac{18}{-6}$$
$$x > -3$$

(Be sure to reverse the inequality symbol when dividing by a negative number.)
Solution set: $\{x|x > -3\}$

CHECK POINT 5

$$5y - 3 \geq 17$$
$$5y - 3 + 3 \geq 17 + 3$$
$$5y \geq 20$$
$$\frac{5y}{5} \geq \frac{20}{5}$$
$$y \geq 4$$

Solution set: $\{y|y \geq 4\}$

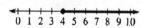

CHECK POINT 6

$$6 - 3x \leq 5x - 2$$
$$6 - 3x - 5x \leq 5x - 2 - 5x$$
$$6 - 8x \leq -2$$
$$6 - 8x - 6 \leq -2 - 6$$
$$-8x \leq -8$$
$$\frac{-8x}{-8} \geq \frac{-8}{-8}$$
$$x \geq 1$$

Solution set: $\{x|x \geq 1\}$

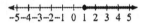

CHECK POINT 7

$$2(x - 3) - 1 \leq 3(x + 2) - 14$$
$$2x - 6 - 1 \leq 3x + 6 - 14$$
$$2x - 7 \leq 3x - 8$$
$$2x - 3x - 7 \leq 3x - 3x - 8$$
$$-x - 7 \leq -8$$
$$-x - 7 + 7 \leq -8 + 7$$
$$-x \leq -1$$
$$-1(-x) \geq -1(-1)$$
$$x \geq 1$$

Solution set: $\{x|x \geq 1\}$

CHECK POINT 8

$$4(x + 2) > 4x + 15$$
$$4x + 8 > 4x + 15$$
$$4x + 8 - 4x > 4x + 15 - 4x$$
$$8 > 15$$

The original inequality is equivalent to the false statement $8 > 15$, which is false for every value of x. The inequality has no solution. The solution set is $\emptyset$, the empty set.

CHECK POINT 9

$$3(x + 1) \geq 2x + 1 + x$$
$$3x + 3 \geq 3x + 1$$
$$3x + 3 - 3x \geq 3x + 1 - 3x$$
$$3 \geq 1$$

The original inequality is equivalent to the true statement $3 \geq 1$, which is true for every value of x. The solution set is the set of all real numbers, written $\{x|x \text{ is a real number}\}$.

CHECK POINT 10

Let $x =$ your grade on the final examination.

$$\text{Average} = \frac{82 + 74 + 78 + x + x}{5}$$

In order to get a B, your average must be at least 80, so

$$\frac{82 + 74 + 78 + x + x}{5} \geq 80.$$

Solve this inequality.

$$\frac{234 + 2x}{5} \geq 80$$
$$5\left(\frac{234 + 2x}{5}\right) \geq 5(80)$$
$$234 + 2x \geq 400$$
$$234 + 2x - 234 \geq 400 - 234$$
$$2x \geq 166$$
$$\frac{2x}{2} \geq \frac{166}{2}$$
$$x \geq 83$$

You must get at least 83% on the final examination to earn a B in the course.

EXERCISE SET 2.7

1. $x > 6$

3. $x < -4$

5. $x \geq -3$

7. $x \leq 4$

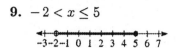

9. $-2 < x \le 5$

11. $-1 < x < 4$

13. $\{x | x > -2\}$

15. $\{x | x \ge 4\}$

17. $\{x | x \ge 3\}$

19. $\quad x - 3 > 2$
$\quad x - 3 + 3 > 2 + 3$
$\quad\quad x > 5$

$\{x | x > 5\}$

21. $\quad x + 4 \le 9$
$\quad x + 4 - 4 \le 9 - 4$
$\quad\quad x \le 5$

$\{x | x \le 5\}$

23. $\quad y - 3 < 0$
$\quad y - 3 + 3 < 0 + 3$
$\quad\quad y < 3$

$\{y | y < 3\}$

25. $\quad 3x + 4 \le 2x + 7$
$\quad 3x - 2x \le 7 - 4$
$\quad\quad x \le 3$

$\{x | x \le 3\}$

27. $\quad 5x - 9 < 4x + 7$
$\quad 5x - 4x < 7 + 9$
$\quad\quad x < 16$

$\{x | x < 16\}$

29. $\quad 7x - 7 > 6x - 3$
$\quad 7x - 6x > -3 + 7$
$\quad\quad x > 4$

$\{x | x > 4\}$

31. $\quad x - \dfrac{2}{3} > \dfrac{1}{2}$
$\quad x - \dfrac{2}{3} + \dfrac{2}{3} > \dfrac{1}{2} + \dfrac{2}{3}$
$\quad\quad x > \dfrac{3}{6} + \dfrac{4}{6}$
$\quad\quad x > \dfrac{7}{6}$

$\{x | x > \frac{7}{6}\}$

33. $\quad y + \dfrac{7}{8} \le \dfrac{1}{2}$
$\quad y + \dfrac{7}{8} - \dfrac{7}{8} \le \dfrac{1}{2} - \dfrac{7}{8}$
$\quad\quad y \le \dfrac{4}{8} - \dfrac{7}{8}$
$\quad\quad y \le -\dfrac{3}{8}$

$\{y | y \le \frac{3}{8}\}$

35.
$$-15y + 13 > 13 - 16y$$
$$-15y + 13 + 16y > 13 - 16y + 16y$$
$$y + 13 > 13$$
$$y + 13 - 13 > 13 - 13$$
$$y > 0$$

$$\{y|y > 0\}$$

37.
$$\frac{1}{2}x < 4$$
$$2\left(\frac{1}{2}x\right) < 2(4)$$
$$1x < 8$$
$$x < 8$$

$$\{x|x < 8\}$$

39.
$$\frac{x}{3} > -2$$
$$3\left(\frac{x}{3}\right) > 3(-2)$$
$$x > -6$$

$$\{x|x > -6\}$$

41.
$$4x < 20$$
$$\frac{4x}{x} < 20$$
$$x < 5$$

$$\{x|x < 5\}$$

43.
$$3x \geq -21$$
$$\frac{3x}{3} \geq \frac{-21}{3}$$
$$x \geq -7$$

$$\{x|x \geq -7\}$$

45.
$$-3x < 15$$
$$\frac{-3x}{-3} > \frac{15}{-3}$$

Notice that the direction of the inequality symbol was reversed when both sides were divided by a negative number.

$$x > -5$$
$$\{x|x > -5\}$$

47.
$$-3x \geq 15$$
$$\frac{-3x}{-3} \leq \frac{15}{-3}$$
$$x \leq -5$$

$$\{x|x \leq -5\}$$

49.
$$-16x > -48$$
$$\frac{-16x}{-16} < \frac{-48}{-16}$$
$$x < 3$$

$$\{x|x < 3\}$$

51.
$$-4y \leq \frac{1}{2}$$
$$2(-4y) \leq 2\left(\frac{1}{2}\right)$$
$$-8y \leq 1$$
$$\frac{-8y}{-8} \geq \frac{1}{-8}$$
$$y \geq -\frac{1}{8}$$

$$\left\{y|y \geq -\tfrac{1}{8}\right\}$$

53.
$$-x < 4$$
$$-1(-x) > -1(4)$$
$$x > -4$$

$$\{x \mid x > -4\}$$

55.
$$2x - 3 > 7$$
$$2x - 3 + 3 > 7 + 3$$
$$2x > 10$$
$$\frac{2x}{2} > \frac{10}{2}$$
$$x > 5$$

$$\{x \mid x > 5\}$$

57.
$$3x + 3 < 18$$
$$3x + 3 - 3 < 18 - 3$$
$$3x < 15$$
$$\frac{3x}{3} < \frac{15}{3}$$
$$x < 5$$

$$\{x \mid x < 5\}$$

59.
$$3 - 7x \le 17$$
$$3 - 7x - 3 \le 17 - 3$$
$$-7x \le 14$$
$$\frac{-7x}{-7} \ge \frac{14}{-7}$$
$$x \ge -2$$

$$\{x \mid x \ge -2\}$$

61.
$$-2x - 3 < 3$$
$$-2x - 3 + 3 < 3 + 3$$
$$-2x < 6$$
$$\frac{-2x}{-2} > \frac{6}{-2}$$
$$x > -3$$

$$\{x \mid x > -3\}$$

63.
$$5 - x \le 1$$
$$5 - x - 5 \le 1 - 5$$
$$-x \le -4$$
$$-1(-x) \ge -1(-4)$$
$$x \ge 4$$

$$\{x \mid x \ge 4\}$$

65.
$$2x - 5 > -x + 6$$
$$2x - 5 + x > -x + 6 + x$$
$$3x - 5 > 6$$
$$3x - 5 + 5 > 6 + 5$$
$$3x > 11$$
$$\frac{3x}{3} > \frac{11}{3}$$
$$x > \frac{11}{3}$$

$$\{x \mid x > \tfrac{11}{3}\}$$

67.
$$2y - 5 < 5y - 11$$
$$2y - 5 - 5y < 5y - 11 - 5y$$
$$-3y - 5 < -11$$
$$-3y - 5 + 5 < -11 + 5$$
$$-3y < -6$$
$$\frac{-3y}{-3} > \frac{-6}{-3}$$
$$y > 2$$

$\{y | y > 2\}$

69. $3(2y - 1) < 9$

$6y - 3 < 9$

$6y - 3 + 3 < 9 + 3$

$6y < 12$

$\dfrac{6y}{6} < \dfrac{12}{6}$

$y < 2$

$\{y | y < 2\}$

71. $3(x + 1) - 5 < 2x + 1$

$3x + 3 - 5 < 2x + 1$

$3x - 2 < 2x + 1$

$3x - 2 - 2x < 2x + 1 - 2x$

$x - 2 < 1$

$x - 2 + 2 < 1 + 2$

$x < 3$

$\{x | x < 3\}$

73. $8x + 3 > 3(2x + 1) - x + 5$

$8x + 3 > 6x + 3 - x + 5$

$8x + 3 > 5x + 8$

$8x + 3 - 5x > 5x + 8 - 5x$

$3x + 3 > 8$

$3x + 3 - 3 > 8 - 3$

$3x > 5$

$x > \dfrac{5}{3}$

$\{x | x > \frac{5}{3}\}$

75. $\dfrac{x}{3} - 2 \geq 1$

$\dfrac{x}{3} - 2 + 2 \geq 1 + 2$

$\dfrac{x}{3} \geq 3$

$3\left(\dfrac{x}{3}\right) \geq 3(3)$

$x \geq 9$

$\{x | x \geq 9\}$

77. $1 - \dfrac{x}{2} > 4$

$1 - \dfrac{x}{2} - 1 > 4 - 1$

$-\dfrac{x}{2} > 3$

$2\left(-\dfrac{x}{2}\right) > 2(3)$

$-x > 6$

$-1(-x) < -1(6)$

$x < -6$

$\{x | x < -6\}$

79. $-4x - 4 < 4(x - 5)$

$-4x - 4 < 4x - 20$

$-4x - 4 + 4 < 4x - 20 + 4$

$-4x < 4x - 16$

$-4x - 4x < 4x - 16 - 4x$

$0 < -16$

The original inequality is equivalent to the false statement $0 < -16$, so the inequality has no solution. The solution set is $\emptyset$ (the empty set).

81.
$$x + 3 < x + 7$$
$$x + 3 - x < x + 7 - x$$
$$3 < 7$$

The original inequality is equivalent to the true statement $3 < 7$, so the solution is the set of all real numbers, written $\{x \mid x \text{ is a real number}\}$.

83.
$$7x \le 7(x - 2)$$
$$7x \le 7x - 14$$
$$7x - 7x \le 7x - 14 - 7x$$
$$0 \le -14$$

Since $0 \le -14$ is a false statement, the original inequality has no solution. The solution set is $\emptyset$.

85.
$$2(x + 3) > 2x + 1$$
$$2x + 6 > 2x + 1$$
$$2x + 6 - 2x > 2x + 1 - 2x$$
$$6 > 1$$

Since $6 > 1$ is a true statement, the original inequality is true for all real numbers. The solution set is $\{x \mid x \text{ is a real number}\}$.

87.
$$5x - 4 \le 4(x - 1)$$
$$5x - 4 \le 4x - 4$$
$$5x - 4 + 4 \le 4x - 4 + 4$$
$$5x \le 4x$$
$$5x - 4x \le 4x - 4x$$
$$x \le 0$$

$\{x \mid x \le 0\}$

89. $x \ge 34.4\%$

The following cities have 34.4% or more of their population ages 25 and older with 16 or more years of education: Raleigh, NC; Seattle, WA; San Francisco, CA; and Austin, TX.

91. $x < 30.0\%$

The only city on the list with less than 30.0% of its population ages 25 and older with 16 or more years of education is San Diego, CA.

93. $30.0\% \le x \le 34.4\%$

The following cities have at least 30.0% but no more than 34.4% of their population ages 25 and older with 16 or more years of education: Washington, DC; Lexington-Fayette, KY; Minneapolis, MN; Boston, MA; and Arlington, TX.

95.
$$3x - 4 < 11$$
$$3x - 4 + 4 < 11 + 4$$
$$3x < 15$$
$$\frac{3x}{3} < \frac{15}{3}$$
$$x < 5$$

The following disorders affect fewer than 5 million people in the United States: antisocial personality and schizophrenia.

97. $N = 550 - 9x; \; N < 370$

$$550 - 9x < 370$$
$$550 - 9x - 550 < 370 - 550$$
$$-9x < -180$$
$$\frac{-9x}{-9} > \frac{-180}{-9}$$
$$x > 20$$

Twenty years after 1988 is 2008. According to the model, there will be 370 billion cigarettes consumed in 2008 and less than 370 billion after 2008 (from 2009 onward).

99. a. Let x = your grade on the final exam.

$$\frac{86 + 88 + x}{3} \geq 90$$

$$3\left(\frac{86 + 88 + x}{3}\right) \geq 3(90)$$

$$86 + 88 + x \geq 270$$

$$174 + x \geq 270$$

$$174 + x - 174 \geq 270 - 174$$

$$x \geq 96$$

You must get at least 96% on the final exam to earn an A in the course.

b.

$$\frac{86 + 88 + x}{3} < 80$$

$$3\left(\frac{86 + 88 + x}{3}\right) < 3(80)$$

$$86 + 88 + x < 240$$

$$174 + x < 240$$

$$174 + x - 174 < 240 - 174$$

$$x < 66$$

If you get less than 66% on the final exam, your grade will be below a B.

101. Let x = number of miles driven.

$$80 + 0.25x \leq 400$$

$$80 + 0.25x - 80 \leq 400 - 80$$

$$0.25x \leq 320$$

$$\frac{0.25x}{0.25} \leq \frac{320}{0.25}$$

$$x \leq 1280$$

You can drive up to 1280 miles.

103. Let x = number of cement bags.

$$245 + 95x \leq 3000$$

$$245 + 95x - 245 \leq 3000 - 245$$

$$95x \leq 2755$$

$$\frac{95x}{95} \leq \frac{2755}{95}$$

$$x \leq 29$$

Up to 29 pounds of cement can safely be listed on the elevator in one trip.

For Exercises 105–109, answers may vary.

111. Let x = number of miles driven.

Weekly cost for Basic Rental: $260
Weekly cost for Continental: $80 + 0.25x$

The cost for Basic Rental is a better deal if

$$80 + 0.25x > 260.$$

Solve this inequality.

$$80 + 0.25x - 80 > 260 - 80$$

$$0.25x > 180$$

$$\frac{0.25x}{0.25} > \frac{180}{0.25}$$

$$x > 720$$

Basic Car Rental is a better deal if you drive more than 720 miles in a week.

113.

$$1.45 - 7.23x > -1.442$$

$$1.45 - 7.23x - 1.45 > -1.442 - 1.45$$

$$-7.23x > -2.892$$

$$\frac{-7.23x}{-7.23} < \frac{-2.892}{-7.23}$$

$$x < 0.4$$

$$\{x | x < 0.4\}$$

Review Exercises

115. $A = PB$, $A = 8$, $P = 40\% = 0.4$

$$A = PB$$

$$8 = 0.4B$$

$$\frac{8}{0.4} = \frac{0.4B}{0.4}$$

$$20 = B$$

8 is 40% of 20.

116. Let $\quad w = \quad$ the width of the rectangle.
Then $w + 5 = \quad$ the length.

The perimeter is 34 inches.

$$2w + 2(w + 5) = 34.$$

Solve this equation.

$$2w + 2w + 10 = 34$$
$$4w + 10 = 34$$
$$4w = 24$$
$$w = 6$$

The width is 6 inches and the length is $6 + 5 = 11$ inches.

117.
$$5x + 16 = 3(x + 8)$$
$$5x + 16 = 3x + 24$$
$$5x + 16 - 3x = 3x + 24 - 3x$$
$$2x + 16 = 24$$
$$2x + 16 - 16 = 24 - 16$$
$$2x = 8$$
$$\frac{2x}{2} = \frac{8}{2}$$
$$x = 4$$

The solution is 4.

Chapter 2 Review Exercises

For Exercises 1–18 and 20–28, students should check all proposed solutions by substituting in the original equations. Checks will not be shown here.

1.
$$x - 10 = 32$$
$$x - 10 + 10 = 32 + 10$$
$$x = 42$$

The solution is 42.

2.
$$-14 = y + 6$$
$$-14 - 6 = y + 6 - 6$$
$$-20 = y$$

The solution is -20.

3.
$$7z - 3 = 6z + 9$$
$$7z - 3 - 6z = 6z + 9 - 6z$$
$$z - 3 = 9$$
$$z - 3 + 3 = 9 + 3$$
$$z = 12$$

The solution is 12.

4.
$$4(x + 3) = 3x - 10$$
$$4x + 12 = 3x - 10$$
$$4x + 12 - 3x = 3x - 10 - 3x$$
$$x + 12 = -10$$
$$x + 12 - 12 = -10 - 12$$
$$x = -22$$

The solution is -22.

5.
$$6x - 3x - 9 + 1 = -5x + 7x - 3$$
$$3x - 8 = 2x - 3$$
$$3x - 8 - 2x = 2x - 3 - 2x$$
$$x - 8 = -3$$
$$x - 8 + 8 = -3 + 8$$
$$x = 5$$

The solution is 5.

6.
$$\frac{x}{7} = 10$$
$$7\left(\frac{x}{7}\right) = 7(10)$$
$$x = 70$$

The solution is 70.

7.
$$\frac{y}{-8} = 4$$
$$-8\left(\frac{y}{-8}\right) = -8(4)$$
$$y = -32$$

The solution is -32.

8.
$$7z = 77$$
$$\frac{7z}{7} = \frac{77}{7}$$
$$z = 11$$

The solution is 11.

9. $-36 = -9y$

$$\frac{-36}{-9} = \frac{-9y}{-9}$$

$$4 = y$$

The solution is 4.

10. $\frac{3}{5}x = -9$

$$\frac{5}{3}\left(\frac{3}{5}x\right) = \frac{5}{3}(-9)$$

$$1x = -15$$

$$x = -15$$

The solution is -15.

11. $30 = -\frac{5}{2}y$

$$-\frac{2}{5} = -\frac{2}{5}\left(-\frac{5}{2}y\right)$$

$$-12 = y$$

The solution is -12.

12. $-x = 14$

$$-1(-x) = -1(14)$$

$$x = -14$$

The solution is -14.

13. $\frac{-x}{3} = -1$

$$3\left(\frac{-x}{3}\right) = 3(-1)$$

$$-x = -3$$

$$-1(-x) = -1(-3)$$

$$x = 3$$

The solution is 3.

14. $4x + 9 = 33$

$$4x + 9 - 9 = 33 - 9$$

$$4x = 24$$

$$\frac{4x}{4} = \frac{24}{4}$$

$$x = 6$$

The solution is 6.

15. $-3y - 2 = 13$

$$-3y - 2 + 2 = 13 + 2$$

$$-3y = 15$$

$$\frac{-3y}{-3} = \frac{15}{-3}$$

$$y = -5$$

The solution is -5.

16. $5z + 20 = 3z$

$$5z + 20 - 3z = 3z - 3z$$

$$2z + 20 = 0$$

$$2z + 20 - 20 = 0 - 20$$

$$2z = -20$$

$$\frac{2z}{2} = \frac{-20}{2}$$

$$z = -10$$

The solution is -10.

17. $5x - 3 = x + 5 = x + 5$

$$5x - 3 - x = x + 5 - x$$

$$4x - 3 = 5$$

$$4x - 3 + 3 = 5 + 3$$

$$4x = 8$$

$$\frac{4x}{4} = \frac{8}{4}$$

$$x = 2$$

The solution is 2.

18. $3 - 2x = 9 - 8x$

$$3 - 2x + 8x = 9 - 8x + 8x$$

$$3 + 6x = 9$$

$$3 + 6x - 3 = 9 - 3$$

$$6x = 6$$

$$\frac{6x}{6} = \frac{6}{6}$$

$$x = 1$$

The solution is 1.

19. $N = 0.07x + 4.1$; $N = 6.2$

$$6.2 = 0.07x + 4.1$$
$$6.2 - 4.1 = 0.07x + 4.1 - 4.1$$
$$2.1 = 0.07x$$
$$\frac{2.1}{0.07} = \frac{0.07x}{0.07}$$
$$30 = x$$

The enrollment for women is expected to reach 6.2 million 30 years after 1984, which is in the year $1984 + 30 = 2014$.

20.
$$5x + 9 - 7x + 6 = x + 18$$
$$-2x + 15 = x + 18$$
$$-2x + 15 - x = x + 18 - x$$
$$-3x + 15 = 18$$
$$-3x + 15 - 15 = 18 - 15$$
$$-3x = 3$$
$$\frac{-3x}{-3} = \frac{3}{-3}$$
$$x = -1$$

The solution is -1.

21.
$$3(x + 4) = 5x - 12$$
$$3x + 12 = 5x - 12$$
$$3x + 12 - 5x = 5x - 12 - 5x$$
$$-2x + 12 = -12$$
$$-2x + 12 - 12 = -12 - 12$$
$$-2x = -24$$
$$\frac{-2x}{-2} = \frac{-24}{-2}$$
$$x = 12$$

The solution is 12.

22.
$$1 - 2(6 - y) = 3y + 2$$
$$1 - 12 + 2y = 3y + 2$$
$$2y - 11 = 3y + 2$$
$$2y - 11 - 3y = 3y + 2 - 3y$$
$$-y - 11 = 2$$
$$-y - 11 + 11 = 2 + 11$$
$$-y = 13$$
$$-1(-y) = -1(13)$$
$$y = -13$$

The solution is -13.

23.
$$2(x - 4) + 3(x + 5) = 2x - 2$$
$$2x - 8 + 3x + 15 = 2x - 2$$
$$5x + 7 = 2x - 2$$
$$5x + 7 - 2x = 2x - 2 - 2x$$
$$3x + 7 = -2$$
$$3x + 7 - 7 = -2 - 7$$
$$3x = -9$$
$$\frac{3x}{3} = \frac{-9}{3}$$
$$x = -3$$

The solution is -3.

24.
$$-2(y - 4) - (3y - 2) = -2 - (6y - 2)$$
$$-2y + 8 - 3y + 2 = -2 - 6y - 2$$
$$-5y + 10 = -6y$$
$$-5y + 10 + 6y = -6y + 6y$$
$$10 + y = 0$$
$$10 + y - 10 = 0 - 10$$
$$y = -10$$

The solution is -10.

25. $\dfrac{2x}{3} = \dfrac{x}{6} + 1$

To clear fractions, multiply both sides by the LCD, which is 6.

$$6\left(\frac{2x}{3}\right) = 6\left(\frac{x}{6} + 1\right)$$
$$6\left(\frac{2x}{3}\right) = 6\left(\frac{x}{6}\right) + 6(1)$$
$$4x = x + 6$$
$$4x - x = x + 6 - x$$
$$3x = 6$$
$$\frac{3x}{3} = \frac{6}{3}$$
$$x = 2$$

The solution is 2.

26. $\dfrac{x}{2} - \dfrac{1}{10} = \dfrac{x}{5} + \dfrac{1}{2}$

Multiply both sides by LCD, which is 10.

$$10\left(\dfrac{x}{2} - \dfrac{1}{10}\right) = 10\left(\dfrac{x}{5} + \dfrac{1}{2}\right)$$

$$10\left(\dfrac{x}{2}\right) - 10\left(\dfrac{1}{10}\right) = 10\left(\dfrac{x}{5}\right) + 10\left(\dfrac{1}{2}\right)$$

$$5x - 1 = 2x + 5$$
$$5x - 1 - 2x = 2x + 5 - 2x$$
$$3x - 1 = 5$$
$$3x - 1 + 1 = 5 + 1$$
$$3x = 6$$
$$\dfrac{3x}{3} = \dfrac{6}{3}$$
$$x = 2$$

The solution is 2.

27. $3(8x - 1) = 6(5 + 4x)$
$$24x - 3 = 30 + 24x$$
$$24x - 3 - 24x = 30 + 24x - 24x$$
$$-3 = 30$$

Since $-3 = 30$ is a false statement, the original equation is inconsistent and has no solution.

28. $4(2x - 3) + 4 = 8x - 8$
$$8x - 12 + 4 = 8x - 8$$
$$8x - 8 = 8x - 8$$
$$8x - 8 - 8x = 8x - 8 - 8x$$
$$-8 = -8$$

Since $-8 = -8$ is a true statement, the original equation is an identity and all real numbers are solutions.

29. $r = 0.6(220 - a)$; $r = 120$
$$r = 0.6(220 - a)$$
$$120 = 0.6(220 - a)$$
$$120 = 132 - 0.6a$$
$$120 - 132 = -0.6a$$
$$-12 = -0.6a$$
$$\dfrac{-12}{-0.6} = \dfrac{-0.6a}{-0.6}$$
$$20 = a$$

If the optimal heart rate is 120 beats per minute, the person is 20 years old.

30. $I = Pr$ for r
$$\dfrac{I}{P} = \dfrac{Pr}{P}$$
$$\dfrac{I}{P} = r \quad \text{or} \quad r = \dfrac{I}{P}$$

31. $V = \dfrac{1}{3}Bh$ for h
$$3V = 3\left(\dfrac{1}{3}Bh\right)$$
$$3V = Bh$$
$$\dfrac{3V}{B} = \dfrac{Bh}{B}$$
$$\dfrac{3V}{B} = h \quad \text{or} \quad h = \dfrac{3V}{B}$$

32. $P = 2l + 2w$ for w
$$P - 2l = 2l + 2w - 2l$$
$$P - 2l = 2w$$
$$\dfrac{P - 2l}{2} = \dfrac{2w}{2}$$
$$\dfrac{P - 2l}{2} = w \quad \text{or} \quad w = \dfrac{P - 2l}{2}$$

33. $A = \dfrac{B + C}{2}$ for B
$$2A = 2\left(\dfrac{B + C}{2}\right)$$
$$2A = B + C$$
$$2A - C = B + C - C$$
$$2A - C = B \quad \text{or} \quad B = 2A - C$$

34. $T = D + pm$ for n

$$T - D = D + pm - D$$
$$T - D = pm$$
$$\frac{T - D}{p} = \frac{pm}{p}$$
$$\frac{T - D}{p} = m \quad \text{or} \quad n = \frac{T - D}{p}$$

35. $0.72 = 72\%$

36. $0.0035 = 0.35\%$

37. $65\% = 0.65$

38. $150\% = 1.5$

39. $3\% = 0.03$

40. $A = PB$; $P = 8\% = 0.08, B = 120$

$$A = PB$$
$$A = 0.08 \cdot 120$$
$$A = 9.6$$

8% of 120 is 9.6.

41. $A = PB$; $A = 90, P = 45\% = 0.45$

$$A = PB$$
$$90 = 0.45B$$
$$\frac{90}{0.45} = \frac{0.45B}{0.45}$$
$$200 = B$$

90 is 4% of 200.

42. $A = PB$; $A = 36, B = 75$

$$A = PB$$
$$36 = P \cdot 75$$
$$\frac{36}{75} = \frac{P \cdot 75}{75}$$
$$0.48 = P$$

36 is 48% of 75.

43. a. $r = \dfrac{h}{7}$

$$7r = 7\left(\frac{h}{7}\right)$$
$$7r = h \text{ or } h = 7r$$

b. $h = 7r; r = 9$
$$h = 7(9) = 63$$

The woman's height is 63 inches or 5 feet, 3 inches.

44. $A = PB$; $A = 1760, P = 22\% = 0.22$

$$A = PB$$
$$1760 = 0.22B$$
$$\frac{1760}{0.22} = \frac{0.22B}{0.22}$$
$$8000 = B$$

8000 Americans suffer spinal cord injuries each year.

45. Let $x =$ the unknown number.

$$6x - 20 = 4x$$
$$6x - 20 - 4x = 4x - 4x$$
$$2x - 20 = 0$$
$$2x - 20 + 20 = 0 + 20$$
$$2x = 20$$
$$x = 10$$

The number is 10. This solution checks because 6 times 10, which is 60, decreased by 20, is 40, which is 4 times the number.

46.   Let $x =$ the number of unhealthy air days in New York.
Then $3x + 48 =$ the number of unhealthy air days in Los Angeles.

$$x + (3x + 48) = 268$$
$$4x + 48 = 268$$
$$4x = 200$$
$$x = 55$$

New York has 55 unhealthy air days and Los Angeles has $3(55) + 48 = 213$ unhealthy air days.

The solution checks since $55 + 213 = 268$.

47. Let $x =$ the smaller page number.
Then $x + 1 =$ the larger page number.

$$x + (x + 1) = 93$$
$$2x + 1 = 93$$
$$2x = 92$$
$$x = 46$$

The page numbers are 46 and 47. This solution check because $46 + 47 = 93$.

48. Let $x =$ the number of Madonna's platinum records.
Then $x + 2 =$ the number of Barbra Streisand's platinum records.

$$x + (x + 2) = 96$$
$$2x + 2 = 96$$
$$2x = 94$$
$$x = 47$$

Madonna has 47 platinum records and Barbra Streisand has $47 + 2 = 49$ platinum records. This solution checks because $47 + 49 = 96$.

49. Let $x =$ the number of years after 2000.

$$567 + 15x = 702$$
$$567 + 15x - 567 = 702 - 567$$
$$15x = 135$$
$$\frac{15x}{15} = \frac{135}{15}$$
$$x = 9$$

According to this model, the average weekly salary will reach $702 in 9 years after 2000, which is the year 2009.

50. Let $x =$ the number of checks written.

$$6 + 0.05x = 6.90$$
$$6 + 0.05x - 6 = 6.90 - 6$$
$$0.05x = 0.90$$
$$\frac{0.05x}{0.05} = \frac{0.90}{0.05}$$
$$x = 18$$

You wrote 18 checks that month.

51. Let $w =$ the width of the field.
Then $3w =$ the length.

The perimeter of a rectangle is twice the length plus twice the width, so the equation is

$$2(3w) + 2w = 400.$$

Solve the equation.

$$6w + 2w = 400$$
$$8w = 400$$
$$w = 50$$

The width is 50 yards and the length is $3(50) = 150$ yards.

52. Let $x =$ the original price of the table.

$$x - 0.25x = 180$$
$$0.75x = 180$$
$$\frac{0.75x}{0.75} = \frac{180}{0.75}$$
$$x = 240$$

The table's price before the reduction was $240.

53. Find the area of a rectangle with length 6.5 ft and width 5 ft.

$$A = lw$$
$$A = (6.5)(5) = 32.5$$

The area is 32.5 ft^2.

54. Find the area of a triangle with base 20 cm and height 5 cm.

$$A = \frac{1}{2}bh$$

$$A = \frac{1}{2}(20)(5) = 50$$

The area is 50 cm².

55. Find the area of a trapezoid with bases 22 yd and 5 yd and height 10 yd.

$$A = \frac{1}{2}h(a+b)$$

$$A = \frac{1}{2}(10)(22+5)$$

$$= \frac{1}{2} \cdot 10 \cdot 27 = 135$$

The area is 135 yd².

56. Since the diameter is 20 m, the radius is $\frac{20}{2} = 10$ m.

$$C = 2\pi r$$
$$C = 2\pi(10)$$
$$C = 20\pi \approx 63$$

The circumference is 20π m or about 63 m.

$$A = \pi r^2$$
$$A = \pi(10)^2$$
$$A = 100 \approx 314$$

The area is 100π m² or about 314 m².

57. $A = \frac{1}{2}bh; A = 42, b = 14$

$$A = \frac{1}{2}bh$$

$$42 = \frac{1}{2} \cdot 14 \cdot h$$

$$42 = 7h$$

$$6 = h$$

The height of the sail is 6 ft.

58. Area of floor:

$$A = bh = (12 \text{ ft})(15 \text{ ft}) = 180 \text{ ft}^2$$

Area of base of stove:

$$A = bh = (3 \text{ ft})(4 \text{ ft}) = 12 \text{ ft}^2$$

Area of bottom of refrigerator:

$$A = bh = (3 \text{ ft})(14 \text{ ft}) = 12 \text{ ft}^2$$

The area to be covered with floor tile is

$$180 \text{ ft}^2 - 12 \text{ ft}^2 - 12 \text{ ft}^2 = 156 \text{ ft}^2.$$

59. First find the area of a trapezoid with bases 80 ft and 100 ft and height 60 ft.

$$A = \frac{1}{2}h(a+b)$$

$$A = \frac{1}{2}(60)(80+100)$$

$$A = 5400$$

The area of the yard is 5400 ft². The cost is

$$\$0.35(5400) = \$1890.$$

60. The radius of the medium pizza is $\frac{1}{2} \cdot 14$ inches = 7 inches, and the radius of each small pizza is $\frac{1}{2} \cdot 8$ inches = 4 inches.

Medium pizza:

$$A = \pi r^2 = \pi(7 \text{ in.})^2$$
$$= 49\pi \text{ in.}^2 \approx 154 \text{ in.}^2$$

Small pizza:

$$A = \pi r^2 = \pi(4 \text{ in.})^2$$
$$= 16\pi \text{ in.}^2 \approx 50.24 \text{ in.}^2$$

The area of one medium pizza is about 154 in.² and the area of two small pizzas is about 2(50.24 in.²) = 100.48 in.². Since the price of one medium pizza is the same as the price of two small pizzas and the medium pizza has the greater area, the medium pizza is the better buy. (Because the prices are the same, it is not necessary to find the prices per square inch in this case.)

61. Find the volume of a rectangular solid with length 5 cm, width 3 cm, and height 4 cm.

$$A = lwh$$
$$A = 5 \cdot 3 \cdot 4 = 60$$

The volume is 60 cm^3.

62. Find the volume of a cylinder with radius 4 yd and height 8 yd.

$$V = \pi r^2 h$$
$$V = \pi(4)^2 \cdot 8$$
$$V = 128\pi \approx 402$$

The volume is 128π yd^3 $\approx$ 402 yd^3.

63. Find the volume of a sphere with radius 6 m.

$$V = \frac{4}{3}\pi r^3$$
$$V = \frac{4}{3}\pi(6)^3$$
$$V = \frac{4}{3} \cdot \pi \cdot 216$$
$$V = 288\pi \approx 904$$

The volume is 288π m^3 $\approx$ 904 m^3.

64. The volume of each box is

$$V = (8 \text{ m})(4 \text{ m})(3 \text{ m}) = 96 \text{ m}^3.$$

The space required for 50 containers is

$$50(96 \text{ m}^3) = 4800 \text{ m}^3.$$

65. Since the diameter of the fish tank is 6 ft, the radius is 3 ft.

$$V = \pi r^2$$
$$V = \pi(3)^2 \cdot 3$$
$$V = 27\pi \approx 84.78$$

The volume of the tank is about 84.78 ft^3.

$$\frac{84.78}{5} \approx 16.96$$

There is enough water in the tank for 16 fish. (There is not quite enough for 17 fish.)

66. The sum of the measures of the three angles of any triangle is 180°, so

$$x + 3x + 2x = 180.$$

Solve this equation.

$$6x = 180$$
$$x = 30$$

If $x = 30$, then $3x = 90$ and $2x = 60$, so the angle measures are 30°, 90°, and 60°.

67. Let $x =$ the measure of the second angle.
Then $2x + 15 =$ the measure of the first angle;
$x + 25 =$ the measure of the third angle.

$$x + (2x + 15) + (x + 25) = 180$$
$$4x + 40 = 180$$
$$4x = 140$$
$$x = 35$$

If $x = 35$, then $2x + 15 = 2(35) + 15 = 85$, and $x + 255 = 35 + 25 = 60$. The measures of the angles are 85°, 35°, and 60°.

68. If the measure of an angle is 57°, the measure of its complement is $90° - 57° = 33°$.

69. If the measure of an angle is 75°, the measure of its supplement is $180° - 75° = 105°$.

70. Let $\quad x =$ the measure of the angle.
Then $90 - x =$ the measure of of its
$\qquad$ complement.

$$x = (90 - x) + 25$$
$$x = 115 - x$$
$$2x = 115$$
$$x = 57.5$$

The measure of the angle is $57.5°$.

71. Let $\quad x =$ the measure of the angle.
Then $180 - x =$ the measure of its supplement.

$$180 - x = 4x - 45$$
$$180 - 5x = -45$$
$$-5x = -225$$
$$x = 45$$

If $x = 45$, then $180 - x = 135$.
The measure of the angle is $45°$ and the
measure of its supplement is $135°$.

72. $x < -1$

73. $-2 < x \leq 4$

74. $\{x | x > 4\}$

75. $\{x | x \leq -3\}$

76. $\quad 2x - 5 < 3$
$$2x - 5 + 5 < 3 + 5$$
$$2x < 8$$
$$\frac{2x}{2} < \frac{8}{2}$$
$$x < 4$$
$$\{x | x < 4\}$$

77. $\quad \dfrac{x}{2} > -4$
$$2\left(\frac{x}{2}\right) > 2(-4)$$
$$x > -8$$
$$\{x | x > -8\}$$

78. $\quad 3 - 5x \leq 18$
$$3 - 5x - 3 \leq 18 - 3$$
$$-5x \leq 15$$
$$\frac{-5x}{-5} \geq \frac{15}{-5}$$
$$x \geq -3$$
$$\{x | x \geq -3\}$$

79. $\quad 4x + 6 < 5x$
$$4x + 6 - 5x < 5x - 5x$$
$$-x + 6 < 0$$
$$-x + 6 - 6 < 0 - 6$$
$$-x < -6$$
$$-1(-x) > -1(-6)$$
$$x > 6$$
$$\{x | x > 6\}$$

80. $\quad 6x - 10 \geq 2(x + 3)$
$$6x - 10 \geq 2x + 6$$
$$6x - 10 - 2x \geq 2x + 6 - 2x$$
$$4x - 10 \geq 6$$
$$4x - 10 + 10 \geq 6 + 10$$
$$4x \geq 16$$
$$\frac{4x}{4} \geq \frac{16}{4}$$
$$x \geq 4$$
$$\{x | x \geq 4\}$$

81.
$$4x + 3(2x - 7) \leq x - 3$$
$$4x + 6x - 21 \leq x - 3$$
$$10x - 21 \leq x - 3$$
$$10x - 21 - x \leq x - 3 - x$$
$$9x - 21 \leq -3$$
$$9x - 21 + 21 \leq -3 + 21$$
$$9x \leq 18$$
$$\frac{9x}{9} \leq \frac{18}{9}$$
$$x \leq 2$$

$$\{x | x \leq 2\}$$

82.
$$2(2x + 4) > 4(x + 2) - 6$$
$$4x + 8 > 4x + 8 - 6$$
$$4x + 8 > 4x + 2$$
$$4x + 8 - 4x > 4x + 2 - 4x$$
$$8 > 2$$

Since $8 > 2$ is a true statement, the original inequality is true for all real numbers, and the solution set is written $\{x | x \text{ is a real number}\}$.

83.
$$-2(x - 4) \leq 3x + 1 - 5x$$
$$-2x + 8 \leq -2x + 1$$
$$-2x + 8 + 2x \leq -2x + 1 + 2x$$
$$8 \leq 1$$

Since $8 \leq 1$ is a false statement, the original inequality has no solution. The solution set is $\emptyset$.

84. Let $x =$ the student's score on the third test.
$$\frac{42 + 74 + x}{3} \geq 60$$
$$3\left(\frac{42 + 74 + x}{3}\right) \geq 3(60)$$
$$42 + 74 + x \geq 180$$
$$116 + x \geq 180$$
$$116 + x - 116 \geq 180 - 116$$
$$x \geq 64$$

The student must score at least 64 on the third test to pass the course.

85. $C = 10 + 5(x - 1); C \leq 500$
$$10 + 5(x - 1) \leq 500$$
$$10 + 5x - 5 \leq 500$$
$$5x + 5 \leq 500$$
$$5x + 5 - 5 \leq 500 - 5$$
$$5x \leq 495$$
$$\frac{5x}{5} \leq \frac{495}{5}$$
$$x \leq 99$$

You can talk no more than 99 minutes.

Chapter 2 Test

1.
$$4x - 5 = 13$$
$$4x + 5 + 5 = 13 + 5$$
$$4x = 18$$
$$\frac{4x}{4} = \frac{18}{4} = \frac{9}{2}$$
$$x = \frac{9}{2}$$

The solution is $\frac{9}{2}$.

2.
$$12x + 4 = 7x - 21$$
$$12x + 4 - 7x = 7x - 21 - 7x$$
$$5x + 4 = -21$$
$$5x + 4 - 4 = -21 - 4$$
$$5x = -25$$
$$\frac{5x}{5} = \frac{-25}{5}$$
$$x = -5$$

The solution is -5.

3.
$$8 - 5(x - 2) = x + 26$$
$$8 - 5x + 10 = x + 26$$
$$18 - 5x = x + 26$$
$$18 - 5x - x = x + 26 - x$$
$$18 - 6x = 26$$
$$18 - 6x - 10 = 26 - 18$$
$$-6x = 8$$
$$\frac{-6x}{-6} = \frac{8}{-6}$$
$$x = -\frac{8}{6}$$
$$= -\frac{4}{3}$$

The solution is $-\frac{4}{3}$.

4.
$$3(2y - 4) = 9 - 3(y + 1)$$
$$6y - 12 = 9 - 3y - 3$$
$$6y - 12 = 6 - 3y$$
$$6y - 12 + 3y = 6 - 3y + 3y$$
$$9y - 12 = 6$$
$$9y - 12 + 12 = 6 + 12$$
$$9y = 18$$
$$\frac{9y}{9} = \frac{18}{9}$$
$$y = 2$$

The solution is 2.

5.
$$\frac{3}{4}x = -15$$
$$\frac{4}{3}\left(\frac{3}{4}x\right) = \frac{4}{3}(-15)$$
$$x = -20$$

The solution is -20.

6.
$$\frac{x}{10} + \frac{1}{3} = \frac{x}{5} + \frac{1}{2}$$

Multiply both sides by the LCD, 30.

$$30\left(\frac{x}{10} + \frac{1}{3}\right) = 30\left(\frac{x}{5} + \frac{1}{2}\right)$$

$$30\left(\frac{x}{10}\right) + 30\left(\frac{1}{3}\right) = 30\left(\frac{x}{5}\right) + 30\left(\frac{1}{2}\right)$$

$$3x + 1- = 6x + 15$$
$$3x + 10 - 6x = 6x + 15 - 6x$$
$$-3x + 10 = 15$$
$$-3x + 10 - 10 = 15 - 10$$
$$-3x = 5$$
$$\frac{-3x}{-3} = \frac{5}{-3}$$
$$z = -\frac{5}{3}$$

The solution is $-\frac{5}{3}$.

7. $N = 2.4x + 180; \ N = 324$

$$2.4x + 180 = 324$$
$$2.4x + 180 - 180 = 324 - 180$$
$$2.4 = 144$$
$$\frac{2.4x}{2.4} = \frac{144}{2.4}$$
$$x = 60$$

The U.S. population is expected to reach 324 million 60 years after 1960, which is in the year 2020.

8. $V = \pi r^2 h$ for h

$$\frac{V}{\pi r^2} = \frac{\pi r^2 h}{\pi r^2}$$
$$\frac{V}{\pi r^2} = h \quad \text{or} \quad h = \frac{V}{\pi r^2}$$

9. $l = \dfrac{P - 2w}{2}$ for w

$$2l = 2\left(\dfrac{P - 2w}{2}\right)$$
$$2l = P - 2w$$
$$2l + 2w = P - 2w + 2w$$
$$2l + 2w = P$$
$$2l + 2w - 2l = P - 2l$$
$$2w = P - 2l$$
$$\dfrac{2w}{2} = \dfrac{P - 2l}{2}$$
$$w = \dfrac{P - 2l}{2}$$

10. $A = PB;\ P = 6\% = 0.06,\ B = 140$

$A = PB$
$A = 0.06(140)$
$A = 8.4$

6% of 140 is 8.4.

11. $A = PB;\ A = 120,\ P = 80\% = 0.80$

$A = PB$
$120 = 0.80B$
$\dfrac{120}{0.80} = \dfrac{0.80B}{0.80}$
$150 = B$

120 is 80% of 150.

12. $A = PB;\ A = 12,\ B = 240$

$A = PB$
$12 = P \cdot 240$
$\dfrac{12}{240} = \dfrac{P \cdot 240}{240}$
$0.05 = P$

12 is 5% of 240.

13. Let x = the unknown number.

$$5x - 9 = 310$$
$$5x - 9 + 9 = 310 + 9$$
$$5x = 319$$
$$\dfrac{5x}{5} = \dfrac{319}{5}$$
$$x = \dfrac{319}{5} = 63.8$$

The number is 63.8.

14. Let B = Buchanan's age.
Then $B + 4$ = Reagan's age.

$$B + (B + 4) = 134$$
$$2B + 4 = 134$$
$$2B = 130$$
$$B = 65$$

Buchanan was 65 years old and Reagan was $65 + 4 = 69$ years old.

15. Let x = number of minutes of long-distance calls.

$$15 + 0.05x = 45$$
$$0.05x = 30$$
$$x = \dfrac{30}{0.05}$$
$$x = 600$$

You can talk long distance for 600 minutes.

16. Let w = width of field (in yards).
Then $2w$ = length of field.

$$2(2w) + 2w = 450$$
$$4w + 2w = 450$$
$$6w = 450$$
$$w = 75$$

The width is 75 yards and the length is $2(75) = 150$ yards.

17. Let $x =$ the book's original price.

$$x - 0.20x = 28$$
$$0.80x = 28$$
$$x = \frac{28}{0.80}$$
$$x = 35$$

The price of the book before the reduction was \$35.

18. Find the area of a triangle with base 47 m and height 22 m.

$$A = \frac{1}{2}bh$$
$$A = \frac{1}{2}(47)(22) = 517$$

The area is 517 m².

19. Find the area of a trapezoid with bases 40 in. and 30 in. and height 15 in.

$$A = \frac{1}{2}h(a + b)$$
$$A = \frac{1}{2}(15)(40 + 30)$$
$$A = \frac{1}{2} \cdot 15 \cdot 70 = 525 \text{ in.}^2$$

The area is 525 in.².

20. Find the volume of a rectangular solid with length 3 in., width 2 in., and height 3 in.

$$V = lwh$$
$$V = 3 \cdot 2 \cdot 3 = 18$$

The volume is 18 in.³.

21. Find the volume of a cylinder with radius 5 cm and height 7 cm.

$$V = \pi r^2 h$$
$$V = \pi(5)^2 \cdot 7 = \pi \cdot 25 \cdot 7$$
$$V = 175\pi \approx 550$$

The volume is 175π cm³ or about 550 cm³.

22. The area of the floor is

$$A = (40 \text{ ft})(50 \text{ ft}) = 2000 \text{ ft}^2.$$

The area of each tile is

$$A = (2 \text{ ft})(2 \text{ ft}) = 4 \text{ ft}^2.$$

The number of tiles needed is

$$\frac{2000 \text{ ft}^2}{4 \text{ ft}^2} = 500.$$

Since there are 10 tiles in a package, the number of packages needed is $\frac{500}{10} = 50$. Since each package costs \$13, the cost for enough tiles to cover the floor is 50(\$13) = \$650.

23. $A = \frac{1}{2}bh$; $A = 56, b = 8$

$$A = \frac{1}{2}bh$$
$$56 = \frac{1}{2} \cdot 8 \cdot h$$
$$56 = 4h$$
$$14 = h$$

The height of the sail is 14 feet.

24. Let $\quad x =$ the measure of the second angle.

Then $3x =$ the measure of the first angle.

$x - 30 =$ the measure of the third angle.

$$x + 3x + (x - 30) = 180$$
$$5x - 30 = 180$$
$$5x = 210$$
$$x = 42$$

Measure of first angle $= 3x = 3(42°)$
$$= 126°$$
Measure of second angle $= x = 42°$
Measure of third angle $= x - 30 = 42° - 30°$
$$= 12°$$

25. Let x = the measure of the angle.

Then $90 - x$ = the measure of its complement.

$$x = (90 - x) + 16$$
$$x = 106 - x$$
$$2x = 106$$
$$x = 53$$

The measure of the angle is $53°$.

26. $x > -2$

27. $-4 \leq x < 1$

28. $\{x | x \leq -1\}$

29. $$\frac{x}{2} < -3$$
$$2\left(\frac{x}{2}\right) < 2(-3)$$
$$x < -6$$
$$\{x | x < -6\}$$

30. $$6 - 9x \geq 33$$
$$6 - 9x - 6 \geq 33 - 6$$
$$-9x \geq 27$$
$$\frac{-9x}{-9} \leq \frac{27}{-9}$$
$$x \leq -3$$
$$\{x | x \leq -3\}$$

31. $$4x - 2 > 2(x + 6)$$
$$4x - 2 > 2x + 12$$
$$4x - 2x > 2x + 12 - 2x$$
$$2x - 2 > 12$$
$$2x > 14$$
$$x > 7$$

$$\{x | x > 7\}$$

32. Let x = the student's score on the fourth exam.

$$\frac{76 + 80 + 72 + x}{4} \geq 80$$
$$4\left(\frac{76 + 80 + 72 + x}{4}\right) \geq 4(80)$$
$$76 + 80 + 72 + x \geq 320$$
$$228 + x \geq 320$$
$$x \geq 92$$

The student must score at least 92 on the fourth exam to have an average of at least 80.

33. Let w = width of rectangle.

$$2(20) + 2w > 56$$
$$40 + 2w > 56$$
$$2w > 16$$
$$w > 8$$

The width must be greater than 8 inches.

Cumulative Review Exercises

(Chapters 1-2)

1. $-8 - (12 - 16) = -8 - (-4)$
$$= -8 + 4 = -4$$

2. $(-3)(-2) + (-2)(4) = 6 + (-8) = -2$

3. $(8 - 10)^3(7 - 11)^2 = (-2)^3(-4)^2$
$$= -8(16)$$
$$= -128$$

4. $2 - 5[x + 3(x + 7)] = 2 - 5(x + 3x + 21)$
$$= 2 - 5(4x + 21)$$
$$= 2 - 20x - 105$$
$$= -103 - 20x$$

5. The rational numbers are $-4, -\frac{1}{3}, 0,$ $\sqrt{4}\,(=2),$ and 1063.

6. Quadrant III

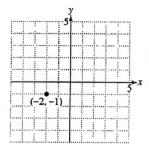

(-2, -1)

7. $-10,000 < -2$ since $-10,000$ is to the left of -2 on the number line.

8. $6(4x - 1 - 5y) = 6(4x) - 6(1) - 6(5y)$
$$= 24x - 6 - 30y$$

9. Unemployment was a minimum in 2000, with about 4% unemployed.

10. The unemployment rate reached a maximum during 1992 of about 7.8%.

11. $\quad 5 - 6(x + 2) = x - 14$
$$5 - 6x - 12 = x - 14$$
$$-7 - 6x = x - 14$$
$$-7 - 6x - x = x - 14 - x$$
$$-7 - 7x = -14$$
$$-7 - 7x + 7 = -14 + 7$$
$$-7x = -7$$
$$\frac{-7x}{-7} = \frac{-7}{-7}$$
$$x = 1$$

The solution is 1.

12. $\dfrac{x}{5} - 2 = \dfrac{x}{3}$

Multiply both sides by the LCD, 15.

$$15\left(\frac{x}{5} - 2\right) = 15\left(\frac{x}{3}\right)$$
$$15\left(\frac{x}{5}\right) - 15(2) = 15\left(\frac{x}{3}\right)$$
$$3x - 30 = 5x$$
$$3x - 30 - 3x = 5x - 3x$$
$$-30 = 2x$$
$$\frac{-30}{2} = \frac{2x}{2}$$
$$-15 = x$$

The solution is -15.

13. $V = \dfrac{1}{3}Ah$ for A

$$V = \frac{1}{3}Ah$$
$$3V = 3\left(\frac{1}{3}Ah\right)$$
$$3V = Ah$$
$$\frac{3V}{h} = \frac{Ah}{h}$$
$$\frac{3V}{h} = A \quad \text{or} \quad A = \frac{3V}{h}$$

14. $A = PB;\ A = 48, P = 30\% = 0.30$

$$A = PB$$
$$48 = 0.30B$$
$$\frac{48}{0.30} = \frac{0.48B}{0.30}$$
$$160 = B$$

48 is 30% of 160.

15. Let $w =$ width of parking lot (in yards).

Then $2w - 10 =$ length of parking lot.

$$2(2w - 10) + 2w = 400$$
$$4w - 20 + 2w = 400$$
$$6w - 20 = 400$$
$$6w = 420$$
$$w = 70$$

The width is 70 yards and the length is $2(70) - 10 = 130$ yards.

16. Let $x =$ number of gallons of gasoline.

$$0.40x = 30,000$$
$$\frac{0.40x}{0.40} = \frac{30,000}{0.40}$$
$$x = 75,000$$

75,000 gallons of gasoline must be sold.

17. $-2 < x \le 3$

18.
$$3 - 3x > 12$$
$$3 - 3x - 3 > 12 - 3$$
$$-3x > 9$$
$$\frac{-3x}{-3} < \frac{9}{-3}$$
$$x < -3$$

$\{x | x < -3\}$

19.
$$5 - 2(2 - x) \le 2(2x + 5) + 1$$
$$5 - 6 + 2x \le 4x + 10 + 1$$
$$2x - 1 \le 4x + 11$$
$$2x - 1 - 4x \le 4x + 11 - 4x$$
$$-2x \le 11$$
$$-2x - 1 \le 11 + 1$$
$$-2x \le 12$$
$$\frac{-2x}{-2} \ge \frac{12}{-2}$$
$$x \ge -6$$

$\{x | x \ge -6\}$

20. Let $x =$ value of medical supplies sold.

$$600 + 0.04x > 2500$$
$$600 + 0.04x - 600 > 2500 - 600$$
$$0.04x > 1900$$
$$\frac{0.04x}{0.04} > \frac{1900}{0.04}$$
$$x > 47,500$$

You must sell more than $47,500 worth of medical supplies.

LINEAR EQUATIONS IN TWO VARIABLES

Graphing Linear Equations

3.1 CHECK POINTS

CHECK POINT 1

$x - 3y = 9$

a. To determine whether $(3, -2)$ is a solution of the equation, substitute 3 for x and -2 for y.

$$x - 3y = 9$$
$$3 - 3(-2) \stackrel{?}{=} 9$$
$$3 - (-6) \stackrel{?}{=} 9$$
$$9 = 9 \text{ true}$$

$(3, -2)$ is a solution.

b. To determine whether $(-2, 3)$ is a solution, substitute -2 for x and 3 for y.

$$x - 3y = 9$$
$$-2 - 3(3) \stackrel{?}{=} 9$$
$$-2 - 9 \stackrel{?}{=} 9$$
$$-11 = 9 \text{ false}$$

$(-2, 3)$ is a not solution.

CHECK POINT 2

$y = 3x + 2$

x	$y = 3x + 2$	(x, y)
-2	$y = 3(-2) + 2 = -4$	$(-2, -4)$
-1	$y = 3(-1) + 2 = -1$	$(-1, -1)$
0	$y = 3(0) + 2 = 2$	$(0, 2)$
1	$y = 3(1) + 2 = 5$	$(1, 5)$
2	$y = 3(2) + 2 = 8$	$(2, 8)$

Five solutions are $y = 3x + 2$ are $(-2, -4)$, $(-1, -1)$, $(0, 2)$, $(1, 5)$, and $(2, 8)$.

CHECK POINT 3

$y = 2x$

x	$y = 2x$	(x, y)
-2	$y = 2(-2) = -4$	$(-2, -4)$
-1	$y = 2(-1) = -2$	$(-1, -2)$
0	$y = 2(0) = 0$	$(0, 0)$
1	$y = 2(1) = 2$	$(1, 2)$
2	$y = 2(2) = 4$	$(2, 4)$

Plot the five ordered pairs from the table and draw a line through the five points.

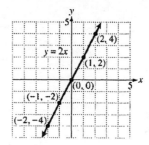

CHECK POINT 4

$y = 2x - 2$

x	$y = 2x - 2$	(x, y)
-2	$y = 2(-2) - 2 = -6$	$(-2, -6)$
-1	$y = 2(-1) - 2 = -4$	$(-1, -4)$
0	$y = 2(0) - 2 = -2$	$(0, -2)$
1	$y = 2(1) - 2 = 0$	$(1, 0)$
2	$y = 2(2) - 2 = 2$	$(2, 2)$

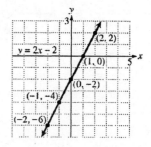

CHECK POINT 5

$$y = \frac{1}{3}x + 2$$

x	$y = \frac{1}{3}x + 2$	(x, y)
-6	$y = \frac{1}{3}(-6) + 2 = 0$	$(-6, 0)$
-3	$y = \frac{1}{3}(-3) + 2 = 1$	$(-3, 1)$
0	$y = \frac{1}{3}(0) + 2 = 2$	$(0, 2)$
3	$y = \frac{1}{3}(3) + 2 = 3$	$(3, 3)$
6	$y = \frac{1}{3}(6) + 2 = 4$	$(6, 4)$

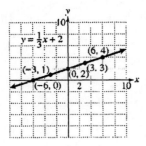

CHECK POINT 6

$$y = x^2 - 1$$

x	$y = x^2 - 1$	(x, y)
-3	$y = (-3)^2 - 1 = 8$	$(-3, 8)$
-2	$y = (-2)^2 - 1 = 3$	$(-2, 3)$
-1	$y = (-1)^2 - 1 = 0$	$(-1, 0)$
0	$y = 0^2 - 1 = -1$	$(0, -1)$
1	$y = 1^2 - 1 = 0$	$(1, 0)$
2	$y = 2^2 - 1 = 3$	$(2, 3)$
3	$y = 3^2 - 1 = 8$	$(3, 8)$

Plot the seven ordered pairs from the table and draw a smooth curve through the second points.

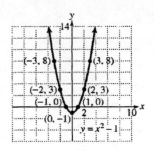

CHECK POINT 7

a. Without the coupon book:

x	$y = 2x$	(x, y)
0	$y = 2(0) = 0$	$(0, 0)$
2	$y = 2(2) = 4$	$(2, 4)$
4	$y = 2(4) = 8$	$(4, 8)$
6	$y = 2(6) = 12$	$(6, 12)$
8	$y = 2(8) = 16$	$(8, 16)$
10	$y = 2(10) = 20$	$(10, 20)$
12	$y = 2(12) = 24$	$(12, 24)$

With the coupon book:

x	$y = 10 + x$	(x, y)
0	$y = 10 + 0 = 10$	$(0, 10)$
2	$y = 10 + 2 = 12$	$(2, 12)$
4	$y = 10 + 4 = 14$	$(4, 14)$
6	$y = 10 + 6 = 16$	$(6, 16)$
8	$y = 10 + 8 = 18$	$(8, 18)$
10	$y = 10 + 10 = 20$	$(10, 20)$
12	$y = 10 + 22 = 22$	$(12, 22)$

b.

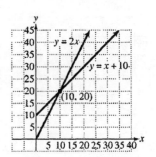

c. The intersection point is $(10, 20)$. This means that your cost for bridge tolls will be the same with or without the coupon book if you use the bridge 10 times a month, namely $20.

EXERCISE SET 3.1

1. $y = 3x$

$(2, 3)$:

$3 \stackrel{?}{=} 3(2)$
$3 = 6$ false

$(2, 3)$ is not a solution.

$(3, 2)$:

$2 \stackrel{?}{=} 3(3)$
$2 = 9$ false

$(3, 2)$ is not a solution.

$(-4, -12)$:

$-12 \stackrel{?}{=} 3(-4)$
$-12 = -12$ true

$(-4, -12)$ is a solution.

3. $y = -4x$

$(-5, -20)$:

$-20 \stackrel{?}{=} -4(-5)$
$-20 = 20$ False

$(-5, -20)$ is not a solution.

$(0, 0)$:

$0 \stackrel{?}{=} -4(0)$
$0 = 0$ true

$(0, 0)$ is a solution.

$(9, -36)$:

$-36 \stackrel{?}{=} -4(9)$
$-36 = -36$ true

$(9, -36)$ is a solution.

5. $y = 2x + 6$

$(0, 6)$:

$6 \stackrel{?}{=} 2(0) + 6$
$6 = 6$ true

$(0, 6)$ is a solution.

$(-3, 0)$:

$0 \stackrel{?}{=} 2(-3) + 6$
$0 = 0$ true

$(-3, 0)$ is a solution.

$(2, -2)$:

$-2 \stackrel{?}{=} 2(2) + 6$
$-2 = 10$ false

$(2, -2)$ is not a solution.

7. $3x + 5y = 15$

$(-5, 6)$:

$3(-5) + 5(6) \stackrel{?}{=} 15$
$-15 + 30 \stackrel{?}{=} 15$
$15 = 15$ true

$(-5, 6)$ is a solution.

$(0, 5)$:

$3(0) + 5(5) \stackrel{?}{=} 15$
$0 + 25 \stackrel{?}{=} 15$
$25 = 15$ false

$(0, 5)$ is not a solution.

$(10, -3)$:

$3(10) + 5(-3) \stackrel{?}{=} 15$
$30 - 15 \stackrel{?}{=} 15$
$15 = 15$ true

$(10, -3)$ is a solution.

9. $x + 3y = 0$

$(0,0)$:

$0 + 3(0) \overset{?}{=} 0$

$\qquad 0 = 0$ true

$(0,0)$ is a solution.

$\left(1, \tfrac{1}{3}\right)$:

$1 + 3\left(\tfrac{1}{3}\right) \overset{?}{=} 0$

$\qquad 1 + 1 \overset{?}{=} 0$

$\qquad\qquad 2 = 0$ false

$\left(1, \tfrac{1}{3}\right)$ is not a solution.

$\left(2, -\tfrac{2}{3}\right)$:

$2 + 2\left(-\tfrac{2}{3}\right) \overset{?}{=} 0$

$\qquad 2 - 2 \overset{?}{=} 0$

$\qquad\qquad 0 = 0$ true

$\left(2, -\tfrac{2}{3}\right)$ is a solution.

11. $x - 4 = 0$

$(4,7)$:

$4 - 4 \overset{?}{=} 0$

$\qquad 0 = 0$ true

$(4,7)$ is a solution.

$(3,4)$:

$3 - 4 \overset{?}{=} 0$

$\qquad -4 = 0$ false

$(3,4)$ is not a solution.

$(0,-4)$:

$(0,-4) \overset{?}{=} 0$

$\qquad -4 = 0$ false

$(0,-4)$ is not a solution.

13. $y = 10x$

x	$y = 10x$	(x,y)
-2	$y = 10(-2) = -20$	$(-2, -20)$
-1	$y = 10(-1) = -10$	$(-1, -10)$
0	$y = 10(0) = 0$	$(0,0)$
1	$y = 10(1) = 10$	$(1, 10)$
2	$y = 10(2) = 20$	$(2, 20)$

15. $y = -6x$

x	$y = -6x$	(x,y)
-2	$y = 6(-2) = 12$	$(-2, 12)$
-1	$y = -6(-1) = 6$	$(-1, 6)$
0	$y = -6(0) = 0$	$(0,0)$
1	$y = -6(1) = -6$	$(1, 6)$
2	$y = -6(2) = -12$	$(2, -12)$

17. $y = 5x - 8$

x	$y = 5x - 8$	(x,y)
-2	$y = 5(-2) - 8 = -18$	$(-2, -18)$
-1	$y = 5(-1) - 8 = -13$	$(-1, -13)$
0	$y = 5(0) - 8 = -8$	$(0, -8)$
1	$y = 5(1) - 8 = -3$	$(1, -3)$
2	$y = 5(2) - 8 = 2$	$(2, 2)$

19. $y = -7x + 3$

x	$y = -7x + 3$	(x,y)
-2	$y = -7(-2) + 3 = 17$	$(-2, 17)$
-1	$y = -7(-1) + 3 = 10$	$(-1, 10)$
0	$y = -7(0) + 3 = 3$	$(0, 3)$
1	$y = -7(1) + 3 = -4$	$(1, -4)$
2	$y = -7(2) + 3 = -11$	$(2, -11)$

21. $y = x$

x	$y = x$	(x, y)
-2	$y = -2$	$(-2, -2)$
-1	$y = -1$	$(-1, -1)$
0	$y = 0$	$(0, 0)$
1	$y = 1$	$(1, 1)$
2	$y = 2$	$(2, 2)$

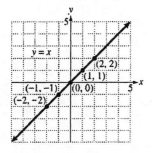

25. $y = 2x + 1$

x	$y = 2x + 1$	(x, y)
-2	$y = 2(-2) + 1 = -3$	$(-2, -3)$
-1	$y = 2(-1) + 1 = -1$	$(-1, -1)$
0	$y = 2(0) + 1 = 1$	$(0, 1)$
1	$y = 2(1) + 1 = 3$	$(1, 3)$
2	$y = 2(2) + 1 = 5$	$(2, 5)$

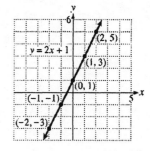

23. $y = x - 1$

x	$y = x - 1$	(x, y)
-2	$y = -2 - 1 = -3$	$(-2, -3)$
-1	$y = -1 - 1 = -2$	$(-1, -2)$
0	$y = 0 - 1 = -1$	$(0, -1)$
1	$y = 1 - 1 = 0$	$(1, 0)$
2	$y = 2 - 1 = 1$	$(2, 1)$

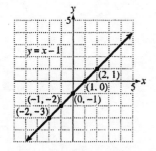

27. $y = -x + 2$

x	$y = -x + 2$	(x, y)
-2	$y = -(-2) + 2 = 4$	$(-2, 4)$
-1	$y = -(-1) + 2 = 3$	$(-1, 3)$
0	$y = -0 + 2 = 2$	$(0, 2)$
1	$y = -1 + 2 = 1$	$(1, 1)$
2	$y = -2 + 2 = 0$	$(2, 0)$

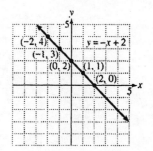

29. $y = -3x - 1$

x	$y = -3x - 1$	(x, y)
-2	$y = -3(-2) - 1 = 5$	$(-2, 5)$
-1	$y = -3(-1) - 1 = 2$	$(-1, 2)$
0	$y = -3(0) - 1 = -1$	$(0, -1)$
1	$y = -3(1) - 1 = -4$	$(1, -4)$
2	$y = -3(2) - 1 = -7$	$(2, -7)$

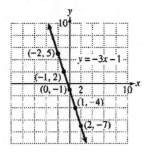

31. $x = \dfrac{1}{2}x$

x	$y = \frac{1}{2}x$	(x, y)
-4	$y = \frac{1}{2}(-4) = -2$	$(-4, -2)$
-2	$y = \frac{1}{2}(-2) = -1$	$(-2, -1)$
0	$y = \frac{1}{2}(0) = 0$	$(0, 0)$
2	$y = \frac{1}{2}(2) = 1$	$(2, 1)$
4	$y = \frac{1}{2}(4) = 2$	$(4, 2)$

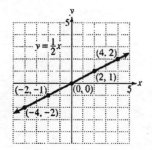

33. $y = -\dfrac{1}{4}x$

x	$y = -\frac{1}{4}x$	(x, y)
-8	$y = -\frac{1}{4}(-8) = 2$	$(-8, 2)$
-4	$y = -\frac{1}{4}(-4) = 1$	$(-4, 1)$
0	$y = -\frac{1}{4}(0) = 0$	$(0, 0)$
4	$y = -\frac{1}{4}(4) = -1$	$(4, -1)$
8	$y = -\frac{1}{4}(8) = -2$	$(8, -2)$

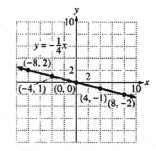

35. $y = \dfrac{1}{3}x + 1$

x	$y = \frac{1}{3}x + 1$	(x, y)
-6	$y = \frac{1}{3}(-6) + 1 = -1$	$(-6, -1)$
-3	$y = \frac{1}{3}(-3) + 1 = 0$	$(-3, 0)$
0	$y = \frac{1}{3}(0) + 1 = 1$	$(0, -1)$
3	$y = \frac{1}{3}(3) + 1 = 2$	$(3, 2)$
6	$y = \frac{1}{3}(6) + 1 = 3$	$(6, 3)$

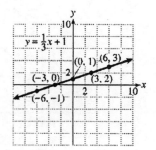

37. $y = -\dfrac{3}{2}x + 1$

x	$y = -\frac{3}{2}x + 1$	(x, y)
-4	$y = -\frac{3}{2}(-4) + 1 = 7$	$(-4, 7)$
-2	$y = -\frac{3}{2}(-2) + 1 = 4$	$(-2, 4)$
0	$y = -\frac{3}{2}(0) + 1 = 1$	$(0, 1)$
2	$y = -\frac{3}{2}(2) + 1 = -2$	$(2, -2)$
4	$y = -\frac{3}{2}(4) + 1 = -5$	$(4, -5)$

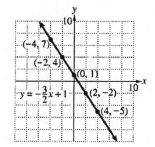

41. $y = x + \dfrac{1}{2}$

x	$y = x + \frac{1}{2}$	(x, y)
-4	$y = -4 + \frac{1}{2} = -3.5$	$(-4, -3.5)$
-2	$y = -2 + \frac{1}{2} = -1.5$	$(-2, -1.5)$
0	$y = 0 + \frac{1}{2} = 0.5$	$(0, 0.5)$
2	$y = 2 + \frac{1}{2} = 2.5$	$(2, 2.5)$
4	$y = 4 + \frac{1}{2} = 4.5$	$(4, 4.5)$

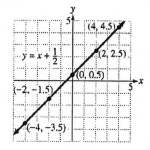

39. $y = -\dfrac{5}{2}x - 1$

x	$y = -\frac{5}{2}x - 1$	(x, y)
-4	$y = -\frac{5}{2}(-4) - 1 = 9$	$(-4, 9)$
-2	$y = -\frac{5}{2}(-2) - 1 = 4$	$(-2, 4)$
0	$y = -\frac{5}{2}(0) - 1 = -1$	$(0, -1)$
2	$y = -\frac{5}{2}(2) - 1 = -6$	$(2, -6)$
4	$y = -\frac{5}{2}(4) - 1 = -11$	$(4, -11)$

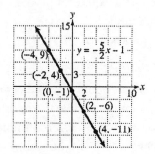

43. $y = 4$, or $y = 0x + 4$

x	$y = 0x + 4$	(x, y)
-6	$y = 0(-6) + 4 = 4$	$(-6, 4)$
-3	$y = 0(-3) + 4 = 4$	$(-3, 4)$
0	$y = 0(0) + 4 = 4$	$(0, 4)$
3	$y = 0(3) + 4 = 4$	$(3, 4)$
6	$y = 0(6) + 4 = 4$	$(6, 4)$

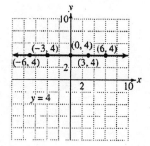

45. $y = x^2$

x	$y = x^2$	(x, y)
-3	$y = (-3)^2 = 9$	$(-3, 9)$
-2	$y = (-2)^2 = 4$	$(-2, 4)$
-1	$y = (-1)^2 = 1$	$(-1, 1)$
0	$y = 0^2 = 0$	$(0, 0)$
1	$y = 1^2 = 1$	$(1, 1)$
2	$y = 2^2 = 4$	$(2, 4)$
3	$y = 3^2 = 9$	$(3, 9)$

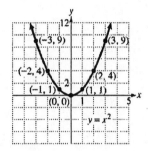

47. $y = x^2 + 1$

x	$y = x^2 + 1$	(x, y)
-3	$y = (-3)^2 + 1 = 10$	$(-3, 10)$
-2	$y = (-2)^2 + 1 = 5$	$(-2, 5)$
-1	$y = (-1)^2 + 1 = 2$	$(-1, 2)$
0	$y = 0^2 + 1 = 1$	$(0, 1)$
1	$y = 1^2 + 1 = 2$	$(1, 2)$
2	$y = 2^2 + 1 = 5$	$(2, 5)$
3	$y = 3^2 + 1 = 10$	$(3, 10)$

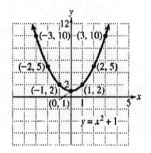

49. $y = 4 - x^2$

x	$y = 4 - x^2$	(x, y)
-3	$y = 4 - (-3)^2 = -5$	$(-3, -5)$
-2	$y = 4 - (-2)^2 = 0$	$(-2, 0)$
-1	$y = 4 - (-1)^2 = 3$	$(-1, 3)$
0	$y = 4 - 0^2 = 4$	$(0, 4)$
1	$y = 4 - 1^2 = 3$	$(1, 3)$
2	$y = 4 - 4^2 = 0$	$(2, 0)$
3	$y = 4 - 3^2 = -5$	$(3, -5)$

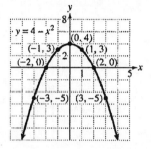

51. a.

x	$y = 2.4x + 180$	(x, y)
40	$y = 2.4(4) + 180 = 276$	$(40, 276)$
50	$y = 2.4(50) + 180 = 300$	$(50, 300)$
60	$y = 2.4(60) + 180 = 324$	$(60, 324)$

b. $x = 40$ represents the year $1960 + 40 = 2000$.

The linear equation predicts a population of 276 million, while the bar graph projects a population of 274.634 million.

$x = 50$ represents the year 2010.

The linear equation predicts a population of 300 million, while the bar graph projects a population of 297.716 million.

$x = 60$ represents the year 2020.

The linear equation predicts a population of 324 million, while the bar graph projects a population of 322.742 million.

In each case, the linear equation models the projections shown in the bar graph quite well.

53. a.

x	$y = 0.85x + 4.05$	(x, y)
11.6	$y = 0.85(11.6) + 4.05 = 13.91$	$(11.6, 13.91)$
8.3	$y = 0.85(8.3) + 4.05 = 11.105$	$(8.3, 11.105)$

b. The linear equation models the actual data quite well.

b.

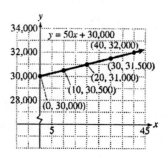

55. a. The x-coordinate of the intersection point is 40. This means that if you drive the moving truck 40 miles, the rental charge will be the same with both companies.

b. A reasonable estimate of the y-coordinate of the intersection point is 55.

c. $y = 40 + 0.35; x = 40$

$y = 40 + 0.35(40)$
$y = 40 + 14 = 54$

$y = 36 + 0.45x; x = 40$

$y = 36 + 0.45(40)$
$y = 36 + 18 = 54$

This value indicates that if you drive the moving truck 40 miles, the rental charge with either company will be $54. This is almost the same as the estimate in part (b).

For Exercises 59–61, answers may vary.

63.

x	$y = |x|$	(x, y)
-3	$y = |-3| = 3$	$(-3, 3)$
-2	$y = |-2| = 2$	$(-2, 2)$
-1	$y = |-1| = 1$	$(-1, 1)$
0	$y = |0| = 0$	$(0, 0)$
1	$y = |1| = 1$	$(1, 1)$
2	$y = |2| = 2$	$(2, 2)$
3	$y = |3| = 3$	$(3, 3)$

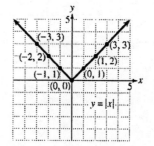

57. a.

x	$y = 50x + 30,000$	(x, y)
0	$y = 50(0) + 30,000 = 30,000$	$(0, 30,000)$
10	$y = 50(10) + 30,000 = 30,500$	$(10, 30,500)$
20	$y = 50(20) + 30,000 = 31,000$	$(20, 31,000)$
30	$y = 50(30) + 30,000 = 31,500$	$(30, 31,500)$
40	$y = 50(40) + 30,000 = 32,000$	$(40, 32,000)$

65. $y = 0.1x^2 - 0.4x + 0.6$

a.

x	$y = 0.1x^2 - 0.4x + 0.6$	(x, y)
0	$y = 0.1 \cdot 0^2 - 0.4 \cdot 0 + 0.6 = 0.6$	$(0, 0.6)$
1	$y = 0.1 \cdot 1^2 - 0.4 \cdot 1 + 0.6 = 0.3$	$(1, 0.3)$
2	$y = 0.1 \cdot 2^2 - 0.4 \cdot 2 + 0.6 = 0.2$	$(2, 0.2)$
3	$y = 0.1 \cdot 3^2 - 0.4 \cdot 3 + 0.6 = 0.3$	$(3, 0.3)$
4	$y = 0.1 \cdot 4^2 - 0.4 \cdot 4 + 0.6 = 0.6$	$(4, 0.6)$
5	$y = 0.1 \cdot 5^2 - 0.4 \cdot 5 + 0.6 = 1.1$	$(5, 1.1)$

b. The air is considered unsafe when $y \geq 0.3$. This occurs when $x \leq 1$ or $x \geq 3$. Since $x = 1$ corresponds to 10 A.M. and $x = 3$ corresponds to noon. To avoid unsafe air, runners should exercise between 10 A.M. and noon.

67. $y = -3x + 2$

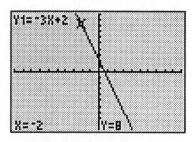

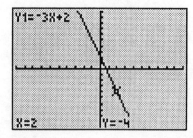

Two points on the graph are $(-2, 8)$ and $(2, -4)$.

69. $y = \dfrac{3}{4}x - 2$

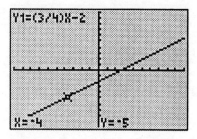

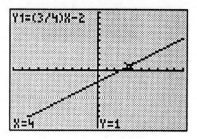

Two points on the graph are $(-4, -5)$ and $(4, 1)$.

71. $y = 2.4x + 180$

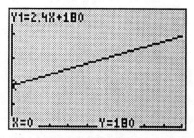

The shape of the graph indicates that the U.S. population is increasing at a steady rate.

Review Exercises

72.
$$3x + 5 = 4(2x - 3) + 7$$
$$3x + 5 = 8x - 12 + 7$$
$$3x + 5 = 8x - 5$$
$$3x + 5 - 8x = 8x - 5 - 8x$$
$$-5x + 5 = -5$$
$$-5x + 5 - 5 = -5 - 5$$
$$-5x = -10$$
$$\frac{-5x}{-5} = \frac{-10}{-5}$$
$$x = 2$$

The solution is 2.

73. $3(1 - 2 \cdot 5) - (-28) = 3(1 - 10) + 28$
$$= 3(-9) + 28$$
$$= -27 + 28 = -1$$

74. $V = \dfrac{1}{3}Ah$ for h

$$V = \frac{1}{3}Ah$$

$$3V = 3\left(\frac{1}{3}Ah\right)$$

$$3V = Ah$$

$$\frac{3V}{A} = \frac{Ah}{A}$$

$$\frac{3V}{A} = h \text{ or } h = \frac{3V}{A}$$

Graphing Linear Equations Using Intercepts

3.2 CHECK POINTS

CHECK POINT 1

a. The graph crosses the x-axis at $(-3, 0)$, so the x-intercept is -3.
The graph crosses the y-axis at $(0, 5)$, so the y-intercept is 5.

b. This horizontal line does not cross the x-axis, so there is no x-intercept. The graph crosses the y-axis $(0, 4)$, so the y-intercept is 4.

c. The graph crosses the x- and y-axes at the same point, the origin. Because the graph crosses both axes at $(0, 0)$, the x-intercept is 0 and the y-intercept is 0.

CHECK POINT 2

$$4x - 3y = 12$$

To find the x-intercept, let $y = 0$ and solve for x.

$$4x - 4y = 12$$
$$4x - 3 \cdot 0 = 12$$
$$4x = 12$$
$$x = 3$$

The x-intercept is 3.

CHECK POINT 3

$$4x - 3y = 12$$

To find the y-intercept, let $x = 0$ and solve for y.

$$4x - 3y = 12$$
$$4 \cdot 0 - 3y = 12$$
$$-3y = 12$$
$$y = 4$$

The y-intercept is -4.

CHECK POINT 4

$2x + 3y = 6$

Step 1 Find the x-intercept.

$$2x + 3y = 6$$
$$2x + 3 \cdot 0 = 6$$
$$2x = 6$$
$$x = 3$$

The x-intercept is 3.

Step 2 Find the y-intercept.

$$2x + 3y = 6$$
$$2 \cdot 0 + 3y = 6$$
$$3y = 6$$
$$y = 2$$

The y-intercept is 2.

Step 3 Find a checkpoint. Let $x = -3$ and find the corresponding value of y.

$$2x + 3y = 6$$
$$2(-3) + 3y = 6$$
$$-6 + 3y = 6$$
$$3y = 12$$
$$y = 4$$

This gives a third ordered pair, $(-3, 4)$. Plot the points $(3, 0), (0, 2)$, and $(-3, 4)$ and draw a line through them.

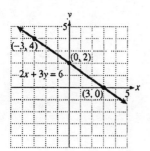

CHECK POINT 5

$x - 2y = 4$

Step 1 Find the x-intercept.

$$x - 2y = 4$$
$$x - 2 \cdot 0 = 4$$
$$x = 4$$

The x-intercept is 4.

Step 2 Find the y-intercept.

$$x - 2y = 4$$
$$0 - 2y = 4$$
$$-2y = 4$$
$$y = -2$$

The y-intercept is -2.

Step 3 Find a checkpoint. Let $x = 2$ and find the corresponding value of y.

$$x - 2y = 4$$
$$2 - 2y = 4$$
$$-2y = 2$$
$$y = -1$$

A checkpoint is $(2, -1)$.
Draw a line through $(4, 0), (0, -2)$, and $(2, -1)$.

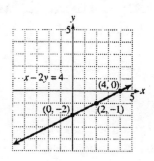

CHECK POINT 6

$x + 3y = 0$

Because the constant on the right is 0, the graph passes through the origin. The x- and y-intercepts are both 0. Two points other than $(0, 0)$ should be found.
Let $y = -1$ to find a second ordered-pair solution, and let $y = 1$ to find a third ordered-pair (checkpoint) solution.

$$x + 3y = 0 \qquad x + 3y = 0$$
$$x + 3(-1) = 0 \qquad x + 3 \cdot 1 = 0$$
$$x + (-3) = 0 \qquad x + 3 = 0$$
$$x = 3 \qquad x = -3$$

Plot the points $(0, 0)$, $(3, -1)$, and $(-3, 1)$ and draw a line through them.

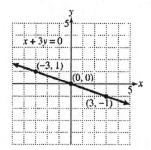

CHECK POINT 7

$y = 3$

All ordered pairs that are solutions of $y = 3$ have a value of y that is 3. Any value can be used for x. Three ordered pairs that are solutions are $(-3, 3)$, $(0, 3)$, and $(4, 3)$.

Plot these three points and draw a line through them. The graph is a horizontal line.

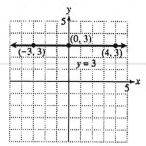

CHECK POINT 8

$x = -2$

All ordered pairs that are solutions have a value of x that is -2. Any value can be used for y. Three ordered pairs that are solutions are $(-2, -4)$, $(-2, 0)$, and $(-2, 3)$. The graph is a vertical line.

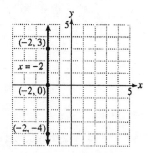

EXERCISE SET 3.2

1. a. The graph crosses the x-axis at $(3, 0)$. Thus, the x-intercept is 3.

b. The graph crosses the y-axis at $(0, 4)$. Thus, the y-intercept is 4.

3. a. The graph crosses the x-axis at $(-2, 0)$. Thus, the x-intercept is -2.

b. The graph crosses the y-axis at $(0, -2)$. Thus, the y-intercept is -2.

5. a. The graph crosses the x-axis at $(0,0)$ (the origin). Thus, the x-intercept is 0.

b. The graph also crosses the y-axis at $(0,0)$. Thus, the y-intercept is 0.

7. a. The graph does not cross the x-axis. Thus, there is no x-intercept.

b. The graph crosses the y-axis at $(0,-2)$. Thus, the y-intercept is -2.

9. $4x + 5y = 20$

To find the x-intercept, let $y = 0$ and solve for x.
$$4x + 5y = 20$$
$$4x + 5(0) = 20$$
$$4x = 20$$
$$x = 5$$
The x-intercept is 5.

To find the y-intercept, let $x = 0$ and solve for y.
$$4x + 5y = 20$$
$$4(0) + 5y = 20$$
$$5y = 20$$
$$y = 4$$
The y-intercept is 4.

11. $7x - 3y = 42$

To find the x-intercept, let $y = 0$ and solve for x.
$$7x - 3y = 42$$
$$7x - 3(0) = 42$$
$$7x = 42$$
$$x = 6$$
The x-intercept is 6.

To find the y-intercept, let $x = 0$ and solve for y.
$$7x - 3y = 42$$
$$7(0) - 3y = 42$$
$$-3y = 42$$
$$y = -14$$
The y-intercept is -14.

13. $-x + 4y = -8$

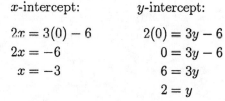

x-intercept: y-intercept:
$$-x + 4(0) = -8 \qquad -0 + 4y = -8$$
$$-x = -8 \qquad\qquad 4y = -8$$
$$x = -8 \qquad\qquad\quad y = -2$$
x–intercept: 8; y-intercept: -2

15. $3x - 5y = 0$

x-intercept: y-intercept:
$$3x - 5(0) = 0 \qquad 3(0) - 5y = 0$$
$$3x = 0 \qquad\qquad -5y = 0$$
$$x = 0 \qquad\qquad\quad y = 0$$
x–intercept: 0; y-intercept: 0

17. $2x = 3y - 6$

x-intercept: y-intercept:
$$2x = 3(0) - 6 \qquad 2(0) = 3y - 6$$
$$2x = -6 \qquad\qquad 0 = 3y - 6$$
$$x = -3 \qquad\qquad 6 = 3y$$
$$\qquad\qquad\qquad\qquad 2 = y$$
x-intercept: -3; y-intercept: 2

In Exercises 19–39, checkpoints will vary.

19. $x + y = 3$

x-intercept: 3
y-intercept: 3
checkpoint: $(2,1)$
Draw a line through $(3,0)$, $(0,3)$, and $(2,1)$.

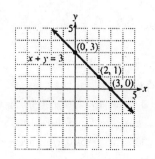

21. $3x + y = 6$

x-intercept: 2
y-intercept: 6
checkpoint: $(1, 3)$
Draw a line through $(2, 0), (0, 6)$,
and $(1, 3)$.

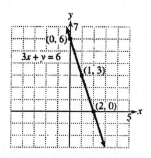

23. $9x - 6y = 18$

x-intercept: 2
y-intercept: -3
checkpoint: $\left(1, -\frac{3}{2}\right)$
Draw a line through $(2, 0), (0, -3)$,
and $\left(1, -\frac{3}{2}\right)$.

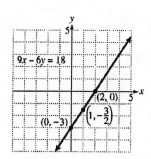

25. $-x + 4y = 8$

x-intercept: -8
y-intercept: 2
checkpoint: $\left(2, \frac{5}{2}\right)$

Draw a line through $(-8, 0), (0, 2)$
and $\left(2, \frac{5}{2}\right)$.

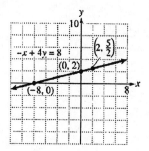

27. $2x - y = 6$

x-intercept: 3
y-intercept: -6
checkpoint: $(1, -4)$
Draw a line through $(3, 0), (0, -6)$,
and $(1, -4)$.

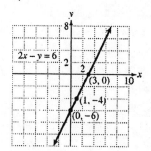

29. $5x = 3y - 15$

x-intercept: -3
y-intercept: 5
checkpoint: $(-6, -5)$
Draw a line through $(-3, 0), (0, 5)$,
and $(-6, -5)$.

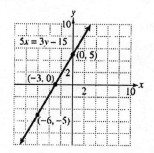

31. $50y = 100 - 25x$

x-intercept: 4
y-intercept: 2
checkpoint: $(-4, 4)$
Draw a line through $(4, 0), (0, 2)$ and $(-4, 4)$.

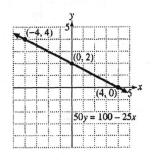

33. $8x - 2y = 12$

x-intercept: $\frac{3}{2}$ or 1.5
y-intercept: -6
checkpoint: $(2, 2)$
Draw a line through $(1.5, 0), (0, -6)$ and $(2, 2)$.

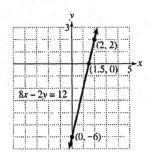

35. $x + y = 0$

x-intercept: 0
y-intercept: 0

The graph passes through the origin. Since both intercepts correspond to the same point, $(0, 0)$, two additional points should be found.
second point: $(-2, 2)$
checkpoint: $(4, -4)$

Draw a line through $(0, 0), (-2, 2)$ and $(4, -4)$.

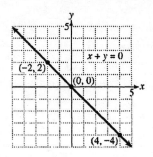

37. $2x + y = 0$

x-intercept: 0
y-intercept: 0
second point: $(1, -2)$
checkpoint: $(-2, -4)$
Draw a line through $(0, 0), (1, -2)$ and $(-2, 4)$.

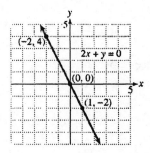

39. $y - 2x = 0$

x-intercept: 0
y-intercept: 0
second point: $(1, 2)$
checkpoint: $(-2, -4)$
Draw a line through $(0, 0), (1, 2)$, and $(-2, -4)$.

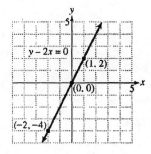

41. The equation for this horizontal line is $y = 3$.

43. The equation for this vertical line is $x = -3$.

45. The equation for this horizontal line, which is the x-axis, is $y = 0$.

47. $y = 4$

All ordered pairs that are solutions will have a value of y that is 4. Any value can be used for x. Three ordered pairs that are solutions are $(-2, 4), (0, 4)$, and $(3, 4)$. Plot these points and draw the line through them. The graph is a horizontal line.

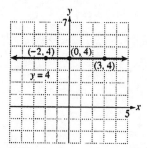

49. $y = -2$

Three ordered pairs are $(-3, -2), (0, -2)$, and $(4, -2)$. The graph is a horizontal line.

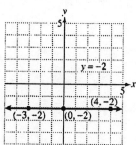

51. $x = 2$

All ordered pairs that are solutions will have a value of x that is 2. Any value can be used for y. Three ordered pairs that are solutions are $(2, -3), (2, 0)$, and $(2, 2)$. The graph is a vertical line.

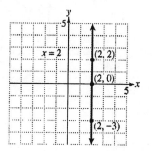

53. $x + 1 = 0$
$$x = -1$$

Three ordered pairs are $(-1, -3), (-1, 0)$, and $(-1, 3)$. The graph is a vertical line.

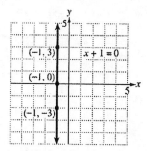

55. $y - 3.5 = 0$
$$y = 3.5$$

Three ordered pairs are $(-2, 3.5), (0, 3.5)$, and $(3.5, 3.5)$. The graph is a horizontal line.

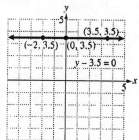

57. $x = 0$

Three ordered pairs are $(0, -2)$, $(0, 0)$, and $(0, 4)$. The graph is a vertical line, the y-axis.

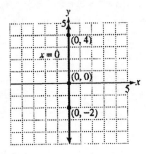

59. $3y = 9$

$\quad y = 3$

Three ordered pairs are $(-3, 3)$, $(0, 3)$, and $(3, 3)$. The graph is a horizontal line.

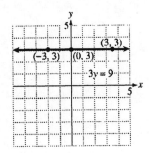

61. $12 - 3x = 0$

$\quad -3x = -12$

$\quad x = 4$

Three ordered pairs are $(4, -2)$, $(4, 1)$, and $(4, 3)$. The graph is a vertical line.

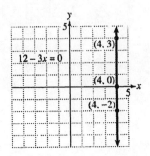

63. The vulture's height is decreasing from 3 seconds to 12 seconds.

65. The y-intercept is 45. This means that the vulture's height was 45 meters at the beginning of the observation.

67. Five x-intercepts of the graph are 12, 13, 14, 15, and 16. During these times (12–16 minutes), the vulture was on the ground.

69. Your temperature is decreasing from 8 A.M. to 11 A.M.

71. Your temperature is increasing from 11 A.M. to 1 P.M.

73. For all age groups, about 80% of people in the United States are satisfied with their lives, so an equation that reasonably models the data is $y = 80$.

For Exercises 75–83, answers may vary.

85. $2x + 5y = 10$ has x-intercept 5 and y-intercept 2.

87. Answers will vary according to the exercises chosen.

89. $\quad 3x - y = 9$

$\quad\quad -y = -3x + 9$

$\quad (-1)(-y) = -1(3x + 9)$

$\quad\quad\quad y = 3x - 9$

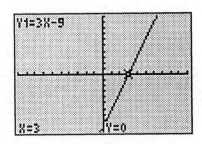

x-intercept: 3; y-intercept: -9

91. $4x - 2y = -40$

$$-2y = -4x - 40$$

$$\frac{-2y}{-2} = \frac{-4x - 40}{-2}$$

$$y = 2x + 20$$

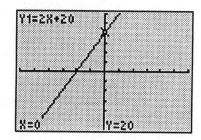

x-intercept: -10; y-intercept: 20

Review Exercises

92. $|-13.4| = 13.4$

93. $7x - (3x - 5) = 7x - 3x + 5 = 4x + 5$

94. $-2 \le x < 4$

$$\xrightarrow{\hspace{0.3cm}\bullet\hspace{1cm}\circ\hspace{0.3cm}}$$
$$-5\ -4\ -3\ -2\ -1\ \ 0\ \ 1\ \ 2\ \ 3\ \ 4\ \ 5$$

Slope

3.3 CHECK POINTS

CHECK POINT 1

a. $(-3, 4)$ and $(-4, -2)$

Let $(x_1, y_1) = (-3, 4)$ and $(x_2, y_2) = (-4, -2)$.

$$m = \frac{\text{Change in } y}{\text{Change in } x} = \frac{y_2 - y_1}{x_2 - x_1}$$

$$= \frac{-2 - 4}{-4 - (-3)}$$

$$= \frac{-6}{-1} = 6$$

The slope of the line through $(-3, 4)$ and $(-4, -2)$ is 6.

b. $(4, -2)$ and $(-1, 5)$

Let $(x_1, y_1) = (4, -2)$ and $(x_2, y_2) = (-1, 5)$.

$$m = \frac{\text{Change in } y}{\text{Change in } x} = \frac{y_2 - y_1}{x_2 - x_1}$$

$$= \frac{5 - (-2)}{-1 - 4}$$

$$= \frac{7}{-5} = -\frac{7}{5}$$

The slope of the line through $(4, -2)$ and $(-1, 5)$ is $-\frac{7}{5}$.

CHECK POINT 2

a. $(6, 5)$ and $(2, 5)$

Let $(x_1, y_1) = (6, 5)$ and $(x_2, y_2) = (2, 5)$.

$$m = \frac{y_2 - y_1}{x_2 - x_1} = \frac{5 - 5}{2 - 6} = \frac{0}{-4} = 0$$

The slope of the line through $(6, 5)$ and $(2, 5)$ is 0. (This is a horizontal line.)

b. $(1, 6)$ and $(1, 4)$

Let $(x_1, y_1) = (1, 6)$ and $(x_2, y_2) = (1, 4)$.

$$m = \frac{y_2 - y_1}{x_2 - x_1} = \frac{4 - 6}{1 - 1} = \frac{-2}{0}$$

Because division by 0 is undefined, the slope of the line through $(1, 6)$ and $(1, 4)$ is undefined. (This is a vertical line.)

CHECK POINT 3

Find the slope of each line.

Line through $(4, 2)$ and $(6, 6)$:

$$m = \frac{6 - 2}{6 - 4} = \frac{4}{2} = 2$$

Line through $(0, -2)$ and $(1, 0)$:

$$m = \frac{0 - (-2)}{1 - 0} = \frac{2}{1} = 2$$

Both slopes are 2. Since their slopes are equal, the lines are parallel.

CHECK POINT 4

Let x represent a year and y the number of men living alone in that year. The two points shown on the line segment for women are $(1995, 10)$ and $(2010, 12)$. Use these points to compute the slope.

$$m = \frac{\text{Change in } y}{\text{Change in } x} = \frac{12 - 10}{2010 - 1995}$$

$$= \frac{2}{15} \approx \frac{0.13 \text{ million people}}{\text{year}}$$

The slope is $\frac{2}{15} \approx 0.13$. This indicates that the number of U.S. men living alone is projected to increase by 0.13 million each year.

EXERCISE SET 3.3

1. $(4, 7)$ and $(8, 10)$

Let $(x_1, y_1) = (4, 7)$ and $(x_2, y_2) = (8, 10)$.

$$m = \frac{\text{Change in } y}{\text{Change in } x} = \frac{y_2 - y_2}{x_2 - x_1}$$

$$= \frac{10 - 7}{8 - 4} = \frac{3}{4}$$

The slope is $\frac{3}{4}$. Since the slope is positive, the line rises.

3. $(-2, 1)$ and $(2, 2)$

$$m = \frac{2 - 1}{2 - (-2)} = \frac{1}{4}$$

Since the slope is positive, the line rises.

5. $(4, -2)$ and $(3, -2)$

$$m = \frac{-2 - (-2)}{3 - 4} = \frac{0}{-1} = 0$$

Since the slope is zero, the line is horizontal.

7. $(-2, 4)$ and $(-1, -1)$

$$m = \frac{-1 - 4}{-1 - (-2)} = \frac{-5}{1} = -5$$

Since the slope is negative, the line falls.

9. $(5, 3)$ and $(5, -2)$

$$m = \frac{-2 - 3}{5 - 5} = \frac{-5}{0}$$

Since the slope is undefined, the line is vertical.

11. Line through $(-2, 2)$ and $(2, 4)$:

$$m = \frac{4 - 2}{2 - (-2)} = \frac{2}{4} = \frac{1}{2}$$

13. Line through $(-3, 4)$ and $(3, 2)$:

$$m = \frac{2 - 4}{3 - (-3)} = \frac{-2}{6} = -\frac{1}{3}$$

15. Line through $(-2, 1), (0, 0)$, and $(2, -1)$ Use any two of these points to find the slope.

$$m = \frac{0 - 1}{0 - (-2)} = \frac{-1}{2} = -\frac{1}{2}$$

17. Line through $(0, 2)$ and $(3, 0)$:

$$m = \frac{0 - 2}{3 - 0} = -\frac{2}{3}$$

19. Line through $(-2, 1)$ and $(4, 1)$:

$$m = \frac{1 - 1}{4 - (-2)} = \frac{0}{6} = 0$$

(Since the line is horizontal, it is not necessary to do this computation. The slope of every horizontal line is 0.)

21. Line through $(-3, 4)$ and $(-3, -2)$:

$$m = \frac{-2 - 4}{-3 - (-3)} = \frac{-6}{0}; \text{ undefined}$$

(Since the line is vertical, it is not necessary to do this computation. The slope of every vertical line is undefined.)

23. Line through $(-2, 0)$ and $(0, 6)$:

$$m = \frac{6 - 0}{0 - (-2)} = 3$$

Line through $(1, 8)$ and $(0, 5)$:

$$m = \frac{5 - 8}{0 - 1} = \frac{-3}{-1} = 3$$

Since their slopes are equal, the lines are parallel.

25. Line through $(0, 3)$ and $(1, 5)$:

$$m = \frac{5 - 3}{1 - 0} = \frac{2}{1} = 2$$

Line through $(-1, 7)$ and $(1, 10)$:

$$m = \frac{10 - 7}{1 - (-1)} = \frac{3}{2}$$

Since their slopes are not equal, the lines are not parallel.

27. Line through $(1999, 1000)$ and $(2001, 1500)$:

$$m = \frac{1500 - 1000}{2001 - 1999} = \frac{500}{2} = 250$$

The amount spent online per U.S. online household was projected to increase by \$250 each year from 1999 to 2001.

29. Line through $(2001, 50)$ and $(2010, -286)$:

$$m = \frac{-286 - 50}{2010 - 2001} = \frac{-336}{9}$$

$$= -\frac{112}{3} \approx 37.33$$

The federal budget surplus will decrease at a projected rate of \$37.33 billion each year from 2001 to 2010.

31. The line segment represents the books sold in horizontal, so its slope is 0. This indicates that the number of books sold has not changed over the years shown on the graph.

33. Line through $(20{,}000, 8000)$ and $(40{,}000, 16{,}000)$:

$$m = \frac{16{,}000 - 8000}{40{,}000 - 20{,}000} = \frac{8000}{20{,}000} = 0.4$$

The cost is \$0.40 or 40¢ per mile.

35. $m = \dfrac{\text{Change in } y}{\text{Change in } x} = \dfrac{6}{18} = \dfrac{1}{3}$

The pitch of the roof is $\frac{1}{3}$.

37. The grade an access ramp is $\frac{1 \text{ foot}}{12 \text{ feet}} = \frac{1}{12} \approx 0.083 = 8.3\%$.

For Exercises 39–43, answers may vary.

45. Statement b is true.

47. Use the graph to observe where each line crosses the y-axis. In order of decreasing size, the y-intercepts are b_2, b_1, b_4, b_3.

49. $y = -3x + 6$

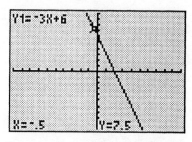

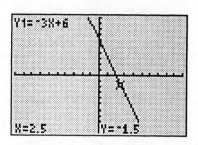

Two points on the graph are $(-0.5, 7.5)$ and $(2.5, -1.5)$.

$$m = \frac{7.5 - (-1.5)}{-0.5 - 2.5} = \frac{9}{-3} = -3$$

51. $y = \frac{3}{4}x - 2$

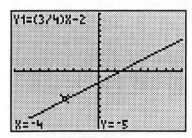

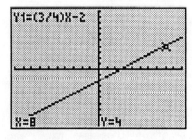

Two points on the graph are $(-4, -5)$ and $(8, 4)$.

$$m = \frac{4 - (-5)}{8 - (-4)} = \frac{9}{12} = \frac{3}{4}$$

Review Exercises

53.   Let x = length of shorter piece
                 (in inches).
Then $2x$ = length of longer piece.

$$x + 2x = 36$$
$$3x = 36$$
$$x = 12$$

The pieces are 12 inches and 24 inches.

54. $-10 + 16 \div 2(-4) = -10 + 8(-4)$
$$= -10 - 32$$
$$= -10 + (-32) = -42$$

55. $2x - 3 \leq 5$
$$2x \leq 8$$
$$x \leq 4$$

$$\{x | x \leq 4\}$$

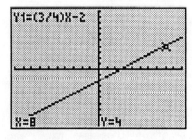
-3 -2 -1 0 1 2 3 4 5 6 7

The Slope-Intercept Form of the Equation of a Line

3.4 CHECK POINTS

CHECK POINT 1

a. $y = 5x - 3$

Write $y = 5x - 3$ as $y = 5x + (-3)$. The slope is the x-coefficient, 5, and the y-intercept is the constant term, -3.

b. $y = \frac{2}{3}x + 4$

This equation is the form $y = mx + b$ with $m = \frac{2}{3}$ and $b = 4$. The slope is $\frac{2}{3}$ and the y-intercept is 4.

c. $7x + y = 6$

Put this equation in the form $y = mx + b$.

$$7x + y = 6$$
$$7x - 7x + y = -7x + 6$$
$$y = -7x + 6$$

The slope is the x-coefficient, -7, and the y-coefficient is the constant term, 6.

CHECK POINT 2

$y = 3x - 2$

Write $y = 3x - 2$ in the form $y = mx + b$.

$$y = 3x + (-2)$$

The slope is 3 and the y-intercept is -2.

Step 1 Plot $(0, -2)$ on the y-axis.

Step 2 Write the slope as a fraction.

$$m = \frac{3}{1} = \frac{\text{Rise}}{\text{Run}}$$

Start at $(0, -2)$. Based on the slope, move 3 units up (the rise) and 1 unit to the *right* (the run) to reach the point $(1, 1)$.

Step 3 Draw a line through $(0, -2)$ and $(1, 1)$.

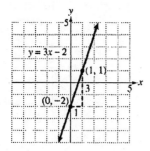

CHECK POINT 3

$y = \frac{3}{5}x + 1$

slope $= \frac{3}{5}$; y-intercept $= 1$

Plot $(0, 1)$. From the point, move 3 units *up* (the rise) and 5 units to the *right* (the run) to reach the point $(5, 4)$. Draw a line through $(0, 1)$ and $(5, 4)$.

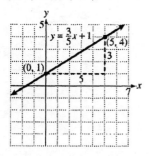

CHECK POINT 4

$3x + 4y = 0$

Put the equation in slope-intercept form by solving for y.

$$3x + 4y = 0$$
$$3x - 3x + 4y = -3x + 0$$
$$4y = -3x + 0$$
$$\frac{4y}{4} = \frac{-3x + 0}{4}$$
$$y = \frac{-3x}{4} + \frac{0}{4}$$
$$y = -\frac{3}{4}x + 0$$

slope $= -\frac{3}{4}$; y-intercept $= 0$

Use the y-intercept to plot $(0, 0)$.

$$m = -\frac{3}{4} = \frac{-3}{4} = \frac{\text{Rise}}{\text{Run}}$$

Because the rise is -3 and the run is 4, move 3 units *down* and 4 units to the *right* to reach the point $(4, -3)$. Draw a line through $(0, 0)$ and $(4, -3)$.

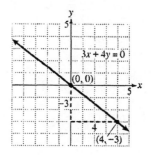

EXERCISE SET 3.4

1. $y = 3x + 2$

The slope is the x-coefficient, which is 3. The y-intercept is the constant term, which is 2.

3. $y = 3x - 5$

$y = 3x + (-5)$

$m = 3$; y-intercept $= -5$

5. $y = -\dfrac{1}{2}x + 5$

$m = -\frac{1}{2};\ y - \text{intercept} = 5$

7. $y = 7x$

$y = 7x + 0$

$m = 7;\ y\text{-intercept} = 0$

9. $y = 10$

$y = 0x + 10$

$m = 0;\ y\text{-intercept} = 10$

11. $y = 4 - x$

$y = -x + 4 = -1x + 4$

$m = -1;\ y\text{-intercept} = 4$

13. $\qquad -5x + y = 7$

$-5x + y + 5x = 5x + 7$

$\qquad\qquad\quad y = 5x + 7$

$m = 5;\ y\text{-intercept} = 7$

15. $x + y = 6$

$\qquad y = -x + 6 = -1x + 6$

$m = -1;\ y\text{-intercept} = 6$

17. $6x + y = 0$

$\qquad y = -6x = -6x + 0$

$m = -6;\ y\text{-intercept: } 0$

19. $3y = 6x$

$\quad y = 2x$

$m = 2;\ y\text{-intercept: } 0$

21. $2x + 7y = 0$

$\qquad 7y = -2x$

$\qquad\ y = -\dfrac{2}{7}x$

$m = -\frac{2}{7};\ y\text{-intercept: } 0$

23. $3x + 2y = 3$

$\qquad 2y = -3x + 3$

$\qquad\ y = \dfrac{-3x + 3}{2}$

$\qquad\ y = -\dfrac{3}{2}x + \dfrac{3}{2}$

$m = -\frac{3}{2};\ y\text{-intercept} = \frac{3}{2}$

25. $3x - 4y = 12$

$\qquad -4y = -3x + 12$

$\qquad \dfrac{-4y}{-4} = \dfrac{-3x + 12}{-4}$

$\qquad\quad y = \dfrac{3}{4}x - 3$

$m = \frac{3}{4};\ y\text{-intercept: } -3$

27. $y = 2x + 3$

Step 1 Plot $(0, 3)$ on the y-axis.

Step 2 $m = \dfrac{2}{1} = \dfrac{\text{Rise}}{\text{Run}}$

Start at $(0, 3)$. Using the slope, move 2 units *up* (the rise) and 1 unit to the *right* (the run) to reach the point $(1, 5)$.

Step 3 Draw a line through $(0, 3)$ and $(1, 5)$.

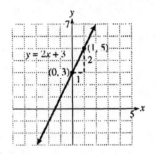

29. $y = -2x + 4$

Slope $= -2 = -\frac{2}{1};\ y\text{-intercept} = 4$
Plot $(0, 4)$ on the y-axis. From this point, move 2 units *down* (because -2 is negative) and 1 unit to the *right* to reach the point $(1, 2)$. Draw a line through $(0, 4)$ and $(1, 2)$.

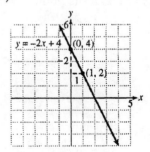

31. $y = \frac{1}{2}x + 3$

Slope $= \frac{1}{2}$; y-intercept $= 3$

Plot $(0, 3)$. From this point, move 1 unit *up* and 2 units to the *right* to reach the point $(2, 4)$. Draw a line through $(0, 3)$ and $(2, 4)$.

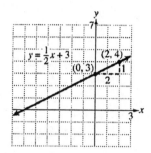

33. $y = \frac{2}{3}x - 4$

Slope $= \frac{2}{3}$; y-intercept $= -4$

Plot $(0, -4)$. From this point, move 3 units *up* and 3 units to the *right* to reach the point $(3, -2)$. Draw a line through $(0, -4)$ and $(3, -2)$.

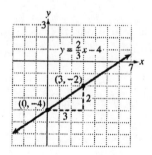

35. $y = -\frac{3}{4}x + 4$

Slope $= -\frac{3}{4} = \frac{-3}{4}$; y-intercept $= 4$

Plot $(0, 4)$. From this point, move 3 units *down* and 4 units to the *right* to reach the point $(4, 1)$.

Draw a line through $(0, 4)$ and $(4, 1)$.

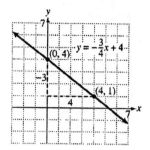

37. $y = -\frac{5}{3}x$

Slope $= -\frac{5}{3} = \frac{-5}{3}$; y-intercept $= 0$

Plot $(0, 0)$. From this point, move 5 units *down* and 3 units to the *right* to reach the point $(3, -5)$. Draw a line through $(0, 0)$ and $(3, -5)$.

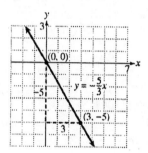

39. a. $3x + y = 0$
$$y = -3x$$

b. $m = -3$; y-intercept $= 0$

c. Plot $(0, 0)$. Since $m = -3 = -\frac{3}{1}$, move 3 units *down* and 1 units to the *right* to reach the point $(1, -3)$. Draw a line through $(0, 0)$ and $(1, -3)$.

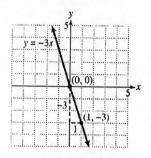

41. a. $3y = 4x$

$y = \dfrac{4}{3}x$

b. $m = \frac{4}{3}$; y-intercept $= 0$

c. Plot $(0,0)$. Move 4 units *up* and 3 units to the *right* to reach the point $(3,4)$. Draw a line through $(0,0)$ and $(3,4)$.

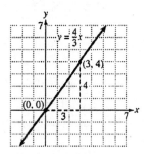

43. a. $2x + y = 3$

$y = -2x + 3$

b. $m = -2$; y-intercept $= 3$

c. Plot $(0,3)$. Since $m = -2 = -\frac{2}{1}$, move 2 units *down* and 1 units to the *right* to reach the point $(1,1)$. Draw a line through $(0,3)$ and $(1,1)$.

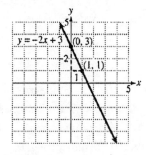

45. a. $7x + 2y = 14$

$2y = -7x + 14$

$\dfrac{2y}{2} = \dfrac{-7x + 14}{2}$

$y = -\dfrac{7}{2}x + 7$

b. $m = -\frac{7}{2}$; y-intercept $= 7$

c. Plot $(0,7)$. Since $m = -\frac{7}{2} = -\frac{7}{2}$, move 7 units *down* and 2 units to the *right* to reach the point $(2,0)$. Draw a line through $(0,7)$ and $(2,4)$.

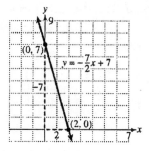

47. $y = 3x + 1$:
$m = 3$; y-intercept $= 1$
$y = 3x - 3$:
$m = 3$, y-intercept $= -3$

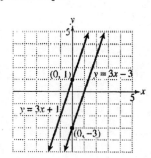

The lines are parallel because their slopes are equal.

49. $y = -3x + 2$:
$m = -3$; y-intercept $= 2$
$y = 3x + 2$:
$m = 3$, y-intercept $= 2$

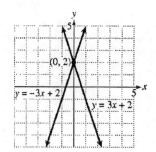

The lines are not parallel because their slopes are not equal.

51. $y = -0.4x + 38$

  a. 1980: $x = 0$
$$y = -0.4(0) + 38 = 38$$
1981: $x = 1$
$$y = -0.4(1) + 38 = 37.6$$
1982: $x = 2$
$$y = -0.4(2) + 38 = 37.2$$
1983: $x = 3$
$$y = -0.4(3) + 38 = 36.8$$
1990: $x = 20$
$$y = -0.4(10) + 38 = 34$$
2000: $x = 20$
$$y = -0.4(20) + 38 = 30$$

According to the formula, 38% of U.S. men smoked in 1980, 37.6% in 1981, 37.2% in 1982, 36.8% in 1983, 34% in 1990, and 30% in 2000.

b. This slope of this model is -0.4. This indicates that the percentage of U.S. men smoking is decreasing by 0.4% each year.

c. The y-intercept is 38. This indicates that in 1980 (the initial year for the model), there were 38% if U.S. men smoking.

53. a. The y-intercept is 24. This indicates that in 1991, the cost of the average prescription was $24.

b. Line through $(0, 24)$ and $(7, 38)$:
$$m = \frac{38 - 24}{7 - 0} = \frac{14}{7} = 2$$
This indicates that the cost was increasing by $2 each year from 1991 to 2000.

c. $y = 2x + 24$

d. The year 2005 corresponds to $x = 14$.
$$y = 2(14) + 24 = 52$$
The model predicts that the average prescription will cost $52 in 2005.

For Exercises 55–57, answers may vary.

59. Each multiple birth corresponds to 2 (if twins), 3 (if triplets), 4 (if quadruplets), or more births. Since this number varies, and most births are single births, the number of multiple births will not increase at the same rate as total births. Therefore, the slopes will not be equal and the lines will not be parallel.

Review Exercises

61. $\dfrac{x}{2} + 7 = 13 - \dfrac{x}{4}$

Multiply by the LCD, which is 4.
$$4\left(\frac{x}{2} + 7\right) = 4\left(13 - \frac{x}{4}\right)$$
$$2x + 28 = 52 - x$$
$$3x + 28 = 52$$
$$3x = 24$$
$$x = 8$$

The solution is 8.

62. $3(12 \div 2^2 - 3)^2 = 3(12 \div 4 - 3)^2$
$$= 3(3 - 3)^2$$
$$= 3 \cdot 0^2 = 3 \cdot 0 = 0$$

63. $A = PB$; $A = 14$, $P = 25\% = 0.25$
$$A = PB$$
$$14 = 0.25 \cdot B$$
$$\frac{14}{0.25} = \frac{0.25B}{0.25}$$
$$56 = B$$

14 is 25% of 56.

The Point-Slope Form of the Equation of a Line

3.5 CHECK POINTS

CHECK POINT 1

Line with slope 6 that passes through the point $(2, -5)$
Begin with the point-slope equation of a line with $m = 6$, $x_1 = 2$, and $y_1 = -5$.

$$y - y_1 = m(x - x_1)$$
$$y - (-5) = 6(x - 2)$$
$$y + 5 = 6(x - 2)$$

Now solve this equation for y and write an equivalent equation in slope-intercept form.

$$y + 5 = 6x - 12$$
$$y = 6x - 17$$

CHECK POINT 2

Line passing through $(-2, -1)$ and $(-1, -6)$

a. First, find the slope of the line.

$$m = \frac{-6 - (-1)}{-1 - (-2)} = \frac{-5}{1} = -5$$

Either point can be used as (x_1, y_1). We will use $(x_1, y_1) = (-2, -1)$.

$$y - y_1 = m(x - x_1)$$
$$y - (-1) = -5[x - (-2)]$$
$$y + 1 = -5(x + 2)$$

Note: If $(-1, -6)$ is used as (x_1, y_1), the equation in point-slope form will be $y + 6 = -5(x + 1)$.

b. Now solve the point-slope equation for y and write an equivalent equation in slope-intercept form.

$$y + 1 = -5(x + 2)$$
$$y + 1 = -5x - 10$$
$$y = -5x - 11$$

Note: If $(-1, -6)$ is used as (x_1, y_1), the point-slope equation will be different, as shown above, but the slope-intercept equation will be the same.

CHECK POINT 3

Passing through $(-2, 5)$ and parallel to the line $y = 3x + 1$
The slope of the line $y = 3x + y$ is 3. Since the lines are parallel, they will have the same slope.
point-slope form:

$$y - y_1 = m(x - x_1)$$
$$y - 5 = (x - (-2))$$
$$y - 5 = 3(x + 2)$$

slope-intercept form:

$$y - 5 = 3(x + 2)$$
$$y - 5 = 3x + 6$$
$$y = 3x + 11$$

CHECK POINT 4

$$x + 3y - 12 = 0$$
$$3y = -x + 12$$
$$y = -\frac{1}{3}x + 4$$

The slope of the line is $-\frac{1}{3}$. The slope of a line perpendicular to this line is 3.

EXERCISE SET 3.5

1. Slope $= 2$, passing through $(3, 5)$
point-slope form: $y - 5 = 2(x - 3)$
$y - 5 = 2x - 6$
slope-intercept form: $y = 2x - 1$

3. Slope $= 6$, passing through $(-2, 5)$
point-slope form: $y - 5 = 6(x + 2)$
$y - 5 = 6x + 12$
slope-intercept form: $y = 6x + 17$

5. Slope $= -3$, passing through $(-2, -3)$
point-slope form: $y + 3 = -3(x + 2)$
$y + 3 = -3x - 6$
slope-intercept form; $y = -3x - 9$

7. Slope $= -4$, passing through $(-4, 0)$
$y - 0 = -4(x + 4)$
point-slope form: $y = -4(x + 4)$
slope-intercept form: $y = -4x - 16$

9. Slope $= -1$, passing through $\left(-\frac{1}{2}, -2\right)$
point-slope form: $y + 2 = -1\left(x + \frac{1}{2}\right)$
$y + 2 = -x - \frac{1}{2}$
slope-intercept form: $y = -x - \frac{5}{2}$

11. Slope $= \frac{1}{2}$, passes through the origin: $(0, 0)$
point-slope form: $y - 0 = \frac{1}{2}(x - 0)$
slope-intercept form: $y = \frac{1}{2}x$

13. Slope $= -\frac{2}{3}$, passing through $(6, -2)$
point-slope form: $y + 2 = -\frac{2}{3}(x - 6)$
$y + 2 = -\frac{2}{3}x + 4$
slope-intercept form: $y = -\frac{2}{3}x + 2$

15. Passing through $(1, 2)$ and $(5, 10)$
slope $= \dfrac{10 - 2}{5 - 1} = \dfrac{8}{4} = 2$
point-slope form: $y - 2 = 2(x - 1)$
or $y - 10 = 2(x - 5)$
$y - 2 = 2x - 2$
slope-intercept form: $y = 2x$

17. Passing through $(-3, 0)$ and $(0, 3)$
slope $= \dfrac{3 - 0}{0 + 3} = \dfrac{3}{3} = 1$
point-slope form: $y - 0 = 1(x + 3)$
or $y - 3 = 1(x - 0)$
slope-intercept form: $y = x + 3$

19. Passing through $(-3, -1)$ and $(2, 4)$
slope $= \dfrac{4 + 1}{2 + 3} = \dfrac{5}{5} = 1$
point-slope form: $y + 1 = 1(x + 3)$
or $y - 4 = 1(x - 2)$
slope-intercept form: $y = x + 2$

21. Passing through $(-3, -2)$ and $(3, 6)$
slope $= \dfrac{6 + 2}{3 + 3} = \dfrac{8}{6} = \dfrac{4}{3}$
point-slope form: $y + 2 = \dfrac{4}{3}(x + 3)$
or $y - 6 = \dfrac{4}{3}(x - 3)$
$y + 2 = \dfrac{4}{3}x + 4$
slope-intercept form: $y = \dfrac{4}{3}x + 2$

23. Passing through $(-3, -1)$ and $(4, -1)$
slope $= \dfrac{-1 + 1}{4 + 3} = \dfrac{0}{7} = 0$
point-slope form: $y + 1 = 0(x + 3)$
or $y + 1 = 0(x - 4)$
slope-intercept form: $y = -1$

25. Passing through $(2,4)$ with x-intercept $= -2$

Use the points $(2,4)$ and $(-2,0)$.

$$\text{slope} = \frac{0-4}{-2-2} = \frac{-4}{-4} = 1$$

point-slope form: $y - 4 = 1(x - 2)$
slope-intercept form: $y = x + 2$

27. x-intercept $= -\frac{1}{2}$ and y-intercept $= 4$

Use the points $\left(-\frac{1}{2}, 0\right)$ and $(0, 4)$.

$$\text{slope} = \frac{4-0}{0+\frac{1}{2}} = \frac{4}{\frac{1}{2}} = 8$$

point-slope form: $y - 0 = 8\left(x + \frac{1}{2}\right)$

or $y - 4 = 8(x - 0)$
slope-intercept form: $y = 8x + 4$

29. For $y = 5x, m = 5$. A line parallel to this line would have the same slope, $m = 5$. A line perpendicular to it would have slope $m = -\frac{1}{5}$.

31. For $y = -7x, m = -7$. A line parallel to this line would have the same slope, $m = -7$. A line perpendicular to it would have slope $m = \frac{1}{7}$.

33. For $y = \frac{1}{2}x + 3, m = \frac{1}{2}$. A line parallel to this line would have the same slope, $m = \frac{1}{2}$. A line perpendicular to it would have slope $m = -2$.

35. For $y = -\frac{2}{5}x - 1, m = -\frac{2}{5}$. A line parallel to this line would have the same slope, $m = -\frac{2}{5}$. A line perpendicular to it would have slope $m = \frac{5}{2}$.

37. $4x + y = 7$
$$y = -4x + 7$$
The slope is -4. A line parallel to this line would have the same slope, $m = -4$. A line perpendicular to it would have slope $m = \frac{1}{4}$.

39. $2x + 4y - 8 = 0$
$$4y = -2x + 8$$
$$y = -\frac{1}{2}x + 2$$
The slope is $-\frac{1}{2}$. A line parallel to this line would have the same slope, $m = -\frac{1}{2}$. A line perpendicular to it would have slope $m = 2$.

41. $2x - 3y - 5 = 0$
$$-3y = -2x + 5$$
$$y = \frac{2}{3}x - \frac{5}{3}$$
The slope is $\frac{2}{3}$. A line parallel to this line would have the same slope, $m = \frac{2}{3}$. A line perpendicular to it would have slope $m = -\frac{3}{2}$.

43. We know that $x = 6$ is a vertical line with undefined slope. A line parallel to it would also be vertical with undefined slope. A line perpendicular to it would be horizontal with slope $m = 0$.

45. Since L is parallel to $y = 2x$, we know it will have slope $m = 2$. We are given that it passes through $(4, 2)$.
point-slope form:
$$y - y_1 = m(x - x_1)$$
$$y - 2 = 2(x - 4)$$
slope-intercept form:
$$y - 2 = 2(x - 4)$$
$$y - 2 = 2x - 8$$
$$y = 2x - 6$$

47. Since L is perpendicular to $y = 2x$, we know it will have slope $m = -\frac{1}{2}$. We are given that it passes through $(2, 4)$.
point-slope form:
$$y - y_1 = m(x - x_1)$$
$$y - 4 = -\frac{1}{2}(x - 2)$$

slope-intercept form:

$$y - 4 = -\frac{1}{2}(x - 2)$$

$$y - 4 = -\frac{1}{2}x + 1$$

$$y = -\frac{1}{2}x + 5$$

49. Since L is parallel to $y = -4x + 3$, we now it will have slope $m = -4$. We are given that it passes through $(-8, -10)$.

point-slope form:

$$y - y_1 = m(x - x_1)$$
$$y - (-10) = -4(x - (-8))$$
$$y + 10 = -4(x + 8)$$

slope-intercept form:

$$y + 10 = -4(x + 8)$$
$$y + 10 = -4x - 32$$
$$y = -4x - 42$$

51. Since L is perpendicular to $y = \frac{1}{5}x + 6$, we know it will have slope $m = -5$. We are given that it passes through $(2, -3)$.

point-slope form:

$$y - y_1 = m(x - x_1)$$
$$y - (-3) = -5(x - 2)$$
$$y + 3 = -5(x - 2)$$

slope-intercept form:

$$y + 3 = -5(x - 2)$$
$$y + 3 = -5x + 10$$
$$y = -5x + 7$$

53. $2x - 3y - 7 = 0$

$$-3y = -2x + 7$$

$$y = \frac{2}{3}x - \frac{7}{3}$$

Since the line parallel to $y = \frac{2}{3}x - \frac{7}{3}$, we know it will have slope $m = \frac{2}{3}$. We are given that it passes through $(-2, 20)$.

point-slope form:

$$y - y_1 = m(x - x_1)$$
$$y - 2 = \frac{2}{3}(x - (-2))$$
$$y - 2 = \frac{2}{3}(x + 2)$$

slope-intercept form:

$$y - 2 = \frac{2}{3}(x + 2)$$
$$y - 2 = \frac{2}{3}x + \frac{4}{3}$$
$$y = \frac{2}{3}x + \frac{10}{3}$$

55. $x - 2y - 3 = 0$

$$-2y = -x + 3$$

$$y = \frac{1}{2}x - \frac{3}{2}$$

Since the line is perpendicular to $y = \frac{1}{2}x - \frac{3}{2}$, we know it will have slope $m = -2$. We are given that it passes through $(4, -7)$.

point-slope form:

$$y - y_1 = m(x - x_1)$$
$$y - (-7) = -2(x - 4)$$
$$y + 7 = -2(x - 4)$$

slope-intercept form:

$$y + 7 = -2(x - 4)$$
$$y + 7 = -2x + 8$$
$$y = -2x + 1$$

57. a. Line through $(2, 162)$ and $(8, 168)$:

$$m = \frac{168 - 162}{8 - 2} = \frac{6}{6} = 1$$

Using the point $(2, 162)$ as (x_1, y_1), the point-slope equation is

$$y - y_1 = m(x - x_1)$$
$$y - 162 = 1(x - 2).$$

b. $y - 162 = x - 2$

$$y = x + 160$$

c. The year 2005 corresponds to $x = 15$.

$$y = 15 + 160 = 175$$

According to the equation, the average American adult will weigh 175 pounds in 2005.

59. Two points on the line are $(12, 3)$ and $(15, 1)$.

$$m = \frac{1 - 3}{15 - 12} = \frac{-2}{3} = -\frac{2}{3}$$

point-slope form using $(12, 3)$:

$$y - 3 = -\frac{2}{3}(x - 12)$$

Use this equation to find the point-slope equation.

$$y - 3 = -\frac{2}{3}x + 8$$

$$y = -\frac{2}{3}x + 11$$

If $x = 7$,

$$y = -\frac{2}{3}(7) + 11 = -\frac{14}{3} + 11 \approx 6.3.$$

The model predicts that a person with 7 years of education will score about 6.3 on the prejudice test.

61. a.

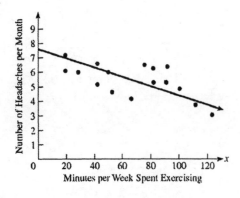

b. Two points on the line are $(50, 6)$ and $(80, 5)$.

The slope is

$$m = \frac{5 - 6}{80 - 50} = -\frac{1}{30}.$$

Using the point $(50, 6)$, the point-slope form is

$$y - 6 = -\frac{1}{30}(x - 50).$$

Use this equation to find the point-slope equation.

$$y - 6 = -\frac{1}{30}x + \frac{5}{3}$$

$$= -\frac{1}{30}x + \frac{23}{3}$$

or approximately

$$y = -0.03x + 7.67$$

c. If $x = 130$,

$$y = -0.03(130) + 7.67 = 3.77.$$

This model predicts that a person exercising 130 minutes a week will have 3.77 or about 4 headaches per week.

63. Answers may vary.

65. Statement c is true.

The line through $(2, -5)$ and $(2, 6)$ is vertical, so its slope is undefined.

67. Using the given information, write two ordered pairs in which $^\circ M$ is the first coordinate and $^\circ E$ is the second coordinate: $(25, 40)$ and $(125, 280)$. Find the slope-intercept equation of the line through these two points.

$$m = \frac{280 - 40}{125 - 25} = \frac{240}{100} = 2.4$$

Use the slope and the point $(25, 40)$ to find the point-slope equation of the line.

$$E - 40 = 2.4(M - 25)$$

Simplify this equation to find the slope-intercept equation.

$$E - 40 = 2.4M - 60$$
$$E = 2.4M - 20$$

69.

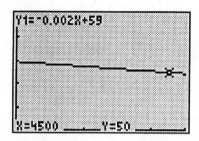

The graph shows that 4500 shirts can be sold at $50 each.

Review Exercises

71. Let $x =$ the number of sheets of paper.

$$4 + 2x \leq 29$$
$$2x \leq 25$$
$$x \leq \tfrac{25}{2} \text{ or } 12\tfrac{1}{2}$$

Since the number of sheets of paper must be a whole number, at most 12 sheets of paper can put in the envelope.

72. The only natural numbers in the given set are 1 and $\sqrt{4}\ (= 2)$.

73. $3x - 5y = 15$
x-intercept: 5
y-intercept: -3
checkpoint: $(-5, -6)$

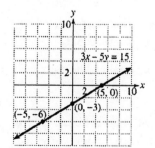

Chapter 3 Review Exercises

1. $y = 3x + 6$

$(-3, 3)$:
$$3 \overset{?}{=} 3(-3) + 6$$
$$3 \overset{?}{=} -6 + 9$$
$$3 = -3 \text{ false}$$

$(-3, 3)$ is a solution.

$(0, 6)$:
$$6 = 3(0) + 6$$
$$6 = 6 \text{ true}$$

$(0, 6)$ is a solution.

$(1, 9)$:
$$9 = 3(1) + 6$$
$$9 = 9 \text{ true}$$

$(1, 9)$ is a solution.

2. $3x - y = 12$

$(0, 4)$:
$$3(0) - 4 \overset{?}{=} 12$$
$$-4 = 12 \text{ false}$$

$(4, 0)$ is not a solution.

$(4, 0)$:
$$3(4) - 0 \overset{?}{=} 12$$
$$12 = 12 \text{ true}$$

$(4, 0)$ is a solution.

$(-1, 15)$:
$$3(-1) - 15 \overset{?}{=} 12$$
$$-3 - 15 \overset{?}{=} 12$$
$$-18 = 12 \text{ false}$$

$(-1, 15)$ is not a solution.

3. $y = 2x - 3$

a.

x	$y = 2x - 3$	(x, y)
-2	$y = 2(-2) - 3 = -7$	$(-2, -7)$
-1	$y = 2(-1) - 3 = -5$	$(-1, -5)$
0	$y = 2(0) - 3 = -5$	$(0, -3)$
1	$y = 2(1) - 3 = -1$	$(1, -1)$
2	$y = 2(2) - 3 = 1$	$(2, 1)$

b.

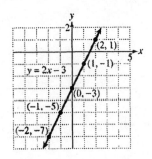

4. $y = \dfrac{1}{2}x + 1$

a.

x	$y = \frac{1}{2}x + 1$	(x, y)
-4	$y = \frac{1}{2}(-4) + 1 = -1$	$(-4, -1)$
-2	$y = \frac{1}{2}(-2) + 1 = 0$	$(-2, 0)$
0	$y = \frac{1}{2}(0) + 1 = 1$	$(0, 1)$
2	$y = \frac{1}{2}(2) + 1 = 2$	$(2, 2)$
4	$y = \frac{1}{2}(4) + 1 = 3$	$(4, 3)$

b.

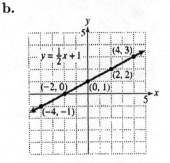

5. $y = x^2 - 3$

x	$y = x^2 - 3$	(x, y)
-3	$y = (-3)^2 - 3 = 6$	$(-3, 6)$
-2	$y = (-2)^2 - 3 = 1$	$(-2, 1)$
-1	$y = (-1)^2 - 3 = -2$	$(-1, -2)$
0	$y = 0^2 - 3 = -3$	$(0, -3)$
1	$y = 1^2 - 3 = -2$	$(1, -2)$
2	$y = 2^2 - 3 = 1$	$(2, 1)$
3	$y = 3^2 - 1 = 6$	$(3, 6)$

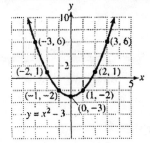

6. a.

x	$y = 5x - 41$	(x, y)
10	$y = 5(10) - 41 = 9$	$(10, 9)$
12	$y = 5(12) - 41 = 19$	$(12, 19)$
14	$y = 5(14) - 41 = 29$	$(14, 29)$
16	$y = 5(16) - 41 = 39$	$(16, 39)$

b. The equation models the data fairly well. The equation value vary from the data by 0.2% to 0.9%.

7. a. The graph crosses the x-axis at $(-2, 0)$, so the x-intercept is -2.

b. The graph crosses the y-axis at $(0, -4)$, so the y-intercept is -4.

8. a. The graph does not cross the x-axis, so there is no x-intercept.

b. The graph crosses the y-axis at $(0, 2)$, so the y-intercept is 2.

9. a. The graph crosses the x-axis at $(0, 0)$ (the origin), so the x-intercept is 0.

b. The graph also crosses the y-axis at $(0,0)$, so the y-intercept is 0.

In Exercises 10–13, checkpoints will vary.

10. $2x + y = 4$

x-intercept: y-intercept:

$$2x + 0 = 4 \qquad 2(0) + y = 4$$
$$2x = 4 \qquad\qquad y = 4$$
$$x = 2$$

x-intercept: $(2,0)$; y-intercept: $(0,4)$
Find one other point as a checkpoint. For example, substitute 1 for x.

$$2(1) + y = 4$$
$$2 + y = 4$$
$$y = 2$$

checkpoint: $(1,2)$
Draw a line through $(2,0), (0,4)$, and $(1,2)$.

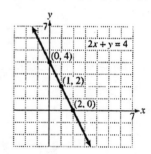

11. $3x - 2y = 12$

x-intercept: $(4,0)$
y-intercept: $(0,-6)$
checkpoint: $(6,3)$
Draw a line through $(4,0), (0,-6)$ and $(6,3)$.

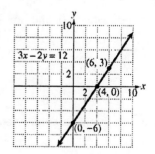

12. $3x = 6 - 2y$

x-intercept: $(2,0)$
y-intercept: $(0,3)$
checkpoint: $(4,-3)$
Draw a line through $(2,0), (0,3)$, and $(4,-3)$.

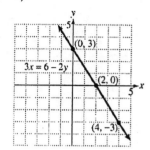

13. $3x - y = 0$

x-intercept: 0
y-intercept: 0
second point: $(1,3)$
checkpoint: $(-1,-3)$
Draw a line through $(0,0), (1,3)$, and $(-1,-3)$.

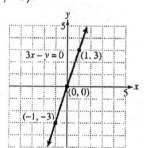

14. $x = 3$

Three ordered pairs are $(3,-2), (3,0)$, and $(3,2)$. The graph is a vertical line.

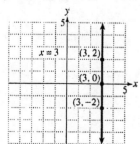

15. $y = -5$

Three ordered pairs are $(-2, -5), (0, -5)$, and $(2, 5)$. The graph is a horizontal line.

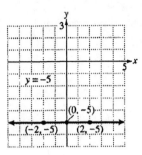

16. $y + 3 = 5$

$\quad\quad y = 2$

Three ordered pairs are $(-4, 2), (0, 2)$, and $(5, 2)$. The graph is a horizontal line.

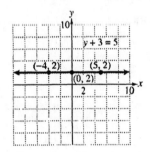

17. $2x = -8$

$\quad\quad x = -4$

Three ordered pairs are $(-4, -2), (-4, 0)$, and $(-4, 2)$. The graph is a vertical line.

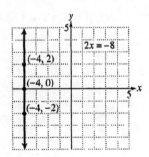

18. a. The minimum temperature occurred at 5 P.M. and was $-4°$F.

b. The maximum temperature occurred at 8 P.M. and was $16°$F.

c. The x-intercepts are 4 and 6. This indicates that at 4 P.M. and 6 P.M., the temperature was $0°$F.

d. The y-intercept is 12. This indicates that at noon the temperature was $12°$F.

e. This indicates that the temperature stayed the same, at $12°$F, from 9 P.M. until midnight.

19. $(3, 2)$ and $(5, 1)$

Let $(x_1, y_1) = (3, 2)$ and $(x_2, y_2) = (5, 1)$.

$$m = \frac{\text{Change in } y}{\text{Change in } x} = \frac{y_2 - y_1}{x_2 - x_2} = \frac{1 - 2}{5 - 3}$$

$$= -\frac{1}{2}$$

The slope is $-\frac{1}{2}$. Since the slope is negative, the line falls.

20. $(-1, 2)$ and $(-3, -4)$

$$m = \frac{-4 - 2}{-3 - (-1)} = \frac{-6}{-2} = 3$$

Since the slope is positive, the line rises.

21. $(-3, 4)$ and $(6, 4)$

$$m = \frac{4 - 4}{6 - (-3)} = \frac{0}{9} = 0$$

Since the slope is 0, the line is horizontal.

22. $(5, 3)$ and $(5, -3)$

$$m = \frac{-3 - 3}{5 - 5} = \frac{-6}{0}; \text{ undefined}$$

Since the slope is undefined, the line is vertical.

23. Line through $(-3, -2)$ and $(2, 1)$:

$$m = \frac{1 - (-2)}{2 - (-3)} = \frac{3}{5}$$

24. Line through $(-2, 3)$ and $(-2, -3)$:

The line is vertical, so its slope is undefined.

25. Line through $(-4, -1)$ and $(2, -3)$:

$$m = \frac{-3 - (-1)}{2 - (-4)} = \frac{-2}{6} = -\frac{1}{3}$$

26. Line through $(-2, 2)$ and $(3, 2)$:

The line is horizontal, so its slope is 0.

27. Line through $(-1, -3)$ and $(2, -8)$:

$$m = \frac{-8 - (-3)}{2 - (-1)} = \frac{-5}{3} = -\frac{5}{3}$$

Line through $(8, -7)$ and $(9, 10)$:

$$m = \frac{10 - (-7)}{9 - 8} = \frac{17}{1} = 17$$

Since their slopes are not equal, the lines are not parallel.

28. Line through $(5, 4)$ and $(9, 7)$:

$$m = \frac{7 - 4}{9 - 5} = \frac{3}{4}$$

Line through $(-6, 0)$ and $(-2, 3)$:

$$m = \frac{3 - 0}{-2 - (-6)} = \frac{3}{4}$$

Since their slopes are equal, the lines are parallel.

29. a. Line through $(1974, 350)$ and $(2000, 1026)$:

$$m = \frac{1026 - 350}{2000 - 1974} = \frac{676}{26} = 26$$

The number of lawyers increased at a rate of 26 thousand each year from 1974 to 2000.

b. Line through $(1950, 200)$ and $(1974, 350)$:

$$m = \frac{350 - 200}{1974 - 1950} = \frac{150}{24} = 6.25$$

The number of lawyers increased at a rate of 6.25 thousand each year from 1950 to 1974.

30. $y = 5x - 7$

$y = 5x + (-7)$

The slope is the x-coefficient, which is 5. The y-intercept is the constant term, which is -7.

31. $y = 6 - 4x$

$y = -4x + 6$

$m = -4$; y-intercept $= 6$

32. $y = 3$

$m = 0$; y-intercept $= 3$

33. $2x + 3y = 6$

$$3y = -2x + 6$$

$$y = \frac{-2x + 6}{3}$$

$$y = -\frac{2}{3}x + 2$$

$m = -\frac{2}{3}$; y-intercept $= 2$

34. $y = 2x - 4$

slope $= 2 = \frac{2}{1}$; y-intercept $= -4$

Plot $(0, -4)$ on the y-axis. From this point, move 2 units *up* (because 2 is positive) and 1 unit to the *right* to reach the point $(1, -2)$. Draw a line through $(0, -4)$ and $(1, -2)$.

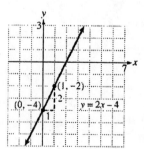

35. $y = \dfrac{1}{2}x - 1$

slope $= \frac{1}{2}$; y-intercept $= -1$

Plot $(0, -1)$. From the point, move 1 unit *up* and 2 units to the *right* to reach the point $(2, 0)$. Draw a line through $(0, -1)$ and $(2, 0)$.

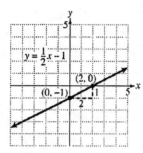

36. $y = -\dfrac{2}{3}x + 5$

slope $= -\frac{2}{3} = \frac{-2}{3}$; y-intercept $= 5$

Plot $(0, 5)$. Move 2 units *down* (because -2 is negative) and 3 units to the *right* to reach the point $(3, 3)$. Draw a line through $(0, 5)$ and $(3, 3)$.

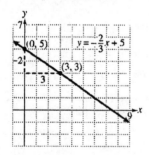

37. $y - 2x = 0$

$\qquad y = 2x$

slope $= 2 = \frac{2}{1}$; y-intercept $= 0$

Plot $(0, 0)$ (the origin). Move 2 units *up* and 1 unit to the *right* to reach the point $(1, 2)$.

Draw a line through $(0, 0)$ and $(1, 2)$.

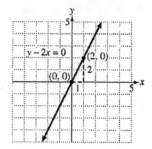

38. $\dfrac{1}{3}x + y = 2$

$\qquad y = -\dfrac{1}{3}x + 2$

slope $= -\frac{1}{3} = \frac{-1}{3}$; y-intercept $= 2$

Plot $(0, 2)$. Move 1 unit *down* and 3 units to the *right* to reach the point $(3, 1)$. Draw line through $(0, 2)$ and $(3, 1)$.

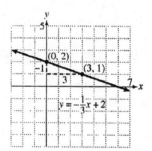

39. $\quad y = -\dfrac{1}{2}x + 4 \qquad\qquad y = -\dfrac{1}{2}x - 1$

$\quad$ slope $= -\frac{1}{2} = \frac{-1}{2} \qquad$ slope $= -\frac{1}{2} = \frac{-1}{2}$

$\quad$ y-intercept $= 4 \qquad\quad$ slope $= -1$

Graph each line using its slope and y-intercept.

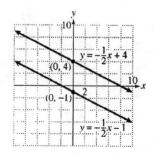

Yes, they are parallel since both lines have slope of $-\frac{1}{2}$.

40. a. The smallest y-intercept is 25. This indicates that in 1990 the average age of U.S. Hispanics was 25.

b. Line through $(0, 35)$ and $(10, 38)$:

$$m = \frac{38 - 35}{10 - 0} = \frac{3}{10} = 0.3$$

This means that the average age for U.S. whites increased at a rate of about 0.3 each year from 1990 to 2000.

c. $y = 0.3x + 35$

d. The year 2010 corresponds to $x = 20$. If $x = 20$,

$$y = 0.3(20) + 35 = 41.$$

According to the model, the average age for U.S. whites in 2010 will be 41 years old.

41. Slope $= 6$, passing through $(-4, 7)$
$y - 7 = 6[x - (-4)]$
point-slope form; $y - 7 = 6(x + 4)$
$y - 7 = 6x + 24$
slope-intercept form: $y = 6x + 31$

42. Passing through $(3, 4)$ and $(2, 1)$

$$m = \frac{1 - 4}{2 - 3} = \frac{-3}{-1} = 3$$

$$y - y_1 = m(x - x_1)$$

Using the point $(3, 4)$, the point-slope equation is

$$y - 4 = 3(x - 3).$$

Rewrite this equation in slope-intercept form.

$$y - 4 = 3x - 9$$
$$y = 3x - 5$$

43. $3x + y - 9 = 0$
$$y = -3x + 9$$

Since the line we are concerned with is parallel to this line, we know it will have slope $m = -3$. We are given that it passes through $(4, -7)$.

point-slope form:

$$y - y_1 = m(x - x_1)$$
$$y - (-7) = -3(x - 4)$$
$$y + 7 = -3(x - 4)$$

slope-intercept form:

$$y + 7 = -3(x - 4)$$
$$y + 7 = -3x + 12$$
$$y = -3x + 5$$

44. The line is perpendicular to $y = \frac{1}{3}x + 4$, so the slope is -3. We are given that it passes through $(-2, 6)$.

point-slope form:

$$y - y_1 = m(x - x_1)$$
$$y - 6 = -3(x - (-2))$$
$$y - 6 = -3(x + 2)$$

slope-intercept form:

$$y - 6 = -3(x + 2)$$
$$y - 6 = -3x - 6$$
$$y = -3x$$

45. Line through $(0, 16)$ and $(30, 12.1)$

a. $m = \dfrac{12.1 - 16}{30 - 0} = \dfrac{-3.9}{30} = -0.13$

Using the point $(0, 16)$, the point slope-form is

$$y - 16 = -0.13(x - 0)$$
$$\text{or} \quad y - 16 = -0.13x.$$

b. $y = -0.13x + 16$

c. The year 1970 corresponds to $x = 70$ and the year 1980 corresponds to $x = 80$. If $x = 70$,

$$y = -0.13(70) + 16 = 6.9.$$

If $x = 80$,

$$y = -0.13(80) + 16 = 5.6.$$

According to the equation, the average surfboard length was 6.9 feet in 1970 and 5.6 feet in 1980.

d. The year 2000 corresponds to $x = 100$. If $x = 100$,

$$y = -0.13(100) + 16 = 3.$$

According to the equation, the average surfboard length in 2000 was 3 feet. It does not seem realistic that surfboards would be this short.

Chapter 3 Test

1. $4x - 2y = 10$

$(0, -5)$:
$$4(0) - 2(-5) \stackrel{?}{=} 10$$
$$0 + 10 \stackrel{?}{=} 10$$
$$10 = 10 \text{ true}$$

$(0, -5)$ is a solution.

$(-2, 1)$:
$$4(-2) - 2(1) \stackrel{?}{=} 10$$
$$-8 - 2 \stackrel{?}{=} 10$$
$$-10 = 10 \text{ false}$$

$(-2, 1)$ is not a solution.

$(4, 3)$:
$$4(4) - 2(3) \stackrel{?}{=} 10$$
$$16 - 6 \stackrel{?}{=} 10$$
$$10 = 10 \text{ true}$$

$(4, 3)$ is a solution.

2. $y = 3x + 1$

x	$y = 3x + 1$	(x, y)
-2	$y = 3(-2) + 1 = -5$	$(-2, -5)$
-1	$y = 3(-1) + 1 = -2$	$(-1, -2)$
0	$y = 3(0) + 1 = 1$	$(0, 1)$
1	$y = 3(1) + 1 = 4$	$(1, 4)$
2	$y = 3(2) + 1 = 7$	$(2, 7)$

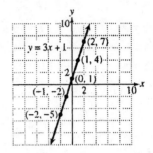

3. $y = x^2 - 1$

x	$y = x^2 - 1$	(x, y)
-3	$y = (-3)^2 - 1 = 8$	$(-3, 8)$
-2	$y = (-2)^2 - 1 = 3$	$(-2, 3)$
-1	$y = (-1)^2 - 1 = 0$	$(-1, 0)$
0	$y = 0^2 - 1 = -1$	$(0, -1)$
1	$y = 1^2 - 1 = 0$	$(1, 0)$
2	$y = 2^2 - 1 = 3$	$(2, 3)$
3	$y = 3^2 - 1 = 8$	$(3, 8)$

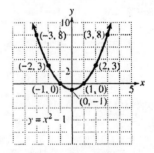

4. a. The graph crosses the x-axis at $(2, 0)$, so the x-intercept is 2.

b. The graph crosses the y-axis at $(0, -3)$, so the y-intercept is -3.

5. $4x - 2y = -8$

x-intercept: y-intercept:

$4x - 2(0) = -8$ $4(0) - 2y = -8$
$4x = -8$ ${-2y} = -8$
$x = -2$ $y = 4$

Find one other point as a checkpoint. For example, substitute -4 for x.

$$4(-4) - 2y = -8$$
$$-16 - 2y = -8$$
$$-2y = -8$$
$$y = -4$$

checkpoint: $(-4, -4)$
Draw a line through $(-2, 0), (0, 4)$ and $(-4, -4)$.

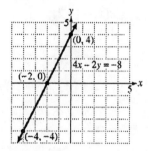

6. $y = 4$

Three ordered pairs are $(-2, 4), (0, 4)$, and $(2, 4)$. The graph is a horizontal line.

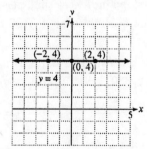

7. $(-3, 4)$ and $(-5, -2)$

$$m = \frac{-2 - 4}{-5 - (-3)} = \frac{-6}{-2} = 3$$

The slope is 3. Since the slope is positive, the line rises.

8. $(6, -1)$ and $(6, 3)$

$$m = \frac{3 - (-1)}{6 - 6} = \frac{4}{0}; \text{ undefined}$$

Since the slope is undefined, the line is vertical.

9. Line through $(-1, -2)$ and $(1, 1)$:

$$m = \frac{1 - (-2)}{1 - (-1)}$$
$$= \frac{3}{2}$$

10. Line through $(2, 4)$ and $(6, 1)$:

$$m = \frac{1 - 4}{6 - 2} = \frac{-3}{4} = -\frac{3}{4}$$

Line through $(-3, 1)$ and $(1, -2)$:

$$m = \frac{-2 - 1}{1 - (-3)} = \frac{-3}{4} = -\frac{3}{4}$$

Since the slopes are equal, the lines are parallel.

11. $y = -x + 10$
$y = -1x + 10$

The slope is the coefficient of x, which is -1. The y-intercept is the constant term, which is 10.

12. $2x + y = 6$
$y = -2x + 6$
$m = -2; y\text{-intercept} = 6$

13. $y = \dfrac{2}{3}x - 1$

slope $= \dfrac{2}{3}$; y-intercept $= -1$

Plot $(0, -1)$. From this point, move 2 units *up* and 3 units to the *right* to reach the point $(3, 1)$. Draw a line through $(0, -1)$ and $(3, 1)$.

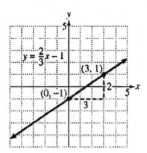

14. $y = -2x + 3$

slope $= -2 = \dfrac{-2}{1} = -2$; y-intercept $= 3$

Plot $(0, 3)$. Move 2 units *down* and 1 unit to the right to reach the point $(1, 1)$. Draw a line through $(0, 3)$ and $(1, 1)$.

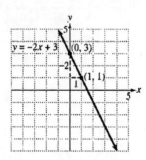

15. Slope $= -2$; passing through $(-1, 4)$
$y - 4 = -2[x - (-1)]$
point-slope form: $y - 4 = -2(x + 1)$
$y - 4 = -2x - 2$
slope-intercept form: $y = -2x + 2$

16. Passing through $(2, 1)$ and $(-1, -8)$
$$m = \frac{-8 - 1}{-1 - 2} = \frac{-9}{-3} = 3$$

Using the point $(2, 1)$, the point-slope equation is

$$y - 1 = 3(x - 2).$$

Rewrite this equation in slope-intercept form

$$y - 1 = 3x - 6$$
$$y = 3x - 5.$$

17. The line is perpendicular to $y = -\frac{1}{2}x - 4$, so the slope is 2. We are given that it passes through $(-2, 3)$.

point-slope form:

$$y - y_1 = m(x - x_1)$$
$$y - 3 = 2(x - (-2))$$
$$y - 3 = 2(x + 2)$$

slope-intercept form:

$$y - 3 = 2(x + 2)$$
$$y - 3 = 2x + 4$$
$$y = 2x + 7$$

18. Line through $(1970, 2100)$ and $(2000, 5280)$:

$$m = \frac{5280 - 2100}{2000 - 1970} = \frac{3180}{30} = 106$$

This slope indicates that per-pupil spending increases by about \$106 each year.

19. a. First, find the slope using the points $(0, 320)$ and $(5, 530)$.
$$m = \frac{530 - 320}{5 - 0} = \frac{210}{5} = 42$$
point-slope form
$$y - y_1 = m(x - x_1)$$
$$y - 320 = 42(x - 0)$$

b. $y - 320 = 42x$
$$y = 42x + 320$$

c. To predict the national average for one-way fares in 2008, let $x = 2008 - 1995 = 13$.

$$f(13) = 42(13) + 320$$
$$= 546 + 320 = 866$$

If the current trend continues, the national average for one-way fares in 2008 will be $866.

Cumulative Review Exercises

(Chapters 1-3)

1. $\dfrac{10 - (-6)}{3^2 - (4 - 3)} = \dfrac{10 + 6}{9 - 1} = \dfrac{16}{8} = 2$

2. $6 - 2[3(x - 1) + 4] = 6 - 2(3x - 3 + 4)$
$$= 6 - 2(3x + 1)$$
$$= 6 - 6x - 2$$
$$= 4 - 6x$$

3. The only irrational number in the given set is $\sqrt{5}$.

4.
$$6(2x - 1) - 6 = 11x + 7$$
$$12x - 6 - 6 = 11x + 7$$
$$12x - 12 = 11x + 7$$
$$12x - 12 - 11x = 11x + 7 - 11x$$
$$x - 12 = 7$$
$$x - 12 + 12 = 7 + 12$$
$$x = 19$$

The solution is 19.

5.
$$x - \frac{3}{4} = \frac{1}{2}$$
$$x - \frac{3}{4} + \frac{3}{4} = \frac{1}{2} + \frac{3}{4}$$
$$x = \frac{2}{4} + \frac{3}{4} = \frac{5}{4}$$

The solution is $\frac{5}{4}$.

6. $y = mx + b$ for x

$$y = mx + b$$
$$y - b = mx + b - b$$
$$y - b = mx$$
$$\frac{y - b}{m} = \frac{mx}{m}$$
$$\frac{y - b}{m} = x \quad \text{or} \quad x = \frac{y - b}{m}$$

7. $A = PB$; $A = 120$; $P = 15\% = 0.15$

$$A = PB$$
$$120 = 0.15 \cdot B$$
$$\frac{120}{0.15} = \frac{0.15B}{0.15}$$
$$800 = B$$

120 is 15% of 800.

8. $y = 4.5x - 46.7$; $y = 133.3$

$$133.3 = 4.5x - 46.7$$
$$133.3 + 46.7 = 4.5x - 46.7 + 46.7$$
$$180 = 4.5x$$
$$\frac{180}{4.5} = \frac{4.5x}{4.5}$$
$$40 = x$$

The car is traveling 40 miles per hour.

9.
$$2 - 6x \geq 2(5 - x)$$
$$2 - 6x \geq 10 - 2x$$
$$2 - 6x + 2x \geq 10 - 2x + 2x$$
$$2 - 4x \geq 10$$
$$2 - 4x - 2 \geq 10 - 2$$
$$-4x \geq 8$$
$$\frac{-4x}{-4} \leq \frac{8}{-4}$$
$$x \leq -2$$

$$\{x | x \leq -2\}$$

10.
$$6(2 - x) > 12$$
$$12 - 6x > 12$$
$$12 - 6x - 12 > 12 - 12$$
$$-6x > 0$$
$$\frac{-6x}{-6} < \frac{0}{-6}$$
$$x < 0$$

$$\{x \mid x < 0\}$$

11. $-x^2 - 10x; \ x = -3$
$$-x^2 - 10x = (-3)^2 - 10(-3)$$
$$= 9 + 30 = 39$$

12. $-2000 < -3;$ -2000 is to be left of -3 on the number line, so -2000 is less than -3.

13. $-4 + (-11) + 21 = -15 + 21 = 6$

The temperature at noon was 6°F.

14. $D = 4x + 30; \ D = 150$
$$150 = 4x + 30$$
$$120 = 4x$$
$$30 = x$$

According to the formula, the average debt will be $150 thousand 30 years after 1985. Since $1985 + 30 = 2015$, this will happen in the year 2015.

15. Let $\quad w =$ the width of the rectangle. Then $2w + 14 =$ the length.
$$2w + 2(2w + 14) = 346$$
$$2w + 4w + 28 = 346$$
$$6w + 28 = 346$$
$$6w = 318$$
$$w = 53$$

If $w = 53$, then $2w + 14 = 2(53) + 14 = 120$. The width is 53 meters and the length is 120 meters.

16. Let $x =$ the person's weight before the weight loss.
$$x - 0.10x = 180$$
$$0.90 = 180$$
$$\frac{0.90x}{0.90} = \frac{180}{0.90}$$
$$x = 200$$

The person's weight was 200 pounds.

17. Let $x =$ the number of hours the plumber worked.
$$18 + 35x = 228$$
$$35x = 210$$
$$x = 6$$

The plumber worked 6 hours.

18. Let $\quad x =$ the measure of the first angle.
Then $x + 20 =$ the measure of the second angle.
$\qquad 2x =$ the measure of the third angle.

$$x + (x + 20) + 2x = 180$$
$$4x + 20 = 180$$
$$4x = 160$$
$$x = 40$$

Measure of first angle $= x = 40°$
Measure of second angle $= x + 20 = 60°$
Measure of third angle $= 2x = 80°$

19. $2x - y = 4$

x-intercept: 2

y-intercept: -4

checkpoint: $(4, 4)$

Draw a line through $(2, 0), (0, -4),$ and $(4, 4)$.

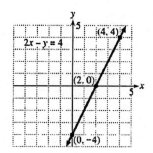

20. $y = -4x + 3$

slope $= -4 = \frac{-4}{1}$; y-intercept $= 3$

Plot $(0, 3)$. Move 4 units *down* and 1 unit to the *right* to reach the point $(3, -1)$. Draw a line through $(0, 3)$ and $(1, -1)$.

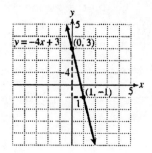

SYSTEMS OF LINEAR EQUATIONS

Solving Systems of Linear Equations by Graphing

4.1 CHECK POINTS

CHECK POINT 1

$$2x - 3y = -4$$
$$2x + y = 4$$

a. $(1, 2)$

To determine if $(1, 2)$ is a solution of the system, replace x with 1 and y with 2 in both equations.

$$2x - 3y = -4 \qquad\qquad 2x + y = 4$$
$$2(1) - 3(2) \overset{?}{=} -4 \qquad 2(1) + 2 \overset{?}{=} 4$$
$$2 - 6 \overset{?}{=} -4 \qquad\qquad 2 + 2 \overset{?}{=} 4$$
$$-4 = -4 \text{ true} \qquad\qquad 4 = 4 \text{ true}$$

The ordered pair $(1, 2)$ satisfies both equations, so it is a solution of the system.

b. $(7, 6)$

$$2x - 3y = -4 \qquad\qquad 2x + y = 4$$
$$2(7) - 3(6) \overset{?}{=} -4 \qquad 2(7) + 6 \overset{?}{=} 4$$
$$14 - 18 \overset{?}{=} -4 \qquad\qquad 14 + 6 \overset{?}{=} 4$$
$$-4 = -4 \text{ true} \qquad\qquad 20 = 4 \text{ false}$$

The ordered pair $(7, 6)$ satisfies the first equation of the system, but not the second one. Because it fails to satisfy *both* equations, $(7, 6)$ is not a solution of the system.

CHECK POINT 2

$$2x + y = 6$$
$$2x - y = -2$$

Step 1 Graph the first equation.
Use intercepts to graph $2x + y = 6$.

x-intercept:	y-intercept:
Set $y = 0$.	Set $x = 0$.
$2x + 0 = 6$	$2 \cdot 0 + y = 6$
$2x = 6$	$y = 6$
$x = 3$	

The x-intercept is 3, so the line passes through $(3, 0)$. The y-intercept is 6, so the graph passes through $(0, 6)$.

Step 2 Graph the second equation on the same axes.
Use intercepts to graph $2x - y = -2$.

x-intercept:	y-intercept:
$2x - 0 = -2$	$2 \cdot 0 - y = -2$
$2x = -2$	$-y = -2$
$x = -1$	$y = 2$

The x-intercept is -1, so the line passes through $(-1, 0)$. The y-intercept is $(0, 2)$, so the line passes through $(0, 2)$.

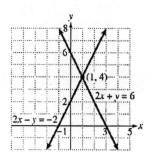

Step 3 Determine the coordinates of the intersection point.

From the graph, it appears that the lines intersect at $(1, 4)$, so the apparent solution of the system is $(1, 4)$.

Step 4 Check the solution in both equations.

$$2x + y = 6 \qquad\qquad 2x - y = -2$$
$$2(1) + 4 \overset{?}{=} 6 \qquad\quad 2(1) - 4 \overset{?}{=} -2$$
$$2 + 4 \overset{?}{=} 6 \qquad\qquad 2 - 4 \overset{?}{=} -2$$
$$6 = 6 \text{ true} \qquad\quad -2 = -2 \text{ true}$$

Because both equations are satisfied $(1, 4)$ is the solution of the system.

CHECK POINT 3

$$y = -x + 6$$
$$y = 3x - 6$$

Step 1 Graph $y = -x + 6$ using the slope, $-1 = \frac{-1}{1}$, and y-intercept, 6. Start at $(0, 6)$ and move 1 unit down and 1 unit to the right to reach the point $(1, 5)$. Draw a line through $(0, 6)$ and $(1, 5)$.

Step 2 Graph $y = 3x - 6$ on the same axes, using the slope, $3 = \frac{3}{1}$, and the y-intercept, -6. Start at $(0, -6)$ and move 3 units up and 1 unit to the right to reach the point $(1, -3)$. Draw a line through $(0, -6)$ and $(1, -3)$.

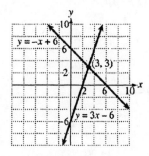

Step 3 From the graph, it appears that the lines intersect at $(3, 3)$.

Step 4 Check the solution in both equations.

$$y = -x + 6 \qquad\qquad y = 3x - 6$$
$$3 \overset{?}{=} -3 + 6 \qquad\quad 3 \overset{?}{=} 3 \cdot 3 - 6$$
$$3 = 3 \text{ true} \qquad\qquad 3 \overset{?}{=} 9 - 6$$
$$\qquad\qquad\qquad\qquad 3 = 3 \text{ true}$$

Because both equations are satisfied, $(3, 3)$ is the solution.

CHECK POINT 4

$$y = 3x - 2$$
$$y = 3x + 1$$

Graph $y = 3x - 2$ using its slope, 3, and y-intercept, -2. Graph $y = 3x + 1$ on the same axes using its slope, 3, and y-intercept, 1.

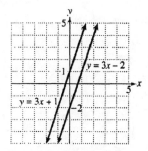

Because the two lines have the same slope, but different y-intercepts, they are parallel. The system is inconsistent and has no solution.

CHECK POINT 5

$$x + y = 3$$
$$2x + 2y = 6$$

Use intercepts to graph each equation.

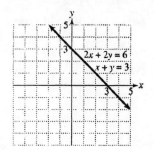

$x + y = 3$

x-intercept: 3, y-intercept: 3

$2x + 2y = 6$

x-intercept: 3, y-intercept: 3

Both lines have the same x-intercept, 3, and the same y-intercept, 3. Thus, the graphs of the two equations are the same line, and the equations have the same equations. Because there are infinitely many points on this line, the system has infinitely many solutions.

EXERCISE SET 4.1

1. $(2, 3)$

$$x + 3y = 11$$
$$2 + 3(3) \overset{?}{=} 11$$
$$2 + 9 \overset{?}{=} 11$$
$$11 = 11 \text{ true}$$

$$x - 5y = -13$$
$$2 - 5(3) \overset{?}{=} -13$$
$$2 - 15 \overset{?}{=} -13$$
$$-13 = -13 \text{ true}$$

Since the ordered pair $(2, 3)$ satisfies both equations, it is solution of the given system of equations.

3. $(-3, -1)$

$$5x - 11y = -4$$
$$5(-3) - 11(-1) \overset{?}{=} -4$$
$$-15 + 11 \overset{?}{=} -4$$
$$-4 = -4 \text{ true}$$

$$6x - 8y = -10$$
$$6(-3) - 8(-1) \overset{?}{=} -10$$
$$-18 + 8 \overset{?}{=} -10$$
$$-10 = -10 \text{ true}$$

$(-3, -1)$ is a solution of the given system.

5. $(2, 5)$

$$2x + 3y = 17$$
$$2(2) + 3(5) \overset{?}{=} 17$$
$$4 + 15 \overset{?}{=} 17$$
$$19 = 17 \text{ false}$$

$$x + 4y = 16$$
$$2 + 4(5) \overset{?}{=} 16$$
$$2 + 20 \overset{?}{=} 16$$
$$22 = 16 \text{ false}$$

Since $(2, 5)$ fails to satisfy either equation, it is not a solution of the given system. *Note:* Since $(2, 5)$ does not satisfy the first equation, it is not necessary to test it in the second one.

7. $\left(\frac{1}{3}, 1\right)$

$$6x - 9y = -7$$
$$6\left(\frac{1}{3}\right) - 9(1) \overset{?}{=} -7$$
$$2 - 9 \overset{?}{=} -7$$
$$-7 = -7 \text{ true}$$

$$9x + 5y = 8$$
$$9\left(\frac{1}{3}\right) + 5(1) \overset{?}{=} 8$$
$$3 + 5 \overset{?}{=} 8$$
$$8 = 8 \text{ true}$$

$(\frac{1}{3}, 1)$ is a solution of the given system.

9. $(8, 5)$

$$5x - 4y = 20$$
$$5(8) - 4(5) \overset{?}{=} 20$$
$$40 - 20 \overset{?}{=} 20$$
$$20 = 20 \text{ true}$$

$$3y = 2x + 1$$
$$3(5) \overset{?}{=} 2(8) + 1$$
$$15 \overset{?}{=} 16 + 1$$
$$15 = 17 \text{ false}$$

$(8, 5)$ fails to satisfy *both* equations; it is not a solution of the given system.

11. $x + y = 6$
$\quad\;\; x - y = 2$

Graph both equations on the same axes.

$x + y = 6$:

x-intercept $= 6$; y-intercept $= 6$

$x - y = 2$:

x-intercept $= 2$; y-intercept $= -2$

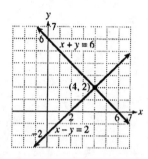

The lines appear to intersect at $(4, 2)$. Check this solution in both equations of the system.

$x + y = 6$	$x - y = 2$
$4 + 2 \overset{?}{=} 6$	$4 - 2 \overset{?}{=} 2$
$6 = 6$ true	$2 = 2$ true

Because both equations are satisfied, $(4, 2)$ is the solution of the system.

In Exercises 13–41, all apparent solutions found from the graphs should be checked in both equations of the given system, as illustrated in the solution for Exercise 1. The checks will not be shown here.

13. $x + y = 1$
$\quad\;\; y - x = 3$

Graph both equations on the same axes.

$x + y = 1$:

x-intercept $= 1$; y-intercept $= 1$

$y - x = 3$

x-intercept $= -3$; y-intercept $= 3$

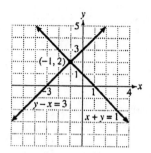

The lines intercept at $(-1, 2)$. $(-1, 2)$ is the solution of the system.

15. $2x - 3y = 6$
$\quad\;\; 4x + 3y = 12$

Graph both equations.

$2x - 3y = 6$:

x-intercept $= 3$; y-intercept $= -2$

$4x + 3y = 12$:

x-intercept $= 3$; y-intercept $= 4$

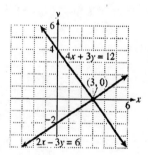

Solution: $(3, 0)$

17. $4x + y = 4$
    $3x - y = 3$

Graph both equations.

x-intercept = 1; y-intercept = 4

$3x - y = 3$:

x-intercept = 1; y-intercept = -3

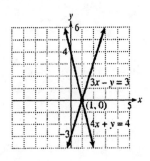

Solution: $(1, 0)$

19. $y = x + 5$
    $y = -x + 3$

Graph both equations.

$y = x + 5$:

slope = 1; y-intercept = 5

$y = -x + 3$:

slope = -1; y-intercept = 3

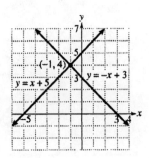

Solution: $(-1, 4)$

21. $y = 2x$
    $y = -x + 6$

Graph both equations.

$y = 2x$:

slope = 2; y-intercept = 0

$y = -x + 6$:

slope = -1; y-intercept = 6

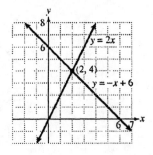

Solution: $(2, 4)$

23. $y = -2x + 3$
    $y = -x + 1$

Graph both equations.

$y = -2x + 3$:

slope = -2; y-intercept = 3

$y = -x + 1$:

slope = -1; y-intercept = 1

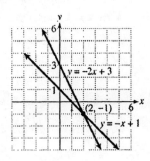

Solution: $(2, -1)$

25. $y = 2x - 1$
$y = 2x + 1$

Graph both equations.

$y = 2x - 1$:

slope $= 2$; y-intercept $= -1$

$y = 2x + 1$:

slope $= 2$; y-intercept $= 1$

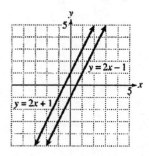

The two lines are parallel. (Note that they have the same slope but different y-intercepts.) The system as no solution.

27. $x + y = 4$
$x = -2$

Graph each equation.

$x + y = 4$

x-intercept $= 4$; y-intercept $= 4$

$x = -2$

vertical line with x-intercept -2

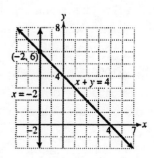

Solution: $(-2, 6)$

29. $x - 2y = 4$
$2x - 4y = 8$

Graph each equation.

$x - 2y = 4$

x-intercept $= 4$; y-intercept $= -2$

$2x - 4y = 8$

x-intercept $= 4$; y-intercept $= -2$

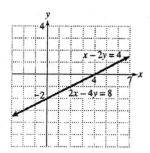

The graph of the two equations are the same line. (Note that they have the same slope and same y-intercept.)
Because the lines coincide, the system has infinitely many solutions.

31. $y = 2x - 1$
$x - 2y = -4$

Graph both lines.

$y = 2x - 1$

slope $= 2$; y-intercept $= -1$

$x - 2y = -4$

x-intercept $= -4$; y-intercept $= 2$

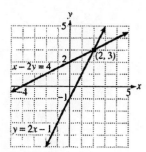

Solution: $(2, 3)$

33. $x + y = 5$
$2x + 2y = 12$

Graph both lines.

$x + y = 5$

x-intercept $= 5$; y-intercept $= 5$

$2x + 2y = 12$

x-intercept $= 6$; y-intercept $= 6$

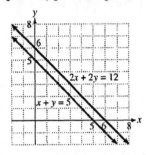

The lines are parallel, so the system has no solution.

35. $x - y = 0$
$y = x$

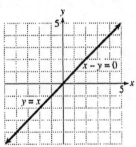

Because the lines coincide, the system has an infinite number of solutions.

37. $x = 2$
$y = 4$

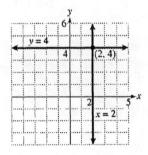

The vertical and horizontal line intersect at $(2, 4)$.

Solution: $(2, 4)$

39. $x = 2$
$x = -1$

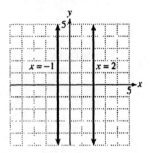

The two vertical lines are parallel, so the system has no solution.

41. $y = 0$
$y = 4$

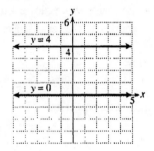

The two horizontal lines are parallel, so the system has no solution.

43. a. The intersection point is approximately $(1996, 40)$. This means that mothers 30 years old and older in Massachusetts had about 40 thousand $(40,000)$ births in 1996.

b. Since 1996, there have been more births in Massachusetts to mothers 30 years old and older than to those under 30 years old.

For Exercises 45–51, answers may vary.

53. Statement c is true.
If two lines have two points in common, they must coincide (be the same line), so they will have equal slopes and equal y-intercepts.

55. Answers may vary.

57. Answers will vary according to the exercises chosen.

59. $y = -x + 5$
$y = x - 7$

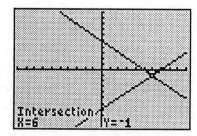

Solution: $(6, -1)$

61. $2x - 3y = 6$
$4x + 3y = 12$

In order to enter the equations into a graphing calculator, each of them must be solved for y.

$$2x - 3y = 6$$
$$-3y = -2x + 6$$
$$\frac{-3y}{-3} = \frac{-2x + 6}{-3}$$
$$y = \frac{2}{3}x - 2$$

$$4x + 3y = 12$$
$$3y = -4x + 12$$
$$\frac{3y}{3} = \frac{-4x + 12}{3}$$
$$y = -\frac{4}{3}x + 4$$

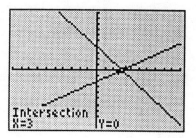

Solution: $(3, 0)$

63. $2x - 3y = 7$
$3x + 5y = 1$

Solve each equation for y.

$$2x - 3y = 7$$
$$-3y = -2x + 7$$
$$\frac{-3y}{-3} = \frac{-2x + 7}{-3}$$
$$y = \frac{2}{3}x - \frac{7}{3}$$

$$3x + 5y = 1$$
$$5y = -3x + 1$$
$$\frac{5y}{5} = \frac{-3x + 1}{5}$$
$$y = -\frac{3}{5}x + \frac{1}{5}$$

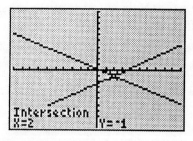

Solution: $(2, -1)$

65. $y = -\frac{1}{2}x + 2$

$y = \frac{3}{4}x + 7$

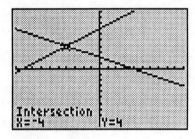

Intersection
X=-4   Y=4

Solution: $(-4, 4)$

Review Exercises

66. $-3 - (-9) = -12$

67. $-3 - (-9) = -3 + 9 = 6$

68. $-3(-9) = 27$

Solving Systems of Linear Equations by the Substitution Method

4.2 CHECK POINTS

CHECK POINT 1

$$y = 5x - 13$$
$$2x + 3y = 12$$

Step 1 Solve either of the equations for one variable in terms of the other.
This step has already been done. The first equation has y solved in terms of x.

Step 2 Substitute the expression from step 1 into the other equation.

$$2x + 3(5x - 13) = 12$$

The variable y has been eliminated.

Step 3 Solve the resulting equation containing one variable.

$$2x + 15x - 39 = 12$$
$$17x - 39 = 12$$
$$17x = 51$$
$$x = 3$$

Step 4 Back-substitute the obtained value into the equation from Step 1.

$$y = 5x - 13$$
$$y = 5(3) - 13$$
$$y = 15 - 13 = 2$$

With $x = 3$ and $y = 2$, the proposed solution is $(3, 2)$.

Step 5 Check the proposed solution in both of the system's given equations.

$$
\begin{array}{ll}
y = 5x - 13 & 2x + 3y = 12 \\
2 \overset{?}{=} 5(3) - 13 & 2(3) + 3(2) \overset{?}{=} 12 \\
2 \overset{?}{=} 15 - 13 & 6 + 6 \overset{?}{=} 12 \\
2 = 2 \text{ true} & 12 = 12
\end{array}
$$

The ordered pair $(3, 2)$ satisfies both equations, so the system's solution is $(3, 2)$.

CHECK POINT 2

$$3x + 2y = -1$$
$$x - y = 3$$

Step 1 Solve the second equation for x.

$$x - y = 3$$
$$x = y + 3$$

Step 2 Substitute $y + 3$ for x in the first equation.

$$3x + 2y = -1$$
$$3(y + 3) + 2y = -1$$

Step 3 Solve the resulting equation.

$$3(y + 3) + 2y = -1$$
$$3y + 9 + 2y = -1$$
$$5y + 9 = -1$$
$$5y = -10$$
$$y = -2$$

Step 4 Back-substitute -2 for y in $3x + 2y = -1$ and solve for x.

$$3x + 2y = -1$$
$$3x + 2(-2) = -1$$
$$3x - 4 = -1$$
$$3x = 3$$
$$x = 1$$

With $x = 1$ and $y = -2$, the proposed solution is $(1, -2)$.

Step 5 Substitute 1 for x and -2 for y in both equations of the original system to verify that the solution is $(1, -2)$.

CHECK POINT 3

$$3x + y = -5$$
$$y = -3x + 3$$

The variable y is isolated in the second equation. Substitute $-3x + 3$ for y in the first equation.

$$3x + y = -5$$
$$3x + (-3x + 3) = -5$$
$$3x - 3x - 3 = -5$$
$$-3 = -5 \text{ false}$$

The false statement $-3 = -5$ indicates that the system is inconsistent and has no solution.

CHECK POINT 4

$$y = 3x - 4$$
$$9x - 3y = 12$$

The variable y is isolated in the first equation. Substitute $3x - 4$ for y in the second equation.

$$9x - 3y = 12$$
$$9x - 3(3x - 4) = 12$$
$$9x - 9x + 12 = 12$$
$$12 = 12 \text{ true}$$

The true statement $12 = 12$ indicates that the system contains dependent equations and has infinitely many solutions.

CHECK POINT 5

$$N = -20p + 1000 \quad \text{Demand model}$$
$$N = 5p + 250 \quad \text{Supply model}$$

To find the price at which supply equals demand, solve the demand-supply linear system. To solve the system by the substitution method, substitute $5p + 250$ for N in the first equation.

$$N = -20p + 1000$$
$$5p + 250 = -20p + 1000$$
$$25p + 250 = 1000$$
$$25p = 750$$
$$p = 30$$

The price at which supply and demand are equal is \$30.
To find the value of N, back substitute into either equation of the system.
Using the supply model,

$$N = 5p + 250$$
$$N = 5 \cdot 30 + 250 = 400.$$

Thus, at \$30, 400 units will be supplied and sold each week.

EXERCISE SET 4.2

1. $x + y = 4$
   $y = 3x$

Step 1 The second equation is already solved for y.

Step 2 Substitute $3x$ for y in the first equation.

$$x + y = 4$$
$$x + (3x) = 4$$

Step 3 Solve this equation of x.

$$4x = 4$$
$$x = 1$$

Step 4 Back-substitute 1 for x into the second equation

$$y = 3x$$
$$y = 3(1) = 3$$

The proposed solution is $(1, 3)$.

Step 5 Check $(1, 3)$ in both of equations of the system.

$$x + y = 4 \qquad y = 3x$$
$$1 + 3 \overset{?}{=} 4 \qquad 3 \overset{?}{=} 3(1)$$
$$4 = 4 \text{ true} \qquad 3 = 3 \text{ true}$$

The ordered pair $(1, 3)$ satisfies both equations, so is the solution of the system.

In Exercises 3–31, the five-step method illustrated in the solution for Exercise 1 should be used. In the remaining solutions, these steps will not be listed and the checks will not be shown.

3. $x + 3y = 8$
$y = 2x - 9$

Substitute $2x - 9$ for y in the first equation and solve for x.

$$x + 3y = 8$$
$$x + 3(2x - 9) = 8$$
$$x + 6x - 27 = 8$$
$$7x - 27 = 8$$
$$7x = 35$$
$$x = 5$$

Back-substitute 5 for x into the second equation and solve for y.

$$y = 2x - 9$$
$$y = 2(5) - 9 = 1$$

Solution: $(5, 1)$

5. $x + 3y = 5$
$4x + 5y = 13$

Solve the first equation for x.

$$x + 3y = 5$$
$$x = 5 - 3y$$

Substitute $5 - 3y$ for x in the second equation and solve for y.

$$4x + 5y = 13$$
$$4(5 - 3y) + 5y = 13$$
$$20 - 12y + 5y = 13$$
$$20 - 7y = 13$$
$$-7y = -7$$
$$y = 1$$

Back-substitute 1 for y in the equation $x = 5 - 3y$ and solve for x.

$$x = 5 - 3y$$
$$x = 5 - 3(1) = 2$$

Solution: $(2, 1)$

7. $2x - y = -5$
$x + 5y = 14$

Solve the second equation for x.

$$x + 5y = 14$$
$$x = 14 - 5y$$

Substitute $14 - 5y$ for x in the first equation.

$$2(14 - 5y) - y = -5$$
$$28 - 10y - y = -5$$
$$28 - 11y = -5$$
$$-11y = -33$$
$$y = 3$$

Back-substitute.

$$x = 14 - 5y$$
$$x = 14 - 5(3) = -1$$

Solution: $(-1, 3)$

9. $2x - y = 3$
$5x - 2y = 10$

Solve the first equation for y.

$$2x - y = 3$$
$$-y = -2x + 3$$
$$y = 2x - 3$$

Substitute $2x-3$ for y in the second equation.

$$5x - 2(2x - 3) = 10$$
$$5x - 4x + 6 = 10$$
$$x + 6 = 10$$
$$x = 4$$

Back-substitute.

$$y = 2x - 3$$
$$y = 2(4) - 3 = 5$$

Solution: $(4, 5)$

11. $x + 8y = 6$
$2x + 4y = -3$

Solve the first equation for x.

$$x + 8y = 6$$
$$x = 6 - 8y$$

$$2x + 4y = -3$$
$$2(6 - 8y) + 4y = -3$$
$$12 - 16y + 4y = -3$$
$$12 - 12y = -3$$
$$-12y = -15$$
$$y = \frac{15}{12} = \frac{5}{4}$$

Back-substitute

$$x = 6 - 8y$$
$$x = 6 - 8\left(\frac{5}{4}\right)$$
$$x = 6 - 10 = -4$$

Solution: $\left(-4, \frac{5}{4}\right)$

13. $x = 9 - 2y$
$x + 2y = 13$

The first equation is already solve for x.
Substitute $9-2y$ for x in the second equation.

$$x + 2y = 13$$
$$(9 - 2y) + 2y = 13$$
$$9 = 13 \text{ false}$$

The false statement $9 = 13$ indicates that the system is inconsistent and has no solution.

15. $y = 3x - 5$
$21x - 35 = 7y$

Substitute $3x-5$ for y in the second equation.

$$21x - 35 = 7y$$
$$21x - 35 = 7(3x - 5)$$
$$21x - 35 = 21x - 35$$
$$21x - 35 - 21x = 21x - 35 - 21x$$
$$-35 = -35 \text{ true}$$

The true statement $-35 = -35$ indicates that the system contains dependent equation and has infinitely many solutions.

17. $5x + 2y = 0$
$x - 3y = 0$

Solve the second equation for x.

$$x - 3y = 0$$
$$x = 3y$$

Substitute $3y$ for x in the first equation.

$$5x + 2y = 0$$
$$5(3y) + 2y = 0$$
$$15y + 2y = 0$$
$$17y = 0$$
$$y = 0$$

Back-substitute.

$$x = 3y$$
$$x = 3(0) = 0$$

Solution: $(0, 0)$

19. $2x + 5y = -4$
$3x - y = 11$

Solve the second equation for y.

$$3x - y = 11$$
$$-y = -3x + 11$$
$$y = 3x - 11$$

Substitute $3x-11$ for y in the first equation.

$$2x + 5(3x - 11) = -4$$
$$2x + 15x - 55 = -4$$
$$17x - 55 = -4$$
$$17x = 51$$
$$x = 3$$

Back-substitute.

$$y = 3x - 11$$
$$y = 3(3) - 11 = -2$$

Solution: $(3, -2)$

21. $2(x - 1) - y = -3$
$y = 2x + 3$

Substitute $2x+3$ for y in the first equation..

$$2(x - 1) - (2x + 3) = -3$$
$$2x - 2 - 2x - 3 = -3$$
$$-5 = -3 \text{ false}$$

The false statement $-5 = -3$ indicates that the system has no solution.

23. $x = 4y - 2$
$x = 6y + 8$

Substitute $4y-2$ for x in the second equation.

$$4y - 2 = 6y + 8$$
$$-2y - 2 = 8$$
$$-2y = 10$$
$$y = -5$$

Back-substitute in the first equation.

$$x = 4y - 2$$
$$x = 4(-5) - 2 = -22$$

Solution: $(-22, -5)$

25. $y = 2x - 8$
$y = 3x - 13$

Substitute $2x-8$ for y in the second equation.

$$2x - 8 = 3x - 13$$
$$-x - 8 = -13$$
$$-x = -5$$
$$x = 5$$

Back-substitute in the first equation.

$$y = 2x - 8$$
$$y = 2(5) - 8 = 2$$

Solution: $(5, 2)$

27. $y = \dfrac{1}{3}x + \dfrac{2}{3}$
$y = \dfrac{5}{7}x - 2$

First, clear both equations of fractions. Multiply the first equation by the LCD, 3.

$$3y = 3\left(\frac{1}{3}x + \frac{2}{3}\right)$$

$$3y = 3x + 2$$

Multiply the second equation by the LCD, 7.

$$7y = 7\left(\frac{5}{7}x - 2\right)$$

$$7y = 5x - 14$$

Now solve the new system

$$3y = x + 2$$
$$7y = 5x - 14$$

Solve the first of these equations for x.

$$3y - 2 = x \quad \text{or} \quad x = 3y - 2$$

Substitute $3y-2$ for x in the second equation of the new system.

$$7y = 5x - 14$$
$$7y = 5(3y - 2) - 14$$
$$7y = 15y - 10 - 14$$
$$7y = 25y - 24$$
$$-8y = -24$$
$$y = 3$$

Back-substitute.

$$x = 3y - 2$$
$$x = 3(3) - 2 = 7$$

Solution: $(7, 3)$

29. $\dfrac{x}{6} - \dfrac{y}{2} = \dfrac{1}{3}$

$x + 2y = -3$

Clear the first equation of fractions by multiplying 6.

$$6\left(\dfrac{x}{6} - \dfrac{y}{2}\right) = 6\left(\dfrac{1}{3}\right)$$
$$x - 3y = 3y = 2$$

Solve this equation for x.

$$x = 3y + 2$$

Substitute $3y + 2$ for x in the second equation of the system.

$$(3y + 2) + 2y = -3$$
$$5y + 2 = -3$$
$$5y = -5$$
$$y = -1$$

Back-substitute.

$$x = 3y + 2$$
$$x = 3(-1) + 2 = -1$$

Solution: $(-1, -1)$

31. $2x - 3y = 8 - 2x$
$3x + 4y = x + 3y + 14$

Simplify the first equation.

$$2x - 3y = 8 - 2x$$
$$2x - 3y + 2x = 8 - 2x + 2x$$
$$4x - 3y = 8$$

Simplify the second equation.

$$3x + 4y = x + 3y + 14$$
$$3x + 4y - x - 3y = x + 3y + 14 - x - 3y$$
$$2x + y = 14$$

Solve the last equation for y.

$$y = 14 - 2x$$

Substitute $14 - 2x$ for y in the equation $4x - 3y = 8$.

$$4x - 3y = 8$$
$$4x - 3(14 - 2x) = 8$$
$$4x - 42 + 6x = 8$$
$$10x - 42 = 8$$
$$10x = 50$$
$$x = 5$$

Back-substitute.

$$y = 14 - 2x$$
$$y = 14 - 2(5) = 4$$

Solution: $(5, 4)$

33. $N = -25p + 7500$ Demand model
$N = 5p + 6000$ Supply model

a. Substitute 40 for p in both models.

$$N = -25p + 7500; \; p = 40$$
$$N = -25(40) + 7500 = 6500$$
$$N = 5p + 6000; \; p = 40$$
$$N = 5(40) + 6000 = 6200$$

At \$40 per ticket, 6500 tickets can be sold, but only 6200 tickets w ill be supplied.

b. To find the price at which supply and demand are equal, solve the demand-supply linear system. Substitute $-25p + 7500$ for N in the supply equation.

$$N = 5p + 6000$$
$$-25p + 7500 = 5p + 6000$$
$$-30 + 7500 = 6000$$
$$-30p = -1500$$
$$p = 50$$

If $p = 50$,

$$N = 5(50) + 6000 = 6250.$$

Supply and demand are equation when the ticket price is \$50. At this price, 6250 tickets are supplied and sold.

35. $y = 1.2x + 1080$ Weekly costs
$y = 1.6x$ Weekly revenue

The station will break even when costs = revenue. Solve the cost-revenue linear system. Substitute $1.6x$ for y in the cost equation.

$$1.6x = 1.2x + 1080$$
$$0.4x = 1080$$
$$\frac{0.4x}{0.4} = \frac{1080}{0.4}$$
$$x = 2700$$

The station will break even if 2700 gallons of gasoline are sold weekly.

37. $M = -0.41x + 22$ Whites
$M = -0.18x + 10$ Blacks

To find out when infant mortality will be the same for blacks and whites, solve this system. Substitute $-0.41x + 22$ for M in the second equation.

$$M = -0.18x + 10$$
$$-0.41x + 22 = -0.18x + 10$$
$$-0.41x + 0.18x = -0.18x + 10 + 0.18x$$
$$-0.23x + 22 = 10$$
$$-0.23x + 22 - 22 = 10 - 22$$
$$-0.23x = -12$$
$$\frac{-0.23x}{-0.23} = \frac{-12}{-0.23}$$
$$x \approx 52$$

$x = 52$ corresponds to the year $1980 + 52 = 2032$.
Substitute 52 for x in either equation of the system.

$$M = -0.18(52) + 10 = 0.6$$

The model projects that the infant mortality for both groups will be about 0.6 deaths per 1000 live births in the year 2032.

For Exercises 39–43, answers may vary.

45. $x = 3 - y - z$
$2x + y - z = -6$
$3x - y + z = 11$

This is a system of three linear equations with three variables. It can be solved by the substitution method.
First substitute $3 - y - z$ for x in the second equation.

$$2x + y - z = -6$$
$$2(3 - y - z) + y - z = -6$$
$$6 - 2y - 2z + y - z = -6$$
$$6 - y - 3z = -6$$
$$6 - y - 3z - 6 = -6 - 6$$
$$-y - 3z = -12$$

Solve this equation for y.

$$-y = -12 + 3z$$
$$y = 12 - 3z$$

Now substitute $3 - y - z$ in the third equation of the given system.

$$3x - y + z = 11$$
$$3(3 - y - z) - y + z = 11$$
$$9 - 3y - 3z - y + z = 11$$
$$9 - 4y - 2z = 11$$

Substitute $12 - 3z$ in the last equation.

$$9 - 4y - 2z = 11$$
$$9 - 4(12 - 3z) - 2z = 11$$
$$9 - 48 + 12z - 2z = 11$$
$$-39 + 10z = 11$$
$$10z = 50$$
$$z = 5$$

Now back-substitute in the equation $y = 12 - 3z$ to find the value of y.

$$y = 12 - 3z$$
$$y = 12 - 3(5) = -3$$

Finally, back-substitute in the equation $x = 3 - y - z$ to find the value of x.

$$x = 3 - y - z$$
$$x = 3 - (-3) - 5 = 1$$

Thus, $x = 1, y = -3$, and $z = 5$.
The solution should be checked by verifying that these values satisfy all three equations of the given system.

Review Exercises

47. $4x + 6y = 12$
x-intercept: 3
y-intercept: 2
checkpoint: $(-3, 4)$
Draw a line through $(3, 0), (0, 2)$, and $(-3, 4)$.

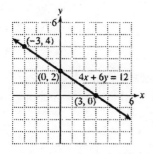

48. $4(x + 1) = 25 + 3(x - 3)$
$$4x + 4 = 25 + 3x - 9$$
$$x + 4 = 16$$
$$x = 12$$

The solution is 12.

49. The integers in the given set are $-73, 0$, and $\frac{3}{1} (= 3)$.

Solving Systems of Linear Equations by the Addition Method

4.3 CHECK POINTS

CHECK POINT 1

$$x + y = 5$$
$$x - y = 9$$

To solve this system by the addition method, add the two left sides and two right sides. This will eliminate the y-terms.

$$\begin{array}{r} x + y = 5 \\ \underline{x - y = 9} \\ 2x + 0y = 14 \\ 2x = 14 \\ x = 7 \end{array}$$

Back-substitute 7 for x into either of the original equations to find y.

$$x + y = 5$$
$$7 + y = 5$$
$$y = -2$$

Check the proposed solution, $(7, -2)$, in both equations of the original system. This will verify that the solution is $(7, -2)$.

CHECK POINT 2

$$4x - y = 22$$
$$3x + 4y = 26$$

To eliminate y, multiply each term of the first equation by 4 and then add the equations.

$$\begin{array}{r} 16x - 4y = 88 \\ \underline{3x + 4y = 26} \\ 19x + 0y = 114 \\ 19x = 114 \\ x = 6 \end{array}$$

Back-substitute 6 for x into either one of the given equations.

$$4x - y = 22$$
$$4 \cdot 6 - y = 22$$
$$24 - y = 22$$
$$-y = -2$$
$$y = 2$$

Check to verify that the solution is $(6, 2)$.

CHECK POINT 3

$$4x + 5y = 3$$
$$2x - 3y = 7$$

To eliminate x, multiply the second equation by -2 and then add the equations.

$$4x + 5y = \quad 3$$
$$\underline{-4x + 6y = -14}$$
$$11y = -11$$
$$y = -1$$

Back-substitute into the first equation.

$$4x + 5y = 3$$
$$4x + 5(-1) = 3$$
$$4x - 5 = 3$$
$$4x = 8$$
$$x = 2$$

Check to verify that the solution is $(2, -1)$.

CHECK POINT 4

$$2x = 9 + 3y$$
$$4y = 8 - 3x$$

First, rewrite both equations in the form $Ax + By = C$.

$$2x - 3y = 9$$
$$3x + 4y = 8$$

To eliminate y, multiply the first equation by 4 and the second equation by 3. Then add the equations.

$$8x - 12y = 36$$
$$\underline{9x + 12y = 24}$$
$$17x \qquad = 60$$
$$x = \frac{60}{17}$$

To avoid working with fractions, instead of substituting $\frac{60}{17}$ for x in one of the given equations, use the addition method again, this time to eliminate x. Go back to the system

$$2x - 3y = 9$$
$$3x + 4y = 8$$

and multiply the first equation by 3 and the second equation by -2. Then add the equations.

$$6x - 9y = \quad 27$$
$$\underline{-6x - 8y = -16}$$
$$-17y = \quad 11$$
$$x = -\frac{11}{17}$$

Check by hand or with a calculator to verify that the solution of the system is $\left(\frac{60}{17}, -\frac{11}{17}\right)$.

CHECK POINT 5

$$x + 2y = 4$$
$$3x + 6y = 13$$

To eliminate x, multiply first equation by -3 and then add the equations.

$$-3x - 6y = -12$$
$$\underline{3x + 6y = \quad 13}$$
$$0 = \quad 1$$

Notice that y has also been eliminated. The false statement $0 = 1$ indicates that the system is inconsistent and has no solution.

CHECK POINT 6

$x - 5y = 7$
$3x - 15y = 21$

To eliminate x, multiply first equation by -3 and then add the equations.

$$-3x + 15y = 7$$
$$\underline{3x - 15y = 21}$$
$$0 = 0$$

Notice that y has also been eliminated. The true statement $0 = 0$ indicates that the system contains dependent equations and has infinitely many solutions.

EXERCISE SET 4.3

1. $x + y = 1$
$x - y = 3$

Add the equations to eliminate the y-terms.

$$x + y = 1$$
$$\underline{x - y = 3}$$
$$2x \quad = 4$$

Now solve for x.

$$2x = 4$$
$$x = 2$$

Back-substitute into either of the original equations to solve for y.

$$x + y = 1$$
$$2 + y = 1$$
$$y = -1$$

The proposed solution, $(2, -1)$, satisfies both equations of the system since $2 + (-1) = 1$ and $2 - (-1) = 3$.
Solution: $(2, -1)$

3. $2x + 3y = 6$
$\underline{2x - 3y = 6}$
$4x = 12$
$x = 3$

$$2(3) + 3y = 6$$
$$3y = 0$$
$$y = 0$$

Solution: $(3, 0)$

5. $x + 2y = 7$
$\underline{-x + 3y = 18}$
$5y = 25$
$y = 5$

$$x + 2(5) = 7$$
$$x + 10 = 7$$
$$x = -3$$

Solution: $(-3, 5)$

7. $5x - y = 14$
$\underline{-5x + 2y = -13}$
$y = 1$

$$5x - 1 = 14$$
$$5x = 15$$
$$x = 3$$

Solution: $(3, 1)$

9. $x + 2y = 2$
$-4x + 3y = 25$

Multiply equation 1 by 4. Don't change equation 2.

$$4x + 8y = 8$$
$$\underline{-4x + 3y = 25}$$
$$11y = 33$$
$$y = 3$$

$$x + 2(3) = 2$$
$$x + 6 = 2$$
$$x = -4$$

Solution: $(-4, 3)$

11. $2x - 7y = 2$
$3x + y = -20$

No change to equation 1.
Multiply equation 2 by 7.

$$2x - 7y = 2$$
$$\underline{21x + 7y = -140}$$
$$23x = -138$$
$$x = -6$$

$$3(-6) + y = -20$$
$$-18 + y = -20$$
$$y = -2$$

Solution: $(-6, -2)$

13. $x + 5y = -1$
$2x + 7y = 1$

Multiply equation 1 by -2.
No change to equation 2.

$$-2x - 10y = 2$$
$$\underline{2x + 7y = 1}$$
$$-3y = 3$$
$$y = -1$$

$$x + 5(-1) = -1$$
$$x - 5 = -1$$
$$x = 4$$

Solution: $(4, -1)$

15. $4x + 3y = 15$
$2x - 5y = 1$

No change to equation 1.
Multiply equation 2 by -2.

$$4x + 3y = 15$$
$$\underline{-4x + 10y = -2}$$
$$13y = 13$$
$$y = 1$$

$$2x - 5(1) = 1$$
$$2x = 6$$
$$x = 3$$

Solution: $(3, 1)$

17. $3x - 4y = 11$
$2x + 3y = -4$

Multiply equation 1 by 3.
Multiply equation 2 by 4.

$$9x - 12y = 33$$
$$\underline{8x + 12y = -16}$$
$$17x = 17$$
$$x = 1$$

$$2(1) + 3y = -4$$
$$3y = -6$$
$$y = -2$$

Solution: $(1, -2)$

19. $3x + 2y = -1$
$-2x + 7y = 9$

Multiply equation 1 by 2.
Multiply equation 2 by 3.

$$6x + 4y = -2$$
$$\underline{-6x + 21y = 27}$$
$$25y = 25$$
$$y = 1$$

$$3x + 2(1) = -1$$
$$3x = -3$$
$$x = -1$$

Solution: $(-1, 1)$

21. $3x = 2y + 7$
$5x = 2y + 13$

Rewrite:

$$3x - 2y = 7$$
$$5x - 2y = 13$$

Multiply equation 1 by -1.
No change to equation 2.

$$-3x + 2y = -7$$
$$\underline{5x - 2y = 13}$$
$$2x = 6$$
$$x = 3$$

$$3(3) = 2y + 7$$
$$2 = 2y$$
$$1 = y$$

Solution: $(3, 1)$

23. $2x = 3y - 6$
$-6x + 12y = 6$

Rewrite equation 1.

$$2x - 3y = -4$$

Multiply this equation by 3 and add to equation 2 of the original system.

$$6x - 9y = -12$$
$$\underline{-6x + 12y = 6}$$
$$3y = -6$$
$$y = -2$$

$$2x - 3(-2) = -4$$
$$2x + 6 = -4$$
$$2x = -10$$
$$x = -5$$

Solution: $(-5, -2)$

25. $2x - y = 3$
$4x + 4y = -1$

Multiply equation 1 by 4.
No change to equation 2.

$$8x - 4y = 12$$
$$\underline{4x + 4y = -1}$$
$$12x = 11$$
$$x = \frac{11}{12}$$

Instead of back-substituting $\frac{11}{12}$ and working with fractions, go back to the original system. Multiply equation 1 by -2 and add the result to equation 2 to eliminate x.

$$-4x + 2y = -6$$
$$\underline{4x + 4y = -1}$$
$$6y = -7$$
$$y = -\frac{7}{6}$$

Solution: $(\frac{11}{12}, -\frac{7}{6})$

27. $4x = 5 + 2y$
$2x + 3y = 4$

Rewrite equation 1.
Multiply equation 2 by -2.

$$4x - 2y = 5$$
$$\underline{-4x - 6y = -8}$$
$$-8x = -3$$
$$y = \frac{3}{8}$$

Instead of back-substituting $\frac{3}{8}$ and working with fractions, go back to the original system, with rewritten equation 1.

$$4x - 2y = 5$$
$$-4x - 6y = -8$$

Multiply the first of these equations by -3 and add to the second.

$$-12x + 6y = -15$$
$$\underline{-4x - 6y = -8}$$
$$-16x = -23$$
$$x = \frac{23}{16}$$

Solution: $(\frac{23}{16}, \frac{3}{8})$

29. $3x - y = 1$
$\underline{3x - y = 2}$

Multiply equation 1 by -1.
No change to equation 2.

$$3x + y = -1$$
$$\underline{3x - y = 2}$$
$$0 = 1 \text{ false}$$

The false statement $0 = 1$ indicates that the system is inconsistent and has no solution.

31. $x + 3y = 2$
$3x + 9y = 6$

Multiply equation 1 by -3.
No change to equation 2.

$$-3x - 9y = -6$$
$$\underline{3x + 9y = 6}$$
$$0 = 0 \text{ true}$$

The true statement $0 = 0$ indicates that the system has infinitely many solutions.

33. $7x - 3y = 4$
$-14x + 6y = -7$

Multiply equation 1 by 2.
No change to equation 2.

$$14x - 6y = 8$$
$$\underline{-14x + 6y = -7}$$
$$0 = 1$$

The false statement $0 = 1$ indicates that the system has no solution.

35. $5x + y = 2$
$3x + y = 1$

No change to equation 1.
Multiply equation 2 by -1.

$$5x + y = 2$$
$$\underline{-3x - y = -2}$$
$$2x = 1$$

$$x = \frac{1}{2}$$

$$3\left(\frac{1}{2}\right) + y = 1$$

$$y = -\frac{1}{2}$$

Solution: $\left(\frac{1}{2}, -\frac{1}{2}\right)$

37. $x = 5 - 3y$
$2x + 6y = 10$

Rewrite equation 1.

$$x + 3y = 5$$

Multiply this equation by -2.
No change to equation 2.

$$-2x - 6y = -10$$
$$2x + 6y = 10$$
$$0 = 0$$

The true statement $0 = 0$ indicates that the system has infinitely many solutions.

39. $4(3x - y) = 0$
$3(x + 3) = 10y$

Rewrite both equations.
First equation:

$$12x - 4y = 0$$

Second equation:

$$3x + 9 = 10y$$
$$3x - 10y = -9$$

Now solve the system

$$12x - 4y = 0$$
$$3x - 10y = -9.$$

Multiply the second equation by -4 and add the result to the first equation.

$$12x - 4y = 0$$
$$\underline{-12x + 40y = 36}$$
$$36y = 36$$
$$y = 1$$

$$12x - 4y = 0$$
$$12x - 4(1) = 0$$
$$12x = 4$$

$$x = \frac{1}{3}$$

Solution: $\left(\frac{1}{3}, 1\right)$

41. $x + y = 11$

$$\frac{x}{5} + \frac{y}{7} = 1$$

Multiply the second equation by the LCD, 35, to clear fractions.

$$35\left(\frac{x}{5} + \frac{y}{7}\right) = 35(1)$$

$$7x + 5y = 35$$

Now solve the system

$$x + y = 11$$
$$7x + 5y = 35.$$

Multiply the first equation by -5 and add the result to the second equation.

$$-5x - 5y = -55$$
$$\underline{7x + 5y = 35}$$
$$2x = -20$$
$$x = -10$$

$$-10 + y = 11$$
$$y = 21$$

Solution: $(-10, 21)$

43. $\frac{4}{5}x - y = -1$

$$\frac{2}{5}x + y = 1$$

Multiply equation 1 by 5.
Multiply equation 2 by 5.

$$4x - 5y = -5$$
$$\underline{2x + 5y = 5}$$
$$6x = 0$$
$$x = 0$$

$$\frac{2}{5}(0) + y = 1$$

$$y = 1$$

Solution: $(0, 1)$

45. $3x - 2y = 8$

$$x = -2y$$

The substitution method is a good choice because the second equation is already solved for x.

Substitute $-2y$ for x in the first equation.

$$3x - 2y = 8$$
$$3(-2y) - 2y = 8$$
$$-6y - 2y = 8$$
$$-8y = 8$$
$$y = -1$$

Back-substitute -1 for y into the second equation.

$$x = -2y$$
$$x = -2(-1) = 2$$

Solution: $(2, -1)$

47. $3x + 2y = -3$

$$2x - 5y = 17$$

The addition method is a good choice because both equations are written in the form $Ax + By = C$.

Multiply equation 1 by 2.
Multiply equation 2 by -3.

$$6x + 4y = -6$$
$$\underline{-6x + 15y = -51}$$
$$19y = -57$$
$$y = -3$$

$$3x + 2(-3) = -3$$
$$3x - 6 = -3$$
$$3x = 3$$
$$x = 1$$

Solution: $(1, -3)$

49. $3x - 2y = 6$
     $y = 3$

The substitution method is a good choice because the second equation is already solved for y.
Substitute 3 for y in the first equation.

$$3x - 2y = 6$$
$$3x - 2(3) = 6$$
$$3x - 6 = 6$$
$$3x = 12$$
$$x = 4$$

It is not necessary to back-substitute to find the value of y because $y = 3$ is one of the equations of the given system.
Solution: $(4, 3)$

51. $y = 2x + 1$
     $y = 2x - 3$

The substitution method is a good choice, because both equations are already solved for y.
Substitute $2x + 1$ for y in the second equation.

$$y = 2x - 3$$
$$2x + 1 = 2x - 3$$
$$2x + 1 - 2x = 2x - 3 - 2x$$
$$1 = -3 \text{ false}$$

The false statement $1 = -3$ indicates that the system has no solution.

53. $2(x + 2y) = 6$
     $3(x + 2y - 3) = 0$

The addition method is a good choice since the left-hand sides of the equation can easily be simplified to give equations of the form $Ax + By = C$.
First equation:

$$2x + 4y = 6$$

Second equation:

$$3x + 6y - 9 = 0$$
$$3x + 6y = 9$$

Now solve the system

$$2x + 4y = 6$$
$$3x + 6y = 9.$$

Multiply the first equation by -3 and the second by 2. Add the results.

$$-6x - 12y = -18$$
$$\underline{6x + 12y = 18}$$
$$0 = 0 \text{ true}$$

The true statement $0 = 0$ indicates that the original system has infinitely many solutions.

55. $3y = 2x$
     $2x + 9y = 24$

The substitution method is a good choice because the first equation can easily be solved for one of the variables. Solve this equation for y.

$$3y = 2x$$
$$y = \frac{2}{3}x$$

Substitute $\frac{2}{3}x$ for y in the second equation.

$$2x + 9y = 24$$
$$2x + 9\left(\frac{2}{3}x\right) = 24$$
$$2x + 6x = 24$$
$$8x = 24$$
$$x = 3$$

Back-substitute 3 for x in the equation $y = \frac{2}{3}x$.

$$y = \frac{2}{3}x$$
$$y = \frac{2}{3}(3) = 2$$

Solution: $(3, 2)$

For Exercises 57–61, answers may vary.

63.
$$\frac{3x}{5} + \frac{4y}{5} = 1$$
$$\frac{x}{4} - \frac{3y}{8} = -1$$

Multiply the first equation by the LCD, 5.

$$5\left(\frac{3x}{5} + \frac{4y}{5}\right) = 5(1)$$
$$3x + 4y = 5$$

Multiply the second equation by the LCD, 8.

$$8\left(\frac{x}{4} - \frac{3y}{8}\right) = 8(-1)$$
$$2x - 3y = -8$$

Now solve the system

$$3x + 4y = 5$$
$$2x - 3y = -8.$$

Multiply the first of these equations by 3 and the second by 4. Then add the equations.

$$\begin{array}{r} 9x + 12y = 15 \\ \underline{8x - 12y = -32} \\ 17x = -17 \\ x = -1 \end{array}$$

Back-substitute -1 for x into the equation that was obtained when the first equation was cleared of fractions.

$$3x + 4y = 5$$
$$3(-1) + 4y = 5$$
$$-3 + 4y = 5$$
$$4y = 8$$
$$y = 2$$

Solution: $(-1, 2)$

65.
$$0.5x - 0.2y = 0.5$$
$$0.4x + 0.7y = 0.4$$

Each equation can be "cleared of decimals" by multiplying by 10.
First equation:

$$10(0.5x - 0.2y) = 10(0.5)$$
$$5x - 2y = 5$$

Second equation:

$$10(0.4x + 0.7y) = 10(0.4)$$
$$4x + 7y = 4$$

Now solve the system

$$5x - 2y = 5$$
$$4x + 7y = 4.$$

Multiply the first of these equations by 4 and the second by -5. Then add the equations.

$$\begin{array}{r} 20x - 8y = 20 \\ \underline{-20x - 35y = -20} \\ -43y = 0 \\ y = 0 \end{array}$$

Back-substitute 0 for y into the equation obtained when the first equation was cleared of decimals.

$$5x - 2y = 5$$
$$5x - 2(0) = 5$$
$$5x = 5$$
$$x = 1$$

Solution: $(1, 0)$

67. Answers will vary according to the exercises chosen.

69. $x = 5y$

$2x - 3y = 7$

Rewrite the first equation in $Ax + By = C$ form.

$$x - 5y = 0$$

Then solve the system

$$x - 5y = 0$$
$$2x - 3y = 7.$$

Enter 2 for two equations in two variables, then the coefficients and constant term for the equations, one equation at a time. After entering all the numbers, press $\boxed{\text{SOLVE}}$ and read the solutions displayed on the screen.

Note: This feature is only available on the TI-85 and higher-numbered TI calculators.

Solution: $(5, 1)$

Review Exercises

71. Let $x =$ the unknown number.

$$5x = x + 40$$
$$40x = 40$$
$$x = 10$$

The number is 10.

72. Because the x-coordinate is negative and the y-coordinate is positive, $\left(-\frac{3}{2}, 15\right)$ is located in quadrant II.

73. $29{,}700 + 150x = 5000 + 1100x$

$29{,}700 + 150x - 1100x = 5000 + 1100x - 1100x$

$29{,}700 - 950x = 5000$

$29{,}700 - 950x - 29{,}700 = 5000 - 29{,}700$

$$-950x = -24{,}700$$

$$\frac{-950x}{-950} = \frac{-24{,}700}{-950}$$

$$x = 26$$

The solution is 26.

Problem Solving Using Systems of Equations

4.4 CHECK POINTS

CHECK POINT 1

Step 1 Use variables to represent unknown quantities.

Let x represent the weight of a bustard.

Let y represent the weight of a condor.

Step 2 Write a system of equations describing the problem's conditions.

Because two bustards and three condors weigh 173 pounds,

$$2x + 3y = 173.$$

Because the bustard's weight increased by double the condor's weight is 100 pounds,

$$x + 2y = 100.$$

Step 3 Solve the system and answer the problem's question. The system

$$2x + 3y = 173$$
$$x + 2y = 100$$

can be solved by substitution or addition. Either method will work well. We will use the addition method.

Multiply the second equation by -2. Then add the equations.

$$\begin{array}{r} 2x + 3y = 173 \\ \underline{-2x - 4y = -200} \\ -y = -27 \\ y = 27 \end{array}$$

Back-substitute 27 for y in the second equation of the original system.

$$x + 2y = 100$$
$$x + 2(27) = 100$$
$$x + 54 = 100$$
$$x = 46$$

A bustard weighs 46 pounds and a condor weighs 27 pounds.

This solution should be checked in the original wording of the problem.

CHECK POINT 2

Let x represent the number of calories in a Quarter Pounder and y represent the number of calories in a Whopper.

The conditions in the problem can be described by the system

$$2x + 3y = 2607$$
$$x + y = 1009.$$

To solve this system by the addition method, multiply the second equation by -2; then add the equations.

$$\begin{array}{r} 2x + 3y = 2607 \\ -2x - 2y = -2018 \\ \hline y = 589 \end{array}$$

To find x, back-substitute into the second equation of the second equation.

$$x + y = 1009$$
$$x + 589 = 1009$$
$$x = 420$$

A Quarter Pounder has 420 calories and a Whopper has 589 calories.

CHECK POINT 3

Let x represent the number of years the heating system is used. Let y represent the total cost for the heating system.

Electric system:

$$y = 5000 + 1100x$$

Gas system:

$$y = 12,000 + 700x$$

To find how long it will take for the heating costs to be equal, solve the system formed by these two equations.

The substitution method will work well because y is isolated in second equation. Substitute $5000 + 1100x$ for y in the second equation.

$$5000 + 1100x = 12,000 + 700x$$
$$5000 + 400x = 12,000$$
$$400 = 7000$$
$$x = 17.5$$

To find y, back-substitute 17.5 for x in the first equation.

$$y = 5000 + 1100(17.5)$$
$$y = 5000 + 19,250$$
$$y = 24,250$$

The total cost for electric and gas heating will be the same after 17.5 years. At the time, the cost for each system will be $24,250.

CHECK POINT 4

Let $x =$ the amount invested in a stock paying 6%

Let $y =$ the amount invested in a stock paying 8%

	Principle	×	Rate	=	Interest
6%	x		0.06		$0.06x$
8%	y		0.08		$0.08y$

$$x + y = 16000$$
$$0.06x + 0.08y = 1180$$

Multiply the first equation by -0.06 and add the second equation.

$$\begin{array}{r} -0.06x - 0.06y = -960 \\ 0.06x + 0.08y = 1180 \\ \hline 0.02y = 220 \\ y = 11000 \end{array}$$

Back-substitute 11000 for y to find x.

$$x + y = 16000$$
$$x + 11000 = 16000$$
$$x = 5000$$

You should invest $5000 at 6% and $11000 at 8%.

CHECK POINT 5

Let $x =$ the amount of 18% acid solution.
Let $y =$ the amount of 45% acid solution.

	# of ml's $\times$	%	= Amount
18%	x	0.18	$0.18x$
45%	y	0.45	$0.45y$
36%	12	0.36	$0.36(12)$

$$x + \qquad = 12$$
$$0.18x + 0.45y = 4.32$$

Multiply the first equation by -0.18 and add to the second equation.

$$-0.18x - 0.18y = -2.16$$
$$\underline{0.18x + 0.45y = 4.32}$$
$$0.27y = 2.16$$
$$y = 8$$

Back-substitute 8 for y to find x.

$$x + y = 12$$
$$x + 8 = 12$$
$$x = 4$$

The chemist must use 4 liters of the 18% solution and 8 liters of the 45% solution.

CHECK POINT 6

Let $x =$ the speed of the boat in still water.
Let $y =$ the speed of the current.

	r $\times$	t =	d
With Current	$x + y$	2	$2(x + y)$
Against the Current	$x - y$	3	$3(x - y)$

$$2(x + y) = 84$$
$$3(x - y) = 84$$

Rewrite the system in $Ax + By = C$ form.

$$2x + 2y = 84$$
$$3x - 3y = 84$$

Multiply the first equation by -3 and the second equation by 2.

$$-6x - 6y = -252$$
$$\underline{6x - 6y = 168}$$
$$-12y = -84$$
$$y = 7$$

Back-substitute 7 for y to find x.

$$2x + 2y = 84$$
$$2x + 2(7) = 84$$
$$2x + 14 = 84$$
$$2x = 70$$
$$x = 35$$

The speed of the boat in still water is 35 miles per hour and the speed of the current is 7 miles per hour.

EXERCISE SET 4.4

1. $x + y = 7$
    $x - y = -1$

Solve the system by the addition method.

$$x + y = 7$$
$$\underline{x - y = -1}$$
$$2x = 6$$
$$x = 3$$

$$3 + y = 7$$
$$y = 4$$

The numbers are 3 and 4.

3. $3x - y = 1$
$x + 2y = 12$

Solve the system by the addition method. Multiply the first equation by 2 and add the result to the second equation.

$$\begin{aligned} 6x - 2y &= 2 \\ x + 2y &= 12 \\ \hline 7x \quad\;\; &= 14 \\ x &= 2 \end{aligned}$$

$$\begin{aligned} 3(2) - y &= 1 \\ 6 - y &= 1 \\ -y &= -5 \\ y &= 5 \end{aligned}$$

The numbers 2 and 5.

5. Let x = the number of millions of pounds of potato chips.
Let y = the number of pounds of tortilla chips.

$$\begin{aligned} x + y &= 10.4 \\ x - y &= 1.2 \\ \hline 2x \quad\;\; &= 11.6 \\ x &= 5.8 \end{aligned}$$

$$\begin{aligned} y + 5.8 &= 10.4 \\ y &= 4.6 \end{aligned}$$

On Super Bowl Sunday, 5.8 million pounds of potato chips and 4.6 million pounds of tortilla chips are consumed.

7. Let x = the number of calories in one pan pizza.
Let y = the number of calories in one beef burrito.

$$\begin{aligned} x + 2y &= 1980 \\ 2x + y &= 2670 \end{aligned}$$

To solve this system by the addition method, multiply the first equation by -2 and add the result to the second equation.

$$\begin{aligned} -2x - 4y &= -3960 \\ 2x + y &= 2670 \\ \hline -3y &= -1290 \\ y &= 430 \end{aligned}$$

$$\begin{aligned} x + 2y &= 1980 \\ x + 2(430) &= 1980 \\ x + 860 &= 1980 \\ x &= 1120 \end{aligned}$$

A pan pizza has 1120 calories and a beef burrito has 430 calories.

9. Let x = number of milligrams of cholesterol in scrambled eggs.
Let y = number of milligrams of cholesterol in Whopper.

$$\begin{aligned} x + y &= -300 + 241 \\ 2x + 3y &= 1257 \end{aligned}$$

$$\begin{aligned} x + y &= 541 \\ 2x + 3y &= 1257 \end{aligned}$$

Multiply the first equation by -2 and add to second equation.

$$\begin{aligned} -2x - 2y &= -1082 \\ 2x + 3y &= 1257 \\ \hline y &= 175 \end{aligned}$$

Back-substitute.

$$\begin{aligned} x + 175 &= 541 \\ x &= 366 \end{aligned}$$

The scrambled eggs have 366 mg of cholesterol, and the Double Beef Whopper has 175 mg of cholesterol.

11. Let $x =$ the price of one sweater.
Let $y =$ the price of one shirt.

$$x + 3y = 42$$
$$3x + 2y = 56$$

Multiply the first equation by -3 and add the result to the second equation.

$$\begin{array}{r} -3x - 9y = -126 \\ 3x + 2y = 56 \\ \hline -7y = -70 \\ y = 10 \end{array}$$

$$x + 3(10) = 42$$
$$x + 30 = 42$$
$$x = 12$$

The price of one sweater is \$12 and the price of one shirt is \$10.

13. a. Let $x =$ the number of minutes of long-distance calls.
Let $y =$ the monthly cost of a telephone plan.

Plan A: $y = 20 + 0.05x$
Plan B: $y = 5 + 0.10x$

To solve this system by the substitution method, substitute $5 + 0.10x$ for y in the first equation.

$$5 + 0.10x = 20 + 0.05x$$
$$5 + 0.05x = 20$$
$$0.05x = 15$$
$$\frac{0.05x}{0.05} = \frac{15}{0.05}$$
$$x = 300$$

If $x = 300$,

$$y = 20 + 0.05(300) = 35.$$

The costs for the two plans will be equal for 300 minutes of long-distance calls per month. The cost of each plan will be \$35.

b. $x = 10(20) = 200$

Plan A: $y = 20 + 0.05(200) = 30$
Plan B: $y = 5 + 0.10(200) = 25$

The monthly cost would be \$30 for Plan A and \$25 for Plan B, so you should select Plan B to get the lower cost.

15. Let $x =$ the number of dollars of merchandise purchased in a year.
Let $y =$ the total cost for a year.

Plan A: $y = 100 + 0.80x$
Plan B: $y = 40 + 0.90x$

Substitute $40 + 0.90x$ for y in the first equation.

$$40 + 0.90x = 100 + 0.80x$$
$$40 + 0.10x = 100$$
$$0.10x = 60$$
$$\frac{0.10x}{0.10} = \frac{60}{0.10}$$
$$x = 600$$

If $x = 600$,

$$y = 100 + 0.80(600) = 580.$$

If you purchase \$600 worth of merchandise, you will pay the \$580 under both plans.

17. Let $x =$ the number of years after 1985.
Let $y =$ the average high school graduate's weekly earnings.

We are interested in the year in which the average college graduate earns twice as much as a high school graduate, so the average college graduate's earnings will be $2y$.

College graduates:

$$2y = 508 + 25x$$

High school graduates:

$$y = 345x + 9x$$

Substitute $345 + 9x$ into the first equation.

$$2(345 + 9x) = 508 + 25x$$
$$690 + 18x = 508 + 25x$$
$$690 - 7x = 508$$
$$-7x = -182$$
$$x = 26$$

$1985 + 26 = 2011$
If $x = 26$,

$$y = 345 + 9(26) = 579$$

and

$$2y = 2(579) = 1158.$$

In 26 years after 1985, which is the year 2011, the average college graduate will earn $1158 per week and the average high school graduate will earn $579 per week.

19. Let $x =$ the number of servings of macaroni.
Let $y =$ the number of servings of broccoli.

$$3x + 2y = 14$$
$$16x + 4y = 48$$

Multiply first equation by -2 and add to second equation.

$$\begin{array}{rcr} -6x - 4y &=& -28 \\ 16x + 4y &=& 48 \\ \hline 10x &=& 20 \\ x &=& 2 \end{array}$$

Back-substitute.

$$3(2) + 2y = 14$$
$$2y = 8$$
$$y = 4$$

It would take 2 servings of macaroni and 4 servings of broccoli to get 14 grams of protein and 48 graphs of carbohydrate.

21. Let $x =$ the amount invested at 7%.
Let $y =$ the amount invested at 9%.

$$x + y = 20000$$
$$0.07x + 0.09y = 1550$$

Solve the first equation for x.

$$x + y = 20000$$
$$x = 20000 - y$$

Substitute $20000 - y$ for x in the second equation.

$$0.07(20000 - y) + 0.09y = 1550$$
$$1400 - 0.07y + 0.09y = 1550$$
$$1400 + 0.02y = 1550$$
$$0.02y = 150$$
$$0.02y = 150$$
$$y = 7500$$

Back-substitute to find x.

$$x + y = 20000$$
$$x + 7500 = 20000$$
$$x = 12500$$

$12,500 was invested at 7% and $7,500 was invested at 9%.

23. Let $x =$ the amount loaned at 8%.
Let $y =$ the amount loaned at 18%.

$$x + y = 250000$$
$$0.08x + 0.18y = 23000$$

Solve the first equation for x.

$$x + y = 250000$$
$$x = 250000 - y$$

Substitute $250000 - y$ for x in the second equation.

$$0.08(250000 - y) + 0.18y = 23000$$
$$20000 - 0.08y + 0.18y = 23000$$
$$20000 + 0.10y = 23000$$
$$0.10y = 3000$$
$$y = 30000$$

Back-substitute to find x.

$$x + 30000 = 250000$$
$$x = 220000$$

$220,000 was loaned at 8% annual mortgage interest and $30,000 was loaned at 18% annual credit card interest.

25. Let $x =$ the amount invested at 12%.
Let $y =$ the amount which lost 5%.

$$x + y = 8000$$
$$0.12x - 0.05y = 620$$

Solve the first equation for x.

$$x + y = 8000$$
$$x = 8000 - y$$

Substitute $8000 - y$ for x in the second equation.

$$0.12(8000 - y) - 0.05y = 620$$
$$960 - 0.12y - 0.05y = 620$$
$$960 - 0.17y = 620$$
$$-0.17y = -340$$
$$y = 2000$$

Back-substitute to find x.

$$x + y = 8000$$
$$x + 2000 = 8000$$
$$x = 6000$$

$6,000 was invested at 12% and $2,000 was invested at a 5% loss.

27. Let $x =$ the number of grams of 45% fat content cheese.
Let $y =$ the number of grams of 20% fat content cheese.

$$x + y = 30$$
$$0.45x + 0.20y = 0.30(30)$$
$$\overline{ x + y = 30}$$
$$0.45x + 0.20y = 9$$

Solve the first equation for x.

$$x + y = 30$$
$$x = 30 - y$$

Substitute $30 - y$ for x in the second equation.

$$0.45x + 0.20y = 9$$
$$0.45(30 - y) + 0.20y = 9$$
$$13.5 - 0.25y = 9$$
$$-0.25y = -4.5$$
$$-0.25y = -4.5$$
$$x = 18$$

Back-substitute to find x.

$$x + 18 = 30$$
$$x = 12$$

Mix 12 grams of 45% fat content cheese with 18 grams of 20% fat content cheese.

29. Let $x =$ the number of students at north campus before the merger.
Let $y =$ the number of students at south campus before the merger.

$$x + y = 1200$$
$$0.10x + 0.50y = 0.40(1200)$$
$$\overline{ x + y = 30}$$
$$0.45x + 0.20y = 9$$

Solve the first equation for x.

$$x + y = 1200$$
$$x = 1200 - y$$

Substitute $1200 - y$ for x in the second equation.

$$0.10(1200 - y) + 0.50y = 480$$
$$120 - 0.10y + 0.50y = 480$$
$$120 + 0.40y = 480$$
$$0.40y = 360$$
$$0.40y = 360$$
$$y = 900$$

Back-substitute to find x.

$$x + y = 1200$$
$$x + 900 = 1200$$
$$x = 300$$

There were 300 students at north campus and 900 students at south campus before the merger.

31. Let $x =$ the amount of \$6.00 per pound tea.
Let $y =$ the amount of \$8.00 per pound tea.

$$x + \ y = 144$$
$$6 \ + 8 \ = 7.50(144)$$
$$x + \ y = 144$$
$$6x + 8y = 1080$$

Solve the first equation for x.

$$x + y = 144$$
$$x = 144 - y$$

Substitute $144 - y$ for x in the second equation.

$$6(144 - y) + 8y = 1080$$
$$864 - 6y + 8y = 1080$$
$$864 + 2y = 1080$$
$$2y = 216$$
$$y = 108$$

Back-substitute to find x.

$$x + y = 144$$
$$x + 108 = 144$$
$$x = 36$$

Mix 36 pounds of the \$6.00 per pound tea with 108 pounds of the \$8.00 per pound tea.

33. Let $x =$ the speed of the plane in still air.
Let $y =$ the speed of the wind.

	r	$\times \ t \ =$	d
With Wind	$x + y$	5	800
Against Wind	$x - y$	8	800

$$5(x + y) = 800$$
$$8(x - y) = 800$$
$$5x + 5y = 800$$
$$8x - 8y = 800$$

Multiply the first equation by 8 and the second equation by 5.

$$40x + 40y = 6400$$
$$40x - 40y = 4000$$
$$80x = 10400$$
$$x = 130$$

Back-substitute to find y.

$$5x + 5y = 800$$
$$5(130) + 5y = 800$$
$$650 + 5y = 800$$
$$5y = 150$$
$$y = 30$$

The speed of the plane in still air is 130 miles per hour and the speed of the wind is 30 miles per hour.

35. Let $x =$ the crew's rowing rate.
Let $y =$ the rate of the current.

	r	$\times \ t \ =$	d
With Current	$x + y$	2	16
Against Current	$x - y$	4	16

$$2(x + y) = 16$$
$$4(x - y) = 16$$

Rewrite the system in $Ax + By = C$ form.

$$2x + 2y = 16$$
$$4x - 4y = 16$$

Multiply the first equation by -2.

$$\begin{array}{r} -4x - 4y = -32 \\ \underline{4x - 4y = 16} \\ -8y = -16 \\ y = 2 \end{array}$$

The crew's rowing rate is 6 kilometers per hour and the rate of the current is 2 kilometers per hour.

37. Let $x =$ the speed in still water.
Let $y =$ the speed of the current.

	$r \times$	$t =$	d
With Current	$x + y$	4	24
Against Current	$x - y$	6	$\frac{3}{4}(24)$

$$4(x + y) = 24$$
$$6(x - y) = \frac{3}{4}(24)$$

Rewrite the system in $Ax + By = C$ form.

$$4x + 4y = 24$$
$$6x - 6y = 18$$

Multiply the first equation by -3 and the second equation by 2.

$$\begin{array}{r} -12x - 12y = -72 \\ \underline{12 - 12y = 36} \\ -24y = -36 \\ y = 1.5 \end{array}$$

Back-substitute to find x.

$$\begin{array}{r} 4x + 4y = 24 \\ 4x + 4(1.5) = 24 \\ 4x + 6 = 24 \\ 4x = 18 \\ x = 4.5 \end{array}$$

The speed in still water is 4.5 miles per hour and the speed of the current is 1.5 miles per hour.

For Exercises 39–41, answers may vary.

43. Let $x =$ the number of birds.
Let $y =$ the number of lions.

Since each bird has one head and each lion has one head,

$$x + y = 30.$$

Since each bird has two feet and each lion has four feet,

$$2x + 4y = 100.$$

Solve the first equation for y.

$$y = 30 - x$$

Substitute $30 - x$ for y in the second equation.

$$\begin{array}{r} 2x + 4(30 - x) = 100 \\ 2x + 120 - 4x = 100 \\ -2x + 120 = 100 \\ -2x = -20 \\ x = 10 \\ 10 + y = 30 \\ y = 20 \end{array}$$

There were 10 birds and 20 lions in the zoo.

45. Let $x =$ the number of people in the downstairs apartment.
Let $y =$ the number of people in the upstairs apartment.

If one of the people in the upstairs apartment goes downstairs, there will be the same number of people in both apartments, so

$$y - 1 = x + 1.$$

If one of the people in the downstairs apartment goes upstairs, there will be twice as many people upstairs as downstairs, so

$$y + 1 = 2(x - 1).$$

Solve the first equation for y.

$$y = x + 2$$

Also solve the second equation for y.

$$y + 1 = 2x - 2$$
$$y = 2x - 3$$

Substitute $x + 2$ for y in the last equation.

$$x + 2 = 2x - 3$$
$$-x + 2 = -3$$
$$-x = -5$$
$$x = 5$$
$$y = 5 + 2 = 7$$

There are 5 people downstairs and 7 people upstairs.

47. Answers will vary depending on the problems chosen.

Review Exercises

48. $(-6, 1)$ and $(2, -1)$

$$m = \frac{-1 - 1}{2 - (-6)} = \frac{-2}{8} = -\frac{1}{4}$$

49. $\dfrac{1}{5} + \left(-\dfrac{3}{4}\right) = \dfrac{4}{20} + \left(-\dfrac{15}{20}\right) = -\dfrac{11}{20}$

50. $y = x^2$

Make a table of values.

x	$y = x^2$	(x, y)
-3	$y = (-3)^2 = 9$	$(-3, 9)$
-2	$y = (-2)^2 = 4$	$(-2, 4)$
-1	$y = (-1)^2 = 1$	$(-1, 1)$
0	$y = 0^2 = 0$	$(0, 0)$
1	$y = 1^2 = 1$	$(1, 1)$
2	$y = 2^2 = 4$	$(2, 4)$
3	$y = 3^2 = 9$	$(3, 9)$

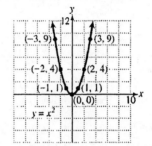

Chapter 4 Review Exercises

1. $(1, -5)$
$$4x - y = 9$$
$$4(1) - (-5) \overset{?}{=} 9$$
$$4 + 5 \overset{?}{=} 9$$
$$9 = 9 \text{ true}$$

$$2x + 3y = -13$$
$$2(1) + 3(-5) \overset{?}{=} -13$$
$$2 - 15 \overset{?}{=} -13$$
$$-13 = -13 \text{ true}$$

Since the ordered pair $(1, -5)$ satisfies both equations, it is a solution of the given system.

2. $(-5, 2)$
$$2x + 3y = -4$$
$$2(-5) + 3(2) \overset{?}{=} -4$$
$$-10 + 6 \overset{?}{=} -4$$
$$-4 = -4 \text{ true}$$

$$x - 4y = -10$$
$$-5 - 4(-2) \stackrel{?}{=} -10$$
$$-5 + 8 \stackrel{?}{=} -10$$
$$3 = -10 \text{ false}$$

Since $(-5, 2)$ fails to satisfy *both* equations, it is not a solution of the given system.

3. $(-1, 3)$
$$x + y = 2$$
$$-1 + 3 \stackrel{?}{=} 2$$
$$2 = 2 \text{ true}$$

$$2x + y = -5$$
$$2(-1) + 3 \stackrel{?}{=} -5$$
$$-2 + 3 \stackrel{?}{=} -5$$
$$1 = -5 \text{ false}$$

Since $(-1, 3)$ fails to satisfy *both* equations, it is not a solution of the given system. Also, the second equation in the system, which can be rewritten as $y = -2x - 5$, is a line with slope -2 and y-intercept -5, while the graph shows a line with slope 2 and y-intercept 5.

4. $x + y = 2$
$x - y = 6$

Graph both lines on the same axes.
$x + y = 2$:
x-intercept $= 2$; y-intercept $= 2$
$x - y = 6$:
x-intercept $= 6$; y-intercept $= -6$

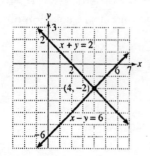

The lines appear to intersect at $(4, -2)$. This apparent solution can be vertified by substituting 4 for x and -2 for y in both equations of the original system.
Solution: $(4, -2)$

5. $2x - 3y = 12$
$-2x + y = -8$

Graph both equations.
$2x - 3y = 12$:
x-intercept $= 6$; y-intercept $= -4$
$-2x + y = -8$
x-intercept $= 4$; y-intercept $= -8$

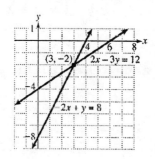

Solution: $(3, -2)$

6. $3x + 2y = 6$
$3x - 2y = 6$

Graph both equations.
$3x + 2y = 6$:
x-intercept $= 2$; y-intercept $= 3$
$3x - 2y = 6$:
x-intercept $= 2$; y-intercept $= -3$

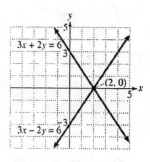

Solution: $(2, 0)$

7. $y = \dfrac{1}{2}x$

$y = 2x - 3$

Graph both equations.

$y = \frac{1}{2}x$:

slope $= \frac{1}{2}$; y-intercept $= 0$

$y = 2x - 3$:
slope $= 2$; y-intercept $= -3$

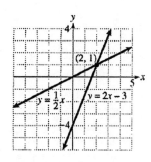

Solution: $(2, 1)$

8. $x + 2y = 2$

$\quad\quad y = x - 5$

Graph both equations.
$x + 2y = 2$:
x-intercept $= 2$; y-intercept $= 1$
$y = x - 5$:
slope $= 1$; y-intercept $= -5$

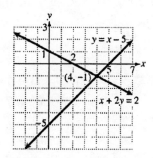

Solution: $(4, -1)$

9. $x + 2y = 8$

$3x + 6y = 12$

Graph both equations.
$x + 2y = 8$:
x-intercept $= 8$; y-intercept $= 4$
$3x + 6y = 12$:
x-intercept $= 4$; y-intercept $= 2$

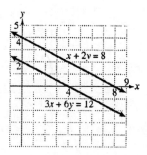

The two lines are parallel. The system has no solution.

10. $2x - 4y = 8$

$\quad x - 2y = 4$

Graph both equations.
$2x - 4y = 8$:
x-intercept: 4; y-intercept $= -2$
$x - 2y = 4$:
x-intercept: 4; y-intercept $= -2$

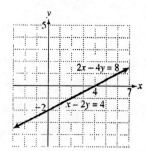

The graphs of the two equations are the same line. The system has infinitely many solutions.

11. $y = 3x - 1$
$y = 3x + 2$

Graph both equations.
$y = 3x - 1$:
slope $= 3$; y-intercept $= -1$
$y = 3x + 2$:
slope $= 3$; y-intercept $= 2$

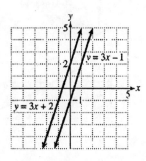

The lines are parallel, so the system has no solution.

12. $x - y = 4$
$\quad x = -2$

Graph both equations:
$x - y = 4$:
x-intercept $= 4$; y-intercept $= -4$
$x = 2$:
vertical line with x-intercept $= -2$

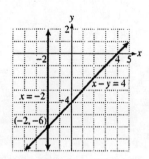

Solution: $(-2, -6)$

13. $x = 2$
$y = 5$

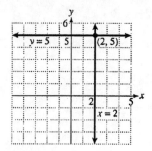

The vertical line and horizontal line intersect at $(2, 5)$.
Solution: $(2, 5)$

14. $x = 2$
$x = 5$

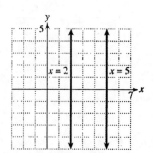

The two vertical lines are parallel, so the system has no solution.

15. $2x - 3y = 7$
$\quad y = 3x - 7$

Substitute $3x - 7$ for y in the first equation.

$$\begin{aligned} 2x - 3y &= 7 \\ 2x - 3(3x - 7) &= 7 \\ 2x - 9x + 21 &= 7 \\ -7x + 21 &= 7 \\ -7x &= -14 \\ x &= 2 \end{aligned}$$

Back-substitute 7 for x into the second equation and solve for y.

$$y = 3x - 7$$
$$y = 3(2) - 7 = -1$$

Solution: $(2, -1)$

16. $2x - y = 6$
   $x = 13 - 2y$

Substitute $13 - 2y$ for x into the first equation.

$$2x - y = 6$$
$$2(13 - 2y) - y = 6$$
$$26 - 4y - y = 6$$
$$26 - 5y = 6$$
$$-5y = -20$$
$$y = 4$$

Back-substitute 4 for y in the second equation.

$$x = 13 - 2y$$
$$x = 13 - 2(4) = 5$$

Solution: $(5, 4)$

17. $2x - 5y = 1$
   $3x + y = -7$

Solve the second equation for y.

$$3x + y = -7$$
$$y = -3x - 7$$

Substitute $-3x - 7$ for y in the first equation.

$$2x - 5y = 1$$
$$2x - 5(-3x - 7) = 1$$
$$2x + 15x + 35 = 1$$
$$17x + 35 = 1$$
$$17x = -34$$
$$x = -2$$

Back-substitute in the equation $y = -3x - 7$.

$$y = -3x - 7$$
$$y = -3(-2) - 7 = -1$$

Solution: $(-2, -1)$

18. $3x + 4y = -13$
   $5y - x = -21$

Solve the second equation for x.

$$5y - x = -21$$
$$-x = -5y - 21$$
$$x = 5y + 21$$

Substitute $5y + 21$ for x in the first equation.

$$3x + 4y = -13$$
$$3(5y + 21) + 4y = -13$$
$$15y + 63 + 4y = -13$$
$$19y + 63 = -13$$
$$19y = -76$$
$$y = -4$$

Back-substitute.

$$3x + 4y = -13$$
$$3x + 4(-4) = -13$$
$$3x - 16 = -13$$
$$3x = 3$$
$$x = 1$$

Solution: $(1, -4)$

19. $y = 39 - 3x$
   $y = 2x - 61$

Substitute $2x - 61$ for y in the first equation.

$$2x - 61 = 39 - 3x$$
$$5x - 61 = 39$$
$$5x = 100$$
$$x = 20$$

Back-substitute.

$$y = 2x - 1$$
$$y = 2(20) - 61 = -21$$

Solution: $(20, -21)$

20. $4x + y = 5$
$12x + 3y = 15$

Solve the first equation for y.

$$4x + y = 5$$
$$y = -4x + 5$$

Substitute $-4x + 5$ for y in the second equation.

$$12x + 3y = 15$$
$$12x + 3(-4x + 5) = 15$$
$$12x - 12x + 15 = 15$$
$$15 = 15 \text{ true}$$

The true statement $15 = 15$ indicates that the given system has infinitely many solutions.

21. $4x - 2y = 10$
    $y = 2x + 3$

Substitute $2x + 3$ for y in the first equation.

$$4x - 2y = 10$$
$$4x - 2(2x + 3) = 10$$
$$4x - 4x - 6 = 10$$
$$-6 = 10 \text{ false}$$

The false statement $-6 = 10$ indicates that the system has no solution.

22. $x - 4 = 0$
$9x - 2y = 0$

Solve the first equation for x.

$$x - 4 = 0$$
$$x = 4$$

Substitute 4 for x in the second equation.

$$9x - 2y = 0$$
$$9(4) - 2y = 0$$
$$36 - 2y = 0$$
$$-2y = -36$$
$$y = 18$$

Solution: $(4, 18)$

23. $8y = 4x$
    $7x + 2y = -8$

Solve the first equation for y.

$$8y = 4x$$
$$y = \frac{1}{2}x$$

Substitute $\frac{1}{2}x$ for y in the second equation.

$$7x + 2y = -8$$
$$7x + 2\left(\frac{1}{2}x\right) = -8$$
$$7x + x = -8$$
$$8x = -8$$
$$x = -1$$

Back-substitute.

$$y = \frac{1}{2}x$$
$$y = \frac{1}{2}(-1) = -\frac{1}{2}$$

Solution: $(-1, -\frac{1}{2})$

24. $N = -60p + 1000$ Demand model
$N = 4p + 200$ Supply model

Substitute $4p + 200$ for N in the demand equation.

$$N = -60p + 1000$$
$$4p + 200 = -60p + 1000$$
$$64p + 200 = 1000$$
$$64p = 800$$
$$p = 12.5$$

If $p = 12.5$,

$$N = 4(12.5) + 200 = 250.$$

Supply and demand are equal when the price of the video is \$12.50. At this price, 250 copies are supplied and sold.

25. $x + y = 6$
$2x + y = 8$

Multiply the first equation by -1 and add the result to the second equation to eliminate the y-terms.

$$\begin{array}{r} -x - y = -6 \\ \underline{2x + y = 8} \\ x = 2 \end{array}$$

Back-substitute into either of the original equations to solve for y.

$$\begin{array}{r} x + y = 6 \\ 2 + y = 6 \\ y = 4 \end{array}$$

Solution: $(2, 4)$

26. $3x - 4y = 1$
$12x - y = -11$

Multiply the first equation by -4 and add the result to the second equation.

$$\begin{array}{r} -12x + 16y = -4 \\ \underline{12x - y = -11} \\ 15y = -15 \\ y = -1 \end{array}$$

Back-substitute.

$$\begin{array}{r} 3x - 4y = 1 \\ 3x - 4(-1) = 1 \\ 3x + 4 = 1 \\ 3x = -3 \\ x = -1 \end{array}$$

Solution: $(-1, -1)$

27. $3x - 7y = 13$
$6x + 5y = 7$

Multiply the first equation by -2. Don't change the second equation.

$$\begin{array}{r} -6x + 14y = -26 \\ \underline{6x - 5y = 7} \\ 19y = -19 \\ y = -1 \end{array}$$

Back-substitute.

$$\begin{array}{r} 3x - 7y = 13 \\ 3x - 7(-1) = 13 \\ 3x + 7 = 13 \\ 3x = 6 \\ x = 2 \end{array}$$

Solution: $(2, -1)$

28. $8x - 4y = 16$
$4x + 5y = 22$

Multiply the second equation by -2. Don't change the first equation.

$$\begin{array}{r} 8x - 4y = 16 \\ \underline{8x - 10y = -44} \\ -14y = -28 \\ y = 2 \end{array}$$

Back-substitute.

$$\begin{array}{r} 8x - 4y = 16 \\ 8x - 4(2) = 16 \\ 8x - 8 = 16 \\ 8x = 24 \\ x = 3 \end{array}$$

Solution: $(3, 2)$

29. $5x - 2y = 8$
$3x - 5y = 1$

Multiply the first equation by 3.
Multiply the second equation by -5.

$$
\begin{array}{r}
-15x - 6y = 24 \\
15x + 25y = -5 \\
\hline
19y = 19 \\
y = 1
\end{array}
$$

Back-substitute.

$$
\begin{aligned}
5x - 2y &= 8 \\
5x - 2(1) &= 8 \\
5x - 2 &= 8 \\
5x &= 10 \\
x &= 2
\end{aligned}
$$

Solution: $(2, 1)$

30. $2x + 7y = 0$
$7x + 2y = 0$

Multiply the first equation by 7.
Multiply the second equation by -2.

$$
\begin{array}{r}
14x + 49y = 0 \\
14x - 4y = 0 \\
\hline
45y = 0 \\
y = 0
\end{array}
$$

Back-substitute.

$$
\begin{aligned}
2x + 7y &= 0 \\
2x + 7(0) &= 0 \\
2x &= 0 \\
x &= 0
\end{aligned}
$$

Solution: $(0, 0)$

31. $x + 3y = -4$
$3x + 2y = 3$

Multiply the first equation by -3.
Don't change the second equation.

$$
\begin{array}{r}
-3x - 9y = 12 \\
3x + 2y = 3 \\
\hline
-7y = 15 \\
y = -\dfrac{15}{7}
\end{array}
$$

Instead of back-substituting $-\frac{15}{7}$ and work-ing with fractions, go back to the original system. Multiply the first equation by 2 and the second equation by -3.

$$
\begin{array}{r}
2x + 6y = -8 \\
9x - 6y = -9 \\
\hline
-7x = -17 \\
x = \dfrac{17}{7}
\end{array}
$$

Solution: $\left(\frac{17}{7}, -\frac{15}{7}\right)$

32. $2x + y = 5$
$2x + y = 7$

Multiply the first equation by -1.
Don't change the second equation.

$$
\begin{array}{r}
-2x - y = -5 \\
2x + y = 7 \\
\hline
0 = 2 \text{ false}
\end{array}
$$

The false statement $0 = 2$ indicates that the system has no solution.

33. $3x - 4y = -1$
$-6x + 8y = 2$

Multiply the first equation by 2.
Don't change the second equation.

$$
\begin{array}{r}
6x - 8y = -2 \\
-6x + 8y = 2 \\
\hline
0 = 0 \text{ true}
\end{array}
$$

The true statement $0 = 0$ indicates that the system has infinitely many solutions.

34.
$$2x = 8y + 24$$
$$3x + 5y = 2$$

Rewrite the first equation in the form $Ax + By = C$.

$$2x - 8y = 24$$

Multiply this equation by 3.
Multiply the second equation by −2.

$$6x - 24y = 72$$
$$\underline{-6x - 10y = -4}$$
$$-34y = 68$$
$$y = -2$$

Back-substitute.

$$3x + 5y = 2$$
$$3x + 5(-2) = 2$$
$$3x - 10 = 2$$
$$3x = 12$$
$$x = 4$$

Solution: $(4, -2)$

35. $5x - 7y = 2$
$3x = 4y$

Rewrite the second equation in the form $Ax + By = C$.

$$3x - 4y = 0$$

Multiply this equation by −5.
Multiply the first equation by 3.

$$15x - 21y = 6$$
$$\underline{-15x + 20y = 0}$$
$$-y = 6$$
$$y = -6$$

Back-substitute.

$$3x - 4y = 0$$
$$3x - 4(-6) = 0$$
$$3x + 24 = 0$$
$$3x = -24$$
$$x = -8$$

Solution: $(-8, -6)$

36. $3x + 4y = -8$
$2x + 3y = -5$

Multiply the first equation by 2.
Multiply the second equation by −3.

$$6x + 8y = -16$$
$$\underline{-6x - 9y = 15}$$
$$-y = -1$$
$$y = 1$$

Back-substitute.

$$3x + 4y = -8$$
$$3x + 4(1) = -8$$
$$3x + 4 = -8$$
$$3x = -12$$
$$x = -4$$

Solution: $(-4, 1)$

37. $6x + 8y = 39$
$y = 2x - 2$

Substitute $2x - 2$ for y in the first equation.

$$6x + 8y = 39$$
$$6x + 8(2x - 2) = 39$$
$$6x + 16x - 16 = 39$$
$$22x - 16 = 39$$
$$22x = 55$$
$$x = \frac{55}{22} = \frac{5}{2}$$

Back-substitute $\frac{5}{2}$ for x into the second equation of the system.

$$y = 2x - 2$$
$$y = 2\left(\frac{5}{2}\right) - 2 = 5 - 2 = 3$$

Solution: $\left(\frac{5}{2}, 3\right)$

38. $x + 2y = 7$
$2x + y = 8$

Multiply the first equation by -2.
Don't change the second equation.

$$\begin{array}{r} -2x - 4y = -14 \\ \underline{2x + \ y = \ \ \ 8} \\ -3y = \ \ -6 \\ y = 2 \end{array}$$

Back-substitute.

$$\begin{aligned} x + 2y &= 7 \\ x + 2(2) &= 7 \\ x + 4 &= 7 \\ x &= 3 \end{aligned}$$

Solution: $(3, 2)$

39. $y = 2x - 3$
$y = -2x - 1$

Substitute $-2x - 1$ for y in the first equation.

$$\begin{aligned} -2x - 1 &= 2x - 3 \\ -4x - 1 &= -3 \\ -4x &= -2 \\ x &= \frac{1}{2} \end{aligned}$$

Back-substitute.

$$y = 2x - 3$$
$$y = 2\left(\frac{1}{2}\right) - 3 = -2$$

Solution: $\left(\frac{1}{2}, -2\right)$

40. $3x - 6y = 7$
$3x = 6y$

Solve the second equation for x.

$$\begin{aligned} 3x &= 6y \\ x &= 2y \end{aligned}$$

Substitute $3y$ for x in the first equation.

$$\begin{aligned} 3x - 6y &= 7 \\ 3(2y) - 6y &= 7 \\ 6y - 6y &= 7 \\ 0 &= 7 \end{aligned}$$

The false statement $0 = 7$ indicates that the system has no solution.

41. $y - 7 = 0$
$7x - 3y = 0$

Solve the first equation for y.

$$\begin{aligned} y - 7 &= 0 \\ y &= 7 \end{aligned}$$

Substitute 7 for y in the second equation.

$$\begin{aligned} 7x - 3y &= 0 \\ 7x - 3(7) &= 0 \\ 7x - 21 &= 0 \\ 7x &= 21 \\ x &= 3 \end{aligned}$$

Solution: $(3, 7)$

42. Let $x =$ the average life span for a horse.
Let $y =$ the average life span for a lion.

$$\begin{array}{r} x + y = 35 \\ \underline{x - y = \ \ 5} \\ 2x \ \ \ \ \ = 40 \\ x = 20 \end{array}$$

$$\begin{aligned} 20 + y &= 35 \\ y &= 15 \end{aligned}$$

The average life span is 20 years for a horse and 15 years for a lion.

43. Let $x =$ the weight of a gorilla.
Let $y =$ the weight of an orangutan.

$$2x + 3y = 1465$$
$$x + 2y = 815$$

Multiply the second equation by -2.
Don't change the first equation.

$$\begin{array}{r} 2x + 3y = 1465 \\ -2x - 4y = -1630 \\ \hline -y = -165 \\ y = 165 \end{array}$$

$$x + 2(165) = 815$$
$$x + 330 = 815$$
$$x = 485$$

The weight of a gorilla is 485 pounds and the weight of an orangutan is 165 pounds.

44. Let $x =$ the cholesterol content of one ounce of shrimp (in milligrams).
Let $y =$ the cholesterol content in one ounce of scallops.

$$3x + 2y = 156$$
$$5x + 3y = 300 - 45$$

Simplify the second equation.

$$5x + 3y = 255$$

Multiply this equation by -2.
Multiply the first equation by 3.

$$\begin{array}{r} 9x + 6y = 468 \\ -10x - 6y = -510 \\ \hline -x = -42 \\ x = 42 \end{array}$$

Back-substitute.

$$3x + 2y = 156$$
$$3(42) + 2y = 156$$
$$126 + 2y = 156$$
$$2y = 30$$
$$y = 15$$

There are 42 mg of cholesterol in an ounce of shrimp and 15 mg in an ounce of scallops.

45. Let $x =$ the length of a tennis table top.
Let $y =$ the width.

Use the formula for the perimeter of a rectangle to write the first equation and the other information in the problem to write the second equation.

$$2x + 2y = 28$$
$$4x - 3y = 21$$

Multiply the first equation by -2.

$$\begin{array}{r} -4x - 4y = -56 \\ 4x - 3y = 21 \\ \hline -7y = -35 \\ y = 5 \end{array}$$

$$2x + 2(5) = 28$$
$$2x + 10 = 28$$
$$2x = 18$$
$$x = 9$$

The length is 9 feet and the width is 5 feet, so the dimensions of the table are 9 feet by 5 feet.

46. Let $ x =$ daily cost for room.
Let $150 - x =$ daily cost for car.

First plan: $3x + 2y = 360$
Second plan: $4x + 3y = 500$

Multiply the first equation by 3.

Multiply the second equation by -2.

$$9x + 6y = 1080$$
$$-8x - 6y = -1000$$
$$x = 80$$

$$3(80) + 2y = 360$$
$$240 + 2y = 360$$
$$2y = 120$$
$$y = 60$$

The cost per day is \$80 for the room and \$60 for the car.

47. Let $x =$ the number of minutes of long-distance calls.
Let $y =$ the monthly cost of a telephone plan.

Plan A: $y = 15 + 0.05x$
Plan B: $y = 10 + 0.075x$

To determine the amount of calling time that will result in the same cost for both plans, solve this system by the substitution method. Substitute $15 + 0.05x$ for x in the first equation.

$$15 + 0.05x = 10 + 0.075x$$
$$15 - 0.025x = 10$$
$$-0.025x = -5$$
$$\frac{-0.025x}{-0.025} = \frac{-5}{-0.025}$$
$$x = 200$$

If $x = 200$,

$$y = 15 + 0.05(200) = 25.$$

The costs for the two plans will be equal for 200 minutes of long-distance calls per month. The cost of each plan will be \$25.

48. Let $x =$ the amount invested at 8%.
Let $y =$ the amount invested at 10%.

$$x + y = 10000$$
$$0.08x + 0.10y = 940$$

Multiply the first equation by -0.08 and add.

$$09.08x - 0.08y = -800$$
$$0.08x + 0.10y = 940$$
$$0.02y = 140$$
$$y = 7000$$

Back-substitute 7000 for y in one of the original equations to find x.

$$x + y = 10000$$
$$x + 7000 = 10000$$
$$x = 3000$$

There was \$3000 invested at 8% and \$7000 invested at 10%.

49. Let $x =$ the amount of the 34% solution.
Let $y =$ the amount of the 4% solution.

$$x + y = 100$$
$$0.34x + 0.04y = 0.07(100)$$

Multiply the first equation by -0.34 and add to the second equation.

$$-0.34x - 0.34y = -34$$
$$0.34x + 0.04y = 7$$
$$-0.30 = -27$$
$$y = 90$$

Back-substitute 90 for y to find x.

$$x + y = 100$$
$$x + 90 = 100$$
$$x = 10$$

10 ml of the 34% solution and 90 ml of the 4% must be used.

50. Let $x =$ the speed of the plane in still air.

Let $y =$ the speed of the wind.

	r	$\times$ t $=$	d
With Wind	$r+w$	3	$3(r+w)$
Against Wind	$r-w$	4	$3(r-w)$

$3(r+w) = 2160$
$4(r-w) = 2160$

The system simplifies as follows.

$3r + 3w = 2160$
$4r - 4w = 2160$

Multiply the first equation by 4, the second equation by 3, and solve by addition.

$$12r + 12w = 8640$$
$$\underline{12r - 12w = 6480}$$
$$24r = 15120$$
$$r = 630$$

Back-substitute 630 for r to find w.

$$3r + 3w = 2160$$
$$3(630) + 3w = 2160$$
$$189 - +3w = 2160$$
$$3w = 270$$
$$w = 90$$

The speed of the plane in still air is 630 miles per hour and the speed of the wind is 90 miles per hour.

Chapter 4 Test

1. $(5, -5)$
$$2x + y = 5$$
$$2(5) + (-5) \overset{?}{=} 5$$
$$10 + (-5) \overset{?}{=} 5$$
$$5 = 5 \text{ true}$$

$$x + 3y = -10$$
$$5 + 3(-5) \overset{?}{=} -10$$
$$5 + (-15) \overset{?}{=} -10$$
$$-10 = -10 \text{ true}$$

Since the ordered pair $(5, -5)$ satisfies both equations, it is a solution of the given system.

2. $(-3, 2)$
$$x + 5y = 7$$
$$-3 + 5(2) \overset{?}{=} 7$$
$$-3 + 10 \overset{?}{=} 7$$
$$7 = 7 \text{ true}$$

$$3x - 4y = 1$$
$$3(-3) - 4(2) \overset{?}{=} 1$$
$$-9 - 8 \overset{?}{=} 1$$
$$-17 = 1 \text{ false}$$

Since the ordered pair $(-3, 2)$ fails to satisfy *both* equations, it is not a solution of the given system.

3. $x + y = 6$
$4x - y = 4$

Graph both lines on the same axes.
$x + y = 6$:
x-intercept $= 6$; y-intercept $= 6$
$4x - y = 4$:
x-intercept: 1; y-intercept $= -4$

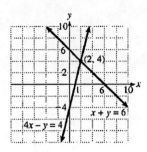

Solution: $(2, 4)$

4. $2x + y = 8$

   $ y = 3x - 2$

Graph both lines on the same axes.

$2x + y = 8$:

x-intercept $= 4$; y-intercept $= 8$

$y = 3x - 2$:

slope $= 3$; y-intercept $= -2$

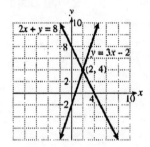

Solution: $(2, 4)$

5. $ x = y + 4$

   $3x + 7y = -18$

Substitute $y + 4$ for x in the second equation.

$$3x + 7y = -18$$
$$3(y + 4) + 7y = -18$$
$$3y + 12 + 7y = -18$$
$$10y + 12 = -18$$
$$10y = -30$$
$$y = -3$$

Back-substitute -3 for y in the first equation.

$$x = y + 4$$
$$x = -3 + 4 = 1$$

Solution: $(1, -3)$

6. $2x - y = 7$

   $3x + 2y = 0$

Solve the first equation for y.

$$2x - y = 7$$
$$-y = -2x + 7$$
$$y = 2x - 7$$

Substitute $2x - 7$ for y in the second equation.

$$3x + 2y = 0$$
$$3x + 2(2x - 7) = 0$$
$$3x + 4x - 14 = 0$$
$$7x - 14 = 0$$
$$7x = 14$$
$$x = 2$$

Back-substitute 2 for x in the equation $3x + 2y = 0$.

$$3x + 2y = 0$$
$$3(2) + 2y = 0$$
$$6 + 2y = 0$$
$$2y = -6$$
$$y = -3$$

Solution: $(2, -3)$

7. $2x - 4y = 3$

   $ x = 2y + 4$

Substitute $2y + 4$ for x in the first equation.

$$2x - 4y = 3$$
$$2(2y + 4) - 4y = 3$$
$$4y + 8 - 4y = 3$$
$$8 = 3 \text{ false}$$

The false statement $8 = 3$ indicates that the system has no solution.

8.
$$2x + y = \ \ 2$$
$$\underline{4x - y = -8}$$
$$6x \qquad = -6$$
$$x = -1$$

Back-substitute.

$$2x + y = 2$$
$$2(-1) + y = 2$$
$$-2 + y = 2$$
$$y = 4$$

Solution: $(-1, 4)$

9. $2x + 3y = 1$
$3x + 2y = -6$

Multiply the first equation by 3.
Multiply the second equation by -2.

$$6x + 9y = \ \ 3$$
$$\underline{-6x - 4y = 12}$$
$$5y = 15$$
$$y = 3$$

Back-substitute.

$$2x + 3y = 1$$
$$2x + 3(3) = 1$$
$$2x + 9 = 1$$
$$2x = -8$$
$$x = -4$$

Solution: $(-4, 3)$

10.
$$3x - 2y = 2$$
$$-9x + 6y = -6$$

Multiply the first equation by 3.
Don't change the second equation.

$$9x - 6y = \ \ 6$$
$$\underline{-9x + 6y = -6}$$
$$0 = \ \ 0 \text{ true}$$

The true statement $0 = 0$ indicates that the equation has infinitely many solutions.

11. Let x = the cost of World War II
(in billions of dollars).
Let y = the cost of the Vietnam War.

$$x + y = 500$$
$$\underline{x - y = 120}$$
$$2x \qquad = 620$$
$$x = 310$$

$$310 + y = 500$$
$$y = 190$$

The cost of World War II was $310 billion and the cost of the Vietnam War was $190 billion (in current dollars).

12. Let x = the number of minutes of long-distance calls.
Let y = the monthly cost of a telephone plan.

Plan A: $y = 15 + 0.05x$
Plan B: $y = 5 + 0.07x$

To determine the amount of calling time that will result in the same cost for both plans, solve this system by the substitution method. Substitute $5 + 0.07x$ for y in the first equation.

$$5 + 0.07x = 15 + 0.05x$$
$$5 + 0.02x = 15$$
$$0.02x = 10$$
$$\frac{0.02x}{0.02} = \frac{10}{0.02}$$
$$x = 500$$

If $x = 500$,

$$y = 15 + 0.05(500) = 40.$$

The costs of the two plans will be equal for 500 calls per month. The cost of each plan will be $40.

13. Let $x =$ the amount invested at 9%.
Let $y =$ the amount invested at 6%.

$$x + \quad y = 6000$$
$$0.09x + 0.06y = 480$$

Multiply the first equation by -0.09 and add to the second equation.

$$-0.09x - 0.09y = -540$$
$$\underline{0.09x + 0.06y = \quad 480}$$
$$-0.03y = -60$$
$$y = 2000$$

Back-substitute 2000 for y to find x.

$$x + y = 6000$$
$$x + 2000 = 6000$$
$$x = 4000$$

There is \$4000 invested at 9% and \$2000 invested at 6%.

14. Let $x =$ the number of ounces of 20% solution.
Let $y =$ the number of ounces of 50% solution.

$$x + y = 60$$
$$0.20x + 0.50y = 0.30 \ (60)$$

Rewrite the system in standard form.

$$x + \quad y = 60$$
$$0.20x + 0.50y = 18$$

Multiply the first equation by -0.20 and add to the second equation.

$$-0.20x - 0.20y = -12$$
$$\underline{0.20x + 0.50y = \quad 18}$$
$$0.30y = 6$$
$$y = 20$$

Back-substitute 20 for y to find x.

$$x + y = 60$$
$$x + 20 = 60$$
$$x = 40$$

40 ounces of 20% solution and 20 ounces of 50% solution must be used.

15. Let $r =$ the speed of the plane in still air.
Let $w =$ the speed of the wind.

	r	$\times$	t	$=$	d
With Wind	$r + w$		2		1600
Against Wind	$r - w$		3		1950

$$2(r + w) = 1600$$
$$3(r - w) = 1950$$

Simplified, the system becomes:

$$2r + 2w = 1600$$
$$3r - 3w = 1950$$

Multiply the first equation by 3, the second equation by 2, and solve by addition.

$$6r - 6w = 4800$$
$$\underline{6r + 6w = 3900}$$
$$12r = 8700$$
$$r = 725$$

Back-substitute 725 for r to find w.

$$2r + 2w = 1600$$
$$2(725) + 2w = 1600$$
$$1450 + 2w = 1600$$
$$2w = 150$$
$$w = 75$$

The speed of the plane in still air is 725 kilometers per hour and the speed of the wind is 75 kilometers per hour.

Cumulative Review Exercises (Chapters 1-4)

1. $-14 - [18 - (6 - 10)] = -14 - [18 - (-4)]$
$$= -14 - 22$$
$$= -14 + (-22)$$
$$= -36$$

2. $6(3x - 2) - (x - 1) = 18x - 12 - x + 1$
$$= 17x - 11$$

3. $17(x+3) = 13 + 4(x-10)$

$17x + 51 = 13 + 4x - 40$

$17x + 51 = 4x - 27$

$13x + 51 = -27$

$13x = -78$

$x = -6$

The solution is -6.

4. $\dfrac{x}{4} - 1 = \dfrac{x}{5}$

To clear fractions, multiply both sides by 20.

$$20\left(\dfrac{x}{4} - 1\right) = 20\left(\dfrac{x}{5}\right)$$

$$5x - 20 = 4x$$

$$x - 20 = 0$$

$$x = 20$$

The solution is 20.

5. $A = P + Prt$ for t

$$A = P + Prt$$

$$A - P = P + Prt - P$$

$$A - P = Prt$$

$$\dfrac{A-P}{Pr} = \dfrac{Prt}{Pr}$$

$$\dfrac{A-P}{Pr} = t \quad \text{or} \quad t = \dfrac{A-P}{Pr}$$

6. $2x - 5 < 5x - 11$

$2x - 5 - 5x < 5x - 11$

$-3x - 5 < -11$

$-3x - 5 + 5 < -11 + 5$

$-3x < -6$

$\dfrac{-3x}{-3} > \dfrac{-6}{-3}$

$x > 2$

$\{x | x > 2\}$

![number line from -5 to 5 with open circle at 2 shaded to right]

7. $x - 3y = 6$

x-intercept: 6

y-intercept: -2

checkpoint: $(3, -1)$

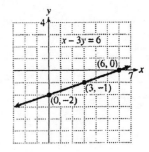

8. $y = 4 - x^2$

Construct a table of values.

x	$y = 4 - x^2$	(x, y)
-3	$y = 4 - (-3)^2 = -5$	$(-3, -5)$
-2	$y = 4 - (-2)^2 = 0$	$(-2, 0)$
-1	$y = 4 - (-1)^2 = 3$	$(-1, 3)$
0	$y = 4 - 0^2 = 4$	$(0, 4)$
1	$y = 4 - 1^2 = 3$	$(1, 3)$
2	$y = 4 - 2^2 = 0$	$(2, 0)$
3	$y = 4 - 3^2 = -5$	$(3, -5)$

Plot the ordered pairs from the table and draw a smooth curve through them.

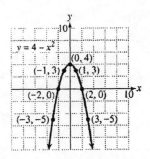

9. $y = -\dfrac{3}{5}x + 2$

slope $= -\frac{3}{5} = \frac{-3}{5}$; y-intercept $= 2$

Plot the point $(0, 2)$. From this point, move 3 units down (because -3 is negative) and 5 units to the right to reach the point $(5, -1)$. Draw a line through $(0, 2)$ and $(5, -1)$.

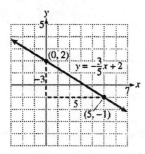

10. $3x - 4y = 8$
$4x + 5y = -10$

To solve this system by the addition method, multiply the first equation by 4 and the second equation by -3. Then add the results.

$$\begin{aligned} 12x - 16y &= 32 \\ -12x - 15y &= 30 \\ \hline -31y &= 62 \\ y &= -2 \end{aligned}$$

Back-substitute.

$$\begin{aligned} 3x - 4y &= 8 \\ 3x - 4(-2) &= 8 \\ 3x + 8 &= 8 \\ 3x &= 0 \\ x &= 0 \end{aligned}$$

Solution: $(0, -2)$

11. $2x - 3y = 9$
$\quad\ y = 4x - 8$

To solve this system by the substitution method, substitute $4x - 8$ for y in the first equation.

$$\begin{aligned} 2x - 3y &= 9 \\ 2x - 3(4x - 8) &= 9 \\ 2x - 12x + 24 &= 9 \\ -10x + 24 &= 9 \\ -10x &= -15 \\ x &= \frac{15}{10} = \frac{3}{2} \end{aligned}$$

Back-substitute $\frac{3}{2}$ for x in the second equation.

$$\begin{aligned} y &= 4x - 8 \\ y &= 4\left(\frac{3}{2}\right) - 8 = -2 \end{aligned}$$

Solution: $\left(\frac{3}{2}, -2\right)$

12. $(5, -6)$ and $(6, -5)$

$$m = \frac{y_2 - y_1}{x_2 - x_1} = \frac{-5 - (-6)}{6 - 5} = \frac{1}{1} = 1$$

13. Passing through $(-1, 6)$ with slope $= -4$ point-slope form:

$$\begin{aligned} y - y_1 &= m(x - x_1) \\ y - 6 &= -4[x - (-1)] \\ y - 6 &= -4(x + 1) \end{aligned}$$

slope-intercept form:

$$\begin{aligned} y - 6 &= -4x - 4 \\ y &= -4x + 2 \end{aligned}$$

14. Let x = the length of the altitude of the triangle.

Use the formula for the area of a triangle.

$$A = \frac{1}{2}bh; \; A = 80, b = 16$$

$$A = \frac{1}{2}bh$$
$$80 = \frac{1}{2} \cdot 16 \cdot h$$
$$80 = 8h$$
$$10 = h$$

The altitude is 10 feet.

15. Let x = the cost of one pen. Then y = the cost of one pad.

$$10x + 15y = 26$$
$$5x + 10y = 16$$

Multiply the second equation by -2 and add the result to the first equation.

$$\begin{array}{r} 10x + 15y = 26 \\ -10x - 20y = -32 \\ \hline -5y = -6 \end{array}$$

$$y = \frac{6}{5} = 1.2$$

$$10x + 15\left(\frac{6}{5}\right) = 26$$
$$10x + 18 = 26$$
$$10x = 8$$

$$x = \frac{8}{10} = 0.8$$

One pen costs $0.80 and one pad costs $1.20.

16. The integers in the given set are $-93, 0$, $\frac{7}{1} (= 7)$ and $\sqrt{100} \, (= 10)$.

17. In 2000, 20% of U.S. households had multiple computers.

Note: In Exercises 17–20, "one computer" means "at least one computer."

18. Both lines are rising from left to right, and the line for one computer is steeper, so the graph for one computer has the greater slope. This means that the percentage of U.S. households with one computer increased at a faster rate than the percentage with multiple computers over the years 1997–2001.

19. Let x = the number of years after 1997. Then y = the percentage of households having one computer.

$$y = 42 + 6x; \; y = 84$$

$$84 = 42 + 6x$$
$$42 = 6x$$
$$7 = x$$

84% of U.S. households will have one computer 7 years after 1997, which will be in the year 2004.

20. $y = \frac{8}{3}x + 12; \; y = 52$

$$52 = \frac{8}{3}x + 12$$
$$40 = \frac{8}{3}x$$
$$\frac{3}{8}(40) = \frac{3}{8}\left(\frac{8}{3}\right)$$
$$15 = x$$

52% of U.S. households will have multiple computers 15 years after 1997, which will be in the year 2012.

Chapter 5

EXPONENTS AND POLYNOMIALS

Adding and Subtracting Polynomials

5.1 CHECK POINTS

CHECK POINT 1

$$(-11x^3 + 7x^2 - 11x - 5)$$
$$+ (16x^3 - 3x^2 + 3x - 15)$$
$$= (-11x^3 + 16x^3) + (7x^2 - 3x^2)$$
$$+ (-11x + 3x) + (-5 - 15)$$
$$= 5x^3 + 4x^2 - 8x - 20$$

CHECK POINT 2

$$\begin{array}{r} -11x^3 \quad 7x^2 - 11x - \ 5 \\ \underline{16x^3 - 3x^2 \quad\ 3x - 15} \\ 5x^3 \quad 4x^2 - \ 8x - 20 \end{array}$$

$$5x^3 + 4x^2 + (-8x) + (-20)$$
$$= 5x^3 + 4x^2 - 8x - 20$$

CHECK POINT 3

$$(9x^2 + 7x - 2) - (2x^2 - 4x - 6)$$
$$= (9x^2 + 7x - 2) + (-2x^2 + 4x + 6)$$
$$= (9x^2 - 2x^2) + (7x + 4x) + (-2 + 6)$$
$$= 7x^2 + 11x + 4$$

CHECK POINT 4

$$(10x^3 - 5x^2 + 7x - 2)$$
$$- (3x^3 - 8x^2 - 5x + 6)$$
$$= (10x^3 - 5x^2 + 7x - 2)$$
$$+ (-3x^3 + 8x^2 + 5x - 6)$$
$$= (10x^3 - 3x^3) + (-5x^2 + 8x^2)$$
$$+ (7x + 5x) + (-2 - 6)$$
$$= 7x^3 + 3x^2 + 12x - 8$$

CHECK POINT 5

$$\begin{array}{r} 8y^3 - 10y^2 - 14y - 2 \\ \underline{-(5y^3 \qquad\quad -\ 3y + 6)} \end{array}$$

$$\begin{array}{r} 8y^3 - 10y^2 - 14y - 2 \\ \underline{+ -\ 5y^3 \qquad\ +\ 3y - 6} \\ 3y^3 - 10y^2 - 11y - 8 \end{array}$$

CHECK POINT 6

$$y = 0.036x^2 - 28.x + 58.14;\ x = 40$$

$$y = 0.036x^2 - 28x + 58.14$$
$$y = 0.036(40)^2 - 2.8(40) + 58.14$$
$$y = 0.036(1600) - 2.8(40) + 58.14$$
$$y = 57.6 - 112 + 58.14$$
$$y = 3.74 \approx 4$$

Approximately 4 people per thousand who are 40 years old die each year. This corresponds to the point $(40, 3.74)$ on the graph, or approximately $(40, 4)$.

EXERCISE SET 5.1

1. $3x + 7$ is a binomial of degree 1.

3. $x^3 - 2x$ is a binomial of degree 3.

5. $8x^2$ is a monomial of degree of 2.

7. 5 is a monomial. Because it is a nonzero constant, its degree is 0.

9. $x^2 - 3x + 4$ is a trinomial of degree 2.

11. $7y^2 - 9y^4 + 5$ is a trinomial of degree 4.

13. $15x - 7x^3$ is a binomial of degree 3.

15. $-9y^{23}$ is a monomial of degree of 23.

17. $(5x + 7) + (-8x + 3)$
$= (5x - 8x) + (7 + 3)$
$= -3x + 10$

19. $(3x^2 + 7x - 9) + (7x^2 + 8x - 2)$
$= (3x^2 + 7x^2) + (7x + 8x) + (-9 - 2)$
$= 10x^2 + 15x - 11$

21. $(5x^2 - 3x) + (2x^2 - x)$
$= (5x^2 + 2x^2) + (-3x - x)$
$= 7x^2 - 4x$

23. $(3x^2 - 7x + 10) + (x^2 + 6x + 8)$
$= (3x^2 + x^2) + (-7x + 6x) + (10 + 8)$
$= 4x^2 - x + 18$

25. $(4y^3 + 7y - 5) + (10y^2 - 6y + 3)$
$= 4y^3 + 10y^2 + (7y - 6y) + (-5 + 3)$
$= 4y^3 + 10y^2 + y - 2$

27. $(2x^2 - 6x + 7) + (3x^3 - 3x)$
$= 3x^3 + 2x^2 + (-6x - 3x) + 7$
$= 3x^3 + 2x^2 - 9x + 7$

29. $(4y^2 + 8y + 11) + (-2y^3 + 5y + 2)$
$= -2y^3 + 4y^2 + (8y + 5y) + (11 + 2)$
$= -2y^3 + 4y^2 + 13y + 13$

31. $(-2y^6 + 3y^4 - y^2) + (-y^6 + 5y^4 + 2y^2)$
$= (-2y^6 - y^6) + (3y^4 + 5y^4) + (-y^2 + 2y^2)$
$= -3y^6 + 8y^4 + y^2$

33. $\left(9x^3 - x^2 - x - \dfrac{1}{3}\right) + \left(x^3 + x^2 + x + \dfrac{4}{3}\right)$

$= (9x^3 + x^3) + (-x^2 + x^2) + (-x + x)$

$\quad + \left(-\dfrac{1}{3} + \dfrac{4}{3}\right)$

$= 10x^2 + \dfrac{3}{3} = 10x^2 + 1$

35. $\left(\dfrac{1}{5}x^4 + \dfrac{1}{3}x^3 + \dfrac{3}{8}x^2 + 6\right)$

$\quad + \left(-\dfrac{3}{5}x^4 + \dfrac{2}{3}x^3 - \dfrac{1}{2}x^2 - 6\right)$

$= \left[\dfrac{1}{5}x^4 + \left(-\dfrac{3}{5}x^4\right)\right] + \left(\dfrac{1}{3}x^2 + \dfrac{2}{3}x^3\right)$

$\quad + \left[\dfrac{3}{8}x^2 + \left(-\dfrac{1}{2}x^2\right)\right] + [6 + (-6)]$

$= -\dfrac{2}{5}x^4 + x^3 - \dfrac{1}{8}x^2$

37. $(0.03x^5 - 0.1x^3 + x + 0.03)$
$\quad + (-0.02x^5 + x^4 - 0.7x + 0.3)$
$\quad = (0.03x^5 - 0.02x^5) + x^4 - 0.1x^3$
$\quad + (x - 0.07x) + (0.03 + 0.3)$
$\quad = 0.01x^5 + x^4 - 0.1x^3 + 0.3x + 0.33$

39. Add:

$$\begin{array}{r} 5y^3 - 7y^2 \\ 6y^3 + 4y^2 \\ \hline 11y^3 - 3y^2 \end{array}$$

41. Add:

$$\begin{array}{r} 3x^2 - 7x + 4 \\ -5x^2 + 6x - 3 \\ \hline -2x^2 - \ x + 1 \end{array}$$

43. Add:

$$\begin{array}{r} \frac{1}{4}x^4 - \ \frac{2}{3}x^3 - 5 \\ -\frac{1}{4}x^4 + \ \frac{1}{5}x^3 + 4.7 \rightarrow \\ \hline \end{array}$$

$$\begin{array}{r} \frac{1}{4}x^4 - \frac{10}{15}x^3 - 5.0 \\ -\frac{2}{4}x^3 + \frac{3}{15}x^3 + 4.7 \\ \hline -\frac{1}{4}x^4 - \frac{7}{15}x^3 - 0.3 \end{array}$$

45. Add:

$$\begin{array}{r} y^3 + 5y^2 - 7y - \ 3 \\ -2y^3 + 3y^2 + 4y - 11 \\ \hline -y^3 + 8y^2 + 4y - 14 \end{array}$$

47. Add:

$$4x^3 - 6x^2 + 5x - 7$$
$$-9x^3 \qquad\;\; - 4x + 3$$
$$\overline{-5x^3 - 6x^2 + \;\; x - 4}$$

49. Add:

$$7x^4 - 3x^3 + x^2$$
$$\qquad x^3 - x^2 + 4x - 2$$
$$\overline{7x^4 - 2x^3 \qquad\;\; + 4x - 2}$$

51. Add:

$$7x^2 - \;\; 9x + 3$$
$$4x^2 + 11x - 2$$
$$\underline{-3x^2 + \;\; 5x - 6}$$
$$8x^2 + \;\; 7x - 6$$

53.
$$1.2x^3 - \;\; 3x^2 + \;\; 9.1$$
$$7.8x^3 - 3.1x^2 + \;\; 8$$
$$\qquad\quad 1.2x^2 - \;\; 6$$
$$\overline{9x^3 - 4.9x^2 + 11.1}$$

55. $(x - 8) - (3x + 2) = (x - 8) + (-3x - 2)$
$$= (x - 3x) + (-8 - 2)$$
$$= -2x - 10$$

57. $(x^2 - 5x - 3) - (6x^2 + 4x + 9)$
$$= (x^2 - 5x - 3) + (-6x^2 - 4x - 9)$$
$$= (x^2 - 6x^2) + (-5x - 4x) + (-3 - 9)$$
$$= -5x^2 - 9x - 12$$

59. $(x^2 - 5x) - (6x^2 - 4x)$
$$= (x^2 - 5x) + (-6x^2 + 4x)$$
$$= (x^2 - 6x^2) + (-5x + 4x)$$
$$= -5x^2 - x$$

61. $(x^2 - 8x - 9) - (5x^2 - 4x - 3)$
$$= (x^2 - 8x - 9) + (-5x^2 + 4x + 3)$$
$$= -4x^2 - 4x - 6$$

63. $(y - 8) - (3y - 2) = (y - 8) + (-3y + 2)$
$$= -2y - 6$$

65. $(6y^3 + 2y^2 - y - 11) - (y^2 - 8y + 9)$
$$= (6y^3 + 2y^2 - y - 11)$$
$$\quad + (-y^2 + 8y - 9)$$
$$= 6y^3 + y^2 + 7y - 20$$

67. $(7n^3 - n^7 - 8) - (6n^3 - n^7 - 10)$
$$= (7n^3 - n^7 - 8) + (-6n^3 + n^7 + 10)$$
$$= (7n^3 - 6n^3) + (-n^7 + n^7) + (-8 + 10)$$
$$= n^3 + 2$$

69. $(y^6 - y^3) - (y^2 - y)$
$$= (y^6 - y^3) + (-y^2 + y)$$
$$= y^6 - y^3 - y^2 + y$$

71. $(7x^4 + 4x^2 + 5x) - (-19x^4 - 5x^2 - x)$
$$= (7x^4 + 4x^2 + 5x) + (19x^4 + 5x^2 + x)$$
$$= 26x^4 + 9x^2 + 6x$$

73. $\left(\dfrac{3}{7}x^3 - \dfrac{1}{5}x - \dfrac{1}{3}\right) - \left(-\dfrac{2}{7}x^3 + \dfrac{1}{4}x - \dfrac{1}{3}\right)$
$$= \left(\dfrac{3}{7}x^3 - \dfrac{1}{5}x - \dfrac{1}{3}\right) + \left(\dfrac{2}{7}x^3 - \dfrac{1}{4}x + \dfrac{1}{3}\right)$$
$$= \left(\dfrac{3}{7}x^3 + \dfrac{2}{7}x^3\right) + \left(-\dfrac{1}{5}x - \dfrac{1}{4}x\right)$$
$$\quad + \left(-\dfrac{1}{3} + \dfrac{1}{3}\right)$$
$$= \left(\dfrac{3}{7}x^3 + \dfrac{2}{7}x^3\right) + \left(-\dfrac{4}{20}x - \dfrac{5}{20}x\right)$$
$$= \dfrac{5}{7}x^3 - \dfrac{9}{20}x$$

75. Subtract:

$$\begin{array}{ll} 7x + 1 & 7x + 1 \\ \underline{-(3x + 5)} \;\to\; + & \underline{-3x + 5} \\ & 4x + 6 \end{array}$$

77. Subtract:

$$\begin{array}{ll} 7x^2 - 3 & 7x^2 - 3 \\ \underline{-(-3x + 4)} \;\to\; + & \underline{3x^2 - 4} \\ & 10x^2 - 7 \end{array}$$

79. Subtract:

$$7y^2 - 5y + 2 \qquad\qquad 7y^2 - 5y + 2$$
$$\underline{-(11y^2 + 2y - 3)} \;\rightarrow\; + \;\underline{-11y^2 - 2y + 3}$$
$$-4y^2 - 7y + 5$$

81. Subtract:

$$7x^3 + 5x^2 - 3 \qquad\qquad 7x^3 + 5x^2 - 3$$
$$\underline{-(-2x^3 - 6x^2 + 5)} \;\rightarrow\; + \;\underline{2x^3 + 6x^2 - 5}$$
$$9x^3 + 11x^2 - 8$$

83. Subtract:

$$5y + 6y^2 - 3y + 10$$
$$\underline{-(6y^3 - 2y^2 - 4y - 4)} \;\rightarrow\;$$

$$\;5y^3 + 6y^2 - 3y + 10$$
$$+ \;\underline{-6y^3 + 2y^2 + 4y + 4}$$
$$-y^3 + 8y^2 + y + 14$$

85. Subtract:

$$7x^4 - 3x^3 + 2x^2$$
$$\underline{-(\quad - x^3 - x^2 + x - 2)} \;\rightarrow\;$$

$$\;7x^4 - 3x^3 + 2x^2$$
$$+ \;\underline{\qquad\quad x^3 + x^2 - x + 2}$$
$$7x^4 - 2x^3 + 3x^2 - x + 2$$

87.

$$0.07x^3 - 0.01x^2 + 0.02x$$
$$\underline{-(0.02x^3 - 0.03x^2 - \quad x)} \;\rightarrow\;$$

$$\;0.07x^3 - 0.01x^2 + 0.02x$$
$$+ \;\underline{-0.02x^3 + 0.03x^2 + \quad x}$$
$$0.05x^3 + 0.02x^2 + 1.02x$$

89. $-0.02A^2 + 2A + 22$
$A = 20$:

$$-0.02(20)^2 + 2(2) + 22 = 54$$

$A = 50$:

$$-0.02(50)^2 + 2(50) + 22 = 72$$

$A = 80$:

$$-0.02(80)^2 + 2(80) + 22 = 54$$

As the level of enthusiasm increases, the level of performance first increases up to a maximum level and then decreases.

91. $y = 0.022x^2 - 0.4x + 60.07$

The year 2000 corresponds to $x = 40$.

$$y = 0.022(40)^2 - 0.4(40) + 60.07$$
$$= 35.2 - 16 + 60.07$$
$$\approx 79.3$$

In 2000, women's earnings were 79.3% of men's.

93. $y = -3.1x^2 + 51.4x + 4024.5$

The year 2000 corresponds to $x = 40$.

$$y = -3.1(40)^2 + 51.4(40) + 4024.5$$
$$= -4960 + 2056 + 4024.5$$
$$= 1120.5$$

According to the formula, the consumption per adult in 2000 was 1120.5 cigarettes. This is a little less than the number shown on the graph, which is approximately 1400 cigarettes.

95. If a dog is 6 years old, the equivalent age is 42 human years.

97. If a person is 25 years old, the equivalent age is 3 dog years.

For Exercises 99–107, answers may vary.

109. $5x^3 - 2x + 1 - (-3x^2 - x - 2)$
$$= (5x^2 - 2x + 1) + (3x^2 + x + 2)$$
$$= 8x^2 - x - 3,$$

so the polynomial is $-3x^2 - x - 2$.

111. In a polynomial of degree 3, the highest degree term has an exponent of 3. The highest degree term of the sum will be the sum of two terms of degree 3, which will be a term of degree 3 or could be 0. It is impossible to get a term of degree 4, so it is impossible to get a polynomial of degree 4.

Review Exercises

112. $(-10)(-7) \div (1-8) = (-10)(-7) \div (-7)$
$$= 70 \div (-7) = -10$$

113. $-4.6 - (-10.2) = -4.6 + 10.2 = 5.6$

114.
$$3(x-2) = 9(x+2)$$
$$3x - 6 = 9x + 18$$
$$3x - 6 - 9x = 9x + 18 - 9x$$
$$-6x - 6 = 18$$
$$-6x - 6 + 6 = 18 + 6$$
$$-6x = 24$$
$$\frac{-6x}{-6} = \frac{24}{-6}$$
$$x = -4$$

The solution is -4.

Multiplying Polynomials

5.2 CHECK POINTS

CHECK POINT 1

a. $2^2 \cdot 2^4 = 2^{2+4} = 2^6$ or 64

b. $x^6 \cdot x^4 = x^{6+4} = x^{10}$

c. $y \cdot y^7 = y^1 \cdot y^7 = y^{1+7} = y^8$

d. $y^4 \cdot y^3 \cdot y^2 = y^{4+3+2} = y^9$

CHECK POINT 2

a. $(3^4)^5 = 3^{4 \cdot 5} = 3^{20}$

b. $(x^9)^{10} = (x^9)^{10} = x^{90}$

c. $[(-5)^7]^3 = (-5)^{7 \cdot 3} = (-5)^{21}$

CHECK POINT 3

a. $(2x)^4 = 2^4 x^4 = 16x^4$

b. $(-4y^3)^3 = (-4)^3(y^2)^3 = (-4)^3 y^{2 \cdot 3} = -64y^6$

CHECK POINT 4

a. $(7x^2)(10x) = (7 \cdot 10)(x^2 \cdot x) = 70x^{2+1}$
$$= 70x^3$$

b. $(-5x^4)(4x^5) = (-5 \cdot 4)(x^4 \cdot x^5)$
$$= -20x^{4+5} = -20x^9$$

CHECK POINT 5

a. $3x(x+5) = 3x \cdot x + 3x \cdot 5$
$$= 3x^2 + 15x$$

b. $6x^2(5x^3 - 2x + 3)$
$$= 6x^2 \cdot 5x^3 - 6x^2 \cdot 2x + 6x^2 \cdot 3$$
$$= 30x^5 - 6x^3 + 18x^2$$

CHECK POINT 6

a. $(x+4)(x+5)$
$$= x(x+5) + 4(x+5)$$
$$= x \cdot x + x \cdot 5 + 4 \cdot x + 4 \cdot 5$$
$$= x^2 + 5x + 4x + 20$$
$$= x^2 + 9x + 20$$

b. $(5x+3)(2x-7)$
$$= 5x(2x-7) + 3(2x-7)$$
$$= 5x \cdot 2x - 5x \cdot 7 + 3 \cdot 2x - 3 \cdot 7$$
$$= 10x^2 - 35x + 6x - 21$$
$$= 10x^2 - 29x - 21$$

CHECK POINT 7

$$(5x + 2)(x^2 - 4x + 3)$$
$$= 5x(x^2 - 4x + 3) + 2(x^2 - 4x + 3)$$
$$= 5x \cdot x^2 - 5x \cdot 4x + 5x \cdot 3 + 2 \cdot x^2$$
$$\quad - 2 \cdot 4x + 2 \cdot 3$$
$$= 5x^3 - 20x^2 + 15x + 2x^2 - 8x + 6$$
$$= 5x^3 - 18x^2 + 7x + 6$$

CHECK POINT 8

$$(3x^2 - 2x)(2x^3 - 5x^2 + 4x)$$

$$\begin{array}{r} 2x^3 - 5x^2 + 4x \\ 3x^2 - 2x \\ \hline -4x^4 + 10x^3 - 8x^2 \\ 6x^5 - 15x^4 + 12x^3 \\ \hline 6x^5 - 19x^4 + 22x^3 - 8x^2 \end{array}$$

EXERCISE SET 5.2

1. $x^{10} \cdot x^5$

To multiply exponential expressions with the same base, use the product rule: $b^m \cdot b^n = b^{m+n}$.

$$x^{10} \cdot x^5 = x^{10+5} = x^{15}$$

3. $y \cdot y^7 = y^1 \cdot y^7 = y^{1+7} = y^8$

5. $x^2 \cdot x^5 \cdot x^4 = x^{2+5+4} = x^{11}$

7. $3^9 \cdot 3^{10} = 3^{19}$

9. $(3^9)^{10}$

To raise an exponential expression to a power, use the power rule: $(b^m)^n = b^{mn}$.

$$(3^9)^{10} = 3^{9 \cdot 10} = 3^{90}$$

11. $(x^4)^5 = x^{4 \cdot 5} = x^{20}$

13. $[(-2)^3]^3 = (-2)^9$

15. $(2x)^3$

To raise a product to a power, use the products-to-powers rule: $(ab)^n = a^n b^n$.

$$(2x)^3 = 2^3 \cdot x^3 = 8x^3$$

17. $(-5x)^2 = (-5)^2 x^2 = 25x^2$

19. $(4x^3)^2 = 4^2 (x^3)^2 = 16x^6$

21. $(-2y^6)^4 = (-2)^4 (y^6)^4 = 16y^{24}$

23. $(-2x^7)^5 = (-2)^5 (x^7)^5 = -32x^{35}$

25. $(7x)(2x) = (7 \cdot 2)(x \cdot x) = 14x^2$

27. $(6x)(4x^2) = (6 \cdot 4)(x \cdot x^2) = 24x^3$

29. $(-5y^4)(3y^3) = (-5 \cdot 3)(y^4 \cdot y^3) = -15y^7$

31. $\left(-\dfrac{1}{2}a^3\right)\left(-\dfrac{1}{4}a^2\right) = \left(-\dfrac{1}{2} \cdot -\dfrac{1}{4}\right)(a^3 \cdot a^2)$
$$= \dfrac{1}{8}a^5$$

33. $(2x^2)(-3x)(8x^4) = -48x^7$

35. $4x(x + 3)$

To multiply a monomial by a binomial, use the distributive property. (Multiply each term of the polynomial by the monomial.)

$$4x(x + 3) = 4x \cdot x + 4x \cdot 3$$
$$= 4x^2 + 12x$$

37. $x(x - 3) = x \cdot x - x \cdot 3$
$$= x^2 - 3x$$

39. $2x(x - 6) = 2x \cdot x - 2x \cdot 6$
$$= 2x^2 - 12x$$

41. $-4y(3y + 5) = -4y \cdot 3y - 4y \cdot 5$
$$= -12y^2 - 20y$$

43. $4x^2(x + 2) = 4x^2 \cdot x + 4x^2 \cdot 2$
$$= 4x^3 + 8x^2$$

45. $2y^2(y^2 + 3y) = 2y^2 \cdot y^2 + 2y^2 \cdot 3y$
$$= 2y^4 + 6y^3$$

47. $2y^2(3y^2 - 4y + 7)$
$$= 2y^2(3y^2) + 2y^2(-4y) + 2y^2(7)$$
$$= 6y^4 - 8y^3 + 14y^2$$

49. $(3x^3 + 4x^2)(2x) = 3x^3 \cdot 2x + 4x^2 \cdot 2x$
$$= 6x^4 + 8x^3$$

51. $(x^2 + 5x - 3)(-2x)$
$$= x^2(-2x) + 5x(-2x) - 3(-2x)$$
$$= -2x^3 - 10x^2 + 6x$$

53. $-3x^2(-4x^2 + x - 5)$
$$= -3x^2(-4x^2) - 3x^2(x) - 3x^2(-5)$$
$$= 12x^4 - 3x^3 + 15x^2$$

55. $(x + 3)(x + 5)$
$$= x(x + 5) + 3(x + 5)$$
$$= x \cdot x + x \cdot 5 + 3 \cdot x + 3 \cdot 5$$
$$= x^2 + 5x + 3x + 15$$
$$= x^2 + 8x + 15$$

57. $(2x + 1)(x + 4)$
$$= 2x(x + 4) + 1(x + 4)$$
$$= 2x^2 + 8x + x + 4$$
$$= 2x^2 + 9x + 4$$

59. $(x + 3)(x - 5)$
$$= x(x - 5) + 3(x - 5)$$
$$= x^2 - 5x + 3x - 15$$
$$= x^2 - 2x - 15$$

61. $(x - 11)(x + 9)$
$$= x(x + 9) - 11(x + 9)$$
$$= x^2 + 9x - 11x - 99$$
$$= x^2 - 2x - 99$$

63. $(2x - 5)(x + 4)$
$$= 2x(x + 4) - 5(x + 4)$$
$$= 2x^2 + 8x - 5x - 20$$
$$= 2x^2 + 3x - 20$$

65. $\left(\dfrac{1}{4}x + 4\right)\left(\dfrac{3}{4}x - 1\right)$
$$= \frac{1}{4}x\left(\frac{3}{4}x - 1\right) + 4\left(\frac{3}{4}x - 1\right)$$
$$= \frac{1}{4}x \cdot \frac{3}{4}x + \frac{1}{4}x(-1)$$
$$+ 4\left(\frac{3}{4}x\right) + 4(-1)$$
$$= \frac{3}{16}x^2 - \frac{1}{4}x + \frac{12}{4}x - 4$$
$$= \frac{3}{16}x^2 + \frac{11}{4}x - 4$$

67. $(x + 1)(x^2 + 2x + 3)$
$$= x(x^2 + 2x + 3) + 1(x^2 + 2x + 3)$$
$$= x^3 + 2x^3 + 3x + x^2 + 2x + 3$$
$$= x^3 + 3x^2 + 5x + 3$$

69. $(y - 3)(y^2 - 3y + 4)$
$$= y(y^2 - 3y + 4) - 3(y^2 - 3y + 4)$$
$$= y^3 - 3y^2 + 4y - 3y^2 + 9y - 12$$
$$= y^3 - 6y^2 + 13y - 12$$

71. $(2a - 3)(a^2 - 3a + 5)$
$$= 2a(a^2 - 3a + 5) - 3(a^2 - 3a + 5)$$
$$= 2a^3 - 6a^2 + 10a - 3a^2 + 9a - 15$$
$$= 2a^3 - 9a^2 + 19a - 15$$

73. $(x + 1)(x^3 + 2x^2 + 3x + 4)$
$$= x(x^3 + 2x^2 + 3x + 4)$$
$$+ 1(x^3 + 2x^2 + 3x + 4)$$
$$= x^4 + 2x^3 + 3x^2 + 4x + x^3 + 2x^2$$
$$+ 3x + 4$$
$$= x^4 + (2x^3 + x^3) + (3x^2 + 2x^2)$$
$$+ (4x + 3x) + 4$$
$$= x^4 + 3x^3 + 5x^2 + 7x + 4$$

75. $\left(x - \dfrac{1}{2}\right)\left(4x^3 - 2x^2 + 5x - 6\right)$

$= x(4x^3 - 2x^2 + 5x - 6)$

$\quad - \dfrac{1}{2}(4x^3 - 2x^2 + 5x - 6)$

$= 4x^4 - 2x^3 + 5x^2 - 6x - 2x^3 + x^2$

$\quad - \dfrac{5}{2}x + 3$

$= 4x^4 - 4x^3 + 6x^2 - \dfrac{17}{2}x + 3$

77. $(x^2 + 2x + 1)(x^2 - x + 2)$

$= x^2(x^2 - x + 2) + 2x(x^2 - x + 2)$

$\quad + 1(x^2 - x + 2)$

$= x^4 - x^3 + 2x^2 + 2x^3 - 2x^2 + 4x$

$\quad + x^2 - x + 2$

$= x^4 + x^3 + x^2 + 3x + 2$

79.
$$
\begin{array}{r}
x^2 - 5x + 3 \\
x + 8 \\
\hline
8x^2 - 40x + 24 \\
x^3 - 5x^2 + 3x \\
\hline
x^3 + 3x^2 - 37x + 24
\end{array}
$$

81.
$$
\begin{array}{r}
x^2 - 3x + 9 \\
2x - 3 \\
\hline
-3x^2 + 9x - 27 \\
2x^3 - 6x^2 + 18x \\
\hline
2x^3 - 6x^2 + 27x - 27
\end{array}
$$

83.
$$
\begin{array}{r}
2x^3 + x^2 + 2x + 3 \\
x + 4 \\
\hline
8x^3 + 4x^2 + 8x + 12 \\
2x^4 + x^3 + 2x^2 + 3x \\
\hline
2x^4 + 9x^3 + 6x^2 + 11x + 12
\end{array}
$$

85.
$$
\begin{array}{r}
4z^3 - 2z^2 + 5z - 4 \\
3z - 2 \\
\hline
-8z^3 + 4z^2 - 10z + 8 \\
12z^4 - 6z^3 + 15z^2 - 12z \\
\hline
12z^4 - 14z^3 + 19z^2 - 22z + 8
\end{array}
$$

87.
$$
\begin{array}{r}
7x^3 - 5x^2 + 6x \\
3x^2 - 4x \\
\hline
-28x^4 + 20x^3 - 24x^2 \\
21x^5 - 15x^4 + 18x^3 \\
\hline
21x^5 - 43x^4 + 38x^3 - 24x^2
\end{array}
$$

89.
$$
\begin{array}{r}
2y^5 - 3y^3 + y^2 - 2y + 3 \\
2y - 1 \\
\hline
-2y^5 + 3y^3 - y^2 + 2y - 3 \\
4y^6 - 6y^4 + 2y^3 - 4y^2 + 6y \\
\hline
4y^6 - 2y^5 - 6y^4 + 5y^3 - 5y^2 + 8y - 3
\end{array}
$$

91.
$$
\begin{array}{r}
x^2 + 7x - 3 \\
x^2 - x - 1 \\
\hline
-x^2 - 7x + 3 \\
-x^3 - 7x^2 + 3x \\
x^4 + 7x^3 - 3x^2 \\
\hline
x^4 + 6x^3 - 11x^2 - 4x + 3
\end{array}
$$

93. Use the formula for the area of a rectangle.

$$A = l \cdot w$$
$$A = (x + 5)(2x - 3)$$
$$= x(2x - 3) + 5(2x - 3)$$
$$= 2x^2 - 3x + 10x - 15$$
$$= 2x^2 + 7x - 15$$

The area of the rug is $(2x^2 + 7x - 15)$ feet.

95. a. $(x + 2)(2x + 1)$

b. $x \cdot 2x + 2 \cdot 2x + x \cdot 1 + 2 \cdot 1$
$$= 2x^2 + 4x + x + 2$$
$$= 2x^2 + 5x + 2$$

c. $(x + 2)(2x + 1) = x(2x + 1) + 2(2x + 1)$
$$= 2x^2 + x + 4x + 2$$
$$= 2x^2 + 5x + 2$$

For Exercises 97–105, answers may vary.

107. The area of the outer square is

$$(x+4)(x+4) = x(x+4) + 4(x+4)$$
$$= x^2 + 4x + 4x + 16$$
$$= x^2 + 8x + 16.$$

The area of the inner square is x^2. The area of the shaded region is the difference between the areas of the two squares, which is

$$(x^2 + 8x + 16) - x^2 = 8x + 16.$$

109. $(-8x^4)\left(-\frac{1}{4}xy^3\right) = 2x^5y^3$, so the missing factor is $-8x^4$.

Review Exercises

110.
$$4x - 7 > 9x - 2$$
$$4x - 7 - 9x > 9x - 2 - 9x$$
$$-5x - 7 > -2$$
$$-5x - 7 + 7 > -2 + 7$$
$$-5x > 5$$
$$\frac{-5x}{-5} < \frac{5}{-5}$$
$$x < -1$$

Solution: $\{x | x < -1\}$

111. $3x - 2y = 6$

x-intercept: 2
y-intercept: -3
checkpoint: $(4, 3)$

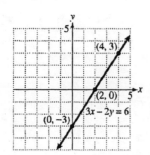

112. $(-2, 8)$ and $(1, 6)$

$$m = \frac{y_2 - y_1}{x_2 - x_2}$$
$$= \frac{6 - 8}{1 - (-2)} = \frac{-2}{3} = -\frac{2}{3}$$

Special Products

5.3 CHECK POINTS

CHECK POINT 1

$$(x + 5)(x + 6)$$
$$= x \overset{F}{\cdot} x + x \overset{O}{\cdot} 6 + 5 \overset{I}{\cdot} x + 5 \overset{L}{\cdot} 6$$
$$= x^2 + 6x + 5x + 30$$
$$= x^2 + 11x + 30$$

CHECK POINT 2

$$(7x + 5)(4x - 3)$$
$$= 7x \overset{F}{\cdot} 4x + 7x \overset{O}{(-3)} + 5 \overset{I}{\cdot} 4x + 5 \overset{L}{(-3)}$$
$$= 28x^2 - 21x + 20x - 15$$
$$= 28x^2 - x - 15$$

CHECK POINT 3

$$(4x - 2x)(5x - 3x)$$
$$= 4 \overset{F}{\cdot} 5 + 4\overset{O}{(-3x)} + \overset{I}{(-2x)}(5) + \overset{L}{(-2x)}(-3x)$$
$$= 20 - 12x - 10x + 6x^2$$
$$= 20 - 22x + 6x^2$$
$$\text{or } 6x^2 - 22x + 20$$

CHECK POINT 4

a. $(7y + 8)(7y - 8) = (7y^2)^2 - 8^2$
$$= 49y^2 - 64$$

b. $(4x - 5)(4x + 5) = (4x)^2 - 5^2$
$$= 16x^2 - 25$$

c. $(2a^3 + 3)(2a^3 - 3) = (2a^3)^2 - 3^2$
$$= 4a^6 - 9$$

CHECK POINT 5

a. $(x + 10)^2 = x^2 + 2 \cdot x \cdot 10 + 10^2$
$$= x^2 + 20x + 100$$

b. $(5x + 4)^2 = (5x)^2 + 2 \cdot 5x \cdot 4 + 4^2$
$$= 25x^2 + 40x + 16$$

CHECK POINT 6

a. $(x - 9)^2 = x^2 - 2 \cdot x + 9 + 9^2$
$$= x^2 - 18x + 81$$

b. $(7x - 3)^2 = (7x)^2 - 2 \cdot 7x \cdot 3 + 3^2$
$$= 49x^2 - 42x + 9$$

EXERCISE SET 5.3

1. $(x + 3)(x + 5)$
$$= \overset{\mathbf{F}}{x \cdot x} + \overset{\mathbf{O}}{x \cdot 5} + \overset{\mathbf{I}}{3 \cdot x} + \overset{\mathbf{L}}{3 \cdot 5}$$
$$= x^2 + 5x + 3x + 15$$
$$= x^2 + 8x + 15$$

3. $(y - 5)(y + 3) = y \cdot y + y \cdot 3 - 5 \cdot y - 5 \cdot 3$
$$= y^2 + 3y - 5y - 15$$
$$= y^2 - 2y - 15$$

5. $(2x - 1)(x + 2)$
$$= 2x \cdot x + 2x \cdot 2 - 1 \cdot x - 1 \cdot 2$$
$$= 2x^2 + 4x - x - 2$$
$$= 2x^2 + 3x - 2$$

7. $(2y - 3)(y + 1)$
$$= 2y \cdot y + 2y \cdot 1 - 3 \cdot y - 3 \cdot 1$$
$$= 2y^2 + 2y - 3y - 3$$
$$= 2y^2 - y - 3$$

9. $(2x - 3)(5x + 3) = 10x^2 + 6x - 15x - 9$
$$= 10x^2 - 9x - 9$$

11. $(3y - 7)(4y - 5) = 12y^2 - 15y - 28y + 35$
$$= 12y^2 - 43y + 35$$

13. $(7 + 3x)(1 - 5x) = 7 - 35x + 3x - 15x^2$
$$= 7 - 32x - 15x^2$$
$$= -15x^2 - 32x + 7$$

15. $(5 - 3y)(6 - 2y) = 30 - 10y - 18y + 6y^2$
$$= 30 - 28y + 6y^2$$
$$= 6y^2 - 28y + 30$$

17. $(5x^2 - 4)(3x^2 - 7)$
$$= (5x^2)(3x^2) + (5x^2)(-7)$$
$$+ (-4)(3x^2) + (-4)(-7)$$
$$= 15x^4 - 35x^2 - 12x^2 + 28$$
$$= 15x^4 - 47x^2 + 28$$

19. $(6x - 5)(2 - x) = 12x - 6x^2 - 10 + 5x$
$$= -6x^2 + 17x - 10$$

21. $(x + 5)(x^2 + 3) = x^3 + 3x + 5x^2 + 15$
$$= x^3 + 5x^2 + 3x + 15$$

23. $(8x^3 + 3)(x^2 + 5) = 8x^5 + 40x^3 + 3x^2 + 15$

In Exercises 25–43, use the rule
$$(A + B)(A - B) + A^2 - B^2.$$

25. $(x + 3)(x - 3) = x^2 - 3^2 = x^2 - 9$

27. $(3x + 2)(3x - 2) = (3x)^2 - 2^2 = 9x^2 - 4$

29. $(3r - 4)(3r + 4) = (3r)^2 - 4^2$
$$= 9r^2 - 16$$

31. $(3 + r)(3 - r) = 3^2 - r^2 = 9 - r^2$

33. $(5 - 7x)(5 + 7x) = 5^2 - (7x^2) = 25 - 49x^2$

35. $\left(2x + \dfrac{1}{2}\right)\left(2x - \dfrac{1}{2}\right) = (2x)^2 - \left(\dfrac{1}{2}\right)^2$
$$= 4x^2 - \dfrac{1}{4}$$

37. $(y^2 + 1)(y^2 - 1) = (y^2)^2 - 1^2 = y^4 - 1$

39. $(r^3 + 2)(r^3 - 2) = (r^3)^2 - 2^2 = r^6 - 4$

41. $(1 - y^4)(1 + y^4) = 1^2 - (y^4)^2 = 1 - y^8$

43. $(x^{10} + 5)(x^{10} - 5) = (x^{10})^2 - 5^2$
$$= x^{20} - 25$$

In Exercises 45–61, use the rules

$$(A + B)^2 = A^2 + 2AB + B^2$$
$$(A - B)^2 = A^2 - 2AB + B^2.$$

45. $(x + 2)^2 = x^2 + 2(2x) + 2^2$
$$= x^2 + 4x + 4$$

47. $(2x + 5)^2 = (2x)^2 + 2(2x)(5) + 5^2$
$$= 4x^2 + 20x + 25$$

49. $(x - 3)^2 = x^2 - 2(3x) + 3^2$
$$= x^2 - 6x + 9$$

51. $(3y - 4)^2 = (3y)^2 - 2(3y)(4) + 4^2$
$$= 9y^2 - 24y + 16$$

53. $(4x^2 - 1)^2 = (4x^2)^2 - 2(4x^2)(1) + 1^2$
$$= 16x^4 - 8x^2 + 1$$

55. $(7 - 2x)^2 = 7^2 - 2(7)(2x) + (2x)^2$
$$= 49 - 28x + 4x^2$$

57. $\left(2x + \dfrac{1}{2}\right)^2 = 4x^2 + 2(2x)\left(\dfrac{1}{2}\right) + \left(\dfrac{1}{2}\right)^2$
$$= 4x^2 + 2x + \dfrac{1}{4}$$

59. $\left(4y - \dfrac{1}{4}\right)^2 = 16y^2 - 2(4y)\left(\dfrac{1}{4}\right) + \left(\dfrac{1}{4}\right)^2$
$$= 16y^2 - 2y + \dfrac{1}{16}$$

61. $(x^8 + 3)^2 = (x^8)^2 + 2(x^8)(3) + 3^2$
$$= x^{16} + 6x^8 + 9$$

63. $(x - 1)(x^2 + x + 1)$
$$= x(x^2 + x + 1) - 1(x^2 + x + 1)$$
$$= x^3 + x^2 + x - x^2 - x - 1$$
$$= x^3 - 1$$

65. $(x - 1)^2 = x^2 - 2(x)(1) + 1^2$
$$= x^2 - 2x + 1$$

67. $(3y + 7)(3y - 7) = (3y^2) - 7^2$
$$= 9y^2 - 49$$

69. $3x^2(4x^2 + x + 9)$
$$= 3x^2(4x^2) + 3x^2(x) + 3x^2(9)$$
$$= 12x^4 + 3x^3 + 27x^2$$

71. $(7y + 3)(10y - 4)$
$$= 70y^2 - 28y + 30y - 12$$
$$= 70y^2 + 2y - 12$$

73. $(x^2 + 1)^2 = (x^2)^2 + 2(x^2)(1) + 1^2$
$$= x^4 + 2x^2 + 1$$

75. $(x^2 + 1)^2(x^2 + 2)$
$$= x^2 \cdot x^2 + x^2 \cdot 2 + 1 \cdot x^2 + 1 \cdot 2$$
$$= x^4 + 3x^2 + 2$$

77. $(x^2 + 4)(x^2 - 4) = (x^2)^2 - 4^2$
$$= x^4 - 16$$

79. $(2 - 3x^5)^2 = 2^2 - 2(2)(3x^5) + (3x^5)^2$
$$= 4 - 12x^5 + 9x^{10}$$

81. $\left(\dfrac{1}{4}x^2 + 12\right)\left(\dfrac{3}{4}x^2 - 8\right)$
$$= \dfrac{1}{4}x^2\left(\dfrac{3}{4}x^2\right) + \dfrac{1}{4}x^2(-8) + 12\left(\dfrac{3}{4}x^2\right)$$
$$+ 12(-8)$$
$$= \dfrac{3}{16}x^4 - 2x^2 + 9x^2 - 96$$
$$= \dfrac{3}{16}x^2 + 7x^2 - 96$$

83. $A = (x + 1)^2 = x^2 + 2x + 1$

85. $A = (2x - 3)(2x + 3) = (2x)^2 - 3^2$
$$= 4x^2 - 9$$

87. Area of outer rectangle:

$$(x + 9)(x + 3) = x^2 + 12x + 27$$

Area of inner rectangle:

$$(x + 5)(x + 1) = x^2 + 6x + 5$$

Area of shaded region:

$$(x^2 + 12x + 27) - (x^2 + 6x + 5) = 6x + 22$$

89. $(x+1)(x+2)$ yards^2

91. $(x+1)(x+2) = (6+1)(6+2) = 7 \cdot 8 = 56$

If the original garden measures 6 yards on a side, the area of the larger garden will be 56 yards^2. This relationship corresponds to the point $(6, 56)$ on the graph.

93. The outer square (square including painting and frame) measures $(x+2)$ inches.

$$(x+2)^2 = x^2 + 4x + 4$$

The area is $(x^2 + 4x + 4)$ square inches.

For Exercises 95–99, answers may vary.

101. To find the correct binomial factors, try different combinations of constants in the binomials that will give a product of -20 as the last term until you find the combination that gives the correct middle term.

$$(x-10)(x+2) = x^2 + 2x - 10x - 20$$
$$= x^2 - 8x - 20,$$

so the two binomials are $(x-10)$ and $(x+2)$.

103. Divide the figure into two rectangles.

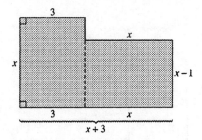

The area of the figure is the sum of the areas of the two rectangles.

$$A = 3 \cdot x + x(x-1)$$
$$= 3x + x^2 - x$$
$$= x^2 + 2x.$$

105.

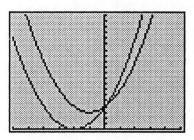

The graphs do not coincide.
$(x+2)^2 = x^2 + 4x + 4$, so $x^2 + 2x + 4$ should be changed to $x^2 + 4x + 4$.

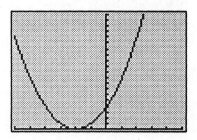

Now the graphs coincide.

107.

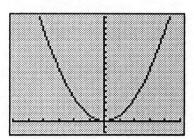

The graphs coincide. This verifies that $(x-2)(x+2) + 4 = x^2$.

Review Exercises

108. $2x + 3y = 1$

$y = 3x - 7$

The substitution method is a good choice because the second equation is already solved for y. Substitute $3x - 7$ for y into the first equation.

$$2x + 3y = 1$$
$$2x + 3(3x - 7) = 1$$
$$2x + 9x - 21 = 1$$
$$11x - 21 = 1$$
$$11x = 22$$
$$x = 2$$

Back-substitute.

$$y = 3x - 7$$
$$y = 3(2) - 7 = 6 - 7 = -1$$

Solution: $(2, -1)$

109. $3x + 4y = 7$

$2x + 7y = 9$

The addition method is a good choice because both equations are written in the form $Ax + By = C$. To eliminate x, multiply the first equation by 2 and the second equation by -3. Then add the results.

$$6x + 8y = 14$$
$$\underline{-6x - 21y = -27}$$
$$-13y = -13$$
$$y = 1$$

Back-substitute 1 for y in either equation of the original system.

$$3x + 4y = 7$$
$$3x + 4(1) = 7$$
$$3x + 4 = 7$$
$$3x = 3$$
$$x = 1$$

Solution: $(1, 1)$

110. $y = \dfrac{1}{3}x$

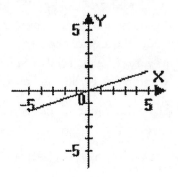

Polynomials in Several Variables

5.4 CHECK POINTS

CHECK POINT 1

$3x^3y + xy^2 + 5y + 6$ for $x = -1$ and $y = 5$

$3x^3y + xy^2 + 5y + 6$
$= 3(-1)^3 \cdot 5 + (-1)(5)^2 + 5 \cdot 5 + 6$
$= 3(-1) \cdot 5 + (-1) \cdot 25 + 5 \cdot 5 + 6$
$= -15 - 25 + 25 + 6$
$= -9$

CHECK POINT 2

$8x^4y^5 - 7x^3y^2 - x^2y - 5x + 11$

Term	Coefficient	Degree
$8x^4y^5$	8	$4 + 5 = 9$
$-7x^3y^2$	-7	$3 + 2 = 5$
$-x^2y$	-1	$2 + 1 = 3$
$-5x$	-5	1
11	11	0

The degree of the polynomial is the highest degree of all its terms, which is 9.

CHECK POINT 3

$(-8x^2y - 3xy + 6) + (10x^2 + 5xy - 10)$
$= (-8x^2y + 10x^2y) + (-3xy + 5xy)$
$\quad + (6 - 10)$
$= 2x^2y + 2xy - 4$

CHECK POINT 4

$(7x^3 - 10x^2y + 2xy^2 - 5)$
$\quad - (4x^3 - 12x^2y - 3xy^2 + 5)$
$\quad = (7x^3 - 10x^2y + 2xy^2 - 5)$
$\quad\quad + (-4x^3 + 12x^2y + 3xy^2 - 5)$
$\quad = (7x^3 - 4x^3) + (-10x^2y + 12x^2y)$
$\quad\quad + (2xy^2 + 3xy^2) + (-5 - 5)$
$\quad = 3x^3 + 2x^2y + 5xy^2 - 10$

CHECK POINT 5

$(6xy^3)(10x^4y^2) = (6 \cdot 10)(x \cdot x^4)(y^3 \cdot y^2)$
$\quad\quad = 60x^{1+4}y^{3+2}$
$\quad\quad = 60x^5y^5$

CHECK POINT 6

$6xy^2(10x^4y^5 - 2x^2y + 3)$
$= 6xy^2 \cdot 10x^4y^5 - 6xy^2 \cdot 2x^2y$
$\quad + 6xy^2 \cdot 3$
$= 60x^{1+4}y^{2+5} - 12x^{1+3}y^{2+1} + 18xy^2$
$= 60x^5y^7 - 12x^4y^3 + 18xy^2$

CHECK POINT 7

a. $(7x - 6y)(3x - y)$
$= (7x)(3x) + (7x)(-y) - 6y(3x)$
$\quad + (-6y)(-y)$
$= 21x^2 - 7xy - 18xy + 6y^2$
$= 21x^2 - 25xy + 6y^2$

b. $(2x + 4y)^2$
$= (2x)^2 + 2 \cdot 2x \cdot 4y + (4y)^2$
$= 4x^2 + 16xy + 16y^2$

CHECK POINT 8

a. $(6xy^2 + 5x)(6xy^2 - 5x)$
$= (6xy^2)^2 - (5x)^2$
$= 36x^2y^4 - 25x^2$

b. $(x - y)(x^2 + xy + y^2)$
$= x(x^2 + xy + y^2)$
$\quad - y(x^2 + xy + y^2)$
$= x \cdot x^2 + x \cdot xy + x \cdot y^2 - y \cdot x^2$
$\quad - y \cdot xy - y \cdot y^2$
$= x^3 + x^2y + xy^2 - x^2y - xy^2 - y^3$
$= x^3 - y^3$

EXERCISE SET 5.4

1. $x^2 + 2xy + y^2; \; x = 2, y = -3$

$$x^2 + 2xy + y^2 = 2^2 + 2(2)(-3) + (-3)^2$$
$$= 4 - 12 + 9 = 1$$

3. $xy^3 - xy + 1 = 2(-3)^3 - 2(-3) + 1$
$\quad\quad = 2(-27) + 6 + 1$
$\quad\quad = -54 + 6 + 1 = -47$

5. $2x^2y - 5y + 3$
$= 2(2^2)(-3) - 5(-3) + 3$
$= 2(4)(-3) - 5(-3) + 3$
$= -24 + 15 + 3 = -6$

7.

Term	Coefficient	Degree
x^3y^2	1	$3 + 2 = 5$
$-5x^2y^7$	-5	$2 + 7 = 9$
$6y^2$	6	2
-3	-3	0

The degree of the polynomial is the highest degree of all its terms, which is 9.

9. $(5x^2y - 3xy) + (2x^2y - xy)$
$= (5x^2y + 2x^2y) + (-3xy - xy)$
$= 7x^2y - 4xy$

11. $(4x^2y + 8xy + 11) + (-2x^2y + 5xy + 2)$
$$= (4x^2y - 2x^2y) + (8xy + 5xy) + (11 + 2)$$
$$= 2x^2y + 13xy + 13$$

13. $(7x^4y^2 - 5x^2y^2 + 3xy)$
$$+ (-18x^4y^2 - 6x^2y^2 - xy)$$
$$= (7x^4y^2 - 18x^4y^2) + (-5x^2y^2 - 6x^2y^2)$$
$$+ (3xy - xy)$$
$$= -11x^4y^2 - 11x^2y^2 + 2xy$$

15. $(x^3 + 7xy - 5y^2) - (6x^3 - xy + 4y^2)$
$$= (x^3 + 7xy - 5y^2) + (-6x^3 + xy - 4y^2)$$
$$= (x^3 - 6x^3) + (7xy + xy) + (-5y^2 - 4y^2)$$
$$= -5x^3 + 8xy - 9y^2$$

17. $(3x^4y^2 + 5x^3y - 3y)$
$$- (2x^4y^2 - 3x^3y - 4y + 6x)$$
$$= (3x^4y^2 + 5x^3y - 3y)$$
$$+ (-2x^4y^2 + 3x^3y + 4y - 6x)$$
$$= (3x^4y^2 - 2x^4y^2) + (5x^3y + 3x^3y)$$
$$+ (-3y + 4y) + (-6x)$$
$$= x^4y^2 + 8x^3y + y - 6x$$

19. $(x^3 - y^3) - (-4x^3 - x^2y + xy^2 + 3y^3)$
$$= (x^3 - y^3) + (4x^3 + x^2y - xy^2 - 3y^3)$$
$$= (x^3 + 4x^3) + x^2y - xy^2 + (-y^3 - 3y^3)$$
$$= 5x^3 + x^2y - xy^2 - 4y^3$$

21. Add:

$$5x^2y^2 - 4xy^2 + 6y^2$$
$$\underline{-8x^2y^2 + 5xy^2 - y^2}$$
$$-3x^2y^2 + xy^2 + 5y^2$$

23. Subtract:

$$3a^2b^4 - 5ab^2 + 7ab$$
$$\underline{-(-5a^2b^4 - 8ab^2 - ab)}$$

Add:

$$3a^2b^4 - 5ab^2 + 7ab$$
$$\underline{5a^2b^4 + 8ab^2 + ab}$$
$$8a^2b^4 + 3ab^2 + 8ab$$

25. $[(7x + 13y) + (-26x + 19y)] - (11x - 5y)$
$$= [(7x - 26x) + (13y + 19y)]$$
$$- (11x - 5y)$$
$$= (-19x + 32y) - (11x - 5y)$$
$$= (-19x + 32y) + (-11x + 5y)$$
$$= (-19x - 11x) + (32y + 5y)$$
$$= -30x + 37y$$

27. $(6x^2y)(3xy) = (6 \cdot 3)(x^2 \cdot x)(y \cdot y)$
$$= 18x^{2+1}y^{1+1}$$
$$= 18x^3y^2$$

29. $(-7x^3y^4)(2x^2y^5) = (-7)(2)x^{3+2}y^{4+5}$
$$= -14x^5y^9$$

31. $5xy(2x + 3y) = 5xy(2x) + 5xy(3y)$
$$= 10x^2y + 15xy^2$$

33. $3xy^2(6x^2 - 2y) = 3xy^2(6x^2) + 3xy^2(-2y)$
$$= 18x^3y^2 - 6xy^3$$

35. $3ab^2(6a^2b^3 + 5ab)$
$$= 3ab^2(6a^2b^3) + 3ab^2(5ab)$$
$$= 18a^3b^5 + 15a^2b^3$$

37. $-b(a^2 - ab + b^2) = -b(a^2) - b(-ab) - b(b^2)$
$$= -a^2b + ab^2 - b^3$$

39. $(x + 5y)(7x + 3y)$
$$= x(7x) + x(3y) + 5y(7x) + 5y(3y)$$
$$= 7x^2 + 3xy + 35xy + 15y^2$$
$$= 7x^2 + 38xy + 15y^2$$

41. $(x - 3y)(2x + 7y)$
$$= x(2x) + x(7y) - 3y(2x) - 3y(7y)$$
$$= 2x^2 + 7xy - 6xy - 21y^2$$
$$= 2x^2 + xy - 21y^2$$

43. $(3xy - 1)(5xy + 2)$
$$= 3xy(5xy) + 3xy(2) - 1(5xy) - 1(2)$$
$$= 15x^2y^2 + 6xy - 5xy - 2$$
$$= 15x^2y^2 + xy - 2$$

45. $(2x + 3y)^2 = (2x)^2 + 2(2x)(3y) + (3y)^2$
$$= 4x^2 + 12xy + 9y^2$$

47. $(xy - 3)^2 = (xy)^2 - 2(xy)(3) + (-3)^2$
$= x^2y^2 - 6xy + 9$

49. $(x^2 + y^2)^2 = (x^2)^2 + 2(x^2)(y^2) + (y^2)^2$
$= x^4 + 2x^2y^2 + y^4$

51. $(x^2 - 2y^2)^2$
$= (x^2) - 2(x^2)(2y^2) + (-2y^2)^2$
$= x^4 - 4x^2y^2 + 4y^4$

53. $(3x + y)(3x - y) = (3x)^2 - y^2 = 9x^2 - y^2$

55. $(ab + 1)(ab - 1) = (ab)^2 - 1^2 = a^2b^2 - 1$

57. $(x + y^2)(x - y^2) = x^2 - (y^2)^2 = x^2 - y^4$

59. $(3a^2b + a)(3a^2b - a) = (3a^2b)^2 - a^2$
$= 9a^4b^2 - a^2$

61. $(3xy^2 - 4y)(3xy^2 + 4y) = (3xy^2)^2 - (4y)^2$
$= 9x^2y^4 - 16y^2$

63. $(a + b)(a^2 - b^2)$
$= a(a^2) + a(-b^2) + b(a^2) + b(-b^2)$
$= a^3 - ab^2 + a^2b - b^3$

65. $(x + y)(x^2 + 3xy + y^2)$
$= x(x^2 + 3xy + y^2) + y(x^2 + 3xy + y^2)$
$= x^3 + 3x^2 + xy^2 + x^2y + 3xy^2 + y^3$
$= x^3 + 4x^2y + 4xy^2 + y^3$

67. $(x - y)(x^2 - 3xy + y^2)$
$= x(x^2 - 3xy + y^2) - y(x^2 - 3xy + y^2)$
$= x^3 - 3x^2y + xy^2 - x^2y + 3xy^2 - y^3$
$= x^3 - 4x^2y + 4xy^2 - y^3$

69. $(xy + ab)(xy - ab) = (xy)^2 - (ab)^2$
$= x^2y^2 - a^2b^2$

71. $(x^2 + 1)(x^4y + x^2 + 1)$
$= x^2(x^4y + x^2 + 1) + 1(x^4y + x^2 + 1)$
$= x^6y + x^4 + x^2 + x^4y + x^2 + 1$
$= x^6y + x^4y + x^4 + 2x^2 + 1$

73. $(x^2y^2 - 3)^2$
$= (x^2y^2)^2 - 2(x^2y^2)(3) + (-3)^2$
$= x^4y^4 - 6x^2y^2 + 9$

75. $(x + y + 1)(x + y - 1)$
$= x(x + y - 1) + y(x + y - 1)$
$\quad + 1(x + y - 1)$
$= x^2 + xy - x + yx + y^2 - y + x + y - 1$
$= x^2 + 2xy + y^2 - 1$

77. $A = (3x + 5y)(x + y)$
$= 3x(x) + 3x(y) + 5y(x) + 5y(y)$
$= 3x^2 + 3xy + 5xy + 5y^2$
$= 3x^2 + 8xy + 5y^2$

79. Area of larger square $= (x + y)^2$
$= x^2 + 2xy + y^2$

Area of smaller square $= x^2$

Area of shaded region $= (x^2 + 2xy + y^2) - x^2$
$= 2xy + y^2$

81. $N = \frac{1}{4}x^2y - 2xy + 4y; \; x = 10, y = 16$

$N = \frac{1}{4}x^2y - 2xy + 4y$

$= \frac{1}{4}(10)^2(16) - 2(10)(16) + 4(16)$

$= \frac{1}{4}(100)(16) - 2(10)(16) + 4(16)$

$= 400 - 320 + 64$

$= 144$

Each tree provides 144 board feet of lumber, so 20 trees will provide $20(144) = 2880$ board feet. This is not enough lumber to complete the job. Since $3000 - 2880 = 120$, the contractor will need 120 more board feet.

83. $s = -16t^2 + v_0t + s_0$; $t = 2$; $v_0 = 80$, $s_0 = 96$

$$s = -16t^2 + v_0t + s_0$$
$$= -16(2)^2 + 80(2) + 96$$
$$= -64 + 160 + 96 = 192$$

The ball will be 192 feet above the ground 2 seconds after being thrown.

85. $s = -16t^2 + v_0t + s_0 = t = 6$, $v_0 = 80$, $s_0 = 96$

$$s = -16t^2 + v_0t + s_0$$
$$= -16(6)^2 + 80(60) + 96$$
$$= -16(36) + 80(6) + 96$$
$$= -576 + 480 + 96 = 0$$

The ball will be 0 feet above the ground after 6 seconds. This means that the ball hits the ground 6 seconds after being thrown.

87. The ball is falling from 2.5 seconds to 6 seconds.

89. $(2, 192)$

91. The ball reaches its maximum height 2.5 seconds after it is thrown. From the graph, a reasonable estimate of the maximum height is 96 feet.

For Exercise 93, answer may vary.

95. Statement c is true.

$$(2x + 3 - 5y)(2x + 3 + 5y)$$
$$= [(2x - 3) - 5y][(2x + 3) + 5y]$$
$$= (2x + 3)^2 - (5y)^2$$
$$= 4x^2 + 12x + 9 - 25y^2$$

97. Area of large rectangle $= (4y)(2y) = 8y^2$
Area of small (unshaded) rectangle $= (2x)(x)$
$$= 2x^2$$
Area of shaded region $= 8y^2 - 2x^2$

99. The storage building is made up of half of a cylinder sitting on top of a rectangular solid.

Rectangular solid:
$$V = lwh = y \cdot 2x \cdot x = 2x^2y$$

Half-cylinder:
$$V = \frac{1}{2}\pi r^2 h = \frac{1}{2}\pi(x)^2 \cdot y$$
$$= \frac{1}{2}\pi x^2 y$$

Volume of storage building $= 2x^2y + \frac{1}{2}\pi x^2 y$

Review Exercises

100. $R = \dfrac{L + 3W}{2}$; for W

$$R = \frac{L + 3W}{2}$$
$$2R = 2\left(\frac{L + 3W}{2}\right)$$
$$2R = L + 3W$$
$$2R - L = L + 3W - L$$
$$2R - L = 3W$$
$$\frac{2R - L}{3} = \frac{3W}{3}$$
$$\frac{2R - L}{3} = W \quad \text{or} \quad W = \frac{2R - L}{3}$$

101. $-6.4 - (-10.2) = -6.4 + 10.2 = 3.8$

102. Since the lines are parallel, they will have the same slope.

$$3x - y = 9$$
$$-y = -3x + 9$$
$$y = 3x - 9$$

The slope is $m = 3$.
point-slope form:
$$y - y_1 = m(x - x_1)$$
$$y - 5 = 3(x - (-2))$$
$$y - 5 = 3(x + 2)$$

slope-intercept form:
$$y - 5 = 3x + 6$$
$$y = 3x + 11$$

Dividing Polynomials

5.5 CHECK POINTS

CHECK POINT 1

a. $\dfrac{5^{12}}{5^4} = 5^{12-4} = 5^8$

b. $\dfrac{x^9}{x^2} = x^{9-2} = x^7$

c. $\dfrac{y^{20}}{y} = \dfrac{y^{20}}{y^1} = y^{20-1} = y^{19}$

CHECK POINT 2

a. $14^0 = 1$ b. $(-10)^0 = 1$

c. $-10^0 = -1$

Only 10 is raised to the 0 power.

d. $20x^0 = 20 \cdot 1 = 20$ e. $(20x)^0$

The entire expression, $20x$, is raised to the 0 power.

CHECK POINT 3

a. $\left(\dfrac{x}{5}\right)^2 = \dfrac{x^2}{5^2} = \dfrac{x^2}{25}$

b. $\left(\dfrac{x^4}{2}\right)^3 = \dfrac{(x^4)^3}{2^3} = \dfrac{x^{4\cdot3}}{2^3} = \dfrac{x^{12}}{8}$

c. $\left(\dfrac{2a^{10}}{b^3}\right)^4 = \dfrac{(2a^{10})^4}{(b^3)^4} = \dfrac{2^4(a^{10})^4}{(b^3)^4}$

$= \dfrac{2^4 a^{40}}{b^{12}} = \dfrac{16a^{40}}{b^{12}}$

CHECK POINT 4

a. $\dfrac{-20x^{12}}{10x^4} = \dfrac{-20}{10}x^{12-4} = -2x^8$

b. $\dfrac{3x^4}{15x^4} = \dfrac{3}{15}x^{4-4} = \dfrac{1}{5}x^0 = \dfrac{1}{5}\cdot 1 = \dfrac{1}{5}$

c. $\dfrac{9x^6y^5}{3xy^2} = \dfrac{9}{3}x^{6-1}y^{5-2} = 3x^5y^3$

CHECK POINT 5

$(-15x^9 + 6x^5 - 9x^3) \div 3x^2$

$\dfrac{-15x^9 + 6x^5 - 9x^3}{3x^2}$

$= \dfrac{-15x^9}{3x^2} + \dfrac{6x^5}{3x^2} - \dfrac{9x^3}{3x^2}$

$= \dfrac{-15}{3}x^{9-7} + \dfrac{6}{3}x^{5-2} - \dfrac{9}{3}x^{3-2}$

$= -5x^2 + 2x^3 - 3x$

CHECK POINT 6

$\dfrac{25x^9 - 7x^4 + 10x^3}{5x^3}$

$= \dfrac{25x^9}{5x^3} - \dfrac{7x^4}{5x^3} + \dfrac{10x^3}{5x^3}$

$= \dfrac{25}{5}x^{9-3} - \dfrac{7}{5}x^{4-3} + \dfrac{10}{5}x^{3-3}$

$= 5x^6 - \dfrac{7}{5}x^1 + 2x^0$

$= 5x - \dfrac{7}{5}x + 2$

CHECK POINT 7

$(18x^7y^6 - 6x^2y^3 + 60xy^2) \div 6xy^2$

$\dfrac{18x^7y^6 - 6x^2y^3 + 60xy^2}{6xy^2}$

$= \dfrac{18x^7y^6}{6xy^2} - \dfrac{6x^2y^3}{6xy^2} + \dfrac{60xy^2}{6xy^2}$

$= 3x^5y^4 - xy + 10$

EXERCISE SET 5.5

1. $\dfrac{3^{20}}{3^5}$

To divide exponential expressions with the same nonzero base, use the quotient rule

$$\dfrac{b^m}{b^n} = b^{m-n},\ b \neq 0.$$

$\dfrac{3^{20}}{3^5} = 3^{20-5} = 3^{15}$

3. $\dfrac{x^6}{x^2} = x^{6-2} = x^4$

5. $\dfrac{y^{13}}{y^5} = y^{13-5} = y^8$

7. $\dfrac{5^6 \cdot 2^8}{5^3 \cdot 2^4} = 5^{6-3} \cdot 2^{8-4} = 5^3 \cdot 2^4$

9. $\dfrac{x^{100}y^{50}}{x^{25}y^{10}} = x^{100-25}y^{50-10} = x^{75}y^{40}$

11. $2^0 = 1$

13. $(-2)^0 = 1$

15. $-2^0 = -(-1) = -1$

17. $100y^0 = 100 \cdot 1 = 100$

19. $(100y^0) = 1$

21. $-5^0 + (-5)^0 = -1 + 1 = 0$

23. $-\pi^0 - (-\pi)^0 = -1 - 1 = -2$

25. $\left(\dfrac{x}{3}\right)^2 = \dfrac{x^2}{9}$

To raise a quotient to a power, use the quotients-to-powers rule

$$\left(\dfrac{a}{b}\right)^n = \dfrac{a^n}{b^n}.$$

$$\left(\dfrac{x}{3}\right)^2 = \dfrac{x^2}{3^2} = \dfrac{x^2}{9}$$

27. $\left(\dfrac{x^2}{4}\right)^3 = \dfrac{(x^2)^3}{4^3} = \dfrac{x^{2 \cdot 3}}{4^3} = \dfrac{x^6}{64}$

29. $\left(\dfrac{2x^3}{5}\right)^2 = \dfrac{2^2(x^3)^2}{5^2} = \dfrac{4x^6}{25}$

31. $\left(\dfrac{-4}{3a^3}\right)^3 = \dfrac{(-4)^3}{3^3(a^3)^3} = \dfrac{-64}{27a^9} = -\dfrac{64}{27a^9}$

33. $\left(\dfrac{-2a^7}{b^4}\right)^5 = \dfrac{(-2a^7)^5}{(b^4)^5} = \dfrac{(-2)^5(a^7)^5}{(b^4)^5}$

$$= \dfrac{-32a^{35}}{b^{20}} = -\dfrac{32a^{35}}{b^{20}}$$

35. $\left(\dfrac{x^2y^3}{2z}\right)^4 = \dfrac{(x^2)^4(y^3)^4}{2^4z^4} = \dfrac{x^8y^{12}}{16z^4}$

In Exercises 37–51, each answer should be checked by showing that the product of the divisor and the quotient is the dividend. The check is shown here only for Exercise 37.

37. $\dfrac{30x^{10}}{10x^5} = \dfrac{30}{10}x^{10-5} = 3x^5$

Check: $10x^5(3x^5) = (10 \cdot 3)x^{5+5} = 30x^{10}$

39. $\dfrac{-8x^{22}}{4x^2} = \dfrac{-8}{4}x^{22-2} = -2x^{20}$

41. $\dfrac{-9y^8}{18y^5} = \dfrac{-9}{18}y^{8-5} = -\dfrac{1}{2}y^3$

43. $\dfrac{7y^{17}}{5y^5} = \dfrac{7}{5}y^{12}$

45. $\dfrac{30x^7y^5}{5x^2y} = \dfrac{30}{5}x^{7-2}y^{5-1} = 6x^5y^4$

47. $\dfrac{-18x^{14}y^2}{36x^2y^2} = \dfrac{-18}{36}x^{14-2}y^{2-2}$

$$= -\dfrac{1}{2}x^{12}y^0 = -\dfrac{1}{2}x^{12} \cdot 1$$

$$= -\dfrac{1}{2}x^{12}$$

49. $\dfrac{9x^{20}y^{20}}{7x^{20}y^{20}} = \dfrac{9}{7}x^0y^0 = \dfrac{9}{7} \cdot 1 \cdot 1 = \dfrac{9}{7}$

51. $\dfrac{-5x^{10}y^{12}z^6}{50x^2y^3z^2} = -\dfrac{1}{10}x^8y^9z^4$

In Exercises 53–77, each answer should be checked by showing that the product of the divisor and the quotient is the dividend. The check is shown here only for Exercise 53.

53. $\dfrac{6x^4 + 2x^3}{2} = \dfrac{6x^4}{2} + \dfrac{2x^3}{2} = 3x^4 + x^3$

Check: $2(3x^4 + x^3) = 2 \cdot 3x^4 + 2 \cdot x^3$
$= 6x^4 + 2x^3$

55. $\dfrac{6x^4 - 2x^3}{2x} = \dfrac{6x^4}{2x} - \dfrac{2x^3}{2x} = 3x^3 - x^2$

57. $\dfrac{y^5 - 3y^2 + y}{y} = \dfrac{y^5}{y} - \dfrac{3y^2}{y} + \dfrac{y}{y}$
$= y^4 - 3y + 1$

59. $\dfrac{15x^3 - 24x^2}{-3x} = \dfrac{15x^3}{-3x} - \dfrac{24x^2}{-3x}$
$= -5x^2 + 8x$

61. $\dfrac{18x^5 + 6x^4 + 9x^3}{3x^2} = \dfrac{18x^5}{3x^2} + \dfrac{6x^4}{3x^2} + \dfrac{9x^3}{3x^2}$
$= 6x^3 + 2x^2 + 3x$

63. $\dfrac{12x^4 - 8x^3 + 40x^2}{4x} = \dfrac{12x^4}{4x} - \dfrac{8x^3}{4x} + \dfrac{40x^2}{4x}$
$= 3x^3 - 2x^2 + 10x$

65. $(4x^2 - 6x) \div x = \dfrac{4x^2 - 6x}{x} = \dfrac{4x^2}{x} - \dfrac{6x}{x}$
$= 4x - 6$

67. $\dfrac{30z^3 + 10z^2}{-5z} = \dfrac{30z^3}{-5z} + \dfrac{10z^2}{-5z} = -6z^2 - 2z$

69. $\dfrac{8x^3 + 6x^2 - 2x}{2} = \dfrac{8x^3}{2x} + \dfrac{6x^2}{2x} - \dfrac{2x}{2x}$
$= 4x^2 + 3x - 1$

71. $\dfrac{25x^7 - 15x^5 - 5x^4}{5x^3} = \dfrac{25x^7}{5x^3} - \dfrac{15x^5}{5x^3} - \dfrac{5x^4}{5x^3}$
$= 5x^4 - 3x^2 - x$

73. $\dfrac{18x^7 - 9x^6 + 20x^5 - 10x^4}{-2x^4}$
$= \dfrac{18x^7}{-2x^4} - \dfrac{9x^6}{-2x^4} + \dfrac{20x^5}{-2x^4} - \dfrac{10x^4}{-2x^4}$
$= -9x^3 + \dfrac{9}{2}x^2 - 10x + 5$

75. $\dfrac{12x^2y^2 + 6x^2y - 15xy^2}{3xy}$
$= \dfrac{12x^2y^2}{3xy} + \dfrac{6x^2y}{3xy} - \dfrac{15xy^2}{3xy}$
$= 4xy + 2x - 5y$

77. $\dfrac{20x^7y^4 - 15x^3y^2 - 10x^2y}{-5x^2y}$
$= \dfrac{20x^7y^4}{-5x^2y} + \dfrac{-15x^3y^2}{-5x^2y} + \dfrac{-10x^2y}{-5x^2y}$
$= -4x^5y^3 + 3xy + 2$

For Exercises 79–85, answers may vary.

87. $\dfrac{18x^8 - 27x^6 + 36x^4}{3x^2} = 6x^6 - 9x^4 + 12x^2,$

so the required polynomial is

$$18x^8 - 27x^6 + 36x^4.$$

One way to find this polynomial is to use the relationship between division and multiplication:

$$3x^2(6x^6 - 9x^4 + 12x^2) = 18x^8 - 36x^6 + 36x^4.$$

89. $\dfrac{3x^{14} - 6x^{12} - ?x^7}{?x^7} = -x^7 + 2x^5 + 3$

To get 2 as the coefficient of the middle term of the quotient, the coefficient in the divisor must be -3. To get the exponents shown in the three terms of the quotient, the exponent in the divisor must be 7. Since we now know that the divisor is $-3x^7$, the coefficient of the last term of the dividend must be -9.
Therefore,

$$\dfrac{3x^{14} - 6x^{12} - ?x^7}{?x^7} = \dfrac{3x^{14} - 6x^{12} - 9x^7}{-3x^7}.$$

Review Exercises

90. $|-20.3| = 20.3$

91.
$$\begin{array}{r} 0.875 \\ 8\overline{)7.000} \\ \underline{6\,4} \\ 60 \\ \underline{56} \\ 40 \\ \underline{40} \\ 0 \end{array}$$

$$\frac{7}{8} = 0.875$$

92. $y = \dfrac{1}{3}x + 2$

slope $= \dfrac{1}{3}$; y-intercept $= 2$

Plot $(0,2)$. From this point move 1 unit *up* and 3 units to the *right* to reach the point $(3,3)$. Draw a line through $(0,2)$ and $(3,3)$.

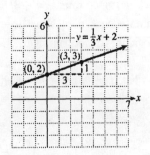

Dividing Polynomials by Binomials

5.6 CHECK POINTS

CHECK POINT 1

Divide $x^2 + 14x + 45$ by $x + 9$.

$$\begin{array}{r} x + 5 \\ x + 9\overline{)x^2 + 14x + 45} \\ \underline{x^2 + 9x} \\ 5x + 45 \\ \underline{5x + 45} \\ 0 \end{array}$$

The quotient is $x+5$ and the remainder is 0. Thus, $(x^2+14x+45) \div (x+9) = x+5$. To check, multiply the divisor and the quotient and add the remainder, 0:

$$(x + 9)(x + 5) + 0$$
$$= x^2 + 5x + 9x + 45 + 0$$
$$= x^2 + 14x + 45.$$

CHECK POINT 2

$$\frac{6x + 8x^2 - 12}{2x + 3}$$

Rewrite the dividend in descending powers of x.

$$6x + 8x^2 - 12 = 8x^2 + 6x - 12$$

$$\begin{array}{r} 4x - 3 \\ 2x + 3\overline{)8x^2 + 6x - 12} \\ \underline{8x^2 + 12x} \\ -6x - 12 \\ \underline{-6x - 9} \\ -3 \end{array}$$

The quotient is $4x - 3$ and the remainder is 0. Thus,

$$\frac{6x + 8x^2 - 12}{2x + 3} = 4x - 3 + \frac{-3}{2x + 3}$$

or

$$\frac{6x + 8x^2 - 12}{2x + 3} = 4x - 3 - \frac{3}{2x + 3}.$$

Check:

$$(2x + 3)(4x - 3) + (-3)$$
$$= 8x^2 - 6x + 12x - 9 - 3$$
$$= 8x^2 + 6x - 12$$
$$\text{or} \quad 6x + 8x^2 - 12$$

CHECK POINT 3

$$\frac{x^3 - 1}{x - 1}$$

Use a coefficient of 0 for the missing x^2- and x-terms in the dividend.

$$\begin{array}{r} x^2 + x + 1 \\ x - 1 \overline{)x^3 + 0x^2 + 0x - 1} \\ \underline{x^3 - x^2} \\ x^2 + 0x \\ \underline{x^2 - x} \\ x - 1 \\ \underline{x - 1} \\ 0 \end{array}$$

The quotient is $x^2 + x + 1$ and the remainder is 0. Thus,

$$\frac{x^3 - 1}{x - 1} = x^2 + x + 1.$$

Check:

$$(x - 1)(x^2 + x + 1)$$
$$= x(x^2 + x + 1) - 1(x^2 + x + 1)$$
$$= x^3 + x^2 + x - x^2 - x - 1$$
$$= x^3 - 1$$

CHECK POINT 4

Divide $x^3 - 7x - 6$ by $x + 2$.

$$\begin{array}{r|rrrr} -2 & 1 & 0 & -7 & -6 \\ & & -2 & 4 & 6 \\ \hline & 1 & -2 & -3 & 0 \end{array}$$

$$(x^3 - 7x - 6) \div (x + 2) = x^2 - 2x - 3$$

EXERCISE SET 5.6

In Exercises 1–35, each answer should be checked by showing that the product of the divisor and the quotient, plus the remainder, is the dividend. Checks will be shown here only for Exercises 1 and 9.

1.
$$\begin{array}{r} x + 4 \\ x + 2 \overline{)x^2 + 6x + 8} \\ \underline{x^2 + 2x} \\ 4x + 8 \\ \underline{4x + 8} \\ 0 \end{array}$$

$$\frac{x^2 + 6x + 8}{x + 2} = x + 4$$

Check: $(x + 2)(x + 4) = x^2 + 4x + 2x + 8$
$$= x^2 + 6x + 8$$

3.
$$\begin{array}{r} 2x + 5 \\ x - 2 \overline{)2x^2 + x - 10} \\ \underline{2x^2 - 4x} \\ 5x - 10 \\ \underline{5x - 10} \\ 0 \end{array}$$

$$\frac{2x^2 + x - 10}{x - 2} = 2x + 5$$

5.
$$\begin{array}{r} x - 2 \\ x - 3 \overline{)x^2 - 5x + 6} \\ \underline{x^2 - 3x} \\ -2x + 6 \\ \underline{-2x + 6} \\ 0 \end{array}$$

$$\frac{x^2 - 5x + 6}{x - 3} = x - 2$$

7.
$$\begin{array}{r} 2y+1 \\ y+2\overline{\smash{\big)}2y^2+5y+2} \\ \underline{2y^2+4y} \\ y+2 \\ \underline{y+2} \\ 0 \end{array}$$

$$\frac{2y^2+5y+2}{y+2}=2y+1$$

9.
$$\begin{array}{r} x-2 \\ x-3\overline{\smash{\big)}x^2-5x+8} \\ \underline{x^2-3x} \\ -2x+8 \\ \underline{-2x+6} \\ 2 \end{array}$$

$$\frac{x^2-5x+8}{x-3}=x-2+\frac{2}{x-3}$$

Check: $(y+2)(y+3)+4=(y^2+5y+6)+4$
$$=y^2+5y+10$$

11.
$$\begin{array}{r} y+3 \\ y+2\overline{\smash{\big)}y^2+5y+10} \\ \underline{y^2+2y} \\ 3y+10 \\ \underline{3y+6} \\ 4 \end{array}$$

$$\frac{5y+10+y^2}{y+2}=\frac{y^2+5y+10}{y+2}$$
$$=y+3+\frac{4}{y+2}$$

13.
$$\begin{array}{r} x^2-5x+2 \\ x-1\overline{\smash{\big)}x^3-6x^2+7x-2} \\ \underline{x^3-x^2} \\ -5x^2+7x \\ \underline{-5x^2+5x} \\ 2x-2 \\ \underline{2x-2} \\ 0 \end{array}$$

$$\frac{x^3-6x^2+7x-2}{x-1}=x^2-5x+2$$

15.
$$\begin{array}{r} 6y-1 \\ 2y-3\overline{\smash{\big)}12y^2-20y+3} \\ \underline{12y^2-18y} \\ -2y+3 \\ \underline{-2y+3} \\ 0 \end{array}$$

$$\frac{12y^2-20y+3}{2y-3}=6y-1$$

17.
$$\begin{array}{r} 2a+3 \\ 2a-1\overline{\smash{\big)}4a^2+4a-3} \\ \underline{4a^2-2a} \\ 6a-3 \\ \underline{6a-3} \\ 0 \end{array}$$

$$\frac{4a^2+4a-3}{2a-1}=2a+3$$

19.
$$\begin{array}{r} y^2-\ y+2 \\ 2y+1\overline{\smash{\big)}2y^3-y^2+3y+2} \\ \underline{2y^3+y^2} \\ -2y^2+3y \\ \underline{-2y^2-\ y} \\ 4y+2 \\ \underline{4y+2} \\ 0 \end{array}$$

$$\frac{3y-y^2+2y^3+2}{2y+1}$$
$$=\frac{2y^3-y^2+3y+2}{2y+1}=y^2-y+2$$

21.
$$\begin{array}{r} x-\ 6 \\ 2x+3\overline{\smash{\big)}2x^2-\ 9x+\ 8} \\ \underline{2x^2+\ 3x} \\ -12x+\ 8 \\ \underline{-12x-18} \\ 26 \end{array}$$

$$\frac{2x^2-9x+8}{2x+3}=x-6+\frac{26}{2x+3}$$

23.
$$
\begin{array}{r}
x^2 + 2x + 8 \\
x-2\overline{)x^3 + 0x^2 + 4x - 3} \\
\underline{x^3 - 2x^2} \\
2x^2 + 4x \\
\underline{2x^2 - 4x} \\
8x - 3 \\
\underline{8x - 16} \\
13
\end{array}
$$

$$\frac{x^3 + 4x - 3}{x - 2} = x^2 + 2x + 8 + \frac{13}{x - 2}$$

25.
$$
\begin{array}{r}
2y^2 + y + 1 \\
2y+3\overline{)4y^3 + 8y^2 + 5y + 9} \\
\underline{4y^3 + 6y^2} \\
2y^2 + 5y \\
\underline{2y^2 + 3y} \\
2y + 9 \\
\underline{2y + 3} \\
6
\end{array}
$$

$$\frac{4y^3 + 8y^2 + 5y + 9}{2y + 3}$$

$$= 2y^2 + y + 1 + \frac{6}{2y + 3}$$

27.
$$
\begin{array}{r}
2y^2 - 3y + 2 \\
3y+2\overline{)6y^3 - 5y^2 + 0y + 5} \\
\underline{6y^3 + 4y^2} \\
-9y^2 + 0y \\
\underline{-9y^2 - 6y} \\
6y + 5 \\
\underline{6y + 4} \\
1
\end{array}
$$

$$\frac{6y^3 - 5y^2 + 5}{3y + 2} = 2y^2 - 3y + 2 + \frac{1}{3y + 2}$$

29.
$$
\begin{array}{r}
9x^2 + 3x + 1 \\
3x-1\overline{)27x^3 + 0x^2 + 0x - 1} \\
\underline{27x^3 - 9x^2} \\
9x^2 + 0x \\
\underline{9x^2 - 3x} \\
3x - 1 \\
\underline{3x - 1} \\
0
\end{array}
$$

$$\frac{27x^3 - 1}{3x - 1} = 9x^2 + 3x + 1$$

31.
$$
\begin{array}{r}
y^3 - 9y^2 + 27y - 27 \\
y-3\overline{)y^4 - 12y^3 + 54y^2 - 108y + 81} \\
\underline{y^4 - 3y^3} \\
-9y^3 + 54y^2 \\
\underline{-9y^3 + 27y^2} \\
27y^2 - 108y \\
\underline{27y^2 - 81y} \\
-27y + 81 \\
\underline{-27y + 81} \\
0
\end{array}
$$

$$\frac{81 - 12y^3 + 54y^2 + y^4 - 108y}{y - 3}$$

$$= \frac{y^4 - 12y^3 + 54y^2 - 108y + 81}{y - 3}$$

$$= y^3 - 9y^2 + 27y - 27$$

33.

$$
\begin{array}{r}
2y+4 \\
2y-1\overline{\smash{)}4y^2+6y+0} \\
\underline{4y^2-2y} \\
8y+0 \\
\underline{8y-4} \\
4
\end{array}
$$

$$\frac{4y^2+6y}{2y-1}=2y+4+\frac{4}{2y-1}$$

35.

$$
\begin{array}{r}
y^3+\ y^2-\ y-1 \\
y-1\overline{\smash{)}y^4+0y^3-2y^2+0y+5} \\
\underline{y^4-\ y^3} \\
y^3-2y^2 \\
\underline{y^3-\ y^2} \\
-y^2+0y \\
\underline{-y^2+\ y} \\
-y+5 \\
\underline{-y+1} \\
4
\end{array}
$$

$$\frac{y^4-2y^2+5}{y-1}=y^3+y^2-y-1+\frac{4}{y-1}$$

37. $(2x^2+x-10)\div(x-2)$

$$
\begin{array}{r|rrr}
2 & 2 & 1 & -10 \\
  &   & 4 & 10 \\
\hline
  & 2 & 5 & 0
\end{array}
$$

$$(2x^2+x-10)\div(x-2)=2x+5$$

39. $(3x^2+7x-20)\div(x+5)$

$$
\begin{array}{r|rrr}
-5 & 3 & 7 & -20 \\
   &   & -15 & 40 \\
\hline
   & 3 & -8 & 20
\end{array}
$$

$$(3x^2+7x-20)\div(x+5)=3x-8+\frac{20}{x+5}$$

41. $(4x^3-3x^2+3x-1)\div(x-1)$

$$
\begin{array}{r|rrrr}
1 & 4 & -3 & 3 & -1 \\
  &   & 4 & 1 & 4 \\
\hline
  & 4 & 1 & 4 & 3
\end{array}
$$

$$(4x^3-3x^2+3x-1)\div(x-1)$$
$$=4x^2+x+4+\frac{3}{x-1}$$

43. $(6x^5-2x^3+4x^2-3x+1)\div(x-2)$

$$
\begin{array}{r|rrrrrr}
2 & 6 & 0 & -2 & 4 & -3 & 1 \\
  &   & 12 & 24 & 44 & 96 & 186 \\
\hline
  & 6 & 12 & 22 & 48 & 93 & 187
\end{array}
$$

$$(6x^5-2x^3+4x^3-3x+1)\div(x-2)$$
$$=6x^4+12x^3+22x^2+48x+93+\frac{187}{x-2}$$

45. $(x^2-5x-5x^3+x^4)\div(5+x)$

Rewrite the polynomials in descending order.

$$(x^4-5x^3+x^2-5x)\div(x+5)$$

$$
\begin{array}{r|rrrrr}
-5 & 1 & -5 & 1 & -5 & 0 \\
   &   & -5 & 50 & -255 & 1300 \\
\hline
   & 1 & -10 & 51 & -260 & 1300
\end{array}
$$

$$(x^2-5x-5x^3+x^4)\div(5+x)$$
$$=x^3-10x^2+51x-260+\frac{1300}{5+x}$$

47. $(3x^3+2x^2-4x+1)\div\left(x-\frac{1}{3}\right)$

$$
\begin{array}{r|rrrr}
\frac{1}{3} & 3 & 2 & -4 & 1 \\
  &   & 1 & 1 & -1 \\
\hline
  & 3 & 3 & -3 & 0
\end{array}
$$

$$(3x^3+2x^2-4x+1)\div\left(x-\frac{1}{3}\right)$$
$$=3x^2+3x-3$$

49. $\dfrac{x^5+x^3-2}{x-1}$

$$
\begin{array}{r|rrrrrr}
1 & 1 & 0 & 1 & 0 & 0 & -2 \\
  &   & 1 & 1 & 2 & 2 & 2 \\
\hline
  & 1 & 1 & 2 & 2 & 2 & 0
\end{array}
$$

$$\frac{x^5+x^3-2}{x-1}=x^4+x^3+2x^2+2x+2$$

51. $\dfrac{x^4-256}{x-4}$

$$
\begin{array}{r|rrrrr}
4 & 1 & 0 & 0 & 0 & -256 \\
  &   & 4 & 16 & 64 & 256 \\
\hline
  & 1 & 4 & 16 & 64 & 0
\end{array}
$$

$$\frac{x^4-256}{x-4}=x^3+4x^2+16x+64$$

53. $\dfrac{2x^5 - 3x^4 + x^3 - x^2 + 2x - 1}{x + 2}$

$$\begin{array}{r|rrrrrr} -2 & 2 & -3 & 1 & -1 & 2 & -1 \\ & & -4 & 14 & -30 & 62 & -128 \\ \hline & 2 & -7 & 15 & -31 & 64 & -129 \end{array}$$

$$\dfrac{2x^5 - 3x^4 + x^3 - x^2 + 2x - 1}{x + 2}$$

$$= 2x^4 - 7x^3 + 15x^2 - 31x + 64 - \dfrac{129}{x+2}$$

55. Solve the formula for the area of rectangle for w. Then substitute the given expressions for A and l.

$$A = lw$$

$$w = \dfrac{A}{l} = \dfrac{2x^2 + 5x - 3}{2x - 1}$$

$$\begin{array}{r} x + 3 \phantom{{}-3} \\ 2x - 1\overline{\smash{\big)}\,2x^2 + 5x - 3} \\ \underline{2x^2 - x} \\ 6x - 3 \\ \underline{6x - 3} \\ 0 \end{array}$$

The width is $(x + 3)$ inches.

57. a. $\dfrac{x + 25}{x + 20} = 1 + \dfrac{5}{x + 20}$

$$\begin{array}{r} 1 \phantom{{}+20} \\ x + 20\overline{\smash{\big)}\,x + 25} \\ \underline{x + 20} \\ 5 \end{array}$$

b.

x	0	5	10	25	50	75
$\dfrac{x + 25}{x + 20}$	$\dfrac{5}{4}$	$\dfrac{6}{5}$	$\dfrac{7}{6}$	$\dfrac{10}{9}$	$\dfrac{15}{14}$	$\dfrac{20}{19}$

c. As x increases, the ratio is decreasing and approaching 1.

For Exercises 59–61, answers may vary.

63. Statement b is true.

65.

$$\begin{array}{r} 8x + 3 \phantom{{}+ k} \\ 2x - 1\overline{\smash{\big)}\,16x^2 - 2x + k} \\ \underline{16x^2 - 8x} \\ 6x + k \\ \underline{6x - 3} \\ 0 \end{array}$$

The remainder will be 0 if

$$k - (-3) = 0$$
$$k + 3 = 0$$
$$k = -3.$$

67.

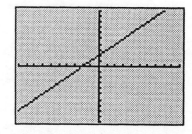

The graphs coincide. This verifies that

$$\dfrac{x^2 - 4}{x - 2} = x + 2.$$

69.

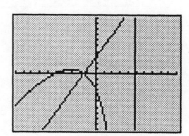

The graphs do not coincide.

$$\begin{array}{r} 2x + 23 \phantom{{}+ 15} \\ x - 5\overline{\smash{\big)}\,2x^2 + 13x + 15} \\ \underline{2x^2 - 10x} \\ 23x + 15 \\ \underline{23x - 115} \\ 130 \end{array}$$

$$\frac{2x^2 + 13x + 15}{x - 5} = 2x + 23 + \frac{130}{x - 5}$$

The expression on the right should be changed to
$2x + 23 + \frac{130}{x-5}$.

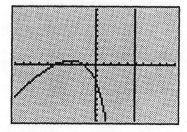

Now the graphs coincide.

71.

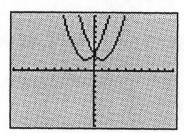

The graphs do not coincide.

$$\begin{array}{r} x^2 + 2x + 3 \\ x + 1\overline{)x^3 + 3x^2 + 5x + 3} \\ \underline{x^2 + x^2} \\ 2x^2 + 5x \\ \underline{2x^2 + 2x} \\ 3x + 3 \\ \underline{3x + 3} \\ 0 \end{array}$$

$$\frac{x^3 + 3x^2 + 5x + 3}{x + 1} = x^2 + 2x + 3$$

The expression on the right should be changed to $x^2 + 2x + 3$.

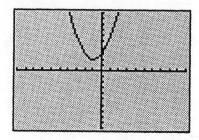

Now the graphs coincide.

Review Exercises

72. $7x - 6y = 17$
  $3x + y = 18$

Multiply the second equation by 6 and solve by addition.

$$\begin{array}{r} 7x - 6y = 17 \\ \underline{18x + 6y = 108} \\ 25x = 125 \\ x = 5 \end{array}$$

Back-substitute 5 for x for y.

$$\begin{aligned} 7x - 6y &= 17 \\ 7(5) - 6y &= 17 \\ 35 - 6y &= 17 \\ -6y &= -18 \\ y &= 3 \end{aligned}$$

The solution is $(5, 3)$.

73. $A = PB$; $P = 6\% = 0.06, B = 20$

$$\begin{aligned} A &= PB \\ A &= (0.06)(20) = 1.2 \end{aligned}$$

1.2 is 60% of 20.

74. $\dfrac{x}{3} + \dfrac{2}{5} = \dfrac{x}{5} - \dfrac{2}{5}x = 5$

To clear fractions, multiply by the LCD, 15.

$$15\left(\dfrac{x}{3} + \dfrac{2}{5}\right) = 15\left(\dfrac{x}{5} - \dfrac{2}{5}\right)$$

$$15\left(\dfrac{x}{3}\right) + 15\left(\dfrac{2}{5}\right) = 15\left(\dfrac{x}{5}\right) - 15\left(\dfrac{2}{5}\right)$$

$$5x + 6 = 3x - 6$$
$$2x + 6 = -6$$
$$2x = -12$$
$$x = -6$$

The solution is -6.

Negative Exponents and Scientific Notation

5.7 CHECK POINTS

CHECK POINT 1

a. $6^{-2} = \dfrac{1}{6^2} = \dfrac{1}{6 \cdot 6} = \dfrac{1}{36}$

b. $5^{-3} = \dfrac{1}{5^3} = \dfrac{1}{5 \cdot 5 \cdot 5} = \dfrac{1}{125}$

c. $(-4)^{-3} = \dfrac{1}{(-4)^3} = \dfrac{1}{(-4)(-4)(-4)}$

$$= \dfrac{1}{-64} = -\dfrac{1}{64}$$

d. $8^{-1} = \dfrac{1}{8^1} = \dfrac{1}{8}$

CHECK POINT 2

a. $\dfrac{2^{-3}}{7^{-2}} = \dfrac{7^2}{2^3} = \dfrac{7 \cdot 7}{2 \cdot 2 \cdot 2} = \dfrac{49}{8}$

b. $\left(\dfrac{4}{5}\right)^{-2} = \dfrac{4^{-2}}{5^{-2}} = \dfrac{5^2}{4^2} = \dfrac{5 \cdot 5}{4 \cdot 4} = \dfrac{25}{16}$

c. $\dfrac{1}{7y^{-2}} = \dfrac{y^2}{7}$

d. $\dfrac{x^{-1}}{y^{-8}} = \dfrac{y^8}{x^1} = \dfrac{y^8}{x}$

CHECK POINT 3

$$x^{-12} \cdot x^2 = x^{-12+2} = x^{-10} = \dfrac{1}{x^{10}}$$

CHECK POINT 4

a. $\dfrac{x^2}{x^{10}} = x^{2-10} = x^{-8} = \dfrac{1}{x^8}$

b. $\dfrac{75x^3}{5x^9} = \dfrac{75}{5} \cdot x^{3-9} = 15x^{-6} = \dfrac{15}{x^6}$

c. $\dfrac{50y^8}{-25y^{14}} = \dfrac{50}{-25}y^{8-14} = -2y^{-6} = -\dfrac{2}{y^6}$

CHECK POINT 5

$$\dfrac{(6x^4)^2}{x^{11}} = \dfrac{6^2(x^4)^2}{x^{11}} = \dfrac{6^2 x^{4\cdot 2}}{x^{11}}$$

$$= \dfrac{36x^8}{x^{11}} = 36x^{8-11}$$

$$= 36x^{-3} = \dfrac{36}{x^3}$$

CHECK POINT 6

$$\left(\dfrac{x^8}{x^4}\right)^{-5} = \dfrac{(x^8)^{-5}}{(x^4)^{-5}} = \dfrac{x^{8(-5)}}{x^{4(-5)}} = \dfrac{x^{-40}}{x^{-20}}$$

$$= x^{-40-(-20)} = x^{-20} = \dfrac{1}{x^{20}}$$

CHECK POINT 7

a. 7.4×10^9

Move the decimal point in 7.4 nine places to the right. This requires adding eight zeros.

$$7.4 \times 10^9 = 7{,}400{,}000{,}000$$

b. 3.07×10^{-6}

Move the decimal point in 3.017 six places to the left. This requires adding five zeros to the right of the decimal point.

$$3.017 \times 10^{-6} = 0.000003017$$

CHECK POINT 8

a. 7,410,000,000

To write this number in scientific notation, move the decimal point nine places to the left. The exponent is positive because the given number is greater than 10.

$$7,410,000,000 = 7.41 \times 10^9$$

b. 0.000000092

To write this number in scientific notation, move the decimal point eight places to the right. The exponent is negative because the given number is between 1 and 10.

CHECK POINT 9

a. $(3 \times 10^8)(2 \times 10^2) = 3 \cdot 2 \cdot 10^8 \cdot 10^2$
$$= 6 \times 10^{8+2}$$
$$= 6 \times 10^{10}$$

b. $\dfrac{8.4 \times 10^7}{4 \times 10^{-4}} = \dfrac{8.4}{4} \times \dfrac{10^7}{10^{-4}}$
$$= 2.1 \times 10^{7-(-4)}$$
$$= 2.1 \times 10^{11}$$

c. $(4 \times 10^{-2})^3 = 4^3 \times (10^{-2})^3$
$$= 4^3 \times 10^{-6}$$
$$= 64 \times 10^{-6}$$
$$= 6.4 \times 10^1 \times 10^{-6}$$
$$= 6.4 \times 10^{-5}$$

CHECK POINT 10

$(2 \times 10^4) \times 26 = (2 \times 26) \times 10^4$
$$= 5.2 \times 10^4$$
$$= 5.2 \times 10^1 \times 10^4$$
$$= 5.2 \times 10^5$$

The total distance covered by all the runners was 5.2×10^6 miles.

EXERCISE SET 5.7

1. $5^{-2} = \dfrac{1}{5^2} = \dfrac{1}{25}$

3. $2^{-3} = \dfrac{1}{2^3} = \dfrac{1}{8}$

5. $(-2)^{-2} = \dfrac{1}{(-2)^2} = \dfrac{1}{4}$

7. $(-3)^{-3} = \dfrac{1}{(-3)^3} = \dfrac{1}{-27} = -\dfrac{1}{27}$

9. $4^{-1} = \dfrac{1}{4^1} = \dfrac{1}{4}$

11. $2^{-1} + 3^{-1} = \dfrac{1}{2^1} + \dfrac{1}{3^1} = \dfrac{1}{2} + \dfrac{1}{3}$
$$= \dfrac{3}{6} + \dfrac{2}{6} = \dfrac{5}{6}$$

13. $\dfrac{1}{3^{-2}} = 3^2 = 9$

15. $\dfrac{1}{(-3)^{-2}} = (-3)^2 = 9$

17. $\dfrac{2^{-3}}{8^{-2}} = \dfrac{8^2}{2^3} = \dfrac{64}{8} = 8$

19. $\left(\dfrac{1}{4}\right)^{-2} = \dfrac{1^{-2}}{4^{-2}} = \dfrac{4^2}{1^2} = \dfrac{16}{1} = 16$

21. $\left(\dfrac{3}{5}\right)^{-3} = \dfrac{3^{-3}}{5^{-3}} = \dfrac{5^3}{3^3} = \dfrac{125}{27}$

23. $\dfrac{1}{6x^{-5}} = \dfrac{1 \cdot x^5}{6} = \dfrac{x^5}{6}$

25. $\dfrac{x^{-8}}{y^{-1}} = \dfrac{y^1}{x^8} = \dfrac{y}{x^8}$

27. $\dfrac{3}{(-5)^{-3}} = 3 \cdot (-5)^3 = 5(-125) = -375$

29. $x^{-8} \cdot x^3 = x^{-8+3} = x^{-5} = \dfrac{1}{x^5}$

31. $(4x^{-5})(2x^2) = 8x^{-5+2} = 8x^{-3} = \dfrac{8}{x^3}$

33. $\dfrac{x^3}{x^9} = x^{3-9} = x^{-6} = \dfrac{1}{x^6}$

35. $\dfrac{y}{y^{100}} = \dfrac{y^1}{y^{100}} = y^{1-100} = y^{-99} = \dfrac{1}{y^{99}}$

37. $\dfrac{30z^5}{10z^{10}} = \dfrac{30}{10} \cdot \dfrac{z^5}{z^{10}} = 3z^{5-10}$

$\qquad = 3z^{-5} = \dfrac{3}{z^5}$

39. $\dfrac{-8x^3}{2x^7} = \dfrac{-8}{2} \cdot \dfrac{x^3}{x^7} = -4x^{-4} = -\dfrac{4}{x^4}$

41. $\dfrac{-9a^5}{27a^8} = \dfrac{-9}{27} \cdot \dfrac{a^5}{a^8} = -\dfrac{1}{3}a^{-3} = -\dfrac{1}{3a^3}$

43. $\dfrac{7w^5}{5w^{13}} = \dfrac{7}{5} \cdot \dfrac{w^5}{w^{13}} = \dfrac{7}{5}w^{-8} = \dfrac{7}{5w^8}$

45. $\dfrac{x^3}{(x^4)^2} = \dfrac{x^3}{x^{4 \cdot 2}} = \dfrac{x^3}{x^8} = x^{-5} = \dfrac{1}{x^5}$

47. $\dfrac{y^{-3}}{(y^4)^2} = \dfrac{y^{-3}}{y^8} = y^{-3-8} = y^{-11} = \dfrac{1}{y^{11}}$

49. $\dfrac{(4x^3)^2}{x^8} = \dfrac{4^2x^6}{x^8} = 16x^{-2} = \dfrac{16}{x^2}$

51. $\dfrac{(6y^4)^3}{y^{-5}} = \dfrac{6^3y^{12}}{y^{-5}} = 216y^{12-(-5)} = 216y^{17}$

53. $\left(\dfrac{x^4}{x^2}\right)^{-3} = (x^2)^{-3} = x^{-6} = \dfrac{1}{x^6}$

55. $\left(\dfrac{4x^5}{2x^2}\right)^{-4} = (2x^3)^{-4} = 2^{-4}x^{-12} = \dfrac{1}{2^4x^{12}}$

$\qquad = \dfrac{1}{16x^{12}}$

57. $(3x^{-1})^{-2} = 3^{-2}(x^{-1})^{-2} = 3^{-2}x^2$

$\qquad = \dfrac{x^5}{3^2} = \dfrac{x^2}{9}$

59. $(-2y^{-1})^{-3} = (-2)^{-3}(y^{-1})^{-3} = \dfrac{y^3}{(-2)^3}$

$\qquad = \dfrac{y^3}{-8} = -\dfrac{y^3}{8}$

61. $\dfrac{2x^5 \cdot 3x^7}{15x^6} = \dfrac{6x^{12}}{15x^6} = \dfrac{6}{15} \cdot \dfrac{x^{12}}{x^6}$

$\qquad = \dfrac{2}{5} \cdot x^6 = \dfrac{2x^6}{5}$

63. $(x^3)^5 \cdot x^{-7} = x^{15} \cdot x^{-7} = x^{15+(-7)} = x^8$

65. $(2y^3)^4y^{-6} = 2^4(y^3)^4y^{-6} = 16y^{12}y^{-6}$

$\qquad = 16y^6$

67. $\dfrac{(y^3)^4}{(y^2)^7} = \dfrac{y^{12}}{y^{14}} = y^{-2} = \dfrac{1}{y^2}$

69. $(y^{10})^{-5} = y^{(10)(-5)} = y^{-50} = \dfrac{1}{y^{50}}$

71. $(a^4b^5)^{-3} = (a^4)^{-3}(b^5)^{-3} = a^{-12}b^{-15}$

$\qquad = \dfrac{1}{a^{12}b^{15}}$

73. $(a^{-2}b^6)^{-4} = a^8b^{-24} = \dfrac{a^8}{b^{24}}$

75. $\left(\dfrac{x^2}{2}\right)^{-2} = \dfrac{x^{-4}}{2^{-2}} = \dfrac{2^2}{x^4} = \dfrac{4}{x^4}$

77. $\left(\dfrac{x^2}{y^3}\right)^{-3} = \dfrac{(x^2)^{-3}}{(y^3)^{-3}} = \dfrac{x^{-6}}{y^{-9}} = \dfrac{y^9}{x^6}$

79. $2.7 \times 10^2 = 270$ (Move decimal point 2 places right.)

81. $9.12 \times 10^5 = 912{,}000$ (Move right 5.)

83. $3.4 \times 10^0 = 3.4$ (Don't move decimal point.)

85. $7.9 \times 10^{-1} = 0.79$ (Move left 1.)

87. $2.15 \times 10^{-2} = 0.0215$ (Move left 2.)

89. $7.86 \times 10^{-4} = 0.000786$ (Move left 4.)

91. $32{,}400 = 3.24 \times 10^4$

93. $220{,}000{,}000 = 2.2 \times 10^8$

95. $713 = 7.13 \times 10^2$

97. $6751 = 6.751 \times 10^3$

99. $0.0027 = 2.7 \times 10^{-3}$

101. $0.000020 = 2.02 \times 10^{-5}$

103. $0.005 = 5 \times 10^{-3}$

105. $3.14159 = 3.14159 \times 10^0$

106. $(2 \times 10^3)(3 \times 10^2) = 6 \times 10^{3+2} = 6 \times 10^5$

109. $(2 \times 10^5)(8 \times 10^3) = 16 \times 10^{5+3} = 16x^8$
$$= 1.6 \times 10^9$$

111. $\dfrac{12 \times 10^6}{4 \times 10^2} = 3 \times 10^{6-2} = 3 \times 10^4$

113. $\dfrac{15 \times 10^4}{5 \times 10^{-2}} = 3 \times 10^{4+2} = 3 \times 10^6$

115. $\dfrac{15 \times 10^{-4}}{5 \times 10^2} = 3 \times 10^{-4-2} = 3 \times 10^{-6}$

117. $\dfrac{180 \times 10^6}{2 \times 10^3} = 90 \times 10^{6-3} = 90 \times 10^3$
$$= 9 \times 10^4$$

119. $\dfrac{3 \times 10^4}{12 \times 10^{-3}} = 0.25 \times 10^{4+3} = 0.25 \times 10^7$
$$= 2.5 \times 10^6$$

121. $(5 \times 10^2)^3 = 5^3 \times 10^{2(3)} = 125 \times 10^6$
$$= 1.25 \times 10^8$$

123. $(3 \times 10^{-2})^4 = 3^4 \times 10^{-2(4)} = 81 \times 10^{-8}$
$$= 8.1 \times 10^{-7}$$

125. $(4 \times 10^6)^{-1} = 4^{-1} \times 10^{6(-1)} = 0.25 \times 10^{-6}$
$$= 2.5 \times 10^{-7}$$

127. $9200 = 9.2 \times 10^3$

129. $0.00000000000000025 = 2.5 \times 10^{-16}$

131. $1,694,300 = 1.6943 \times 10^6$
1 million $= 10^6$

$$1,694,300 \text{ million} = (1.6943 \times 10^6)(10^6)$$
$$= 1.6943 \times 10^{12}$$

133. $60 = 6 \times 10^1$
1 billion $= 10^9$
60 billion $= (6 \times 10^1)(10^9) = 6 \times 10^{10}$

135. 1.6 trillion $= 1.6 \times 10^{12}$

25% of 1.6 trillion $= 0.25(1.6 \times 10^{12})$
$$= 0.4 \times 10^{12} = 4 \times 10^{11}$$

The United States government spends approximately $\$4 \times 10^{11}$ per year on Social Security.

137. $120(2.7 \times 10^8) = 324 \times 10^8 = 3.2410^{10}$

The total annual spending in the United States on ice cream is about $\$3.24 \times 10^{10}$.

For Exercises 139–143, answers may vary.

145. Statement b is true.
$5^{-2} = \frac{1}{25}$ and $2^{-5} = \frac{1}{32}$.
Since $\frac{1}{25} > \frac{1}{32}, 5^{-2} > 2^{-5}$.

147. There is no advantage in using scientific notation to represent a number greater than or equal to 1 and less than 10 because the decimal point will not be moved and it is simpler to write it without the zero exponent.

Example: $7.75 = 7.75 \times 10^0$

149. Students will check their work with a calculator. Results will depend on the exercises chosen.

151. Students will check their work with a calculator. Results will depend on the exercises chosen.

Review Exercises

153. $8 - 6x > 4x - 12$
$8 - 10x > -12$
$-10x > -20$
$x < 2$

The solution set is $\{x | x < 2\}$.

154. $24 \div 8 \cdot 3 + 28 \div (-7) = 3 \cdot 3 + 28 \div (-7)$
$$= 9 + (-4) = 5$$

155. The whole numbers in the given set are 0 and $\sqrt{16}\ (= 4)$.

Chapter 5 Review Exercises

1. $7x^4 + 9x$ is a binomial of degree 4.

2. $3x + 5x^2 - 2$ is a trinomial of degree 2.

3. $16x$ is a monomial of degree 1.

4. $(-6x^2 + 7x^2 - 9x + 3)$
  $+ (14x^3 + 3x^2 - 11x - 7)$
  $= (-6x^3 + 14x^3) + (7x^2 + 3x^2)$
  $+ (-9x - 11x) + (3 - 7)$
  $= 8x^3 + 10x^2 - 20x - 4$

5. $(9y^3 - 7y^2 + 5) + (4y^3 - y^2 + 7y - 10)$
  $= (9y^3 + 4y^3) + (-7y^2 - y^2) + 7y$
  $+ (5 - 10)$
  $= 13y^3 - 8y^2 + 7y - 5$

6. $(5y^2 - y - 8) - (-6y^2 + 3y - 4)$
  $= (5y^2 - y - 8) + (6y^2 - 3y + 4)$
  $= (5y^2 + 6y^2) + (-y - 3y) + (-8 + 4)$
  $= 11y^2 - 4y - 4$

7. $(13x^4 - 8x^3 + 2x^2) - (5x^4 - 3x^3 + 2x^2 - 6)$
  $= (13x^4 - 8x^3 + 2x^2)$
  $+ (-5x^4 + 3x^3 - 2x^2 + 6)$
  $= (13x^4 - 5x^4) + (-8x^3 + 3x^3)$
  $+ (2x^2 - 2x^2) + 6$
  $= 8x^4 - 5x^3 + 6$

8. $(-13x^4 - 6x^2 + 5x) - (x^4 + 7x^2 - 11x)$
  $= (-13x^4 - 6x^2 + 5x)$
  $+ (-x^4 - 7x^2 + 11x)$
  $= (-13x^4 - x^4) + (-6x^2 - 7x^2)$
  $+ (5x + 11x)$
  $= -14x^4 - 13x^2 + 16x$

9. Add:
$$\begin{array}{r} 7y^4 - 6y^3 + 4y^2 - 4y \\ \underline{y^3 - \ y^2 + 3y - 4} \\ 7y^4 - 5y^3 + 3y^2 - \ y - 4 \end{array}$$

10. Subtract:
$$\begin{array}{r} 7x^2 - 9x + 2 \\ \underline{-(4x^2 - 2x - 7)} \end{array}$$
Add:
$$\begin{array}{r} 7x^2 - 9x + 2 \\ \underline{-4x^2 + 2x + 7} \\ 3x^2 - 7x + 9 \end{array}$$

11.
$$\begin{array}{r} 5x^3 - 6x^2 - \ 9x + 14 \\ \underline{-(-5x^3 + 3x^2 - 11x + \ 3)} \end{array}$$
Add:
$$\begin{array}{r} 5x^3 - 6x^2 - \ 9x + 14 \\ \underline{5x^3 - 3x^2 + 11x - \ 3} \\ 10x^3 - 9x^2 + \ 2x + 11 \end{array}$$

12. $104.5x^2 - 1501.5x + 6016; x = 10$
$$104.5x^2 - 1501.5x + 6016$$
$$= 104.5(10^2) - 1501.5(10) + 6016$$
$$= 10{,}450 - 15{,}015 + 6016$$
$$= 1451$$

The death rate for men averaging 10 hours of sleep per night is 1451 men per 10,000 men.

13. $x^{20} \cdot x^3 = x^{20+3} = x^{23}$

14. $y \cdot y^5 \cdot y^8 = y^1 \cdot y^5 \cdot y^8 = y^{1+5+8} = y^{14}$

15. $(x^{20})^5 = x^{20 \cdot 5} = x^{100}$

16. $(10y)^2 = 10^2 y^2 = 100y^2$

17. $(-4x^{10})^3 = (-4)^3 (x^{10})^3 = -64x^{30}$

18. $(5x)(10x^3) = (5 \cdot 10)(x^1 \cdot x^3) = 50x^4$

19. $(-12y^7)(3y^4) = -36y^{11}$

20. $(-2x^5)(-3x^4)(5x^3) = 30x^{12}$

21. $7x(3x+9) = 7x(3x) + (7x)(9) = 21x^2 + 63x$

22. $5x^3(4x^2 - 11x) = 5x^3(4x^2) - 5x^3(11x)$
$$= 20x^5 - 55x^4$$

23. $3y^2(-7y^2 + 3y - 6)$
$$= 3y^2(-7y^2) + 3y^2(3y) + 3y^2(-6)$$
$$= -21y^4 + 9y^3 - 18y^2$$

24. $2y^5(8y^3 - 10y^2 + 1)$
$$= 2y^5(8y^3) + 2y^5(-10y^2) + 2y^5(1)$$
$$= 16y^8 - 20y^7 + 2y^5$$

25. $(x+3)(x^2 - 5x + 2)$
$$= x(x^2 - 5x + 2) + 3(x^2 - 5x + 2)$$
$$= x^3 - 5x^2 + 2x + 3x^2 - 15x + 6$$
$$= x^3 - 2x^2 - 13x + 6$$

26. $(3y - 2)(4y^2 + 3y - 5)$
$$= 3y(4y^2 + 3y - 5) - 2(4y^2 + 3y - 5)$$
$$= 12y^3 + 9y^2 - 15y - 8y^2 - 6y + 10$$
$$= 12y^3 + y^2 - 21y + 10$$

27.
$$
\begin{array}{r}
y^2 - 4y + 7 \\
3y - 5 \\
\hline
-5y^2 + 20y - 35 \\
3y^3 - 12y^2 + 21y \\
\hline
3y^3 - 17y^2 + 41y - 35
\end{array}
$$

28.
$$
\begin{array}{r}
4x^3 - 2x^2 - 6x - 1 \\
2x + 3 \\
\hline
12x^3 - 6x^2 - 18x - 3 \\
8x^4 - 4x^3 - 12x^2 - 2x \\
\hline
8x^4 + 8x^3 - 18x^2 - 20x - 3
\end{array}
$$

29. $(x+6)(x+2)$
$$= x \cdot x + x \cdot 2 + 6 \cdot x + 6 \cdot 2$$
$$= x^2 + 2x + 6x + 12$$
$$= x^2 + 8x + 12$$

30. $(3y - 5)(2y + 1) = 6y^2 + 3y - 10y - 5$
$$= 6y^2 - 7y - 5$$

31. $(4x^2 - 2)(x^2 - 3)$
$$= 4x^2 \cdot x^2 + 4x^2(-3) - 2 \cdot x^2 - 2(-3)$$
$$= 4x^4 - 12x^2 - 2x^2 + 6$$
$$= 4x^4 - 14x^2 + 6$$

32. $(5x + 4)(5x - 4) = (5x)^2 - 4^2$
$$= 25x^2 - 16$$

33. $(7 - 2y)(7 + 2y) = 7^2 - (2y)^2 = 49 - 4y^2$

34. $(y^2 + 1)(y^2 - 1) = (y^2)^2 - 1^2 = y^4 - 1$

35. $(x + 3)^2 = x^2 + 2(x)(3) + 3^2$
$$= x^2 + 6x + 9$$

36. $(3y + 4)^2 = (3y)^2 + 2(3y)(4) + 16$
$$= 9y^2 + 24y + 16$$

37. $(y - 1)^2 = y^2 - 2y + 1$

38. $(5y - 2)^2 = (5y)^2 - 2(5y)(2) + 2^2$
$$= 25y^2 - 20y + 4$$

39. $(x^2 + 4)^2 = (x^2)^2 + 2(x^2)(4) + 4^2$
$$= x^4 + 8x^2 + 16$$

40. $(x^2 + 4)(x^2 - 4) = (x^2)^2 - 4^2 = x^4 - 16$

41. $(x^2 + 4)(x^2 - 5) = (x^2)^2 - 5x^2 + 4x^2 - 20$
$$= x^4 - x^2 - 20$$

42. $A = (x + 3)(x + 4)$
$$= x^2 + 4x + 3x + 12$$
$$= x^2 + 7x + 12$$

43. $A = (x + 30)(x + 20)$
$$= x^2 + 20x + 30x + 600$$
$$= x^2 + 50x + 600$$

The area of the expanded garage is $(x^2 + 50x + 600)$ yards^2.

44. $2x^3y - 4xy^2 + 5y + 6; x = -1, y = 2$

$2x^3y - 4xy^2 + 5y + 6$
$$= 2(-1)^3(2) - 4(-1)(2)^2 + 5(2) + 6$$
$$= 2(-1)(2) - 4(1)(4) + 5(2) + 6$$
$$= -4 + 16 + 10 + 6 = 28$$

45.

Term	Coefficient	Degree
$4x^2y$	4	$2+1=3$
$9x^3y^2$	9	$3+2=5$
$-17x^4$	-17	4
-12	-12	0

Degree of the polynomial $= 5$

46. $(7x^2 - 8xy + y^2) + (-8x^2 - 9xy + 4y^2)$
$= (7x^2 - 8x^2) + (-8xy - 9xy)$
$\quad + (y^2 + 4y^2)$
$= -x^2 - 17xy + 5y^2$

47. $(13x^3y^2 - 5x^2y - 9x^2)$
$\quad - (11x^3y^2 - 6x^2y - 3x^2 + 4)$
$= (13x^3y^2 - 5x^2y - 9x^2)$
$\quad + (-11x^3y^2 + 6x^2y + 3x^2 - 4)$
$= (13x^3y^2 - 11x^3y^2) + (-5x^2y + 6x^2y)$
$\quad + (-9x^2 + 3x^2) - 4$
$= 2x^3y^3 + x^2y - 6x^2 - 4$

48. $(-7x^2y^3)(5x^4y^6)$
$= (-7)(-5)x^{2+4}y^{3+6}$
$= -35x^6y^9$

49. $5ab^2(3a^2b^3 - 4ab)$
$= 5ab^2(3a^2b^3) + 5ab^2(-4ab)$
$= 15a^3b^5 - 20a^2b^3$

50. $(x + 7y)(3x - 5y)$
$= x(3x) + x(-5y) + 7y(3x) + 7y(-5y)$
$= 3x^2 - 5xy + 21xy - 35y^2$
$= 3x^2 + 16xy - 35y^2$

51. $(4xy - 3)(9xy - 1)$
$= 4xy(9xy) + 4xy(-1) - 3(9xy) - 3(-1)$
$= 36x^2y^2 - 4xy - 27xy + 3$
$= 36x^2y^2 - 31xy + 3$

52. $(3x + 5y)^2 = (3x)^2 + 2(3x)(5y) + (5y)^2$
$= 9x^2 + 30xy + 25y^2$

53. $(xy - 7)^2 = (xy)^2 - 2(xy)(7) + 7^2$
$= x^2y^2 - 14xy + 49$

54. $(7x + 4y)(7x - 4y) = (7x)^2 - (4y)^2$
$= 49x^2 - 16y^2$

55. $(a - b)(a^2 + ab + b^2)$
$= a(a^2 + ab + b^2) - b(a^2 + ab + b^2)$
$= a^3 + a^2b + ab^2 - a^2b - ab^2 - b^3$
$= a^3 + (a^2b - a^2b) + (ab^2 - ab^2) - b^3$
$= a^3 - b^3$

56. $\dfrac{6^{40}}{6^{10}} = 6^{40-10} = 6^{30}$

57. $\dfrac{x^{18}}{x^3} = x^{18-x} = x^{15}$

58. $(-10)^0 = 1$

59. $-10^0 = -(1) = -1$

60. $400x^0 = 400 \cdot 1 = 400$

61. $\left(\dfrac{x^4}{2}\right)^3 = \dfrac{(x^4)^3}{2^3} = \dfrac{x^{4 \cdot 3}}{8} = \dfrac{x^2}{8}$

62. $\left(\dfrac{-3}{2y^6}\right)^4 = \dfrac{(-3)^4}{(2y^6)^4} = \dfrac{81}{(2^4y^6)^4} = \dfrac{81}{16y^{24}}$

63. $\dfrac{-15y^8}{3y^2} = \dfrac{-15}{3} \cdot \dfrac{y^8}{y^2} = -5y^6$

64. $\dfrac{40x^8y^6}{5xy^3} = \dfrac{40}{5} \cdot \dfrac{x^8}{x^1} \cdot \dfrac{y^6}{y^3} = 5x^7y^3$

65. $\dfrac{18x^4 - 12x^2 + 36x}{6x} = \dfrac{18x^4}{6x} - \dfrac{12x^2}{6x} + \dfrac{36x}{6x}$
$= 3x^3 - 2x + 6$

66. $\dfrac{30x^8 - 25x^7 - 40x^5}{-5x^3}$
$= \dfrac{30x^8}{-5x^3} - \dfrac{25x^7}{-5x^3} - \dfrac{40x^5}{-5x^3}$
$= -6x^5 + 5x^4 + 8x^2$

67. $\dfrac{27x^3y - 9x^2y - 18xy^2}{3xy}$
$= \dfrac{27x^3y}{3xy} - \dfrac{9x^2y}{3xy} - \dfrac{18xy^2}{3xy}$
$= 9x^2 - 3x - 6y$

68.

$$
\begin{array}{r}
2x + 7 \\
x - 2\overline{)2x^2 + 3x - 14} \\
\underline{2x^2 - 4x} \\
7x - 14 \\
\underline{7x - 14} \\
0
\end{array}
$$

$$\frac{2x^2 + 3x - 14}{x - 2} = 2x + 7$$

69.

$$
\begin{array}{r}
y^2 - 3y + 5 \\
2y + 1\overline{)2y^3 - 5y^2 + 7y + 5} \\
\underline{2y^3 + y^2} \\
-6y^2 + 7y \\
\underline{-6y^2 - 3y} \\
10y + 5 \\
\underline{10y + 5} \\
0
\end{array}
$$

$$\frac{2y^3 - 5y^2 + 7y + 5}{2y + 1} = y^2 - 3y + 5$$

70.

$$
\begin{array}{r}
z^2 + 5z + 2 \\
z - 7\overline{)z^3 - 2z^2 - 33z - 7} \\
\underline{z^3 - 7z^2} \\
5z^2 - 33z \\
\underline{5z^2 - 35z} \\
2z - 7 \\
\underline{2z - 14} \\
7
\end{array}
$$

$$\frac{z^3 - 2z^2 - 33z - 7}{z - 7} = z^2 + 5z + 2 + \frac{7}{z - 7}$$

71.

$$
\begin{array}{r}
y^2 + 3y + 9 \\
y - 3\overline{)y^3 + 0y^2 + 0y - 27} \\
\underline{y^3 - 3y^2} \\
3y^2 + 0y \\
\underline{3y^2 - 9y} \\
9y - 27 \\
\underline{9y - 27} \\
0
\end{array}
$$

$$\frac{y^3 - 27}{y - 3} = y^2 + 3y + 9$$

72. $(4x^3 - 3x^2 - 2x + 1) \div (x + 1)$

$$
\begin{array}{r|rrrr}
-1 & 4 & -3 & -2 & 1 \\
   &   & -4 & 7 & -5 \\
\hline
   & 4 & -7 & 5 & -4
\end{array}
$$

$(4x^3 - 3x^2 - 2x + 1) \div (x + 1)$

$$= 4x^2 - 7x + 5 - \frac{4}{x + 1}$$

73. $(3x^4 - 2x^2 - 10x - 20) \div (x - 2)$

$$
\begin{array}{r|rrrrr}
2 & 3 & 0 & -2 & -10 & -20 \\
  &   & 6 & 12 & 20 & 20 \\
\hline
  & 3 & 6 & 10 & 10 & 0
\end{array}
$$

$(3x^4 - 2x^2 - 10x - 20) \div (x - 2)$
$$= 3x^3 + 6x^2 + 10x + 10$$

74. $(x^4 + 16) \div (x + 4)$

$$
\begin{array}{r|rrrrr}
-4 & 1 & 0 & 0 & 0 & 16 \\
   &   & -4 & 16 & -64 & 256 \\
\hline
   & 1 & -4 & 16 & -64 & 272
\end{array}
$$

$(x^4 + 16) \div (x + 4)$

$$= x^3 - 4x^2 + 16x - 64 + \frac{272}{x + 4}$$

75. $7^{-2} = \dfrac{1}{7^2} = \dfrac{1}{49}$

76. $(-4)^{-3} = \dfrac{1}{(-4)^3} = \dfrac{1}{-64} = -\dfrac{1}{64}$

77. $2^{-1} + 4^{-1} = \dfrac{1}{2} + \dfrac{1}{4} = \dfrac{3}{4}$

78. $\dfrac{1}{5^{-2}} = 5^2 = 25$

79. $\left(\dfrac{2}{5}\right)^{-3} = \dfrac{2^{-3}}{5^{-3}} = \dfrac{5^3}{2^3} = \dfrac{125}{8}$

80. $\dfrac{x^3}{x^9} = x^{3-9} = x^{-6} = \dfrac{1}{x^6}$

81. $\dfrac{30y^6}{5y^8} = \dfrac{30}{5} \cdot \dfrac{y^6}{y^8} = 6y^{-2} = \dfrac{6}{y^2}$

82. $(5x^{-7})(6x^2) = (5 \cdot 6)(x^{-7+2})$

$$= 30x^{-5} = \frac{30}{x^5}$$

83. $\dfrac{x^4 \cdot x^{-2}}{x^{-6}} = \dfrac{x^{4+(-2)}}{x^{-6}} = \dfrac{x^2}{x^{-6}}$

$$= x^{2-(-6)} = x^8$$

84. $\dfrac{(3y^3)^4}{y^{10}} = \dfrac{3^4 y^{3(4)}}{y^{10}} = \dfrac{81y^{12}}{y^{10}}$

$$= 81y^{12-10} = 81y^2$$

85. $\dfrac{y^{-7}}{(y^4)^3} = \dfrac{y^{-7}}{y^{12}} = y^{-7-12} = y^{-19} = \dfrac{1}{y^{19}}$

86. $(2x^{-1})^{-3} = 2^{-3}(x^{-1})^{-3} = 2^{-3}x^3$

$$= \dfrac{x^3}{2^{-3}} = \dfrac{x^3}{8}$$

87. $\left(\dfrac{x^7}{x^4}\right)^{-2} = (x^3)^{-2} = x^{-6} = \dfrac{1}{x^6}$

88. $\dfrac{(y^3)^4}{(y^{-2})^4} = \dfrac{y^{12}}{y^{-8}} = y^{12-(-8)} = y^{20}$

89. $2.3 \times 10^4 = 23{,}000$

(Move decimal point to right 4 places.)

90. $1.76 \times 10^{-3} = 0.00176$ (Move left 3 places.)

91. $9 \times 10^{-1} = 0.9$

92. $73{,}900{,}000 = 7.39 \times 10^7$

93. $0.00062 = 6.2 \times 10^{-4}$

94. $0.38 = 3.8 \times 10^{-1}$

95. $3.8 = 3.8 \times 10^0$

96. $(6 \times 10^{-3})(1.5 \times 10^6) = 6(1.5) \times 10^{-3+6}$

$$= 9 \times 10^3$$

97. $\dfrac{2 \times 10^2}{4 \times 10^{-3}} = \dfrac{10^{2+3}}{2} = 0.5 \times 10^5$

$$= 5 \times 10^{-1} \times 10^5$$
$$= 5.0 \times 10^4$$

98. $(4 \times 10^{-2})^2 = 4^2 \times 10^{-2(2)} = 16 \times 10^{-4}$

$$= 1.6 \times 10^{-4} = 1.6 \times 10^{1-4}$$
$$= 1.6 \times 10^{-3}$$

99. $\dfrac{10^{-6}}{10^{-9}} = \dfrac{10^9}{10^6} = 10^{9-6} = 10^3 = 1000$

There are 1000 nanoseconds in a mircosecond.

100. $2(6.1 \times 10^9) = 12.2 \times 10^9 = 1.22 \times 10^{10}$

In 40 years, there will be approximately 1.22×10^{10} people in the world.

Chapter 5 Test

1. $9x + 6x^2 - 4$ is a trinomial of degree 2.

2. $(7x^3 + 3x^2 - 5x - 11)$
$\quad + (6x^3 - 2x^2 + 4x - 13)$
$\quad = (7x^3 + 6x^3) + (3x^2 - 2x^2)$
$\quad\quad + (-5x + 4x) + (-11 - 13)$
$\quad = 13x^3 + x^2 - x - 24$

3. $(9x^3 - 6x^2 - 11x - 4)$
$\quad - (4x^3 - 8x^2 - 13x + 5)$
$\quad = (9x^3 - 6x^2 - 11x - 4)$
$\quad\quad + (-4x^3 + 8x^2 + 13x - 5)$
$\quad = (9x^3 - 4x^3) + (-6x^2 + 8x^2)$
$\quad\quad + (-11x + 13x) + (-4 - 5)$
$\quad = 5x^3 + 2x^2 + 2x - 9$

4. $(-7x^3)(5x^8) = (-7 \cdot 5)(x^{3+8}) = -35x^{11}$

5. $6x^2(8x^3 - 5x - 2)$
$\quad = 6x^2(8x^3) + 6x^2(-5x) + 6x^2(-2)$
$\quad = 48x^5 - 30x^3 - 12x^2$

6. $(3x + 2)(x^2 - 4x - 3)$
$\quad = 3x(x^2 - 4x - 3) + 2(x^2 - 4x - 3)$
$\quad = 3x^3 - 12x^2 - 9x + 2x^2 - 8x - 6$
$\quad = 3x^3 - 10x^2 - 17x - 6$

7. $(3y + 7)(2y - 9) = 6y^2 + 14y - 27y - 63$
$$= 6y^2 - 13y - 63$$

8. $(7x + 5)(7x - 5) = (7x)^2 - 5^2 = 49x^2 - 25$

9. $(x^2 + 3)^2 = (x^2)^2 + 2(x^2)(3) + 3^2$
$$= x^4 + 6x^2 + 9$$

10. $(5x - 3)^2 = (5x)^2 - 2(5x)(3) + 3^2$
$$= 25x^2 - 30x + 9$$

11. $4x^2 + 5xy - 6x;\ x = -2, y = 3$

$4x^2 + 5xy - 6x$
$$= 4(-2)^2(3) + 5(-2)(3) - 6(-2)$$
$$= 4(4)(3) + 5(-2)(3) - 6(-2)$$
$$= 48 - 30 + 12 = 30$$

12. $(8x^2y^3 - xy + 2y^2) - (6x^2y^3 - 4xy - 10y^2)$
$$= (8x^2y^3 - xy + 2y^2)$$
$$+ (-6x^2y^3 + 4xy + 10y^2)$$
$$= (8x^2y^3 - 6x^2y^3) + (-xy + 4xy)$$
$$+ (2y^2 + 10y^2)$$
$$= 2x^2y^3 + 3xy + 12y^2$$

13. $(3a - 7b)(4a + 5b)$
$$= (3a)(4a) + (3a)(5b) - (7b)(4a)$$
$$- (7b)(5b)$$
$$= 12a^2 + 15ab - 28ab - 35b^2$$
$$= 12a^2 - 13ab - 35b^2$$

14. $(2x + 3y)^2 = (2x)^2 + 2(2x)(3y) + (3y)^2$
$$= 4x^2 + 12xy + 9y^2$$

15. $\dfrac{-25x^{16}}{5x^4} = \dfrac{-25}{5} \cdot \dfrac{x^{16}}{x^4} = -5x^{16-4}$
$$= -5x^{12}$$

Check by multiplication:
$$5x^4(-5x^{12}) = -25x^{4+12} = -25x^{16}$$

16. $\dfrac{15x^4 - 10x^3 + 25x^2}{5x}$
$$= \dfrac{15x^4}{5x} - \dfrac{10x^3}{5x} + \dfrac{25x^2}{5x}$$
$$= 3x^3 - 2x^2 + 5x$$

Check by multiplication:

$5x(3x^3 - 2x^2 + 5x)$
$$= 5x(3x^3) + 5x(-2x^2) + 5x(5x)$$
$$= 15x^4 - 10x^3 + 25x^2$$

17.
$$\begin{array}{r} x^2 - 2x + 3 \\ 2x+1{\overline{\smash{\big)}\,2x^3 - 3x^2 + 4x + 4}} \\ \underline{2x^3 +\ \ x^2} \\ -4x^2 + 4x \\ \underline{-4x^2 - 2x} \\ 6x + 4 \\ \underline{6x + 3} \\ 1 \end{array}$$

$$\dfrac{2x^3 - 3x^2 + 4x + 4}{2x + 1} = x^2 - 2x + 3 + \dfrac{1}{2x + 1}$$

Check by multiplication:

$(2x + 1)(x^2 - 2x + 3) + 1$
$$= [2x(x^2 - 2x + 3) + 1(x^2 - 2x + 3)] + 1$$
$$= (2x^3 - 4x^2 + 6x + x^2 - 2x + 3) + 1$$
$$= (2x^3 - 3x^2 + 4x + 3) + 1$$
$$= 2x^3 - 3x^2 + 4x + 4$$

18. $(3x^4 + 11x^3 - 20x^2 + 7x + 35) + (x + 5)$

$$\begin{array}{r|rrrrr} -5 & 3 & 11 & -20 & 7 & 35 \\ & & -15 & 20 & 0 & -35 \\ \hline & 3 & -4 & 0 & 7 & 0 \end{array}$$

$$(3x^4 - 2x^2 - 10x) \div (x - 2) = 3x^3 - 4x^2 + 7$$

19. $10^{-2} = \dfrac{1}{10^2} = \dfrac{1}{100}$

20. $\dfrac{1}{4^{-3}} = 1 \cdot 4^3 = 4^3 = 64$

21. $(-3x^2)^3 = (-3)^3(x^2)^3 = -27x^6$

22. $\dfrac{20x^3}{5x^8} = \dfrac{4}{x^5}$

23. $(-7x^{-8})(3x^2) = -21x^{-6} = -\dfrac{21}{x^6}$

24. $\dfrac{(2x^3)^4}{x^8} = \dfrac{2^4(x^3)^4}{x^8} = \dfrac{16x^{12}}{x^8} = 16x^4$

25. $(5x^{-4})^{-2} = 5^{-2}(x^{-4})^{-2} = 5^{-2}x^8 = \dfrac{x^8}{5^2} = \dfrac{x^8}{25}$

26. $\left(\dfrac{x^{10}}{x^5}\right)^{-3} = (x^{10-5})^{-3} = (x^5)^{-3}$

$$= x^{-15} = \dfrac{1}{x^{15}}$$

27. $3.7 \times 10^{-4} = 0.00037$

28. $7,600,000 = 7.6 \times 10^6$

29. $(4.1 \times 10^2)(3 \times 10^{-5})$
$$= (4.1 \cdot 3)(10^2 \cdot 10^{-5})$$
$$= 12.3 \times 10^{-3}$$
$$= 1.23 \times 10^{-2}$$

30. $\dfrac{8.4 \times 10^6}{4 \times 10^{-2}} = \dfrac{8.4}{4} \times \dfrac{10^6}{10^{-2}}$
$$= 2.1 \times 10^{6-(-2)}$$
$$= 2.1 \times 10^8$$

Cumulative Review Exercises (Chapters 1-5)

1. $(-7)(-5) \div (12 - 3) = (-7)(-5) \div 9$
$$= 35 \div 9 = \dfrac{35}{9}$$

2. $(3 - 7)^2(9 - 11)^3 = (-4)^2(-2)^3$
$$= 16(-8) = -128$$

3. $14,300 - (-750) = 14,300 + 750$
$$= 15,050$$

The difference in elevation between the plane and the submarine is 15,050 feet.

4. $2(x + 3) + 2x = x + 4$
$$2x + 6 + 2x = x + 4$$
$$4x + 6 = x + 4$$
$$3x + 6 = 4$$
$$3x = -2$$
$$x = -\dfrac{2}{3}$$
The solution is $-\frac{2}{3}$.

5. $\dfrac{x}{5} - \dfrac{1}{3} = \dfrac{x}{10} - \dfrac{1}{2}$

To clear fractions, multiply by the LCD $= 30$.

$$30\left(\dfrac{x}{5} - \dfrac{1}{3}\right) = 30\left(\dfrac{x}{10} - \dfrac{1}{2}\right)$$
$$30\left(\dfrac{x}{5}\right) - 30\left(\dfrac{1}{3}\right) = 30\left(\dfrac{x}{10}\right) - 30\left(\dfrac{1}{2}\right)$$
$$6x - 10 = 3x - 15$$
$$3x - 10 = -15$$
$$3x = -5$$
$$x = -\dfrac{5}{3}$$

The solution is $-\frac{5}{3}$.

6. Let $\quad x = $ width of sign.
Then $3x - 2 = $ length of sign.

$$2x + 2(3x - 2) = 28$$
$$2x + 6x - 4 = 28$$
$$8x - 4 = 28$$
$$8x = 32$$
$$x = 4$$
$$3x - 2 = 3(4) - 2 = 10$$

The length of the sign is 10 feet and the width is 4 feet, so the dimensions are 10 feet by 4 feet.

7. $$7 - 8x \le -6x - 5$$
$$7 - 8x + 6x \le -6x - 5 + 6x$$
$$-2x + 7 \le -5$$
$$-2x + 7 - 7 \le -5 - 7$$
$$-2x \le -12$$
$$\dfrac{-2x}{-2} \ge \dfrac{-12}{-2}$$
$$x \ge 6$$

$\{x | x \ge 6\}$

8. Let x = the amount invested at 12%.
   Let y = the amount invested at 14%.

$$x + y = 6000$$
$$0.12x + 0.14y = 772$$

Solve the first equation for y.

$$x + y = 6000$$
$$y = 6000 - x$$

Substitute for y in the second equation to find x.

$$0.12x + 0.14(6000 - x) = 772$$
$$0.12x + 840 - 0.14x = 772$$
$$840 - 0.02x = 772$$
$$-0.02x = -68$$
$$x = 3400$$

Back-substitute to find y.

$$y = 6000 - x = 6000 - 3400 = 2600$$

$3400 should be invested at 12% and $2600 should be invested at 14%.

9. Let x = the amount of 70% antifreeze.
   Let y = the amount of 30% antifreeze.

$$x + \qquad y = 20$$
$$\underline{0.70x + 0.30y = 0.60(20)}$$
$$x + \qquad y = 20$$
$$0.70x + 0.30y = 12$$

Solve the first equation for y.

$$x + y = 20$$
$$y = 20 - x$$

Substitute for y in the second equation to find x.

$$0.70x + 0.30(20 - x) = 12$$
$$0.70x + 6 - 0.30x = 12$$
$$0.40x + 6 = 12$$
$$0.40x = 6$$
$$x = 15$$

Back-substitute to find y.

$$y = 20 - x = 20 - 15 = 5$$

15 liters of the 70% antifreeze solution should be mixed with 5 liters of the 30% antifreeze solution.

10. $y = -\dfrac{2}{5}x + 2$

slope $= -\frac{2}{5} = \frac{-2}{5}$; y-intercept $= 2$

Plot $(0, 2)$. Move 2 units *down* (since -2 is negative) and 5 units to the *right* to reach the point $(5, 0)$.
Draw a line through $(0, 2)$ and $(5, 0)$.

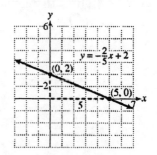

11. $x - 2y = 4$
    x-intercept: 4
    y-intercept: -2
    checkpoint: $(-2, -3)$

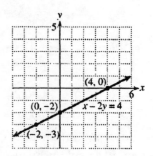

12. $(-3, 2)$ and $(2, -4)$

$$m = \frac{y_2 - y_1}{x_2 - x_1}$$
$$= \frac{-4 - 2}{2 - (-3)} = \frac{-6}{5} = -\frac{6}{5}$$

Because the slope is negative, the line is falling.

13. Slope $= -2$; passing through $(3, -1)$

Substitute -2 for m, 3 for x_1, and -1 for y_1 in the point-slope form.

$$y - y_1 = m(x - x_1)$$
$$y - (-1) = -2(x - 3)$$
$$y + 1 = -2(x - 3)$$

Now rewrite the equation in slope-intercept from.

$$y + 1 = -2x + 6$$
$$y = -2x + 5$$

14. $3x + 2y = 10$

$4x - 3y = -15$

The addition method is a good choice because both equations are written in the form $Ax + By = C$. Multiply the first equation by 3 and the second equation by 2; then add the equations.

$$\begin{array}{r} 9x + 6y = 30 \\ 8x - 6y = -30 \\ \hline 17x = 0 \\ x = 0 \end{array}$$

Back-substitute into the first equation of the given system.

$$3x + 2y = 10$$
$$3(0) + 2y = 10$$
$$2y = 10$$
$$y = 5$$

Solution: $(0, 5)$

15. $2x + 3y = -6$

$y = 3x - 13$

The substitution methods is a good choice since the second equation is already solved for y. Substitute $3x - 13$ for y in the first equation.

$$2x + 3y = -6$$
$$2x + 3(3x - 13) = -6$$
$$2x + 9x - 39 = -6$$
$$11x - 39 = -6$$
$$11x = 33$$
$$x = 3$$

Back-substitute.

$$y = 3x - 13$$
$$y = 3(3) - 13 = -4$$

Solution: $(3, -4)$

16. Let $\quad x = $ the number of minutes of long-distance calls.

Then $y = $ the monthly cost of a telephone plan.

First plan: $y = 15 + 0.05x$

Second plan: $y = 5 + 0.07x$

To solve this system by the substitution method, substitute $5 + 0.07x$ for y in the first equation.

$$5 + 0.07x = 15 + 0.05x$$
$$5 + 0.07x - 0.05x = 15 + 0.05x - 0.05x$$
$$5 + 0.02x = 15$$
$$0.02x = 10$$
$$\frac{0.02x}{0.02} = \frac{10}{0.02}$$
$$x = 500$$

If $x = 500$,

$$y = 15 + 0.05(500) = 40.$$

The plans will cost the same for 500 minutes of long-distance calls per month. The cost of each plan will be $40.

17. $(9x^5 - 3x^3 + 2x - 7) - (6x^5 + 3x^3 - 7x - 9)$

$= (9x^5 - 3x^3 + 2x - 7)$
$\quad + (-6x^5 - 3x^3 + 7x + 9)$
$= (9x^5 - 6x^5) + (-3x^3 - 3x^3) + (2x + 7x)$
$\quad + (-7 + 9)$
$= 3x^5 - 6x^3 + 9x + 2$

18.

$$\begin{array}{r} x^2 + 2x + 3 \\ x+1{\overline{\smash{\big)}\,x^3 + 3x^2 + 5x + 3}} \\ \underline{x^3 + x^2} \\ 2x^2 + 5x \\ \underline{2x^2 + 2x} \\ 3x + 3 \\ \underline{3x + 3} \\ 0 \end{array}$$

$$\frac{x^3 + 3x^2 + 5x + 3}{x + 1} = x^2 + 2x + 3$$

19. $\dfrac{(3x^2)^4}{x^{10}} = \dfrac{3^4(x^2)^4}{x^{10}} = \dfrac{81x^8}{x^{10}}$

$\quad = 81x^{8-10} = 81x^{-2} = \dfrac{81}{x^2}$

20. $2.4 \times 10^{-3} = 0.024$

FACTORING POLYNOMIALS

The Greatest Common Factor and Factoring by Grouping

6.1 CHECK POINTS

CHECK POINT 1

a. $18x^3$ and $15x^2$

The greatest integer that divides 18 and 15 is 3. The variable, x, raised to the smallest exponent, is x^2. Therefore, the GCF (greatest common factor) of $18x^3$ and $15x^2$ is $3x^2$.

b. The GCF of $-20x^2, 12x^4$, and $40x^3$ is $4x^2$.

c. The GCF of x^4y, x^3y^2, and x^2y is x^2y. Notice that all three terms have a numerical coefficient of 1.

CHECK POINT 2

$6x^2 + 18$

The GCF of $6x^2$ and 18 is 6.

$$6x^2 + 18 = 6(x^2 + 3)$$

CHECK POINT 3

$25x^2 + 35x^3$

The GCF of $25x^2$ and $35x^3$ is $5x^2$.

$$25x^2 + 35x^3 = 5x^2(5 + 7x)$$

CHECK POINT 4

$15x^2 + 12x^4 - 27x^3$

The GCF is $3x^3$.

$$15x^7 + 12x^4 - 27x^3 = 3x^3(5x^2 + 4x - 9)$$

CHECK POINT 5

$8x^3y^2 - 14x^2y + 2xy$

The GCF is $2xy$.

$$8x^3y^2 - 14x^2y + 2xy = 2xy(4x^2y - 7x + 1)$$

CHECK POINT 6

a. $x^2(x+1) + 7(x+1)$

The greatest common factor is the binomial $x + 1$. Factor out this common binomial factor.

$$x^2(x+1) + 7(x+1) = (x+1)(x^2+7)$$

b. $x(y+4) - 7(y+4)$

The greatest common factor is the binomial $y + 4$.

$$x(y+4) - 7(y+4) = (y+4)(x-7)$$

CHECK POINT 7

$x^3 + 5x^2 + 2x + 10$

First, group terms with common factors.

$$(x^3 + 5x^2) + (2x + 10)$$

Factor out the common monomial factor from each group.

$$x^2(x+5) + 2(x+5)$$

Factor out the common binomial factor, $x + 5$.

$$(x+5)(x^2+2)$$

Thus,

$$x^3 + 5x^2 + 2x + 10 = (x+5)(x^2+2).$$

CHECK POINT 8

$$xy + 3x - 5y - 15 = (xy + 3x) + (-5y - 15)$$
$$= x(y - 3) - 5(y + 3)$$
$$= (y + 3)(x - 5)$$

EXERCISE SET 6.1

1. Possible answers:

$$8x^3 = (2x)(4x^2)$$
$$8x^3 = (4x)(2x^2)$$
$$8x^3 = (8x)(x^2)$$

3. Possible answers:

$$-12x^5 = (-4x^3)(3x^2)$$
$$-12x^5 = (2x^2)(-6x^3)$$
$$-12x^5 = (-3)(4x^5)$$

5. Possible answers:

$$36x^4 = (6x^2)(6x^2)$$
$$36x^4 = (-2x)(-18x^3)$$
$$36x^4 = (4x^3)(9x)$$

7. The GCF (greatest common factor) of 4 and $8x$ is 4.

9. $12x^2 + 8x$

Since 4 is the numerical coefficient of the GCF, and x is the variable factor of the GCF, the GCF of $12x^2$ and $8x$ is $4x$.

11. The GCF of $-2x^4$ and $6x^3$ is $2x^3$.

13. The GCF of $9y^5, 18y^2$, and $-3y$ and $3y$.

15. The GCF of xy, xy^2, and xy^3 is xy.

17. The GCF of $16x^5y^4$, $8x^6y^3$, and $20x^4y^5$ is $4x^4y^3$.

19. $5x + 5 = 5 \cdot x + 5 \cdot 1 = 5(x + 1)$

21. $3y - 3 = 3 \cdot y - 3 \cdot 1 = 3(y - 1)$

23. $8x + 16 = 8 \cdot x + 8 \cdot 2 = 8(x + 2)$

25. $25x - 10 = 5(5x) - 5(2) = 5(5x - 2)$

27. $x^2 + x = x \cdot x + x \cdot 1 = x(x + 1)$

29. $18y^2 + 24 = 6(3y^2) + 6(4)$
$$= 6(3y^2 + 4)$$

31. $36x^3 + 24x^2 = 6x^2(6x) + 6x^2(4)$
$$= 6x^2(6x + 4)$$

33. $25y^2 - 13y = y(25y) - y(13)$
$$= y(25y - 13)$$

35. $9y^4 + 27y^6 = 9y^4 \cdot 1 + 9y^4 \cdot 3y^3$
$$= 9y^4(1 + 3y^3)$$

37. $8x^2 - 4x^4 = 4x^2(2) - 4x^2(x^2)$
$$= 4x^2(2 - x^2)$$

39. $12y^2 + 16y - 8 = 4(3y^2) + 4(4y) - 4(2)$
$$= 4(3y^2 + 4y - 2)$$

41. $9x^4 + 18x^3 + 6x^2$
$$= 3x^2(3x^2) + 3x^2(6x) + 3x^2(2)$$
$$= 3x^2(3x^2 + 6x + 2)$$

43. $100y^5 - 50y^3 + 100y^2$
$$= 50y^2(2y^3) - 50y^2(y) + 50y^2(2)$$
$$= 50y^2(2y^3 - y + 2)$$

45. $10x - 20x^2 + 5x^3$
$$= 5x(2) - 5x(4x) + 5x(x^2)$$
$$= 5x(2 - 4x + x^2)$$

47. $11x^2 - 23$ cannot be factored because the two terms have no common factor other than 1.

49. $6x^3y^2 + 9xy = 3xy(2x^2y) + 3xy(3)$
$$= 3xy(2x^2y + 3)$$

51. $30x^2y^2 - 10xy^2 + 20xy$
$$= 10xy(3xy^2) - 10xy(y) + 10xy(2)$$
$$= 10xy(3xy^2 - y + 2)$$

53. $32x^3y^2 - 24x^3y - 16x^2y$
$= 8x^2y(4xy) - 8x^2y(3x) - 8x^2y(2)$
$= 8x^2y(4xy - 3x - 2)$

55. $x(x+5) + 3(x+5) = (x+5)(x+3)$

Here, $(x+5)$ is the greatest common binomial factor.

57. $x(x+2) - 4(x+2) = (x+2)(x-4)$

59. $x(y+6) - 7(y+6) = (y+6)(x-7)$

61. $3x(x+y) - (x+y) = 3x(x+y) - 1(x+y)$
$= (x+y)(3x-1)$

63. $4x(3x+1) + 3x + 1 = 4x(3x+1) + 1(3x+1)$
$= (3x+1)(4x+1)$

65. $7x^2(5x+4) + 5x + 4$
$= 7x^2(5x+4) + 1(5x+4)$
$= (5x+4)(7x^2+1)$

67. $x^2 + 2x + 4x + 8 = (x^2 + 2x) + (4x + 8)$
$= x(x+2) + 4(x+2)$
$= (x+2)(x+4)$

69. $x^2 + 3x - 5x - 15 = (x^2 + 3x) + (-5x - 15)$
$= x(x+3) - 5(x+3)$
$= (x-5)(x+3)$

71. $x^3 - 2x^2 + 5x - 10 = (x^3 - 2x^2) + (5x - 10)$
$= x^2(x-2) + 5(x-2)$
$= (x-2)(x^2+5)$

73. $x^3 - x^2 + 2x - 2 = x^2(x-1) + 2(x-1)$
$= (x-1)(x^2+2)$

75. $xy + 5x + 9y + 45 = x(y+5) + 9(y+5)$
$= (y+5)(x+9)$

77. $xy - x + 5y - 5 = x(y-1) + 5(y-1)$
$= (y-1)(x+5)$

79. $3x^2 - 6xy + 5xy - 10y^2$
$= 3x(x-2y) + 5y(x-2y)$
$= (x-2y)(3x+5y)$

81. $3x^3 - 2x^2 - 6x + 4$
$= x^2(3x-2) - 2(3x-2)$
$= (3x-2)(x^2-2)$

83. $x^2 - ax - bx + ab = x(x-a) - b(x-a)$
$= (x-a)(x-b)$

85. $8x^2 + 20x + 2488$

a. The year 2003 corresponds to $x = 10$.

$8x^2 + 20x + 2488$
$= 8(10)^2 + 20(1) + 2488$
$= 800 + 200 + 2488$
$= 3488$

According to the model, 3488 thousand (or 3,488,000) students will graduate from U.S. high schools in 2003.

b. The greatest common factor of the three terms is 4, so

$$8x^2 + 20x + 2488 = 4(2x^2 + 5x + 622).$$

c. $4(2x^2 + 5x + 622)$; $x = 10$

$4(2x^2 + 5x + 622) = 4[2(10)^2 + 5(10) + 622]$
$= 4[200 + 50 + 622]$
$= 4(872)$
$= 3488$

The factored form also predicts that 3488 thousand (or 3,488,000) students will graduate from U.S. high schools in 2003. Getting the same answer in parts (a) and (b) suggests that the factorization is correct. However, it only *proves* that the two expressions (unfactored and factored forms) are equal when $x = 10$. To prove that the two expressions are equal, you need to show they are equal for *all* possible values of x (all real numbers).

87. Use the formula for the area of a rectangle. Substitute $5x^4 - 10x$ for A and $5x$ for w.

$$A = l \cdot w$$
$$5x^4 - 10x = l(5x)$$

To find a polynomial representing l, factor $5x^4 - 10x$.

$$5x^4 - 10x = 5x(x^3 - 2)$$
$$\text{or } (x^3 - 2)5x$$

Therefore, the length is $(x^3 - 2)$ units.

For Exercises 89–93, answers may vary.

95. Statement d is true.
Either $-4x$ or $4x$ can be used as the GCF.

97. $x^{4n} + x^{2n} + x^{3n}$

Because n is a natural number (positive integer), $4n, 2n,$ and $3n$ are all natural numbers with $4n > 3n > 2n$. Therefore, the GCF is x^{2n}.

$$x^{4n} + x^{2n} + x^{3n} = x^{2n}(x^{2n} + 1 + x^n)$$

99. Answers will vary. One example is

$$5x^2 + 10x - 4x - 8.$$

101.

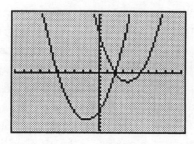

The graphs do not coincide.

Factor by grouping.

$$x^2 - 2x + 5x - 10 = x(x - 2) + 5(x - 2)$$
$$= (x - 2)(x + 5)$$

Change the expression on the right side to $(x - 2)(x + 5)$.

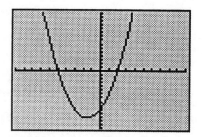

Now the graphs coincide.

Review Exercises

103. $(x + 7)(x + 10) = x^2 + 10x + 7x + 70$
$\qquad\qquad\qquad\quad = x^2 + 17x + 70$

104. $2x - y = -4$
$\quad\;\; x - 3y = 3$

Graph both equations on the same axes.

$2x - y = -4$:
x-intercept: -2; y-intercept: 4
$x - 3y = 3$:
x-intercept: 3; y-intercept: -1

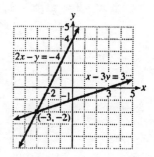

The lines interseect as $(-3, -2)$.
Solution: $(-3, -2)$

105. Line through $(-7, 2)$ and $(-4, 5)$

First, find the slope.

$$m = \frac{5-2}{-4-(-7)} = \frac{3}{3} = 1$$

Write the point-slope equation using $m = 1$ and $(x_1, y_1) = (-7, 2)$.

$$y - y_1 = m(x - x_1)$$
$$y - 2 = 1[x - (-7)]$$
$$y - 2 = 1(x + 7)$$

Now rewrite this equation in slope-intercepet form.

$$y - 2 = x + 7$$
$$y = x + 9$$

Note: If $(-4, 5)$ is used as (x_1, y_1), the point-slope equation will be

$$y - 5 = 1[x - (-4)]$$
$$y - 5 = x + 4.$$

This also leads to the slope-intercept equation $y = x + 9$.

Factoring Trinomials Whose Leading Coefficient Is One

6.2 CHECK POINTS

CHECK POINT 1

$x^2 + 5x + 6 = (x + 2)(x + 3)$

The product of the First terms is $x \cdot x = x^2$.

The product of the Last terms is $2 \cdot 3 = 6$.

The sum of the Outside and inside products is $3x + 2x = 5x$.

CHECK POINT 2

$x^2 - 6x + 8$

Factors of 8	1, 8	2, 4	−1, −8	−2, −4
Sum of Factors	9	6	−9	−6

The factors of 8 whose sum is −6, the coefficient of the middle term of the binomial, are −2 and −4. Thus,

$$x^2 - 6x + 8 = (x - 2)(x - 4).$$

CHECK POINT 3

$x^2 + 3x - 10$

Factors of −10	−10, 1	−5, 2	5, −2	10, −1
Sum of Factors	−9	−3	3	9

$$x^2 + 3x - 10 = (x + 5)(x - 2)$$

CHECK POINT 4

$y^2 - 6y - 27$

Factors of −27	−27, 1	−9, 3	−3, 9	−1, 27
Sum of Factors	−26	−6	6	26

$$y^2 - 6y - 27 = (y - 9)(y + 3)$$

242

CHECK POINT 5

$x^2 + x - 7$

Factors of -7	$-7, 1$	$7, -1$
Sum of Factors	-6	6

Because neither pair has a sum of 1, $x^2 + x - 7$ cannot be factored using integers. This trinomial is prime.

CHECK POINT 6

$x^2 - 4xy + 3y^2$

The factors will have the form $(x \quad ?y)$ $\cdot (x \quad ?y)$.

Factors of 3	$3, 1$	$-3, -1$
Sum of Factors	4	-4

$$x^2 - 4xy + 3y^2 = (x - 3y)(x - y)$$

CHECK POINT 7

$2x^3 + 6x^2 - 56x$

First factor out the GCF, $2x$.

$$2x^3 + 6x^2 - 56x = 2x(x^2 + 3x - 28)$$

Now factor $x^2 + 3x - 28$ by finding two intergers whose product is -28 and whose sum is 3.

$$x^2 + 3x - 28 = (x - 4)(x + 7)$$

Thus, the complete factorization is

$$2x^3 + 6x^2 - 56x = 2x(x - 4)(x + 7).$$

EXERCISE SET 6.2

In Exercises 1–61, each factorization should be checked using FOIL multiplication. The check will only be shown here for Exercise 1.

1. $x^2 + 6x + 5$

Factors of 5	$5, 1$	$-5, -1$
Sum of Factors	6	-6

The factors of 5 whose sum is 6 are 5 and 1. Thus,

$$x^2 + 6x + 5 = (x + 5)(x + 1).$$

Check:

$$(x + 5)(x + 1) = x^2 + x + 5x + 5$$
$$= x^2 + 6x + 5$$

3. $x^2 + 8x + 15 = (x + 3)(x + 5)$
$(3)(5) = 15;\ 3 + 5 = 8$

5. $x^2 + 12x + 11 = (x + 1)(x + 11)$
$(1)(11) = 11;\ 1 + 11 = 12$

7. $x^2 - 8x + 15 = (x - 5)(x - 3)$
$(-5)(-3) = 15;\ (-5) + (-3) = -8$

9. $x^2 - 14x + 49 = (x - 7)(x - 7)$
$(-7)(-7) = 49;\ (-7) + (-7) = -14$

11. $y^2 - 15y + 36 = (y - 3)(y - 12)$
$(-3)(-12) = 36;\ (-3) + (-12) = -15$

13. $x^2 + 3x - 10 = (x + 5)(x - 2)$
$(5)(-2) = -10;\ 5 + (-2) = 3$

15. $y^2 + 10y - 39 = (y + 13)(y - 3)$
$(13)(-3) = -39;\ 13 + (-3) = 10$

17. $x^2 - 2x - 15 = (x - 5)(x + 3)$
$(-5)(3) = -15;\ -5 + 3 = -2$

19. $x^2 - 2x - 8 = (x - 4)(x + 2)$
$(-4)(2) = -8; -4 + 2 = -2$

21. $x^2 + 4x + 12$ is prime because there is no pair of integers whose product is 12 and whose sum is 4.

23. $y^2 - 16y + 48 = (y - 4)(y - 12)$
$(-4)(-12) = 48; (-4) + (-12) = -16$

25. $x^2 - 3x + 6$ is prime because there is no pair of integers whose product is 6 and whose sum is -3.

27. $w^2 - 30w - 64 = (w - 32)(w + 2)$
$(-32)(2) = -64; -32 + 2 = -30$

29. $y^2 - 18y + 65 = (y - 5)(y - 13)$
$(-5)(-13) = 65; (-5) + (-13) = -18$

31. $r^2 + 12r + 27 = (r + 3)(r + 9)$
$(3)(9) = 27; 3 + 9 = 12$

33. $y^2 - 7y + 5$ is prime because there is no pair of integers whose product is 5 and whose sum is -7.

35. $x^2 + 7xy + 6y^2 = (x + 6y)(x + y)$
$(6)(1) = 6; 6 + 1 = 7$

37. $x^2 - 8xy + 15y^2 = (x - 3y)(x - 5y)$
$(-3)(-5) = 15; (-3) + (-5) = -8$

39. $x^2 - 3xy - 18y^2 = (x - 6y)(x + 3y)$
$(-6)(3) = -18; (-6) + 3 = -3$

41. $a^2 - 18ab + 45b^2 = (a - 15b)(a - 3b)$
$(-15)(-3) = 45; (-15) + (-3) = -18$

43. $3x^2 + 15x + 18$

First factor out the GCF, 3. Then factor the resulting binomial.

$$3x^2 + 15x + 18 = 3(x^2 + 5x + 6)$$
$$= 3(x + 2)(x + 3)$$

45. $4y^2 - 4y - 8 = 4(y^2 - y - 2)$
$$= 4(y - 2)(y + 1)$$

47. $10x^2 - 40x - 600 = 10(x^2 - 4x - 60)$
$$= 10(x - 10)(x + 6)$$

49. $3x^2 - 33x + 54 = 3(x^2 - 11x + 18)$
$$= 3(x - 2)(x - 9)$$

51. $2r^3 + 6r^2 + 4r = 2r(r^2 + 3r + 2)$
$$= 2r(r + 2)(r + 1)$$

53. $4x^3 + 12x^2 - 72x = 4x(x^2 + 3x - 18)$
$$= 4x(x + 6)(x - 3)$$

55. $2r^3 + 8r^2 - 64r = 2r(r^2 + 4r - 32)$
$$= 2r(r + 8)(r - 4)$$

57. $y^4 + 2y^3 - 80y^2 = y^2(y^2 + 2y - 80)$
$$= y^2(y + 10)(y - 8)$$

59. $x^4 - 3x^3 - 10x^2 = x^2(x^2 - 3x - 10)$
$$= x^2(x - 5)(x + 2)$$

61. $2w^4 - 26w^3 - 96w^2 = 2w^2(w^2 - 13w - 48)$
$$= 2w^2(w - 16)(w + 3)$$

63. $-16t^2 + 16t + 32 = -16(t^2 - t - 2)$
$$= -16(t - 2)(t + 1)$$

For Exercises 65–67, answers may vary.

69. Statement c is true.

$$y^2 + 5y - 24 = (y - 3)(y + 8)$$

71. In order for $x^2 + 4x + b$ to be factorable, b must be an integer with two positive factors whose sum is 4. The only such pairs are 3 and 1, or 2 and 2.

$$(x + 3)(x + 1) = x^2 + 4x + 3$$
$$(x + 2)(x + 2) = x^2 + 4x + 4$$

Therefore, the possible values of b are 3 and 4.

73.
$$4x^3 - 28x^2 + 48x = 4x(x^2 - 7x + 12)$$
$$= 4x(x-4)(x-3)$$

The box has the following dimensions:

$$\text{length} = 8 - 2x = 2(4 - x)$$
$$\text{width} = 6 - 2x = 2(3 - x)$$
$$\text{height} = x.$$

Therefore, the volume is

$$V = lwh$$
$$= 2(4-x) \cdot 2(3-x) \cdot x$$
$$= 4[(-1)(x-4) \cdot (-1)(x-3)]x$$
$$= 4x(x-4)(x-3),$$

which is the factored form obtained above.

75.

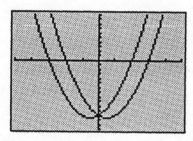

$$2x^2 + 2x - 12 = 2(x^2 + x - 6)$$
$$= 2(x+3)(x-2)$$

Change the polynomial on the right to $2(x+3)(x-2)$.

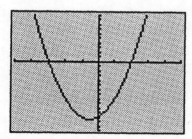

Now the graphs coincide.

77.

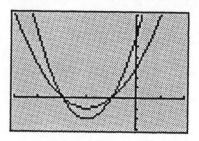

$$2x^2 + 8x + 6 = 2(x^2 + 4x + 3)$$
$$= 2(x+3)(x+1)$$

Change the polynomial on the right to $2(x+3)(x+1)$.

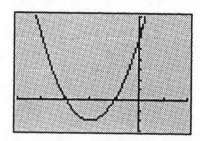

Now the graphs coincide.

Review Exercises

78. $(2x+3)(x-2) = 2x^2 - 4x + 3x - 6$
$$= 2x^2 - x - 6$$

79. $(3x+4)(3x+1) = 9x^2 + 3x + 12x + 4$
$$= 9x^2 + 15x + 4$$

80. $4(x-2) = 3x + 5$
$$4x - 8 = 3x + 5$$
$$x - 8 = 5$$
$$x = 13$$

The solution is 13.

Factoring Trinomials Whose Leading Coefficient Is Not One

6.3 CHECK POINTS

CHECK POINT 1

$5x^2 - 14x + 8$

Step 1 Find two First terms whose product is $5x^2$.

$$5x^2 - 14x + 8 = (5x \qquad)(x \qquad)$$

Step 2 Find two Last terms whose product is 8. The number 8 has pairs of factors that are either both positive or both negative. Because the middle term, $-14x$, is negative, both factors must be negative. The negative factorizations of 8 are $-1(-8)$ and $-2(-4)$.

Step 3 Try various combinations of these factors to find the one in which the sum of the Outside and Inside products is equal to $-14x$.

Possible Factors of $5x^2 - 14x + 8$	Sum of Outside and Inside Products
$(5x - 1)(x - 8)$	$-40x - x = -41x$
$(5x - 8)(x - 1)$	$-5x - 8x = -13x$
$(5x - 2)(x - 4)$	$-20x - 2x = -22x$
$(5x - 4)(x - 2)$	$-10x - 4x = -14x$

Thus,

$$5x^2 - 14x + 8 = (5x - 4)(x - 2).$$

CHECK POINT 2

$6x^2 + 19x - 7$

Step 1 There are two possiblities of the first terms.

$$6x^2 + 19x - 7 \overset{?}{=} (6x \qquad)(x \qquad)$$
$$6x^2 + 19x - 7 \overset{?}{=} (6x \qquad)(x \qquad)$$

Step 2 The only possible factorizations of -7 are $1(-7)$ and $-1(7)$.

Step 3

Possible Factors of $6x^2 + 19x - 7$	Sum of Outside and Inside Products
$(6x + 7)(x - 1)$	$-6x + 7x = x$
$(6x - 7)(x + 1)$	$6x - 7x = -x$
$(6x + 1)(x - 7)$	$-42x + x = -41x$
$(6x - 1)(x + 7)$	$42x - x = 41x$
$(3x + 7)(2x - 1)$	$-3x + 14x = 11x$
$(3x - 7)(2x + 1)$	$3x - 14x = -11x$
$(3x + 1)(2x - 7)$	$-21x + 2x = -19x$
$(3x - 1)(2x + 7)$	$21x - 2x = 19x$

Thus,

$$6x^2 + 19x - 7 = (3x - 1)(2x + 7).$$

CHECK POINT 3

$3x^2 - 13xy + 4y^2$

Step 1 Find two First terms whose product is $3x^2$.

$$3x^2 - 13xy + 4y^2 = (3x \qquad)(x \qquad)$$

Step 2 Find two Last terms whose product is $4y^2$. The possible factorizations are $(y)(4y), (-y)(-4y), (2y)(2y)$, and $(-2y)(-2y)$. Because the middle term is negative, the factors must be $(-y)(-4y)$ and $(-2y)(-2y)$.

Step 3 Try various combinations of these factors.

Possible Factors of $3x^2 - 13xy + 4y^2$	Sum of Outside and Inside Products
$(3x - 4y)(3x - y)$	$-3xy - 4xy = -7xy$
$(3x - y)(x - 4y)$	$-12xy - xy = -13xy$
$(3x - 2y)(x - 2y)$	$-6xy - 2xy = -8xy$

Thus,

$$3x^2 - 13xy + 4y^2 = (3x - y)(x - 4y).$$

CHECK POINT 4

$3x^2 - x - 10$

Step 1 Multiply the leading coefficient, a, and the constant, c.

$$ac = 3(-10) = -30$$

Step 2 Find the factors of ac whose sum is b.
The factors of $ac = -30$ whose sum is $b = -1$ are -6 and 5.

Step 3 Rewrite the middle term, $-x$, using the factors -6 and 5.

$$3x^2 - x - 10 = 3x^2 - 6x + 5x - 10$$

Step 4 Factor by grouping.

$$\begin{aligned}
3x^2 - x - 10 &= 3x^2 - 6x + 5x - 10 \\
&= 3x(x - 2) + 5(x - 2) \\
&= (x - 2)(3x + 5) \\
&\quad \text{or} \quad (3x + 5)(x - 2)
\end{aligned}$$

CHECK POINT 5

$8x^2 - 10x + 3$

Here, $ac = 8(3) = 24$. Find the factors of 24 whose sum is -10. These factors are -6 and -4. Rewrite $-10x$ as $-6x - 4x$; then factor by grouping.

$$\begin{aligned}
8x^2 - 10x + 3 &= 8x^2 - 6x - 4x + 3 \\
&= 2x(4x - 3) - 1(4x - 3) \\
&= (4x - 3)(2x - 1) \\
&\quad \text{or} \quad (2x - 1)(4x - 3)
\end{aligned}$$

CHECK POINT 6

$5y^4 + 13y^3 + 6y^2$

First factor out the GCF, y^2. Then factor the resulting trinomial using trial and error or grouping.

$$\begin{aligned}
5y^4 + 13y^3 + 6y^2 &= y^2(5y^2 + 13y + 6) \\
&= y^2(5y + 3)(y + 2)
\end{aligned}$$

EXERCISE SET 6.3

In Exercises 1–57, each trinomial may be factored by either trial and error or by factoring. Both methods will be illustrated here. Each factorization should be checked by FOIL multiplication. The check will be shown here only for Exercise 1. In all answers, the factors maybe written either order.

1. $2x^2 + 7x + 3$

Factor by trial and error.

Step 1 $2x^2 + 7x + 3 = (2x \quad)(x \quad)$

Step 2 The number 3 has pairs of factors that are either both positive or both negative. Because the middle term, $7x$, is positive, both factors must be positive. The only positive factorization is $(1)(3)$.

Step 3

Possible Factors of $2x^2 + 7x + 3$	Sum of Outside and Inside Products
$(2x + 1)(x + 3)$	$6x + x = 7x$
$(2x + 3)(x + 1)$	$2x + 3x = 5x$

Thus,

$$2x^2 + 7x + 3 = (2x + 1)(x + 3).$$

Check:

$$(2x + 1)(x + 3) = 2x^2 + 6x + x + 3$$
$$= 2x^2 + 7x + 3$$

3. $3x^2 + 8x + 4$

Factor by trial and error.
The only possibility for the First terms is $(3x)(x) = 3x^2$.
Because the middle term is positive and the last term is also positive, the possible factorizations of 4 are $(1)(4)$ and $(2)(2)$.

Possible Factors of $3x^2 + 8x + 4$	Sum of Outside and Inside Products
$(3x + 1)(x + 4)$	$12x + x = 13x$
$(3x + 4)(x + 1)$	$3x + 4x = 7x$
$(3x + 2)(x + 2)$	$6x + 2x = 8x$

Thus,

$$3x^2 + 8x + 4 = (3x + 2)(x + 2).$$

5. $2x^2 + 13x + 20$

Factor by grouping.
$a = 2$ and $c = 20$, so $ac = 2(20) = 40$.
The factors of 40 whose sum is 13 are 8 and 5.

$$2x^2 + 13x + 20 = 2x^2 + 8x + 5x + 20$$
$$= 2x(x + 4) + 5(x + 4)$$
$$= (x + 4)(2x + 5)$$

7. $5y^2 - 8y + 3$

Factor by trial and error. The First terms must be $5y$ and y. Beause the middle term is negative, the factors of 3 must be -3 and -1.

$$(5y - 1)(y - 3) = 5y^2 - 16y + 3$$
$$(5y - 3)(y - 1) = 5y^2 - 8y + 3$$

Thus,

$$(5y - 3)(y - 1) = y^2 - 8y + 3.$$

9. $3y^2 - y - 2$

Factor of trial and error.

$$(3y + 1)(y - 2) = 3y^2 - 5y + 2$$
$$(3y - 1)(y + 2) = 3y^2 - 5y - 2$$
$$(3y + 2)(y - 1) = 3y^2 - y - 2$$
$$(3y - 2)(y + 1) = 3y^2 + y - 2$$

Thus,

$$3y^2 - y - 2 = (3y + 2)(y - 1).$$

11. $3x^2 + x - 10$

Factor by grouping.
$a = 3$ and $c = -10$, so $ac = -30$.
The factors of -30 whose sum is 1 are 6 and -5.

$$3x^2 + x - 10 = 3x^2 + 6x - 5x - 10$$
$$= 3x(x + 2) - 5(x + 2)$$
$$= (x + 2)(3x - 5)$$

13. $3x^2 - 22x + 7$

Factor by trial and error.

$$(3x - 7)(x - 1) = 3x^2 - 10x + 7$$
$$(3x - 1)(x - 7) = 3x^2 - 22x + 7$$

Thus,

$$3x^2 - 22x + 7 = (3x - 1)(x - 7).$$

15. $5y^2 - 16y + 3$

Factor by trial and error.

$$(5y - 3)(y - 1) = 5y^2 - 8y + 3$$
$$(5y - 1)(y - 3) = 5y^2 - 16y + 3$$

Thus,

$$5y^2 - 16y + 3 = (5y - 1)(y - 3).$$

17. $3x^2 - 17x + 10$

Factor by grouping.
$a = 3$ and $c = 10$, so $ac = 10$.
The factors of 30 whose sum is -17 are
-15 and -2.

$$3x^2 - 17x + 10 = 3x^2 - 15x - 2x + 10$$
$$= 3x(x - 5) - 2(x - 5)$$
$$= (x - 5)(3x - 2)$$

19. $6w^2 - 11w + 4$

Factor by grouping.
$a = 6$ and $c = 4$, so $ac = 24$.
The factors of 24 whose sum is -11 are
-3 and -8.

$$6w^2 - 11w + 4 = 6w^2 - 3w - 8w + 4$$
$$= 3w(2w - 1) - 4(2w - 1)$$
$$= (2w - 1)(3w - 4)$$

21. $8x^2 + 33x + 4$

Factor by grouping.
$a = 8$ and $c = 4$, so $ac = 32$.
The factors of 32 whose sum is 33 are 32
and 1.

$$8x^2 + 33x + 4 = 8x^2 + 32x + x + 4$$
$$= 8x(x + 4) + 1(x + 4)$$
$$= (x + 4)(8x + 1)$$

23. $5x^2 + 33x - 14$

Factor by trial and error.

$$(5x - 7)(x + 2) = 5x^2 + 3x - 14$$
$$(5x + 7)(x - 2) = 5x^2 - 3x - 14$$
$$(5x - 2)(x + 7) = 5x^2 + 33x - 14$$

Because the correct factorization has been
found, there is no need to try additional
possibilities.

$$5x^2 + 33x - 14 = (5x - 2)(x + 7).$$

25. $14y^2 + 15y - 9$

Factor by trial and error. Try various
combinations until the correct one is obtained.

$$(7y + 9)(2y - 1) = 14y^2 + 11y - 9$$
$$(7y + 1)(2y - 9) = 14y^2 - 61y - 9$$
$$(7y + 3)(2y - 3) = 14y^2 - 15y - 9$$
$$(7y - 3)(2y + 3) = 14y^2 + 15y - 9$$

Thus,

$$14y^2 + 15y - 9 = (7y - 3)(2y + 3).$$

27. $6x^2 - 7x + 3$

Use trial and error. List all of the possi-
blilities in which both signs are negative.

$$(6x - 1)(x - 3) = 6x^2 - 19x + 3$$
$$(6x - 3)(x - 1) = 6x^2 - 9x + 3$$
$$(3x - 1)(2x - 3) = 6x^2 - 11x + 3$$
$$(3x - 3)(2x - 1) = 6x^2 - 9x + 3$$

None of these possibilities gives the required middle term, $-7x$, and there are
no more possibilities to try, so $6x^2 - 7x + 3$
is prime.

29. $25z^2 - 30z + 9$

Use trial and error until the correct factorization is obtained. The signs in both factors must be negative.

$$(5z - 1)(5z - 9) = 25z^2 - 50z + 9$$
$$(5z - 3)(5z - 3) = 25z^2 - 30z + 9$$

Thus,

$$25z^2 - 30z + 9 = (5z - 3)(5z - 3).$$

31. $15y^2 - y - 2$

Factor by grouping.
$a = 15$ and $c = -2$, so $ac = -30$.
The factors of -30 whose sum is -1 are -6 and 5.

$$15y^2 - y - 2 = 15y^2 - 6y + 5y - 2$$
$$= 3y(5y - 2) + 1(5y - 2)$$
$$= (5y - 2)(3y + 1)$$

33. $5x^2 + 2x + 9$

Use trial and error. The signs in both factors must be positive.

$$(5x + 3)(x + 3) = 5x^2 + 18x + 9$$
$$(5x + 9)(x + 1) = 5x^2 + 14x + 9$$
$$(5x + 1)(x + 9) = 5x^2 + 46x + 9$$

None of these possiblities gives the required middle term, $2x$, and there are no more possibilities to try, so $5x^2 + 2x + 9$ is prime.

35. $10y^2 + 43y - 9$

Factor by grouping.
$a = 10$ and $c = -9$, so $ac = -90$.
The factors of -90 whose sum is 43 are 45 and -2.

$$10y^2 + 43y - 9 = 10y^2 + 45y - 2y - 9$$
$$= 5y(2y + 9) - 1(2y + 9)$$
$$= (2y + 9)(5y - 1)$$

37. $8x^2 - 2x - 1$

Use trial and error until the correct factorization is obtained. The sign just be negative in one factor and positive in the other.

$$(4x - 1)(2x + 1) = 8x^2 + 2x - 1$$
$$(4x + 1)(2x - 1) = 8x^2 - 2x - 1$$

Thus,

$$8x^2 - 2x - 1 = (4x + 1)(2x - 1).$$

39. $9y^2 - 9y + 2$

Factor by grouping.
$a = 9$ and $c = 2$, so $ac = 18$.
The factors of 18 whose sum is -9 are -3 and -6.

$$9y^2 - 9y + 2 = 9y^2 - 3y - 6y + 2$$
$$= 3y(3y - 1) - 2(3y - 1)$$
$$= (3y - 1)(3y - 2)$$

41. $20x^2 + 27x - 8$

Factor by grouping.
$a = 20$ and $c = -8$, so $ac = -160$.
The factors of -160 whose sum is 27 are -5 and 32.

$$20x^2 + 27x - 8 = 20x^2 - 5x + 32x - 8$$
$$= 5x(4x - 1) + 8(4x - 1)$$
$$= (4x - 1)(5x + 8)$$

43. $2x^2 + 3xy + y^2 = (2x + y)(x + y)$

(In this case, there are no other combinations to try.)

45. $3x^2 + 5xy + 2y^2$

Factor by trial and error.

$$(3x + y)(x + 2y) = 3x^2 + 7xy + 2y^2$$
$$(3x + 2y)(x + y) = 3x^2 + 5xy + 2y^2$$

Thus,

$$3x^2 + 5xy + 2y^2 = (3x + 2y)(x + y).$$

47. $2x^2 - 9xy + 9y^2 = (2x - 3y)(x - 3y)$

49. $6x^2 - 5xy - 6y^2 = (2x - 3y)(3x + 2y)$

51. $15x^2 + 11xy - 14y^2 = (3x - 2y)(5x + 7y)$

53. $2a^2 + 7ab + 5b^2 = (2a + 5b)(a + b)$

55. $15a^2 - ab - 6b^2 = (3a - 2b)(5a + 3b)$

57. $12x^2 - 25xy + 12y^2 = (3x - 4y)(4x - 3y)$

59. $4x^2 + 26x + 30$

First factor out the GCF, 2. Then factor the resulting trinomial by trial and error or grouping.

$$4x^2 + 26x + 30 = 2(2x^2 + 13x + 15)$$
$$= 2(2x + 3)(x + 5)$$

61. $9x^2 - 6x - 24$
The GCF is 3.

$$9x^2 - 6x - 24 = 3(3x^2 - 2x - 8)$$
$$= 3(3x + 4)(x - 2)$$

63. $4y^2 + 2y - 30 = 2(2y^2 + y - 15)$
$$= 2(2y - 5)(y + 3)$$

65. $9y^2 + 33y - 60 = 3(3y^2 + 11y - 20)$
$$= 3(3y - 4)(y + 5)$$

67. $3x^3 + 4x^2 + x$
The GCF is x.

$$3x^3 + 4x^2 + x = x(3x^2 + 4x + 1)$$
$$= x(3x + 1)(x + 1)$$

69. $2x^3 - 3x^2 - 5x = x(2x^2 - 3x - 5)$
$$= x(2x - 5)(x + 1)$$

71. $9y^3 - 39y^2 + 12y$
The GCF is $3y$.

$$9y^3 - 39y^2 + 12y = 3y(3y^2 - 13y + 4)$$
$$= 3y(3y - 1)(y - 4)$$

73. $60z^3 + 40z^2 + 5z = 5z(12z^2 + 8z + 1)$
$$= 5z(6z + 1)(2z + 1)$$

75. $15x^4 - 39x^3 + 18x^2 = 3x^2(5x^2 - 13x + 6)$
$$= 3x^2(5x - 3)(x - 2)$$

77. $10x^5 - 17x^4 + 3x^3 = x^3(10x^2 - 17x + 3)$
$$= x^3(2x - 3)(5x - 1)$$

79. $6x^2 - 3xy - 18y^2 = 3(2x^2 - xy - 6y^2)$
$$= 3(2x + 3y)(x - 2y)$$

81. $12x^2 + 10xy - 8y^2 = 2(6x^2 + 5xy - 4y^2)$
$$= 2(2x - y)(3x + 4y)$$

83. $8x^2y + 34xy - 84y = 2y(4x^2 + 17x - 42)$
$$= 2y(4x - 7)(x + 6)$$

85. $12a^2b - 46ab^2 + 14b^3$
$$= 2b(6a^2 - 23ab + 7b^2)$$
$$= 2b(2a - 7b)(3a - b)$$

87. a. $x^2 + 3x + 2$

b. $(x + 2)(x + 1)$

c. Yes, the pieces are the same in both figures: one large square, three long rectangles, and two small squares. This geometric model illustrates the factorization

$$x^2 + 3x + 2 = (x + 2)(x + 1).$$

For Exercises 89–91, answers may vary.

93. Statement a is true.

$18y^2 - 6y + 6 = 9(y^2 - 3y + 3)$, and $y^2 - 3y + 3$ is prime.

95. $2x^2 + bx + 3$

The possible factorizations that will give $2x^2$ as the first term and 3 as the last term are:

$$(2x + 3)(x + 1) = 2x^2 + 5x + 3$$
$$(2x + 1)(x + 3) = 2x^2 + 7x + 3$$
$$(2x - 3)(x - 1) = 2x^2 - 5x + 3$$
$$(2x - 1)(x - 3) = 2x^2 - 7x + 3.$$

The possible middle terms are $5x, 7x, -5x,$ and $-7x$, so $2x^2 + bx + 3$ can be factored if b is $5, 7, -5,$ or -7.

97. $2x^{2n} - 7x^n - 4$

Since $x^n \cdot x^n = x^{n+n} = x^{2n}$, the first terms of the factors will be $2x^n$ and x^n. Use trial and error or grouping to obtain the correct factorization.

$$2x^{2n} - 7x^n - 4 = (2x^n + 1)(x^n - 4)$$

Review Exercises

98. $(9x + 10)(9x - 10) = (9x)^2 - 10^2$
$$= 81x^2 - 100$$

99. $(4x + 5y)^2 = (4x)^2 + 2(4x)(5y) + (5y)^2$
$$= 16x^2 + 40xy + 25y^2$$

100. $(x + 2)(x^2 - 2x + 4)$
$$= x(x^2 - 2x + 4) + 2(x^2 - 2x + 4)$$
$$= x^3 - 2x^2 + 4x + 2x^2 - 4x + 8$$
$$= x^3 + 8$$

Factoring Special Forms

6.4 CHECK POINTS

CHECK POINT 1

Use the formula for factoring the difference of two squares:

$$A^2 - B^2 = (A + B)(A - B).$$

a. $x^2 - 81 = x^2 - 9^2 = (x + 9)(x - 9)$

b. $36x^2 - 25 = (6x)^2 - 5^2$
$$= (6x + 5)(6x - 5)$$

CHECK POINT 2

a. $25 - 4x^{10} = 5^2 - (2x^5)^2$
$$= (5 + 2x^5)(2 - 2x^5)$$

b. $100x^2 - 9y^2 = (10x)^2 - (3y)^2$
$$= (10x + 3y)(10x - 3y)$$

CHECK POINT 3

Factor out the GCF, then factor the resulting polynomial as the difference of two squares.

a. $18x^3 - 2x = 2x(9x^2 - 1)$
$$= 2x[(3x)^2 - 1^2]$$
$$= 2x(3x + 1)(3x - 1)$$

b. $72 - 18x^2 = 18(4 - x^2) = 18(2^2 - x^2)$
$$= 18(2 + x)(2 - x)$$

CHECK POINT 4

$$81x^4 - 16 = (9x^2)^2 - 4^2$$
$$= (9x^2 + 4)(9x^2 - 4)$$

Notice that $9x^2 - 4$ is also the difference of two squares, so the factorizations must be continued. The complete factorization is

$$81x^4 - 16 = (9x^2 + 4)(9x^2 - 4)$$
$$= (9x^2 + 4)[(3x)^2 - 2^2]$$
$$= (9x^2 + 4)(3x + 2)(3x - 2).$$

CHECK POINT 5

Use the formulas for factoring perfect square trinomials:

$$A^2 + 2AB + B^2 = (A + B)^2$$
$$A^2 - 2AB + B^2 = (A - B)^2.$$

a. $x^2 + 14x + 49 = x^2 + 2 \cdot x \cdot 7 + 7^2$
$$= (x + 7)^2$$

b. $x^2 - 6x + 9 = x^2 - 2 \cdot x \cdot 3 + 3^2$
$$= (x - 3)^2$$

c. $16x^2 - 56x + 49 = (4x)^2 - 2 \cdot 4x \cdot 7 + 7^2$
$$= (4x - 7)^2$$

CHECK POINT 6

$$4x^2 + 12xy + 9y^2$$
$$= (2x)^2 + 2 \cdot 2x \cdot 3y + (3y)^2$$
$$= (2x + 3y)^2$$

CHECK POINT 7

Use the formula for factoring the sum of two cubes:

$$A^3 + B^3 = (A + B)(A^2 - AB + B^2)$$
$$x^3 + 27 = x^3 + 3^3$$
$$= (x + 3)(x^2 - x \cdot 3 + 3^2)$$
$$= (x + 3)(x^2 - 3x + 9)$$

CHECK POINT 8

Use the formula for factoring the difference of two cubes:

$$A^3 - B^3 = (A - B)(A^2 + AB + B^2)$$
$$1 - y^3 = 1^3 - y^3$$
$$= (1 - y)(1^2 + 1 \cdot y + y^2)$$
$$= (1 - y)(1 + y + y^2)$$

CHECK POINT 9

Use the formula for factoring the sum of two cubes.

$$125x^3 + 8$$
$$= (5x)^3 + 2^3$$
$$= (5x + 2)[(5x)^2 - 5x \cdot 2 + 2^2]$$
$$= (5x + 2)(25x^2 - 10x + 4)$$

EXERCISE SET 6.4

1. $x^2 - 25 = x^2 - 5^2 = (x + 5)(x - 5)$

3. $y^2 - 1 = y^2 - 1^2 = (y + 1)(y - 1)$

5. $4x^2 - 9 = (2x)^2 - 3^2 = (2x + 3)(2x - 3)$

7. $25 - x^2 = 5^2 - x^2 = (5 + x)(5 - x)$

9. $1 - 49x^1 = 1^2 - (7x)^2 = (1 + 7x)(1 - 7x)$

11. $9 - 25y^2 = 3^2 - (5y)^2 = (3 + 5y)(3 - 5y)$

13. $x^4 - 9 = (x^2)^2 - 3^2 = (x^2 + 3)(x^2 - 3)$

15. $49y^4 - 16 = (7y^2) - 4^2 = (7y^2 + 4)(7y^2 - 4)$

17. $x^{10} - 9 = (x^5) - 3^2 = (x^5 + 3)(x^5 - 3)$

19. $25x^2 - 16y^2 = (5x)^2 - (4y)^2$
$$= (5x + 4y)(5x - 4y)$$

21. $x^4 - y^{10} = (x^2)^2 - (y^5)^2$
$$= (x^2 + y^5)(x^2 - y^5)$$

23. $x^4 - 16 = (x^2)^2 - 4^2 = (x^2 + 4)(x^2 - 4)$

Because $x^2 - 4$ is also the difference of two squares, the factorization must be continued. The complete factorization is

$$x^4 - 16 = (x^2 + 4)(x^2 - 4)$$
$$= (x^2 + 4)(x^2 - 2^2)$$
$$= (x^2 + 4)(x + 2)(x - 2).$$

25. $16x^4 - 81 = (4x^2) - 9^2$
$$= (4x^2 + 9)(4x^2 - 9)$$
$$= (4x^2 + 9)[(2x)^2 - 3^2]$$
$$= (4x^2 + 9)(2x + 3)(2x - 3)$$

27. $2x^2 - 18 = 2(x^2 - 9) = 2(x + 3)(x - 3)$

29. $2x^3 - 72x = 2x(x^2 - 36)$
$$= 2x(x + 6)(x - 6)$$

31. $x^2 + 36$ is prime because it is the sum of two squares with no common factor other than 1.

33. $2x^3 + 72x = 2x(x^2 + 36)$

35. $50 - 2y^2 = 2(25 - y^2) = 2(5 + y)(5 - y)$

37. $8y^3 - 2y = 2y(4y^2 - 1)$
$$= 2y(2y + 1)(2y - 1)$$

39. $2x^3 - 2x = 2x(x^2 - 1) = 2x(x + 1)(x - 1)$

41. $x^2 + 2x + 1 = x^2 + 2 \cdot x \cdot 1 + 1^2$
$$= (x + 1)^2$$

43. $x^2 - 14x + 49 = x^2 - 2 \cdot x \cdot 7 + 7 + 7^2$
$$= (x - 7)^2$$

45. $x^2 - 2x + 1 = x^2 - 2 \cdot x + 1 + 1^2$
$$= (x - 1)^2$$

47. $x^2 + 22x + 121 = x^2 + 2 \cdot x \cdot 11 + 11^2$
$$= (x + 11)^2$$

49. $4x^2 + 4x + 1 = (2x)^2 + 2 \cdot 2x \cdot 1$
$$= (2x + 1)^2$$

51. $25y^2 - 10y + 1 = (5y)^2 - 2 \cdot 5y \cdot 1 + 1^2$
$$= (5y - 1)^2$$

53. $x^2 - 10x + 100$ is prime.

To be a perfect square trinomial, the middle term would have to be $-20x$, rather than $-10x$.

55. $x^2 + 14xy + 49y^2 = x^2 + 2 \cdot x \cdot 7y + (7y)^2$
$$= (x + 7y)^2$$

57. $x^2 - 12xy + 36y^2 = x^2 - 2 \cdot x \cdot 6y + (6y)^2$
$$= (x - 6y)^2$$

59. $x^2 - 8xy + 64y^2$ is prime.

To be a perfect square trinomial, the middle term would have to be $-16xy$ rather than $-8xy$.

61. $16x^2 - 40xy + 25y^2$
$$= (4x)^2 - 2 \cdot 4x \cdot 5y + (5y)^2$$
$$= (4x - 5y)^2$$

63. $12x^2 - 12x + 3 = 3(4x^2 - 4x + 1)$
$$= 3[(2x)^2 - 2 \cdot 2x \cdot 1 + 1^2]$$
$$= 3(2x - 1)^2$$

65. $9x^3 + 6x^2 + x$
$$= x(9x^2 + 6x + 1)$$
$$= x[(3x)^2 + 2 \cdot 3x \cdot 1 + 1^2]$$
$$= x(3x + 1)^2$$

67. $2y^2 - 4y + 2 = 2(y^2 - 2y + 1)$
$$= 2(y - 1)^2$$

69. $2y^3 + 28y^2 + 98y = 2y(y^2 + 14y + 49)$
$$= 2y(y + 7)^2$$

71. $x^3 + 1$
$$= x^3 + 1^3$$
$$= (x + 1)(x^2 - x \cdot 1 + 1^2)$$
$$= (x + 1)(x^2 - x + 1)$$

73. $x^3 - 27$
$$= x^3 - 3^3$$
$$= (x - 3)(x^2 + x \cdot 3 + 3^2)$$
$$= (x - 3)(x^2 + 3x + 9)$$

75. $8y^3 - 1$
$$= (2y)^3 - 1$$
$$= (2y - 1)[(2y)^2 + 2y + 1]$$
$$= (2y - 1)(4y^2 + 2y + 1)$$

77. $27x^3 + 8$
$$= (3x)^3 + 2^3$$
$$= (3x + 2)[(3x)^2 - 3x \cdot 2 + 2^2]$$
$$= (3x + 2)(9x^2 - 6x + 4)$$

79. $x^3y^3 - 64$
$$= (xy)^3 - 4^3$$
$$= (xy - 4)[(xy)^2 + xy \cdot 4 + 4^2]$$
$$= (xy - 4)(x^2y^2 + 4xy + 16)$$

81. $27y^4 + 8y$
$$= y(27y^3 + 8)$$
$$= y[(3y)^3 + 2^3]$$
$$= y(3y + 2)[(3y)^2 - 3y \cdot 2 + 2^2]$$
$$= y(3y + 2)(9y^2 - 6y + 4)$$

83. $54 - 16y^3$
$$= 2(27 - 8y^3)$$
$$= 2[3^3 - (2y)^3]$$
$$= 2(3 - 2y)[3^2 + 3 \cdot 2y + (2y)^2]$$
$$= 2(3 - 2y)(9 + 6y + 4y^2)$$

85. $64x^3 + 27y^3$
$$= (4x)^3 + (3y)^3$$
$$= (4x + 3y)(4x)^2 - 4x \cdot 3y + (3y)^2]$$
$$= (4x + 3y)(16x^2 - 12xy + 9y^2)$$

87. $125x^3 - 64y^3$
$$= (5x)^3 - (4y)^3$$
$$= (5x - 4y)[(5x)^2 + 5x \cdot 4y + (4y)^2]$$
$$= (5x - 4y)(25x^2 + 20xy + 16y^2)$$

89. Area of outer square $= x^2$
Area of inner square $= 5^2 = 25$
Area of shaded region $= x^2 - 25$
$$= (x + 5)(x - 5)$$

91. Area of large square $= x^2$
Area of each small (corner) square $= 2^2$
$$= 4$$
Area of four corner squares $= 4 \cdot 4 = 16$
Area of shaded region $= x^2 - 16$
$$= (x + 4)(x - 4)$$

For Exercises 93–95, answers may vary.

97. Statement b is true.

99. $(x + 1)^2 - 25$
$$= (x + 1)^2 - 5^2$$
$$= [(x + 1) + 5][(x + 1) - 5]$$
$$= (x + 6)(x - 4)$$

101. $4x^{2n} + 12x^n + 9$
$$= (2x^n)^2 + 2 \cdot 2x^n \cdot 3 + 3^2$$
$$= (2x^n + 3)^2$$

103. $(x + 3)^2 - 2(x + 3) + 1$
$$= [(x + 3) - 1]^2$$
$$= (x + 2)^2$$

105. $64x^2 - 16x + k$

Let r be the number such that $r^2 = k$. Then

$$64x^2 - 16x + k = (8x)^2 - 2 \cdot 8x \cdot r + r^2.$$

Comparing the middle terms, we see that

$$-2 \cdot 8x \cdot r = -16x$$
$$-16xr = -16x$$
$$r = 1.$$

Therefore, $k = r^2 = 1^2 = 1$.

107.

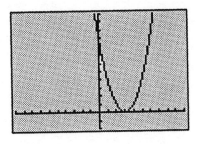

The graphs coincide. This verfies that

$$x^2 - 6x + 9 = (x-3)^2.$$

109.

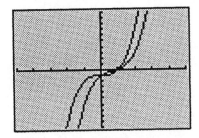

The graphs do not coincide.

$$x^3 - 1 = x^3 - 1^3 = (x+1)(x^2+1)$$

The polynomial on the right should be changed to $(x-1)(x^2 - x + 1)$.

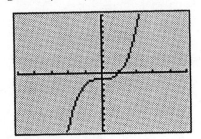

Now the graphs coincide.

Review Exercises

110. $(2x^2 y^3)^4 (5xy^2)$
$$= [2^4 (x^2)^4 (y^3)^4] \cdot (5xy^2)$$
$$= (16x^8 y^{12})(5xy^2)$$
$$= (16 \cdot 5)(x^8 \cdot x^1)(y^{12} \cdot y^2)$$
$$= 80x^9 y^{14}$$

111. $(10x^2 - 5x + 2) - (14x^2 - 5x - 1)$
$$= (10x^2 - 5x + 2) + (-14x^2 + 5x + 1)$$
$$= (10x^2 - 14x^2) + (-5x + 5x) + (2 - 1)$$
$$= -4x^2 + 3$$

112.

$$
\begin{array}{r}
2x + 5 \\
3x - 2 \overline{)6x^2 + 11x - 10} \\
\underline{6x^2 - 4x} \\
15x - 10 \\
\underline{15x - 10} \\
0
\end{array}
$$

$$\frac{6x^2 + 11x - 10}{3x - 2} = 2x + 5$$

A General Factoring Strategy

6.5 CHECK POINTS

CHECK POINT 1

$5x^4 - 45x^2$

Step 1 Factor out the GCF, which is $5x^2$.

$$5x^4 - 45x^2 = 5x^2(x^2 - 9)$$

Step 2 The factor $x^2 - 9$ has two terms and is the difference of two squares.

$$5x^4 - 45x^2 = 5x^2(x^2 - 9)$$
$$= 5x^2(x+3)(x-3)$$

Step 3 No factor with more than one term can be factored further.

Step 4 Check by multiplying.

$$5x^2(x+3)(x-3) = 5x^2(x^2 - 9)$$
$$= 5x^4 - 45x^2$$

CHECK POINT 2

$4x^2 - 16x - 48$

Step 1 Factor out the GCF, which is 4.

$$4x^2 - 16x - 48 = 4(x^2 - 4x - 12)$$

Step 2 The factor $x^2 - 4x - 12$ has three terms, but it is not a perfect square trinomial. Factor it by using trial and error.

$$4x^2 - 16x - 48 = 4(x^2 - 4x - 12)$$
$$= 4(x - 6)(x + 2)$$

Step 3 No factor with more than one term can be factored further.

Step 4 Check by multiplying.

$$4(x - 6)(x + 2) = 4(x^2 - 4x - 12)$$
$$= 4x^2 - 16x - 48$$

CHECK POINT 3

$4x^5 - 64x$

Step 1 Factor out the GCF, which is $4x$.

$$4x^5 - 64x = 4x(x^4 - 16)$$

Step 2 The factor $x^4 - 16$ has two terms. This binomial can be expressed as the difference of two squares, $(x^2)^2 - 4^2$, so it can be factored as the difference of two squares.

$$4x^5 - 64x = 4x(x^4 - 16)$$
$$= 4x(x^2 + 4)(x^2 - 4)$$

Step 3 $x^2 - 4$ is also the difference of two squares, so continue factoring.

$$4x^5 - 64x = 4x(x^4 - 16)$$
$$= 4x(x^2 + 4)(x^2 - 4)$$
$$= 4x(x^2 + 4)(x + 2)(x - 2)$$

Step 4 Check by multiplying.

$$4x(x^2 + 4)(x + 2)(x - 2)$$
$$= 4x(x^2 + 4)(x^2 - 4)$$
$$= 4x(x^4 - 16)$$
$$= 4x^5 - 64x$$

CHECK POINT 4

$x^3 - 4x^2 - 9x + 36$

Step 1 Other than 1, there is no common factor.

Step 2 There are four terms. Try factoring by grouping.

$$x^3 - 4x^2 - 9x + 36$$
$$= (x^3 - 4x^2) + (-9x + 36)$$
$$= x^2(x - 4) - 9(x - 4)$$
$$= (x - 4)(x^2 - 9)$$

Step 3 Since $x^2 - 9$ is the difference of two squares, continue factoring.

$$x^3 - 4x^2 - 9x + 36$$
$$= (x - 4)(x^2 - 9)$$
$$= (x - 4)(x + 3)(x - 3)$$

Step 4

$$(x - 4)(x + 3)(x - 3)$$
$$= (x - 4)(x^2 - 9)$$
$$= x^3 - 9x - 4x^2 + 36$$
$$= x^3 - 4x^2 - 9x + 36$$

CHECK POINT 5

$3x^3 - 30x^2 + 75x$

Step 1 Factor out the GCF, which is $3x$.

$$3x^3 - 30x^2 + 75x = 3x(x^2 - 10x + 25)$$

Step 2 The factor $x^2 - 10x + 25$ has three terms and is a perfect square trinomial.

$$3x^3 - 30x^2 + 75x$$
$$= 3x(x^2 - 10x + 25)$$
$$= 3x(x^2 - 2 \cdot x \cdot 5 + 5^2)$$
$$= 3x(x - 5)^2$$

Step 3 The factorization is complete.

Step 4 Check by multiplying.

$$3x(x-5)^2 = 3x(x^2 - 10x + 25)$$
$$= 3x^3 - 30x^2 + 75x$$

CHECK POINT 6

$2x^5 + 54x^2$

Step 1 Factor out the GCF, which is $2x^2$.

$$2x^5 + 54x^2 = 2x^2(x^3 + 27)$$

Step 2 The factor $x^3 + 27$ has two terms and is the sum of two cubes.

$$2x^5 + 54x^2 = 2x^2(x^3 + 3^3)$$
$$= 2x^2(x+3)(x^2 - 3x + 9)$$

Step 3 The factorization is complete.

Step 4 Check by multiplyling.

$$2x^2(x+3)(x^2 - 3x + 9) = 2x^2(x^3 + 27)$$
$$= 2x^5 + 54x^2$$

CHECK POINT 7

$3x^4 y - 48y^5$

Step 1 Factor out the GCF, which is $3y$.

$$3x^4 y - 48y^5 = 3y(x^4 - 16y^4)$$

Step 2 The factor $x^4 - 16y^4$ has two terms and is the difference of two squares.

$$3x^4 - 48y^5 = 3y(x^4 - 16y^4)$$
$$= 3y[(x^2)^2 - (4y^2)^2]$$
$$= 3y(x^2 + 4y^2)(x^2 - 4y^2)$$

Step 3 The last factor, $x^2 - 4y^2$, is also the difference of two squares, so continue factoring.

$$3x^2 y - 48y^5$$
$$= 3y(x^2 + 4y^2)(x^2 - 4y^2)$$
$$= 3y(x^2 + 4y^2)(x + 2y)(x - 2y)$$

Step 4 Check by multiplying.

$$3y(x^2 + 4y^2)(x + 2y)(x - 2y)$$
$$= 3y(x^2 + 4y^2)(x^2 - 4y^2)$$
$$= 3y(x^4 - 16y^4)$$
$$= 3x^4 y - 48y^5$$

CHECK POINT 8

$12x^3 + 36x^2 y + 27xy^2$

Step 1 Factor out the GCF, which is $3x$.

$$12x^3 + 36y^2 + 27xy^2$$
$$= 3x(4x^2 + 12xy + 9y^2)$$

Step 2 The factor $4x^2 + 12xy + 9y^2$ has three terms and is a perfect square trinomial.

$$12x^3 + 36x^2 y + 27xy^2$$
$$= 3x(4x^2 + 12xy + 9y^2)$$
$$= 3x[(2x)^2 + 2 \cdot 2x \cdot 3y + (3y)^2]$$
$$= 3x(2x + 3y)^2$$

Step 3 The factorization is complete.

Step 4 Check by multiplying.

$$3x(2x + 3y)^2$$
$$= 3x[(2x)^2 + 2 \cdot 2x \cdot 3y + (3y)^2]$$
$$= 3x(4x^2 + 12xy + 9y^2)$$
$$= 12x^3 + 36x^2 y + 27xy^2$$

EXERCISE SET 6.5

In Exercises 1–61, all factorizations should be checked using multiplication or a graphing utility. Checks will not be shown here.

1. $3x^3 - 3x = 3x(x^2 - 1)$
$$= 3x(x + 1)(x - 1)$$

3. $3x^3 + 3x = 3x(x^2 + 1)$

5. $4x^2 - 4x - 24 = 4(x^2 - x - 6)$
$$= 4(x - 3)(x + 2)$$

7. $2x^4 - 162 = 2(x^4 - 81)$
$$= 2(x^2 + 9)(x^2 - 9)$$
$$= 2(x^2 + 9)(x + 3)(x - 3)$$

9. $x^3 + 2x^2 - 9x - 18$
$$= (x^3 + 2x^2) + (-9x - 18)$$
$$= x^2(x + 2) - 9(x + 2)$$
$$= (x + 2)(x^2 - 9)$$
$$= (x + 2)(x + 3)(x - 3)$$

11. $3x^3 - 24x^2 + 48x = 3x(x^2 - 8x + 16)$
$$= 3x(x - 4)^2$$

13. $2x^5 + 2x^2 = 2x^2(x^3 + 1)$
$$= 2x^2(x + 1)(x^2 - x + 1)$$

15. $6x^2 + 8x = 2x(3x + 4)$

17. $2y^2 - 2y - 112 = 2(y^2 - y - 56)$
$$= 2(y - 8)(y + 7)$$

19. $7y^4 + 14y^3 + 7y^2 = 7y^2(y^2 + 2y + 1)$
$$= 7y^2(y + 1)^2$$

21. $y^2 + 8y - 16$ is prime because there are no two integers whose product is -16 and whose sum is 8.

23. $16y^2 - 4y - 2 = 2(8y^2 - 2y - 1)$
$$= 2(4y + 1)(2y - 1)$$

25. $r^2 - 25r = r(r - 25)$

27. $4w^2 + 8w - 5 = (2w + 5)(2w - 1)$

29. $x^3 - 4x = x(x^2 - 4) = x(x + 2)(x - 2)$

31. $x^2 + 64$ is prime because it is the sum of two squares with no common fator other than 1.

33. $9y^2 + 13y + 4 = (9y + 4)(y + 1)$

35. $y^3 + 2y^2 - 4y - 8$
$$= (y^3 + 2y^2) + (-4y - 8)$$
$$= y^2(y + 2) - 4(y + 2)$$
$$= (y + 2)(y^2 - 4)$$
$$= (y + 2)(y + 2)(y - 2)$$
or $(y + 2)^2(y - 2)$

37. $9y^2 + 24y + 16$
$$= (3y)^2 + 2 \cdot 3y \cdot 4 + 4^2$$
$$= (3y + 4)^2$$

39. $5y^3 - 45y^2 + 70y$
$$= 5y(y^2 - 9y + 14)$$
$$= 5y(y - 7)(y - 2)$$

41. $y^5 - 81y$
$$= y(y^4 - 81)$$
$$= y(y^2 + 9)(y^2 - 9)$$
$$= y(y^2 + 9)(y + 3)(y - 3)$$

43. $20a^4 - 45a^2$
$$= 5a^2(4a^2 - 9)$$
$$= 5a^2(2a + 3)(2a - 3)$$

45. $12y^2 - 11y + 2 = (4y - 1)(3y - 2)$

47. $9y^2 - 64 = (3y)^2 - 8^2$
$$= (3y + 8)(3y - 8)$$

49. $9y^2 + 64$ is prime because it is the sum of two squares with no common factor other than 1.

51. $2y^3 + 3y^2 - 50y - 75$
$= (2y^3 + 3y^2) + (-50y - 75)$
$= y^2(2y + 3) - 25(2y + 3)$
$= (2y + 3)(y^2 - 25)$
$= (2y + 3)(y + 5)(y - 5)$

53. $2r^3 + 30r^2 - 68r$
$= 2r(r^2 + 15r - 34)$
$= 2r(r + 17)(r - 2)$

55. $8x^5 - 2x^3 = 2x^3(4x^2 - 1)$
$= 2x^2[(2x)^2 - 1^2]$
$= 2x^2(2x + 1)(2x - 1)$

57. $3x^2 + 243 = 3(x^2 + 81)$

59. $x^4 + 8x = x(x^3 + 8)$
$= x(x^3 + 2^3)$
$= x(x + 2)(x^2 - 2x + 4)$

61. $2y^5 - 2y^2$
$= 2y^2(y^3 - 1)$
$= 2y^2(y - 1)(y^2 + y + 1)$

63. $6x^2 + 8xy = 2x(3x + 4y)$

65. $xy - 7x + 3y - 21$
$= (xy - 7x) + (3y - 21)$
$= x(y - 7) + 3(y - 7)$
$= (y - 7)(x + 3)$

67. $x^2 - 3xy - 4y^2 = (x - 4y)(x + y)$

69. $72a^3b^2 + 12a^2 - 24a^4b^2$
$= 12a^2(6ab^2 + 1 - 2a^2b^2)$

71. $3a^2 + 27ab + 54b^2$
$= 3(a^2 + 9ab + 18b^2)$
$= 3(a + 6b)(a + 3b)$

73. $48x^4y - 3x^2y$
$= 3x^2y(16x^2 - 1)$
$= 3x^2y(4x + 1)(4x - 1)$

75. $6a^2b + ab - 2b$
$= b(6a^2 + a - 2)$
$= b(3a + 2)(2a - 1)$

77. $7x^5y - 7xy^5$
$= 7xy(x^4 - y^4)$
$= 7xy(x^2 + y^2)(x^2 - y^2)$
$= 7xy(x^2 + y^2)(x + y)(x - y)$

79. $10x^3y - 14x^2y^2 + 4xy^3$
$= 2xy(5x^2 - 7xy + 2y^2)$
$= 2xy(5x - 2y)(x - y)$

81. $2bx^2 + 44bx + 242b$
$= 2b(x^2 + 22x + 121)$
$= 2b(x^2 + 2 \cdot x \cdot 11 + 11^2)$
$= 2b(x + 11)^2$

83. $15a^2 + 11ab - 14b^2 = (5a + 7b)(3a - 2b)$

85. $36x^3y - 62x^2y^2 + 12xy^3$
$= 2xy(18x^2 - 31xy + 6y^2)$
$= 2xy(9x - 2y)(2x - 3y)$

87. $a^2y - b^2y - a^2x + b^2x$
$= (a^2y - b^2y) + (-a^2x + b^2x)$
$= y(a^2 - b^2) - x(a^2 - b^2)$
$= (a^2 - b^2)(y - -x)$
$= (a + b)(a - b)(y - x)$

89. $9ax^3 + 15ax^2 - 14ax$
$= ax(9x^2 + 15x - 14)$
$= ax(3x + 7)(3x - 2)$

91. $81x^4y - y^5$
$$= y(81x^4 - y^4)$$
$$= y(9x^2 + y^2)(9x^2 - y^2)$$
$$= y(9x^2 + y^2)(3x + y)(3x - y)$$

93. $256 - 16t^2 = 16(16 - t^2)$
$$= 16(4 + t)(4 - t)$$

95. Area of outer circle $= \pi b^2$
Area of inner circle $= \pi a^2$
Area of shaded ring $= \pi b^2 - \pi a^2$

$$\pi b^2 - \pi a^2 = \pi(b^2 - a^2)$$
$$= \pi(b + a)(b - a)$$

97. Answers may vary.

99. Statement d is true.

$$3x^2y^3 + 9xy^2 + 21xy$$
$$= 3xy(xy^2 + 3y + 7),$$

and $xy^2 + 3y + 7$ cannot be factored further.

101. $5y^5 - 5y^4 - 20y^3 + 20y^2$
$$= 5y^2(y^3 - y^2 - 4y + 4)$$
$$= 5y^2[y^2(y - 1) - 4(y - 1)]$$
$$= 5y^2(y - 1)(y^2 - 4)$$
$$= 5y^2(y - 1)(y + 2)(y - 2)$$

103. $(x + 5)^2 - 20(x + 5) + 100$

This is a perfect square trinomial.

$$(x + 5)^2 - 20(x + 5) + 100$$
$$= (x + 5)^2 - 2(x + 5)(10) + 10^2$$
$$= [(x + 5) - 10]^2$$
$$= (x - 5)^2$$

105.

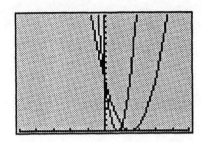

The graphs do not coincide.

$$4x^2 - 12x + 9 = (2x)^2 - 2 \cdot 2x \cdot 3 + 3^2$$
$$= (2x - 3)^2$$

Change the polynomial on the right side to $(4x - 3)^2$.

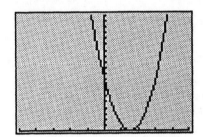

Now the graphs coincide.

107.

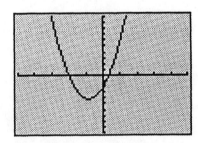

The graphs coincide.
This verifies that the factorization

$$6x^2 + 10x - 4 = 2(3x - 1)(x + 2)$$

is correct.

109.

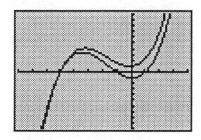

The graphs do not coincide.

$$2x^3 + 10x^2 - 2x - 10$$
$$= 2(x^3 + 5x^2 - x - 5)$$
$$= 2[(x^3 + 5x^2) + (-x - 5)]$$
$$= 2[x^2(x + 5) - 1(x + 5)]$$
$$= 2(x + 5)(x^2 - 1)$$
$$= 2(x + 5)(x + 1)(x - 1)$$

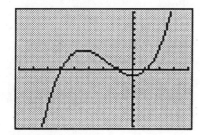

Review Exercises

110. $9x^2 - 16 = (3x)^2 - 4^2$
$$= (3x + 4)(3x - 4)$$

111. $5x - 2y = 10$
x-intercept: 2
y-intercept: -5
checkpoint: $(4, 5)$

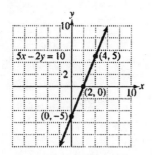

112. Let $\quad x = $ the measure of the first angle.

Then $3x = $ the measure of the second angle;

$x + 80 = $ the measure of the third angle.

$$x + 3x + (x + 80) = 180$$
$$5x + 80 = 180$$
$$5x = 100$$
$$x = 20$$

Measure of first angle $= x = 20°$
Measure of second angle $= 3x = 60°$
Measure of third angle $= x + 80 = 100°$

Solving Quadratic Equations by Factoring
7.6 CHECK POINTS

CHECK POINT 1

$(2x + 1)(x - 4) = 0$

Set each factor equal to zero and solve each resulting equation for x.

$$(2x + 1)(x - 4) = 0$$
$$2x + 1 = 0 \quad \text{or} \quad x - 4 = 0$$
$$2x = -1 \qquad\qquad x = 4$$
$$x = -\frac{1}{2}$$

Check each of these solutions in the equation $(2x+1)(x-4)$. The equation has two solutions, $-\frac{1}{2}$ and 4.

CHECK POINT 2

$x^2 - 6x + 5 = 0$

Step 1 The equation is already written in standard form.

Step 2 Factor the trinomial.

$$x^2 - 6x + 5 = 0$$
$$(x - 5)(x - 1) = 0$$

Step 3 and 4 Set each factor equal to zero and solve the resulting equation.

$$x - 5 = 0 \quad \text{or} \quad x - 1 = 0$$
$$x = 5 \qquad\qquad x = 1$$

Step 5 Check the solutions in the original equation.

Check 5:

$$x^2 - 6x + 5 = 0$$
$$5^2 - 6 \cdot 5 + 5 \stackrel{?}{=} 0$$
$$25 - 30 + 5 \stackrel{?}{=} 0$$
$$-5 + 5 \stackrel{?}{=} 0$$
$$0 = 0 \text{ true}$$

Check 1:

$$x^2 - 6x + 5 = 0$$
$$1^2 - 6 \cdot 1 + 5 \stackrel{?}{=} 0$$
$$1 - 6 + 5 \stackrel{?}{=} 0$$
$$-5 + 5 \stackrel{?}{=} 0$$
$$0 = 0 \text{ true}$$

The solutions are 5 and 1.

CHECK POINT 3

$$4x^2 = 2x$$

Step 1 Write the equation in standard form.

$$4x^2 = 2x$$
$$4x^2 - 2x = 0$$

Step 2 Factor the binomial by factoring out the GCF, $2x$.

$$2x(2x - 1) = 0$$

Step 3 and 4 Set each factor equal to zero and solve the resulting equations.

$$2x = 0 \quad \text{or} \quad 2x - 1 = 0$$
$$x = 0 \qquad\qquad 2x = 1$$
$$x = \frac{1}{2}$$

Step 5 Check the solutions in the original equation:

Check 0:   Check: $\frac{1}{2}$:

$$4x^2 = 2x$$
$$4 \cdot 0^2 = 2 \cdot 0$$
$$0 = 0 \text{ true}$$

$$4x^2 = 2x$$
$$4\left(\frac{1}{2}\right)^2 = 2\left(\frac{1}{2}\right)$$
$$4 \cdot \frac{1}{4} = 1$$
$$1 = 1 \text{ true}$$

The solutions are 0 and $\frac{1}{2}$.

CHECK POINT 4

$$x^2 = 10x - 25$$

Step 1

$$x^2 - 10x + 25 = 10x - 10x - 25 + 25$$
$$x^2 - 10x + 25 = 0$$

Step 2 $x^2 - 10x + 25$ is a perfect square trinomial.

$$(x - 5)^2 = 0$$

Step 3 and 4 Because both factors are the same, it is only necessary to set one of them equal to zero.

$$x - 5 = 0$$
$$x = 5$$

Step 5 Check 5:

$$x^2 = 10x - 25$$
$$5^2 \stackrel{?}{=} 10 \cdot 5 - 25$$
$$25 \stackrel{?}{=} 50 - 25$$
$$25 = 25 \text{ true}$$

The solution is 5.

CHECK POINT 5

$16x^2 = 25$

Step 1

$$16x^2 - 25 = 25 - 25$$
$$16x^2 - 25 = 0$$

Step 2 $16x^2 - 25$ is the difference of two squares.

$$(4x + 5)(4x - 5) = 0$$

Step 3 and 4

$$4x + 5 = 0 \quad \text{or} \quad 4x - 5 = 0$$
$$4x = -5 \qquad\qquad 4x = 5$$
$$x = -\frac{5}{4} \qquad\qquad x = \frac{5}{4}$$

Step 5

Check $-\frac{5}{4}$:

$$16x^2 = 25$$
$$16\left(-\frac{5}{4}\right)^2 \stackrel{?}{=} 25$$
$$16 \cdot \frac{25}{16} \stackrel{?}{=} 25$$
$$25 = 25 \text{ true}$$

Check: $\frac{5}{4}$:

$$16x^2 = 25$$
$$16\left(\frac{5}{4}\right)^2 \stackrel{?}{=} 25$$
$$16 \cdot \frac{25}{16} \stackrel{?}{=} 25$$
$$25 = 25 \text{ true}$$

The solutions are $-\frac{5}{4}$ and $\frac{5}{4}$.

CHECK POINT 6

$(x - 5)(x - 2) = 28$

Step 1

$$x^2 - 2x - 5x + 10 = 28$$
$$x^2 - 7x + 10 = 28$$
$$x^2 - 7x + 10 - 28 = 28 - 28$$
$$x^2 - 7x - 8 = 0$$

Step 2

$$(x - 9)(x + 2) = 0$$

Step 3 and 4

$$x - 9 = 0 \quad \text{or} \quad x + 2 = 0$$
$$x = 9 \qquad\qquad x = -2$$

Step 5

Check 9:

$$(x - 5)(x - 2) = 28$$
$$(9 - 5)(9 - 2) \stackrel{?}{=} 28$$
$$4 \cdot 7 \stackrel{?}{=} 28$$
$$28 = 28 \text{ true}$$

Check -2:

$$(x - 5)(x - 2) = 28$$
$$(-2 - 5)(-2 - 2) \stackrel{?}{=} 28$$
$$(-7)(-4) \stackrel{?}{=} 28$$
$$28 = 28 \text{ true}$$

The solutions are 9 and -2.

CHECK POINT 7

$h = -16t^2 + 48t + 160$

Substitute 192 for h and solve for t.

$$192 = -16t^2 + 48t + 160$$
$$16t^2 + 48t + 192 - 160 = -16t^2 + 16t^2 + 48t$$
$$- 48t + 160 - 160$$
$$16t^2 - 48t + 32 = 0$$
$$16(t^2 - 3t + 2) = 0$$
$$16(t - 1)(t - 2) = 0$$

$$t - 1 = 0 \quad \text{or} \quad t - 2 = 0$$
$$t = 1 \qquad\qquad t = 0$$

The ball's height is 192 feet after 1 second and after 2 seconds. These solutionss correspond to the points $(1, 192)$ and $(2, 192)$ on the graph.

CHECK POINT 8

Let $\quad x = $ the width of the sign.

Then $x + 3 = $ the length of the floor.

Use the formula for the area of a rectangle.

$$l \cdot w = A$$
$$(x + 3)(x) = 54$$
$$x^2 + 3x = 54$$
$$x^2 + 3x - 54 = 0$$
$$(x + 9)(x - 6) = 0$$
$$x + 9 = 0 \quad \text{or} \quad x - 6 = 0$$
$$x = -9 \qquad\qquad x = 6$$

A rectangle cannot have a negative length. Thus, $x = 6$ and $x + 3 = 9$. The length of the sign is 9 feet and the width is 6 feet. This solution checks because

$$A = lw = (9 \text{ feet})(6 \text{ feet})$$
$$= 54 \text{ square feet.}$$

EXERCISE SET 6.6

1. $x(x + 3) = 0$

$$x = 0 \quad \text{or} \quad x + 3 = 0$$
$$x = -3$$

The solutions are 0 and -3.

3. $(x - 8)(x + 5) = 0$

$$x - 8 = 0 \quad \text{or} \quad x + 5 = 0$$
$$x = 8 \qquad\qquad x = -5$$

The solutions are 8 and -5.

5. $(x - 2)(4x + 5) = 0$

$$x - 2 = 0 \quad \text{or} \quad 4x + 5 = 0$$
$$x = 2 \qquad\qquad 4x = -5$$
$$x = -\frac{5}{4}$$

The solutions are 2 and $-\frac{5}{4}$.

7. $4(x - 3)(2x + 7) = 0$

$$x - 3 = 0 \quad \text{or} \quad 2x + 7 = 0$$
$$x = 3 \qquad\qquad 2x = -7$$
$$x = -\frac{7}{2}$$

The solutions are 3 and $-\frac{7}{2}$.

In Exercises 9–55, all solutions should be checked by substitution or by using a graphing utility and identifying x-intercepts. The check by substitution will be shown here for Exercise 9 only.

9. $\quad x^2 + 8x + 15 = 0$

$$(x + 5)(x + 3) = 0$$
$$x + 5 = 0 \quad \text{or} \quad x + 3 = 0$$
$$x = 5 \qquad\qquad x = -3$$

Check -5:

$$x^2 + 8x + 15 = 0$$
$$(-5)^2 + 8(-5) + 15 \stackrel{?}{=} 0$$
$$25 - 40 + 15 \stackrel{?}{=} 0$$
$$-15 + 15 \stackrel{?}{=} 0$$
$$0 = 0 \text{ true}$$

Check 3:

$$x^2 + 8x + 15 = 0$$
$$(-3)^2 + 8(-3) + 15 \stackrel{?}{=} 0$$
$$9 - 24 + 15 \stackrel{?}{=} 0$$
$$-15 + 15 \stackrel{?}{=} 0$$
$$0 = 0 \text{ true}$$

The solutions are -5 and -3.

11. $\quad x^2 - 2x - 15 = 0$

$$(x + 3)(x - 5) = 0$$
$$x + 3 = 0 \quad \text{or} \quad x - 5 = 0$$
$$x = -3 \qquad\qquad x = 5$$

The solutions are -3 and 5.

13.
$$x^2 - 4x = 21$$
$$x^2 - 4x - 21 = 0$$
$$(x+3)(x-7) = 0$$
$$x + 3 = 0 \quad \text{or} \quad x - 7 = 0$$
$$x = -3 \qquad\qquad x = 7$$

The solutions are -3 and 7.

15.
$$x^2 + 9x = -8$$
$$x^2 + 9x + 8 = 0$$
$$(x+8)(x+1) = 0$$
$$x + 8 = 0 \quad \text{or} \quad x + 1 = 0$$
$$x = -8 \qquad\qquad x = -1$$

The solutions are -8 and -1.

17. $x^2 + 4x = 0$
$$x(x+4) = 0$$
$$x = 0 \quad \text{or} \quad x + 4 = 0$$
$$x = -4$$

The solutions are 0 and -4.

19. $x^2 - 5x = 0$
$$x(x-5) = 0$$
$$x = 0 \quad \text{or} \quad x - 5 = 0$$
$$x = 5$$

The solutions are 0 and 5.

21.
$$x^2 = 4x$$
$$x^2 - 4x = 0$$
$$x(x-4) = 0$$
$$x = 0 \quad \text{or} \quad x - 4 = 0$$
$$x = 4$$

The solutions are 0 and 4.

23.
$$2x^2 = 5x$$
$$2x^2 - 5x = 0$$
$$x(2x-5) = 0$$
$$x = 0 \quad \text{or} \quad 2x - 5 = 0$$
$$2x = 5$$
$$x = \frac{5}{2}$$

The solutions are 0 and $\frac{5}{2}$.

25.
$$3x^2 = -5x$$
$$3x^2 + 5x = 0$$
$$x(3x+5) = 0$$
$$x = 0 \quad \text{or} \quad 3x + 5 = 0$$
$$3x = -5$$
$$x = -\frac{5}{3}$$

The only solution is 0 and $-\frac{5}{3}$.

27. $x^2 + 4x + 4 = 0$
$$(x-2)^2 = 0$$
$$x + 2 = 0$$
$$x = -2$$

The only solution is -2.

29.
$$x^2 = 12x - 36$$
$$x^2 - 12x + 36 = 0$$
$$(x-6)^2 = 0$$
$$x - 6 = 0$$
$$x = 6$$

The only solution is 6.

31.
$$4x^2 = 12x - 9$$
$$4x^2 - 12x + 9 = 0$$
$$(2x-3)^2 = 0$$
$$2x - 3 = 0$$
$$2x = 3$$
$$x = \frac{3}{2}$$

The only solution is $\frac{3}{2}$.

33.
$$2x^2 = 7x + 4$$
$$2x^2 - 7x - 4 = 0$$
$$(2x+1)(x-4) = 0$$
$$2x + 1 = 0 \quad \text{or} \quad x - 4 = 0$$
$$2x = -1 \qquad\qquad x = 4$$
$$x = -\frac{1}{2}$$

The solutions are $-\frac{1}{2}$ and 4.

35.
$$5x^2 = 18 - x$$
$$5x^2 + x - 18 = 0$$
$$(5x - 9)(x + 2) = 0$$
$$5x - 9 = 0 \quad \text{or} \quad x + 2 = 0$$
$$5x = 9 \qquad\qquad x = -2$$
$$x = \frac{9}{5}$$

The solutions are $\frac{9}{5}$ and -2.

37.
$$x^2 - 49 = 0$$
$$(x + 7)(x - 7) = 0$$
$$x + 7 = 0 \quad \text{or} \quad x - 7 = 0$$
$$x = -7 \qquad\qquad x = 7$$

The solutions are -7 and 7.

39.
$$4x^2 - 25 = 0$$
$$(2x + 5)(2x - 5) = 0$$
$$2x + 5 = 0 \quad \text{or} \quad 2x - 5 = 0$$
$$2x = -5 \qquad\qquad 2x = 5$$
$$x = -\frac{5}{2} \qquad\qquad x = \frac{5}{2}$$

The solutions are $-\frac{5}{2}$ and $\frac{5}{2}$.

41.
$$81x^2 = 25$$
$$81x^2 - 25 = 0$$
$$(9x + 5)(9x - 5) = 0$$
$$9x + 5 = 0 \quad \text{or} \quad 9x - 5 = 0$$
$$9x = -5 \qquad\qquad 9x = 5$$
$$x = -\frac{5}{9} \qquad\qquad x = \frac{5}{9}$$

The solutions are $-\frac{5}{9}$ and $\frac{5}{9}$.

43.
$$x(x - 4) = 21$$
$$x^2 - 4x = 21$$
$$x^2 - 4x - 21 = 0$$
$$(x + 3)(x - 7) = 0$$
$$x + 3 = 0 \quad \text{or} \quad x - 7 = 0$$
$$x = -3 \qquad\qquad x = 7$$

The solutions are -3 and 7.

45.
$$4x(x + 1) = 15$$
$$4x^2 + 4x = 15$$
$$4x^2 + 4x - 15 = 0$$
$$(2x + 5)(2x - 3) = 0$$
$$2x + 5 = 0 \quad \text{or} \quad 2x - 3 = 0$$
$$2x = -5 \qquad\qquad 2x = 3$$
$$x = -\frac{5}{2} \qquad\qquad x = \frac{3}{2}$$

The solutions are $-\frac{5}{2}$ and $\frac{3}{2}$.

47. $(x - 1)(x + 4) = 14$
$$x^2 + 3x - 4 = 14$$
$$x^2 + 3x - 18 = 0$$
$$(x + 6)(x - 3) = 0$$
$$x + 6 = 0 \quad \text{or} \quad x - 3 = 0$$
$$x = -6 \qquad\qquad x = 3$$

The solutions are -6 and 3.

49. $(x + 1)(2x + 5) = -1$
$$2x^2 + 7x + 5 = -1$$
$$2x^2 + 7x + 6 = 0$$
$$(2x + 3)(x + 2) = 0$$
$$2x + 3 = 0 \quad \text{or} \quad x + 2 = 0$$
$$2x = -3 \qquad\qquad x = -2$$
$$x = -\frac{3}{2}$$

The solutions are $-\frac{3}{2}$ and -2.

51.
$$y(y + 8) = 16(y - 1)$$
$$y^2 + 8y = 16y - 16$$
$$y^2 - 8y + 16 = 0$$
$$(y - 4)^2 = 0$$
$$y - 4 = 0$$
$$y = 4$$

The only solution is 4.

53. $4y^2 + 20y + 25 = 0$

$$(2y + 5)^2 = 0$$
$$2y + 5 = 0$$
$$2y = -5$$
$$y = -\frac{5}{2}$$

The only solution is $-\frac{5}{2}$.

55. $$64w^2 = 48w - 9$$
$$64w^2 - 48w + 9 = 0$$
$$(8w - 3)^2 = 0$$
$$8w - 3 = 0$$
$$8w = 3$$
$$w = \frac{3}{8}$$

The only solution is $\frac{3}{8}$.

57. $h = -16t^2 + 20t + 300$

Substitute 0 for h and solve for t.

$$0 = -16t^2 + 20t + 300$$
$$16t^2 - 20t - 300 = 0$$
$$4t(4t^2 - 5t - 75) = 0$$
$$4t(4t + 15)(t - 5) = 0$$

$$4t + 15 = 0 \quad \text{or} \quad t - 5 = 0$$
$$4t = -15 \qquad\qquad t = 5$$
$$t = -\frac{15}{4}$$

Discard $t = -\frac{15}{4}$ since time cannot be negative. It will take 5 seconds for the ball to reach the ground.

59. Substitute 276 for h and solve for t.

$$276 = -16t^2 + 20t + 300$$
$$16t^2 - 20t - 24 = 0$$
$$4(4t^2 - 5t - 6) = 0$$
$$4(4t + 3)(t - 2) = 0$$

$$4t + 3 = 0 \quad \text{or} \quad t - 2 = 0$$
$$4t = -3 \qquad\qquad t = 2$$
$$t = -\frac{3}{4}$$

Discard $t = \frac{3}{4}$ since time cannot be negative. The ball's height will be 276 feet 2 seconds after it is thrown. This corresponds to the point $(2, 276)$ on the graph.

61. $h = -16t^2 + 72t$

Substitute 32 for h and solve for t.

$$32 = -16t^2 + 72t$$
$$16t^2 + 72t + 32 = 0$$
$$8(2t^2 + 9t + 4) = 0$$
$$8(2t - 1)(t - 4) = 0$$

$$2t - 1 = 0 \quad \text{or} \quad t - 4 = 0$$
$$t = \frac{1}{2} \qquad\qquad t = 4$$

The debris will be 32 feet above the ground $\frac{1}{2}$ second after the explosion and 4 seconds after the explosion.

63. $N = 2x^2 + 22x + 320$

Substitute 1100 for N and solve for x.

$$1100 = 2x^2 + 22x + 320$$
$$0 = 2x^2 + 22x - 780$$
$$0 = 2(x^2 + 11x - 390)$$
$$0 = 2(x + 26)(x - 15)$$

$$x + 26 = 0 \quad \text{or} \quad x - 15 = 0$$
$$x = -26 \qquad\qquad x = 15$$

Discard $x = -26$ because the model starts at $x = 0$ to represent 1980. Since $x = 15$ represents the year 1995, the model shows that there were 1100 thousand inmates in U.S state and federal prisons in 1995. This corresponds to the point $(15, 1100)$ on the graph.

65. $P = -10x^2 + 475x + 3500$

Substitute 7250 for P and solve for x.

$$7250 = -10x^2 + 475x + 3500$$
$$10x^2 - 475x + 3750 = 0$$
$$5(2x^2 - 95x + 750) = 0$$
$$5(x - 10)(2x - 75) = 0$$

$$x - 10 = 0 \quad \text{or} \quad 2x - 75 = 0$$
$$x = 10 \qquad\qquad 2x = 75$$
$$x = \frac{75}{2} \text{ or } 37.5$$

The alligator population will have increased to 7250 after 10 years. (Discard 37.5 because this value is outside of $0 \le x \le 12$.)

67. The solution in Exercise 65 corresponds to the point $(10, 7250)$ on the graph.

69. $N = \dfrac{t^2 - t}{2}$

Substitute 45 for N and solve for t.

$$45 = \frac{t^2 - t}{2}$$
$$2 \cdot 45 = 2\left(\frac{t^2 - t}{2}\right)$$
$$90 = t^2 - t$$
$$0 = t^2 - t - 90$$
$$0 = (t - 10)(t + 9)$$

$$t - 10 = 0 \quad \text{or} \quad t + 9 = 0$$
$$t = 10 \qquad\qquad t = -9$$

Discard $t = -9$ since the number of teams cannot be negative. If 45 games are scheduled, there are 10 teams in the league.

71. Let $x =$ the width of the parking lot.

Then $x + 3 =$ the length.

$$l \cdot w = A$$
$$(x + 3)(x) = 180$$
$$x^2 + 3x = 180$$
$$x^2 + 3x - 180 = 0$$
$$(x + 15)(x - 12) = 0$$

$$x + 15 = 0 \quad \text{or} \quad x - 12 = 0$$
$$x = -15 \qquad\qquad x = 12$$

Discard $x = -15$ since the width cannot be negative. Then $x = 12$ and $x + 3 = 15$, so the length is 15 yards and the width is 12 yards.

73. Use the formula for the area of a triangle where x is the base and $x + 1$ is the height.

$$\frac{1}{2}bh = A$$
$$\frac{1}{2}x(x + 1) = 15$$
$$2\left[\frac{1}{2}x(x + 1)\right] = 2 \cdot 15$$
$$x(x + 1) = 30$$
$$x^2 + x = 30$$
$$x^2 + x - 30 = 0$$
$$(x + 6)(x - 5) = 0$$

$$x + 6 = 0 \quad \text{or} \quad x - 5 = 0$$
$$x = -6 \qquad\qquad x = 5$$

Discard $x = -6$ since the length of the base cannot be negative. Then $x = 5$ and $x + 1 = 6$, so the base is 5 centimeters and the height is 6 centimeters.

75. a. Area of large rectangle
$$(2x + 12)(2x + 10)$$
$$= 4x^2 + 20x + 24x + 120$$
$$= 4x^2 + 44x + 120$$
Area of flower bed $= 10 \cdot 12 = 120$
Area of border
$$= (4x^2 + 44x + 120) - 120$$
$$= 4x^2 + 44x$$

b. Find the width of the border for which the area of the border would be 168 square feet.

$$4x^2 + 44x = 168$$
$$4x^2 + 44x - 168 = 0$$
$$4(x^2 + 11x - 42) = 0$$
$$4(x + 14)(x - 3) = 0$$
$$x + 14 = 0 \quad \text{or} \quad x - 3 = 0$$
$$x = -14 \quad\quad\quad x = 3$$

Discard $x = -14$ since the width of the border cannot be negative. You should prepare a strip that is 3 feet wide for the border.

For Exercises 77–79, answers may vary.

81. If -3 and 5 are solutions of the quadratic equation, then $x - (-3) = x + 3$ and $x - 5$ must be factors of the polynomial on the left side when the quadratic equation is written in standard form.

$$(x + 3)(x - 5) = 0$$
$$x^2 - 5x + 3x - 15 = 0$$
$$x^2 - 2x - 15 = 0$$

Thus, $x^2 - 2x - 15 = 0$ is a quadratic equation in standard form whose solutions are -3 and 5.

83. $x^3 + 3x^2 - 10x = 0$

This is a cubic equation (equation of degree 3), rather than a quadratic equation, but it can be solved by factoring following the same method that is used with quadratic equations.

$$x^3 + 3x^2 - 10x = 0$$
$$x(x^2 + 3x - 10) = 0$$
$$x(x + 5)(x - 2) = 0$$
$$x = 0 \quad \text{or} \quad x + 5 = 0 \quad \text{or} \quad x - 2 = 0$$
$$x = -5 \quad\quad\quad x = 2$$

The equation has three solutions, $0, -5,$ and 2.

85. $(x^2 - 5x + 5)^3 = 1$

The only number that can be cubed (raised to the third power) to give 1 is 1. Therefore, the given equation is equivalent to the quadratic equation

$$x^2 - 5x + 5 = 1.$$

Solve this equation.

$$x^2 - 5x + 4 = 0$$
$$(x - 1)(x - 4) = 0$$
$$x - 1 = 0 \quad \text{or} \quad x - 4 = 0$$
$$x = 1 \quad\quad\quad x = 4$$

The solutions are 1 and 4.

87. $y = x^2 + x - 2$

To match this equation with its graph find the intercepts.

y-intercept:
Let $x = 0$ and solve for y.

$$y = 0^2 + 0 - 2$$
$$y = -2$$

The y-intercept is -2.

x-intercepts:
Let $y = 0$ and solve for x.

$$0 = x^2 + x - 2$$
$$0 = (x + 2)(x - 1)$$

$$x + 2 = 0 \quad \text{or} \quad x - 1 = 0$$
$$x = -2 \qquad\qquad x = 1$$

The x-intercepts are -2 and 1.
The only graph with y-intercept -2 and x-intercepts -2 and 1 is graph a.

89. $y = x^2 - 4x$

To match this equation with its graph, find the intercepts.

y-intercept:
Let $x = 0$ and solve for y.

$$y = 0^2 - 4(0) = 0$$

The y-intercept is 0, which means that the graph passes through the origin.

x-intercepts:
Let $y = 0$ and solve for x.

$$0 = x^2 - 4x$$
$$0 = x(x - 4)$$
$$x = 0 \quad \text{or} \quad x - 4 = 0$$
$$x = 4$$

The x-intercepts are 0 and 4.
The only graph with y-intercept 0 and x-intercepts 0 and 4 is graph b.

91. $y = x^2 + x - 6$
$x^2 + x - 6 = 0$

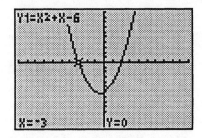

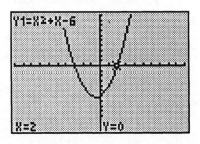

The calculator shows that the x-intercepts for the graph are -3 and 2. This means that the solutions of the equation $x^2 + x - 6 = 0$ are -3 and 2.

Check -3:

$$x^2 + x - 6 = 0$$
$$(-3)^2 + (-3) - 6 \overset{?}{=} 0$$
$$9 - 3 - 6 \overset{?}{=} 0$$
$$6 - 6 = 0$$
$$0 = 0 \text{ true}$$

Check 2:

$$x^2 + x - 6 = 0$$
$$2^2 + 2 - 6 \overset{?}{=} 0$$
$$4 + 2 - 6 \overset{?}{=} 0$$
$$6 - 6 \overset{?}{=} 0$$
$$0 = 0 \text{ true}$$

The check verify that the solutions of $x^2 + x - 6 = 0$ are -3 and 2.

93. $y = x^2 - 2x + 1$
$x^2 - 2x + 1 = 0$

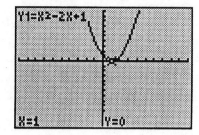

The calculator shows that the graph has one x-intercept, 1. This means that the only solution of the equation $x^2 - 2x + 1 = 0$ is 1.

Check 1:

$$x^2 - 2x + 1 = 0$$
$$1^2 - 2(1) + 1 \stackrel{?}{=} 0$$
$$1 - 2 + 1 \stackrel{?}{=} 0$$
$$-1 + 1 \stackrel{?}{=} 0$$
$$0 = 0 \text{ true}$$

The check verifies that the solution of $x^2 + 2x + 1$ is 1.

95. Answers will vary depending on the exercises chosen.

Review Exercises

96. $y > -\dfrac{2}{3}x + 1$

Graph $y = -\frac{2}{3}x + 1$ as a dashed line using the slope $-\frac{2}{3} = \frac{-2}{3}$ and y-intercept 1. (Plot $(0, 1)$ and move 2 units *down* and 3 units to the *right* to reach the point $(3, -1)$. Draw a line through $(0, 1)$ and $(3, -1)$.)

Use $(0, 0)$ as a test point. Since $0 > -\frac{2}{3}(0) + 1$ is false, shade the half-plane *not* containing $(0, 0)$.

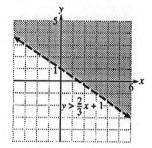

97. $\left(\dfrac{8x^4}{4x^7}\right)^2 = \left(\dfrac{8}{4} \cdot x^{4-7}\right) = (2x^{-3})^2$

$$= 2^2 \cdot (x^{-3})^2 = 4x^{-6} = \dfrac{4}{x^6}$$

98.
$$5x + 28 = 6 - 6x$$
$$5x + 6x + 28 = 6 - 6x + 6x$$
$$11x + 28 = 6$$
$$11x + 28 - 28 = 6 - 28$$
$$11x = -22$$
$$\dfrac{11x}{11} = \dfrac{-22}{11}$$
$$x = -2$$

Chapter 6 Review Exercises

1. $30x - 45 = 15(2x - 3)$

2. $12x^3 + 16x^2 - 400x = 4x(3x^2 + 4x - 100)$

3. $30x^4y + 15x^3y + 5x^2y = 5x^2(6x^2 + 3x + 1)$

4. $7(x + 3) - 2(x + 3) = (x + 3)(7 - 2)$
$$= (x + 3) \cdot 5 \text{ or } 5(x + 3)$$

5. $7x^2(x + y) - (x + y) = 7x^2(x + y) - 1(x + y)$
$$= (x + y)(7x^2 - 1)$$

6. $x^3 + 3x^2 + 2x + 6 = (x^3 + 3x^2) + (2x + 6)$
$$= x^2(x + 3) + 2(x + 3)$$
$$= (x + 3)(x^2 + 2)$$

7. $xy + y + 4x + 4 = (xy + y) + (4x + 4)$
$$= y(x + 1) + 4(x + 1)$$
$$= (x + 1)(y + 4)$$

8. $x^3 + 5x + x^2 + 5 = (x^3 + 5x) + (x^2 + 5)$
$$= x(x^2 + 5) + 1(x^2 + 5)$$
$$= (x^2 + 5)(x + 1)$$

9. $xy + 4x - 2y - 8 = (xy + 4x) + (-2y - 8)$
$$= x(y + 4) - 2(y + 4)$$
$$= (y + 4)(x - 2)$$

10. $x^2 - 3x + 2 = (x - 2)(x - 1)$

11. $x^2 - x - 20 = (x - 5)(x + 4)$

12. $x^2 + 19x + 48 = (x + 3)(x + 16)$

13. $x^2 - 6xy + 8y^2 = (x - 4y)(x - 2y)$

14. $x^2 + 5x - 9$ is prime because there is no pair of integers whose product is -9 and whose sum is 5.

15. $x^2 + 16xy - 17y^2 = (x + 17y)(x - y)$

16. $3x^2 + 6x - 24 = 3(x^2 + 2x - 8)$
$$= 3(x + 4)(x - 2)$$

17. $3x^3 - 36x^2 + 33x = 3x(x^2 - 12x + 11)$
$$= 3x(x - 11)(x - 1)$$

18. $3x^2 + 17x + 10$

Factor by trial and error or by grouping. To factor by grouping, find two integers whose product is $ac = 3 \cdot 10 = 30$ and whose sum is $b = 17$. These integers are 15 and 2.

$$3x^2 + 17x + 10 = 3x^2 + 15x + 2x + 10$$
$$= 3x(x + 5) + 2(x + 5)$$
$$= (x + 5)(3x + 2)$$

19. $5y^2 - 17y + 6$

Factor by trial and error or by grouping. To factor by trial and error, start with the First terms, which must be $5y$ and y. Because the middle term is negative, the factors of 6 must both be negative. Try various combinations until the correct middle term is obtained.

$$(5y - 1)(y - 6) = 5y^2 - 31y + 6$$
$$(5y - 6)(y - 1) = 5y^2 - 11y + 6$$
$$(5y - 3)(y - 2) = 5y^2 - 13y + 6$$
$$(5y - 2)(y - 3) = 5y^2 - 17y + 6$$

Thus,

$$5y^2 - 17y + 6 = (5y - 2)(y - 3).$$

20. $4x^2 + 4x - 15 = (2x + 5)(2x - 3)$

21. $5y^2 + 11y + 4$

Use trial and error. The First terms must be $5y$ and 4. Because the middle term is positive, the factors of 4 must both be positive. Try various combinations.

$$(5y + 2)(y + 2) = 5y^2 + 12y + 4$$
$$(5y + 4)(y + 1) = 5y^2 + 9y + 4$$
$$(5y + 1)(y + 4) = 5y^2 + 21y + 4$$

None of these possibilities gives the required middle term, $11x$, and there are no more possibilities to try, so $5y^2 + 11y + 4$ is prime.

22. $8x^2 + 8x - 6$

First factor out the GCF, 2. Then factor the resulting trinomial by trial and error or by grouping.

$$8x^2 + 8x - 6 = 2(4x^2 + 4x - 3)$$
$$= 2(2x + 3)(2x - 1)$$

23. $2x^3 + 7x^2 - 72x = x(2x^2 + 7x - 72)$
$$= x(2x - 9)(x + 8)$$

24. $12y^3 + 28y^2 + 8y = 4y(3y^2 + 7y + 2)$
$$= 4y(3y + 1)(y + 2)$$

25. $2x^2 - 7xy + 3y^2 = (2x - y)(x - 3y)$

26. $5x^2 - 6xy - 8y^2 = (5x + 4y)(x - 2y)$

27. $4x^2 - 1 = (2x)^2 - 1^2 = (2x + 1)(2x - 1)$

28. $81 - 100y^2 = 9^2 - (10y)^2$
$$= (9 + 10y)(9 - 10y)$$

29. $25a^2 - 49b^2 = (5a)^2 - (7b)^2$
$$= (5a + 7b)(5a - 7b)$$

30. $z^4 - 16 = (z^2)^2 - 4^2$
$$= (z^2 + 4)(z^2 - 4)$$
$$= (z^2 + 4)(z + 2)(z - 2)$$

31. $2x^2 - 18 = 2(x^2 - 9) = 2(x + 3)(x - 3)$

32. $x^2 + 1$ is prime because it is the sum of two squares with no common factor other than 1.

33. $9x^3 - x = x(9x^2 - 1) = x(3x + 1)(3x - 1)$

34. $18xy^2 - 8x = 2x(9y^2 - 4)$
$$= 2x(3y + 2)(3y - 2)$$

35. $x^2 + 22x + 121 = x^2 + 2 \cdot x \cdot 11 + 11^2$
$$= (x + 11)^2$$

36. $x^2 - 16x + 64 = x^2 - 2 \cdot x \cdot 8 + 8^2$
$$= (x - 8)^2$$

37. $9y^2 + 48y + 64 = (3y)^2 + 2 \cdot 3y \cdot 8 + 8^2$
$$= (3y + 8)^2$$

38. $16x^2 - 40x + 25 = (4x)^2 - 2 \cdot 4x \cdot 5 + 5^2$
$$= (4x - 5)^2$$

39. $25x^2 + 15x + 9$ is prime.
(To be a perfect square trinomial, the middle term would have to be 30x.)

40. $36x^2 + 60xy + 25y^2$
$$= (6x)^2 + 2 \cdot 6x \cdot 5y + (5y)^2$$
$$= (6x + 5y)^2$$

41. $25x^2 - 40xy + 16y^2$
$$= (5x)^2 - 2 \cdot 5x \cdot 4y + (4y)^2$$
$$= (5x - 4y)^2$$

42. $x^3 - 27 = x^3 - 3^2 = (x - 3)(x^2 + 3x + 9)$

43. $64x^3 + 1$
$$= (4x)^3 + 1^3$$
$$= (4x + 1)[(4x)^2 - 4x \cdot 1 + 1^2]$$
$$= (4x + 1)(16x^2 - 4x + 1)$$

44. $54x^3 - 16y^3$
$$= 2(27x^3 - 8y^3)$$
$$= 2[(3x)^3 - (2y)^3]$$
$$= 2(3x - 2y)[(3x)^2 + 3x \cdot 2y + (2y)^2]$$
$$= 2(3x - 2y)(9x^2 + 6xy + 4y^2)$$

45. $27x^3y + 8y$
$$= y(27x^3 + 8)$$
$$= y[(3x)^3 + 2^3]$$
$$= y(3x + 2)[(3x)^2 - 3x \cdot 2 + 2^2]$$
$$= y(3x + 2)(9x^2 - 6x + 4)$$

46. Area of outer square $= a^2$
Area of inner square $= 3^2 = 9$
Area of shaded region $= a^2 - 9$
$$= (a + 3)(a - 3)$$

47. Area of large square $= a^2$
Area of each small (corner) square $= b^2$
Area of four corner squares $= 4b^2$
Area of shaded region $= a^2 - 4b^2$
$$= (a + 2b)(a - 2b)$$

48. Area on the left:

Area of large square $= A^2$

Area of each rectangle: $A \cdot 1 = A$

Area of two rectangles $= 2A$

Area of small square $= 1^2 = 1$

On the right:

Area of square $= (A+1)^2$

This geometric model illustrates the factorization

$$A^2 + 2A + 1 = (A+1)^2.$$

49. $x^3 - 8x^2 + 7x = x(x^2 - 8x + 7)$
$$= x(x-7)(x-1)$$

50. $10y^2 + 9y + 2 = (5y+2)(2y+1)$

51. $128 - 2y^2 = 2(64 - y^2)$
$$= 2(8+y)(8-y)$$

52. $9x^2 + 6x + 1 = (3x)^2 + 2 \cdot 3x \cdot 1 + 1^2$
$$= (3x+1)^2$$

53. $20x^7 - 36x^3 = 4x^3(5x^4 - 9)$

54. $x^3 - 3x^2 - 9x + 27$
$$= (x^3 - 3x^2) + (-9x + 27)$$
$$= x^2(x-3) - 9(x-3)$$
$$= (x-3)(x^2 - 9)$$
$$= (x-3)(x+3)(x-3)$$
$$= (x-3)^2(x+3)$$

55. $y^2 + 16$ is prime because it is the sum of two squares with no common factor other than 1.

56. $2x^3 + 19x^2 + 35x = x(2x^2 + 19x + 35)$
$$= x(2x+5)(x+7)$$

57. $3x^3 - 30x^2 + 75x = 3x(x^2 - 10x + 25)$
$$= 3x(x-5)^2$$

58. $3x^5 - 24x^2 = 3x^2(x^3 - 8)$
$$= 3x^2(x^3 - 2^3)$$
$$= 3x^2(x-2)(x^2 + 2x + 4)$$

59. $4y^4 - 36y^2 = 4y^2(y^2 - 9)$
$$= 4y^2(y+3)(y-3)$$

60. $5x^2 + 20x - 105 = 5(x^2 + 4x - 21)$
$$= 5(x+7)(x-3)$$

61. $9x^2 + 8x - 3$ is prime.

62. $10x^5 - 44x^2 + 16x^3 = 2x^3(5x^2 - 22x + 8)$
$$= 2x^3(5x-2)(x-4)$$

63. $100y^2 - 49 = (10y)^2 - 7^2$
$$= (10y+7)(10y-7)$$

64. $9x^5 - 18x^4 = 9x^4(x-2)$

65. $x^4 - 1 = (x^2)^2 - 1^2$
$$= (x^2 + 1)(x^2 - 1)$$
$$= (x^2 + 1)(x+1)(x-1)$$

66. $2y^3 - 16 = 2(y^3 - 8)$
$$= 2(y^3 - 2^3)$$
$$= 2(y-2)(y^2 + 2y + 2^2)$$
$$= 2(y-2)(y^2 + 2y + 4)$$

67. $x^3 + 64 = x^3 + 4^3$
$$= (x+4)(x^2 - 4x + 4^2)$$
$$= (x+4)(x^2 - 4x + 16)$$

68. $6x^2 + 11x - 10 = (3x-2)(2x+5)$

69. $3x^4 - 12x^2 = 3x^2(x^2 - 4)$
$$= 3x^2(x+2)(x-2)$$

70. $x^2 - x - 90 = (x-10)(x+9)$

71. $25x^2 + 25xy + 6y^2 = (5x+2y)(5x+3y)$

72. $x^4 + 125x = x(x^3 + 125)$
$$= x(x^3 + 5^3)$$
$$= x(x+5)(x^2 - 5x + 5^2)$$
$$= x(x+5)(x^2 - 5x + 25)$$

73. $32y^3 + 32y^2 + 6y = 2y(16y^2 + 16y + 3)$
$$= 2y(4y+3)(4y+1)$$

74. $2y^2 - 16y + 32 = 2(y^2 - 8y + 16)$
$$= 2(y - 4)^2$$

75. $x^2 - 2xy - 35y^2 = (x + 5y)(x - 7y)$

76. $x^2 + 7x + xy + 7y = x(x + 7) + y(x + 7)$
$$= (x + 7)(x + y)$$

77. $9x^2 + 24xy + 16y^2$
$$= (3x)^2 + 2 \cdot 3x \cdot 4y + (4y)^2$$
$$= (3x + 4y)^2$$

78. $2x^4y - 2x^2y = 2x^2y(x^2 - 1)$
$$= 2x^2y(x + 1)(x - 1)$$

79. $100y^2 - 49z^2 = (10y)^2 - (7z)^2$
$$= (10y + 7z)(10y - 7z)$$

80. $x^2 + xy + y^2$ is prime.
(To be a perfect square trinomial, the middle term would have to be $2xy$.)

81. $3x^4y^2 - 12x^2y^4 = 3x^2y^2(x^2 - 4y^2)$
$$= 3x^2y^2(x + 2y)(x - 2y)$$

82. $x(x - 12) = 0$
$x = 0$ or $x - 12 = 0$
$$x = 12$$

The solutions are 0 and 12.

83. $3(x - 7)(4x + 9) = 0$
$x - 7 = 0$ or $4x + 9 = 0$
$x = 7$ $\qquad 4x = -9$
$$x = -\frac{9}{4}$$

The solutions are 7 and $-\frac{9}{4}$.

84. $x^2 + 5x - 14 = 0$
$(x + 7)(x - 2) = 0$
$x + 7 = 0$ or $x - 2 = 0$
$x = -7$ $\qquad x = 2$

The solutions are -7 and 2.

85. $5x^2 + 20x = 0$
$5x(x + 4) = 0$
$5x = 0$ or $x + 4 = 0$
$x = 0$ $\qquad x = -4$

The solutions are 0 and -4.

86. $2x^2 + 15x = 8$
$2x^2 + 15x - 8 = 0$
$(2x - 1)(x + 8) = 0$
$2x - 1 = 0$ or $x + 8 = 0$
$2x = 1$ $\qquad x = -8$
$$x = \frac{1}{2}$$

The solutions are $\frac{1}{2}$ and -8.

87. $x(x - 4) = 32$
$x^2 - 4x = 32$
$x^2 - 4x - 32 = 0$
$(x + 4)(x - 8) = 0$
$x + 4 = 0$ or $x - 8 = 0$
$x = -4$ $\qquad x = 8$

The solutions are -4 and 8.

88. $(x + 3)(x - 2) = 50$
$x^2 + x - 6 = 50$
$x^2 + x - 56 = 0$
$(x + 8)(x - 7) = 0$
$x + 8 = 0$ or $x - 7 = 0$
$x = -8$ $\qquad x = 7$

The solutions are -8 and 7.

89. $x^2 = 14x - 49$
$x^2 - 14x + 49 = 0$
$(x - 7)^2 = 0$
$x - 7 = 0$
$$x = 7$$

The only solution is 7.

90.
$$9x^2 = 100$$
$$9x^2 - 100 = 0$$
$$(3x + 10)(3x - 10) = 0$$
$$3x + 10 = 0 \quad \text{or} \quad 3x - 10 = 0$$
$$3x = -10 \qquad\qquad 3x = 10$$
$$x = -\frac{10}{3} \qquad\qquad x = \frac{10}{3}$$

The solutions are $-\frac{10}{3}$ and $\frac{10}{3}$.

91.
$$3x^2 + 21x + 30 = 0$$
$$3(x^2 + 7x + 10) = 0$$
$$3(x + 5)(x + 2) = 0$$
$$x + 5 = 0 \quad \text{or} \quad x + 2 = 0$$
$$x = -5 \qquad\qquad x = -2$$

The solutions are -5 and -2.

92.
$$3x^2 = 22x - 7$$
$$3x^2 - 22x + 7 = 0$$
$$(3x - 1)(x - 7) = 0$$
$$3x - 1 = 0 \quad \text{or} \quad x - 7 = 0$$
$$3x = 1 \qquad\qquad x = 7$$
$$x = \frac{1}{3}$$

The solutions are $\frac{1}{3}$ and 7.

93. $h = -16t^2 + 16t + 32$

Substitute 0 for h and solve for t.

$$0 = -16t^2 + 16t + 32$$
$$16t^2 - 16t - 32 = 0$$
$$16(t^2 - t - 2) = 0$$
$$16(t + 1)(t - 2) = 0$$

$$t = 1 = 0 \quad \text{or} \quad t - 2 = 0$$
$$t = -1 \qquad\qquad t = 2$$

Because time cannot be negative, discard the solution $t = -1$. The solution $t = 2$ indicates that you will hit the water after 2 seconds.

94. Let $\quad x =$ the width of the sign.
Then $x + 3 =$ the length of the floor.

Use the formula for the area of a rectangle.

$$l \cdot w = A$$
$$(x + 3)(x) = 40$$
$$x^2 + 3x = 40$$
$$x^2 + 3x - 40 = 0$$
$$(x + 8)(x - 5) = 0$$
$$x + 8 = 0 \quad \text{or} \quad x - 5 = 0$$
$$x = -8 \qquad\qquad x = 5$$

A rectangle cannot have a negative length. Thus, $x = 5$ and $x + 3 = 8$. The length of the sign is 8 feet and the width is 5 feet. This solution checks because

$$A = lw = (9 \text{ feet})(6 \text{ feet})$$
$$= 54 \text{ square feet.}$$

95. Area of garden $= x(x - 3) = 88$

$$x(x - 3) = 88$$
$$x^2 - 3x = 88$$
$$x^2 - 3x - 88 = 0$$
$$(x - 11)(x + 8) = 0$$
$$x - 11 = 0 \quad \text{or} \quad x + 8 = 0$$
$$x = 11 \qquad\qquad x = -8$$

Because a length cannot be negative, discard $x = -8$. Each side of the square lot is 11 meters, that is, the dimensions of the square lot are 11 meters by 11 meters.

Chapter 6 Test

1. $x^2 - 9x + 18 = (x - 3)(x - 6)$

2. $x^2 - 14x + 49 = x^2 - 2 \cdot x \cdot 7 + 7^2$
$= (x - 7)^2$

3. $15y^4 - 35y^3 + 10y^2 = 5y^2(3y^2 - 7y + 2)$
$= 5y^2(3y - 1)(y - 2)$

4. $x^3 + 2x^2 + 3x + 6 = (x^3 + 2x^2) + (3x + 6)$
$= x^2(x + 2) + 3(x + 2)$
$= (x + 2)(x^2 + 3)$

5. $x^2 - 9x = x(x - 9)$

6. $x^3 + 6x^2 - 7x = x(x^2 + 6x - 7)$
$= x(x + 7)(x - 1)$

7. $14x^2 + 64x - 30 = 2(7x^2 + 32x - 15)$
$= 2(7x - 3)(x + 5)$

8. $25x^2 - 9 = (5x)^2 - 3^2$
$= (5x + 3)(5x - 3)$

9. $x^3 + 8 = x^3 + 2^3 = (x + 2)(x^2 - 2x + 2^2)$
$= (x + 2)(x^2 - 2x + 4)$

10. $x^2 - 4x - 21 = (x + 3)(x - 7)$

11. $x^2 + 4$ is prime.

12. $6y^3 + 9y^2 + 3y = 3y(2y^2 + 3y + 1)$
$= 3y(2y + 1)(y + 1)$

13. $4y^2 - 36 = 4(y^2 - 9) = 4(y + 3)(y - 3)$

14. $16x^2 + 48x + 36$
$= 4(4x^2 + 12x + 9)$
$= 4[(2x)^2 + 2 \cdot 4x \cdot 3 + 3^2]$
$= 4(2x + 3)^2$

15. $2x^4 - 32 = 2(x^4 - 16)$
$= 2(x^2 + 4)(x^2 - 4)$
$= 2(x^2 + 4)(x + 2)(x - 2)$

16. $36x^2 - 84x + 49 = (6x)^2 - 2 \cdot 6x \cdot 7 + 7^2$
$= (6x - 7)^2$

17. $7x^2 - 50x + 7 = (7x - 1)(x - 7)$

18. $x^3 + 2x^2 - 5x - 10 = (x^3 + 2x^2) + (-5x - 10)$
$= x^2(x + 2) - 5(x + 2)$
$= (x + 2)(x^2 - 5)$

19. $12y^3 - 12y^2 - 45y = 3y(4y^2 - 4y - 15)$
$= 3y(2y + 3)(2y - 5)$

20. $y^3 - 125 = y^3 - 5^3$
$= (y - 5)(y^2 + 5y + 5^2)$
$= (y - 5)(y^2 + 5y + 25)$

21. $5x^2 - 5xy - 30y^2 = 5(x^2 - xy - 6y^2)$
$= 5(x - 3y)(x + 2y)$

22. $x^2 + 2x - 24 = 0$
$(x + 6)(x - 4) = 0$
$x + 6 = 0 \quad \text{or} \quad x - 4 = 0$
$x = -6 \qquad\qquad x = 4$

The solutions are -6 and 4.

23. $3x^2 - 5x = 2$
$3x^2 - 5x - 2 = 0$
$(3x + 1)(x - 2) = 0$
$3x + 1 = 0 \quad \text{or} \quad x - 2 = 0$
$3x = -1 \qquad\qquad x = 2$
$x = -\dfrac{1}{3}$

The solutions are $-\frac{1}{3}$ and 2.

24. $x(x - 6) = 16$
$x^2 - 6x = 16$
$x^2 - 6x - 16 = 0$
$(x + 2)(x - 8) = 0$
$x + 2 = 0 \quad \text{or} \quad x - 8 = 0$
$x = -2 \qquad\qquad x = 8$

The solutions are -2 and 8.

25.
$$6x^2 = 21x$$
$$6x^2 - 21x = 0$$
$$3x(2x - 7) = 0$$
$$3x = 0 \quad \text{or} \quad 2x - 7 = 0$$
$$x = 0 \qquad\qquad 2x = 7$$
$$x = \frac{7}{2}$$

The solutions are 0 and $\frac{7}{2}$.

26.
$$16x^2 = 81$$
$$16x^2 - 81 = 0$$
$$(4x + 9)(4x - 9) = 0$$
$$4x + 9 = 0 \quad \text{or} \quad 4x - 9 = 0$$
$$4x = -9 \qquad\qquad 4x = 9$$
$$x = -\frac{9}{4} \qquad\qquad x = \frac{9}{4}$$

The solutions are $-\frac{9}{4}$ and $\frac{9}{4}$.

27.
$$(5x + 4)(x - 1) = 2$$
$$5x^2 - x - 4 = 2$$
$$5x^2 - x - 6 = 0$$
$$(5x - 6)(x + 1) = 0$$
$$5x - 6 = 0 \quad \text{or} \quad x + 1 = 0$$
$$5x = 6$$
$$x = \frac{6}{5} \qquad\qquad x = -1$$

The solutions are $\frac{6}{5}$ and -1.

28. Area of large square = x^2
Area of each small (corner) square
$$= 1^2 = 1$$
Area of four corner squares = 4
Area of shaded region = $x^2 - 4$
$$= (x + 2)(x - 2)$$

29. $h = -16t^2 + 80t + 96$

Substitute 96 for h and solve for t.
$$0 = -16t^2 + 80t + 96$$
$$16t^2 - 80t - 96 = 0$$
$$16(t^2 - 5t - 6) = 0$$
$$16(t - 6)(t + 1) = 0$$
$$t - 6 = 0 \quad \text{or} \quad t + 1 = 0$$
$$t = 6 \qquad\qquad t = -1$$

Since time cannot be negative, discard $t = -1$. The rocket will reach the ground after 6 seconds.

30. Let x = the width of the garden.
Then $x + 6$ = the width.
$$(x + 6)(x) = 55$$
$$x^2 + 6x = 55$$
$$x^2 + 6x - 55 = 0$$
$$(x + 11)(x - 5) = 0$$
$$x + 11 = 0 \quad \text{or} \quad x - 5 = 0$$
$$x = -11 \qquad\qquad x = 5$$

Since the width cannot be negative, discard $x = 11$. Then $x = 5$ and $x + 6 = 11$, so the length is 11 feet and the width is 5 feet.

Cumulative Review Exercises (Chapters 1-6)

1. $6[5 + 2(3 - 8) - 3] = 6[5 + 2(-5) - 3]$
$$= 6[5 - 10 - 3]$$
$$= 6(-8) = -48$$

2. $4(x - 2) = 2(x - 4) + 3x$
$$4x - 8 = 2x - 8 + 3x$$
$$4x - 8 = 5x - 8$$
$$4x - 5x = -8 + 8$$
$$-x = 0$$
$$x = 0$$

The solution is 0.

3.
$$\frac{x}{2} - 1 = \frac{x}{3} + 1$$
$$6\left(\frac{x}{2} - 1\right) = 6\left(\frac{x}{3} + 1\right)$$
$$3x - 6 = 2x + 6$$
$$3x - 2x = 6 + 6$$
$$x = 12$$

The solution is 12.

4.
$$5 - 5x > 2(5 - x) + 1$$
$$5 - 5x > 10 - 2x + 1$$
$$5 - 5x > 11 - 2x$$
$$5 - 5x + 2x > 11 - 2x + 2x$$
$$5 - 3x > 11$$
$$5 - 3x - 5 > 11 - 5$$
$$-3x > 6$$
$$\frac{-3x}{-3} < \frac{6}{-3}$$
$$x < -2$$

Solution set: $\{x | x < -2\}$

$$\xleftarrow{\hspace{0.3cm}} \underset{-5\ -4\ -3\ -2\ -1\ \ 0\ \ 1\ \ 2\ \ 3\ \ 4\ \ 5}{\circ} \xrightarrow{\hspace{0.3cm}}$$

5. Let $x =$ the measure of each
             of the base angles.
Then $3x - 10 =$ the measure of the
             three angles of any
             triangle is 180°, so

$$x + x + (3x - 10) = 180.$$

Solve this equation.

$$5x - 10 = 180$$
$$5x = 190$$
$$x = 38$$

If $x = 38$, $3x - 10 = 3(38) - 10 = 104$.
The measures of the three angles of the
triangle are $38°, 38°$, and $104°$.

6. Let $x =$ the cost of the dinner
before tax.

$$x + 0.06x = 159$$
$$1.06x = 159$$
$$\frac{1.06x}{1.06} = \frac{159}{1.06}$$
$$x \approx 150$$

The cost of the dinner before tax was $150.

7. $y = -\frac{3}{5}x + 2$

slope $= -\frac{3}{5} = \frac{-3}{5}$; y-intercept $= 2$
Plot $(0, 3)$. From this point, move 3 units
down (because -3 is negative) and 5 units
to the *right* to reach the point $(5, 0)$. Draw
a line through $(0, 3)$ and $(5, 0)$.

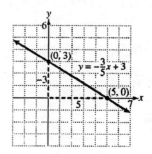

8. Line passing through $(2, -4)$ and $(3, 1)$

$$m = \frac{1 - (-4)}{3 - 2} = \frac{5}{1} = 5$$

Use the point $(2, -4)$ in the point-slope
equation.

$$y - y_1 = m(x - x_1)$$
$$y - (-4) = 5(x - 2)$$
$$y + 4 = 5(x - 2)$$

Rewrite this equation in slope-intercept
form.

$$y + 4 = 5x - 10$$
$$y = 5x - 14$$

9. $5x - 6y = 30$

Graph using the intercepts $(6, 0)$ and $(0, -5)$.

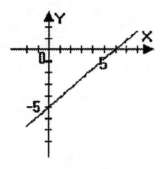

10. $5x + 2y = 13$
$y = 2x - 7$

The substitution method is a good choice for solving this system because the second equation is already solve for y.
Substitute $2x - 7$ for y in the first equation.

$$5x + 2y = 13$$
$$5x + 2(2x - 7) = 13$$
$$5x + 4x - 14 = 13$$
$$9x - 14 = 13$$
$$9x = 27$$
$$x = 3$$

Back-substitute into the second given equation.

$$y = 2x - 7$$
$$y = 2(3) - 7 = -1$$

Solution: $(3, -1)$

11. $2x + 3y = 5$
$3x - 2y = -4$

The addition method is a good choice for solving this system because both equations are written in the form $Ax + By = C$.
Multiply equation 1 by 2 and equation 2 by 3; then add the results.

$$
\begin{array}{r}
4x + 6y = 10 \\
9x - 6y = -12 \\
\hline
13x = -2
\end{array}
$$
$$x = -\frac{2}{13}$$

Instead of back-substituting $-\frac{2}{13}$ and working with fractions, go back to the original system and eliminate x. Multiply equation 1 by 3 and equation 2 by -2; then add the results.

$$
\begin{array}{r}
6x + 9y = 15 \\
-6x + 4y = 8 \\
\hline
13y = 23
\end{array}
$$
$$y = \frac{23}{3}$$

Solution: $\left(-\frac{2}{13}, \frac{23}{3}\right)$

12. $\dfrac{4}{5} - \dfrac{9}{8} = \dfrac{4}{5} \cdot \dfrac{8}{8} - \dfrac{9}{8} \cdot \dfrac{5}{5}$

$$= \frac{32}{40} - \frac{45}{40} = -\frac{13}{40}$$

13. $\dfrac{6x^5 - 3x^4 + 9x^2 + 27x}{3x}$

$$= \frac{6x^5}{3x} - \frac{3x^4}{3x} + \frac{9x^2}{3x} + \frac{27x}{3x}$$

$$= 2x^4 - x^3 + 3x + 9$$

14. $(3x - 5y)(2x + 9y)$
$ = 6x^2 + 27xy - 10xy - 45y^2$
$ = 6x^2 + 17xy - 45y^2$

15.

$$
\begin{array}{r}
2x^2 + 5x - 3 \\
3x - 5{\overline{\smash{\big)}\,6x^3 + 5x^2 - 34x + 13}} \\
\underline{6x^3 - 10x^2} \\
15x^2 - 34x \\
\underline{15x^2 - 25x} \\
-9x + 13 \\
\underline{-9x + 15} \\
-2
\end{array}
$$

$$
\frac{6x^3 + 5x^2 - 34x + 13}{3x - 5}
$$

$$
= 2x^2 + 5x + 3 + \frac{-20}{3x - 5}
$$

$$
\text{or} \quad 2x^2 + 5x + 3 - \frac{20}{3x - 5}
$$

16. To write 0.0071 in scienific notation, move the decimal point 3 places to the right. Because the given number is between 0 and 1, the exponent will be negative.

$$
0.0071 = 7.1 \times 10^{-3}
$$

17. $3x^2 + 11x + 6$

Factor by trial and error by grouping. To factor by grouping, find two integers whose product is $ac = 3 \cdot 6 = 18$ and whose sum is $b = 11$. These integers are 9 and 2.

$$
\begin{aligned}
3x^2 + 11x + 6 &= 3x^2 + 9x + 2x + 6 \\
&= 3x(x + 3) + 2(x + 3) \\
&= (x + 3)(3x + 2)
\end{aligned}
$$

18.
$$
\begin{aligned}
y^5 - 16y &= y(y^4 - 16) \\
&= y(y^2 + 4)(y^2 - 4) \\
&= y(y^2 + 4)(y + 2)(y - 2)
\end{aligned}
$$

19.
$$
\begin{aligned}
4x^2 + 12x + 9 &= (2x)^2 + 2 \cdot 2x \cdot 3 + 3^2 \\
&= (2x + 3)^2
\end{aligned}
$$

20. Let $x =$ the width of the rectangle. Then $x + 2 =$ the length.

Use the formula for the area of a rectangle.

$$
\begin{aligned}
l \cdot w &= A \\
(x + 2)(x) &= 24 \\
x^2 + 2x &= 24 \\
x^2 + 2x - 24 &= 0 \\
(x + 6)(x - 4) &= 0 \\
x + 6 = 0 \quad &\text{or} \quad x - 4 = 0 \\
x = -6 \quad & \qquad x = 4
\end{aligned}
$$

Discard -6 because the width cannot be negative. Then $x = 4$ and $x + 2 = 6$, so the length is 6 feet and the width is 4 feet. The dimensions of the rectangle are 6 feet by 4 feet.

Chapter 7

RATIONAL EXPRESSIONS

Rational Expressions and Their Simplification

7.1 CHECK POINTS

CHECK POINT 1

a. $\dfrac{7x-28}{8x-40}$

Set the denominator equal to 0 and solve for x.

$$8x - 40 = 0$$
$$8x = 40$$
$$x = 5$$

The rational expression is undefined for $x = 5$.

b. $\dfrac{8x-40}{x^2+3x-28}$

Set the denominator equal to 0 and solve for x.

$$x^2 + 3x - 28 = 0$$
$$(x+7)(x-4) = 0$$

$$x + 7 = 0 \quad \text{or} \quad x - 4 = 0$$
$$x = -7 \qquad\qquad x = 4$$

The rational expression is undefined for $x = -7$ and $x = 4$.

CHECK POINT 2

$$\frac{7x+28}{21x} = \frac{\overset{1}{\cancel{7}}(x+4)}{\underset{1}{\cancel{7}}\cdot 3x} = \frac{x+4}{3x}$$

CHECK POINT 3

$$\frac{x^3-x^2}{7x-7} = \frac{x^2(x-1)}{7(x-1)} = \frac{x^2}{7}, \; x \neq 1$$

CHECK POINT 4

$$\frac{x^2-1}{x^2+2x+1} = \frac{(x+1)(x-1)}{(x+1)(x+1)} = \frac{x-1}{x+1}$$

CHECK POINT 5

$$\frac{9x^2-49}{28-12x} = \frac{(3x+7)(3x-7)}{4(7x-3)}$$
$$= \frac{(3x+7)(3x-7)}{4(7x-3)}$$
$$= \frac{-(3x+7)}{4} \quad \text{or} \quad -\frac{3x+7}{4}$$
$$\text{or} \quad \frac{-3x-7}{4}$$

EXERCISE SET 7.1

1. $\dfrac{7}{2x}$

Set the denominator equal to 0 and solve for x.

$$2x = 0$$
$$x = 0$$

The rational expression is undefined for $x = 0$.

3. $\dfrac{x}{x-7}$

Set the denominator equal to 0 and solve for x.

$$x - 7 = 0$$
$$x = 7$$

The rational expression is undefined for $x = 7$.

5. $\dfrac{7}{5x - 15}$

$$5x - 15 = 0$$
$$5x = 15$$
$$x = 3$$

The rational expression is undefined for $x = 3$.

7. $\dfrac{x + 4}{(x + 7)(x - 3)}$

$$(x + 7)(x - 3) = 0$$
$$x + 7 = 0 \quad \text{or} \quad x - 3 = 0$$
$$x = -7 \qquad\qquad x = 3$$

The rational expression is undefined for $x = -7$ and $x = 3$.

9. $\dfrac{13x}{(3x - 15)(x + 2)}$

$$(3x - 15)(x + 2) = 0$$
$$3x - 15 = 0 \quad \text{or} \quad x + 2 = 0$$
$$3x = 15 \qquad\qquad x = -2$$
$$x = 5$$

The rational expression is undefined for $x = 5$ and $x = -2$.

11. $\dfrac{x + 5}{x^2 + x - 12}$

$$x^2 + x - 12 = 0$$
$$(x + 4)(x - 3) = 0$$
$$x + 4 = 0 \quad \text{or} \quad x - 3 = 0$$
$$x = -4 \qquad\qquad x = 3$$

The rational expression is undefined for $x = -4$ and $x = 3$.

13. $\dfrac{x + 5}{5}$

Because the denominator, 5, is not zero for any value of x, the rational expression is defined for all real numbers.

15. $\dfrac{y + 3}{4y^2 + y - 3}$

$$4y^2 + y - 3 = 0$$
$$(y + 1)(4y - 3) = 0$$
$$y + 1 = 0 \quad \text{or} \quad 4y - 3 = 0$$
$$y = -1 \qquad\qquad 4y = 3$$
$$y = \dfrac{3}{4}$$

The rational expression is undefined for $y = -1$ and $y = \frac{3}{4}$.

17. $\dfrac{y + 5}{y^2 - 25}$

$$y^2 - 25 = 0$$
$$(y + 5)(y - 5) = 0$$
$$y + 5 = 0 \quad \text{or} \quad y - 5 = 0$$
$$y = -5 \qquad\qquad y = 5$$

The rational expression is undefined for $y = -5$ and $y = 5$.

19. $\dfrac{5}{x^2 + 1}$

The smallest possible value of x^2 is 0, so $x^2 + 1 \geq 1$ for all real numbers x. This means that there is no real number x for which $x^2 + 1 = 0$. Thus, the rational expression is defined for all real numbers.

21. $\dfrac{14x^2}{7x} = \dfrac{2 \cdot 7 \cdot x \cdot x}{7 \cdot x} = 2x$

23. $\dfrac{5x - 15}{25} = \dfrac{5(x - 3)}{5 \cdot 5} = \dfrac{x - 3}{5}$

25. $\dfrac{2x - 8}{4x} = \dfrac{2(x - 4)}{2 \cdot 2x} = \dfrac{x - 4}{2x}$

27. $\dfrac{3}{3x - 9} = \dfrac{3}{3(x - 3)} = \dfrac{1}{x - 3}$

29. $\dfrac{-15}{3x-9} = \dfrac{-15}{3(x-3)} = \dfrac{-5}{x-3}$ or $-\dfrac{5}{x-3}$

31. $\dfrac{3x+9}{x+3} = \dfrac{3(x+3)}{x+3} = 3$

33. $\dfrac{x+5}{x^2-25} = \dfrac{x+5}{(x+5)(x-5)} = \dfrac{1}{x-5}$

35. $\dfrac{2y-10}{3y-15} = \dfrac{2(y-5)}{3(y-5)} = \dfrac{2}{3}$

37. $\dfrac{x+1}{x^2-2x-3} = \dfrac{x+1}{(x+1)(x-3)} = \dfrac{1}{x-3}$

39. $\dfrac{4x-8}{x^2-4x+4} = \dfrac{4(x-2)}{(x-2)(x-2)} = \dfrac{4}{x-2}$

41. $\dfrac{y^2-3y+2}{y^2+7y-18} = \dfrac{(y-1)(y-2)}{(y+9)(y-2)} = \dfrac{y-1}{y+9}$

43. $\dfrac{2y^2-7y+3}{2y^2-5y+2} = \dfrac{(2y-1)(y-3)}{(2y-1)(y-2)} = \dfrac{y-3}{y-2}$

45. $\dfrac{2x+3}{2x+5}$

The numerator and denominator have no common factor (other than 1), so this rational expression cannot be simplified.

47. $\dfrac{x^2+12x+36}{x^2-36} = \dfrac{(x+6)(x+6)}{(x+6)(x-6)} = \dfrac{x+6}{x-6}$

49. $\dfrac{x^3-2x^2+x-2}{x-2} = \dfrac{x^2(x-2)+1(x-2)}{x-1}$

$\qquad = \dfrac{(x-2)(x^2+1)}{x-2}$

$\qquad = x^2+1$

51. $\dfrac{x^3-8}{x-2} = \dfrac{(x-2)(x^2+2x+4)}{x-2}$

$\qquad = x^2+2x+4$

53. $\dfrac{(x-4)^2}{x^2-16} = \dfrac{(x-4)(x-4)}{(x+4)(x-4)} = \dfrac{x-4}{x+4}$

55. $\dfrac{x}{x+1}$

The numerator and denominator have no common factor (other than 1), so this rational expression cannot be simplified.

57. $\dfrac{x+4}{x^2+16}$

The numerator and denominator are both prime polynomials. They have no common factor (other than 1), so this rational expression cannot be simplified.

59. $\dfrac{x-5}{5-x} = \dfrac{-1(5-x)}{x-5} = -1$

Notice that the numerator and denominator of the given rational expression are additive inverses.

61. $\dfrac{2x-3}{3-2x}$

The numerator and denominator of this rational expression are additive inverses, so

$$\frac{2x-3}{3-2x} = -1.$$

63. $\dfrac{x-5}{x+5}$

The numerator and denominator have no common factor, so this rational expression cannot be simplified.

65. $\dfrac{4x-6}{3-2x} = \dfrac{2(2x-3)}{3-2x} = \dfrac{-2(3-2x)}{3-2x} = -2$

67. $\dfrac{4-6x}{3x^2-2x} = \dfrac{2(2-3x)}{x(3x-2)}$

$\qquad = \dfrac{-2(3x-2)}{x(3x-2)}$

$\qquad = -\dfrac{2}{x}$

69. $\dfrac{x^2-1}{1-x} = \dfrac{(x+1)(x-1)}{1-x}$

$\qquad = \dfrac{(x+1)\cdot-1(1-x)}{1-x}$

$\qquad = -1(x+1) = -x-1$

71. $\dfrac{y^2 - y - 12}{4 - y} = \dfrac{(y-4)(y+3)}{4-y}$

$$= \dfrac{-1(4-y)(y+3)}{4-y}$$

$$= -1(y+3) = -y - 3$$

73. $\dfrac{x^2 y - x^2}{x^3 - x^3 y} = \dfrac{x^2(y-1)}{x^3(1-y)}$

$$= \dfrac{x^2 \cdot -1(1-y)}{x^3(1-y)}$$

$$= -\dfrac{1}{x}$$

75. $\dfrac{x^2 + 2xy - 3y^2}{2x^2 + 5xy - 3y^2} = \dfrac{(x-y)(x+3y)}{(2x-y)(x+3y)}$

$$= \dfrac{x-y}{2x-y}$$

77. The conviction rate is the ratio of the number of drug convictions to the number of drug arrests. Therefore, the conviction rate can be described by the polynomial

$$\dfrac{6t^4 - 207t^3 + 2128t^2 - 6622t + 15{,}220}{28t^4 - 711t^3 + 5963t^2 - 1695t + 27{,}424},$$

where t is the number of years after 1984.

79. $\dfrac{130x}{100 - x}$

a. $x = 40$:

$$\dfrac{130x}{100 - x} = \dfrac{130(40)}{100 - 40}$$

$$= \dfrac{5200}{60}$$

$$\approx 86.67$$

$x = 80$:

$$\dfrac{130x}{100 - x} = \dfrac{130(80)}{100 - 80}$$

$$= \dfrac{10{,}400}{20}$$

$$= 520$$

$x = 90$:

$$\dfrac{130x}{100 - x} = \dfrac{130(90)}{100 - 90}$$

$$= \dfrac{11{,}700}{10}$$

$$= 1170$$

These results mean that it costs \$86.67 million to inoculate 40% of the population, \$520 million to inoculate 80% of the population, and \$1170 million to inoculate 90% of the population.

b. Set the denominator equal to 0 and solve for x.

$$100 - x = 0$$

$$100 = x$$

The rational expression is undefined for $x = 100$.

c. The cost keeps rising as x approaches 100. No amount of money will be enough to inoculate 100% of the population.

81. $\dfrac{DA}{A + 12}$; $D = 1000$, $A = 8$

$$\dfrac{DA}{A + 12} = \dfrac{1000 \cdot 8}{8 + 12}$$

$$= \dfrac{8000}{20} = 400$$

The correct dosage for an 8-year-old is 400 milligrams.

83. $C = \dfrac{100x + 100{,}000}{x}$

a. $x = 500$

$$C = \dfrac{100(500) + 100{,}000}{500}$$

$$= \dfrac{150{,}000}{500} = 300$$

The cost per bicycle when manufacturing 500 bicycles is \$300.

b. $x = 4000$

$$C = \frac{100(4000) + 100{,}000}{4000}$$
$$= \frac{400{,}000 + 100{,}000}{4000}$$
$$= \frac{500{,}000}{4000} = 125$$

c. The cost per bicycle decreases as more bicycles are manufactured. One possible reason for this is that there could be fixed costs for equipment, so the more the equipment is used, the lower the cost per bicycle.

85. $y = \dfrac{5x}{x^2 + 1}; x = 3$

$$y = \frac{5 \cdot 3}{3^2 + 1} = \frac{15}{10} = 1.5$$

The equation indicates that the drug's concentration after 3 hours is 1.5 milligram per liter. The point $(3, 1.5)$ on the graph conveys this information.

87. The graph shows that the drug reaches its maximum concentration after 1 hour. If $x = 1$,

$$y = \frac{5 \cdot 1}{1^2 + 1} = \frac{5}{2} = 2.5,$$

so the drug's concentration after 1 hour is 2.5 milligrams per liter.

For Exercises 89–93, answers may vary.

95. Any rational expression in which the numerator and denominator have no common factor other than 1 cannot be simplified. Student examples will vary.

97. $x^2 - x - 6 = (x - 3)(x + 2)$

Therefore,

$$\frac{x^2 - x - 6}{x + 2} = x - 3,$$

so

$$\frac{x^2 - x - 6}{x + 2}$$

is the desired rational expression.

99.

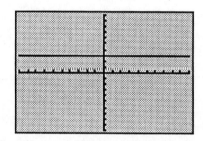

The graphs coincide. This verifies that the simplification

$$\frac{3x + 15}{x + 5} = 3, x \neq -5.$$

is correct.

101.

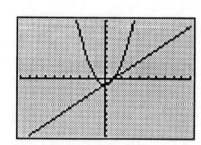

The graphs do not coincide.

$$\frac{x^2 - x}{x} = \frac{x(x - 1)}{x}$$
$$= x - 1, x \neq 0$$

Change the expression on the right from $x^2 - 1$ to $x - 1$.

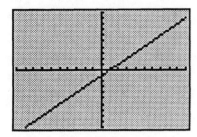

Now the graphs coincide.

Review Exercises

103. $\dfrac{5}{6} \cdot \dfrac{9}{25} = \dfrac{45}{150} = \dfrac{\cancel{15} \cdot 3}{\cancel{15} \cdot 10} = \dfrac{3}{10}$

104. $\dfrac{2}{3} \div 4 = \dfrac{2}{3} \cdot \dfrac{1}{4} = \dfrac{2}{12} = \dfrac{\cancel{2} \cdot 1}{\cancel{2} \cdot 6} = \dfrac{1}{6}$

105. $2x - 5y = -2$
$3x + 4y = 20$

Multiply the first equation by 3 and the second equation by -2; then add the results.

$$
\begin{array}{r}
6x - 15y = {-6} \\
-6x - 8y = -40 \\
\hline
-23y = -46 \\
y = 2
\end{array}
$$

Back-substitute into the first equation of the original system.

$$
\begin{aligned}
2x - 5y &= -2 \\
2x - 5(2) &= -2 \\
2x - 10 &= -2 \\
2x &= 8 \\
x &= 4
\end{aligned}
$$

Solution: $(4, 2)$

Multiplying and Dividing Rational Expressions

7.2 CHECK POINTS

CHECK POINT 1

$$\frac{9}{x+4} \cdot \frac{x-5}{2} = \frac{9(x-5)}{(x+4)2}$$
$$= \frac{9x - 45}{2x + 8}$$

CHECK POINT 2

$$\frac{x+4}{x-7} \cdot \frac{3x-21}{8x+32} = \frac{x+4}{x-7} \cdot \frac{3(x-7)}{8(x+4)} = \frac{3}{8}$$

CHECK POINT 3

$$\frac{x-5}{x-2} \cdot \frac{x^2-4}{9x-45} = \frac{x-5}{x-2} \cdot \frac{(x+2)(x-2)}{9(x-5)}$$
$$= \frac{x+2}{9}$$

CHECK POINT 4

$$\frac{5x+5}{7x-7x^2} \cdot \frac{2x^2+x-3}{4x^2-9}$$
$$= \frac{5(x+1)}{7x(1-x)} \cdot \frac{(2x+3)(x-1)}{(2x+3)(2x-3)}$$
$$= \frac{-5(x+1)}{7x(2x-3)} \quad \text{or} \quad -\frac{5(x+1)}{7x(2x-3)}$$

CHECK POINT 5

$$(x+3) \div \frac{x-4}{x+7} = \frac{x+3}{1} \cdot \frac{x+7}{x-4}$$
$$= \frac{(x+3)(x+7)}{x-4}$$
$$\text{or} \quad \frac{x^2+10x+7}{x-4}$$

CHECK POINT 6

$$\frac{x^2+5x+6}{x^2-25} \div \frac{x+2}{x+5}$$
$$=\frac{x^2+5x+6}{x^2-25} \cdot \frac{x+5}{x+2}$$
$$=\frac{(x+3)(x+2)}{(x+5)(x-5)} \cdot \frac{x+5}{x+2}$$
$$=\frac{x+3}{x-5}$$

CHECK POINT 7

$$\frac{y^2+3y+2}{y^2+1} \div (5y^2+10y)$$
$$=\frac{y^2+3y+2}{y^2+1} \cdot \frac{1}{5y^2+10y}$$
$$=\frac{(y+2)(y+1)}{y^2+1} \cdot \frac{1}{5y(y+2)}$$
$$=\frac{y+1}{5y(y^2+1)}$$

EXERCISE SET 7.2

1. $\frac{5}{x+2} \cdot \frac{x-3}{7} = \frac{5(x-3)}{(x+2)7} = \frac{5x-15}{7x+14}$

3. $\frac{x}{2} \cdot \frac{4}{x+1} = \frac{4x}{2(x+1)} = \frac{2x}{x+1}$

5. $\frac{3}{x} \cdot \frac{2x}{9} = \frac{6x}{9x} = \frac{2}{3}$

7. $\frac{x-2}{x+3} \cdot \frac{2x+6}{5x-10} = \frac{x-2}{x+3} \cdot \frac{2(x+3)}{5(x-2)}$
$$= \frac{2}{5}$$

9. $\frac{x^2+7x+12}{x+4} \cdot \frac{1}{x+3}$
$$= \frac{(x+4)(x+3)\cdot 1}{(x+4)(x+3)} = 1$$

11. $\frac{x^2-25}{x^2-3x-10} \cdot \frac{x+2}{x}$
$$= \frac{(x+5)(x-5)}{(x+2)(x-5)} \cdot \frac{(x+2)}{x}$$
$$= \frac{x+5}{x}$$

13. $\frac{4y+30}{y^2-3y} \cdot \frac{y-3}{2y+15}$
$$= \frac{2(2y+15)}{y(y-3)} \cdot \frac{(y-3)}{(2y+15)}$$
$$= \frac{2}{y}$$

15. $\frac{y^2-7y-30}{y^2-6y-40} \cdot \frac{2y^2+5y+2}{2y^2+7y+3}$
$$= \frac{(y+3)(y-10)}{(y+4)(y-10)} \cdot \frac{(2y+1)(y+2)}{(2y+1)(y+3)}$$
$$= \frac{y+2}{y+4}$$

17. $(y^2-9) \cdot \frac{4}{y-3}$
$$= \frac{y^2-9}{1} \cdot \frac{4}{y-3}$$
$$= \frac{(y+3)(y-3)}{1} \cdot \frac{4}{y-3}$$
$$= 4(y+3) \quad \text{or} \quad 4y+12$$

19. $\frac{x^2-5x+6}{x^2-2x-3} \cdot \frac{x^2-1}{x^2-4}$
$$= \frac{(x-2)(x-3)}{(x+1)(x-3)} \cdot \frac{(x+1)(x-1)}{(x+2)(x-2)}$$
$$= \frac{x-1}{x+2}$$

21. $\frac{x^3-8}{x^2-4} \cdot \frac{x+2}{3x}$
$$= \frac{(x-2)(x^2+2x+4)}{(x+2)(x-2)} \cdot \frac{(x+2)}{3x}$$
$$= \frac{x^2+2x+4}{3x}$$

23. $\dfrac{(x-2)^3}{(x-1)^2} \cdot \dfrac{x^2-2x+1}{x^2-4x+4}$

$= \dfrac{(x-2)^3}{(x-1)^2} \cdot \dfrac{(x-1)^2}{(x-2)^2}$

$= \dfrac{x-2}{x-1}$

25. $\dfrac{6x+2}{x^2-1} \cdot \dfrac{1-x}{3x^2+x}$

$= \dfrac{2(3x+1)}{(x+1)(x-1)} \cdot \dfrac{(1-x)}{x(3x+1)}$

$= \dfrac{2(3x+1)}{(x+1)(x-1)} \cdot \dfrac{-1(x-1)}{x(3x+1)}$

$= \dfrac{-2}{x(x+1)}$ or $-\dfrac{2}{x(x+1)}$

27. $\dfrac{25-y^2}{y^2-2y-35} \cdot \dfrac{y^2-8y-20}{y^2-3y-10}$

$= \dfrac{(5+y)(5-y)}{(y+5)(y-7)} \cdot \dfrac{(y-10)(y+2)}{(y-5)(y+2)}$

$= \dfrac{-(y-10)}{y-7}$ or $-\dfrac{y-10}{y-7}$

29. $\dfrac{x^2-y^2}{x} \cdot \dfrac{x^2+xy}{x+y}$

$= \dfrac{(x+y)(x-y)}{x} \cdot \dfrac{x(x+y)}{(x+y)}$

$= (x-y)(x+y)$ or x^2-y^2

31. $\dfrac{x^2+2xy+y^2}{x^2-2xy+y^2} \cdot \dfrac{4x-4y}{3x+3y}$

$= \dfrac{(x+y)(x+y)}{(x-y)(x-y)} \cdot \dfrac{4(x-y)}{3(x+y)}$

$= \dfrac{4(x+y)}{3(x-y)}$

33. $\dfrac{x}{7} \div \dfrac{5}{3} = \dfrac{x}{7} \cdot \dfrac{3}{5} = \dfrac{3x}{35}$

35. $\dfrac{3}{x} \div \dfrac{12}{x} = \dfrac{3}{x} \cdot \dfrac{x}{12} = \dfrac{1}{4}$

37. $\dfrac{15}{x} \div \dfrac{3}{2x} = \dfrac{\overset{5}{\cancel{15}}}{\cancel{x}} \cdot \dfrac{\overset{1}{\cancel{2x}}}{\cancel{3}} = 10$

39. $\dfrac{x+1}{3} \div \dfrac{3x+3}{7} = \dfrac{x+1}{3} \cdot \dfrac{7}{3x+3}$

$= \dfrac{x+1}{3} \cdot \dfrac{7}{3(x+1)}$

$= \dfrac{7}{9}$

41. $\dfrac{7}{x-5} \div \dfrac{28}{3x-15} = \dfrac{7}{x-5} \cdot \dfrac{3x-15}{28}$

$= \dfrac{7}{(x-5)} \cdot \dfrac{3(x-5)}{7\cdot4}$

$= \dfrac{3}{4}$

43. $\dfrac{x^2-4}{x} \div \dfrac{x+2}{x-2} = \dfrac{x^2-4}{x} \cdot \dfrac{x-2}{x+2}$

$= \dfrac{(x+2)(x-2)}{x} \cdot \dfrac{x-2}{x+2}$

$= \dfrac{(x-2)^2}{x}$

45. $(y^2-16) \div \dfrac{y^2+3y-4}{y^2+4}$

$= \dfrac{y^2-16}{1} \cdot \dfrac{y^2+4}{y^2+3y-4}$

$= \dfrac{(y+4)(y-4)}{1} \cdot \dfrac{y^2+4}{(y+4)(y-1)}$

$= \dfrac{(y-4)(y^2+4)}{y-1}$

47. $\dfrac{y^2-y}{15} \div \dfrac{y-1}{4} = \dfrac{y^2-y}{15} \cdot \dfrac{5}{y-1}$

$= \dfrac{y(y-1)}{15} \cdot \dfrac{5}{(y-1)}$

$= \dfrac{y}{3}$

49. $\dfrac{4x^2+10}{x-3} \div \dfrac{6x^2+15}{x^2-9}$

$= \dfrac{4x^2+10}{x-3} \cdot \dfrac{x^2-9}{6x^2+15}$

$= \dfrac{2(2x^2+5)}{(x-3)} \cdot \dfrac{(x+3)(x-3)}{3(2x^2+5)}$

$= \dfrac{2(x+3)}{3}$ or $\dfrac{2x+6}{3}$

51. $\dfrac{x^2 - 25}{2x - 2} \div \dfrac{x^2 + 10x + 25}{x^2 + 4x - 5}$

$= \dfrac{x^2 - 25}{2x - 2} \cdot \dfrac{x^2 + 4x - 5}{x^2 + 10x + 25}$

$= \dfrac{(x+5)(x-5)}{2(x-1)} \cdot \dfrac{(x+5)(x-1)}{(x+5)(x+5)}$

$= \dfrac{x - 5}{2}$

53. $\dfrac{y^3 + y}{y^2 - y} \div \dfrac{y^3 - y^2}{y^2 - 2y + 1}$

$= \dfrac{y^3 + y}{y^2 - y} \cdot \dfrac{y^2 - 2y + 1}{y^3 - y^2}$

$= \dfrac{y(y^2 + 1)}{y(y - 1)} \cdot \dfrac{(y - 1)(y - 1)}{y^2(y - 1)}$

$= \dfrac{y^2 + 1}{y^2}$

55. $\dfrac{y^2 + 5y + 4}{y^2 + 12y + 32} \div \dfrac{y^2 - 12y + 35}{y^2 + 3y - 40}$

$= \dfrac{y^2 + 5y + 4}{y^2 + 12y + 32} \cdot \dfrac{y^2 + 3y - 40}{y^2 - 12y + 35}$

$= \dfrac{(y + 4)(y + 1)}{(y + 4)(y + 8)} \cdot \dfrac{(y + 8)(y - 5)}{(y - 7)(y - 5)}$

$= \dfrac{y + 1}{y - 7}$

57. $\dfrac{2y^2 - 128}{y^2 + 16y + 64} \div \dfrac{y^2 - 6y - 16}{3y^2 + 30y + 48}$

$= \dfrac{2y^2 - 128}{y^2 + 16y + 64} \cdot \dfrac{3y^2 + 30y + 48}{y^2 - 6y - 16}$

$= \dfrac{2(y^2 - 64)}{(y + 8)(y + 8)} \cdot \dfrac{3(y^2 + 10y + 16)}{(y + 2)(y - 8)}$

$= \dfrac{2(y + 8)(y - 8)}{(y + 8)(y + 8)} \cdot \dfrac{3(y + 2)(y + 8)}{(y + 2)(y - 8)} = 6$

59. $\dfrac{2x + 2y}{3} \div \dfrac{x^2 - y^2}{x - y}$

$= \dfrac{2x + 2y}{3} \cdot \dfrac{x - y}{x^2 - y^2}$

$= \dfrac{2(x + y)}{3} \cdot \dfrac{x - y}{(x + y)(x - y)} = \dfrac{2}{3}$

61. $\dfrac{x^2 - y^2}{8x^2 - 16xy + 8y^2} \div \dfrac{4x - 4y}{x + y}$

$= \dfrac{x^2 - y^2}{8x^2 - 16xy + 8y^2} \cdot \dfrac{x + y}{4x - 4y}$

$= \dfrac{(x + y)(x - y)}{8(x^2 - 2xy + y^2)} \cdot \dfrac{x + y}{4(x - y)}$

$= \dfrac{(x + y)(x - y)}{8(x - y)(x - y)} \cdot \dfrac{(x + y)}{4(x - y)}$

$= \dfrac{(x + y)^2}{32(x - y)^2}$

63. $\dfrac{xy - y^2}{x^2 + 2x + 1} \div \dfrac{2x^2 + xy - 3y^2}{2x^2 + 5xy + 3y^2}$

$= \dfrac{xy - y^2}{x^2 + 2x + 1} \cdot \dfrac{2x^2 + 5xy + 3y^2}{2x^2 + xy - 3y^2}$

$= \dfrac{y(x - y)}{(x + 1)(x + 1)} \cdot \dfrac{(2x + 3y)(x + y)}{(2x + 3y)(x - y)}$

$= \dfrac{y(x + y)}{(x + 1)^2}$

65. $\dfrac{1}{2} \cdot \dfrac{250x}{100 - x} = \dfrac{125x}{100 - x}$

The rational expression

$$\dfrac{125x}{100 - x}$$

represents the reduced cost.

For Exercises 67–69, answers may vary.

71.

$$\frac{\boxed{}}{\boxed{}} \cdot \frac{3x - 12}{2x} = \frac{3}{2}$$

$$\frac{\boxed{}}{\boxed{}} \cdot \frac{3(x - 4)}{2x} = \frac{3}{2}$$

The numerator of the unknown rational expression must contain a factor of x. The denominator of the unknown rational expression must contain a factor of $(x - 4)$. Therefore, the simplest pair of polynomials that will work are x in the numerator and $x - 4$ in the denominator, to give the rational expression $\frac{x}{x-4}$.

Check:

$$\frac{x}{x - 4} \cdot \frac{3x - 12}{2x} = \frac{x}{x - 4} \cdot \frac{3(x - 4)}{2x} = \frac{3}{2}$$

73.

$$\left(\frac{y - 2}{y^2 - 9y + 18} \cdot \frac{y^2 - 4y - 12}{y + 2} \right)$$

$$\div \frac{y^2 - 4}{y^2 + 5y + 6}$$

$$= \frac{y - 2}{y^2 - 9y + 18} \cdot \frac{y^2 - 4y - 12}{y + 2}$$

$$\cdot \frac{y^2 + 5y + 6}{y^2 - 4}$$

$$= \frac{(y - 2)}{(y - 3)(y - 6)} \cdot \frac{(y - 6)(y + 2)}{(y + 2)}$$

$$\cdot \frac{(y + 2)(y + 3)}{(y + 2)(y - 2)}$$

$$= \frac{y + 3}{y - 3}$$

75.

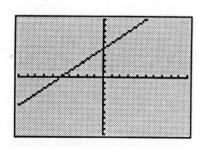

The graph coincides. This verifies that

$$\frac{x^3 - 25x}{x^2 - 3x - 10} \cdot \frac{x + 2}{x} = x + 5.$$

77.

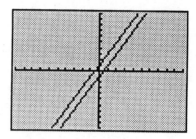

The graphs do not coincide.

$$(x - 5) \div \frac{2x^2 - 11x + 5}{4x^2 - 1}$$

$$= \frac{x - 5}{1} \cdot \frac{4x^2 - 1}{2x^2 - 11x + 5}$$

$$= \frac{x - 5}{1} \cdot \frac{(2x + 1)(2x - 1)}{(2x - 1)(x - 5)}$$

$$= 2x + 1$$

Change the expression on the right from $(2x - 1)$ to $(2x + 1)$.

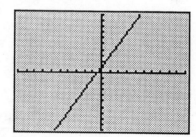

Now the graphs coincide.

Review Exercises

78.
$$2x + 3 < 3(x - 5)$$
$$2x + 3 < 3x - 15$$
$$-x + 3 < -15$$
$$-x < -18$$
$$x > 18$$
$$\{x | x > 18\}$$

79. $3x^2 - 15x - 42 = 3(x^2 - 5x - 14)$
$$= 3(x-7)(x+2)$$

80. $x(2x+9) = 5$
$$2x^2 + 9x = 5$$
$$2x^2 + 9x - 5 = 0$$
$$(2x - 1)(x + 5) = 0$$
$$2x - 1 = 0 \quad \text{or} \quad x + 5 = 0$$
$$2x = 1 \qquad\qquad x = -5$$
$$x = \frac{1}{2}$$

The solutions are $\frac{1}{2}$ and -5.

Adding and Subtracting Rational Expressions with the Same Denominator

7.3 CHECK POINTS

CHECK POINT 1

$$\frac{3x-2}{5} + \frac{2x+12}{5} = \frac{3x - 2 + 2x + 12}{5}$$
$$= \frac{5x + 10}{5}$$
$$= \frac{5(x+2)}{5}$$
$$= x + 2$$

CHECK POINT 2

$$\frac{x^2}{x^2 - 25} + \frac{25 - 10x}{x^2 - 25} = \frac{x^2 - 10x + 25}{x^2 - 25}$$
$$= \frac{(x-5)(x-5)}{(x+5)(x-5)}$$
$$= \frac{x-5}{x+5}$$

CHECK POINT 3

a. $\dfrac{4x+5}{x+7} - \dfrac{x}{x+7} = \dfrac{4x + 5 - x}{x+7}$
$$= \frac{3x+5}{x+7}$$

b. $\dfrac{3x^2 + 4x}{x-1} - \dfrac{11x - 4}{x-1} = \dfrac{(3x^2 + 4x) - (11x - 4)}{x-1}$
$$= \frac{3x^2 + 4x - 11x + 4}{x-1}$$
$$= \frac{3x^2 - 7x + 4}{x-1}$$
$$= \frac{(3x-4)(x-1)}{x-1}$$
$$= 3x - 4$$

CHECK POINT 4

$$\frac{y^2 + 3y - 6}{y^2 - 5y + 4} - \frac{4y - 4 - 2y^2}{y^2 - 5y + 4}$$
$$= \frac{(y^2 + 3y - 6) - (4y - 4 - 2y^2)}{y^2 - 5y + 4}$$
$$= \frac{y^2 + 3y - 6 - 4y + 4 + 2y^2}{y^2 - 5y + 4}$$
$$= \frac{3y^2 - y - 2}{y^2 - 5y + 4}$$
$$= \frac{(3y+2)(y-1)}{(y-4)(y-1)}$$
$$= \frac{3y+2}{y-4}$$

CHECK POINT 5

$$\frac{x^2}{x-7} + \frac{4x + 21}{7 - x}$$
$$= \frac{x^2}{x-7} + \frac{(-1)}{(-1)} \cdot \frac{(4x + 21)}{(7 - x)}$$
$$= \frac{x^2}{x-7} + \frac{-4x - 21}{-7 + x}$$
$$= \frac{x^2 + (-4x - 21)}{x - 7}$$
$$= \frac{x^2 - 4x - 21}{x - 7}$$
$$= \frac{(x-7)(x+3)}{x-7}$$
$$= x + 3$$

CHECK POINT 6

$$\frac{7x - x^2}{x^2 - 2x - 9} - \frac{5x - 3x^2}{9 + 2x - x^2}$$

$$= \frac{7x - x^2}{x^2 - 2x - 9} - \frac{(-1)}{(-1)} \cdot \frac{5x - 3x^2}{9 - 2x - x^2}$$

$$= \frac{7x - x^2}{x^2 - 2x - 9} - \frac{-5x + 3x^2}{x^2 - 2x - 9}$$

$$= \frac{(7x - x^2) - (-5x + 3x^2)}{x^2 - 2x - 9}$$

$$= \frac{7x - x^2 + 5x - 3x^2}{x^2 - 2x - 9}$$

$$= \frac{-4x^2 + 12x}{x^2 - 2x - 9}$$

EXERCISE SET 7.3

1. $\dfrac{4x}{9} + \dfrac{3x}{9} = \dfrac{7x}{9}$

3. $\dfrac{7x}{12} + \dfrac{x}{12} = \dfrac{8x}{12} = \dfrac{2x}{3}$

5. $\dfrac{x - 3}{8} + \dfrac{3x + 7}{8} = \dfrac{4x + 4}{8}$

$$= \frac{4(x + 1)}{8}$$

$$= \frac{x + 1}{2}$$

7. $\dfrac{5}{x} + \dfrac{3}{x} = \dfrac{8}{x}$

9. $\dfrac{7}{9x} + \dfrac{5}{9x} = \dfrac{12}{9x} = \dfrac{4}{3x}$

11. $\dfrac{5}{x + 3} + \dfrac{4}{x + 3} = \dfrac{9}{x + 3}$

13. $\dfrac{x}{x - 3} + \dfrac{4x + 5}{x - 3} = \dfrac{5x + 5}{x - 3}$

15. $\dfrac{4x + 1}{6x + 5} + \dfrac{8x + 9}{6x + 5} = \dfrac{12x + 10}{6x + 5}$

$$= \frac{2(6x + 5)}{6x + 5} = 2$$

17. $\dfrac{y^2 + 7y}{y^2 - 5y} + \dfrac{y^2 - 4y}{y^2 - 5y} = \dfrac{y^2 + 7y + y^2 - 4y}{y^2 - 5y}$

$$= \frac{2y^2 + 3y}{y^2 - 5y}$$

$$= \frac{y(2y + 3)}{y(y - 5)}$$

$$= \frac{2y + 3}{y - 5}$$

19. $\dfrac{4y - 1}{5y^2} + \dfrac{3y + 1}{5y^2} = \dfrac{4y - 1 + 3y + 1}{5y^2}$

$$= \frac{7y}{5y^2} = \frac{7}{5y}$$

21. $\dfrac{x^2 - 2}{x^2 + x - 2} + \dfrac{2x - x^2}{x^2 + x - 2} = \dfrac{x^2 - 2 + 2x - x^2}{x^2 + x - 2}$

$$= \frac{2x - 2}{x^2 + x - 2}$$

$$= \frac{2(x - 1)}{(x + 2)(x - 1)}$$

$$= \frac{2}{x + 2}$$

23. $\dfrac{x^2 - 4x}{x^2 - x - 6} + \dfrac{4x - 4}{x^2 - x - 6}$

$$= \frac{x^2 - 4x + 4x - 4}{x^2 - x - 6}$$

$$= \frac{x^2 - 4}{x^2 - x - 6}$$

$$= \frac{(x + 2)(x - 2)}{(x - 3)(x + 2)}$$

$$= \frac{x - 2}{x - 3}$$

25. $\dfrac{3x}{5x - 4} - \dfrac{4}{5x - 4} = \dfrac{3x - 4}{5x - 4}$

27. $\dfrac{4x}{4x - 3} - \dfrac{3}{4x - 3} = \dfrac{4x - 3}{4x - 3} = 1$

29. $\dfrac{14y}{7y+2} - \dfrac{7y-2}{7y+2} = \dfrac{14y - (7y - 2)}{7y+2}$

$\qquad\qquad = \dfrac{14y - 7y + 2}{7y+2}$

$\qquad\qquad = \dfrac{7y+2}{7y+2} = 1$

31. $\dfrac{3x+1}{4x-2} - \dfrac{x+1}{4x-2} = \dfrac{(3x+1) - (x+1)}{4x-2}$

$\qquad\qquad = \dfrac{3x+1-x-1}{4x-2}$

$\qquad\qquad = \dfrac{2x}{4x-2}$

$\qquad\qquad = \dfrac{2x}{2(2x-1)}$

$\qquad\qquad = \dfrac{x}{2x-1}$

33. $\dfrac{3y^2-1}{3y^3} - \dfrac{6y^2-1}{3y^3}$

$\qquad = \dfrac{(3y^2-1) - (6y^2-1)}{3y^3}$

$\qquad = \dfrac{3y^2-1-6y^2+1}{3y^3}$

$\qquad = \dfrac{-3y^2}{3y^3} = -\dfrac{1}{y}$

35. $\dfrac{4y^2+5}{9y^2-64} - \dfrac{y^2-y+29}{9y^2-64}$

$\qquad = \dfrac{(4y^2+5) - (y^2-y+29)}{9y^2-64}$

$\qquad = \dfrac{4y^2+5-y^2+y-29}{9y^2-64}$

$\qquad = \dfrac{3y^2+y-24}{9y^2-64}$

$\qquad = \dfrac{(3y-8)(y+3)}{(3y+8)(3y-8)}$

$\qquad = \dfrac{y+3}{3y+8}$

37. $\dfrac{6y^2+y}{2y^2-9y+9} - \dfrac{2y+9}{2y^2-9y+9} - \dfrac{4y-3}{2y^2-9y+9}$

$\qquad = \dfrac{(6y^2+y) - (2y+9) - (4y-3)}{2y^2-9y+9}$

$\qquad = \dfrac{6y^2+y-2y-9-4y+3}{2y^2-9y+9}$

$\qquad = \dfrac{6y^2-5y-6}{2y^2-9y+9}$

$\qquad = \dfrac{(2y-3)(3y+2)}{(2y-3)(y-3)}$

$\qquad = \dfrac{3y+2}{y-3}$

39. $\dfrac{4}{x-3} + \dfrac{2}{3-x} = \dfrac{4}{x-3} + \dfrac{(-1)}{(-1)} \cdot \dfrac{2}{3-x}$

$\qquad\qquad = \dfrac{4}{x-3} + \dfrac{-2}{x-3}$

$\qquad\qquad = \dfrac{2}{x-3}$

41. $\dfrac{6x+7}{x-6} + \dfrac{3x}{6-x} = \dfrac{6x+7}{x-6} + \dfrac{(-1)}{(-1)} \cdot \dfrac{3x}{6-x}$

$\qquad\qquad = \dfrac{6x+7}{x-6} + \dfrac{-3x}{x-6}$

$\qquad\qquad = \dfrac{3x+7}{x-6}$

43. $\dfrac{5x-2}{3x-4} + \dfrac{2x-3}{4-3x}$

$\qquad = \dfrac{5x-2}{3x-4} + \dfrac{(-1)}{(-1)} \cdot \dfrac{2x-3}{4-3x}$

$\qquad = \dfrac{5x-2}{3x-4} + \dfrac{-2x+3}{3x-4}$

$\qquad = \dfrac{5x-2-2x+3}{3x-4}$

$\qquad = \dfrac{3x+1}{3x-4}$

45. $\dfrac{x^2}{x-2} + \dfrac{4}{2-x} = \dfrac{x^2}{x-2} + \dfrac{(-1)}{(-1)} \cdot \dfrac{4}{2-x}$

$\qquad\qquad = \dfrac{x^2}{x-2} + \dfrac{-4}{x-2}$

$\qquad\qquad = \dfrac{x^2-4}{x-2}$

$\qquad\qquad = \dfrac{(x+2)(x-2)}{x-2}$

$\qquad\qquad = x+2$

47. $\dfrac{y-3}{y^2-25} + \dfrac{y-3}{25-y^2}$

$\qquad = \dfrac{y-3}{y^2-25} + \dfrac{(-1)}{(-1)} \cdot \dfrac{y-3}{25-y^2}$

$\qquad = \dfrac{y-3}{y^2-25} + \dfrac{-y+3}{y^2-25}$

$\qquad = \dfrac{y-3-y+3}{y^2-25}$

$\qquad = \dfrac{0}{y^2-25} = 0$

49. $\dfrac{6}{x-1} - \dfrac{5}{1-x} = \dfrac{6}{x-1} - \dfrac{(-1)}{(-1)} \cdot \dfrac{5}{1-x}$

$\qquad\qquad = \dfrac{6}{x-1} - \dfrac{-5}{x-1}$

$\qquad\qquad = \dfrac{6+5}{x-1} = \dfrac{11}{x-1}$

51. $\dfrac{10}{x+3} - \dfrac{2}{-x-3} = \dfrac{10}{x+3} - \dfrac{(-1)}{(-1)} \cdot \dfrac{2}{-x-3}$

$\qquad\qquad = \dfrac{10}{x+3} - \dfrac{-2}{x+3}$

$\qquad\qquad = \dfrac{10+2}{x+3} = \dfrac{12}{x+3}$

53. $\dfrac{y}{y-1} - \dfrac{1}{1-y} = \dfrac{y}{y-1} - \dfrac{(-1)}{(-1)} \cdot \dfrac{1}{1-y}$

$\qquad\qquad = \dfrac{y}{y-1} - \dfrac{-1}{y-1}$

$\qquad\qquad = \dfrac{y+1}{y-1}$

55. $\dfrac{3-x}{x-7} - \dfrac{2x-5}{7-x}$

$\qquad = \dfrac{3-x}{x-7} - \dfrac{(-1)}{(-1)} \cdot \dfrac{2x-5}{7-x}$

$\qquad = \dfrac{3-x}{x-7} - \dfrac{-2x+5}{x-7}$

$\qquad = \dfrac{(3-x)-(-2x+5)}{x-7}$

$\qquad = \dfrac{3-x+2x-5}{x-7}$

$\qquad = \dfrac{x-2}{x-7}$

57. $\dfrac{x-2}{x^2-25} - \dfrac{x-2}{25-x^2}$

$\qquad = \dfrac{x-2}{x^2-25} - \dfrac{(-1)}{(-1)} \cdot \dfrac{x-2}{x^2-25}$

$\qquad = \dfrac{x-2}{x^2-25} - \dfrac{-x+2}{x^2-25}$

$\qquad = \dfrac{(x-2)-(-x+2)}{x^2-25}$

$\qquad = \dfrac{x-2+x-2}{x^2-25}$

$\qquad = \dfrac{2x-4}{x^2-25}$

59. $\dfrac{x}{x-y} + \dfrac{y}{y-x} = \dfrac{x}{x-y} + \dfrac{(-1)}{(-1)} \cdot \dfrac{y}{y-x}$

$\qquad\qquad = \dfrac{x}{x-y} + \dfrac{-y}{x-y}$

$\qquad\qquad = \dfrac{x-y}{x-y} = 1$

61. $\dfrac{2x}{x^2 - y^2} + \dfrac{2y}{y^2 - x^2}$

$$= \frac{2x}{x^2 - y^2} + \frac{(-1)}{(-1)} \cdot \frac{2y}{y^2 - x^2}$$

$$= \frac{2x}{x^2 - y^2} + \frac{-2y}{x^2 - y^2}$$

$$= \frac{2x - 2y}{x^2 - y^2}$$

$$= \frac{2(x - y)}{(x + y)(x - y)}$$

$$= \frac{2}{x + y}$$

63. $\dfrac{x^2 - 2}{x^2 + 6x - 7} + \dfrac{19 - 4x}{7 - 6x - x^2}$

$$= \frac{x^2 - 2}{x^2 + 6x - 7} + \frac{(-1)}{(-1)} \cdot \frac{19 - 4x}{7 - 6x - x^2}$$

$$= \frac{x^2 - 2}{x^2 + 6x - 7} + \frac{-19 + 4x}{7 - 6x - x^2}$$

$$= \frac{x^2 - 2 - 19 + 4x}{x^2 + 6x - 7}$$

$$= \frac{x^2 + 4x - 21}{x^2 + 6x - 7}$$

$$= \frac{(x + 7)(x - 3)}{(x + 7)(x - 1)}$$

$$= \frac{x - 3}{x - 1}$$

65. a. $\dfrac{L + 60W}{L} - \dfrac{L - 40W}{L}$

$$= \frac{(L + 60W) - (L - 40W)}{L}$$

$$= \frac{L + 60W - L + 40W}{L}$$

$$= \frac{100W}{L}$$

b. $\dfrac{100W}{L}$; $W = 5, L = 6$

$$\frac{100W}{L} = \frac{100 \cdot 5}{6}$$

$$\approx 83.3$$

Since this value is over 80, the skull is round.

67. $P = 2L + 2W$

$$= 2\left(\frac{5x + 10}{x + 3}\right) + 2\left(\frac{5}{x + 3}\right)$$

$$= \frac{10x + 20}{x + 3} + \frac{10}{x + 3}$$

$$= \frac{10x + 30}{x + 3}$$

$$= \frac{10(x + 3)}{x + 3} = 10$$

The perimeter is 10 meters.

For Exercises 69–71, answers may vary.

73. Statement d. is true.

$$\frac{2x + 1}{x - 7} + \frac{3x + 1}{x - 7} - \frac{5x + 2}{x - 7}$$

$$= \frac{5x + 2}{x - 7} - \frac{5x + 2}{x - 7} = 0$$

75. $\left(\dfrac{3x - 1}{x^2 + 5x - 6} - \dfrac{2x - 7}{x^2 + 5x - 6}\right) \div \dfrac{x + 2}{x^2 - 1}$

$$= \left(\frac{(3x - 1) - (2x - 7)}{x^2 + 5x - 6}\right) \div \frac{x + 2}{x^2 - 1}$$

$$= \frac{3x - 1 - 2x + 7}{x^2 + 5x - 6} \div \frac{x + 2}{x^2 - 1}$$

$$= \frac{x + 6}{x^2 + 5x - 6} \div \frac{x + 2}{x^2 - 1}$$

$$= \frac{x + 6}{x^2 + 5x - 6} \cdot \frac{x^2 - 1}{x + 1}$$

$$= \frac{(x + 6)}{(x + 6)(x - 1)} \cdot \frac{(x + 1)(x - 1)}{(x + 2)}$$

$$= \frac{x + 1}{x + 2}$$

77. $\dfrac{2x}{x+3} + \dfrac{\boxed{}}{x+3} = \dfrac{4x+1}{x+3}$

The sum of numerators on the left side must be $4x+1$, so the missing expression is $2x+1$.

Check:

$$\dfrac{2x}{x+3} + \dfrac{2x+1}{x+3} = \dfrac{2x+2x+1}{x+3}$$
$$= \dfrac{4x+1}{x+3}$$

79. $\dfrac{6}{x-2} + \dfrac{\boxed{}}{2-x} = \dfrac{13}{x-2}$

$\dfrac{6}{x-2} + \dfrac{(-1)}{(-1)} \cdot \dfrac{\boxed{}}{2-x} = \dfrac{13}{x-2}$

$\dfrac{6}{x-2} + \dfrac{(-1)\boxed{}}{x-2} = \dfrac{13}{x-2}$

Since $6+7 = 13$, the opposite of the missing expression must be 7, so the missing expression is -7.

Check:

$$\dfrac{6}{x-2} + \dfrac{-7}{2-x} = \dfrac{6}{x-2} + \dfrac{7}{x-2} = \dfrac{13}{x-2}$$

81. $\dfrac{3x}{x-5} + \dfrac{\boxed{}}{5-x} = \dfrac{7x+1}{x-5}$

$\dfrac{3x}{x-5} + \dfrac{(-1)}{(-1)} \cdot \dfrac{\boxed{}}{5-x} = \dfrac{7x+1}{x-5}$

$\dfrac{3x}{x-5} + \dfrac{(-1)\boxed{}}{x-5} = \dfrac{7x+1}{x-5}$

Since $3x+(4x+1) = 7x+1$, the opposite of the missing expression must be $4x+1$, so the missing expression is $-4x-1$.

Check:

$$\dfrac{3x}{x-5} + \dfrac{-4x-1}{5-x} = \dfrac{3x}{x-5} + \dfrac{4x+1}{x-5}$$
$$= \dfrac{7x+1}{x-5}$$

83.

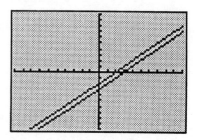

The graphs do not coincide.

$$\dfrac{x^2+4x+3}{x+2} - \dfrac{5x+9}{x+2}$$
$$= \dfrac{(x^2+4x+3)-(5x+9)}{x+2}$$
$$= \dfrac{x^2+4x+3-5x-9}{x+2}$$
$$= \dfrac{x^2-x-6}{x+2}$$
$$= \dfrac{(x+2)(x-3)}{x+2}$$
$$= x-3$$

Change $x-2$ to $x-3$.

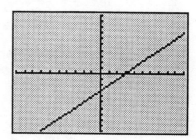

Now the graphs coincide.

Review Exercises

85. $\dfrac{13}{15} - \dfrac{8}{45} = \dfrac{13}{15} \cdot \dfrac{3}{3} - \dfrac{8}{45}$
$$= \dfrac{39}{45} - \dfrac{8}{45} = \dfrac{31}{45}$$

86. $81x^4 - 1 = (9x^2+1)(9x^2-1)$
$$= (9x^2+1)(3x+1)(3x-1)$$

87.

$$\begin{array}{r} 3x^2 - 7x - 5 \\ x+3{\overline{\smash{\big)}\,3x^3 + 2x^2 - 26x - 15}} \\ \underline{3x^3 + 9x^2} \\ -7x^2 - 26x \\ \underline{-7x^2 - 21x} \\ -5x - 15 \\ \underline{-5x - 15} \\ 0 \end{array}$$

$$\frac{3x^3 + 2x^2 - 26x - 15}{x+3} = 3x^2 - 7x - 5$$

Adding and Subtracting Rational Expressions with Different Denominators

7.4 CHECK POINTS

CHECK POINT 1

$$\frac{3}{10x^2} \text{ and } \frac{7}{15x}$$

Step 1 Factor each denominator completely.

$$10x^2 = 2 \cdot 5x^2$$
$$15x = 3 \cdot 5x$$

Step 2 List the factors of the first denominator.

$$2, 5, x^2$$

Step 3 Add any unlisted factors from the second denominator. The only unlisted factor is 3, giving the list

$$2, 3, 5, x^2.$$

Step 4 The LCD is the product of all factors in the final list. Thus, the LCD is

$$2 \cdot 3 \cdot 5x^2 = 30x^2.$$

CHECK POINT 2

$$\frac{2}{x+3} \text{ and } \frac{4}{x-3}$$

The LCD is $(x+3)(x-3)$.

CHECK POINT 3

$$\frac{9}{7x^2 + 28x} \text{ and } \frac{11}{x^2 + 8x + 16}$$

$$7x^2 + 28x = 7x(x+4)$$
$$x^2 + 8x + 16 = (x+4)^2$$

$$\text{LCD} = 7x(x+4)(x+4) \text{ or } 7(x+4)^2$$

CHECK POINT 4

$$\frac{3}{10x^2} + \frac{7}{15x}$$

Step 1 Find the LCD. In CHECK POINT 1, you found that the LCD for these rational expressions is $30x^2$.

Step 2 Write equivalent rational expressions with LCD as denominators.

$$\frac{3}{10x^2} \cdot \frac{3}{3} = \frac{9}{30x^2}$$
$$\frac{7}{15x} \cdot \frac{2x}{2x} = \frac{14x}{30x^2}$$

Thus,

$$\frac{3}{10x^2} + \frac{7}{15x} = \frac{9}{30x^2} + \frac{14x}{30x^2}.$$

Steps 3 and 4

Add numerators, putting this sum over the LCD. Simplify if possible.

$$\frac{9}{30x^2} + \frac{14x}{30x^2} = \frac{9 + 14x}{30x^2}$$

The numerator is prime and further simplification is not possible.

CHECK POINT 5

$$\frac{2}{x+3} + \frac{4}{x-3}$$

In CHECK POINT 2, you found that the LCD for these rational expressions is $(x+3)(x-3)$.

$$\frac{2}{x+3} + \frac{4}{x-3}$$

$$= \frac{2(x-3)}{(x+3)(x-3)} + \frac{4(x+3)}{(x+3)(x-3)}$$

$$= \frac{2(x-3) + 4(x+3)}{(x+3)(x-3)}$$

$$= \frac{2x-6+4x+12}{(x+3)(x-3)}$$

$$= \frac{6x+6}{(x+3)(x-3)}$$

CHECK POINT 6

$$\frac{x}{x+5} - 1$$

The LCD is $x+5$.

$$\frac{x}{x+5} - 1 = \frac{x}{x+5} - \frac{1(x+5)}{1(x+5)}$$

$$= \frac{x-(x+5)}{x+5}$$

$$= \frac{x-x-5}{x+5}$$

$$= \frac{-5}{x+5} \text{ or } -\frac{5}{x+5}$$

CHECK POINT 7

$$\frac{5}{y^2-5y} - \frac{y}{5y-25}$$

First, find the LCD.

$$y^2 - 5y = y(y-5)$$
$$5y - 25 = 5(y-5)$$

The LCD is $5y(y-5)$.

$$\frac{5}{y^2-5y} - \frac{y}{5y-25} = \frac{5}{y(y-5)} - \frac{y}{5(y-5)}$$

$$= \frac{5 \cdot 5}{5y(y-5)} - \frac{y \cdot y}{5y(y-5)}$$

$$= \frac{25 - y^2}{5y(y-5)}$$

$$= \frac{(5+y)(5-y)}{5y(y-5)}$$

$$= \frac{-1(5+y)}{5y}$$

$$= -\frac{5+y}{5y}$$

CHECK POINT 8

$$\frac{4x}{x^2-25} + \frac{3}{5-x}$$

Find the LCD.

$$x^2 - 25 = (x+5)(x-5)$$
$$5 - x = 1(5-x)$$

Notice that $x-5$ and $5-x$ are opposite factors, so either rational expression may be multiplied by $\frac{-1}{-1}$. Here, the second expression will be multiplied by $\frac{-1}{-1}$, and $(x+5)(x-5)$ will be used as the LCD.

$$\frac{4x}{x^2-25} + \frac{3}{5-x}$$

$$= \frac{4x}{(x+5)(x-5)} + \frac{(-1)}{(-1)} \cdot \frac{3}{5-x}$$

$$= \frac{4x}{(x+5)(x-5)} + \frac{-3(x+5)}{(x+5)(x-5)}$$

$$= \frac{4x - 3(x+5)}{(x+5)(x-5)}$$

$$= \frac{4x - 3x - 15}{(x+5)(x-5)}$$

$$= \frac{x - 15}{(x+5)(x-5)}$$

EXERCISE SET 7.4

1. $\dfrac{7}{15x^2}$ and $\dfrac{13}{24x}$

$$15x^2 = 3 \cdot 5x^2$$
$$24x = 2^3 \cdot 3x$$

$$\text{LCD} = 2^3 \cdot 3 \cdot 5x^2 = 120x^2$$

3. $\dfrac{8}{15x^2}$ and $\dfrac{5}{6x^5}$

$$15x^2 = 3 \cdot 5x^2$$
$$6x^5 = 2 \cdot 3x^5$$

$$\text{LCD} = 2 \cdot 3 \cdot 5 \cdot x^5 = 30x^5$$

5. $\dfrac{4}{x-3}$ and $\dfrac{7}{x+1}$

$$\text{LCD} = (x-3)(x+1)$$

7. $\dfrac{5}{7(y+2)}$ and $\dfrac{10}{y}$

$$\text{LCD} = 7y(y+2)$$

9. $\dfrac{2}{x+3}$ and $\dfrac{5}{x^2-9}$

$$x + 3 = 1(x+3)$$
$$x^2 - 9 = (x+3)(x-3)$$

$$\text{LCD} = (x+3)(x-3)$$

11. $\dfrac{7}{y^2-4}$ and $\dfrac{15}{y(y+2)}$

$$y^2 - 4 = (y+2)(y-2)$$
$$y(y+2) = y(y+2)$$

$$\text{LCD} = y(y+2)(y-2)$$

13. $\dfrac{3}{y^2-25}$ and $\dfrac{y}{y^2-10y+25}$

$$y^2 - 25 = (y+5)(y-5)$$
$$y^2 - 10y + 25 = (y-5)(y-5)$$

$$\text{LCD} = (y+5)(y-5)(y-5)$$

15. $\dfrac{3}{x^2-x-20}$ and $\dfrac{x}{2x^2+7x-4}$

$$x^2 - x - 20 = (x-5)(x+4)$$
$$2x^2 + 7x - 4 = (2x-1)(x+4)$$

$$\text{LCD} = (x-5)(x+1)(2x-1)$$

17. $\dfrac{3}{x} + \dfrac{5}{x^2}$

$$\text{LCD} = x^2$$

$$\frac{3}{x} + \frac{5}{x^2} = \frac{3}{x} \cdot \frac{x}{x} + \frac{5}{x^2} = \frac{3x+5}{x^2}$$

19. $\dfrac{2}{9x} + \dfrac{11}{6x}$

$$\text{LCD} = 18x$$

$$\frac{2}{9x} + \frac{11}{6x} = \frac{2 \cdot 2}{18x} + \frac{11 \cdot 3}{18x}$$
$$= \frac{4}{18x} + \frac{33}{18x} = \frac{37}{18x}$$

21. $\dfrac{4}{x} + \dfrac{7}{2x^2}$

$$\text{LCD} = 2x^2$$

$$\frac{4}{x} + \frac{7}{2x^2} = \frac{4 \cdot 2x}{2x^2} + \frac{7}{2x^2} = \frac{8x+7}{2x^2}$$

23. $1 + \dfrac{1}{x}$

$$\text{LCD} = x$$

$$1 + \frac{1}{x} = \frac{1 \cdot x}{x} + \frac{1}{x} = \frac{x+1}{x}$$

25. $\dfrac{3}{x} + 5$

$$\text{LCD} = x$$

$$\frac{3}{x} + 5 = \frac{3}{x} + \frac{5 \cdot x}{x} = \frac{3+5x}{x}$$

27. $\dfrac{x-1}{6} + \dfrac{x+2}{3}$

LCD $= 6$

$$
\begin{aligned}
\frac{x-1}{6} + \frac{x+2}{3} &= \frac{x-1}{6} + \frac{(x+2)(2)}{6} \\
&= \frac{x-1+2x+4}{6} \\
&= \frac{3x+3}{6} \\
&= \frac{3(x+1)}{6} \\
&= \frac{x+1}{2}
\end{aligned}
$$

29. $\dfrac{4}{x} + \dfrac{3}{x-5}$

LCD $= x(x-5)$

$$
\begin{aligned}
\frac{4}{x} + \frac{3}{x-5} &= \frac{4(x-5)}{x(x-5)} + \frac{3x}{x(x-5)} \\
&= \frac{4(x-5)+3x}{x(x-5)} \\
&= \frac{4x-20+3x}{x(x-5)} \\
&= \frac{7x-20}{x(x-5)}
\end{aligned}
$$

31. $\dfrac{2}{x-1} + \dfrac{3}{x+2}$

LCD $= (x-1)(x+2)$

$$
\begin{aligned}
&\frac{2}{x-1} + \frac{3}{x+2} \\
&= \frac{2(x+2)}{(x-1)(x+2)} + \frac{3(x-1)}{(x-1)(x+2)} \\
&= \frac{2x+4+3x-3}{(x-1)(x+2)} \\
&= \frac{5x+1}{(x-1)(x+2)}
\end{aligned}
$$

33. $\dfrac{2}{y+5} + \dfrac{3}{4y}$

LCD $= 4y(y+5)$

$$
\begin{aligned}
\frac{2}{y+5} + \frac{3}{4y} &= \frac{2(4y)}{4y(y+5)} + \frac{3(y+5)}{4y(y+5)} \\
&= \frac{2(4y)+3(y+5)}{4y(y+5)} \\
&= \frac{8y+3y+15}{4y(y+5)} \\
&= \frac{11y+15}{4y(y+5)}
\end{aligned}
$$

35. $\dfrac{x}{x+7} - 1$

LCD $= x+7$

$$
\begin{aligned}
\frac{x}{x+7} - 1 &= \frac{x}{x+7} - \frac{x+7}{x+7} \\
&= \frac{x-(x+7)}{x+7} \\
&= \frac{x-x-7}{x+7} \\
&= \frac{-7}{x+7} \text{ or } -\frac{7}{x+7}
\end{aligned}
$$

37. $\dfrac{7}{x+5} - \dfrac{4}{x-5}$

LCD $= (x+5)(x-5)$

$$
\begin{aligned}
&\frac{7}{x+5} - \frac{4}{x-5} \\
&= \frac{7(x-5)}{(x+5)(x-5)} - \frac{4(x+5)}{(x+5)(x-5)} \\
&= \frac{7(x-5)-4(x+5)}{(x+5)(x-5)} \\
&= \frac{7x-35-4x-20}{(x+5)(x-5)} \\
&= \frac{3x-55}{(x+5)(x-5)}
\end{aligned}
$$

39. $\dfrac{2x}{x^2 - 16} + \dfrac{x}{x - 4}$

$$x^2 - 16 = (x + 4)(x - 4)$$
$$x - 4 = 1(x - 4)$$

$$\text{LCD} = (x + 4)(x - 4)$$

$$\dfrac{2x}{x^2 - 16} + \dfrac{x}{x - 4}$$
$$= \dfrac{2x}{(x + 4)(x - 4)} + \dfrac{x}{x - 4}$$
$$= \dfrac{2x}{(x + 4)(x - 4)} + \dfrac{x(x + 4)}{(x + 4)(x - 4)}$$
$$= \dfrac{2x + x(x + 4)}{(x + 4)(x - 4)}$$
$$= \dfrac{2x + x^2 + 4x}{(x + 4)(x - 4)}$$
$$= \dfrac{x^2 + 6x}{(x + 4)(x - 4)}$$

41. $\dfrac{5y}{y^2 - 9} - \dfrac{4}{y + 3}$

$$\text{LCD} = (y + 3)(y - 3)$$

$$\dfrac{5y}{y^2 - 9} - \dfrac{4}{y + 3}$$
$$= \dfrac{5y}{(y + 3)(y - 3)} - \dfrac{4}{y + 3}$$
$$= \dfrac{5y}{(y + 3)(y - 3)} - \dfrac{4(y - 3)}{(y + 3)(y - 3)}$$
$$= \dfrac{5y - 4(y - 3)}{(y + 3)(y - 3)}$$
$$= \dfrac{5y - 4y + 12}{(y + 3)(y - 3)}$$
$$= \dfrac{y + 12}{(y + 3)(y - 3)}$$

43. $\dfrac{7}{x - 1} - \dfrac{3}{(x - 1)(x - 1)}$

$$\text{LCD} = (x - 1)(x - 1)$$

$$\dfrac{7}{x - 1} - \dfrac{3}{(x - 1)(x - 1)}$$
$$= \dfrac{7(x - 1)}{(x - 1)(x - 1)} - \dfrac{3}{(x - 1)(x - 1)}$$
$$= \dfrac{7x - 7 - 3}{(x - 1)(x - 1)}$$
$$= \dfrac{7x - 10}{(x - 1)(x - 1)} \quad \text{or} \quad \dfrac{7x - 10}{(x - 1)^2}$$

45. $\dfrac{3y}{4y - 20} + \dfrac{9y}{6y - 30}$

$$4y - 20 = 4(y - 5)$$
$$6y - 30 = 6(y - 5)$$

$$\text{LCD} = 12(y - 5)$$

$$\dfrac{3y}{4y - 20} + \dfrac{9y}{6y - 30} = \dfrac{3y}{4(y - 5)} + \dfrac{9y}{6(y - 5)}$$
$$= \dfrac{3y \cdot 3}{12(y - 5)} + \dfrac{9y \cdot 2}{12(y - 5)}$$
$$= \dfrac{9y + 18y}{12(y - 5)} = \dfrac{27y}{12(y - 5)}$$
$$= \dfrac{9y}{4(y - 5)}$$

47. $\dfrac{y + 4}{y} - \dfrac{y}{y + 4}$

$$\text{LCD} = y(y + 4)$$

$$\dfrac{y + 4}{y} - \dfrac{y}{y + 4}$$
$$= \dfrac{(y + 4)(y + 4)}{y(y + 4)} - \dfrac{y \cdot y}{y(y + 4)}$$
$$= \dfrac{y^2 + 8y + 16 - y^2}{y(y + 4)}$$
$$= \dfrac{8y + 16}{y(y + 4)}$$

49. $\dfrac{2x+9}{x^2-7x+12} - \dfrac{2}{x-3}$

$$x^2 - 7x + 12 = (x-3)(x-4)$$
$$x - 3 = 1(x-3)$$

$$LCD = (x-3)(x-4)$$

$$\dfrac{2x+9}{x^2-7x+12} - \dfrac{2}{x-3}$$

$$= \dfrac{2x+9}{(x-3)(x-4)} - \dfrac{2}{x-3}$$

$$= \dfrac{2x+9}{(x-3)(x-4)} - \dfrac{2(x-4)}{(x-3)(x-4)}$$

$$= \dfrac{2x+9-2(x-4)}{(x-3)(x-4)}$$

$$= \dfrac{2x+9-2x+8}{(x-3)(x-4)}$$

$$= \dfrac{17}{(x-3)(x-4)}$$

51. $\dfrac{3}{x^2-1} + \dfrac{4}{(x+1)^2}$

$$x^2 - 1 = (x+1)(x-1)$$
$$(x+1)^2 = (x+1)(x+1)$$

$$LCD = (x+1)(x+1)(x-1)$$

$$\dfrac{3}{x^2-1} + \dfrac{4}{(x+1)^2}$$

$$= \dfrac{3}{(x+1)(x-1)} + \dfrac{4}{(x+1)(x+1)}$$

$$= \dfrac{3(x+1)}{(x+1)(x+1)(x-1)}$$

$$+ \dfrac{4(x-1)}{(x+1)(x+1)(x-1)}$$

$$= \dfrac{3(x+1)+4(x-1)}{(x+1)(x+1)(x-1)}$$

$$= \dfrac{3x+3+4x-4}{(x+1)(x+1)(x-1)}$$

$$= \dfrac{7x-1}{(x+1)(x+1)(x-1)}$$

53. $\dfrac{3x}{x^2+3x-10} - \dfrac{2x}{x^2+x-6}$

$$x^2 + 3x - 10 = (x-2)(x+5)$$
$$x^2 + x - 6 = (x+3)(x-2)$$

$$LCD = (x+3)(x-2)(x+5)$$

$$\dfrac{3x}{x^2+3x-10} - \dfrac{2x}{x^2+x-6}$$

$$= \dfrac{3x}{(x-2)(x+5)} - \dfrac{2x}{(x+3)(x-2)}$$

$$= \dfrac{3x(x+3)}{(x+3)(x-2)(x+5)}$$

$$- \dfrac{2x(x+5)}{(x+3)(x-2)(x+5)}$$

$$= \dfrac{3x(x+3)-2x(x+5)}{(x+3)(x-2)(x+5)}$$

$$= \dfrac{3x^2+9x-2x^2-10x}{(x+3)(x-2)(x+5)}$$

$$= \dfrac{x^2-x}{(x+3)(x-2)(x+5)}$$

55. $\dfrac{y}{y^2+2y+1} + \dfrac{4}{y^2+5y+4}$

$$y^2 + 2y + 1 = (y+1)(y+1)$$
$$y^2 + 5y + 4 = (y+4)(y+1)$$

$$LCD = (y+4)(y+1)(y+1)$$

$$\dfrac{y}{y^2+2y+1} + \dfrac{4}{y^2+5y+4}$$

$$= \dfrac{y}{(y+1)(y+1)} + \dfrac{4}{(y+4)(y+1)}$$

$$= \dfrac{y(y+4)}{(y+4)(y+1)(y+1)}$$

$$+ \dfrac{4(y+1)}{(y+4)(y+1)(y+1)}$$

$$= \dfrac{y(y+4)+4(y+1)}{(y+4)(y+1)(y+1)}$$

$$= \dfrac{y^2+4y+4y+4}{(y+4)(y+1)(y+1)}$$

$$= \dfrac{y^2+8y+4}{(y+4)(y+1)(y+1)}$$

57. $\dfrac{x-5}{x+3} + \dfrac{x+3}{x-5}$

$\text{LCD} = (x+3)(x-5)$

$\dfrac{x-5}{x+3} + \dfrac{x+3}{x-5}$

$= \dfrac{(x-5)(x-5)}{(x+3)(x-5)} + \dfrac{(x+3)(x+3)}{(x+3)(x-5)}$

$= \dfrac{(x-5)(x-5) + (x+3)(x+3)}{(x+3)(x-5)}$

$= \dfrac{(x^2 - 10x + 25) + (x^2 + 6x + 9)}{(x+3)(x-5)}$

$= \dfrac{2x^2 - 4x + 34}{(x+3)(x-5)}$

59. $\dfrac{5}{2y^2 - 2y} - \dfrac{3}{2y - 2}$

$2y^2 - 2y = 2y(y-1)$

$2y - 2 = 2(y-1)$

$\text{LCD} = 2y(y-1)$

$\dfrac{5}{2y^2 - 2y} - \dfrac{3}{2y - 2} = \dfrac{5}{2y(y-1)} - \dfrac{3}{2(y-1)}$

$= \dfrac{5}{2y(y-1)} - \dfrac{3 \cdot y}{2y(y-1)}$

$= \dfrac{5 - 3y}{2y(y-1)}$

61. $\dfrac{4x+3}{x^2 - 9} - \dfrac{x+1}{x-3}$

$\text{LCD} = (x+3)(x-3)$

$\dfrac{4x+3}{x^2 - 9} - \dfrac{x+1}{x-3}$

$= \dfrac{4x+3}{(x+3)(x-3)} - \dfrac{(x+1)(x+3)}{(x+3)(x-3)}$

$= \dfrac{(4x+3) - (x+1)(x+3)}{(x+3)(x-3)}$

$= \dfrac{(4x+3) - (x^2 + 4x + 3)}{(x+3)(x-3)}$

$= \dfrac{4x + 3 - x^2 - 4x - 3}{(x+3)(x-3)}$

$= \dfrac{-x^2}{(x+3)(x-3)} = -\dfrac{x^2}{(x+3)(x-3)}$

63. $\dfrac{y^2 - 39}{y^2 + 3y - 10} - \dfrac{y-7}{y-2}$

$y^2 + 3y - 10 = (y-2)(y+5)$

$y - 2 = 1(y-2)$

$\text{LCD} = (y-2)(y+5)$

$\dfrac{y^2 - 39}{y^2 + 3y - 10} - \dfrac{y-7}{y-2}$

$= \dfrac{y^2 - 39}{(y-2)(y+5)} - \dfrac{y-7}{y-2}$

$= \dfrac{y^2 - 39}{(y-2)(y+5)} - \dfrac{(y-7)(y+5)}{(y-2)(y+5)}$

$= \dfrac{(y^2 - 39) - (y-7)(y+5)}{(y-2)(y+5)}$

$= \dfrac{(y^2 - 39) - (y^2 - 2y - 35)}{(y-2)(y+5)}$

$= \dfrac{y^2 - 39 - y^2 + 2y + 35}{(y-2)(y+5)}$

$= \dfrac{2y - 4}{(y-2)(y+5)}$

$= \dfrac{2(y-2)}{(y-2)(y+5)}$

$= \dfrac{2}{y+5}$

65. $4 + \dfrac{1}{x-3}$

$\text{LCD} = x - 3$

$4 + \dfrac{1}{x-3} = \dfrac{4(x-3)}{x-3} + \dfrac{1}{x-3}$

$= \dfrac{4(x-3) + 1}{x-3}$

$= \dfrac{4x - 12 + 1}{x-3}$

$= \dfrac{4x - 11}{x-3}$

67. $3 - \dfrac{3y}{y+1}$

$LCD = y + 1$

$$3 - \frac{3y}{y+1} = \frac{3(y+1)}{y+1} - \frac{3y}{y+1}$$
$$= \frac{3(y+1) - 3y}{y+1}$$
$$= \frac{3y + 3 - 3y}{y+1}$$
$$= \frac{3}{y+1}$$

69. $\dfrac{9x+3}{x^2-x-6} + \dfrac{x}{3-x}$

$$x^2 - x - 6 = (x-3)(x+2)$$
$$-1(3-x) = x - 3$$

$LCD = (x-3)(x+2)$

$$\frac{9x+3}{x^2-x-6} + \frac{x}{3-x}$$
$$= \frac{9x+3}{(x-3)(x+2)} + \frac{(-1)}{(-1)} \cdot \frac{x}{3-x}$$
$$= \frac{9x+3}{(x-3)(x+2)} + \frac{-x}{x-3}$$
$$= \frac{9x+3}{(x-3)(x+2)} + \frac{-x(x+2)}{(x-3)(x+2)}$$
$$= \frac{9x+3 - x(x+2)}{(x-3)(x+2)}$$
$$= \frac{9x+3 - x^2 - 2x}{(x-3)(x+2)}$$
$$= \frac{-x^2 + 7x + 3}{(x-3)(x+2)}$$

71. $\dfrac{x+3}{x^2+x-2} - \dfrac{2}{x^2-1}$

$$x^2 + x - 2 = (x-1)(x+2)$$
$$x^2 - 1 = (x+1)(x-1)$$

$LCD = (x+1)(x-1)(x+2)$

$$\frac{x+3}{x^2+x-2} - \frac{2}{x^2-1}$$
$$= \frac{x+3}{(x-1)(x+2)} - \frac{2}{(x+1)(x-1)}$$
$$= \frac{(x+3)(x+1)}{(x+1)(x-1)(x+2)}$$
$$\quad - \frac{2(x+2)}{(x+1)(x-1)(x+2)}$$
$$= \frac{(x+3)(x+1) - 2(x+2)}{(x+1)(x-1)(x+2)}$$
$$= \frac{x^2 + 4x + 3 - 2x - 4}{(x+1)(x-1)(x+2)}$$
$$= \frac{x^2 + 2x - 1}{(x+1)(x-1)(x+2)}$$

73. $\dfrac{y+3}{5y^2} - \dfrac{y-5}{15y}$

$LCD = 15y^2$

$$\frac{y+3}{5y^2} - \frac{y-5}{15y} = \frac{(y+3)(3)}{15y^2} - \frac{(y-5)(y)}{15y^2}$$
$$= \frac{(3y+9) - (y^2 - 5y)}{15y^2}$$
$$= \frac{3y + 9 - y^2 + 5y}{15y^2}$$
$$= \frac{-y^2 + 8y + 9}{15y^2}$$

75. $\dfrac{x+3}{3x+6} + \dfrac{x}{4-x^2}$

$$3x+6 = 3(x+2)$$
$$4-x^2 = (2+x)(2-x)$$

Note that $-1(2-x) = x-2$.
LCD $= 3(x+2)(x-2)$

$$\frac{x+3}{3x+6} + \frac{x}{4-x^2}$$
$$= \frac{x+3}{3(x+2)} + \frac{x}{(2+x)(2-x)}$$
$$= \frac{x+3}{3(x+2)} + \frac{(-1)}{(-1)}\cdot\frac{x}{(2+x)(2-x)}$$
$$= \frac{x+3}{3(x+2)} + \frac{-x}{(x+2)(x-2)}$$
$$= \frac{(x+3)(x-2)}{3(x+2)(x-2)} + \frac{-x(3)}{3(x+2)(x-2)}$$
$$= \frac{x^2+x-6-3x}{3(x+2)(x-2)}$$
$$= \frac{x^2-2x-6}{3(x+2)(x-2)}$$

77. $\dfrac{y}{y^2-1} + \dfrac{2y}{y-y^2}$

$$y^2-1 = (y+1)(y-1)$$
$$y-y^2 = y(1-y)$$

Note that $-1(1-y) = y-1$.
LCD $= y(y+1)(y-1)$

$$\frac{y}{y^2-1} + \frac{2y}{y-y^2}$$
$$= \frac{y}{(y+1)(y-1)} + \frac{2y}{y(1-y)}$$
$$= \frac{y}{(y+1)(y-1)} + \frac{(-1)}{(-1)}\cdot\frac{2y}{y(1-y)}$$
$$= \frac{y}{(y+1)(y-1)} + \frac{-2y}{y(y-1)}$$

$$= \frac{y\cdot y}{y(y+1)(y-1)} + \frac{-2y(y+1)}{y(y+1)(y-1)}$$
$$= \frac{y^2-2y(y+1)}{y(y+1)(y-1)} = \frac{y^2-2y^2-2y}{y(y+1)(y-1)}$$
$$= \frac{-y^2-2y}{y(y+1)(y-1)} = \frac{-y(y+2)}{y(y+1)(y-1)}$$
$$= -\frac{-1(y+2)}{(y+1)(y-1)} = \frac{-y-2}{(y+1)(y-1)}$$

79. $\dfrac{x-1}{x} + \dfrac{y+1}{y}$

LCD $= xy$

$$\frac{x-1}{x} + \frac{y+1}{y} = \frac{(x-1)(y)}{xy} + \frac{(y+1)(x)}{xy}$$
$$= \frac{xy-y+xy+x}{xy}$$
$$= \frac{x+2xy-y}{xy}$$

81. $\dfrac{3x}{x^2-y^2} - \dfrac{2}{y-x}$

$$x^2-y^2 = (x+y)(x-y)$$

Note that $y-x = -1(x-y)$.
LCD $= (x+y)(x-y)$

$$\frac{3x}{x^2-y^2} - \frac{2}{y-x}$$
$$= \frac{3x}{(x+y)(x-y)} - \frac{(-1)}{(-1)}\cdot\frac{2}{y-x}$$
$$= \frac{3x}{(x+y)(x-y)} - \frac{-2}{x-y}$$
$$= \frac{3x}{(x+y)(x-y)} - \frac{-2(x+y)}{(x+y)(x-y)}$$
$$= \frac{3x+2(x+y)}{(x+y)(x-y)} = \frac{3x+2x+2y}{(x+y)(x-y)}$$
$$= \frac{5x+2y}{(x+y)(x-y)}$$

83. Young's Rule: $C = \dfrac{DA}{A+12}$

$A = 8$:

$$C = \frac{D \cdot 8}{8+12} = \frac{8D}{20} = \frac{2D}{5}$$

$A = 3$:

$$C = \frac{D \cdot 3}{3+12} = \frac{3D}{15} = \frac{D}{5}$$

Difference:

$$\frac{2D}{5} - \frac{D}{5} = \frac{D}{5}$$

The difference is dosages for an 8-year-old child and a 3-year-old child is $\frac{D}{5}$. This means that an 8-year-old should be given $\frac{1}{5}$ more of the adult dosage than a 3-year-old.

85. Young's Rule:

$$C = \frac{DA}{A+12}$$

Cowling's Rule:

$$C = \frac{D(A+1)}{24}$$

For $A = 12$, Young's Rule gives

$$C = \frac{D \cdot 12}{12+12} = \frac{12D}{24} = \frac{D}{2}$$

and Cowling's Rule gives

$$C = \frac{D(12+1)}{24} = \frac{13D}{24}.$$

The difference between the dosages given by Cowling's Rule and Young's Rule is

$$\frac{13D}{24} - \frac{12D}{24} = \frac{D}{24}.$$

This means that Cowling's Rule says to give a 12-year-old $\frac{1}{24}$ of the adult dose more than Young's Rule says the dosage should be.

87. No, because the graphs cross, neither formula gives a consistently smaller dosage.

89. The difference in dosage is greatest at 13 years.

91. $P = 2L + 2W$

$$= 2\left(\frac{x}{x+3}\right) + 2\left(\frac{x}{x+4}\right)$$

$$= \frac{2x}{x+3} + \frac{2x}{x+4}$$

$$= \frac{2x(x+4)}{(x+3)(x+4)} + \frac{2x(x+3)}{(x+3)(x+4)}$$

$$= \frac{2x^2 + 8x + 2x^2 + 6x}{(x+3)(x+4)}$$

$$= \frac{4x^2 + 14x}{(x+3)(x+4)}$$

93. Answers may vary.

95. Explanations will vary. The right side of the equation should be charged from $\frac{3}{x+5}$ to $\frac{5+2x}{5x}$.

97. Answers may vary.

99. $\dfrac{x+6}{x^2-4} - \dfrac{x+3}{x+2} + \dfrac{x-3}{x-2}$

$\text{LCD} = (x+2)(x-2)$

$\dfrac{x+6}{x^2-4} - \dfrac{x+3}{x+2} + \dfrac{x-3}{x-2}$

$= \dfrac{x+6}{(x+2)(x-2)} - \dfrac{x+3}{x+2} + \dfrac{x-3}{x-2}$

$= \dfrac{x+6}{(x+2)(x-2)} - \dfrac{(x+3)(x-2)}{(x+2)(x-2)}$

$\quad + \dfrac{(x-3)(x+2)}{(x+2)(x-2)}$

$= \dfrac{(x+6) - (x+3)(x-2) + (x-3)(x+2)}{(x+2)(x-2)}$

$= \dfrac{(x+6) - (x^2+x-6) + (x^2-x-6)}{(x+2)(x-2)}$

$= \dfrac{x+6-x^2-x+6+x^2-x-6}{(x+2)(x-2)}$

$= \dfrac{-x+6}{(x+2)(x-2)}$

101. $\dfrac{y^2+5y+4}{y^2+2y-3} \cdot \dfrac{y^2+y-6}{y^2+2y-3} - \dfrac{2}{y-1}$

$= \dfrac{(y+4)(y+1)}{(y+3)(y-1)} \cdot \dfrac{(y+3)(y-2)}{(y+3)(y-1)} - \dfrac{2}{y-1}$

$= \dfrac{(y+4)(y+1)(y-2)}{(y+3)(y-1)(y-1)} - \dfrac{2}{y-1}$

$\text{LCD} = (y+3)(y-1)(y-1)$

$= \dfrac{(y+4)(y+1)(y-2)}{(y+3)(y-1)(y-1)}$

$\quad - \dfrac{2(y+3)(y-1)}{(y+3)(y-1)(y-1)}$

$= \dfrac{(y+3)(y+1)((y-2) - 2(y+3)(y-1)}{(y+3)(y-1)(y-1)}$

$= \dfrac{(y+4)(y^2-y-2) - 2(y^2+2y-3)}{(y+3)(y-1)(y-1)}$

$= \dfrac{y^3+3y^2-6y-8 - 2y^2-4y+6}{(y+3)(y-1)(y-1)}$

$= \dfrac{y^3+y^2-10y-2}{(y+3)(y-1)(y-1)}$

103. $\dfrac{4}{x-2} - \boxed{} = \dfrac{2x+8}{(x-2)(x+1)}$

The missing rational expression must have $(x+1)$ as a factor in its denominator or as the complete denominator.

Let $x = $ the numerator of the missing rational expression.

$$\dfrac{4}{x-2} - \dfrac{y}{x+1} = \dfrac{2x+8}{(x-2)(x+1)}$$

Then

$$\dfrac{4(x+1) - y(x-2)}{(x-2)(x+1)} = \dfrac{2x+8}{(x-2)(x+1)},$$

so

$$4x+4 - yx+2y = 2x+8,$$

which implies that

$$4x - yx = 2x$$

and

$$4 + 2y = 8.$$

Both of these equations give $y = 2$.
Thus, the missing rational expression is

$$\dfrac{2}{x+1}.$$

Review Exercises

104. $(3x+5)(2x-7) = 6x^2 - 21x + 10x - 35$
$\qquad\qquad\qquad\quad = 6x^2 - 11x - 35$

105. $3x - y = 3$

$$-y = -3x + 3$$
$$y = 3x - 3$$

Graph $3x - y = 3$ using the x-intercept, 1, and the y-intercept, -3. .

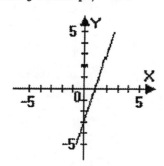

106. Line passing through $(-3, -4)$ and $(1, 0)$
First, find the slope.

$$m = \frac{0 - (-4)}{1 - (-3)} = \frac{4}{4} = 1$$

Use $m = (1, 0)$ and $(x_1, y_1) = (1, 0)$ in the point-slope form and simplify to find the slope-intercept form.

$$y - y_1 = m(x - x_1)$$
$$y - 0 = 1(x - 1)$$
$$y = x - 1$$

Complex Rational Expressions

7.5 CHECK POINTS

CHECK POINT 1

$$\frac{\dfrac{1}{4} + \dfrac{2}{3}}{\dfrac{2}{3} - \dfrac{1}{4}}$$

Step 1 Add to get a single rational expression in the numerator.

$$\frac{1}{4} + \frac{2}{3} = \frac{1}{4} \cdot \frac{3}{3} + \frac{2}{3} \cdot \frac{4}{4}$$
$$= \frac{3}{12} + \frac{8}{11} = \frac{11}{12}$$

Step 2 Subtract to get a single rational expression in the denominator.

$$\frac{2}{3} - \frac{1}{4} = \frac{2}{3} \cdot \frac{4}{4} - \frac{1}{4} \cdot \frac{3}{3}$$
$$= \frac{8}{12} - \frac{3}{12} = \frac{5}{12}$$

Step 3 and 4 Perform the division indicated by the main fraction bar: Invert and multiply. If possible, simplify.

$$\frac{\dfrac{1}{4} + \dfrac{2}{3}}{\dfrac{2}{3} - \dfrac{1}{4}} = \frac{\dfrac{11}{12}}{\dfrac{5}{12}} = \frac{11}{12} \cdot \frac{12}{5} = \frac{11}{5}$$

CHECK POINT 2

$$\frac{2 - \dfrac{1}{x}}{2 + \dfrac{1}{x}}$$

Step 1

$$2 - \frac{1}{x} = \frac{2 \cdot x}{1 \cdot x} - \frac{1}{x} = \frac{2x - 1}{x}$$

Step 2

$$2 + \frac{1}{x} = \frac{2 \cdot x}{1 \cdot x} + \frac{1}{x} = \frac{2x + 1}{x}$$

Step 3 and 4

$$\frac{2 - \dfrac{1}{x}}{2 + \dfrac{1}{x}} = \frac{\dfrac{2x - 1}{x}}{\dfrac{2x + 1}{x}} = \frac{2x - 1}{x} \cdot \frac{x}{2x + 1}$$
$$= \frac{2x - 1}{2x + 1}$$

CHECK POINT 3

$$\frac{\dfrac{1}{x} - \dfrac{1}{y}}{\dfrac{1}{xy}} = \frac{\dfrac{y-x}{xy}}{\dfrac{1}{xy}} = \frac{y-x}{xy} \cdot \frac{xy}{1} = y - x$$

CHECK POINT 4

$$\frac{\dfrac{1}{4} + \dfrac{2}{3}}{\dfrac{2}{3} - \dfrac{1}{4}}$$

$$\text{LCD} = 12$$

$$\frac{\dfrac{1}{4} + \dfrac{2}{3}}{\dfrac{2}{3} - \dfrac{1}{4}} = \frac{12}{12} \cdot \frac{\left(\dfrac{1}{4} + \dfrac{2}{3}\right)}{\left(\dfrac{2}{3} - \dfrac{1}{4}\right)}$$

$$= \frac{12 \cdot \dfrac{1}{4} + 12 \cdot \dfrac{2}{3}}{12 \cdot \dfrac{2}{3} - 12 \cdot \dfrac{1}{4}}$$

$$= \frac{3+8}{8-3} = \frac{11}{5}$$

CHECK POINT 5

$$\frac{2 - \dfrac{1}{x}}{2 + \dfrac{1}{x}}$$

$$\text{LCD} = x$$

$$\frac{2 - \dfrac{1}{x}}{2 + \dfrac{1}{x}} = \frac{x\left(2 - \dfrac{1}{x}\right)}{x\left(2 + \dfrac{1}{x}\right)}$$

$$= \frac{x \cdot 2 - x \cdot \dfrac{1}{x}}{x \cdot 2 + x \cdot \dfrac{1}{x}}$$

$$= \frac{2x - 1}{2x + 1}$$

CHECK POINT 6

$$\frac{\dfrac{1}{x} - \dfrac{1}{y}}{\dfrac{1}{xy}}$$

$$\text{LCD} = xy$$

$$\frac{\dfrac{1}{x} - \dfrac{1}{y}}{\dfrac{1}{xy}} = \frac{xy}{xy} \cdot \frac{\left(\dfrac{1}{x} - \dfrac{1}{y}\right)}{\left(\dfrac{1}{xy}\right)} = \frac{xy \cdot \dfrac{1}{x} - xy \cdot \dfrac{1}{x}}{xy \cdot \dfrac{1}{xy}}$$

$$= \frac{y-x}{1} = y - x$$

EXERCISE SET 7.5

In Exercises 1–39, each complex rational expression can be simlified by either of the two methods introduced in this section of the textbook. Both methods will be illustrated here.

1. $\dfrac{\dfrac{1}{2} + \dfrac{1}{4}}{\dfrac{1}{2} + \dfrac{1}{3}}$

Add to get a single rational expression in the numerator.

$$\frac{1}{2} + \frac{1}{4} = \frac{2}{4} + \frac{1}{4} = \frac{3}{4}$$

Add to get a single rational expression in the denominator.

$$\frac{1}{2} + \frac{1}{3} = \frac{3}{6} + \frac{2}{6} = \frac{5}{6}$$

Perform the division indicated by the fraction bar: Invert and multiply.

$$\frac{\dfrac{1}{2} + \dfrac{1}{4}}{\dfrac{1}{2} + \dfrac{1}{3}} = \frac{\dfrac{3}{4}}{\dfrac{5}{6}} = \frac{3}{\cancel{4}} \cdot \frac{\cancel{6}^{3}}{5} = \frac{9}{10}$$

3. $\dfrac{3+\dfrac{1}{2}}{4-\dfrac{1}{4}}$

$$3+\dfrac{1}{2}=\dfrac{6}{2}+\dfrac{1}{2}=\dfrac{7}{2}$$

$$4-\dfrac{1}{4}=\dfrac{16}{4}-\dfrac{1}{4}=\dfrac{15}{4}$$

$$\dfrac{3+\dfrac{1}{2}}{4-\dfrac{1}{4}}=\dfrac{\dfrac{7}{2}}{\dfrac{15}{4}}=\dfrac{7}{\cancel{2}_{1}}\cdot\dfrac{\cancel{4}^{2}}{15}=\dfrac{14}{15}$$

5. $\dfrac{\dfrac{2}{5}-\dfrac{1}{3}}{\dfrac{2}{3}-\dfrac{3}{4}}$

LCD $=60$

$$\dfrac{\dfrac{2}{5}-\dfrac{1}{3}}{\dfrac{2}{3}-\dfrac{3}{4}}=\dfrac{60}{60}\cdot\dfrac{\left(\dfrac{2}{5}-\dfrac{1}{3}\right)}{\left(\dfrac{2}{3}-\dfrac{3}{4}\right)}$$

$$=\dfrac{60\cdot\dfrac{2}{5}-60\cdot\dfrac{1}{3}}{60\cdot\dfrac{2}{3}-60\cdot\dfrac{3}{4}}$$

$$=\dfrac{24-20}{40-45}$$

$$=\dfrac{4}{-5}=-\dfrac{4}{5}$$

7. $\dfrac{\dfrac{3}{4}-x}{\dfrac{3}{4}+x}=\dfrac{\dfrac{3}{4}-\dfrac{4x}{x}}{\dfrac{3}{4}+\dfrac{4x}{x}}$

$$=\dfrac{\dfrac{3-4x}{4}}{\dfrac{3+4x}{4}}$$

$$=\dfrac{3-4x}{4}\cdot\dfrac{4}{3+4x}$$

$$=\dfrac{3-4x}{3+4x}$$

9. $\dfrac{5-\dfrac{2}{x}}{3+\dfrac{1}{x}}=\dfrac{\dfrac{5x-2}{x}}{\dfrac{3x+1}{x}}=\dfrac{5x-2}{x}\cdot\dfrac{x}{3x+1}$

$$=\dfrac{5x-2}{3x+1}$$

11. $\dfrac{2+\dfrac{3}{7}}{1-\dfrac{7}{y}}=\dfrac{\dfrac{2y+3}{y}}{\dfrac{y-7}{y}}$

$$=\dfrac{2y+3}{y}\cdot\dfrac{y}{y-7}$$

$$=\dfrac{2y+3}{y-7}$$

13. $\dfrac{\dfrac{1}{y}-\dfrac{3}{2}}{\dfrac{1}{y}+\dfrac{3}{4}}=\dfrac{\dfrac{2-3y}{2y}}{\dfrac{4+3y}{4y}}$

$$=\dfrac{2-3y}{2y}\cdot\dfrac{4y}{4+3y}$$

$$=\dfrac{2(2-3y)}{4+3y}=\dfrac{4-6y}{4+3y}$$

15. $\dfrac{\dfrac{x}{5}-\dfrac{5}{x}}{\dfrac{1}{5}+\dfrac{1}{x}}$

LCD $=5x$

$$\dfrac{\dfrac{x}{5}-\dfrac{5}{x}}{\dfrac{1}{5}+\dfrac{1}{x}}=\dfrac{5x}{5x}\cdot\dfrac{\left(\dfrac{x}{5}-\dfrac{5}{x}\right)}{\left(\dfrac{1}{5}+\dfrac{1}{x}\right)}$$

$$=\dfrac{5x\cdot\dfrac{x}{5}-5x\cdot\dfrac{5}{x}}{5x\cdot\dfrac{1}{5}+5x\cdot\dfrac{1}{x}}$$

$$=\dfrac{x^2-25}{x+5}$$

$$=\dfrac{(x+5)(x-5)}{x+5}=x-5$$

17. $\dfrac{1+\dfrac{1}{x}}{1-\dfrac{1}{x^2}} = \dfrac{\dfrac{x+1}{x}}{\dfrac{x^2-1}{x^2}}$

$\qquad = \dfrac{x+1}{x}\cdot\dfrac{x}{x^2-1}$

$\qquad = \dfrac{x+1}{x}\cdot\dfrac{x^2}{(x+1)(x-1)}$

$\qquad = \dfrac{x}{x-1}$

19. $\dfrac{\dfrac{1}{7}-\dfrac{1}{y}}{\dfrac{7-y}{7}}$

$\text{LCD} = 7y$

$\dfrac{\dfrac{1}{7}-\dfrac{1}{y}}{\dfrac{7-y}{7}} = \dfrac{7y}{7y}\cdot\dfrac{\left(\dfrac{1}{7}-\dfrac{1}{y}\right)}{\left(\dfrac{7-y}{7}\right)}$

$\qquad = \dfrac{7y\left(\dfrac{1}{7}\right)-7y\left(\dfrac{1}{y}\right)}{7y\left(\dfrac{7-y}{7}\right)}$

$\qquad = \dfrac{y-7}{y(7-y)}$

$\qquad = \dfrac{-1(7-y)}{y(7-y)} = -\dfrac{1}{y}$

21. $\dfrac{x+\dfrac{1}{y}}{\dfrac{x}{y}} = \dfrac{\dfrac{xy+1}{y}}{\dfrac{x}{y}}$

$\qquad = \dfrac{xy+1}{y}\cdot\dfrac{y}{x}$

$\qquad = \dfrac{xy+1}{x}$

23. $\dfrac{\dfrac{1}{x}+\dfrac{1}{y}}{xy}$

$\text{LCD} = xy$

$\dfrac{\dfrac{1}{x}+\dfrac{1}{y}}{xy} = \dfrac{xy}{xy}\cdot\dfrac{\left(\dfrac{1}{x}+\dfrac{1}{y}\right)}{(xy)} = \dfrac{y+x}{x^2y^2}$

25. $\dfrac{\dfrac{x}{y}+\dfrac{1}{x}}{\dfrac{y}{x}+\dfrac{1}{x}} = \dfrac{\dfrac{x^2+y}{xy}}{\dfrac{y+1}{x}} = \dfrac{x^2+y}{xy}\cdot\dfrac{x}{y+1}$

$\qquad = \dfrac{x^2+y}{y(y+1)}$

27. $\dfrac{\dfrac{1}{y}+\dfrac{2}{y^2}}{\dfrac{2}{y}+1}$

$\text{LCD} = y^2$

$\dfrac{\dfrac{1}{y}+\dfrac{2}{y^2}}{\dfrac{2}{y}+1} = \dfrac{y^2}{y^2}\cdot\dfrac{\left(\dfrac{1}{y}+\dfrac{2}{y^2}\right)}{\left(\dfrac{2}{y}+1\right)}$

$\qquad = \dfrac{y^2\left(\dfrac{1}{y}\right)+y^2\left(\dfrac{2}{y^2}\right)}{y^2\left(\dfrac{2}{y}\right)+y^2(1)}$

$\qquad = \dfrac{y+2}{2y+y^2}$

$\qquad = \dfrac{(y+2)}{y(2+y)} = \dfrac{1}{y}$

29. $\dfrac{\dfrac{12}{x^2}-\dfrac{3}{x}}{\dfrac{15}{x}-\dfrac{9}{x^2}} = \dfrac{\dfrac{12}{x^2}-\dfrac{3x}{x^2}}{\dfrac{15x}{x^2}-\dfrac{9}{x^2}} = \dfrac{\dfrac{12-3x}{x^2}}{\dfrac{15x-9}{x^2}}$

$\qquad = \dfrac{12-3x}{x^2}\cdot\dfrac{x^2}{15x-9} = \dfrac{12-3x}{15x-9}$

$\qquad = \dfrac{3(4-x)}{3(5x-3)} = \dfrac{4-x}{5x-3}$

31. $\dfrac{2+\dfrac{6}{y}}{1-\dfrac{9}{y^2}}$

$\text{LCD} = y^2$

$$\dfrac{2+\dfrac{6}{y}}{1-\dfrac{9}{y^2}} = \dfrac{y^2}{y^2}\cdot\dfrac{\left(2+\dfrac{6}{y}\right)}{\left(1-\dfrac{9}{y^2}\right)}$$

$$= \dfrac{2y^2+6y}{y^2-9}$$

$$= \dfrac{2y(y+3)}{(y+3)(y-3)}$$

$$= \dfrac{2y}{y-3}$$

33. $\dfrac{\dfrac{1}{x+2}}{1+\dfrac{1}{x+2}}$

$\text{LCD} = x+2$

$$\dfrac{\dfrac{1}{x+2}}{1+\dfrac{1}{x+2}} = \dfrac{x+2}{x+2}\cdot\dfrac{\left(\dfrac{1}{x+2}\right)}{\left(1+\dfrac{1}{x+2}\right)}$$

$$= \dfrac{1}{x+2+1} = \dfrac{1}{x+3}$$

35. $\dfrac{x-5+\dfrac{3}{x}}{x-7+\dfrac{2}{x}}$

$\text{LCD} = x$

$$\dfrac{x-5+\dfrac{3}{x}}{x-7+\dfrac{2}{x}} = \dfrac{x}{x}\cdot\dfrac{\left(x-5+\dfrac{3}{x}\right)}{\left(x-7+\dfrac{2}{x}\right)}$$

$$= \dfrac{x^2-5x+3}{x^2-7x+2}$$

37. $\dfrac{\dfrac{3}{xy^2}+\dfrac{2}{x^2y}}{\dfrac{1}{x^2y}+\dfrac{2}{xy^3}} = \dfrac{\dfrac{3x}{x^2y^2}+\dfrac{2y}{x^2y^2}}{\dfrac{y^2}{x^2y^3}+\dfrac{2x}{x^2y^3}}$

$$= \dfrac{\dfrac{3x+2y}{x^2y^2}}{\dfrac{y^2+2x}{x^2+y^3}}$$

$$= \dfrac{3x+2y}{x^2y^2}\cdot\dfrac{x^2y^3}{y^2+2x}$$

$$= \dfrac{(3x+2y)(y)}{y^2+2x}$$

$$= \dfrac{3xy+2y^2}{y^2+2x}$$

39. $\dfrac{\dfrac{3}{x+1}-\dfrac{3}{x-1}}{\dfrac{5}{x^2-1}}$

$$= \dfrac{\dfrac{3(x-1)-3(x+1)}{(x+1)(x-1)}}{\dfrac{5}{x^2-1}}$$

$$= \dfrac{\dfrac{3x-3-3x-3}{(x+1)(x-1)}}{\dfrac{5}{x^2-1}}$$

$$= \dfrac{\dfrac{-6}{(x+1)(x-1)}}{\dfrac{5}{x^2-1}}$$

$$= \dfrac{-6}{(x+1)(x-1)}\cdot\dfrac{x^2-1}{5}$$

$$= \dfrac{-6}{(x+1)(x-1)}\cdot\dfrac{(x+1)(x-1)}{5}$$

$$= -\dfrac{6}{5}$$

41. $\dfrac{2d}{\dfrac{d}{r_1}+\dfrac{d}{r_2}}$

LCD $= r_1 r_2$

$$\dfrac{2d}{\dfrac{d}{r_1}+\dfrac{d}{r_2}} = \dfrac{r_1 r_2}{r_1 r_2}\cdot\dfrac{2d}{\left(\dfrac{d}{r_1}+\dfrac{d}{r_2}\right)}$$

$$= \dfrac{2r_1 r_2 d}{r_2 d + r_1 d}$$

If $r_1 = 40$ and $r_2 = 30$, the value of this expression will be

$$\dfrac{2\cdot 40\cdot 30\cdot d}{30d+40d} = \dfrac{2400d}{70d}$$

$$= \dfrac{240}{7}$$

$$= 34\tfrac{2}{7}.$$

Your average speed will be $34\tfrac{2}{7}$ miles per hour.

For Exercises 43–45, answers may vary.

47. Simplify the given complex fraction

LCD $= x^6$

$$\dfrac{x^6}{x^6}\cdot\dfrac{\left(\dfrac{1}{x}+\dfrac{1}{x^2}+\dfrac{1}{x^3}\right)}{\left(\dfrac{1}{x^4}+\dfrac{1}{x^5}+\dfrac{1}{x^6}\right)}$$

$$= \dfrac{\dfrac{x^6}{x}+\dfrac{x^6}{x^2}+\dfrac{x^6}{x^3}}{\dfrac{x^6}{x^4}+\dfrac{x^6}{x^5}+\dfrac{x^6}{x^6}}$$

$$= \dfrac{x^5+x^4+x^3}{x^2+x+1}$$

$$= \dfrac{x^3(x^2+x+1)}{x^3}$$

$$= x^3$$

Because the rational expression can be simplified to x^3, this is what it does it each number x: It cubes x.

49. $\dfrac{1+\dfrac{1}{y}-\dfrac{6}{y^2}}{1-\dfrac{5}{y}+\dfrac{6}{y^2}} - \dfrac{1-\dfrac{1}{y}}{1-\dfrac{2}{y}-\dfrac{3}{y^2}}$

Simplify the first complex rational expression using by the LCD method.

$$\dfrac{y^2}{y^2}\cdot\dfrac{\left(1+\dfrac{1}{y}-\dfrac{6}{y^2}\right)}{\left(1-\dfrac{5}{y}+\dfrac{6}{y^2}\right)} = \dfrac{y^2+y-6}{y^2-5y+6}$$

Simplify the second complex algebraic expression by the LCD method.

$$\dfrac{y^2}{y^2}\cdot\dfrac{\left(1-\dfrac{1}{y}\right)}{\left(1-\dfrac{2}{y}-\dfrac{3}{y^2}\right)} = \dfrac{y^2-y}{y^2-2y-3}$$

Now subtract.

$$\dfrac{y^2+y-6}{y^2-5y+6} - \dfrac{y^2-y}{y^2-2y-3}$$

$$= \dfrac{y^2+y-6}{(y-2)(y-3)} - \dfrac{y^2-y}{(y-3)(y+1)}$$

$$= \dfrac{(y-2)(y+3)}{(y-2)(y-3)} - \dfrac{y^2-y}{(y-3)(y+1)}$$

$$= \dfrac{y+3}{y-3} - \dfrac{y^2-y}{(y-3)(y+1)}$$

LCD $= (y-3)(y+1)$

$$= \dfrac{(y+3)(y+1)}{(y-3)(y+1)} - \dfrac{y^2-y}{(y-3)(y+1)}$$

$$= \dfrac{(y+3)(y+1)-(y^2-y)}{(y-3)(y+1)}$$

$$= \dfrac{(y^2+4y+3)-(y^2-y)}{(y-3)(y+1)}$$

$$= \dfrac{y^2+4y+3-y^2+y}{(y-3)(y+1)}$$

$$= \dfrac{5y+3}{(y-3)(y+1)}$$

51.

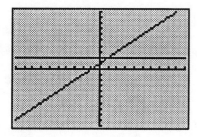

The graphs do not coincide.

$$\frac{\frac{1}{x}+1}{\frac{1}{x}} = \frac{\frac{1}{x}+\frac{x}{x}}{\frac{1}{x}} = \frac{\frac{1+x}{x}}{\frac{1}{x}}$$

$$= \frac{1+x}{x} \cdot \frac{x}{1} = 1+x$$

Change the expression on the right to $1+x$.

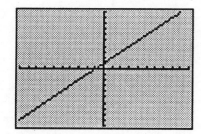

Review Exercises

53. $2x^3 - 20x^2 + 50x = 2x(x^2 - 10x + 25)$
$$= 2x(x-5)^2$$

54. $2 - 3(x-2) = 5(x+5) - 1$
$$2 - 3x + 6 = 5x + 25 - 1$$
$$8 - 3x = 5x + 24$$
$$8 - 3x - 5x = 5x + 24 - 5x$$
$$8 - 8x = 24$$
$$8 - 8x - 8 = 24 - 8$$
$$-8x = 16$$
$$\frac{-8x}{-8} = \frac{16}{-8}$$
$$x = -2$$

The solution is -2.

55. $(x+y)(x^2 - xy + y^2)$
$$= x(x^2 - xy + y^2) + y(x^2 - xy + y^2)$$
$$= x^3 - x^2y + xy^2 + x^2y - xy^2 + y^3$$
$$= x^3 + y^3$$

Solving Rational Equations

7.6 CHECK POINTS

CHECK POINT 1

$$\frac{x}{6} = \frac{1}{6} + \frac{x}{8}$$

The LCD is 24. To clear the equation of fractions, multiply both sides by 24.

$$\frac{x}{6} = \frac{1}{6} + \frac{x}{8}$$
$$24\left(\frac{x}{6}\right) = 24\left(\frac{1}{6} + \frac{x}{8}\right)$$
$$24 \cdot \frac{x}{6} = 24 \cdot \frac{1}{6} + 24 \cdot \frac{x}{8}$$
$$4x = 4 + 3x$$
$$x = 4$$

Check by substituting 4 for x in the original equation:

$$\frac{x}{6} = \frac{1}{6} + \frac{x}{8}$$
$$\frac{4}{6} \overset{?}{=} \frac{1}{6} + \frac{4}{8}$$
$$\frac{4}{6} \overset{?}{=} \frac{1}{6} + \frac{1}{2}$$
$$\frac{4}{6} \overset{?}{=} \frac{1}{6} + \frac{3}{6}$$
$$\frac{4}{6} = \frac{4}{6} \text{ true}$$

The solution is 4.

CHECK POINT 2

$$\frac{5}{2x} = \frac{17}{18} - \frac{1}{3x}$$

The denominators are $2x, 18$, and $3x$, so the LCD is $18x$. In this equation, x cannot equal zero because that would make two of the denominator equal to zero.

$$\frac{5}{2x} = \frac{17}{18} - \frac{1}{3x}, x \neq 0$$

$$18x \cdot \frac{5}{2x} = 18x \left(\frac{17}{18} - \frac{1}{3x} \right)$$

$$18x \cdot \frac{5}{2x} = 18x \cdot \frac{17}{18} - 18x \cdot \frac{1}{3x}$$

$$45 = 17x - 6$$

$$51 = 17x$$

$$3 = x$$

Check by substituting 3 for x in the original equation. Note that the original restriction that $x \neq 0$ is met. The solution is 3.

CHECK POINT 3

$$x + \frac{6}{x} = -5$$

Step 1 List restrictions on the variable. The restriction is $x \neq 0$.

Step 2 Multiply both sides by the LCD. The LCD is x.

$$x + \frac{6}{x} = -5, x \neq 0$$

$$x \left(x + \frac{6}{x} \right) = x(-5)$$

$$x \cdot x + x \cdot \frac{6}{x} = x(-5)$$

$$x^2 + 6 = -5x$$

Step 3 Solve the resulting equation.

$$x^2 + 5x + 6 = 0$$

$$(x + 3)(x + 2) = 0$$

$$x + 3 = 0 \quad \text{or} \quad x + 2 = 0$$

$$x = -3 \qquad x = -2$$

Step 4 Check proposed solutions in the original equation.

The proposed solutions, -3 and -2, are not part of the restriction that $x \neq 0$.

Check -3:

$$x + \frac{6}{x} = -5$$

$$-3 + \frac{6}{-3} \overset{?}{=} -5$$

$$-3 - 2 \overset{?}{=} -5$$

$$-5 = -5 \text{ true}$$

Check -2:

$$x + \frac{6}{x} = -5$$

$$-2 + \frac{6}{-2} \overset{?}{=} -5$$

$$-3 + (-2) \overset{?}{=} -5$$

$$-5 = -5 \text{ true}$$

The solutions are -3 and -2.

CHECK POINT 4

$$\frac{11}{x^2 - 25} + \frac{4}{x + 5} = \frac{3}{x - 5}$$

Factor the first denominator.

$$\frac{11}{(x + 5)(x - 5)} + \frac{4}{x + 5} = \frac{3}{x - 5}$$

The restrictions are $x \neq -5, x \neq 5$. The LCD is $(x + 5)(x - 5)$.

$$(x + 5)(x - 5) \left[\frac{11}{(x + 5)(x - 5)} + \frac{4}{x + 5} \right]$$

$$= (x + 5)(x - 5) \cdot \frac{3}{x - 5}$$

$$11 + 4(x - 5) = (x + 5) \cdot 3$$

$$11 + 4x - 20 = 3x + 15$$

$$4x - 9 = 3x + 15$$

$$x - 9 = 15$$

$$x = 24$$

The proposed solution, 24, is not part of the restriction that $x \neq -5, x \neq 5$. Substitute 24 for x in the given equation to verify that 24 is the solutions.

CHECK POINT 5

$$\frac{x}{x-3} = \frac{3}{x-3} + 9$$

The restriction is $x \neq 3$.
The LCD is $x - 3$.

$$\frac{x}{x-3} = \frac{3}{x-3} + 9, x \neq 3$$
$$(x-3)\cdot\frac{x}{x-3} = (x-3)\left(\frac{3}{x-3} + 9\right)$$
$$(x-3)\cdot\frac{x}{x-3} = (x-3)\cdot\frac{3}{x-3}$$
$$+ (x-3)\cdot 9$$
$$x = 3 + 9x - 27$$
$$-8x = -24$$
$$x = 3$$

The proposed solution, 3, is *not* a solution because of the restriction $x \neq 3$. Notice that 3 makes two of the denominators zero in the original equation. Therefore, this equation has no solution.

CHECK POINT 6

$$y = \frac{250x}{100-x}; y = 750$$

$$750 = \frac{250x}{100-x}$$
$$(100-x)(750) = (100-x)\cdot\frac{250x}{100-x}$$
$$75{,}000 - 750x = 250x$$
$$75{,}000 = 1000x$$
$$75 = x$$

If the government spends \$750 million, 75% of the pollutants can be removed.

EXERCISE SET 7.6

In Exercises 1–43, all proposed solutions that are on the list of restrictions on the variable should be rejected and all other proposed solutions should be checked in the original equation. Checks will not be shown here.

1. $\frac{x}{3} = \frac{x}{2} - 2$

There are no restrictions on the variable because the variable does not appear in any denominator.
The LCD is 6.

$$\frac{x}{3} = \frac{x}{2} - 2$$
$$6\left(\frac{x}{3}\right) = 6\left(\frac{x}{2} - 2\right)$$
$$6\cdot\frac{x}{3} = 6\cdot\frac{x}{2} - 6\cdot 2$$
$$2x = 3x - 12$$
$$0 = x - 12$$
$$12 = x$$

The solution is 12.

3. $\frac{4x}{3} = \frac{x}{18} - \frac{x}{6}$

There are no restrictions.
The LCD is 18.

$$\frac{4x}{3} = \frac{x}{18} - \frac{x}{6}$$
$$18\left(\frac{4x}{3}\right) = 18\left(\frac{x}{18} - \frac{x}{6}\right)$$
$$18\cdot\frac{4x}{3} = 18\cdot\frac{x}{18} - 18\cdot\frac{x}{6}$$
$$24x = x - 3x$$
$$24x = -2x$$
$$26x = 0$$
$$x = 0$$

The solution is 0.

5. $2 - \dfrac{8}{x} = 6$

The restriction is $x \neq 0$.

The LCD is x.

$$2 - \frac{8}{x} = 6$$

$$x\left(2 - \frac{8}{x}\right) = x \cdot 6$$

$$x \cdot 2 - x \cdot \frac{8}{x} = x \cdot 6$$

$$2x - 8 = 6x$$

$$-8 = 4x$$

$$-2 = x$$

The solution is -2.

7. $\dfrac{4}{x} + \dfrac{1}{2} = \dfrac{5}{x}$

The restriction is $x \neq 0$.

The LCD is $2x$.

$$\frac{4}{x} + \frac{1}{2} = \frac{5}{x}$$

$$2x\left(\frac{4}{x} + \frac{1}{2}\right) = 2x\left(\frac{5}{x}\right)$$

$$2x \cdot \frac{4}{x} + 2x \cdot \frac{1}{2} = 2x \cdot \frac{5}{x}$$

$$8 + x = 10$$

$$x = 2$$

The solution is 2.

9. $\dfrac{2}{x} + 3 = \dfrac{5}{2x} + \dfrac{13}{4}$

The restriction is $x \neq 0$.

The LCD is $4x$.

$$\frac{2}{x} + 3 = \frac{5}{2x} + \frac{13}{4}$$

$$4x\left(\frac{2}{x} + 3\right) = 4x\left(\frac{5}{2x} + \frac{13}{4}\right)$$

$$8 + 12x = 10 + 13x$$

$$8 = 10 + x$$

$$-2 = x$$

The solution is -2.

11. $\dfrac{2}{3x} + \dfrac{1}{4} = \dfrac{11}{6x} - \dfrac{1}{3}$

The restriction is $x \neq 0$.

The LCD is $12x$.

$$\frac{2}{3x} + \frac{1}{4} = \frac{11}{6x} - \frac{1}{3}$$

$$12\left(\frac{2}{3x} + \frac{1}{4}\right) = 12x\left(\frac{11}{6x} - \frac{1}{3}\right)$$

$$8 + 3x = 22 - 4x$$

$$8 + 7x = 22$$

$$7x = 14$$

$$x = 2$$

The solution is 2.

13. $\dfrac{6}{x+3} = \dfrac{4}{x-3}$

Restrictions: $x \neq -3, x \neq 3$

$\text{LCD} = (x+3)(x-3)$

$$\frac{6}{x+3} = \frac{4}{x-3}$$

$$(x-3)(x-3) \cdot \frac{6}{x+3} = (x+3)(x-3) \cdot \frac{4}{x-3}$$

$$(x-3) \cdot 6 = (x+3) \cdot 4$$

$$6x - 18 = 4x + 12$$

$$2x - 18 = 12$$

$$2x = 30$$

$$x = 15$$

The solution is 15.

15. $\dfrac{x-2}{2x} + 1 = \dfrac{x+1}{x}$

Restriction: $x \neq 0$

$\text{LCD} = 2x$

$$\frac{x-2}{2x} + 1 = \frac{x+1}{x}$$

$$2x\left(\frac{x-2}{2x} + 1\right) = 2x\left(\frac{x+1}{x}\right)$$

$$x - 2 + 2x = 2(x+1)$$

$$3x - 2 = 2x + 2$$

$$x - 2 = 2$$

$$x = 4$$

The solution is 4.

17. $x + \dfrac{6}{x} = -7$

Restriction: $x \neq 0$
LCD $= x$

$$x + \frac{6}{x} = -7$$

$$x\left(x + \frac{6}{x}\right) = x(-7)$$

$$x^2 + 6 = -7x$$

$$x^2 + 7x + 6 = 0$$

$$(x + 6)(x + 1) = 0$$

$$x + 6 = 0 \quad \text{or} \quad x + 1 = 0$$

$$x = -6 \qquad\qquad x = -1$$

The solutions are -6 and -1.

19. $\dfrac{x}{5} - \dfrac{5}{x} = 0$

Restriction: $x \neq 0$
LCD $= 5x$

$$\frac{x}{5} - \frac{5}{x} = 0$$

$$5x\left(\frac{x}{5} - \frac{5}{x}\right) = 5x \cdot 0$$

$$5x \cdot \frac{x}{5} - 5x \cdot \frac{5}{x} = 0$$

$$x^2 - 25 = 0$$

$$(x + 5)(x - 5) = 0$$

$$x + 5 = 0 \quad \text{or} \quad x - 5 = 0$$

$$x = -5 \qquad\qquad x = 5$$

The solutions are -5 and 5.

21. $x + \dfrac{3}{x} = \dfrac{12}{x}$

Restriction: $x \neq 0$
LCD $= x$

$$x + \frac{3}{x} = \frac{12}{x}$$

$$x\left(x + \frac{3}{x}\right) = x\left(\frac{12}{x}\right)$$

$$x^2 + 3 = 12$$

$$x^2 - 9 = 0$$

$$(x + 3)(x - 3) = 0$$

$$x + 3 = 0 \quad \text{or} \quad x - 3 = 0$$

$$x = -3 \qquad\qquad x = 3$$

The solutions are -3 and 3.

23. $\dfrac{4}{y} - \dfrac{y}{2} = \dfrac{7}{2}$

Restrictions: $y \neq 0$
LCD $= 2y$

$$\frac{4}{y} - \frac{y}{2} = \frac{7}{2}$$

$$2y\left(\frac{4}{y} - \frac{y}{2}\right) = 2y\left(\frac{7}{2}\right)$$

$$8 - y^2 = 7y$$

$$0 = y^2 + 7y - 8$$

$$0 = (y + 8)(y - 1)$$

$$y + 8 = 0 \quad \text{or} \quad y - 1 = 0$$

$$y = -8 \qquad\qquad y = 1$$

The solutions are -8 and 1.

25. $\dfrac{x - 4}{x} = \dfrac{15}{x + 4}$

Restrictions: $x \neq 0, x \neq -4$
LCD $= x(x + 4)$

$$\frac{x - 4}{x} = \frac{15}{x + 4}$$

$$x(x + 4)\left(\frac{x - 4}{x}\right) = x(x + 4)\left(\frac{15}{x + 4}\right)$$

$$(x + 4)(x - 4) = x \cdot 15$$

$$x^2 - 16 = 15x$$

$$x^2 - 15x - 16 = 0$$

$$(x + 1)(x - 16) = 0$$

$$x + 1 = 0 \quad \text{or} \quad x - 16 = 0$$
$$x = -1 \qquad\qquad x = 16$$

The solutions are -1 and 16.

27. $\dfrac{1}{x-1} + 5 = \dfrac{11}{x-1}$

Restriction: $x \neq 1$
LCD $= x - 1$

$$\frac{1}{x-1} + 5 = \frac{11}{x-1}$$
$$(x-1)\left(\frac{1}{x-1} + 5\right) = (x-1)\left(\frac{11}{x-1}\right)$$
$$1 + (x-1)\cdot 5 = 11$$
$$1 + 5x - 5 = 11$$
$$5x - 4 = 11$$
$$5x = 15$$
$$x = 3$$

The solution is 3.

29. $\dfrac{8y}{y+1} = 4 - \dfrac{8}{y+1}$

Restriction: $y \neq -1$
LCD $= y + 1$

$$\frac{8y}{y+1} = 4 - \frac{8}{y+1}$$
$$(y+1)\left(\frac{8y}{y+1}\right) = (y+1)\left(4 - \frac{8}{y+1}\right)$$
$$8y = (y+1)\cdot 4 - 8$$
$$8y = 4y + 4 - 8$$
$$8y = 4y - 4$$
$$4y = -4$$
$$y = -1$$

The proposed solution, -1, is a solution because of the restriction $x \neq -1$. Notice that -1 makes two of the denominators zero in the original equation. Therefore, the equation has no solution.

31. $\dfrac{3}{x-1} + \dfrac{8}{x} = 3$

Restrictions: $x \neq 1, x \neq 0$
LCD $= x(x-1)$

$$\frac{3}{x-1} + \frac{8}{x} = 3$$
$$x(x-1)\left(\frac{3}{x-1} + \frac{8}{x}\right) = x(x-1)\cdot 3$$
$$x(x-1)\cdot\frac{3}{x-1} + x(x-1)\cdot\frac{8}{x} = 3x(x-1)$$
$$3x + 8(x-1) = 3x^2 - 3x$$
$$3x + 8x - 8 = 3x^2 - 3x$$
$$11x - 8 = 3x^2 - 3x$$
$$0 = 3x^2 - 14x + 8$$
$$0 = (3x - 2)(x - 4)$$

$$0 = 3x - 2 \text{ or } x - 4 = 0$$
$$3x - 2 = 0 \quad \text{or} \quad x - 4 = 0$$
$$3x = 2 \qquad\qquad x = 4$$
$$x = \frac{2}{3}$$

The solutions are $\frac{2}{3}$ and 4.

33. $\dfrac{3y}{y-4} - 5 = \dfrac{12}{y-4}$

Restriction: $y \neq 4$
LCD $= y - 4$

$$\frac{3y}{y-4} - 5 = \frac{12}{y-4}$$
$$(y-4)\left(\frac{3y}{y-4} - 5\right) = (y-4)\left(\frac{12}{y-4}\right)$$
$$3y - 5(y-4) = 12$$
$$3y - 5y + 20 = 12$$
$$-2y + 20 = 12$$
$$-2y = -8$$
$$y = 4$$

The proposed solution, 4, is *not* a solution because of the restriction $y \neq 4$. Therefore, equation has no solution.

35. $\dfrac{1}{x} + \dfrac{1}{x-3} = \dfrac{x-2}{x-3}$

Restrictions: $x \neq 0, x \neq 3$

LCD $= x(x-3)$

$$\dfrac{1}{x} + \dfrac{1}{x-3} = \dfrac{x-2}{x-3}$$

$$x(x-3)\left(\dfrac{1}{x} + \dfrac{1}{x-3}\right) = x(x-3)\cdot\dfrac{x-2}{x-3}$$

$$x-3+x = x(x-2)$$
$$2x-3 = x^2 - 2x$$
$$0 = x^2 - 4x + 3$$
$$0 = (x-3)(x-1)$$
$$x - 3 = 0 \quad \text{or} \quad x - 1 = 0$$
$$x = 3 \qquad\qquad x = 1$$

The proposed solution 3 is *not* a solution because of the restriction $x \neq -3$.
The proposed solution 1 checks in the original equation.
The solution is 1.

37. $\dfrac{x+1}{3x+9} + \dfrac{x}{2x+6} = \dfrac{2}{4x+12}$

To find any restrictions and the LCD, factor the denominators.

$$\dfrac{x+1}{3(x+3)} + \dfrac{x}{2(x+3)} = \dfrac{2}{4(x+3)}$$

Restriction: $x \neq -3$

LCD $= 12(x+3)$

$$12(x+3)\left[\dfrac{x+1}{3(x+3)} + \dfrac{x}{2(x+3)}\right]$$

$$= 12(x+3)\left[\dfrac{2}{4(x+3)}\right]$$

$$4(x+1) + 6x = 6$$
$$4x + 4 + 6x = 6$$
$$10x + 4 = 6$$
$$10x = 2$$
$$x = \dfrac{2}{10} = \dfrac{1}{5}$$

The solution is $\frac{1}{5}$.

39. $\dfrac{4y}{y^2 - 25} + \dfrac{2}{y-5} = \dfrac{1}{y+5}$

To find any restrictions and the LCD, factor the first denominator.

$$\dfrac{4y}{(y+5)(y-5)} + \dfrac{2}{y-5} = \dfrac{1}{y+5}$$

Restrictions: $y \neq -5, y \neq 5$

LCD $= (y+5)(y-5)$

$$(y+5)(y-5)\left[\dfrac{4y}{(y+5)(y-5)} + \dfrac{2}{y-5}\right]$$

$$= (y+5)(y-5)\cdot\dfrac{1}{y+5}$$

$$4y + 2(y+5) = y - 5$$
$$4y + 2y + 10 = y - 5$$
$$6y + 10 = y - 5$$
$$5y + 10 = -5$$
$$5y = -15$$
$$y = -3$$

The solution is -3.

41. $\dfrac{1}{x-4} - \dfrac{5}{x+2} = \dfrac{6}{x^2 - 2x - 8}$

Factor the last denominator.

$$\dfrac{1}{x-4} - \dfrac{5}{x+2} = \dfrac{6}{(x-4)(x+2)}$$

Restrictions: $x \neq 4, x \neq -2$

LCD $= (x-4)(x+2)$

$$(x-4)(x+2)\left[\dfrac{1}{x-4} - \dfrac{5}{x+2}\right]$$

$$= (x-4)(x+2)\left[\dfrac{6}{(x-4)(x+2)}\right]$$

$$(x+2)\cdot 1 - (x-4)\cdot 5 = 6$$
$$x + 2 - 5x + 20 = 6$$
$$-4x + 22 = 6$$
$$-4x = -16$$
$$x = 4$$

The proposed solution 4 is *not* a solution because of the restriction $x \neq 4$. Therefore, the given equation has no solution.

43. $\dfrac{2}{x+3} - \dfrac{2x+3}{x-1} = \dfrac{6x-5}{x^2+2x-3}$

Factor the last denominator.

$$\dfrac{2}{x+3} - \dfrac{2x+3}{x-1} = \dfrac{6x-5}{(x+3)(x-1)}$$

Restrictions: $x \neq -3, x \neq 1$
LCD $= (x+3)(x-1)$

$$(x+3)(x-1)\left[\dfrac{2}{x+3} - \dfrac{2x+3}{x-1}\right]$$

$$= (x+3)(x-1)\left[\dfrac{6x-5}{(x+3)(x-1)}\right]$$

$$(x-1)\cdot 2 - (x+3)(2x+3) = 6x-5$$
$$2x-2-(2x^2+9x+9) = 6x-5$$
$$2x-2-2x^2-9x-9 = 6x-5$$
$$-2x^2-7x-11 = 6x-5$$
$$0 = 2x^2+13x+6$$
$$0 = (x+6)(2x+1)$$

$$x+6=0 \quad \text{or} \quad 2x+1=0$$
$$x=-6 \qquad\qquad 2x=-1$$
$$x=-\dfrac{1}{2}$$

The solutions are -6 and $-\frac{1}{2}$.

45. $C = \dfrac{400x+500,000}{x}; C = 450$

$$450 = \dfrac{400x+500,000}{x}$$

LCD $= x$

$$x\cdot 450 = x\left(\dfrac{400x+500,000}{x}\right)$$

$$450x = 40x + 500,000$$
$$50x = 500,000$$
$$x = 10,000$$

At an average cost of $450 per wheelchair, 10,000 wheelchairs can be produced.

47. $C = \dfrac{2x}{100-x}; C = 2$

$$2 = \dfrac{2x}{100-x}$$

LCD $= 100-x$

$$(100-x)\cdot 2 = (100-x)\cdot\dfrac{2x}{100-x}$$

$$200 - 2x = 2x$$
$$200 = 4x$$
$$50 = x$$

For $2 million, 50% of the contaminants can be removed.

49. $C = \dfrac{DA}{A+12}; C = 300, D = 1000$

$$300 = \dfrac{1000A}{A+12}$$

LCD $= A+12$

$$(A+12)\cdot 300 = (A+12)\left(\dfrac{1000A}{A+12}\right)$$

$$300A + 3600 = 1000A$$
$$3600 = 700A$$
$$\dfrac{3600}{700} = A$$
$$A = \dfrac{36}{7} \approx 5.14$$

To the nearest year, the child is 5 years old.

51. $C = \dfrac{10,000}{x} + 3x; C = 350$

$$350 = \dfrac{10,000}{x} + 3x$$

LCD $= x$

$$x\cdot 350x = x\left(\dfrac{10,000}{x} + 3x\right)$$

$$350x = 10,000 + 3x^2$$
$$0 = 3x^2 - 350x + 10,000$$
$$0 = (3x-200)(x-50)$$

$$3x - 200 = 0 \qquad \text{or} \quad x - 50 = 0$$
$$3x = 200 \qquad\qquad\qquad x = 50$$
$$x = \frac{200}{3}$$
$$= 66\tfrac{2}{3} \approx 67$$

For yearly inventory costs to be \$350, the owner should order either 50 or approximately 67 cases. These solutions correspond to the points $(50, 350)$ and $(67, 350)$ on the graph.

53. Let $x =$ the number of additional hits needed.
After x additional consecutive hits, the player's batting average will be

$$\frac{12 + x}{40 + x},$$

so solve the equation

$$\frac{12 + x}{40 + x} = 0.440.$$

Multiply both sides by the LCD, $40 + x$.

$$(40 + x)\left(\frac{12 + x}{40 + x}\right) = (40 + x)(0.440)$$
$$12 + x = 17.6 + 0.44x$$
$$12 + x - 12 = 17.6 + 0.44x - 12$$
$$x = 5.6 + 0.44x$$
$$x - 0.44x = 5.6 + 0.44x - 0.44x$$
$$0.56 = 5.6$$
$$\frac{0.56x}{0.56} = \frac{5.6}{0.56}$$
$$x = 10$$

The player must get 10 additional consecutive hits to achieve a batting average of 0.440.

For Exercises 55–59, answers may vary.

61. Statement b is true.
The given equation is equivalent to the false statement $1 = 0$, so it has no solution.

63. $f = \dfrac{f_1 f_2}{f_1 + f_2}$ for f_2

$$f = \frac{f_1 f_2}{f_1 + f_2}$$

Multiply both sides by the LCD, $f_1 + f_2$.

$$(f_1 + f_2) \cdot f = (f_1 + f_2)\left(\frac{f_1 f_2}{f_1 + f_2}\right)$$
$$f f_1 + f f_2 = f_1 f_2$$

Get all terms containing f_2 on one side and all terms not containing f_2 on the other side.

$$f f_2 - f_1 f_2 = -f_1 f$$

Factor out the common factor f_2 on the left side.

$$f_2(f - f_1) = -f_1 f$$

Divide both sides by $f - f_1$.

$$\frac{f_2(f - f_1)}{f - f_1} = \frac{-f_1 f}{f - f_1}$$
$$f_2 = \frac{-f_1 f}{f - f_1} \quad \text{or} \quad \frac{f f_1}{f_1 - f}$$

65. $\left(\dfrac{x+1}{x+7}\right)^2 \div \left(\dfrac{x+1}{x+7}\right)^4 = 0$

$$\left(\dfrac{x+1}{x+7}\right)^2 \cdot \left(\dfrac{x+7}{x+1}\right)^4 = 0$$

$$\left(\dfrac{x+1}{x+7}\right)^2 \cdot \dfrac{(x+7)^4}{(x+1)^4} = 0$$

Restrictions: $x \neq -7, x \neq -1$

$$\dfrac{(x+7)^2}{(x+1)^2} = 0$$

Multiply both sides by $(x+1)^2$.

$$(x+1)^2 \left[\dfrac{(x+7)^2}{(x+1)^2}\right] = (x+1)^2 \cdot 0$$

$$(x+7)^2 = 0$$

$$x+7 = 0$$

$$x = -7$$

The proposed solution, -7, *not* a solution of the original equation because it is on the list of restrictions. Therefore, the given equation has no solution.

67. $\dfrac{x}{2} + \dfrac{x}{4} = 6$

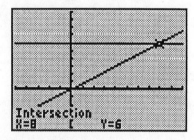

The solution is 8.
Check:

$$\dfrac{x}{2} + \dfrac{x}{4} = 6$$

$$\dfrac{8}{2} + \dfrac{8}{4} \overset{?}{=} 6$$

$$4 + 2 \overset{?}{=} 6$$

$$6 = 6 \text{ true}$$

69. $x + \dfrac{6}{x} = -5$

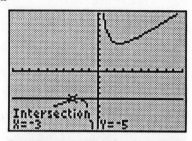

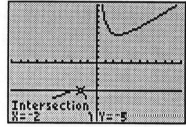

The solutions are -3 and -2.

Check -3:   Check -3:

$$x + \dfrac{6}{x} = -5 \qquad\qquad x + \dfrac{6}{x} = -5$$

$$-3 + \dfrac{6}{-3} \overset{?}{=} -5 \qquad -2 + \dfrac{6}{-2} \overset{?}{=} -5$$

$$-3 + (-2) \overset{?}{=} -5 \qquad -2 + (-3) \overset{?}{=} -5$$

$$-5 = -5 \text{ true} \qquad\qquad -5 = -5 \text{ true}$$

Review Exercises

70. $x^4 + 2x^3 - 3x - 6$

Factor by grouping.

$$x^4 + 2x^3 - 3x - 6 = (x^4 + 2x^3) + (-3x - 6)$$
$$= x^3(x+2) - 3(x+2)$$
$$= (x+2)(x^3 - 3)$$

71. $(3x^2)(-4x^{-10}) = (3 \cdot -4)(x^2 \cdot x^{-10})$
$$= -12x^{2+(-10)} = -12x^{-8}$$
$$= -\dfrac{12}{x^8}$$

72. $-5[4(x-2) - 3] = -5[4x - 8 - 3]$
$$= -5[4x - 11]$$
$$= -20x + 55$$

Applications Using Rational Equations and Proportions

7.7 CHECK POINTS

CHECK POINT 1

Let $\quad x =$ the rate of current.
Then $3 + x =$ the boat's rate with the current
and $\quad 3 - x =$ the boat's rate against the current.

	$d \times$	r	$= t$
With the Current	10	$3 + x$	$\dfrac{10}{3 + x}$
Against the Current	2	$3 - x$	$\dfrac{2}{3 - x}$

The times are equal, so

$$\frac{10}{3 + x} = \frac{2}{3 - x}.$$

Multiply both sides by the LCD, $(3 + x)(3 - x)$.

$$(3 + x)(3 - x) \cdot \frac{10}{3 + x} = (3 + x)(3 - x) \cdot \frac{2}{3 - x}$$
$$10(3 - x) = 2(3 + x)$$
$$30 - 10x = 6 + 2x$$
$$30 = 6 + 12x$$
$$24 = 12x$$
$$2 = x$$

The rate of the current is 2 miles per hour.
Check the proposed solution in the original wording of the problem.

Time to travel 10 miles with the current $= \dfrac{\text{Distance}}{\text{Time}} = \dfrac{10}{3 + 2} = \dfrac{10}{5} = 2$ hours

Time to travel 2 miles against the current $= \dfrac{\text{Distance}}{\text{Time}} = \dfrac{2}{3 - 2} = \dfrac{2}{1} = 2$ hours

The times are the same, which checks with the original conditions of the problem.

CHECK POINT 2

Let $x =$ the time, in hours, for both people to paint the house together.

	Fractional part of job completed in 1 hour	Time working together	Fractional part of job completed in x hours
First Person	$\dfrac{1}{8}$	x	8
Second Person	$\dfrac{1}{4}$	x	$\dfrac{x}{4}$

Working together, the two people complete one whole job, so

$$\frac{x}{8} + \frac{x}{4} = 1.$$

Multiply both sides by the LCD, 8.

$$8\left(\frac{x}{8} + \frac{x}{4}\right) = 8 \cdot 1$$

$$8 \cdot \frac{x}{8} + 8 \cdot \frac{x}{4} = 8$$

$$x + 2x = 8$$

$$3x = 8$$

$$x = \frac{8}{3} = 2\tfrac{2}{3}$$

It will take the two people $2\tfrac{2}{3}$ hours or 2 hours 40 minutes to paint the house working together.

CHECK POINT 3

Let $x =$ the tax on a house assesed at \$112,500.

$$\frac{\text{Tax on \$45,000 house}}{\text{Assessed value (\$45,000)}} = \frac{\text{Tax on \$112,500 house}}{\text{Assessed value (\$112,500)}}$$

$$\frac{\$600}{\$45,000} = \frac{x}{\$112,500}$$

$$\frac{600}{45,000} = \frac{x}{112,500}$$

$$45,000x = (600)(112,500)$$

$$45,000x = 67,500,000$$

$$\frac{45,000x}{45,000} = \frac{67,500,000}{45,000}$$

$$x = 1500$$

The tax on a house with an assessed value of \$112,500 is \$1500.

CHECK POINT 4

Let $x =$ the total number of deer in the refuge.

$$\frac{\text{Original number}}{\text{Total number}} = \frac{\text{Number of tagged}}{\text{Total number of}}$$
$$\frac{\text{of tagged deer}}{\text{of deer}} = \frac{\text{deer in sample}}{\text{deer in sample}}$$

$$\frac{120}{x} = \frac{25}{150}$$
$$(120)(150) = 25x$$
$$18,000 = 25x$$
$$\frac{18,000}{25} = \frac{25x}{25}$$
$$720 = x$$

There are approximately 720 deer in the refuge.

CHECK POINT 5

$$\frac{3}{8} = \frac{12}{x}$$

Because this equation is a proportion, the cross-products principle can be used. (This method will give the same result as multiplying both sides by the LCD, $12x$, but using the cross-products principle requires one less step.)

$$3x = 8 \cdot 12$$
$$3x = 96$$
$$x = 32$$

The length of the side marked x is 32 inches.

EXERCISE SET 7.7

1. The times are equal, so

$$\frac{10}{x} = \frac{15}{x+3}.$$

To solve this equation, multiply both sides by the LCD, $x(x+3)$.

$$x(x+3) \cdot \frac{10}{x} = x(x+3) \cdot \frac{15}{x+3}$$
$$10(x+3) = 145$$
$$10x + 30 = 15x$$
$$30 = 5x$$
$$6 = x$$

If $x = 6, x + 3 = 9$.
Note: The equation

$$\frac{10}{x} = \frac{15}{x+3}$$

is a proportion, so it can also be solved by using the cross-products principle. This allows you to skip the first step of the solution process shown above.
The walking rate is 6 miles per hour and the car's rate is 9 miles per hour.

3. Let $x =$ the jogger's rate running uphill.
Then $x + 4 =$ the jogger's rate running downhill.

	$d \times$	r	$= t$
Downhill	5	$x + 4$	$\frac{5}{x+4}$
Uphill	3	x	$\frac{3}{x}$

The times are equal, so

$$\frac{5}{x+4} = \frac{3}{x}.$$

Use the cross-products principle to solve this equation.

$$5x = 3(x + 4)$$
$$5x = 3x + 12$$
$$2x = 12$$
$$x = 6$$

If $x = 6, x + 4 = 10$.
The jogger runs 10 miles per hour downhill and 6 miles per hour uphill.

5. Let $x =$ the rate of the current.
Then $15 + x =$ the boat's rate with the current.
and $15 - x =$ the boat's rate against the current.

	$d \times$	r	$= t$
With the Current	20	$15 + x$	$\dfrac{20}{15 + x}$
Against the Current	10	$15 - x$	$\dfrac{10}{15 - x}$

Use the cross-products principle to solve this equation.

$$20(15 - x) = 10(15 + x)$$
$$300 - 20x = 150 + 10x$$
$$300 = 150 + 30x$$
$$150 = 30x$$
$$5 = x$$

The rate of the current is 5 miles per hour.

7. Let $x =$ walking rate.
Then $2x =$ jogging rate.

	$d \times$	r	$= t$
Walking	2	x	$\dfrac{2}{x}$
Jogging	2	$2x$	$\dfrac{2}{2x}$

The total time is 1 hour, so

$$\frac{2}{x} + \frac{2}{2x} = 1$$
$$\frac{2}{x} + \frac{1}{x} = 1.$$

To solve this equation, multiply both sides by the LCD, x.

$$x\left(\frac{2}{x} + \frac{1}{x}\right) = x \cdot 1$$
$$2 + 1 = x$$
$$3 = x$$

If $x = 3, 2x = 6$.
The walking rate is 3 miles per hour and the jogging rate is 6 miles per hour.

9. Let $x =$ the boat's average rate in still water.
Then $x + 2 =$ the boat's rate with the current.
and $x - 2 =$ the boat's rate against the current.

	$d \times$	r	$= t$
With the Current	6	$x + 2$	$\dfrac{6}{x + 2}$
Against the Current	4	$x - 2$	$\dfrac{4}{x - 2}$

$$\frac{6}{x + 2} = \frac{4}{x - 2}$$
$$6(x - 2) = 4(x + 2)$$
$$6x - 12 = 4x + 8$$
$$2x - 12 = 8$$
$$2x = 20$$
$$x = 10$$

The boat's average rate in still water is 4 miles per hour.

11. Let $x =$ the time, in minutes, for both people to shovel the driveway together.

	Fractional part of job completed in 1 hour	Time working together	Fractional part of job completed in x hours
You	$\dfrac{1}{20}$	x	$\dfrac{x}{20}$
Your Brother	$\dfrac{1}{15}$	x	$\dfrac{x}{15}$

Working together, the two people complete on whole job, so

$$\frac{x}{20} + \frac{x}{15} = 1.$$

Multiply both sides by the LCD, 60.

$$60 \left(\frac{x}{20} + \frac{x}{15} \right) = 60 \cdot 1$$
$$60 \cdot \frac{x}{20} + 60 \cdot \frac{x}{15} = 60$$
$$3x + 4x = 60$$
$$7x = 60$$
$$x = \frac{60}{7} \approx 8.6$$

It will take about 8.6 minutes, which is enough time.

13. Let $x =$ the time, in minutes, for both teams to clean the streets working together.

	Fractional part of job completed in 1 hour	Time working together	Fractional part of job completed in x hours
First Team	$\dfrac{1}{400}$	x	$\dfrac{x}{400}$
Second Team	$\dfrac{1}{300}$	x	$\dfrac{x}{300}$

Working together, the two teams complete one whole job, so

$$\frac{x}{400} + \frac{x}{300} = 1.$$

Multiply both sides by the LCD, 1200.

$$1200 \left(\frac{x}{400} + \frac{x}{300} \right) = 1200 \cdot 1$$

$$3x + 4x = 1200$$

$$7x = 1200$$

$$x = \frac{1200}{7} \approx 171.4$$

It will take about 171.4 hours for both teams to clean the streets working together. One week is $7 \cdot 24 = 168$ hours, so even if both crews work 24 hours a day, there is not enough time.

15. Let $x =$ the time, in hours, for both pipes to fill in pool.

$$\frac{x}{4} + \frac{x}{6} = 1$$

$$12 \left(\frac{x}{4} + \frac{x}{6} \right) = 12 \cdot 1$$

$$3x + 2x = 12$$

$$5x = 12$$

$$x = \frac{12}{5} = 2.4$$

Using both pipes, it will take 2.4 hours or 2 hours 24 minutes to fill the pool.

17. Let $x =$ the tax on a property with an assessed value of \$162,500.

$$\frac{\text{Tax on \$65,000 property}}{\text{Assessed value (\$65,000)}} = \frac{\text{Tax on \$162,000 property}}{\text{Assessed value (\$162,500)}}$$

$$\frac{\$720}{\$65,000} = \frac{\$x}{\$162,500}$$

$$\frac{720}{65,000} = \frac{x}{\$162,500}$$

$$65,000x = (720)(162,500)$$

$$65,000x = 117,000,000$$

$$\frac{65,000x}{65,000} = \frac{117,000,000}{65,000}$$

$$x = 1800$$

The tax on a property assessed at \$162,500 is \$1800.

19. Let $x =$ the total number of fur seal pups in the rookery.

$$\frac{\text{Original number of tagged fur seal pups}}{\text{Total number of fur seal pups}} = \frac{\text{Number of tagged fur seal pups in sample}}{\text{Number of fur seal pups in sample}}$$

$$\frac{4963}{x} = \frac{218}{900}$$

$$218x = (4963)(900)$$

$$218x = 4,466,700$$

$$\frac{218x}{218} = \frac{4,466,700}{218}$$

$$x \approx 20,490$$

There were about 20,490 fur seal pups in the rookery.

21. Let $x =$ the monthly amount of child support for a father earning \$38,000 annually.

$$\frac{x}{\$38,000} = \frac{1}{40}$$

$$\frac{x}{\$38,000} = \frac{1}{40}$$

$$40x = 38,000$$

$$x = 950$$

A father earning \$38,000 annually should pay \$950 in monthly child support.

23. Let $x =$ the height of the critter.

$$\frac{\text{Foot length of person}}{\text{Height of person}} = \frac{\text{Foot length of critter}}{\text{Height of critter}}$$

$$\frac{10 \text{ inches}}{67 \text{ inches}} = \frac{23 \text{ inches}}{x}$$

$$\frac{10}{67} = \frac{23}{x}$$

$$10x = (67)(23)$$

$$10x = 1541$$

$$x = 154.1$$

The height of the critter is 154.1 inches.

25. $\dfrac{18}{9} = \dfrac{10}{x}$

$18x = 9 \cdot 10$

$18x = 90$

$x = 5$

The length of the side marked x is 5 inches.

27. $\dfrac{10}{30} = \dfrac{x}{18}$

$30x = 10 \cdot 18$

$30x = 180$

$x = 6$

The length of the side marked x is 6 meters.

29. $\dfrac{20}{15} = \dfrac{x}{12}$

$15x = 12 \cdot 20$

$15x = 240$

$x = 16$

The length of the side marked x is 16 inches.

31. $\dfrac{8}{6} = \dfrac{x}{12}$

$6x = 8 \cdot 12$

$6x = 96$

$x = 16$

The tree is 16 feet tall.

For Exercises 33-41, answers may vary.

43. Let $x =$ the time, in hours, for the experienced carpenter to panel the room. Then $3x =$ the time, in hours, for the apprentice to panel the room.

Note: Because the experienced carpenter can do the job 3 times faster, the apprentice takes 3 times as long as the experienced carpenter.

	Fractional part of job completed in 1 hour	Time working together	Fractional part of job completed in x hours
Experienced Carpenter	$\dfrac{1}{x}$	6	$\dfrac{6}{x}$
Apprentice	$\dfrac{1}{3x}$	6	$\dfrac{6}{3x}$

Together, the two carpenters complete one whole job, so

$$\frac{6}{x} + \frac{6}{3x} = 1$$

or

$$\frac{6}{x} + \frac{2}{x} = 1.$$

To solve this equation, multiply both sides by the LCD, x.

$$x\left(\frac{6}{x} + \frac{2}{x}\right) = x \cdot 1$$

$$6 + 2 = x$$

$$8 = x$$

If $x = 8, 3x = 24$.
Walking alone, it would take the experienced carpenter 8 hours and the apprentice 24 hours to panel the room.

45. The current front:rear ratio is $\frac{60}{20} = \frac{3}{1}$ or 3:1. To change the ratio to 5:1, either change the rear sprocket to 12, since $\frac{60}{12} = \frac{5}{1}$ or 5:1, or else change the front sprocket to 100 teeth since $\frac{100}{20} = \frac{5}{1}$ or 5:1.

Review Exercises

46. $25x^2 - 81 = (5x)^2 - 9^2$
$\qquad\qquad = (5x + 9)(5x - 9)$

47. $x^2 - 12x + 36 = 0$
$\qquad (x - 6)^2 = 0$
$\qquad\quad x - 6 = 0$
$\qquad\qquad\quad x = 6$

The only solution is 6.

48. $y = -\frac{2}{3}x + 4$

slope $= -\frac{2}{3} = \frac{-2}{3}$

y-intercept $= 4$

Plot $(0, 4)$. From this point, move 2 units *down* and 3 units to the *right* to reach the point $(3, 2)$. Draw a line through $(0, 4)$ and $(3, 2)$.

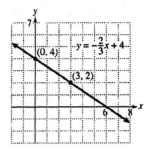

Modeling Using Variation

7.8 CHECK POINTS

CHECK POINT 1

1. $P = kd$

Find k.

$$25 = k60$$

$$k = \frac{5}{12}$$

The equation becomes $P = \frac{5}{12}d$. When $d = 330$ feet, $P = \frac{5}{12}d = \frac{5}{12}(330) = 137.5$.

A submarine 330 feet below the surface will experience a pressur of 137.5 pounds per square inch.

CHECK POINT 2

$P = \dfrac{k}{V}$

Find k.

$$12 = \frac{k}{8}$$

$$k = 96$$

The equation becomes $P = \frac{96}{V}$. When $V = 22$,

$$P = \frac{99}{22} \approx 4.36.$$

When the volume is 22 square inches, the pressure is 4.36 pounds per squrae inch.

CHECK POINT 3

$t = \dfrac{kn}{p}$

Find k.

$$t = \frac{kn}{p}$$
$$32 = \frac{k(16)}{4}$$
$$32 = k(4)$$
$$8 = k$$

The equation becomes $t = \frac{8n}{p}$. When $p = 8$ and $n = 24, t = \frac{8n}{p} = \frac{8(24)}{8} = 24$.

It will take 24 minutes for 8 people to solve 24 problems.

CHECK POINT 4

$V = khr^2$

Find k.

$$V = khr^2$$
$$120\pi = k(10)(6)^2$$
$$120\pi = k(10)(36)$$
$$120\pi = k(360)$$
$$\frac{1}{3}\pi = k$$

The equation becomes $V = \frac{1}{3}\pi hr^2$. When $r = 12$ feet and $h = 2$ feet, we have the following.

$$V = \frac{1}{3}\pi(2)(120^2 = \frac{1}{3}\pi(2)(144)$$
$$= \frac{1}{3}\pi(288) = 96\pi$$

A cone with a height of 2 feet and a radius of 12 feet has a volume of 96π cubic feet.

EXERCISE SET 7.8

1. $y = kx$.

Find k.

$$y = kx$$
$$35 = k \cdot 5$$
$$7 = k$$

The equation becomes $y = 7x$.
When $x = 12, y = 7x = 7 \cdot 12 = 84$.

3. $y = \dfrac{k}{x}$

Find k.

$$y = \frac{k}{x}$$
$$10 = \frac{k}{5}$$
$$50 = k$$

The equation becomes $y = \frac{50}{x}$.
When $x = 2, y = \frac{50}{2} = 25$.

5. $y = \dfrac{kx}{z^2}$

Find k.

$$y = \frac{kx}{z^2}$$
$$20 = \frac{k(50)}{5^2}$$
$$20 = \frac{k(50)}{25}$$
$$20 = 2k$$
$$10 = k$$

The equation becomes $y = \frac{10x}{z^2}$.
When $x = 3$ and $z = 6$,
$$y = \frac{10x}{z^2} = \frac{10(3)}{6^2} = \frac{10(3)}{36} = \frac{30}{36} = \frac{5}{6}.$$

7. $y = kxy$

Find k.

$$y = kxy$$
$$25 = k(2)(5)$$
$$25 = k(10)$$
$$\frac{5}{2} = k$$

The equation becomes $y = \frac{5}{2}xy$.
When $x = 8$ and $z = 12$,

$$y = \frac{5}{2}(8)(12) = \frac{5}{\cancel{2}}(\cancel{8}^2)(12) = 240.$$

9. **a.** $G = kW$
   b. $G = 0.02W$
   c. $G = 0.02(52) = 1.04$
   At the end of the year, the fingernails would be 1.04 inches long.

11. $C = kM$
    Find k.

$$C = km$$
$$400 = k(3000)$$
$$k = \frac{400}{3000} = \frac{2}{15}$$

The equation becomes $C = \frac{2}{15}M$.
When $M = 450$,

$$C = \frac{2}{15}M = \frac{2}{\cancel{15}}(\cancel{450}^{30}) = 60.$$

The ticket for a 450 mile trip will cost $60.

13. $s = km$
    Find k.

$$s = km$$
$$1502.2 = k(2.03)$$
$$740 = k$$

The equation becomes $s = 740m$.
When $m = 3.3, s = 740(3.3) = 2442$.
The Blackbird's speed is 2442 miles per hour.

15. $w = kh^3$
    Find k.

$$w = kh^3$$
$$170 = k(70)^3$$
$$170 = k(343,000)$$
$$0.000496 = k$$

The equation becomes $w = 0.000496h^3$.
When $h = 107$,

$$w = .000496(107)^3$$
$$= .000496(1,225,043)$$
$$\approx 607.$$

Robert Wadlow's weight was approximately 607 pounds.

17. $t = \frac{k}{d}$
    Find k.

$$t = \frac{k}{d}$$
$$1.5 = \frac{k}{20}$$
$$30 = k$$

The equation becomes $t = \frac{30}{d}$.
When $d = 60, t = \frac{30}{60} = 0.5$.

When the average rate is 60 miles per hour, it will take $\frac{1}{2}$ hour to get to campus.

19. $v = \frac{k}{p}$
    Use the given values to find k.

$$v = \frac{k}{p}$$
$$32 = \frac{k}{8}$$
$$256 = k$$

The equation becomes $v = \frac{256}{p}$.
When $d = 40, v = \frac{256}{40} = 6.4$.

When the pressure is 40 cubic centimeters, the volume is 6.4 pounds.

21. $I = \dfrac{kw}{h}$

Find k.

$$I = \frac{kw}{h}$$
$$21 = \frac{k(150)}{70}$$
$$k = \frac{70}{150}(21)$$
$$k = 9.8$$

The equation becomes $I = \frac{9.8w}{h}$.

When $w = 240$ and $h = 74$, $I = \frac{9.8(240)}{74} \approx$ 31.8.

The body mass index is approximately 32. This is not in the desirable range.

23. $I = \dfrac{k}{d^2}$

Find k.

$$I = \frac{k}{d^2}$$
$$25 = \frac{k}{4^2}$$
$$25 = \frac{k}{16}$$
$$400 = k$$

The equation becomes $I = \frac{400}{6^2} = \frac{400}{36} \approx$ 11.1.

At a distance of 6 feet, the intensity of illumination is 11.1 foot-candles.

25. $E = kmv^2$

Find k.

$$E = kmv^2$$
$$36 = k(8)(3)^2$$
$$36 = k(72)$$
$$0.5 = k$$

The equation becomes $E = 0.5mv^2$.
When $m = 4$ and $v = 6$,

$$E = 0.5(4)(6)^2 = 0.5(4)(36) = 72.$$

A mass of 4 grams and velocity of 6 centimeters per second has a kinetic energy of 72 ergs.

27. $n = \dfrac{kp_1p_2}{d^2}$

Find k.

$$n = \frac{kp_1p_2}{d^2}$$
$$158{,}233 = \frac{k(2538)(1818)}{(608)^2}$$
$$158{,}233 = \frac{k(4{,}614{,}084)}{369{,}664}$$
$$158{,}233 = 12.4818k$$
$$12677.1 \approx k$$

The equation becomes $n = \frac{12677.1p_1p_2}{d^2}$.

When $p_1 = 1225$, $p_2 = 2970$ and $d = 3403$,

$$n = \frac{12677.1(1225)(2970)}{(3403)^2}$$
$$= \frac{46{,}122{,}459{,}090}{11{,}580{,}409} \approx 3982.8.$$

The average number of phone calls between Orlando and Seattle is about 3983 per day.

29. $f = kas^2$

Find k.

$$f = kas^2$$
$$150 = k(4 \cdot 5)(30)^2$$
$$150 = k(20)(900)$$
$$150 = k(18{,}000)$$
$$\frac{1}{120} = k$$

The equation becomes $f = \frac{1}{120}as^2$.
When $s = 60$, $a = 3 \cdot 4 = 12$,

$$f\frac{1}{120}(12)(60)^2 = \frac{1}{10}(3600) = 360.$$

The force is 360 pounds. Since the windows are only made to withstand a 300 pound force, the hurrican shutters should be placed on the windows.

For Exercises 31-37, answers may vary.

39. Since wind pressure varies directly as the square of the wind velocityu, $P = kv^2$. Velocity is squared in the variation equation. If velocity is doubled, when it is squared, it will be multiplied by 2^2 or 4. Therefore, if the wind speed doubles, the wind pressure is multiplied by 4.

41. Since heat varies directly as the square of the voltage and inversely as the resistance, we have $H = \frac{kv^2}{r}$. To triple the amount of heat generated while voltage remains constant, we must change the resistance.

$$H = \frac{kv^2}{r}$$

$$3(H) = 3\left(\frac{kv^2}{r}\right)$$

$$3H = \frac{3kv^2}{r}$$

$$3H = \frac{\frac{1}{3}(3kv^2)}{\frac{1}{3}(r)}$$

$$3H = \frac{kv^2}{\frac{1}{3}r}$$

For the neat to be tripled, the resistance must be multiplied by $\frac{1}{3}$.

43. Answers will vary. For examplel, consider Exercise 11.

$$C = \frac{2}{15}M$$

Graph the equation $y = \frac{2}{15}x$.

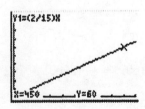

The ticket for a 450 mile trip will cost $60.

Review Exercises

44. $8(2 - x) = -5x$

$$16 - 8x = -5x$$

$$16 = 3x$$

$$x = \frac{16}{3}$$

45. $\dfrac{27x^3 - 8}{3x + 2}$

$$
\begin{array}{r}
9x^2 - 6x + 4 \\
3x + 2\overline{)27x^3 + 0x^2 + 0x - 8} \\
\underline{27x^3 + 18x^2} \\
-18x^2 + 0x \\
\underline{-18x^2 - 12x} \\
12x - 8 \\
\underline{12x - 8} \\
-16
\end{array}
$$

$$\frac{27x^3 - 8}{3x + 2} = 9x^2 - 6x + 4 - \frac{16}{3x + 2}$$

46. $6x^3 - 6x^2 - 120x = 6x(x^2 - x - 20)$
$$= 6x(x - 5)(x + 4)$$

Chapter 7 Review Exercises

1. $\dfrac{5x}{6x - 24}$

Set the denominator equal to 0 and solve for x.

$$6x - 24 = 0$$
$$6x = 24$$
$$x = 4$$

The rational expression is undefined for $x = 4$.

2. $\dfrac{x+3}{(x-2)(x+5)}$

Set the denominator equal to 0 and solve for x.

$$(x-2)(x+5) = 0$$
$$x-2=0 \quad \text{or} \quad x+5=0$$
$$x=2 \qquad\qquad x=-5$$

The rational expression is undefined for $x=2$ and $x=-5$.

3. $\dfrac{x^2+3}{x^2-3x+2}$

$$(x-1)(x-2) = 0$$
$$x-1=0 \quad \text{or} \quad x-1=0$$
$$x=1 \qquad\qquad x=2$$

The rational expression is undefined for $x=1$ and $x=2$.

4. $\dfrac{7}{x^2+81}$

The smallest possible value of x^2 is 0, so $x^2+81 \geq 81$ for all real numbers x. This means that there is no real number x for which $x^2+81 = 0$. Thus, the rational expression is defined for all real numbers.

5. $\dfrac{16x^2}{12x} = \dfrac{4 \cdot 4 \cdot x \cdot x}{4 \cdot 3 \cdot x} = \dfrac{4x}{3}$

6. $\dfrac{x^2-4}{x-2} = \dfrac{(x+2)(x-2)}{(x-2)} = x+2$

7. $\dfrac{x^3+2x^2}{x+2} = \dfrac{x^2(x+2)}{(x+2)} = x^2$

8. $\dfrac{x^2+3x-18}{x^2-36} = \dfrac{(x+6)(x-3)}{(x+6)(x-6)}$

$$= \dfrac{x-3}{x-6}$$

9. $\dfrac{x^2-4x-5}{x^2+8x+7} = \dfrac{(x+1)(x-5)}{(x+1)(x+7)}$

$$= \dfrac{x-5}{x+7}$$

10. $\dfrac{y^2+2y}{y^2+4y+4} = \dfrac{y(y+2)}{(y+2)(y+2)}$

$$= \dfrac{y}{y+2}$$

11. $\dfrac{x^2}{x^2+4}$

The numerator and denominator have no common factor, so this rational expression cannot be simplified.

12. $\dfrac{2x^2-18y^2}{3y-x} = \dfrac{2(x^2-9y^2)}{3y-x}$

$$= \dfrac{2(x+3y)(x-3y)}{(3y-x)}$$

$$= \dfrac{2(x+3y)(-1)(3y-x)}{(3y-x)}$$

$$= -2(x+3y) \text{ or } -2x-6y$$

13. $\dfrac{x^2-4}{12x} \cdot \dfrac{3x}{x+2} = \dfrac{(x+2)(x-2)}{12x} \cdot \dfrac{3x}{(x+2)}$

$$= \dfrac{x-2}{4}$$

14. $\dfrac{5x+5}{6} \cdot \dfrac{3x}{x^2+x} = \dfrac{5(x+1)}{6} \cdot \dfrac{3x}{x(x+1)}$

$$= \dfrac{5}{2}$$

15. $\dfrac{x^2+6x+9}{x^2-4} \cdot \dfrac{x-2}{x+3}$

$= \dfrac{(x+3)(x+3)}{(x+2)(x-2)} \cdot \dfrac{x-2}{x+3}$

$= \dfrac{x+3}{x+2}$

16. $\dfrac{y^2-2y+1}{y^2-1} \cdot \dfrac{2y^2+y-1}{5y-5}$

$= \dfrac{(y-1)(y-1)}{(y+1)(y-1)} \cdot \dfrac{(2y-1)(y+1)}{5(y-1)}$

$= \dfrac{2y-1}{5}$

17. $\dfrac{2y^2+y-3}{4y^2-9} \cdot \dfrac{3y+3}{5y-5y^2}$

$= \dfrac{(2y+3)(y-1)}{(2y+3)(2y-3)} \cdot \dfrac{3(y+1)}{5y(1-y)}$

$= \dfrac{-3(y+1)}{5y(2y-3)} \text{ or } -\dfrac{3(y+1)}{5y(2y-3)}$

18. $\dfrac{x^2+x-2}{10} \div \dfrac{2x+4}{5}$

$= \dfrac{x^2+x-2}{10} \cdot \dfrac{5}{2x+4}$

$= \dfrac{(x-1)(x+2)}{10} \cdot \dfrac{5}{2(x+2)}$

$= \dfrac{x-1}{4}$

19. $\dfrac{6x+2}{x^2-1} \div \dfrac{3x^2+x}{x-1}$

$= \dfrac{6x+2}{x^2-1} \cdot \dfrac{x-1}{3x^2+x}$

$= \dfrac{2(3x+1)}{(x+1)(x-1)} \cdot \dfrac{(x-1)}{x(3x+1)}$

$= \dfrac{2}{x(x+1)}$

20. $\dfrac{1}{y^2+8y+15} \div \dfrac{7}{y+5}$

$= \dfrac{1}{y^2+8y+15} \cdot \dfrac{y+5}{7}$

$= \dfrac{1}{(y+3)(y+5)} \cdot \dfrac{(y+5)}{7}$

$= \dfrac{1}{7(y+3)}$

21. $\dfrac{y^2+y-42}{y-3} \div \dfrac{y+7}{(y-3)^2}$

$= \dfrac{y^2+y-42}{y-3} \cdot \dfrac{(y-3)^2}{y+7}$

$= \dfrac{(y+7)(y-6)}{(y-3)} \cdot \dfrac{(y-3)(y-3)}{y+7}$

$= (y-6)(y-3) \text{ or } y^2-9y+18$

22. $\dfrac{8x+8y}{x^2} \div \dfrac{x^2-y^2}{x^2}$

$= \dfrac{8x+8y}{x^2} \cdot \dfrac{x^2}{x^2-y^2}$

$= \dfrac{8(x+y)}{x^2} \cdot \dfrac{x^2}{(x+y)(x-y)}$

$= \dfrac{8}{x-y}$

23. $\dfrac{4x}{x+5} + \dfrac{20}{x+5} = \dfrac{4x+20}{x+5} = \dfrac{4(x+5)}{x+5} = 4$

24. $\dfrac{8x-5}{3x-1} + \dfrac{4x+1}{3x-1} = \dfrac{8x-5+4x+1}{3x-1}$

$= \dfrac{12x-4}{3x-1}$

$= \dfrac{4(3x-1)}{3x-1} = 4$

25. $\dfrac{3x^2 + 2x}{x-1} - \dfrac{10x-5}{x-1}$

$= \dfrac{(3x^2 + 2x) - (10x - 5)}{x-1}$

$= \dfrac{3x^2 + 2x - 10x + 5}{x-1}$

$= \dfrac{3x^2 - 8x + 5}{x-1}$

$= \dfrac{(3x-5)(x-1)}{x-1}$

$= 3x - 5$

26. $\dfrac{6y^2 - 4y}{2y-3} - \dfrac{12 - 3y}{2y-3}$

$= \dfrac{(6y^2 - 4y) - (12 - 3y)}{2y-3}$

$= \dfrac{6y^2 - 4y - 12 + 3y}{2y-3}$

$= \dfrac{6y^2 - y - 12}{2y-3}$

$= \dfrac{(2y-3)(3y+4)}{2y-3}$

$= 3y + 4$

27. $\dfrac{x}{x-2} + \dfrac{x-4}{2-x} = \dfrac{x}{x-2} + \dfrac{(-1)}{(-1)} \cdot \dfrac{x-4}{x-2}$

$= \dfrac{x}{x-2} + \dfrac{-x+4}{x-2}$

$= \dfrac{x-x+4}{x-2} = \dfrac{4}{x-2}$

28. $\dfrac{x+5}{x-3} - \dfrac{x}{3-x} = \dfrac{x+5}{x-3} - \dfrac{(-1)}{(-1)} \cdot \dfrac{x}{3-x}$

$= \dfrac{x+5}{x-3} + \dfrac{x}{x-3}$

$= \dfrac{x+5+x}{x-3} = \dfrac{2x+5}{x-5}$

29. $\dfrac{7}{9x^3}$ and $\dfrac{5}{12x}$

$$9x^3 = 3^2 x^3$$
$$12x = 2^2 \cdot 3x$$

$$\text{LCD} = 2^2 \cdot 3^2 \cdot x^3 = 36x^3$$

30. $\dfrac{3}{x^2(x-1)}$ and $\dfrac{11}{x(x-1)^2}$

$\text{LCD} = x^2(x-1)^2$

31. $\dfrac{x}{x^2 + 4x + 3}$ and $\dfrac{17}{x^2 + 10x + 21}$

$$x^2 + 4x + 3 = (x+3)(x+1)$$
$$x^2 + 10x + 21 = (x+3)(x+7)$$

$\text{LCD} = (x+3)(x+1)(x+7)$

32. $\dfrac{7}{3x} + \dfrac{5}{2x^2}$

$\text{LCD} = 6x^2$

$$\dfrac{7}{3x} + \dfrac{5}{2x^2} = \dfrac{7}{3x} \cdot \dfrac{2x}{2x} + \dfrac{5}{2x^2} \cdot \dfrac{3}{3}$$

$$= \dfrac{14x + 15}{6x^2}$$

33. $\dfrac{5}{x+1} + \dfrac{2}{x}$

$\text{LCD} = x(x+1)$

$$\dfrac{5}{x+1} + \dfrac{2}{x} = \dfrac{5x}{x(x+1)} + \dfrac{2(x+1)}{x(x+1)}$$

$$= \dfrac{5x + 2(x+1)}{x(x+1)} = \dfrac{5x + 2x + 2}{x(x+1)}$$

$$= \dfrac{7x + 2}{x(x+1)}$$

34. $\dfrac{7}{x+3} + \dfrac{4}{(x+3)^2}$

$\text{LCD} = (x+3)^2$ or $(x+3)(x+3)$

$$\dfrac{7}{x+3} + \dfrac{4}{(x+3)^2}$$

$$= \dfrac{7}{x+3} + \dfrac{4}{(x+3)(x+3)}$$

$$= \dfrac{7(x+3)}{(x+3)(x+3)} + \dfrac{4}{(x+3)(x+3)}$$

$$= \dfrac{7(x+3) + 4}{(x+3)(x+3)} = \dfrac{7x + 21 + 4}{(x+3)(x+3)}$$

$$= \dfrac{7x + 25}{(x+3)(x+3)} \text{ or } \dfrac{7x + 25}{(x+3)^2}$$

35. $\dfrac{6y}{y^2 - 4} - \dfrac{3}{y + 2}$

$$y^2 - 4 = (y + 2)(y - 2)$$
$$y + 2 = 1(y + 2)$$

$$\text{LCD} = (y + 2)(y - 2)$$

$$\dfrac{6y}{y^2 - 4} - \dfrac{3}{y + 2}$$
$$= \dfrac{6y}{(y + 2)(y - 2)} - \dfrac{3}{y + 2}$$
$$= \dfrac{6y}{(y + 2)(y - 2)} - \dfrac{3(y - 2)}{(y + 2)(y - 2)}$$
$$= \dfrac{6y - 3(y - 2)}{(y + 2)(y - 2)}$$
$$= \dfrac{6y - 3y + 6}{(y + 2)(y - 2)}$$
$$= \dfrac{3y + 6}{(y + 2)(y - 2)}$$
$$= \dfrac{3(y + 2)}{(y + 2)(y - 2)}$$
$$= \dfrac{3}{y - 2}$$

36. $\dfrac{y - 1}{y^2 + 2y + 1} - \dfrac{y + 1}{y - 1}$

$$= \dfrac{y - 1}{(y - 1)(y - 1)} - \dfrac{y + 1}{y - 1}$$
$$= \dfrac{1}{y - 1} - \dfrac{y + 1}{y - 1}$$
$$= \dfrac{1 - (y + 1)}{y - 1}$$
$$= \dfrac{1 - y - 1}{y - 1}$$
$$= \dfrac{-y}{y - 1} \text{ or } -\dfrac{y}{y - 1}$$

37. $\dfrac{x + y}{y} - \dfrac{y - x}{x}$

$$\text{LCD} = xy$$

$$\dfrac{x + y}{y} - \dfrac{y - x}{x}$$
$$= \dfrac{(x + y)}{y} \cdot \dfrac{x}{x} - \dfrac{(x - y)}{x} \cdot \dfrac{y}{y}$$
$$= \dfrac{x^2 + xy}{xy} - \dfrac{xy - y^2}{xy}$$
$$= \dfrac{(x^2 + xy) - (xy - y^2)}{xy}$$
$$= \dfrac{x^2 + xy - xy + y^2}{xy}$$
$$= \dfrac{x^2 + y^2}{xy}$$

38. $\dfrac{2x}{x^2 + 2x + 1} + \dfrac{x}{x^2 - 1}$

$$x^2 + 2x + 1 = (x + 1)(x + 1)$$
$$x^2 - 1 = (x + 1)(x - 1)$$

$$\text{LCD} = (x + 1)(x + 1)(x - 1)$$

$$\dfrac{2x}{x^2 + 2x + 1} + \dfrac{x}{x^2 - 1}$$
$$= \dfrac{2x}{(x + 1)(x + 1)} + \dfrac{x}{(x + 1)(x + 1)}$$
$$= \dfrac{2x(x - 1)}{(x + 1)(x + 1)(x - 1)}$$
$$\quad + \dfrac{x(x + 1)}{(x + 1)(x + 1)(x - 1)}$$
$$= \dfrac{2x(x - 1) + x(x + 1)}{(x + 1)(x + 1)(x - 1)}$$
$$= \dfrac{2x^2 - 2x + x^2 + x}{(x + 1)(x + 1)(x - 1)}$$
$$= \dfrac{3x^2 - x}{(x + 1)(x + 1)(x - 1)}$$
$$= \dfrac{3x(x - 1)}{(x + 1)(x + 1)(x - 1)}$$
$$= \dfrac{3x}{(x + 1)(x + 1)} \text{ or } \dfrac{3x}{(x + 1)^2}$$

39. $\dfrac{5x}{x+1} - \dfrac{2x}{1-x^2}$

$x + 1 = 1(x+1)$

$1 - x^2 = -1(x^2-1) = -(x+1)(x-1)$

$\text{LCD} = (x+1)(x-1)$

$\dfrac{5x}{x+1} - \dfrac{2x}{1-x^2}$

$= \dfrac{5x}{x+1} - \dfrac{(-1)}{(-1)} \cdot \dfrac{2x}{1-x^2}$

$= \dfrac{5x}{x+1} - \dfrac{-2x}{(x+1)(x-1)}$

$= \dfrac{5x(x-1)}{x+1} - \dfrac{-2x}{(x+1)(x-1)}$

$= \dfrac{5x(x-1)+2x}{(x+1)(x-1)}$

$= \dfrac{5x^2 - 5x + 2x}{(x+1)(x-1)}$

$= \dfrac{5x^2 - 3x}{(x+1)(x-1)}$

40. $\dfrac{4}{x^2-x-6} - \dfrac{4}{x^2-4}$

$x^2 - x - 6 = (x+2)(x-3)$

$x^2 - 4 = (x+2)(x-2)$

$\text{LCD} = (x+2)(x-3)(x-2)$

$\dfrac{4}{x^2-x-6} - \dfrac{4}{x^2-4}$

$= \dfrac{4}{(x+2)(x-3)} - \dfrac{4}{(x+2)(x-2)}$

$= \dfrac{4(x-2)}{(x+2)(x-3)(x-2)}$

$\quad - \dfrac{4(x-3)}{(x+2)(x-3)(x-2)}$

$= \dfrac{4(x-2) - 4(x-3)}{(x+2)(x-3)(x-2)}$

$= \dfrac{4x - 8 - 4x + 12}{(x+2)(x-3)(x-2)}$

$= \dfrac{4}{(x+2)(x-3)(x-2)}$

41. $\dfrac{7}{x+3} + 2$

$\text{LCD} = x+3$

$\dfrac{7}{x+3} + 2 = \dfrac{7}{x+3} + \dfrac{2(x+3)}{x+3}$

$= \dfrac{7 + 2(x+3)}{x+3}$

$= \dfrac{7 + 2x + 6}{x+3}$

$= \dfrac{2x + 13}{x+3}$

42. $\dfrac{2y-5}{6y+9} - \dfrac{4}{2y^2+3y}$

$6y + 9 = 3(2y+3)$

$2y^2 + 3y = y(2y+3)$

$\text{LCD} = 3(2y+3)$

$\dfrac{2y-5}{6y+9} - \dfrac{4}{2y^2+3y}$

$= \dfrac{2y-5}{3(2y+3)} - \dfrac{4}{y(2y+3)}$

$= \dfrac{(2y-5)(y)}{3y(2y+3)} - \dfrac{4\cdot 3}{3y(2y+3)}$

$= \dfrac{2y^2 - 5y - 12}{3y(2y+3)} = \dfrac{(2y+3)(y-4)}{3y(2y+3)}$

$= \dfrac{y-4}{3y}$

In Exercises 43–47, each complex rational expression can be simplified by either of the two methods introduced in Section 8.5 of the textbook. Both methods will be illustrated here.

43. $\dfrac{\frac{1}{2} + \frac{3}{8}}{\frac{3}{4} - \frac{1}{2}} = \dfrac{\frac{4}{8} + \frac{3}{8}}{\frac{3}{4} - \frac{2}{4}} = \dfrac{\frac{7}{8}}{\frac{1}{4}} = \dfrac{7}{8} \cdot \dfrac{4}{1} = \dfrac{7}{2}$

44. $\dfrac{\dfrac{1}{x}}{1-\dfrac{1}{x}}$

$\text{LCD} = x$

$$\frac{\dfrac{1}{x}}{1-\dfrac{1}{x}} = \frac{x}{x} \cdot \frac{\left(\dfrac{1}{x}\right)}{\left(1-\dfrac{1}{x}\right)}$$

$$= \frac{x \cdot \dfrac{1}{x}}{x \cdot 1 - x \cdot \dfrac{1}{x}}$$

$$= \frac{1}{x-1}$$

45. $\dfrac{\dfrac{1}{x}+\dfrac{1}{y}}{\dfrac{1}{xy}}$

$\text{LCD} = xy$

$$\frac{\dfrac{1}{x}+\dfrac{1}{y}}{\dfrac{1}{xy}} = \frac{xy}{xy} \cdot \frac{\left(\dfrac{1}{x}+\dfrac{1}{y}\right)}{\left(\dfrac{1}{xy}\right)}$$

$$= \frac{xy \cdot \dfrac{1}{x} + xy \cdot \dfrac{1}{y}}{xy \cdot \dfrac{1}{xy}}$$

$$= \frac{y+x}{1} = y+x \text{ or } x+y$$

46. $\dfrac{\dfrac{1}{x}-\dfrac{1}{2}}{\dfrac{1}{3}-\dfrac{x}{6}} = \dfrac{\dfrac{2}{2x}-\dfrac{x}{2x}}{\dfrac{2}{6}-\dfrac{x}{6}} = \dfrac{\dfrac{2-x}{2x}}{\dfrac{2-x}{6}}$

$$= \frac{2-x}{2x} \cdot \frac{6}{2-x} = \frac{3}{x}$$

47. $\dfrac{3+\dfrac{12}{x}}{1-\dfrac{16}{x^2}}$

$\text{LCD} = x^2$

$$\frac{3+\dfrac{12}{x}}{1-\dfrac{16}{x^2}} = \frac{x^2}{x^2} \cdot \frac{\left(3+\dfrac{12}{x}\right)}{\left(1-\dfrac{16}{x^2}\right)}$$

$$= \frac{x^2 \cdot 3 + x^2 \cdot \dfrac{12}{x}}{x^2 \cdot 1 - x^2 \cdot \dfrac{16}{x^2}}$$

$$= \frac{3x^2 + 12x}{x^2 - 16}$$

$$= \frac{3x(x+4)}{(x+4)(x-4)}$$

$$= \frac{3x}{x-4}$$

48. $\dfrac{3}{x} - \dfrac{1}{6} = \dfrac{1}{x}$

The restriction is $x \neq 0$.
The LCD is $6x$.

$$\frac{3}{x} - \frac{1}{6} = \frac{1}{x}$$

$$6x\left(\frac{3}{x} - \frac{1}{6}\right) = 6x\left(\frac{1}{x}\right)$$

$$6x \cdot \frac{3}{x} - 6x \cdot \frac{1}{6} = 6x \cdot \frac{1}{x}$$

$$18 - x = 6$$

$$-x = 12$$

$$x = 12$$

The solution is 12.

49. $\dfrac{3}{4x} = \dfrac{1}{x} + \dfrac{1}{4}$

The restriction is $x \neq 0$.
The LCD is $4x$.

$$\frac{3}{4x} = \frac{1}{x} + \frac{1}{4}$$

$$4x\left(\frac{3}{4x}\right) = 4x\left(\frac{1}{x} + \frac{1}{4}\right)$$

$$3 = 4 + x$$

$$-1 = x$$

The solution is -1.

50. $x + 5 = \dfrac{6}{x}$

The restriction is $x \neq 0$.
The LCD is x.

$$x + 5 = \frac{6}{x}$$

$$x(x + 5) = x\left(\frac{6}{x}\right)$$

$$x^2 + 5x = 6$$

$$x^2 + 5x - 6 = 0$$

$$(x + 6)(x - 1) = 0$$

$$x + 6 = 0 \quad \text{or} \quad x - 1 = 0$$

$$x = -6 \qquad\qquad x = 1$$

The equation has two solutions, -6 and 1.

51. $4 - \dfrac{x}{x + 5} = \dfrac{5}{x + 5}$

The restriction is $x \neq -5$.
The LCD is $x + 5$.

$$(x + 5)\left(4 - \frac{x}{x + 5}\right) = (x + 5)\left(\frac{5}{x + 5}\right)$$

$$(x + 5) \cdot 4 - (x + 5)\left(\frac{x}{x + 5}\right) = (x + 5)\left(\frac{5}{x + 5}\right)$$

$$4x + 20 = 5$$

$$3x + 20 = 5$$

$$3x = -15$$

$$x = -5$$

The only proposed solution, -5, is *not* a solution because of the restriction $x \neq -5$. Notice that -5 makes two of the denominators zero in the original equation. Therefore, the given equation has no solution.

52. $\dfrac{2}{x - 3} = \dfrac{4}{x + 3} + \dfrac{8}{x^2 - 9}$

To find any restrictions and the LCD, all denominators should be written in factored form.

$$\frac{2}{x - 3} = \frac{4}{x + 3} + \frac{8}{(x + 3)(x - 3)}$$

Restrictions: $x \neq 3, x \neq -3$
LCD $= (x + 3)(x - 3)$

$$(x + 3)(x - 3) \cdot \frac{2}{x + 3}$$

$$= (x+3)(x-3)\left(\frac{4}{x + 3} + \frac{8}{(x + 3)(x - 3)}\right)$$

$$2(x - 3) = 4(x - 3) + 8$$

$$2x - 6 = 4x - 12 + 8$$

$$2x - 6 = 4x - 4$$

$$-6 = 2x - 4$$

$$10 = 2x$$

The solution is 5.

53. $\dfrac{2}{x} = \dfrac{2}{3} + \dfrac{x}{6}$

Restriction: $x \neq 0$
LCD $= 6x$

$$6x\left(\frac{2}{x}\right) = 6x\left(\frac{2}{3} + \frac{x}{6}\right)$$

$$12 = 4x + x^2$$

$$0 = x^2 + 4x - 12$$

$$0 = (x + 6)(x - 2)$$

$$x + 6 = 0 \quad \text{or} \quad x - 2 = 0$$

$$x = -6 \qquad\qquad x = 2$$

The solutions are -6 and 2.

54. $\dfrac{13}{y-1} - 3 = \dfrac{1}{y-1}$

Restriction: $y \neq 1$

LCD $= y - 1$

$$(y-1)\left(\dfrac{13}{y-1} - 3\right) = (y-1)\left(\dfrac{1}{y-1}\right)$$
$$13 - 3(y-1) = 1$$
$$13 - 3y + 3 = 1$$
$$16 - 3y = 1$$
$$-3y = -15$$
$$y = 5$$

The solution is 5.

55. $\dfrac{1}{x+3} - \dfrac{1}{x-1} = \dfrac{x+1}{x^2+2x-3}$

$$\dfrac{1}{x+3} - \dfrac{1}{x-1} = \dfrac{x+1}{(x+3)(x-1)}$$

Restrictions: $x \neq -3, x \neq 1$

LCD $= (x+3)(x-1)$

$$(x+3)(x-1)\left[\dfrac{1}{x+3} - \dfrac{1}{x-1}\right]$$
$$= (x+3)(x-1) \cdot \left[\dfrac{x+1}{(x+3)(x-1)}\right]$$
$$(x-1) - (x+3) = x+1$$
$$x - 1 - x - 3 = x + 1$$
$$-4 = x + 1$$
$$-5 = x$$

The solution is -5.

56. $P = \dfrac{250(3t+5)}{t+25}; P = 125$

$$125 = \dfrac{250(3t+5)}{t+25}$$
$$125(t+25) = \dfrac{250(3t+5)}{t+25} \cdot (t+25)$$
$$125t + 3125 = 250(3t+5)$$
$$125t + 3125 = 750t + 1250$$
$$3125 = 625t + 1250$$
$$1875 = 625t$$
$$3 = t$$

It will take 3 years for the population to reach 125 elk.

57. $S = 1 - r; S = 200, C = 140$

$$200 = \dfrac{140}{1-r}$$
$$200(1-r) = \dfrac{140}{1-r} \cdot 1 - r$$
$$200 - 200r = 140$$
$$-200r = -60$$
$$r = \dfrac{-60}{-200} = \dfrac{3}{10} = 30\%$$

The markup is 30%.

58. Let $x =$ the rate of the current.

Then $20 + x =$ the rate of the boat with the current

and $20 - x =$ the rate of the boat against the current.

	$d \times$	r	$= t$
With the Current	72	$20+x$	$\dfrac{72}{20+x}$
Against the Current	48	$20-x$	$\dfrac{48}{20-x}$

The times are equal, so

$$\dfrac{72}{20+x} = \dfrac{48}{20-x}$$

This equation is a proportion, so it can be solved using the cross-products principle.

$$72(20-x) = 48(20+x)$$
$$1440 - 72x = 960 + 48x$$
$$1440 = 960 + 120x$$
$$480 = 120x$$
$$4 = x$$

The rate of the current is 4 miles per hour.

59. Let $\quad x =$ the rate of the slower car.
Then $x + 10 =$ the rate of the faster car.

	$d \times$	r	$= t$
Slower Car	60	x	$\dfrac{60}{x}$
Faster Car	90	$x + 10$	$\dfrac{90}{x + 10}$

$$\frac{60}{x} = \frac{90}{x + 10}$$
$$60(x + 10) = 90x$$
$$60x + 600 = 90x$$
$$600 = 30x$$
$$20 = x$$

If $x = 20, x + 10 = 30$.
The rate of the slower car is 20 miles per hour and the rate of the faster car is 30 miles per hour.

60. Let $x =$ the time, in hours, for both people to paint the fence together.

	Fractional part of job completed in 1 hour	Time working together	Fractional part of job completed in x hours
Painter	$\dfrac{1}{6}$	x	$\dfrac{x}{6}$
Apprentice	$\dfrac{1}{12}$	x	$\dfrac{x}{12}$

Working together, the two people complete one whole job, so
$$\frac{x}{6} + \frac{x}{12} = 1.$$
Multiply both sides by the LCD, 12.
$$12\left(\frac{x}{6} + \frac{x}{12}\right) = 12 \cdot 1$$
$$2x + x = 12$$
$$3x = 12$$
$$x = 4$$

It would take them 4 hours to paint the fence working together.

61. Let x = number of teachers needed for 5400 students.

$$\frac{3}{50} = \frac{x}{5400}$$
$$50x = 3 \cdot 5400$$
$$50x = 16{,}200$$
$$\frac{50x}{50} = \frac{16{,}200}{50}$$
$$x = 324$$

For an enrollment of 5400 students, 324 teachers are needed.

62. Let x = number of trout in the lake.

$$\frac{\text{Original number of tagged trout}}{\text{Total number of trout}} = \frac{\text{Number of tagged trout in sample}}{\text{Number of trout in sample}}$$

$$\frac{112}{x} = \frac{32}{82}$$
$$32x = 112 \cdot 82$$
$$32x = 9184$$
$$\frac{32x}{32} = \frac{9184}{32}$$
$$x = 287$$

There are 287 trout in the lake.

63. $$\frac{8}{4} = \frac{10}{x}$$
$$8x = 40$$
$$x = 5$$

The length of the side marked with an x is 5 feet.

64. $b = ke$

Find k.
$$b = ke$$
$$98 = k(1400)$$
$$0.07 = k$$

The equation becomes $b = 0.07e$. When $e = 2200$ kilowatts, $b = 0.07(2200) = 154$.

If 2200 kilowatts are used, the electric bill will be \$154.

65. $t = \dfrac{k}{r}$

Find k.
$$t = \frac{k}{r}$$
$$4 = \frac{k}{50}$$
$$200 = k$$

The equation becomes $t = \frac{200}{r}$. When $r = 40$, $t = \frac{200}{40} = 5$.

It will take 5 hours at 40 miles per hour.

66. $l = \dfrac{k}{d^2}$

Find k.
$$l = \frac{k}{d^2}$$
$$28 = \frac{k}{8^2}$$
$$28 = \frac{k}{64}$$
$$1792 \quad k$$

The equation becomes $l = \frac{1792}{d^2}$. When $d = 4$,
$$l = \frac{1792}{(4)^2} = \frac{1792}{16} = 112.$$

At a distance of 4 feet, the loudness of the stereo is 112 decibels.

67. $t = \dfrac{kn}{w}$

Find k.
$$t = \frac{kn}{w}$$
$$10 = \frac{k(30)}{6}$$
$$10 = 5k$$
$$2 = k$$

The equation becomes $t = \frac{2n}{w}$. When $n = 40$ and $w = 5$, $t = \frac{2(40)}{5} = \frac{80}{5} = 16$.

It will take 16 hours for 5 workers to assemble 40 computers.

68. $v = kha$

Find k.

$$175 = k(15)(35)$$
$$175 = k(525)$$
$$\frac{1}{3} = k$$

The equation becomes $v = \frac{1}{3}ha$. When $h = 20$ feet and $a = 120$ square feet, $v = \frac{1}{3}(20)(120) = 800$.

If the height is 20 feet and the area is 120 square feet, the volume will be 800 cubic feet.

Chapter 7 Test

1. $\dfrac{x+7}{x^2+5x-36}$

Set the denominator equal to 0 and solve for x.

$$x^2 + 5x - 36 = 0$$
$$(x+9)(x-4) = 0$$
$$x + 9 = 0 \quad \text{or} \quad x - 4 = 0$$
$$x = -9 \qquad\qquad x = 4$$

The rational expression is undefined for $x = -9$ and $x = 4$.

2. $\dfrac{x^2+2x-3}{x^2-3x+2} = \dfrac{(x-1)(x+3)}{(x-1)(x-2)} = \dfrac{x+3}{x-2}$

3. $\dfrac{4x^2-20x}{x^2-4x-5} = \dfrac{4x(x-5)}{(x+1)(x-5)} = \dfrac{4x}{x+1}$

4. $\dfrac{x^2-16}{10} \cdot \dfrac{5}{x+4} = \dfrac{(x+4)(x-4)}{10} \cdot \dfrac{5}{(x+4)}$

$$= \dfrac{x-4}{2}$$

5. $\dfrac{x^2-7x+12}{x^2-4x} \cdot \dfrac{x^2}{x^2-9}$

$$= \dfrac{(x-3)(x-4)}{x(x-4)} \cdot \dfrac{x^2}{(x+3)(x-3)}$$

$$= \dfrac{x}{x+3}$$

6. $\dfrac{2x+8}{x-3} \div \dfrac{x^2+5x+4}{x^2-9}$

$$= \dfrac{2x+8}{x-3} \cdot \dfrac{x^2-9}{x^2+5x+4}$$

$$= \dfrac{2(x+4)}{(x-3)} \cdot \dfrac{(x+3)(x-3)}{(x+4)(x+1)}$$

$$= \dfrac{2(x+3)}{x+1} = \dfrac{2x+6}{x+1}$$

7. $\dfrac{5y+5}{(y-3)^2} \div \dfrac{y^2-1}{y-3}$

$$= \dfrac{5y+5}{(y-3)^2} \cdot \dfrac{y-3}{y^2-1}$$

$$= \dfrac{5(y+1)}{(y-3)(y-3)} \cdot \dfrac{(y-3)}{(y+1)(y-1)}$$

$$= \dfrac{5}{(y-3)(y-1)}$$

8. $\dfrac{2y^2+5}{y+3} + \dfrac{6y-5}{y+3}$

$$= \dfrac{(2y^2+5)+(6y-5)}{y+3}$$

$$= \dfrac{2y^2+5+6y-5}{y+3}$$

$$= \dfrac{2y^2+6y}{y+3}$$

$$= \dfrac{2y(y+3)}{y+3} = 2y$$

9. $\dfrac{y^2 - 2y + 3}{y^2 + 7y + 12} - \dfrac{y^2 - 4y - 5}{y^2 + 7y + 12}$

$$= \dfrac{(y^2 - 2y + 3) - (y^2 - 4y - 5)}{y^2 + 7y + 12}$$

$$= \dfrac{y^2 - 2y + 3 - y^2 + 4y + 5}{y^2 + 7y + 12}$$

$$= \dfrac{2y + 8}{y^2 + 7y + 12}$$

$$= \dfrac{2(y + 4)}{y^2 + 7y + 12}$$

$$= \dfrac{2(y + 4)}{(y + 3)(y + 4)}$$

$$= \dfrac{2}{y + 3}$$

$\dfrac{2}{x^2 - 4x + 3} + \dfrac{6}{x^2 + x - 2}$

$$= \dfrac{2}{(x - 1)(x - 3)} + \dfrac{6}{(x - 1)(x + 2)}$$

$$= \dfrac{2(x + 2)}{(x - 1)(x - 3)(x + 2)}$$

$$+ \dfrac{6(x - 3)}{(x - 1)(x - 3)(x + 2)}$$

$$= \dfrac{2(x + 2) + 6(x - 3)}{(x - 1)(x - 3)(x + 2)}$$

$$= \dfrac{2x + 4 + 6x - 18}{(x - 1)(x - 3)(x + 2)}$$

$$= \dfrac{8x - 14}{(x - 1)(x - 3)(x + 2)}$$

10. $\dfrac{x}{x + 3} + \dfrac{5}{x - 3}$

$\text{LCD} = (x + 3)(x - 3)$

$\dfrac{x}{x + 3} + \dfrac{5}{x - 3}$

$$= \dfrac{x(x - 3)}{(x + 3)(x - 3)} + \dfrac{5(x + 3)}{(x + 3)(x - 3)}$$

$$= \dfrac{x(x - 3) + 5(x + 3)}{(x + 3)(x - 3)}$$

$$= \dfrac{x^2 - 3x + 5x + 15}{(x + 3)(x - 3)}$$

$$= \dfrac{x^2 + 2x + 15}{(x + 3)(x - 3)}$$

12. $\dfrac{4}{x - 3} + \dfrac{x + 5}{3 - x}$

$$3 - x = -1(x - 3)$$

$\text{LCD} = x - 3$

$\dfrac{4}{x - 3} + \dfrac{x + 5}{3 - x}$

$$= \dfrac{4}{x - 3} + \dfrac{(-1)}{(-1)} \cdot \dfrac{(x + 5)}{(3 - x)}$$

$$= \dfrac{4}{x - 3} + \dfrac{-x - 5}{x - 3}$$

$$= \dfrac{4 - x - 5}{x - 3} = \dfrac{-x - 1}{x - 3}$$

11. $\dfrac{2}{x^2 - 4x + 3} + \dfrac{6}{x^2 + x - 2}$

$$x^2 - 4x + 3 = (x - 1)(x - 3)$$
$$x^2 + x - 2 = (x - 1)(x + 2)$$

$$\text{LCD} = (x - 1)(x - 3)(x + 2)$$

13. $1 + \dfrac{3}{x - 1}$

$\text{LCD} = x - 1$

$$1 + \dfrac{3}{x - 1} = \dfrac{1(x - 1)}{x - 1} + \dfrac{3}{x - 1}$$

$$= \dfrac{x - 1 + 3}{x - 1} = \dfrac{x + 2}{x - 1}$$

14. $\dfrac{2x+3}{x^2-7x+12}-\dfrac{2}{x-3}$

$$x^2-7x+12=(x-3)(x-4)$$
$$x-3=1(x-3)$$

$$\text{LCD}=(x-3)(x-4)$$

$$\dfrac{2x+3}{x^2-7x+12}-\dfrac{2}{x-3}$$

$$=\dfrac{2x+3}{(x-3)(x-4)}-\dfrac{2(x-4)}{(x-3)(x-4)}$$

$$=\dfrac{2x+3-2(x-4)}{(x-3)(x-4)}$$

$$=\dfrac{2x+3-2x+8}{(x-3)(x-4)}$$

$$=\dfrac{11}{(x-3)(x-4)}$$

15. $\dfrac{8y}{y^2-16}-\dfrac{4}{y-4}$

$$y^2-16=(y+4)(y-4)$$
$$y-4=1(y-4)$$

$$\text{LCD}=(y+4)(y-4)$$

$$\dfrac{8y}{y^2-16}-\dfrac{4}{y-4}$$

$$=\dfrac{8y}{(y+4)(y-4)}-\dfrac{4}{y-4}$$

$$=\dfrac{8y}{(y+4)(y-4)}-\dfrac{4(y+4)}{(y+4)(y-4)}$$

$$=\dfrac{8y-4(y+4)}{(y+4)(y-4)}$$

$$=\dfrac{8y-4y-16}{(y+4)(y-4)}$$

$$=\dfrac{4y-16}{(y+4)(y-4)}$$

$$=\dfrac{4(y-4)}{(y+4)(y-4)}$$

$$=\dfrac{4}{y+4}$$

16. $\dfrac{(x-y)^2}{x+y}\div\dfrac{x^2-xy}{3x+3y}$

$$=\dfrac{(x-y)^2}{x+y}\cdot\dfrac{3x+3y}{x^2-xy}$$

$$=\dfrac{(x-y)(x-y)}{(x+y)}\cdot\dfrac{3(x+y)}{x(x-y)}$$

$$=\dfrac{3(x-y)}{x}$$

$$=\dfrac{3x-3y}{x}$$

17. $\dfrac{5+\dfrac{5}{x}}{2+\dfrac{1}{x}}=\dfrac{\dfrac{5x}{x}+\dfrac{5}{x}}{\dfrac{2x}{x}+\dfrac{1}{x}}$

$$=\dfrac{\dfrac{5x+5}{x}}{\dfrac{2x+1}{x}}$$

$$=\dfrac{5x+5}{x}\cdot\dfrac{x}{2x+1}$$

$$=\dfrac{5x+5}{2x+1}$$

18. $\dfrac{\dfrac{1}{x}-\dfrac{1}{y}}{\dfrac{1}{x}}$

$$\text{LCD}=xy$$

$$\dfrac{\dfrac{1}{x}-\dfrac{1}{y}}{\dfrac{1}{x}}=\dfrac{xy}{xy}\cdot\dfrac{\left(\dfrac{1}{x}-\dfrac{1}{y}\right)}{\left(\dfrac{1}{x}\right)}$$

$$=\dfrac{xy\cdot\dfrac{1}{x}-xy\cdot\dfrac{1}{y}}{xy\cdot\dfrac{1}{x}}$$

$$=\dfrac{y-x}{y}$$

19. $\dfrac{5}{x} + \dfrac{2}{3} = 2 - \dfrac{2}{x} - \dfrac{1}{6}$

Restriction: $x \neq 0$

LCD $= 6x$

$$6x\left(\dfrac{5}{x} + \dfrac{2}{3}\right) = 6x\left(2 - \dfrac{2}{x} - \dfrac{1}{6}\right)$$

$$6x \cdot \dfrac{5}{x} + 6x \cdot \dfrac{2}{3} = 6x \cdot 2 - 6x \cdot \dfrac{2}{x} - 6x \cdot \dfrac{1}{6}$$

$$30 + 4x = 12x - 12 - 6$$

$$30 + 4x = 12x - 18$$

$$30 = 8x - 18$$

$$48 = 8x$$

$$6 = x$$

The solution is 6.

20. $\dfrac{3}{y+5} - 1 = \dfrac{4-y}{2y+10}$

$\dfrac{3}{y+5} - 1 = \dfrac{4-y}{2(y+5)}$

Restriction: $y \neq -5$

LCD $= 2(y+5)$

$$2(y+5)\left(\dfrac{3}{y+5} - 1\right) = 2(y+5)\left[\dfrac{4-y}{2(y+5)}\right]$$

$$6 - 2(y+5) = 4 - y$$

$$6 - 2y - 10 = 4 - y$$

$$-4 - 2y = 4 - y$$

$$-4 = 4 + y$$

$$-8 = y$$

The solution is -8.

21. $\dfrac{2}{x-1} = \dfrac{3}{x^2-1} + 1$

$\dfrac{2}{x-1} = \dfrac{3}{(x+1)(x-1)} + 1$

Restrictions: $x \neq 1, x \neq -1$

LCD $= (x+1)(x-1)$

$$(x+1)(x-1)\left(\dfrac{2}{x-1}\right)$$

$$= (x+1)(x-1)\left[\dfrac{3}{(x+1)(x-1)} + 1\right]$$

$$2(x+1) = 3(x+1)(x-1)$$

$$2x + 2 = 3 + x^2 - 1$$

$$2x + 2 = 2 + x^2$$

$$0 = x^2 - 2x$$

$$0 = x(x-2)$$

$$x = 0 \quad \text{or} \quad x - 2 = 0$$

The equation has two solutions, 0 and 2.

22. Let $\quad x =$ the rate of the current.

Then $30 - x =$ the rate of the boat with the current.

and $\quad 30 - x =$ the rate of the boat against the current..

	$d \times$	r	$= t$
With the Current	16	$30 + x$	$\dfrac{16}{30+x}$
Against the Current	14	$30 - x$	$\dfrac{14}{30-x}$

$$\dfrac{16}{30+x} = \dfrac{14}{30-x}$$

$$16(30-x) = 14(30+x)$$

$$480 - 16x = 420 + 14x$$

$$480 = 420 + 30x$$

$$60 = 30x$$

$$2 = x$$

The rate of the current is 2 miles per hour.

23. Let $x =$ the time (in minutes) for both pipes to fill the hot tub.

$$\frac{x}{20} + \frac{x}{30} = 1$$

LCD $= 60$

$$60\left(\frac{x}{20} + \frac{x}{30}\right) = 60 \cdot 1$$
$$3x + 2x = 60$$
$$5x = 60$$
$$x = 12$$

It will take 12 minutes for both pipes to fill the hot tub.

24. Let $x =$ number of tule elk in the park.

$$\frac{200}{x} = \frac{5}{150}$$
$$5x = 30{,}000$$
$$x = 6000$$

There are 6000 tule elk in the park.

25. $\quad \dfrac{10}{4} = \dfrac{8}{x}$

$$10x = 8 \cdot 4$$
$$10x = 32$$
$$x = 3.2$$

The length of the side marked with an x is 3.2 inches.

26. Let $\quad C =$ the current (in amperes).
Then $R =$ the resistance (in ohms).

Step 1 $C = \dfrac{k}{R}$

Step 2 To find k, substitute 42 for C and 5 for R.

$$42 = \frac{k}{5}$$
$$42 \cdot 5 = \frac{k}{5} \cdot 5$$
$$210 = k$$

Step 3 $C = \dfrac{210}{R}$

Step 4 Substitute 4 for R and solve for C.

$$C = \frac{210}{4} = 52.5$$

When the resistance is 4 ohms, the current is 52.5 amperes.

Cumulative Review Exercises (Chapters 1-7)

1. $2(x - 3) + 5x = 8(x - 1)$
$$2x - 6 + 5x = 8x - 8$$
$$7x - 6 = 8x - 8$$
$$-6 = x - 8$$
$$2 = x$$

The solution is 2.

2. $-3(2x - 4) > 2(6x - 12)$
$$-6x + 12 > 12x - 24$$
$$-18x + 12 > -24$$
$$-18x > -36$$
$$\frac{-18x}{-18} < \frac{-36}{-18}$$
$$x < 2$$

Solution set: $\{x \mid x < 2\}$

3. $\qquad x^2 + 3x = 18$
$$x^2 + 3x - 18 = 0$$
$$(x + 6)(x - 3) = 0$$
$$x + 6 = 0 \quad \text{or} \quad x - 3 = 0$$
$$x = -6 \qquad\qquad x = 3$$

The solutions are -6 and 3.

4. $\dfrac{2x}{x^2-4} + \dfrac{1}{x-2} = \dfrac{2}{x+2}$

$$x^2 - 4 = (x+2)(x-2)$$

Restrictions: $x \neq -2, x = 2$
LCD $= (x+2)(x-2)$

$$\frac{2x}{(x+2)(x-2)} + \frac{1}{x-2} = \frac{2}{x+2}$$

$$(x+2)(x-2)\left[\frac{2x}{(x+2)(x-2)} + \frac{1}{x-2}\right]$$

$$= (x+2)(x-2)\cdot\frac{2}{x+2}$$

$$2x + (x+2) = 2(x-2)$$
$$3x + 2 = 2x - 4$$
$$x = -6$$

The solution is -6.

5. $y = 2x - 3$
$x + 2y = 9$

To solve this system by the substitution method, substitute $2x-3$ for y in the second equation.

$$x + 2y = 9$$
$$x + 2(2x-3) = 9$$
$$x + 4x - 6 = 9$$
$$5x - 6 = 9$$
$$5x = 15$$
$$x = 3$$

Back-substitute 3 for x into the first equation.

$$y = 2x - 3$$
$$y = 2\cdot 3 - 3 = 3$$

Solution: $(3,3)$

6. $3x + 2y = -2$
$-4x + 5y = 18$

To solve this system by the addition method, multiply the first equation by 4 and the second equation by 3.
Then add the equations.

$$12x + 8y = -8$$
$$\underline{-12x + 15y = 54}$$
$$23y = 46$$
$$y = 2$$

Back-substitute 2 for y in the first equation of the original system.

$$3x + 2y = -2$$
$$3x + 2(2) = -2$$
$$3x + 4 = -2$$
$$3x = -6$$
$$x = -2$$

Solution: $(-2, 2)$

7. $3x - 2y = 6$
x-intercept: 2
y-intercept: -3
checkpoint: $(4,3)$
Draw a line through $(2,0)$, $(0,-3)$ and $(4,3)$.

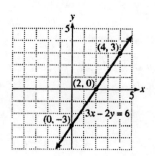

8. $y = -2x + 3$

Graph $y = -2x + 3$ using its slope, $-2 = \frac{-2}{1}$, and its y-intercept, 3.

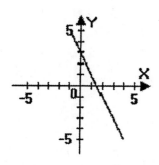

9. $y = -3$

The graph is a horizontal line with y-intercept -3.

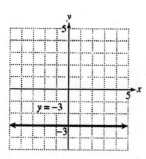

10. $-21 - 16 - 3(2 - 8) = -21 - 16 - 3(-6)$
$$= -21 - 16 + 18$$
$$= -37 + 18 = -19$$

11. $\left(\dfrac{4x^5}{2x^2}\right)^3 = (2x^3)^3 = 2^3 \cdot (x^3)^3 = 8x^9$

12. $\dfrac{\dfrac{1}{x} - 2}{4 - \dfrac{1}{x}}$

LCD $= x$

$$\frac{\dfrac{1}{x} - 2}{4 - \dfrac{1}{x}} = \frac{x\left(\dfrac{1}{x} - 2\right)}{x\left(4 - \dfrac{1}{x}\right)}$$

$$= \frac{x \cdot \dfrac{1}{x} - x \cdot 2}{x \cdot 4 - x \cdot \dfrac{1}{x}}$$

$$= \frac{1 - 2x}{4x - 1}$$

13. $4x^2 - 13x + 3$

Factor by trial and error. Try various combinations until the correct one is found.

$$4x^2 - 13x + 3 = (4x - 1)(x - 3)$$

14. $4x^2 - 20x + 25 = (2x)^2 - 2 \cdot 2x \cdot 5 + 5^2$
$$= (2x - 5)^2$$

15. $3x^2 - 75 = 3(x^2 - 25)$
$$= 3(x + 5)(x - 5)$$

16. $(4x^2 - 3x + 2) - (5x^2 - 7x - 6)$
$$= (4x^2 - 3x + 2) + (-5x^2 + 7x + 6)$$
$$= -x^2 + 4x + 8$$

17. $\dfrac{-8x^6 + 12x^4 - 4x^2}{4x^2} = \dfrac{-8x^6}{4x^2} + \dfrac{12x^4}{4x^2} - \dfrac{4x^2}{4x^2}$
$$= -2x^4 + 3x^2 - 1$$

18. $\dfrac{x+6}{x-2} + \dfrac{2x+1}{x+3}$

LCD $= (x-2)(x+3)$

$\dfrac{x+6}{x-2} + \dfrac{2x+1}{x+3}$

$= \dfrac{(x+6)(x+3)}{(x-2)(x+3)} + \dfrac{(2x+1)(x-2)}{(x-2)(x+3)}$

$= \dfrac{(x+6)(x+3) + (2x+1)(x-2)}{(x-2)(x+3)}$

$= \dfrac{x^2 + 9x + 18 + 2x^2 - 3x - 2}{(x-2)(x+3)}$

$= \dfrac{3x^2 + 6x + 16}{(x-2)(x+3)}$

19. Let $x =$ the amount invested at 5%.

Then $4000 - x =$ the amount invested at 9%.

$0.05x + 0.09(4000 - x) = 311$
$0.05x + 360 - 0.09x = 311$
$-0.04x + 360 = 311$
$-0.04x = -49$
$x = \dfrac{-49}{-0.04}$
$= 1225$

If $x = 1225$, then $4000 - x = 2775$.
$1225 was invested at 5% and $2775 at 9%.

20. Let $x =$ the length of the shorter piece.

Then $3x =$ the length of the larger piece.

$x + 3x = 68$
$4x = 68$
$x = 17$

If $x = 17$, then $3x = 51$.
The lengths of the pieces are 17 inches and 51 inches.

Chapter 8

FUNCTIONS; MORE ON SYSTEMS OF LINEAR EQUATIONS

Introduction to Functions

8.1 CHECK POINTS

CHECK POINT 1

domain $\{5, 10, 15, 20, 25\}$

range $\{12.8, 16.2, 18.9, 20.7, 21.8\}$

CHECK POINT 2

a. The relation is not a function. The domain element 5 is paired with more than one element of the range.
b. The relation is a function.

CHECK POINT 3

a. $f(6) = 4(6) + 5 = 24 + 5 = 29$
b. $g(-5) = 3(-5)^2 - 10$
   $= 3(25) - 10 = 75 - 10 = 65$
c. $h(-4) = (-4)^2 - 7(-4) + 2$
   $= 16 + 28 + 2 = 46$
d. $F(a+h) = 6(a+h) + 9 = 6a + 6h + 9$

CHECK POINT 4

a. The vertical line test shows that this is the graph of a function.
b. The vertical line test shows that this is the graph of a function.
c. The vertical line test shows that this is not the graph of a function.

CHECK POINT 5

a. $f(10) \approx 16$
b. $x \approx 8$

EXERCISE SET 8.1

1. The relation is a function.
   Domain $\{1, 3, 5\}$
   Range $\{2, 4, 5\}$

3. The relation is not a function.
   Domain $\{3, 4\}$
   Range $\{4, 5\}$

5. The relation is a function.
   Domain $\{-3, -2, -1, 0\}$
   Range $\{-3, -2, -1, 0\}$

7. The relation is not a function.
   Domain $\{1\}$
   Range $\{4, 5, 6\}$

9. a. $f(0) = 0 + 1 = 1$
   b. $f(5) = 5 + 1 = 6$
   c. $f(-8) = -8 + 1 = -7$
   d. $f(2a) = 2a + 1$
   e. $f(a+2) = (a+2) + 1$
      $= a + 2 + 1 = a + 3$

11. a. $g(0) = 3(0) - 2 = 0 - 2 = -2$
    b. $g(-5) = 3(-5) - 2 = -15 - 2 = -17$
    c. $g\left(\dfrac{2}{3}\right) = 3\left(\dfrac{2}{3}\right) - 2 = 2 - 2 = 0$
    d. $g(4b) = 3(4b) - 2 = 12b - 2$
    e. $g(b+4) = 3(b+4) - 2$
       $= 3b + 12 - 2 = 3b + 10$

13. a. $h(0) = 3(0)^2 + 5 = 3(0) + 5$
       $= 0 + 5 = 5$
    b. $h(-1) = 3(-1)^2 + 5 = 3(1) + 5$
       $= 3 + 5 = 8$
    c. $h(4) = 3(4)^2 + 5 = 3(16) + 5$
       $= 48 + 5 = 53$
    d. $h(-3) = 3(-3)^2 + 5 = 3(9) + 5$
       $= 27 + 5 = 32$
    e. $h(4b) = 3(4b)^2 + 5 = 3(16b^2) + 5$
       $= 48b^2 + 5$

15.   **a.** $f(0) = 2(0)^2 + 3(0) - 1 = -1$

     b. $f(3) = 2(3)^2 + 3(3) - 1$
$$= 2(9) + 9 - 1 = 18 + 9 - 1 = 26$$

     c. $f(-4) = 2(-4)^2 + 3(-4) - 1$
$$= 2(16) - 12 - 1$$
$$= 32 - 12 - 1 = 19$$

     d. $f(b) = 2(b)^2 + 3(b) - 1 = 2b^2 + 3b - 1$

     e. $f(5a) = 2(5a)^2 + 3(5a) - 1$
$$= 2(25a^2) + 15a - 1$$
$$= 50a^2 + 15a - 1$$

17.   **a.** $f(0) = \dfrac{2(0) - 3}{(0) - 4} = \dfrac{-3}{-4} = \dfrac{3}{4}$

     b. $f(3) = \dfrac{2(3) - 3}{(3) - 4} = \dfrac{6 - 3}{3 - 4} = \dfrac{3}{-1} = -3$

     c. $f(-4) = \dfrac{2(-4) - 3}{(-4) - 4} = \dfrac{-8 - 3}{-8}$
$$= \dfrac{-11}{-8} = \dfrac{11}{8}$$

     d. $f(-5) = \dfrac{2(-5) - 3}{(-5) - 4} = \dfrac{-10 - 3}{-9}$
$$= \dfrac{-13}{-9} = \dfrac{13}{9}$$

     e. $f(a + h) = \dfrac{2(a + h) - 3}{(a + h) - 4}$
$$= \dfrac{2a + 2h - 3}{a + h - 4}$$

     f.   Four must be excluded from the domain, because 4 would make the denominator zero. Division by zero is undefined.

19.   The vertical line test shows that the graph represents a function.

21.   The vertical line test shows that the graph represents a function.

23.   The vertical line test shows that the graph

does not represent a function.

25.   The vertical line test shows that the graph represents a function.

27. $f(-2) = -4$

29. $f(4) = 4$

31. $f(-3) = 0$

33. $g(-4) = 2$

35. $g(-10) = 2$

37.   When $x = -2$, $g(x) = 1$.

39. $\{(1, 31), (2, 53), (3, 70), (4, 86), (5, 86)\}$
Domain $\{1, 2, 3, 4, 5\}$
Range $\{31, 53, 70, 86\}$
The relation is a function.

41. $W(16) = 0.07(16) + 4.1 = 1.12 + 4.1 = 5.22$

In 2000, there were 5.22 million women enrolled in U.S. colleges. This is represented by the point (16, 5.2) on the graph. (Coordinates are approximate.)

43. $W(20) = 0.07(20) + 4.1 = 1.4 + 4.1 = 5.5$

$M(20) = 0.01(20) + 3.9 = 0.2 + 3.9 = 4.1$

$W(20) - M(20) = 5.5 - 4.1 = 1.4$

In 2004, there will be 1.4 million more women than men enrolled in U.S. colleges.

45. $f(20) = 0.4(20)^2 - 36(20) + 1000$
$$= 0.4(400) - 720 + 1000$$
$$= 160 - 720 + 1000$$
$$= -560 + 1000 = 440$$

Twenty-year-old drivers have 440 accidents per 50 million miles driven.

47.   The graph reaches its lowest point at $x = 45$.

$$f(45) = 0.4(45)^2 - 36(45) + 1000$$
$$= 0.4(2025) - 1620 + 1000$$
$$= 810 - 1620 + 1000$$
$$= -810 + 1000 = 190$$

Drivers at age 45 have 190 accidents per 50 million miles driven. This is the least number of accidents for any driver between ages 16 and 74.

49. $f(60) \approx 3.1$

In 1960, 3.1% of the U.S. population was made up of Jewish Americans.

51. In 1919 and 1964, $f(x) = 3$. This means that in 1919 and 1964, 3% of the U.S. population was made up of Jewish Americans.

53. The percentage of Jewish Americans in the U.S. population reached a maximum in 1940. Using the graph to estimate, approximately 3.7% of the U.S. population were Jewish Americans.

55. Each year is paired with exactly one percentage. This means that each member of the domain is paired with one member of the range.

57. $f(3) = 0.76$

The cost of mailing a first-class letter weighing 3 ounces is $0.76.

59. The cost to mail a letter weighing 1.5 ounces is $0.55.

For Exercises 61-67, answers may vary.

69. $f(a+h) = 3(a+h) + 7 = 3a + 3h + 7$
$f(a) = 3a + 7$
$$\frac{f(a+h) - f(a)}{h} = \frac{(3a + 3h + 7) - (3a + 7)}{h}$$
$$= \frac{3a + 3h + 7 - 3a - 7}{h}$$
$$= \frac{3h}{h} = 3$$

71. We know that $f(x+y) = f(x) + f(y)$ and $f(1) = 3$.
$f(2) = f(1+1) = f(1) + f(1) = 3 + 3 = 6$
$f(3) = f(2+1) = f(2) + f(1) = 6 + 3 = 9$
$f(4) = f(3+1) = f(3) + f(1) = 9 + 3 = 12$
While $f(x+y) = f(x) + f(y)$ is true for this function, it is not true for all functions.

73.

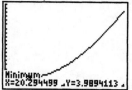

The number of physician's visits first decreases, then increases over time.

These are the approximate coordinates of the point (20.3, 4.0). The minimum number of physician's visits per year is approximately 4. This occurs around age 20.

Review Exercises

74. $24 \div 4\left[2 - (5-2)\right]^2 - 6$
$$= 24 \div 4\left[2 - (3)\right]^2 - 6$$
$$= 24 \div 4\left[-1\right]^2 - 6 = 24 \div 4\left[1\right] - 6$$
$$= 6\left[1\right] - 6 = 6 - 6 = 0$$

75. $\left(\frac{3x^2 y^{-2}}{y^3}\right)^{-2} = \left(\frac{3x^2}{y^2 y^3}\right)^{-2} = \left(\frac{3x^2}{y^5}\right)^{-2}$
$$= \left(\frac{y^5}{3x^2}\right)^2 = \frac{y^{5 \cdot 2}}{3^2 x^{2 \cdot 2}} = \frac{y^{10}}{9x^4}$$

76. $\frac{x}{3} = \frac{3x}{5} + 4$
$$15\left(\frac{x}{3}\right) = 15\left(\frac{3x}{5} + 4\right)$$

$$15\left(\frac{x}{3}\right)=15\left(\frac{3x}{5}\right)+15(4)$$
$$5x=3(3x)+60$$
$$5x=9x+60$$
$$-4x=60$$
$$x=-15$$

The Algebra of Functions

8.2 CHECK POINTS

CHECK POINT 1

a. Domain of $f=\{x|x \text{ is a real number}\}$.

b. Domain of $g=\{x|x \text{ is a real number and } x\neq-5\}$.

CHECK POINT 2

a. $(f+g)(x)=f(x)+g(x)$
$$=(3x^2+4x-1)+(2x+7)$$
$$=3x^2+4x-1+2x+7$$
$$=3x^2+6x+6$$

b. $(f+g)(4)=3(4)^2+6(4)+6$
$$=3(16)+24+6$$
$$=48+24+6=78$$

CHECK POINT 3

a. $(f+g)(x)=f(x)+g(x)$
$$=\frac{5}{x}+\frac{7}{x-8}$$

b. Domain of $f+g=\{x|x \text{ is a real number and, } x\neq0 \text{ and } x\neq8\}$

CHECK POINT 4

a. $f(5)=(5)^2-2(5)=25-10=15$
$$g(5)=5+3=8$$
$$(f+g)(5)=f(5)+g(5)=15+8=23$$

b. $(f-g)(x)=f(x)-g(x)=(x^2-2x)-(x+3)$
$$=x^2-2x-x-3=x^2-3x-3$$

$$(f-g)(-1)=(-1)^2-3(-1)-3$$
$$=1+3-3=1$$

c. $f(-4)=(-4)^2-2(-4)=16+8=24$
$$g(-4)=-4+3=-1$$
$$(fg)(-4)=f(-4)\cdot g(-4)=24(-1)=-24$$

d. $\left(\dfrac{f}{g}\right)(x)=\dfrac{f(x)}{g(x)}=\dfrac{x^2-2x}{x+3}$

$$\left(\frac{f}{g}\right)(7)=\frac{7^2-2(7)}{7+3}=\frac{49-14}{10}=\frac{35}{10}=\frac{7}{2}$$

EXERCISE SET 8.2

1. Domain of $f=\{x|x \text{ is a real number}\}$

3. Domain of $g=\{x|x \text{ is a real number and } x\neq-4\}$.

5. Domain of $f=\{x|x \text{ is a real number and } x\neq3\}$.

7. Domain of $g=\{x|x \text{ is a real number and } x\neq5\}$.

9. Domain of $f=\{x|x \text{ is a real number and } x\neq-7 \text{ and } x\neq9\}$

11. **a.** $(f+g)(x)=(3x+1)+(2x-6)$
$$=3x+1+2x-6=5x-5$$
b. $(f+g)(5)=5(5)-5=25-5=20$

13. **a.** $(f+g)(x)=(x-5)+(3x^2)$
$$=x-5+3x^2=3x^2+x-5$$
b. $(f+g)(5)=3(5)^2+5-5$
$$=3(25)=75$$

15. **a.** $(f+g)(x)=(2x^2-x-3)+(x+1)$
$$=2x^2-x-3+x+1=2x^2-2$$

b. $(f+g)(5) = 2(5)^2 - 2 = 2(25) - 2$
$$= 50 - 2 = 48$$

17. Domain of $f+g = \{x | x \text{ is a real number}\}$.

19. Domain of $f+g = \{x | x \text{ is a real number}$ and $x \neq 5\}$.

21. Domain of $f+g = \{x | x \text{ is a real number}$ and $x \neq 0$ and $x \neq 5\}$.

23. Domain of $f+g = \{x | x \text{ is a real number}$ and $x \neq 2$ and $x \neq -3\}$.

25. Domain of $f+g = \{x | x \text{ is a real number}$ and $x \neq 2\}$.

27. Domain of $f+g = \{x | x \text{ is a real number}\}$.

29. $(f+g)(x) = f(x) + g(x)$
$$= x^2 + 4x + 2 - x = x^2 + 3x + 2$$
$(f+g)(3) = (3)^2 + 3(3) + 2 = 9 + 9 + 2 = 20$

31. $f(-2) = (-2)^2 + 4(-2) = 4 + (-8) = -4$
$g(-2) = 2 - (-2) = 2 + 2 = 4$
$f(-2) + g(-2) = -4 + 4 = 0$

33. $(f-g)(x) = f(x) - g(x) = (x^2 + 4x) - (2 - x)$
$$= x^2 + 4x - 2 + x = x^2 + 5x - 2$$
$(f-g)(3) = (5)^2 + 5(5) - 2$
$$= 25 + 25 - 2 = 48$$

35. From Exercise 31, we know
$f(-2) = -4$, and $g(-2) = 4$.
$f(-2) - g(-2) = -4 - 4 = -8$

37. $(fg)(x) = f(x) \cdot g(x) = (x^2 + 4x)(2 - x)$
$$= 2x^2 - x^3 + 8x - 4x^2$$

$$= -x^3 - 2x^2 + 8x$$
$(fg)(2) = -(2)^3 - 2(2)^2 + 8(2)$
$$= -8 - 2(4) + 16 = -8 - 8 + 16 = 0$$

39. From Exercise 37, we know
$(fg)(x) = -x^3 - 2x^2 + 8x$.
$(fg)(5) = -(5)^3 - 2(5)^2 + 8(5)$
$$= -125 - 2(25) + 40$$
$$= -125 - 50 + 40 = -135$$

41. $\left(\dfrac{f}{g}\right)(x) = \dfrac{f(x)}{g(x)} = \dfrac{x^2 + 4x}{2 - x}$
$\left(\dfrac{f}{g}\right)(1) = \dfrac{(1)^2 + 4(1)}{2 - (1)} = \dfrac{1 + 4}{1} = \dfrac{5}{1} = 5$

43. $\left(\dfrac{f}{g}\right)(-1) = \dfrac{(-1)^2 + 4(-1)}{2 - (-1)} = \dfrac{1 - 4}{3} = \dfrac{-3}{3} = -1$

45. Domain of $f+g = \{x | x \text{ is a real number}\}$

47. $\left(\dfrac{f}{g}\right)(x) = \dfrac{f(x)}{g(x)} = \dfrac{x^2 + 4x}{2 - x}$
Domain of $\dfrac{f}{g} = \{x | x \text{ is a real number and}$
$x \neq 2\}$.

49. $(D+C)(2000) = (D)(2000) + (C)(2000)$
$$= 14 + 6 = 20$$
This means that the total veterinary costs for dogs and cats in the year 2000 was $20 billion.

51. Domain of $D + C$ = {1983, 1987, 1991, 1996, 2000}.

53. $(f+g)(x)$ represents the total world population, $h(x)$.

55. $(f+g)(2000) = f(2000) + g(2000)$
$$= h(2000) = 5.9$$

This means that the total world population in the year 2000 was approximately 5.9 billion.

57.
$$(R - C)(x) = 65x - (600,000 + 45x)$$
$$= 65x - 600,000 - 45x$$
$$= 20x - 600,000$$
$$(R - C)(20,000) = 20(20,000) - 600,000$$
$$= 400,000 - 600,000$$
$$= -200,000$$

This means that if the company produces and sells 20,000 radios, it will lose $200,000.
$$(R - C)(30,000) = 20(30,000) - 600,000$$
$$= 600,000 - 600,000 = 0$$

If the company produces and sells 30,000 radios, it will break even with its costs equal to its revenue.
$$(R - C)(40,000) = 20(40,000) - 600,000$$
$$= 800,000 - 600,000$$
$$= 200,000$$

This means that if the company produces and sells 40,000 radios, it will make a profit of $200,000.

For Exercises 59-63, answers may vary.

65. To create a graph that shows the population, in billions, of the world's less-developed regions from 1950 through 2050, at each year, x, subtract the population of the world's more-developed regions, $f(x)$, from the total world population, $h(x)$. This will yield the population of the world's less-developed regions, $g(x)$. See graphing answer section.

67. $y_1 = 2x + 3$ $y_2 = 2 - 2x$
$y_3 = y_1 + y_2$

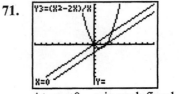

69. $y_1 = x$ $y_2 = x - 4$
$y_3 = y_1 \cdot y_2$

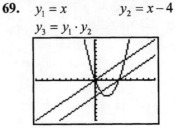

71.

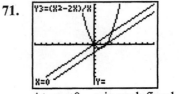

At $x = 0$, y is undefined. This is because at $x = 0$, the function, y_3 is undefined.

Review Exercises

72. $11x + 4y = -3$
$-13x + \ \ y = 15$

Multiply the second equation by -4 and solve by addition.
$$11x + 4y = -3$$
$$\underline{52x - 4y = -60}$$
$$63x = -63$$
$$x = -1$$

Back-substitute -1 for x to find y.
$$11(-1) + 4y = -3$$
$$-11 + 4y = -3$$
$$4y = 8$$
$$y = 2$$

The solution is $(-1, 2)$.

73. $3(6 - x) = 3 - 2(x - 4)$
$$18 - 3x = 3 - 2x + 8$$
$$18 - 3x = 11 - 2x$$
$$18 = 11 + x$$
$$7 = x$$

74. $f(b + 2) = 6(b + 2) - 4$
$$= 6b + 12 - 4 = 6b + 8$$

Systems of Linear Equations in Three Variables

8.3 CHECK POINTS

CHECK POINT 1

$$-1-2(-4)+3(5)=22$$
$$-1+8+15=22$$
$$22=22$$

$$2(-1)-3(-4)-5=5$$
$$-2+12-5=5$$
$$5=5$$

$$3(-1)+(-4)-5(5)=-32$$
$$-3-4-25=-32$$
$$-32=-32$$

The triple is a solution of the system.

CHECK POINT 2

Add the first and second equations to eliminate z.

$$\begin{array}{r} x+4y-\ z=\ 20 \\ 3x+2y+\ z=\ \ \ 8 \\ \hline 4x+6y=28 \end{array}$$

Multiply the first equation by 2 and add to the third equation.

$$\begin{array}{r} 2x+8y-2z=\ \ 40 \\ 2x-3y+2z=-16 \\ \hline 4x+5y=24 \end{array}$$

We have the following system of two equations in two variables.

$$4x+6y=28$$
$$4x+5y=24$$

Multiply the first equation by -1 and add.

$$\begin{array}{r} -4x-6y=-28 \\ 4x+5y=\ \ 24 \\ \hline -y=-4 \\ y=4 \end{array}$$

Back-substitute 4 for y to find x.

$$4x+6(4)=28$$
$$4x+24=28$$
$$4x=4$$
$$x=1$$

Back-substitute 1 for x and 4 for y to find z.

$$1+4(4)-z=20$$
$$1+16-z=20$$
$$17-z=20$$
$$-3=z$$

The solution is $(1,4,-3)$.

CHECK POINT 3

Multiply the second equation by -2 and add to the third equation.

$$\begin{array}{r} -2x-4y-2z=-34 \\ 2x-3y+2z=\ \ -1 \\ \hline -7y=-35 \\ y=5 \end{array}$$

Substitute 6 for y in the first equation to find z.

$$2(5)-z=7$$
$$10-z=7$$
$$3=z$$

Back-substitute 6 for y and 5 for z to find x.

$$x+2(5)+3=17$$
$$x+10+3=17$$
$$x+13=17$$
$$x=4$$

The solution is $(4,5,3)$.

CHECK POINT 4

When $x=1$ and $y=4$,

$$4=a(1)^2+b(1)+c$$
$$4=a(1)+b+c$$
$$4=a+b+c$$
$$\text{or } a+b+c=4$$

When $x=2$ and $y=1$,

$$1=a(2)^2+b(2)+c$$
$$1=a(4)+2b+c$$
$$1=4a+2b+c$$
$$\text{or } 4a+2b+c=1$$

When $x = 3$ and $y = 4$,

$4 = a(3)^2 + b(3) + c$

$4 = a(9) + 3b + c$

$4 = 9a + 3b + c$

or $9a + 3b + c = 4$

The resulting system is as follows.

$a + b + c = 4$

$4a + 2b + c = 1$

$9a + 3b + c = 4$

Multiply the first equation by -1 and add to the second equation to eliminate c.

$-a - b - c = -4$

$\underline{4a + 2b + c = 1}$

$3a + b = -3$

Multiply the first equation by -1 and add to the third equation.

$-a - b - c = -4$

$\underline{9a + 3b + c = 4}$

$8a + 2b = 0$

The resulting system is as follows.

$3a + b = -3$

$8a + 2b = 0$

Solve the first equation for b.

$3a + b = -3$

$b = -3a - 3$

Substitute $-3a - 3$ for b in the second equation.

$8a + 2(-3a - 3) = 0$

$8a - 6a - 6 = 0$

$2a - 6 = 0$

$2a = 6$

$a = 3$

Back-substitute 3 for a to find b.

$b = -3(3) - 3 = -9 - 3 = -12$

Back-substitute to find c.

$3 + (-12) + c = 4$

$-9 + c = 4$

$c = 13$

Now substitute the values for a, b, and c into $y = ax^2 + bx + c$. The function that models the given data is $y = 3x^2 - 12x + 13$.

EXERCISE SET 8.3

1. $2 - 1 + 3 = 4$ $\qquad$ $2 - 2(-1) - 3 = 1$

$4 = 4$ $\qquad$ $2 + 2 - 3 = 1$

$\qquad\qquad\qquad\qquad\qquad1 = 1$

$2(2) - (-1) - 3 = -1$

$4 + 1 - 3 = -1$

$1 = -1$

The triple does not make each equation true, so it is not a solution.

3. $4 - 2(1) = 2$ $\qquad$ $2(4) + 3(1) = 11$

$4 - 2 = 2$ $\qquad$ $8 + 3 = 11$

$2 = 2$ $\qquad\qquad$ $11 = 11$

$1 - 4(2) = -7$

$1 - 8 = -7$

$-7 = -7$

The triple makes each equation true, so it is a solution.

5.   Multiply the second equation by -1 and add to the first equation..

$x + y + 2z = 11$

$\underline{-x - y - 3z = -14}$

$-z = -3$

$z = 3$

Back-substitute 3 for z in the first and third equations.

$x + y + 2(3) = 11$ $\qquad$ $x + 2y - 3 = 5$

$+ 6 = 11$... $x + y + 6 = 11$ $\qquad$ $x + 2y = 8$

$+ y = 5$... $x + y = 5$

We now have two equations in two variables.

$x + y = 5$

$x + 2y = 8$

Multiply the first equation by -1 and solve by addition.

$-x - y = -5$

$\underline{x + 2y = 8}$

$y = 3$

Back-substitute 3 for y to find x.

$x + 3 = 5$

$x = 2$

The solution is $(2,3,3)$.

7. Multiply the second equation by –4 and add to the first equation.

$$4x-\ y+2z=11$$
$$\underline{-4x-8y+4z=\ \ 4}$$
$$-9y+6z=15$$

Multiply the second equation by –2 and add it to the third equation.

$$-2x-4y+2z=\ \ 2$$
$$\underline{2x+2y-3z=-1}$$
$$-2y-\ z=\ \ 1$$

We now have two equations in two variables.

$$-9y+6z=15$$
$$-2y-\ z=\ \ 1$$

Multiply the second equation by 6 and solve by addition.

$$-9y+6z=15$$
$$\underline{-12y-6z=\ \ 6}$$
$$-21y\qquad=21$$
$$y\qquad=21$$

Back-substitute –1 for y in one of the equations in two variables.

$$-2(-1)-z=1$$
$$2-z=1$$
$$1=z$$

Back-substitute –1 for y and 1 for z in one of the original equations in three variables.

$$x+2(-1)-1=-1$$
$$x-2-1=-1$$
$$x-3=-1$$
$$x=2$$

The solution is $(2,-1,1)$.

9. Multiply the second equation by –2 and add to the third equation.

$$-4x+10y-4z=4$$
$$\underline{4x-\ 3y+4z=10}$$
$$7y\qquad=14$$
$$y\qquad=\ 2$$

Back-substitute 2 for y in the first and third equations to obtain two equations in two unknowns.

$$3x+2(2)-3z=-2$$
$$3x+4-3z=-2$$
$$3x-3z=-6$$

$$4x-3(2)+4z=10$$
$$4x-6+4z=10$$
$$4x+4z=16$$

The system of two equations in two variables is as follows.

$$3x-3z=-6$$
$$4x+4z=16$$

Multiply the first equation by –4 and the second equation by 3.

$$-12x+12z=24$$
$$\underline{12x+12z=48}$$
$$24z=72$$
$$z=\ 3$$

Back-substitute 3 for z to find x.

$$3x-3(3)=-6$$
$$3x-9=-6$$
$$3x=3$$
$$x=1$$

The solution is $(1,2,3)$.

11. Multiply the second equation by –1 and add it to the third equation.

$$-x-2y+z=0$$
$$\underline{4x-\ y-z=6}$$
$$3x-3y\qquad=6$$

Multiply the second equation by 3 and add it to the first equation.

$$2x-4y+3z=17$$
$$\underline{3x+6y-3z=\ \ 0}$$
$$5x+2y\qquad=17$$

The system in two variables is as follows.

$$3x-3y=6$$
$$5x+2y=17$$

Multiply the first equation by 2 and the second equation by 3 and solve by addition.

$$6x - 6y = 12$$
$$\underline{15x + 6y = 51}$$
$$21x \quad = 63$$
$$x \quad = 3$$

Back-substitute 3 for x in one of the equations in two variables.

$$3(3) - 3y = 6$$
$$9 - 3y = 6$$
$$-3y = -3$$
$$y = 1$$

Back-substitute 3 for x and 1 for y in one of the original equations in three variables.

$$3 + 2(1) - z = 0$$
$$3 + 2 - z = 0$$
$$5 - z = 0$$
$$5 = z$$

The solution is $(3, 1, 5)$.

13. Add the second and third equations to obtain an equation in two variables.

$$x + y - z = 4$$
$$\underline{3x + 2y + z = 0}$$
$$4x + 3y \quad = 4$$

We now have a system of two equations in two variables.

$$2x + y = 2$$
$$4x + 3y = 4$$

Multiply the first equation by -2 and solve by addition.

$$-4x - 2y = -4$$
$$\underline{4x + 3y = \;\; 4}$$
$$y = \;\; 0$$

Back-substitute 0 for y in one of the equations in two unknowns.

$$2x + 0 = 2$$
$$2x = 2$$
$$x = 1$$

Back-substitute 1 for x and 0 for y in one of the equations in three unknowns.

$$1 + 0 - z = 4$$
$$1 - z = 4$$
$$-3 = z$$

The solution is $(1, 0, -3)$.

15. Multiply the first equation by -1 and add to the second equation.

$$-x - y \quad = 4$$
$$\underline{\quad\;\; y - z = 1}$$
$$-x \quad - z = 5$$

Multiply the second equation by -1 and add to the third equation.

$$-y + z = \;\; -1$$
$$\underline{2x + y + 3z = -21}$$
$$2x \quad + 4z = -22$$

The system of two equations in two variables is as follows.

$$-x - z = \;\;\; 5$$
$$2x + 4z = -22$$

Multiply the first equation by 2 and add to the second equation.

$$-2x - 2z = \;\; 10$$
$$\underline{2x + 4z = -22}$$
$$2z = -12$$
$$z = -6$$

Back-substitute -6 for z to find x.

$$-x - (-6) = 5$$
$$-x + 6 = 5$$
$$1 = x$$

Back-substitute 1 for x in the first equation of the original system.

$$1 + y = -4$$
$$y = -5$$

The solution is $(1, -5, -6)$.

17. Add the first and second equations to eliminate y.

$$2x + y + 2z = 1$$
$$\underline{3x - y + \;\; z = 2}$$
$$5x \quad + 3z = 3$$

Multiply the second equation by -2 and add to the third equation.

$$-6x + 2y - 2z = -4$$
$$\underline{\quad\; x - 2y - \;\; z = \;\; 0}$$
$$-5x \quad - 3z = -4$$

We obtain two equations in two variables which can be solved by addition.

$$5x+3z = 3$$
$$-5x-3z = -4$$
$$0 = -1$$

The system is inconsistent. There are no triples, (x, y, z) for which $0 = -1$.

19. Multiply the first equation by -2 and add to the second equation.
$$-10x+4y+10z = -2$$
$$10x-4y-10z = 2$$
$$0 = 0$$
The system is dependent and has infinitely many solutions.

21. Rewrite each equation and obtain the system of three equations in three variables.
$$6x+3y+5z = -1$$
$$2x-6y+8z = -9$$
$$4x-9y+3z = -4$$
Multiply the second equation by -3 and add to the first equation.
$$6x+ 3y+ 5z = -1$$
$$-6x+18y-24z = 27$$
$$21y-19z = 26$$
Multiply the second equation by -2 and add to the third equation.
$$-4x+12y-16z = 18$$
$$4x- 9y+ 3z = -4$$
$$3y-13z = 14$$
The system of two variables in two equations is as follows.
$$21y-19z = 26$$
$$3y-13z = 14$$
Multiply the second equation by -7 and add to the third equation.
$$21y-19z = 26$$
$$-21y+91z = -98$$
$$72z = -72$$
$$z = -1$$
Back-substitute -1 for z in one of the equations in two variables to find y.
$$3y-13(-1) = 14$$
$$3y+13 = 14$$
$$3y = 1$$

$$y = \frac{1}{3}$$

Back-substitute -1 for z and $\frac{1}{3}$ for y to find x.
$$6x+1-5 = -1$$
$$6x-4 = -1$$
$$6x = 3$$
$$x = \frac{1}{2}$$

The solution is $\left(\frac{1}{2}, \frac{1}{3}, -1\right)$.

23. $(x, y) = (-1, 6)$
$$6 = a(-1)^2 + b(-1) + c$$
$$6 = a - b + c$$
$(x, y) = (1, 4)$
$$4 = a(1)^2 + b(1) + c$$
$$4 = a + b + c$$
$(x, y) = (2, 9)$
$$9 = a(2)^2 + b(2) + c$$
$$9 = a(4) + 2b + c$$
$$9 = 4a + 2b + c$$
The resulting system is as follows.
$$a - b + c = 6$$
$$a + b + c = 4$$
$$4a + 2b + c = 9$$
Add the first and second equations.
$$a-b+ c = 6$$
$$a+b+ c = 4$$
$$2a +2c = 10$$
Multiply the first equation by 2 and add to the third equation.
$$2a - 2b + 2c = 12$$
$$4a + 2b + c = 9$$
$$6a +3c = 21$$
The system of two equations in two variables is as follows.
$$2a + 2c = 10$$
$$6a + 3c = 21$$
Multiply the first equation by -3 and add to the second equation.

$$-6a - 6c = -30$$
$$\underline{6a + 3c =\ \ 21}$$
$$-3c = -9$$
$$c = 3$$

Back-substitute 3 for c to find a.
$$2a + 2(3) = 10$$
$$2a + 6 = 10$$
$$2a = 4$$
$$a = 2$$

Back-substitute 3 for c and 2 for a in one of the equations in three variables.
$$2 + b + 3 = 4$$
$$b + 5 = 4$$
$$b = -1$$

The quadratic function is $y = 2x^2 - x + 3$.

25. $(x, y) = (-1, -4)$
$$-4 = a(-1)^2 + b(-1) + c$$
$$-4 = a - b + c$$
$(x, y) = (1, -2)$
$$-2 = a(1)^2 + b(1) + c$$
$$-2 = a + b + c$$
$(x, y) = (2, 5)$
$$5 = a(2)^2 + b(2) + c$$
$$5 = a(4) + 2b + c$$
$$5 = 4a + 2b + c$$

The resulting system is as follows.
$$a - b + c = -4$$
$$a + b + c = -2$$
$$4a + 2b + c =\ \ 5$$

Multiply the second equation by -1 and add to the first equation.
$$a - b + c = -4$$
$$\underline{-a - b - c =\ \ 2}$$
$$-2b = -2$$
$$b = 1$$

Back-substitute 4 for b in the first and third equations to obtain two equations in two variables.

$$a - b + c = -4 \qquad 4a + 2b + c = 5$$
$$a - 1 + c = -4 \qquad 4a + 2(1) + c = 5$$
$$a + c = -3 \qquad\ \ 4a + 2 + c = 5$$
$$\qquad\qquad\qquad\qquad 4a + c = 3$$

The resulting system is as follows.
$$a + c = -3$$
$$4a + c =\ \ 3$$

Multiply the first equation by -1 and add to the second equation.
$$-a - c = 3$$
$$\underline{4a + c = 3}$$
$$3a = 6$$
$$a = 2$$

Back-substitute 2 for a and 1 for b in one of the equations in three variables.
$$2 - 1 + c = -4$$
$$1 + c = -4$$
$$c = -5$$

The quadratic function is $y = 2x^2 + x - 5$.

27.   Let x = the first number
Let y = the second number
Let z = the third number
$$x +\ \ y +\ \ z = 16$$
$$2x + 3y + 4z = 46$$
$$5x -\ y\qquad = 31$$

Multiply the first equation by -4 and add to the second equation.
$$-4x - 4y - 4z = -64$$
$$\underline{2x + 3y + 4z =\ \ 46}$$
$$-2x - y \qquad = -18$$

The system of two equations in two variables is as follows.
$$5x - y =\ \ 31$$
$$-2x - y = -18$$

Multiply the first equation by -1 and add to the second equation.
$$-5x + y = -31$$
$$\underline{-2x - y = -18}$$
$$-7x = -49$$
$$x = 7$$

Back-substitute 7 for x in one of the equations in two variables.

$$5(7) - y = 31$$
$$35 - y = 31$$
$$4 = y$$

Back-substitute 7 for x and 4 for y in one of the equations in two variables.

$$7 + 4 + z = 16$$
$$11 + z = 16$$
$$z = 5$$

The numbers are 7, 4 and 5.

29. a.

1960	$(0, 5.4)$
1970	$(10, 4.7)$
1980	$(20, 6.2)$

b.
$$5.4 = a(0)^2 + b(0) + c$$
$$5.4 = 0a + 0b + c$$

$$4.7 = a(10)^2 + b(10) + c$$
$$4.7 = a(100) + b(10) + c$$
$$4.7 = 100a + 10b + c$$

$$6.2 = a(20)^2 + b(20) + c$$
$$6.2 = a(400) + b(20) + c$$
$$6.2 = 400a + 20b + c$$

The resulting system is as follows.
$$0a + 0b + c = 5.4$$
$$100a + 10b + c = 4.7$$
$$400a + 20b + c = 6.2$$

31. a. $(x, y) = (1, 224)$
$$224 = a(1)^2 + b(1) + c$$
$$224 = a(1) + b + c$$
$$224 = a + b + c$$
$(x, y) = (3, 176)$
$$176 = a(3)^2 + b(3) + c$$
$$176 = a(9) + 3b + c$$
$$176 = 9a + 3b + c$$
$(x, y) = (4, 104)$
$$104 = a(4)^2 + b(4) + c$$
$$104 = a(16) + 4b + c$$
$$104 = 16a + 4b + c$$
The resulting system is as follows.

$$a + b + c = 224$$
$$9a + 3b + c = 176$$
$$16a + 4b + c = 104$$

Multiply the second equation by -1 and add to the first.

$$a + b + c = 224$$
$$\underline{-9a - 3b - c = -176}$$
$$-8a - 2b = 48$$

Multiply the second equation by -1 and add to the third.

$$-9a - 3b - c = -176$$
$$\underline{16a + 4b + c = 104}$$
$$7a + b = 72$$

The system of two equations in two variables is as follows.

$$-8a - 2b = 48$$
$$7a + b = -72$$

Multiply the second equation by 2 and solve by addition.

$$-8a - 2b = 48$$
$$\underline{14a + 2b = -144}$$
$$6a = -96$$
$$a = -16$$

Back-substitute to find b.

$$-8(-16) - 2b = 48$$
$$128 - 2b = 48$$
$$-2b = -80$$
$$b = 40$$

Back-substitute -16 for a and 40 for b to find c.

$$-16 + 40 + c = 224$$
$$24 + c = 224$$
$$c = 200$$

The quadratic function is $y = -16x^2 + 40x + 200$.

b.
$$-16x^2 + 40x + 200 = 0$$
$$-8(2x^2 - 5x - 25) = 0$$
$$-8(x - 5)(2x + 5) = 0$$
$$-8(x - 5) = 0 \quad \text{or} \quad 2x + 5 = 0$$
$$x - 5 = 0 \qquad\qquad 2x = -5$$
$$x = 5 \qquad\qquad x = -\frac{5}{2}$$

Disregard $-\dfrac{5}{2}$ because we can't have a negative time measurement. The ball will hit the ground after 5 seconds.

33. Let x = the starting salary of CEs
Let y = the starting salary of MEs
Let z = the starting salary of EEs

$$x + y + z = 121421$$
$$x - y \quad\;\; = \quad 2906$$
$$\quad\; y - z = \quad 1041$$

Multiply the second equation by -1 and add to the first equation.

$$\begin{aligned} x + y + z &= 121421 \\ -x + y \quad\;\; &= -2906 \\ \hline 2y + z &= 118515 \end{aligned}$$

We obtain a system of two equations in two unknowns. Add the equations to eliminate z.

$$\begin{aligned} y - z &= \quad 1041 \\ 2y + z &= 118515 \\ \hline 3y &= 119556 \\ y &= 39852 \end{aligned}$$

Back-substitute 39852 for y to find z.
$$39852 - z = 1041$$
$$38811 = z$$
Back-substitute 39852 for y in one of the equations in two variables.
$$x - 39852 = 2906$$
$$x \quad\;\; = 42758$$

The starting salaries are \$42,758 for Chemical Engineers, \$39,852 for Mechanical Engineers and \$38,811 for Electrical Engineers.

35. Let x = the amount invested at 8%
Let y = the amount invested at 10%
Let z = the amount invested at 12%

$$x + y + z = 6700$$
$$0.08x + 0.10y + 0.12z = \quad 716$$
$$z - x - y = \quad 300$$

Rewrite the system in $Ax + By + Cz = D$ form.

$$x + \quad\; y + \quad\; z = 6700$$
$$0.08x + 0.10y + 0.12z = \quad 716$$
$$-x - \quad\; y + \quad\; z = \quad 300$$

Add the first and third equations to find z.

$$\begin{aligned} x + y + z &= 6700 \\ -x - y + z &= \quad 300 \\ \hline 2z &= 7000 \\ z &= 3500 \end{aligned}$$

Back-substitute 3500 for z to obtain two equations in two variables.
$$x + y + 3500 = 6700$$
$$x + y = 3200$$

$$0.08x + 0.10y + 0.12(3500) = 716$$
$$0.08x + 0.10y + 420 = 716$$
$$0.08x + 0.10y - 296$$

The new system is as follows.
$$x + \quad\; y = 3200$$
$$0.08x + 0.10y = \quad 296$$

Multiply the second equation by -10 and add it to the first equation.

$$\begin{aligned} x + y &= \quad 3200 \\ -0.8x + -y &= -2960 \\ \hline 0.2x &= 240 \\ x &= 1200 \end{aligned}$$

Back-substitute 1200 for x in one of the equations in two variables.
$$1200 + y = \quad 3200$$
$$y = \quad 2000$$

\$1200 was invested at 8%, \$2000 was invested at 10%, and \$3500 was invested at 12%.

37. Let x = the number of \$8 tickets
Let y = the number of \$10 tickets
Let z = the number of \$12 tickets

$$x + \quad\; y + \quad\; z = \quad 400$$
$$8x + 10y + 12z = 3700$$
$$x + \quad\; y \quad\;\;\;\; = \quad 7z$$

Rewrite the third equation.
$$x + \quad\; y + \quad\; z = \quad 400$$
$$8x + 10y + 12z = 3700$$
$$x + \quad\; y - 7z = \quad\;\;\; 0$$

Multiply the first equation by –1 and add to the third equation.

$$\begin{aligned} -x-y-z &= -400 \\ x+y-7z &= 0 \\ \hline -8z &= -400 \\ z &= 50 \end{aligned}$$

Back-substitute 50 for z in two of the original equations to obtain two of equations in two variables.

$$\begin{aligned} x+y+50 &= 400 \\ x+y &= 350 \end{aligned}$$

$$\begin{aligned} 8x+10y+12(50) &= 3700 \\ 8x+10y+600 &= 3700 \\ 8x+10y &= 3100 \end{aligned}$$

The resulting system is as follows.

$$\begin{aligned} x+y &= 350 \\ 8x+10y &= 3100 \end{aligned}$$

Multiply the first equation by –8 and add to the second equation.

$$\begin{aligned} -8x-8y &= -2800 \\ 8x+10y &= 3100 \\ \hline 2y &= 300 \\ y &= 150 \end{aligned}$$

Back-substitute 50 for z and 150 for y in one of the original equations.

$$\begin{aligned} x+150+50 &= 400 \\ x+200 &= 400 \\ x &= 200 \end{aligned}$$

There were 200 \$8 tickets, 150 \$10 tickets, and 50 \$12 tickets sold.

39. Let A = the number of servings of A
Let B = the number of servings of B
Let C = the number of servings of C

$$\begin{aligned} 40A+200B+400C &= 660 \\ 5A+2B+4C &= 25 \\ 30A+10B+300C &= 425 \end{aligned}$$

Multiply the second equation by –8 and add to the first equation.

$$\begin{aligned} 40A+200B+400C &= 660 \\ -40A-16B-32C &= -200 \\ \hline 184B+368C &= 460 \end{aligned}$$

Multiply the second equation by –6 and add to the third equation.

$$\begin{aligned} -30A-12B-24C &= -150 \\ 30A+10B+300C &= 425 \\ \hline -2B+276C &= 275 \end{aligned}$$

The resulting system is as follows.

$$\begin{aligned} 184B+368C &= 460 \\ -2B+276C &= 275 \end{aligned}$$

Multiply the second equation by 92 and eliminate B.

$$\begin{aligned} 184B+368C &= 460 \\ -184B+25392C &= 25300 \\ \hline 25760C &= 25760 \\ C &= 1 \end{aligned}$$

Back-substitute 1 for C in one of the equations in two variables.

$$\begin{aligned} -2B+276(1) &= 275 \\ -2B+276 &= 275 \\ -2B &= -1 \\ B &= \frac{1}{2} \end{aligned}$$

Back-substitute 1 for C and $\frac{1}{2}$ for B to find A.

$$\begin{aligned} 5A+2\left(\frac{1}{2}\right)+4(1) &= 25 \\ 5A+1+4 &= 25 \\ 5A+5 &= 25 \\ 5A &= 20 \\ A &= 4 \end{aligned}$$

To meet the requirements, 4 ounces of Food A, $\frac{1}{2}$ ounce of Food B, and 1 ounce of Food C should be used.

For Exercises 41-45, answers may vary.

47. Statement **c.** is true. The variable terms of the second equation are a multiple of the variable terms in the first equation, but the constants are not. Multiple the first equation by 2 results in a contradiction.

$$-2x - 2y + 2z = -20$$
$$\underline{2x + 2y - 2z = 7}$$
$$0 = -13$$

Statement **a.** is false. The ordered triple is one solution to the equation, but there are an infinite number of other ordered triples which satisfy the equation.

Statement **b.** is false.
$$2 - (-3) - 5 = -6$$
$$2 + 3 - 5 = -6$$
$$0 \neq -6$$

Statement **d.** is false. An equation with four variables can be satisfied by real numbers.

49. Let t = the number of triangles
Let r = the number of rectangles
Let p = the number of pentagons
$$t + r + p = 40$$
$$3t + 4r + 5p = 153$$
$$2r + 5p = 72$$

Multiply the first equation by -3 and add to the second equation.
$$-3t - 3r - 3p = -120$$
$$\underline{3t + 4r + 5p = 153}$$
$$r + 2p = 33$$

We have two equations in two variables.
$$2r + 5p = 72$$
$$r + 2p = 33$$

Multiply the second equation by -2 and add to eliminate r.
$$2r + 5p = 72$$
$$\underline{-2r - 4p = -66}$$
$$p = 6$$

Back-substitute 6 for p in one of the equations in two variables.
$$r + 2(6) = 33$$
$$r + 12 = 33$$
$$r = 21$$

Back-substitute 21 for r and 6 for p to find t.

$$t + 21 + 6 = 40$$
$$t + 27 = 40$$
$$t = 13$$

There are 13 triangles, 21 rectangles, and 6 pentagons.

For Exercise 51, answers may vary.

Review Exercises

53.
$$4x - 5y = 20$$
$$-5y = -4x + 20$$
$$y = \frac{4}{5}x - 4$$
$$m = \frac{4}{5} \qquad y - \text{intercept} = -4$$

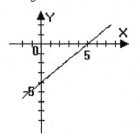

54.
$$2(x - 3) > 4x + 10$$
$$2x - 6 > 4x + 10$$
$$-2x - 6 > 10$$
$$-2x > 16$$
$$x < -8$$
The solution set is $\{x | x < -8\}$.

55.
$$\frac{1}{x^2 - 17x + 30} \div \frac{1}{x^2 + 7x - 18}$$
$$= \frac{1}{x^2 - 17x + 30} \cdot \frac{x^2 + 7x - 18}{1}$$
$$= \frac{1}{(x - 15)(x - 2)} \cdot \frac{(x + 9)(x - 2)}{1}$$
$$= \frac{1}{(x - 15)\cancel{(x - 2)}} \cdot \frac{(x + 9)\cancel{(x - 2)}}{1}$$
$$= \frac{x + 9}{x - 15}$$

Matrix Solutions to Systems of Linear Equations

8.4 CHECK POINTS

CHECK POINT 1
$$x - y + z = 8$$
$$0x + 1y - 12z = -15$$
$$0x + 0y + 1z = 1$$
Simplify the system.
$$x - y + z = 8$$
$$y - 12z = -15$$
$$z = 1$$
Back-substitute 1 for z to find y.
$$y - 12(1) = -15$$
$$y - 12 = -15$$
$$y = -3$$
Back-substitute -3 for y and 1 for z to find x.
$$x - (-3) + 1 = 8$$
$$x + 3 + 1 = 8$$
$$x + 4 = 8$$
$$x = 4$$
The solution is $(4, -3, 1)$.

CHECK POINT 2

a. $$\begin{bmatrix} 1 & 6 & -3 & | & 7 \\ 4 & 12 & -20 & | & 8 \\ -3 & -2 & 1 & | & -9 \end{bmatrix}$$

b. $$\begin{bmatrix} 1 & 3 & -5 & | & 2 \\ 1 & 6 & -3 & | & 7 \\ -3 & -2 & 1 & | & -9 \end{bmatrix}$$

c. $$\begin{bmatrix} 4 & 12 & -20 & | & 8 \\ 1 & 6 & -3 & | & 7 \\ 0 & 16 & -8 & | & 12 \end{bmatrix}$$

CHECK POINT 3
$$\begin{bmatrix} 2 & -1 & | & -4 \\ 1 & 3 & | & 5 \end{bmatrix} \quad R_1 \leftrightarrow R_2$$
$$= \begin{bmatrix} 1 & 3 & | & 5 \\ 2 & -1 & | & -4 \end{bmatrix} \quad -2R_1 + R_2$$

$$= \begin{bmatrix} 1 & 3 & | & 5 \\ 0 & -7 & | & -14 \end{bmatrix} \quad -\frac{1}{7}R_2$$
$$= \begin{bmatrix} 1 & 3 & | & 5 \\ 0 & 1 & | & 2 \end{bmatrix}$$
$$x + 3y = 5$$
$$y = 2$$
Back-substitute 2 for y to find x.
$$x + 3(2) = 5$$
$$x + 6 = 5$$
$$x = -1$$
The solution is $(-1, 2)$.

CHECK POINT 4
$$\begin{bmatrix} 2 & 1 & 2 & | & 18 \\ 1 & -1 & 2 & | & 9 \\ 1 & 2 & -1 & | & 6 \end{bmatrix} \quad R_1 \leftrightarrow R_2$$
$$= \begin{bmatrix} 1 & -1 & 2 & | & 9 \\ 2 & 1 & 2 & | & 18 \\ 1 & 2 & -1 & | & 6 \end{bmatrix} \quad -2R_1 + R_2$$
$$= \begin{bmatrix} 1 & -1 & 2 & | & 9 \\ 0 & 3 & -2 & | & 0 \\ 1 & 2 & -1 & | & 6 \end{bmatrix} \quad -R_1 + R_3$$
$$= \begin{bmatrix} 1 & -1 & 2 & | & 9 \\ 0 & 3 & -2 & | & 0 \\ 0 & 3 & -3 & | & -3 \end{bmatrix} \quad -R_2 + R_3$$
$$= \begin{bmatrix} 1 & -1 & 2 & | & 9 \\ 0 & 3 & -2 & | & 0 \\ 0 & 0 & -1 & | & -3 \end{bmatrix} \quad -\frac{1}{3}R_2$$
$$= \begin{bmatrix} 1 & -1 & 2 & | & 9 \\ 0 & 1 & -2/3 & | & 0 \\ 0 & 0 & -1 & | & -3 \end{bmatrix} \quad -R_3$$
$$= \begin{bmatrix} 1 & -1 & 2 & | & 9 \\ 0 & 1 & -2/3 & | & 0 \\ 0 & 0 & 1 & | & 3 \end{bmatrix}$$
$$x - y + 2z = 9$$
$$y - \frac{2}{3}z = 0$$
$$z = 3$$
Back-substitute 3 for z to find y.

$$y - \frac{2}{3}(3) = 0$$
$$y - 2 = 0$$
$$y = 2$$

Back-substitute 2 for y and 3 for z to find x.

$$x - 2 + 2(3) = 9$$
$$x - 2 + 6 = 9$$
$$x + 4 = 9$$
$$x = 5$$

The solution is $(5, 2, 3)$.

EXERCISE SET 8.4

1. $x - 3y = 11$
$$y = -3$$

Substitute -3 for y in the first equation.

$$x - 3(-3) = 11$$
$$x + 9 = 11$$
$$x = 2$$

The solution is $(2, -3)$.

3. $x - 3y = 1$
$$y = -1$$

Substitute -1 for y to find x.

$$x - 3(-1) = 1$$
$$x + 3 = 1$$
$$x = -2$$

The solution is $(-2, -1)$.

5. $x \quad\; -4z = 5$
$$y - 12z = 13$$
$$z = -\frac{1}{2}$$

Substitute $-\frac{1}{2}$ for z to find y.

$$y - 12\left(-\frac{1}{2}\right) = 13$$
$$y + 6 = 13$$
$$y = 7$$

Substitute 7 for y to find x.

$$x - 4\left(-\frac{1}{2}\right) = 5$$
$$x + 2 = 5$$
$$x = 3$$

The solution is $\left(3, 7, -\frac{1}{2}\right)$.

7. $x + \frac{1}{2}y + \quad z = \frac{11}{2}$
$$y + \frac{3}{2}z = 7$$
$$z = 4$$

Substitute 4 for z to find y.

$$y + \frac{3}{2}(4) = 7$$
$$y + 6 = 7$$
$$y = 1$$

Substitute 1 for y and 4 for z to find x.

$$x + \frac{1}{2}(1) + 4 = \frac{11}{2}$$
$$x + \frac{9}{2} = \frac{11}{2}$$
$$x = \frac{2}{2} = 1$$

The solution is $(1, 1, 4)$.

9. $\begin{bmatrix} 2 & 2 & | & 5 \\ 1 & -\frac{3}{2} & | & 5 \end{bmatrix} R_1 \leftrightarrow R_2 = \begin{bmatrix} 1 & -\frac{3}{2} & | & 5 \\ 2 & 2 & | & 5 \end{bmatrix}$

11. $\begin{bmatrix} -6 & 8 & | & -12 \\ 3 & 5 & | & -2 \end{bmatrix} -\frac{1}{6}R_1$

$$= \begin{bmatrix} 1 & -\frac{4}{3} & | & 2 \\ 3 & 5 & | & -2 \end{bmatrix}$$

13. $\begin{bmatrix} 1 & -3 & | & 5 \\ 2 & 6 & | & 4 \end{bmatrix} -2R_1 + R_2$

$$= \begin{bmatrix} 1 & -3 & | & 5 \\ 0 & 12 & | & -6 \end{bmatrix}$$

15. $\begin{bmatrix} 1 & -3/2 & | & 7/2 \\ 3 & 4 & | & 2 \end{bmatrix}$ $-3R_1 + R_2$

$= \begin{bmatrix} 1 & -3/2 & | & 7/2 \\ 0 & 17/2 & | & -17/2 \end{bmatrix}$

17. $\begin{bmatrix} 2 & -6 & 4 & | & 10 \\ 1 & 5 & -5 & | & 0 \\ 3 & 0 & 4 & | & 7 \end{bmatrix}$ $\frac{1}{2}R_1$

$= \begin{bmatrix} 1 & -3 & 2 & | & 5 \\ 1 & 5 & -5 & | & 0 \\ 3 & 0 & 4 & | & 7 \end{bmatrix}$

19. $\begin{bmatrix} 1 & -3 & 2 & | & 0 \\ 3 & 1 & -1 & | & 7 \\ 2 & -2 & 1 & | & 3 \end{bmatrix}$ $-3R_1 + R_2$

$= \begin{bmatrix} 1 & -3 & 2 & | & 0 \\ 0 & 10 & -7 & | & 7 \\ 2 & -2 & 1 & | & 3 \end{bmatrix}$

21. $\begin{bmatrix} 1 & 1 & -1 & | & 6 \\ 2 & -1 & 1 & | & -3 \\ 3 & -1 & -1 & | & 4 \end{bmatrix}$ $\begin{matrix}-2R_1 + R_2 \\ \text{and} \\ -3R_1 + R_3\end{matrix}$

$= \begin{bmatrix} 1 & 1 & -1 & | & 6 \\ 0 & -3 & 3 & | & -15 \\ 0 & -4 & 2 & | & -14 \end{bmatrix}$

23. $\begin{bmatrix} 1 & 1 & | & 6 \\ 1 & -1 & | & 2 \end{bmatrix}$ $-R_1 + R_2$

$= \begin{bmatrix} 1 & 1 & | & 6 \\ 0 & -2 & | & -4 \end{bmatrix}$ $-\frac{1}{2}R_2$

$= \begin{bmatrix} 1 & 1 & | & 6 \\ 0 & 1 & | & 2 \end{bmatrix}$

$x + y = 6$
$y = 2$
Back-substitute 2 for y.
$x + y = 6$
$x + 2 = 6$
$x = 4$
The solution is $(4, 2)$.

25. $\begin{bmatrix} 2 & 1 & | & 3 \\ 1 & -3 & | & 12 \end{bmatrix}$ $R_1 \leftrightarrow R_2$

$= \begin{bmatrix} 1 & -3 & | & 12 \\ 2 & 1 & | & 3 \end{bmatrix}$ $-2R_1 + R_2$

$= \begin{bmatrix} 1 & -3 & | & 12 \\ 0 & 7 & | & -21 \end{bmatrix}$ $\frac{1}{7}R_2$

$= \begin{bmatrix} 1 & -3 & | & 12 \\ 0 & 1 & | & -3 \end{bmatrix}$

$x - 3y = 12$
$y = -3$
Back-substitute -3 for y.
$x - 3(-3) = 12$
$x + 9 = 12$
$x = 3$
The solution is $(3, -3)$.

27. $\begin{bmatrix} 5 & 7 & | & -25 \\ 11 & 6 & | & -8 \end{bmatrix}$ $\frac{1}{5}R_1$

$= \begin{bmatrix} 1 & \frac{7}{5} & | & -5 \\ 11 & 6 & | & -8 \end{bmatrix}$ $-11R_1 + R_2$

$= \begin{bmatrix} 1 & \frac{7}{5} & | & -5 \\ 0 & -\frac{47}{5} & | & 47 \end{bmatrix}$ $-\frac{5}{47}R_2$

$= \begin{bmatrix} 1 & \frac{7}{5} & | & -5 \\ 0 & 1 & | & -5 \end{bmatrix}$

$x + \frac{7}{5}y = -5$
$y = -5$
Back-substitute -5 for y.
$x + \frac{7}{5}(-5) = -5$
$x - 7 = -5$
$x = 2$
The solution is $(2, -5)$.

29. $\begin{bmatrix} 4 & -2 & | & 5 \\ -2 & 1 & | & 6 \end{bmatrix}$ $\frac{1}{4}R_1$

$$= \begin{bmatrix} 1 & -\dfrac{1}{2} & \bigg| & \dfrac{5}{2} \\ -2 & 1 & \bigg| & 6 \end{bmatrix} \quad 2R_1 + R_2$$

$$= \begin{bmatrix} 1 & -\dfrac{1}{2} & \bigg| & \dfrac{5}{2} \\ 0 & 0 & \bigg| & \dfrac{17}{2} \end{bmatrix}$$

$$x - \frac{1}{2}y = \frac{5}{2}$$
$$0x + 0y = \frac{17}{2}$$

This is a contradiction. The system is inconsistent.

31. $\begin{bmatrix} 1 & -2 & | & 1 \\ -2 & 4 & | & -2 \end{bmatrix} \quad 2R_1 + R_2$

$$= \begin{bmatrix} 1 & -2 & | & 1 \\ 0 & 0 & | & 0 \end{bmatrix}$$

$$x - 2y = 1$$
$$0x + 0y = 0$$

The system is dependent. There are infinitely many solutions.

33. $\begin{bmatrix} 1 & 1 & -1 & | & -2 \\ 2 & -1 & 1 & | & 5 \\ -1 & 2 & 2 & | & 1 \end{bmatrix} \quad -2R_1 + R_2$

$$= \begin{bmatrix} 1 & 1 & -1 & | & -2 \\ 0 & -3 & 3 & | & 9 \\ -1 & 2 & 2 & | & 1 \end{bmatrix} \quad R_1 + R_3$$

$$= \begin{bmatrix} 1 & 1 & -1 & | & -2 \\ 0 & -3 & 3 & | & 9 \\ 0 & 3 & 1 & | & -1 \end{bmatrix} \quad R_2 + R_3$$

$$= \begin{bmatrix} 1 & 1 & -1 & | & -2 \\ 0 & -3 & 3 & | & 9 \\ 0 & 0 & 4 & | & 8 \end{bmatrix} \quad \frac{1}{4}R_3$$

$$= \begin{bmatrix} 1 & 1 & -1 & | & -2 \\ 0 & -3 & 3 & | & 9 \\ 0 & 0 & 1 & | & 2 \end{bmatrix}$$

$$x + y - z = -2$$
$$y - z = -3$$
$$z = 2$$

Back-substitute 2 for z to find y.

$$y - 2 = -3$$
$$y = -1$$

Back-substitute 2 for z and -1 for y to find x.

$$x - 1 - 2 = -2$$
$$x - 3 = -2$$
$$x = 1$$

The solution is $(1, -1, 2)$.

35. $\begin{bmatrix} 1 & 3 & 0 & | & 0 \\ 1 & 1 & 1 & | & 1 \\ 3 & -1 & -1 & | & 11 \end{bmatrix} \quad -R_1 + R_2$

$$= \begin{bmatrix} 1 & 3 & 0 & | & 0 \\ 0 & -2 & 1 & | & 1 \\ 3 & -1 & -1 & | & 11 \end{bmatrix} \quad -3R_1 + R_3$

$$= \begin{bmatrix} 1 & 3 & 0 & | & 0 \\ 0 & -2 & 1 & | & 1 \\ 0 & -10 & -1 & | & 11 \end{bmatrix} \quad -\frac{1}{2}R_2$

$$= \begin{bmatrix} 1 & 3 & 0 & | & 0 \\ 0 & 1 & -1/2 & | & -1/2 \\ 0 & -10 & -1 & | & 11 \end{bmatrix} \quad -\frac{1}{10}R_3$

$$= \begin{bmatrix} 1 & 3 & 0 & | & 0 \\ 0 & 1 & -1/2 & | & -1/2 \\ 0 & 1 & 1/10 & | & -11/10 \end{bmatrix} \quad -R_2 + R_3$

$$= \begin{bmatrix} 1 & 3 & 0 & | & 0 \\ 0 & 1 & -1/2 & | & -1/2 \\ 0 & 0 & 3/5 & | & -3/5 \end{bmatrix} \quad \frac{5}{3}R_3$

$$= \begin{bmatrix} 1 & 3 & 0 & | & 0 \\ 0 & 1 & -1/2 & | & -1/2 \\ 0 & 0 & 1 & | & -1 \end{bmatrix}$$

$$x + 3y \qquad = 0$$
$$y - \frac{1}{2}z = -\frac{1}{2}$$
$$z = -1$$

Back-substitute -1 for z to find y.

$$y - \frac{1}{2}(-1) = -\frac{1}{2}$$
$$y + \frac{1}{2} = -\frac{1}{2}$$
$$y = -1$$

Back-substitute -1 for y to find x.

$x+3(-1)=0$

$x-3=0$

$x=3$

The solution is $(3,-1,-1)$.

37. $\begin{bmatrix} 2 & 2 & 7 & | & -1 \\ 2 & 1 & 2 & | & 2 \\ 4 & 6 & 1 & | & 15 \end{bmatrix} \quad \frac{1}{2}R_1$

$= \begin{bmatrix} 1 & 1 & 7/2 & | & -1/2 \\ 2 & 1 & 2 & | & 2 \\ 4 & 6 & 1 & | & 15 \end{bmatrix} \quad -2R_1+R_2$

$= \begin{bmatrix} 1 & 1 & 7/2 & | & -1/2 \\ 0 & -1 & -5 & | & 3 \\ 4 & 6 & 1 & | & 15 \end{bmatrix} \quad -R_2$

$= \begin{bmatrix} 1 & 1 & 7/2 & | & -1/2 \\ 0 & 1 & 5 & | & -3 \\ 4 & 6 & 1 & | & 15 \end{bmatrix} \quad -4R_1+R_3$

$= \begin{bmatrix} 1 & 1 & 7/2 & | & -1/2 \\ 0 & 1 & 5 & | & -3 \\ 0 & 2 & -13 & | & 17 \end{bmatrix} \quad -2R_2+R_3$

$= \begin{bmatrix} 1 & 1 & 7/2 & | & -1/2 \\ 0 & 1 & 5 & | & -3 \\ 0 & 0 & -23 & | & 23 \end{bmatrix} \quad -R_3$

$= \begin{bmatrix} 1 & 1 & 7/2 & | & -1/2 \\ 0 & 1 & 5 & | & -3 \\ 0 & 0 & 1 & | & -1 \end{bmatrix}$

$x+y+\dfrac{7}{2}z=-\dfrac{1}{2}$

$y+5z=-3$

$z=-1$

Back-substitute -1 for z to find y.

$y+5(-1)=-3$

$y-5=-3$

$y=2$

Back-substitute -1 for z and 2 for y to find x.

$x+2+\dfrac{7}{2}(-1)=-\dfrac{1}{2}$

$x+2-\dfrac{7}{2}=-\dfrac{1}{2}$

$x-\dfrac{3}{2}=-\dfrac{1}{2}$

$x=1$

The solution is $(1,2,-1)$.

39. $\begin{bmatrix} 1 & 1 & 1 & | & 6 \\ 1 & 0 & -1 & | & -2 \\ 0 & 1 & 3 & | & 11 \end{bmatrix} \quad R_2 \leftrightarrow R_3$

$= \begin{bmatrix} 1 & 1 & 1 & | & 6 \\ 0 & 1 & 3 & | & 11 \\ 0 & -1 & -2 & | & -8 \end{bmatrix} \quad R_2+R_3$

$= \begin{bmatrix} 1 & 1 & 1 & | & 6 \\ 0 & 1 & 3 & | & 11 \\ 0 & 0 & 1 & | & 3 \end{bmatrix}$

$x+y+z=6$

$y+3z=11$

$z=3$

Back-substitute to find y.

$y+3(3)=11$

$y+9=11$

$y=2$

Back-substitute to find x.

$x+2+3=6$

$x+5=6$

$x=1$

The solution is $(1,2,3)$.

41. $\begin{bmatrix} 1 & -1 & 3 & | & 4 \\ 2 & -2 & 6 & | & 7 \\ 3 & -1 & 5 & | & 14 \end{bmatrix} \quad \begin{matrix} -2R_1+R_2 \\ \text{and} \\ -3R_1+R_3 \end{matrix}$

$= \begin{bmatrix} 1 & -1 & 3 & | & 4 \\ 0 & 0 & 0 & | & -1 \\ 0 & 2 & -4 & | & 2 \end{bmatrix}$

$x-y+3z=4$

$0x+0y+0z=-1$

$2y-4z=2$

The second row is a contradiction. $0x+0y+0z$ cannot equal -1. The system is dependent and there are infinitely many solutions.

43. $\begin{bmatrix} 1 & -2 & 1 & | & 4 \\ 5 & -10 & 5 & | & 20 \\ -2 & 4 & -2 & | & -8 \end{bmatrix} \begin{matrix} \\ \frac{1}{5}R_2 \\ \\ \end{matrix}$

$= \begin{bmatrix} 1 & -2 & 1 & | & 4 \\ 1 & -2 & 1 & | & 4 \\ -2 & 4 & -2 & | & -8 \end{bmatrix}$

R_1 and R_2 are the same. The system is dependent and there are infinitely many solutions.

45. $\begin{bmatrix} 1 & 1 & 0 & | & 1 \\ 0 & 1 & 2 & | & -2 \\ 2 & 0 & -1 & | & 0 \end{bmatrix} \begin{matrix} \\ \\ -2R_1 + R_3 \end{matrix}$

$= \begin{bmatrix} 1 & 1 & 0 & | & 1 \\ 0 & 1 & 2 & | & -2 \\ 0 & -2 & -1 & | & -2 \end{bmatrix} \begin{matrix} \\ 2R_2 + R_3 \\ \end{matrix}$

$= \begin{bmatrix} 1 & 1 & 0 & | & 1 \\ 0 & 1 & 2 & | & -2 \\ 0 & 0 & 3 & | & -6 \end{bmatrix} \begin{matrix} \\ \frac{1}{3}R_3 \\ \end{matrix}$

$= \begin{bmatrix} 1 & 1 & 0 & | & 1 \\ 0 & 1 & 2 & | & -2 \\ 0 & 0 & 1 & | & -2 \end{bmatrix}$

$x + y \qquad = 1$
$\qquad y + 2z = -2$
$\qquad\qquad z = -2$

Back-substitute -2 for z to find y.
$y + 2(-2) = -2$
$y - 4 = -2$
$y = 2$

Back-substitute 2 for y to find x.
$x + 2 = 1$
$x = -1$

The solution is $(-1, 2, -2)$.

47. a. $(x, y) = (1, 344)$
$344 = a(1)^2 + b(1) + c$
$344 = a + b + c$
$(x, y) = (5, 480)$
$480 = a(5)^2 + b(5) + c$
$480 = a(25) + 5b + c$
$480 = 25a + 5b + c$

$(x, y) = (10, 740)$
$740 = a(10)^2 + b(10) + c$
$740 = a(100) + 10b + c$
$740 = 100a + 10b + c$

The new system is as follows.
$a + b + c = 344$
$25a + 5b + c = 480$
$100a + 10b + c = 740$

$\begin{bmatrix} 1 & 1 & 1 & | & 344 \\ 25 & 5 & 1 & | & 480 \\ 100 & 10 & 1 & | & 740 \end{bmatrix} \begin{matrix} -25R_1 + R_2 \\ \text{and} \\ -100R_1 + R_3 \end{matrix}$

$= \begin{bmatrix} 1 & 1 & 1 & | & 344 \\ 0 & -20 & -24 & | & -8120 \\ 0 & -90 & -99 & | & -33660 \end{bmatrix} \begin{matrix} \\ -\frac{1}{20}R_2 \\ \end{matrix}$

$= \begin{bmatrix} 1 & 1 & 1 & | & 344 \\ 0 & 1 & 6/5 & | & 406 \\ 0 & -90 & -99 & | & -33660 \end{bmatrix} \begin{matrix} \\ -\frac{1}{90}R_3 \\ \end{matrix}$

$= \begin{bmatrix} 1 & 1 & 1 & | & 344 \\ 0 & 1 & 6/5 & | & 406 \\ 0 & 1 & 11/10 & | & 374 \end{bmatrix} \begin{matrix} \\ -R_2 + R_3 \\ \end{matrix}$

$= \begin{bmatrix} 1 & 1 & 1 & | & 344 \\ 0 & 1 & 6/5 & | & 406 \\ 0 & 0 & -1/10 & | & -32 \end{bmatrix} \begin{matrix} \\ -10R_3 \\ \end{matrix}$

$= \begin{bmatrix} 1 & 1 & 1 & | & 344 \\ 0 & 1 & 6/5 & | & 406 \\ 0 & 0 & 1 & | & 320 \end{bmatrix}$

$x + y + z = 344$
$\qquad y + \dfrac{6}{5}z = 406$
$\qquad\qquad z = 320$

Back-substitute to find y.
$y + \dfrac{6}{5}(320) = 406$
$y + 384 = 406$
$y = 22$

Back-substitute to find x.
$x + 22 + 320 = 344$
$x + 342 = 344$
$x = 2$

The solution set is $\{(2, 22, 320)\}$.

The quadratic function is $y = 2x^2 + 22x + 320$.

b. $f(30) = 2(30)^2 + 22(30) + 320$
$= 2(900) + 660 + 320$
$= 1800 + 660 + 320 = 2780$
The model predicts that there will be 2,780,000 inmates in 2010.

c. Answers may vary.

49. Let x=the percentage in youngest group
Let y=the percentage in middle group
Let z=the percentage in oldest group
$$x + z = y + 2$$
$$2z = x - 3$$
$$x + y + z = 100$$
Rewrite the system in $Ax + By + Cz = D$ form.
$$x - y + z = 2$$
$$-x + 2z = -3$$
$$x + y + z = 100$$

$\begin{bmatrix} 1 & -1 & 1 & | & 2 \\ -1 & 0 & 2 & | & -3 \\ 1 & 1 & 1 & | & 100 \end{bmatrix}$ $\begin{matrix} R_1 + R_2 \\ \text{and} \\ -R_1 + R_3 \end{matrix}$

$= \begin{bmatrix} 1 & -1 & 1 & | & 2 \\ 0 & -1 & 3 & | & -1 \\ 0 & 2 & 0 & | & 98 \end{bmatrix}$ $R_2 \leftrightarrow R_3$

$= \begin{bmatrix} 1 & -1 & 1 & | & 2 \\ 0 & 2 & 0 & | & 98 \\ 0 & -1 & 3 & | & -1 \end{bmatrix}$ $\frac{1}{2} R_2$

$= \begin{bmatrix} 1 & -1 & 1 & | & 2 \\ 0 & 1 & 0 & | & 49 \\ 0 & -1 & 3 & | & -1 \end{bmatrix}$ $R_2 + R_3$

$= \begin{bmatrix} 1 & -1 & 1 & | & 2 \\ 0 & 1 & 0 & | & 49 \\ 0 & 0 & 3 & | & 48 \end{bmatrix}$ $\frac{1}{3} R_3$

$= \begin{bmatrix} 1 & -1 & 1 & | & 2 \\ 0 & 1 & 0 & | & 49 \\ 0 & 0 & 1 & | & 16 \end{bmatrix}$

$$x - y + z = 2$$
$$y = 49$$
$$z = 16$$
Back-substitute 49 for y and 16 for z to find x.
$$x - 49 + 16 = 2$$
$$x - 33 = 2$$
$$x = 35$$
35% of the online users are in the youngest group, 49% of the online users are in the middle group, and 16% of the online users are in the oldest group.

For Exercises 51-55, answers may vary.

57. Statement **d.** is true.

Statement **a.** is false. Multiplying a row by a negative fraction is permitted.

Statement **b.** is false because there are three variables in the system. The corrected augmented matrix is as follows.
$$\begin{bmatrix} 1 & -3 & 0 & | & 5 \\ 0 & 1 & -2 & | & 7 \\ 2 & 0 & 1 & | & 4 \end{bmatrix}$$

Statement **c.** is false. When solving a system of three equations in three variables, we use row operations to obtain ones along the diagonal and zeros below the ones.

59. a. $\begin{bmatrix} 3 & 1 & 3 & | & 14 \\ 7 & 5 & 8 & | & 32 \\ 1 & 3 & 2 & | & 9 \end{bmatrix}$ $R_3 \leftrightarrow R_1$

$= \begin{bmatrix} 1 & 3 & 2 & | & 9 \\ 7 & 5 & 8 & | & 32 \\ 3 & 1 & 3 & | & 14 \end{bmatrix}$ $-7R_1 + R_2$

$= \begin{bmatrix} 1 & 3 & 2 & | & 9 \\ 0 & -16 & -6 & | & -31 \\ 3 & 1 & 3 & | & 14 \end{bmatrix}$ $-3R_1 + R_3$

$$= \begin{bmatrix} 1 & 3 & 2 & | & 9 \\ 0 & -16 & -6 & | & -31 \\ 0 & -8 & -3 & | & -13 \end{bmatrix} \quad -\frac{1}{2}R_2 + R_3$$

$$= \begin{bmatrix} 1 & 3 & 2 & | & 9 \\ 0 & -16 & -6 & | & -31 \\ 0 & 0 & 0 & | & -13 \end{bmatrix}$$

This is a contradiction.

$0x + 0y + 0z = -13$

$0 = -13$

There is no solution to this system. No combination of these foods will meet the requirements.

b.
$$\begin{bmatrix} 3 & 1 & 3 & | & 14 \\ 7 & 5 & 8 & | & 37 \\ 1 & 3 & 2 & | & 9 \end{bmatrix} \quad R_3 \leftrightarrow R_1$$

$$= \begin{bmatrix} 1 & 3 & 2 & | & 9 \\ 7 & 5 & 8 & | & 37 \\ 3 & 1 & 3 & | & 14 \end{bmatrix} \quad -7R_1 + R_2$$

$$= \begin{bmatrix} 1 & 3 & 2 & | & 9 \\ 0 & -16 & -6 & | & -26 \\ 3 & 1 & 3 & | & 14 \end{bmatrix} \quad -3R_1 + R_3$$

$$= \begin{bmatrix} 1 & 3 & 2 & | & 9 \\ 0 & -16 & -6 & | & -26 \\ 0 & -8 & -3 & | & -13 \end{bmatrix} \quad -\frac{1}{2}R_2 + R_3$$

$$= \begin{bmatrix} 1 & 3 & 2 & | & 9 \\ 0 & -16 & -6 & | & -26 \\ 0 & 0 & 0 & | & 0 \end{bmatrix}$$

The system is dependent. There are infinitely many combinations of foods A, B, and C that will meet the requirements.

61. Answers will vary. Consider Exercise 24.

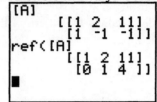

Review Exercises

62. $f(2a-1) = -3(2a-1)+10$
$$= -6a+3+10 = -6a+13$$

63. $(fg)(x) = f(x) \cdot g(x)$
$$= 3x(2x-3) = 6x^2 - 9x$$
$(fg)(-1) = 6(-1)^2 - 9(-1)$
$$= 6(1)+9 = 6+9 = 15$$

64. $2x^3 - 16x^2 + 30x = 2x(x^2 - 8x + 15)$
$$= 2x(x-5)(x-3)$$

Matrix Solutions of Systems of Linear Equations

8.5 CHECK POINTS

CHECK POINT 1

a. $\begin{vmatrix} 10 & 9 \\ 6 & 5 \end{vmatrix} = 10(5) - 6(9) = 50 - 54 = -4$

b. $\begin{vmatrix} 4 & 3 \\ -5 & -8 \end{vmatrix} = 4(-8) - (-5)(3) = -32 + 15 = -17$

CHECK POINT 2

$5x + 4y = 12$

$3x - 6y = 24$

$$D = \begin{vmatrix} 5 & 4 \\ 3 & -6 \end{vmatrix} = 5(-6) - 3(4) = -30 - 12 = -42$$

$$D_x = \begin{vmatrix} 12 & 4 \\ 24 & -6 \end{vmatrix} = 12(-6) - 24(4) = -72 - 96 = -168$$

$$D_y = \begin{vmatrix} 5 & 12 \\ 3 & 24 \end{vmatrix} = 5(24) - 3(12) = 120 - 36 = 84$$

$$x = \frac{D_x}{D} = \frac{-168}{-42} = 4 \qquad y = \frac{D_y}{D} = \frac{84}{-42} = -2$$

The solution is $(4, -2)$.

CHECK POINT 3

$$\begin{vmatrix} 2 & 1 & 7 \\ -5 & 6 & 0 \\ -4 & 3 & 1 \end{vmatrix} = 2 \begin{vmatrix} 6 & 0 \\ 3 & 1 \end{vmatrix} - (-5) \begin{vmatrix} 1 & 7 \\ 3 & 1 \end{vmatrix} + (-4) \begin{vmatrix} 1 & 7 \\ 6 & 0 \end{vmatrix} = 2(6(1) - 3(0)) + 5(1(1) - 3(7)) - 4(1(0) - 6(7))$$

$$= 2(6 - 0) + 5(1 - 21) - 4(0 - 42) = 2(6) + 5(-20) - 4(-42) = 12 - 120 + 168 = 80$$

CHECK POINT 4

$$D = \begin{vmatrix} 3 & -2 & 1 \\ 2 & 3 & -1 \\ 1 & 4 & 3 \end{vmatrix} = 3 \begin{vmatrix} 3 & -1 \\ 4 & 3 \end{vmatrix} - 2 \begin{vmatrix} -2 & 1 \\ 4 & 3 \end{vmatrix} + 1 \begin{vmatrix} -2 & 1 \\ 3 & -1 \end{vmatrix}$$

$$= 3(3(3) - 4(-1)) - 2(-2(3) - 4(1)) + 1(-2(-1) - 3(1)) = 3(9 + 4) - 2(-6 - 4) + 1(2 - 3)$$

$$= 3(13) - 2(-10) + 1(-1) = 39 + 20 - 1 = 58$$

$$D_x = \begin{vmatrix} 16 & -2 & 1 \\ -9 & 3 & -1 \\ 2 & 4 & 3 \end{vmatrix} = 16 \begin{vmatrix} 3 & -1 \\ 4 & 3 \end{vmatrix} - (-9) \begin{vmatrix} -2 & 1 \\ 4 & 3 \end{vmatrix} + 2 \begin{vmatrix} -2 & 1 \\ 3 & -1 \end{vmatrix}$$

$$= 16(3(3) - 4(-1)) + 9(-2(3) - 4(1)) + 2(-2(-1) - 3(1)) = 16(9 + 4) + 9(-6 - 4) + 2(2 - 3)$$

$$= 16(13) + 9(-10) + 2(-1) = 208 - 90 - 2 = 116$$

$$D_y = \begin{vmatrix} 3 & 16 & 1 \\ 2 & -9 & -1 \\ 1 & 2 & 3 \end{vmatrix} = 3 \begin{vmatrix} -9 & -1 \\ 2 & 3 \end{vmatrix} - 2 \begin{vmatrix} 16 & 1 \\ 2 & 3 \end{vmatrix} + 1 \begin{vmatrix} 16 & 1 \\ -9 & -1 \end{vmatrix}$$

$$= 3(-9(3) - 2(-1)) - 2(16(3) - 2(1)) + 1(16(-1) - (-9)(1)) = 3(-27 + 2) - 2(48 - 2) + 1(-16 + 9)$$

$$= 3(-25) - 2(46) + 1(-7) = -75 - 92 - 7 = -174$$

$$D_z = \begin{vmatrix} 3 & -2 & 16 \\ 2 & 3 & -9 \\ 1 & 4 & 2 \end{vmatrix} = 3 \begin{vmatrix} 3 & -9 \\ 4 & 2 \end{vmatrix} - 2 \begin{vmatrix} -2 & 16 \\ 4 & 2 \end{vmatrix} + 1 \begin{vmatrix} -2 & 16 \\ 3 & -9 \end{vmatrix}$$

$$= 3\big(3(2)-4(-9)\big)-2\big(-2(2)-4(16)\big)+1\big(-2(-9)-3(16)\big)$$
$$= 3(6+36)-2(-4-64)+1(18-48)=3(42)-2(-68)+1(-30)=126+136-30=232$$

$$x=\frac{D_x}{D}=\frac{116}{58}=2 \qquad y=\frac{D_y}{D}=\frac{-174}{58}=-3 \qquad z=\frac{D_z}{D}=\frac{232}{58}=4$$

The solution is $(2,-3,4)$.

EXERCISE SET 8.5

1.
$$\begin{vmatrix} 5 & 7 \\ 2 & 3 \end{vmatrix}=5(3)-2(7)=15-14=1$$

3.
$$\begin{vmatrix} -4 & 1 \\ 5 & 6 \end{vmatrix}=-4(6)-5(1)=-24-5=-29$$

5.
$$\begin{vmatrix} -7 & 14 \\ 2 & -4 \end{vmatrix}=-7(-4)-2(14)=28-28=0$$

7.
$$\begin{vmatrix} -5 & -1 \\ -2 & -7 \end{vmatrix}=-5(-7)-(-2)(-1)$$
$$=35-2=33$$

9.
$$\begin{vmatrix} 1/2 & 1/2 \\ 1/8 & -3/4 \end{vmatrix}=\frac{1}{2}\left(-\frac{3}{4}\right)-\frac{1}{8}\left(\frac{1}{2}\right)=-\frac{3}{8}-\frac{1}{16}$$
$$=-\frac{6}{16}-\frac{1}{16}=-\frac{7}{16}$$

11.
$$D=\begin{vmatrix} 1 & 1 \\ 1 & -1 \end{vmatrix}=1(-1)-1(1)=-1-1=-2$$

$$D_x=\begin{vmatrix} 7 & 1 \\ 3 & -1 \end{vmatrix}=7(-1)-3(1)=-7-3=-10$$

$$D_y=\begin{vmatrix} 1 & 7 \\ 1 & 3 \end{vmatrix}=1(3)-1(7)=3-7=-4$$

$$x=\frac{D_x}{D}=\frac{-10}{-2}=5 \qquad y=\frac{D_y}{D}=\frac{-4}{-2}=2$$

The solution is $(5,2)$.

13.
$$D=\begin{vmatrix} 12 & 3 \\ 2 & -3 \end{vmatrix}=12(-3)-2(3)$$
$$=-36-6=-42$$

$$D_x=\begin{vmatrix} 15 & 3 \\ 13 & -3 \end{vmatrix}=15(-3)-13(3)$$
$$=-45-39=-84$$

$$D_y=\begin{vmatrix} 12 & 15 \\ 2 & 13 \end{vmatrix}=12(13)-2(15)$$
$$=156-30=126$$

$$x=\frac{D_x}{D}=\frac{-84}{-42}=2 \qquad y=\frac{D_y}{D}=\frac{126}{-42}=-3$$

The solution is $(2,-3)$.

15.
$$D=\begin{vmatrix} 4 & -5 \\ 2 & 3 \end{vmatrix}=4(3)-2(-5)=12+10=22$$

$$D_x=\begin{vmatrix} 17 & -5 \\ 3 & 3 \end{vmatrix}=17(3)-3(-5)$$
$$=51+15=66$$

$$D_y=\begin{vmatrix} 4 & 17 \\ 2 & 3 \end{vmatrix}=4(3)-2(17)$$
$$=12-34=-22$$

$$x=\frac{D_x}{D}=\frac{66}{22}=3 \qquad y=\frac{D_y}{D}=\frac{-22}{22}=-1$$

The solution is $(3,-1)$.

17.
$$D=\begin{vmatrix} 1 & -3 \\ 3 & -4 \end{vmatrix}=1(-4)-3(-3)=-4+9=5$$

$$D_x=\begin{vmatrix} 4 & -3 \\ 12 & -4 \end{vmatrix}=4(-4)-12(-3)$$
$$=-16+36=20$$

$$D_y=\begin{vmatrix} 1 & 4 \\ 3 & 12 \end{vmatrix}=1(12)-3(4)=12-12=0$$

$$x=\frac{D_x}{D}=\frac{20}{5}=4 \qquad y=\frac{D_y}{D}=\frac{0}{5}=0$$

The solution is $(4,0)$.

19.

$$D = \begin{vmatrix} 3 & -4 \\ 2 & 2 \end{vmatrix} = 3(2) - 2(-4) = 6 + 8 = 14$$

$$D_x = \begin{vmatrix} 4 & -4 \\ 12 & 2 \end{vmatrix} = 4(2) - 12(-4) = 8 + 48 = 56$$

$$D_y = \begin{vmatrix} 3 & 4 \\ 2 & 12 \end{vmatrix} = 3(12) - 2(4) = 36 - 8 = 28$$

$$x = \frac{D_x}{D} = \frac{56}{14} = 4$$

$$y = \frac{D_y}{D} = \frac{28}{14} = 2$$

The solution is $(4, 2)$.

21. Rewrite the system in $Ax + By = C$ form.

$$2x - 3y = 2$$
$$5x + 4y = 51$$

$$D = \begin{vmatrix} 2 & -3 \\ 5 & 4 \end{vmatrix} = 2(4) - 5(-3) = 8 + 15 = 23$$

$$D_x = \begin{vmatrix} 2 & -3 \\ 51 & 4 \end{vmatrix} = 2(4) - 51(-3)$$
$$= 8 + 153 = 161$$

$$D_y = \begin{vmatrix} 2 & 2 \\ 5 & 51 \end{vmatrix} = 2(51) - 5(2) = 102 - 10 = 92$$

$$x = \frac{D_x}{D} = \frac{161}{23} = 7 \qquad y = \frac{D_y}{D} = \frac{92}{23} = 4$$

The solution is $(7, 4)$.

23. Rewrite the system in $Ax + By = C$ form.

$$3x + 3y = 2$$
$$2x + 2y = 3$$

$$D = \begin{vmatrix} 3 & 3 \\ 2 & 2 \end{vmatrix} = 3(2) - 2(3) = 6 - 6 = 0$$

$$D_x = \begin{vmatrix} 2 & 3 \\ 3 & 2 \end{vmatrix} = 2(2) - 3(3) = 4 - 9 = -5$$

$$D_y = \begin{vmatrix} 2 & 3 \\ 3 & 2 \end{vmatrix} = 2(2) - 3(3) = 4 - 9 = -5$$

Because $D = 0$ but neither D_x nor D_y is zero, Cramer's Rule cannot be used to solve the system. Instead, use matrices.

$$\begin{bmatrix} 3 & 3 & | & 2 \\ 2 & 2 & | & 3 \end{bmatrix} \frac{1}{3}R_1$$

$$= \begin{bmatrix} 1 & 1 & | & 2/3 \\ 2 & 2 & | & 3 \end{bmatrix} -2R_1 + R_2$$

$$= \begin{bmatrix} 1 & 1 & | & 2/3 \\ 0 & 0 & | & 5/3 \end{bmatrix}$$

This is a contradiction. There are no pairs, (x, y), for which $0 = \frac{5}{3}$. The solution set is $\varnothing$ and the system is inconsistent.

25. Rewrite the system in $Ax + By = C$ form.

$$3x + 4y = 16$$
$$6x + 8y = 32$$

$$D = \begin{vmatrix} 3 & 4 \\ 6 & 8 \end{vmatrix} = 3(8) - 6(4) = 24 - 24 = 0$$

$$D_x = \begin{vmatrix} 16 & 4 \\ 32 & 8 \end{vmatrix} = 16(8) - 32(4)$$
$$= 128 - 128 = 128$$

$$D_y = \begin{vmatrix} 3 & 16 \\ 6 & 32 \end{vmatrix} = 3(32) - 6(16) = 96 - 96 = 0$$

Since $D = 0$ and all determinants in the numerators are 0, the equations in the system are dependent and there are infinitely many solutions.

27.

$$\begin{vmatrix} 3 & 0 & 0 \\ 2 & 1 & -5 \\ 2 & 5 & -1 \end{vmatrix}$$

$$= 3\begin{vmatrix} 1 & -5 \\ 5 & -1 \end{vmatrix} - 2\begin{vmatrix} 0 & 0 \\ 5 & -1 \end{vmatrix} + 2\begin{vmatrix} 0 & 0 \\ 1 & -5 \end{vmatrix}$$

$$= 3(1(-1) - 5(-5)) - 2(0(-1) - 5(0))$$
$$+ 2(0(-5) - 1(0))$$

$$= 3(-1 + 25) - 2(0 - 0) + 2(0 - 0)$$

$$= 3(24) - 2(0) + 2(0) = 72$$

29.

$$\begin{vmatrix} 3 & 1 & 0 \\ -3 & 4 & 0 \\ -1 & 3 & -5 \end{vmatrix} = 3\begin{vmatrix} 4 & 0 \\ 3 & -5 \end{vmatrix} - (-3)\begin{vmatrix} 1 & 0 \\ 3 & -5 \end{vmatrix} + (-1)\begin{vmatrix} 1 & 0 \\ 4 & 0 \end{vmatrix} = 3(4(-5)-3(0)) + 3(1(-5)-3(0)) - 1(1(0)-4(0))$$

$$= 3(-20-0) + 3(-5-0) - 1(0-0) = 3(-20) + 3(-5) - 1\cancel{(0)} = -60-15 = -75$$

31.

$$\begin{vmatrix} 1 & 1 & 1 \\ 2 & 2 & 2 \\ -3 & 4 & -5 \end{vmatrix} = 1\begin{vmatrix} 2 & 2 \\ 4 & -5 \end{vmatrix} - 2\begin{vmatrix} 1 & 1 \\ 4 & -5 \end{vmatrix} + (-3)\begin{vmatrix} 1 & 1 \\ 2 & 2 \end{vmatrix} = 1(2(-5)-4(2)) - 2(1(-5)-4(1)) - 3(1(2)-2(1))$$

$$= 1(-10-8) - 2(-5-4) - 3(2-2) = 1(-18) - 2(-9) - 3\cancel{(0)} = -18+18 = 0$$

33. $x + y + z = 0$
$2x - y + z = -1$
$-x + 3y - z = -8$

$$D = \begin{vmatrix} 1 & 1 & 1 \\ 2 & -1 & 1 \\ -1 & 3 & -1 \end{vmatrix} = 1\begin{vmatrix} -1 & 1 \\ 3 & -1 \end{vmatrix} - 2\begin{vmatrix} 1 & 1 \\ 3 & -1 \end{vmatrix} - 1\begin{vmatrix} 1 & 1 \\ -1 & 1 \end{vmatrix} = 1(-1(-1)-3(1)) - 2(1(-1)-3(1)) - 1(1(1)-(-1)(1))$$

$$= 1(1-3) - 2(-1-3) - 1(1+1) = 1(-2) - 2(-4) - 1(2) = -2+8-2 = 4$$

$$D_x = \begin{vmatrix} 0 & 1 & 1 \\ -1 & -1 & 1 \\ -8 & 3 & -1 \end{vmatrix} = 0\cancel{\begin{vmatrix} -1 & 1 \\ 3 & -1 \end{vmatrix}} - (-1)\begin{vmatrix} 1 & 1 \\ 3 & -1 \end{vmatrix} - 8\begin{vmatrix} 1 & 1 \\ -1 & 1 \end{vmatrix} = 1(1(-1)-3(1)) - 8(1(1)-(-1)(1))$$

$$= 1(-1-3) - 8(1+1) = 1(-4) - 8(2) = -4-16 = -20$$

$$D_y = \begin{vmatrix} 1 & 0 & 1 \\ 2 & -1 & 1 \\ -1 & -8 & -1 \end{vmatrix} = 1\begin{vmatrix} -1 & 1 \\ -8 & -1 \end{vmatrix} - 2\begin{vmatrix} 0 & 1 \\ -8 & -1 \end{vmatrix} - 1\begin{vmatrix} 0 & 1 \\ -1 & 1 \end{vmatrix} = 1(-1(-1)-(-8)1) - 2(0(-1)-(-8)1) - 1(0(1)-(-1)1)$$

$$= 1(1+8) - 2(0+8) - 1(0+1) = 1(9) - 2(8) - 1(1) = 9-16-1 = -8$$

$$D_z = \begin{vmatrix} 1 & 1 & 0 \\ 2 & -1 & -1 \\ -1 & 3 & -8 \end{vmatrix} = 1\begin{vmatrix} -1 & -1 \\ 3 & -8 \end{vmatrix} - 2\begin{vmatrix} 1 & 0 \\ 3 & -8 \end{vmatrix} - 1\begin{vmatrix} 1 & 0 \\ -1 & -1 \end{vmatrix} = 1(-1(-8)-3(-1)) - 2(1(-8)-3(0)) - 1(1(-1)-(-1)0)$$

$$= 1(8+3) - 2(-8-0) - 1(-1+0) = 1(11) - 2(-8) - 1(-1) = 11+16+1 = 28$$

$$x = \frac{D_x}{D} = \frac{-20}{4} = -5 \qquad y = \frac{D_y}{D} = \frac{-8}{4} = -2 \qquad z = \frac{D_z}{D} = \frac{28}{4} = 7$$

The solution is $(-5, -2, 7)$.

35. $4x - 5y - 6z = -1$
$x - 2y - 5z = -12$
$2x - y \quad\quad = 7$

$$D = \begin{vmatrix} 4 & -5 & -6 \\ 1 & -2 & -5 \\ 2 & -1 & 0 \end{vmatrix} = 4 \begin{vmatrix} -2 & -5 \\ -1 & 0 \end{vmatrix} - 1 \begin{vmatrix} -5 & -6 \\ -1 & 0 \end{vmatrix} + 2 \begin{vmatrix} -5 & -6 \\ -2 & -5 \end{vmatrix}$$

$$= 4 \left(-2(0) - (-1)(-5) \right) - 1 \left(-5(0) - (-1)(-6) \right) + 2 \left(-5(-5) - (-2)(-6) \right)$$

$$= 4(-5) - 1(-6) + 2(25 - 12) = -20 + 6 + 2(13) = -20 + 6 + 26 = 12$$

$$D_x = \begin{vmatrix} -1 & -5 & -6 \\ -12 & -2 & -5 \\ 7 & -1 & 0 \end{vmatrix} = -1 \begin{vmatrix} -2 & -5 \\ -1 & 0 \end{vmatrix} - (-12) \begin{vmatrix} -5 & -6 \\ -1 & 0 \end{vmatrix} + 7 \begin{vmatrix} -5 & -6 \\ -2 & -5 \end{vmatrix}$$

$$= -1 \left(-2(0) - (-1)(-5) \right) - (-12) \left(-5(0) - (-1)(-6) \right) + 7 \left(-5(-5) - (-2)(-6) \right)$$

$$= -1(-5) - (-12)(-6) + 7(25 - 12) = 5 - 72 + 7(13) = 5 - 72 + 91 = 24$$

$$D_y = \begin{vmatrix} 4 & -1 & -6 \\ 1 & -12 & -5 \\ 2 & 7 & 0 \end{vmatrix} = 4 \begin{vmatrix} -12 & -5 \\ 7 & 0 \end{vmatrix} - 1 \begin{vmatrix} -1 & -6 \\ 7 & 0 \end{vmatrix} + 2 \begin{vmatrix} -1 & -6 \\ -12 & -5 \end{vmatrix}$$

$$= 4 \left(-12(0) - 7(-5) \right) - 1 \left(-1(0) - 7(-6) \right) + 2 \left(-1(-5) - (-12)(-6) \right)$$

$$= 4(35) - 1(42) + 2(5 - 72) = 140 - 42 + 2(-67) = 140 - 42 - 134 = -36$$

$$D_z = \begin{vmatrix} 4 & -5 & -1 \\ 1 & -2 & -12 \\ 2 & -1 & 7 \end{vmatrix} = 4 \begin{vmatrix} -2 & -12 \\ -1 & 7 \end{vmatrix} - 1 \begin{vmatrix} -5 & -1 \\ -1 & 7 \end{vmatrix} + 2 \begin{vmatrix} -5 & -1 \\ -2 & -12 \end{vmatrix}$$

$$= 4 \left(-2(7) - (-1)(-12) \right) - 1 \left(-5(7) - (-1)(-1) \right) + 2 \left(-5(-12) - (-2)(-1) \right)$$

$$= 4(-14 - 12) - 1(-35 - 1) + 2(60 - 2) = 4(-26) - 1(-36) + 2(58) = -104 + 36 + 116 = 48$$

$$x = \frac{D_x}{D} = \frac{24}{12} = 2 \qquad y = \frac{D_y}{D} = \frac{-36}{12} = -3 \qquad z = \frac{D_z}{D} = \frac{48}{12} = 4$$

The solution is $(2, -3, 4)$.

37. $x + y + z = 4$
$x - 2y + z = 7$
$x + 3y + 2z = 4$

$$D = \begin{vmatrix} 1 & 1 & 1 \\ 1 & -2 & 1 \\ 1 & 3 & 2 \end{vmatrix} = 1 \begin{vmatrix} -2 & 1 \\ 3 & 2 \end{vmatrix} - 1 \begin{vmatrix} 1 & 1 \\ 3 & 2 \end{vmatrix} + 1 \begin{vmatrix} 1 & 1 \\ -2 & 1 \end{vmatrix} = 1(-2(2) - 3(1)) - 1(1(2) - 3(1)) + 1(1(1) - (-2)1)$$

$$= 1(-4 - 3) - 1(2 - 3) + 1(1 + 2) = 1(-7) - 1(-1) + 1(3) = -7 + 1 + 3 = -3$$

$$D_x = \begin{vmatrix} 4 & 1 & 1 \\ 7 & -2 & 1 \\ 4 & 3 & 2 \end{vmatrix} = 4 \begin{vmatrix} -2 & 1 \\ 3 & 2 \end{vmatrix} - 7 \begin{vmatrix} 1 & 1 \\ 3 & 2 \end{vmatrix} + 4 \begin{vmatrix} 1 & 1 \\ -2 & 1 \end{vmatrix} = 4(-4 - 3) - 7(2 - 3) + 4(1 + 2)$$

$$= 4(-2(2) - 3(1)) - 7(1(2) - 3(1)) + 4(1(1) - (-2)1) = 4(-7) - 7(-1) + 4(3) = -28 + 7 + 12 = -9$$

$$D_y = \begin{vmatrix} 1 & 4 & 1 \\ 1 & 7 & 1 \\ 1 & 4 & 2 \end{vmatrix} = 1\begin{vmatrix} 7 & 1 \\ 4 & 2 \end{vmatrix} - 1\begin{vmatrix} 4 & 1 \\ 4 & 2 \end{vmatrix} + 1\begin{vmatrix} 4 & 1 \\ 7 & 1 \end{vmatrix} = 1\big(7(2)-4(1)\big) - 1\big(4(2)-4(1)\big) + 1\big(4(1)-7(1)\big)$$

$$= 1(14-4)-1(8-4)+1(4-7) = 1(10)-1(4)+1(-3) = 10-4-3 = 3$$

$$D_z = \begin{vmatrix} 1 & 1 & 4 \\ 1 & -2 & 7 \\ 1 & 3 & 4 \end{vmatrix} = 1\begin{vmatrix} -2 & 7 \\ 3 & 4 \end{vmatrix} - 1\begin{vmatrix} 1 & 4 \\ 3 & 4 \end{vmatrix} + 1\begin{vmatrix} 1 & 4 \\ -2 & 7 \end{vmatrix} = 1\big(-2(4)-3(7)\big) - 1\big(1(4)-3(4)\big) + 1\big(1(7)-(-2)4\big)$$

$$= 1(-8-21)-1(4-12)+1(7+8) = 1(-29)-1(-8)+1(15) = -29+8+15 = -6$$

$$x = \frac{D_x}{D} = \frac{-9}{-3} = 3 \qquad y = \frac{D_y}{D} = \frac{3}{-3} = -1 \qquad z = \frac{D_z}{D} = \frac{-6}{-3} = 2$$

The solution is $(3,-1,2)$.

39.
$$\begin{aligned} x \quad\quad + 2z &= 4 \\ 2y - z &= 5 \\ 2x + 3y \quad\quad &= 13 \end{aligned}$$

$$D = \begin{vmatrix} 1 & 0 & 2 \\ 0 & 2 & -1 \\ 2 & 3 & 0 \end{vmatrix} = 1\begin{vmatrix} 2 & -1 \\ 3 & 0 \end{vmatrix} - 0\begin{vmatrix} 0 & 2 \\ 3 & 0 \end{vmatrix} + 2\begin{vmatrix} 0 & 2 \\ 2 & -1 \end{vmatrix} = 1\big(2(0)-3(-1)\big) + 2\big(0(-1)-2(2)\big)$$

$$= 1(3) + 2(-4) = 3-8 = -5$$

$$D_x = \begin{vmatrix} 4 & 0 & 2 \\ 5 & 2 & -1 \\ 13 & 3 & 0 \end{vmatrix} = 4\begin{vmatrix} 2 & -1 \\ 3 & 0 \end{vmatrix} - 5\begin{vmatrix} 0 & 2 \\ 3 & 0 \end{vmatrix} + 13\begin{vmatrix} 0 & 2 \\ 2 & -1 \end{vmatrix} = 4\big(2(0)-3(-1)\big) - 5\big(0(0)-3(2)\big) + 13\big(0(-1)-2(2)\big)$$

$$= 4(3) - 5(-6) + 13(-4) = 12+30-52 = -10$$

$$D_y = \begin{vmatrix} 1 & 4 & 2 \\ 0 & 5 & -1 \\ 2 & 13 & 0 \end{vmatrix} = 1\begin{vmatrix} 5 & -1 \\ 13 & 0 \end{vmatrix} - 0\begin{vmatrix} 4 & 2 \\ 13 & 0 \end{vmatrix} + 2\begin{vmatrix} 4 & 2 \\ 5 & -1 \end{vmatrix} = 1\big(5(0)-13(-1)\big) + 2\big(4(-1)-5(2)\big)$$

$$= 1(13) + 2(-4-10) = 1(13) + 2(-14) = 13-28 = -15$$

$$D_z = \begin{vmatrix} 1 & 0 & 4 \\ 0 & 2 & 5 \\ 2 & 3 & 13 \end{vmatrix} = 1\begin{vmatrix} 2 & 5 \\ 3 & 13 \end{vmatrix} - 0\begin{vmatrix} 0 & 4 \\ 3 & 13 \end{vmatrix} + 2\begin{vmatrix} 0 & 4 \\ 2 & 5 \end{vmatrix} = 1\big(2(13)-3(5)\big) + 2\big(0(5)-2(4)\big)$$

$$= 1(26-15) + 2(-8) = 1(11)-16 = 11-16 = -5$$

$$x = \frac{D_x}{D} = \frac{-10}{-5} = 2 \qquad y = \frac{D_y}{D} = \frac{-15}{-5} = 3 \qquad z = \frac{D_z}{D} = \frac{-5}{-5} = 1$$

The solution is $(2,3,1)$.

41.
$$\text{Area} = \pm\frac{1}{2}\begin{vmatrix} 3 & -5 & 1 \\ 2 & 6 & 1 \\ -3 & 5 & 1 \end{vmatrix} = \pm\frac{1}{2}\left[3\begin{vmatrix} 6 & 1 \\ 5 & 1 \end{vmatrix} - 2\begin{vmatrix} -5 & 1 \\ 5 & 1 \end{vmatrix} - 3\begin{vmatrix} -5 & 1 \\ 6 & 1 \end{vmatrix} \right]$$

$$= \pm\frac{1}{2}\left[3\big(6(1)-5(1)\big)-2\big(-5(1)-5(1)\big)-3\big(-5(1)-6(1)\big)\right]$$

$$= \pm\frac{1}{2}\left[3(6-5)-2(-5-5)-3(-5-6)\right] = \pm\frac{1}{2}\left[3(1)-2(-10)-3(-11)\right]$$

$$= \pm\frac{1}{2}\left[3+20+33\right] = \pm\frac{1}{2}\left[56\right] = \pm28$$

The area is 28 square units.

43.
$$\begin{vmatrix} 3 & -1 & 1 \\ 0 & -3 & 1 \\ 12 & 5 & 1 \end{vmatrix} = 3\begin{vmatrix} -3 & 1 \\ 5 & 1 \end{vmatrix} - 0\begin{vmatrix} -1 & 1 \\ 5 & 1 \end{vmatrix} + 12\begin{vmatrix} -1 & 1 \\ -3 & 1 \end{vmatrix} = 3\big(-3(1)-5(1)\big)+12\big(-1(1)-(-3)1\big)$$

$$= 3(-3-5)+12(-1+3) = 3(-8)+12(2) = -24+24 = 0$$

Because the determinant is equal to zero, the points are collinear.

45.
$$\begin{vmatrix} x & y & 1 \\ 3 & -5 & 1 \\ -2 & 6 & 1 \end{vmatrix} = x\begin{vmatrix} -5 & 1 \\ 6 & 1 \end{vmatrix} - 3\begin{vmatrix} y & 1 \\ 6 & 1 \end{vmatrix} - 2\begin{vmatrix} y & 1 \\ -5 & 1 \end{vmatrix} = x\big(-5(1)-6(1)\big)-3\big(y(1)-6(1)\big)-2\big(y(1)-(-5)1\big)$$

$$= x(-5-6)-3(y-6)-2(y+5) = x(-11)-3y+18-2y-10 = -11x-5y+8$$

To find the equation of the line, set the determinant equal to zero.

$$-11x-5y+8 = 0$$
$$-5y = 11x-8$$
$$y = -\frac{11}{5}x+\frac{8}{5}$$

For Exercises 47-53, answers may vary.

55. Statement **d.** is true. Only one determinant is necessary to evaluate the determinant.

$$\begin{vmatrix} 2 & 3 & -2 \\ 0 & 1 & 3 \\ 0 & 4 & -1 \end{vmatrix}$$

$$= 2\begin{vmatrix} 1 & 3 \\ 4 & -1 \end{vmatrix} - 0\begin{vmatrix} 3 & -2 \\ 4 & -1 \end{vmatrix} + 0\begin{vmatrix} 3 & -2 \\ 1 & 3 \end{vmatrix}$$

Statement **a.** is false. For the determinant to equal zero, not every variable in the system must be zero.

Statement **b.** is false. Using Cramer's rule, we use $\dfrac{D_y}{D}$ to find y.

Statement **c.** is false. Despite determinants being different (i.e., all entries are not identical), they can have the same value. This means that the numerators of the x and y when using Cramer's rule can have the same value, without being the same determinant. As a result, x and y can have the same value.

57.
$$\begin{vmatrix} 1 & 3 \\ 2 & 4 \end{vmatrix} = 1(4)-2(3) = 4-6 = -2$$

Switch the columns and re-evaluate.

$$\begin{vmatrix} 3 & 1 \\ 4 & 2 \end{vmatrix} = 3(2)-4(1) = 6-4 = 2$$

When the columns of a second-order determinant are interchanged, the value of the determinant is multiplied by -1.

59. We are given two points, (x_1, y_1) and (x_2, y_2). To find the equation of a line using two points, we first find the slope, and then use the slope and one of the points to write the equation of the line in point-slope form. Here, the slope is: $m = \dfrac{y_2 - y_1}{x_2 - x_1}$. Using point slope form, we obtain:

$y - y_1 = \dfrac{y_2 - y_1}{x_2 - x_1}(x - x_1)$. To determine that this is equivalent to what is obtained when the determinant is set equal to zero, we multiply as follows:

$$y - y_1 = \frac{y_2 - y_1}{x_2 - x_1}(x - x_1)$$
$$(x_2 - x_1)(y - y_1) = (y_2 - y_1)(x - x_1)$$
$$x_2 y - x_2 y_1 - x_1 y + x_1 y_1 = xy_2 - x_1 y_2 - xy_1 + x_1 y_1$$

Now, evaluate the determinant to see if they are equivalent.

$$\begin{vmatrix} x & y & 1 \\ x_1 & y_1 & 1 \\ x_2 & y_2 & 1 \end{vmatrix} = 0$$

$$x\begin{vmatrix} y_1 & 1 \\ y_2 & 1 \end{vmatrix} - x_1\begin{vmatrix} y & 1 \\ y_2 & 1 \end{vmatrix} + x_2\begin{vmatrix} y & 1 \\ y_1 & 1 \end{vmatrix} = 0$$

$$x\big(y_1(1) - y_2(1)\big) - x_1\big(y(1) - y_2(1)\big) + x_2\big(y(1) - y_1(1)\big) = 0$$
$$x(y_1 - y_2) - x_1(y - y_2) + x_2(y - y_1) = 0$$
$$xy_1 - xy_2 - x_1 y + x_1 y_2 + x_2 y - x_2 y_1 = 0$$
$$x_2 y - x_2 y_1 - x_1 y = xy_2 - x_1 y_2 - xy_1$$

When we compare, we see that the equations are not the same. Using the Addition Property of Equality, we add $x_1 y_1$ to both sides of the equation and see that the expressions are the equivalent. This shows that the equation of a line through (x_1, y_1) and (x_2, y_2) is given by the determinant

$$\begin{vmatrix} x & y & 1 \\ x_1 & y_1 & 1 \\ x_2 & y_2 & 1 \end{vmatrix} = 0.$$

61. Answers will vary depending upon personal preference.

Review Exercises

62. $2x - 1 = x^2 - 4x + 4$
$$0 = x^2 - 6x + 5$$
$$0 = (x - 5)(x - 1)$$
$$x - 5 = 0 \quad \text{or} \quad x - 1 = 0$$
$$x = 5 \qquad\qquad x = 1$$

The solutions are 1 and 5.

63.
$$\left(2x^2\right)^{-3} = \left(\frac{1}{2x^2}\right)^3 = \frac{1}{8x^6}$$

64.
$$\frac{x^2 - 6x + 9}{12} \cdot \frac{3}{x^2 - 9}$$

$$= \frac{(x-3)^2}{4(3)} \cdot \frac{3}{(x+3)(x-3)}$$

$$= \frac{(x-3)^{\cancel{2}}}{4\cancel{(3)}} \cdot \frac{\cancel{3}}{(x+3)\cancel{(x-3)}}$$

$$= \frac{x-3}{4(x+3)}$$

Chapter 8 Review Exercises

1. The relation is a function.
Domain {3, 4, 5}
Range {10}

2. The relation is a function.
Domain {1, 2, 3, 4}
Range {−6, π, 12, 100}

3. The relation is not a function.
Domain {13, 15}
Range {14, 16, 17}

4.
a. $f(0) = 7(0) - 5 = 0 - 5 = -5$

b. $f(3) = 7(3) - 5 = 21 - 5 = 16$

c. $f(-10) = 7(-10) - 5 = -70 - 5 = -75$

d. $f(2a) = 7(2a) - 5 = 14a - 5$

e. $f(a+2) = 7(a+2) - 5$
$$= 7a + 14 - 5 = 7a + 9$$

5.
a.
$$g(0) = 3(0)^2 - 5(0) + 2$$
$$= 0 - 0 + 2 = 2$$

b.
$$g(5) = 3(5)^2 - 5(5) + 2$$
$$= 3(25) - 25 + 2$$
$$= 75 - 25 + 2 = 52$$

c.
$$g(-4) = 3(-4)^2 - 5(-4) + 2$$
$$= 3(16) + 20 + 2$$
$$= 48 + 20 + 2 = 70$$

d.
$$g(b) = 3(b)^2 - 5(b) + 2$$
$$= 3b^2 - 5b + 2$$

e.
$$g(4a) = 3(4a)^2 - 5(4a) + 2$$
$$= 3(16a^2) - 20a + 2$$
$$= 48a^2 - 20a + 2$$

6.

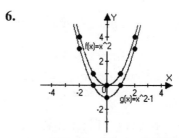

g shifts the graph of *f* down one unit

7.

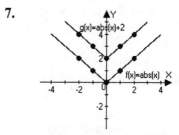

g shifts the graph of *f* up two units

8. The vertical line test shows that this is not the graph of a function.

9. The vertical line test shows that this is the graph of a function.

10. The vertical line test shows that this is the graph of a function.

11. The vertical line test shows that this is not the graph of a function.

12. $f(-2) = -3$

13. $f(0) = -2$

14. When $x = 3$, $f(x) = -5$.

15. **a.** The vulture's height is a function of its time in flight because every time, t, is associated with at most one height.

b. $f(15) = 0$

At time $t = 15$ seconds, the vulture is at height zero. This means that after 15 seconds, the vulture is on the ground.

c. The vulture's maximum height is 45 meters.

d. For $x = 7$ and 22, $f(x) = 20$. This means that at times 7 seconds, and 20 seconds, the vulture is at a height of 22 meters.

e. The vulture began the flight at 45 meters and remained there for approximately 3 seconds. At that time, the vulture began to descend. It landed on the ground and stayed there from approximately 12 seconds to 17 seconds. The vulture then began to climb back up to a height of 44 meters.

16. Domain of $f = \{x | x \text{ is a real number}\}$

17. Domain of $f = \{x | x \text{ is a real number and } x \neq -8\}$

18. Domain of $f = \{x | x \text{ is a real number and } x \neq 5\}$

19. **a.** $(f+g)(x) = (4x-5) + (2x+1)$
$$= 4x - 5 + 2x + 1 = 6x - 4$$

b. $(f+g)(3) = 6(3) - 4 = 18 - 4 = 14$

20. **a.** $(f+g)(x) = (5x^2 - x + 4) + (x - 3)$
$$= 5x^2 - x + 4 + x - 3$$
$$= 5x^2 + 1$$

b. $(f+g)(3) = 5(3)^2 + 1 = 5(9) + 1$
$$= 45 + 1 = 46$$

21. Domain of $f + g = \{x | x \text{ is a real number}$ and $x \neq 4\}$

22. Domain of $f + g = \{x | x \text{ is a real number}$ and $x \neq -6$ and $x \neq -1\}$

23. $f(x) = x^2 - 2x$, $g(x) = x - 5$
$$(f+g)(x) = (x^2 - 2x) + (x - 5)$$
$$= x^2 - 2x + x - 5 = x^2 - x - 5$$
$$(f+g)(-2) = (-2)^2 - (-2) - 5$$
$$= 4 + 2 - 5 = 1$$

24. Recall from Exercise 23: $(f+g)(x) = x^2 - x - 5$.

$$f(3) + g(3) = (f+g)(3) = (3)^2 - (3) - 5$$
$$= 9 - 3 - 5 = 1$$

25. $(f-g)(x) = (x^2 - 2x) - (x - 5)$
$$= x^2 - 2x - x + 5 = x^2 - 3x + 5$$
$$(f-g)(1) = (1)^2 - 3(1) + 5 = 1 - 3 + 5 = 3$$

26. Recall from Exercise 25: $(f-g)(x) = x^2 - 3x + 5$.

$$f(4) - g(4) = (f-g)(4)$$
$$= (4)^2 - 3(4) + 5$$
$$= 16 - 12 + 5 = 9$$

27. $(fg)(x) = (x^2 - 2x)(x - 5)$
$$= x^3 - 5x^2 - 2x^2 + 10x$$
$$= x^3 - 7x^2 + 10x$$
$$(fg)(-3) = (-3)^3 - 7(-3)^2 + 10(-3)$$
$$= -27 - 7(9) - 30 = -120$$

28. $\left(\dfrac{f}{g}\right)(x) = \dfrac{x^2 - 2x}{x - 5}$

$$\left(\dfrac{f}{g}\right)(4) = \dfrac{(4)^2 - 2(4)}{4-5} = \dfrac{16-8}{-1} = \dfrac{8}{-1} = -8$$

29. $(f-g)(x) = x^2 - 3x + 5$

Domain of $f - g = \{x | x \text{ is a real number}\}$.

30. $\left(\dfrac{f}{g}\right)(x) = \dfrac{x^2 - 2x}{x - 5}$

Domain of $\dfrac{f}{g} = \{x | x \text{ is a real number and }$

$x \neq 5\}$

31. $-3 + (-2) + 5 = 0$

$\qquad -5 + 5 = 0$

$\qquad\qquad 0 = 0$

$2(-3) - 3(-2) + 5 = 5$

$\qquad -6 + 6 + 5 = 5$

$\qquad\qquad 5 = 5$

$4(-3) + 2(-2) + 4(5) = 3$

$\qquad -12 - 4 + 20 = 3$

$\qquad\qquad 4 \cancel{=} 3$

The triple does not satisfy all three equations, so it is not a solution.

32. Multiply the first equation by –2 and add to the third.

$-4x + 2y - 2z = -2$

$\underline{4x - 2y + 3z = 4}$

$\qquad\qquad z = 2$

Back-substitute 2 for z in two of the original equations to obtain a system of two equations in two variables.

$2x - y + z = 1 \qquad 3x - 3y + 4z = 5$

$2x - y + 2 = 1 \qquad 3x - 3y + 4(2) = 5$

$\quad 2x - y = -1 \qquad\quad 3x - 3y + 8 = 5$

$\qquad\qquad\qquad\qquad\qquad 3x - 3y = -3$

The resulting system is as follows.

$2x - y = -1$

$3x - 3y = -3$

Multiply the first equation by –3 and add solve by addition.

$-6x + 3y = 3$

$\underline{3x - 3y = -3}$

$-3x = 0$

$\qquad x = 0$

Back-substitute 0 for x to find y.

$2(0) - y = -1$

$\qquad -y = -1$

$\qquady = 1$

The solution is $(0, 1, 2)$.

33. Multiply the first equation by –2 and add to the second equation.

$-2x - 4y + 2z = -10$

$\underline{2x - y + 3z = 0}$

$\qquad -5y + 5z = -10$

We now have two equations in two variables.

$2y + z = 1$

$-5y + 5z = -10$

Multiply the first equation by –5 and solve by addition.

$-10y - 5z = -5$

$\underline{-5y + 5z = -10}$

$-15y = -15$

$\quady = 1$

Back-substitute 1 for y to find z.

$2(1) + z = 1$

$\quad 2 + z = 1$

$\qquad z = -1$

Back-substitute to find x.

$x + 2(1) - (-1) = 5$

$\quad x + 2 + 1 = 5$

$\qquad x + 3 = 5$

$\qquad\qquad x = 2$

The solution is $(2, 1, -1)$.

34. Multiply the second equation by –3 and add to the third equation.

$-3x + 3y + 6z = -6$

$\underline{2x - 3y + 6z = 5}$

$-x + 12z = -1$

Multiply the second equation by –4 and add to the first equation.

$$3x - 4y + 4z = 7$$
$$\underline{-4x + 4y + 8z = -8}$$
$$-x \quad\quad + 12z = -1$$

The equations are identical. The system is dependent. There are an infinite number of solutions to the system.

35. $(x, y) = (1, 4)$

$$4 = a(1)^2 + b(1) + c$$
$$4 = a + b + c$$

$(x, y) = (3, 20)$

$$20 = a(3)^2 + b(3) + c$$
$$20 = a(9) + 3b + c$$
$$20 = 9a + 3b + c$$

$(x, y) = (-2, 25)$

$$25 = a(-2)^2 + b(-2) + c$$
$$25 = a(4) - 2b + c$$
$$25 = 4a - 2b + c$$

The resulting system is as follows.

$$a + b + c = 4$$
$$9a + 3b + c = 20$$
$$4a - 2b + c = 25$$

Multiply the first equation by -1 and add to the second equation.

$$-a - b - c = -4$$
$$\underline{9a + 3b + c = 20}$$
$$8a + 2b = 16$$

Multiply the first equation by -1 and add to the third equation.

$$-a - b - c = -4$$
$$\underline{4a - 2b + c = 25}$$
$$3a - 3b = 21$$

The system of two equations in two variables is as follows.

$$8a + 2b = 16$$
$$3a - 3b = 21$$

Multiply the first equation by 3, the second equation by 2 and solve by addition.

$$24a + 6b = 48$$
$$\underline{6a - 6b = 42}$$
$$30a = 90$$
$$a = 3$$

Back-substitute 3 for a to find b.

$$3(3) - 3b = 21$$
$$9 - 3b = 21$$
$$-3b = 12$$
$$b = -4$$

Back-substitute 3 for a and -4 for b to find c.

$$3 + (-4) + c = 4$$
$$-1 + c = 4$$
$$c = 5$$

The quadratic function is $f(x) = 3x^2 - 4x + 5$.

36. $x + y + z = 45$
$$x = y + 1$$
$$2z - 12 = x$$

Rewrite the system in $Ax + By = C$ form.

$$x + y + z = 45$$
$$x - y \quad = 1$$
$$-x \quad + 2z = 12$$

Add the first and second equations to eliminate y.

$$x + y + z = 45$$
$$\underline{x - y \quad = 1}$$
$$2x + z = 46$$

We obtain a system of two equations in two variables.

$$-x + 2z = 12$$
$$2x + z = 46$$

Multiply the first equation by 2 and solve by addition.

$$-2x + 4z = 24$$
$$\underline{2x + z = 46}$$
$$5z = 70$$
$$z = 14$$

Back-substitute 14 for z to find x.

$$-x + 2(14) = 12$$
$$-x + 28 = 12$$
$$16 = x$$

Back-substitute 16 for x to find y.

$$16 - y = 1$$
$$15 = y$$

The savings rate for Japan is 16%, the savings rate for Germany is 15%, and the savings rate for France is 14%.

37. $2x + 3y = -10$
$y = -6$
Back-substitute -6 for y to find x.
$2x + 3(-6) = -10$
$2x - 18 = -10$
$2x = 8$
$x = 4$
The solution is $(4, -6)$.

38. Back-substitute 3 for z to find y.
$y - 2(3) = -4$
$y - 6 = -4$
$y = 2$
Back-substitute 2 for y and 3 for z to find x.
$x + 2 + 3(3) = 12$
$x + 2 + 9 = 12$
$x + 11 = 12$
$x = 1$
The solution is $(1, 2, 3)$.

39. $\begin{bmatrix} 1 & -8 & | & 3 \\ 0 & 1 & | & -2 \end{bmatrix}$

40. $\begin{bmatrix} 1 & -3 & | & 1 \\ 0 & 7 & | & -7 \end{bmatrix}$

41. $\begin{bmatrix} 1 & -1 & 1/2 & | & -1/2 \\ 1 & 2 & -1 & | & 2 \\ 6 & 4 & 3 & | & 5 \end{bmatrix}$

42. $\begin{bmatrix} 1 & 2 & 2 & | & 2 \\ 0 & 1 & -1 & | & 2 \\ 0 & 0 & 9 & | & -9 \end{bmatrix}$

43. $\begin{bmatrix} 1 & 4 & | & 7 \\ 3 & 5 & | & 0 \end{bmatrix}$ $-3R_1 + R_2$

$= \begin{bmatrix} 1 & 4 & | & 7 \\ 0 & -7 & | & -21 \end{bmatrix}$ $-\dfrac{1}{7}R_2$

$= \begin{bmatrix} 1 & 4 & | & 7 \\ 0 & 1 & | & 3 \end{bmatrix}$

$x + 4y = 7$
$y = 3$
Back-substitute 3 for y to find x.
$x + 4(3) = 7$
$x + 12 = 7$
$x = -5$
The solution is $(-5, 3)$.

44. $\begin{bmatrix} 2 & -3 & | & 8 \\ -6 & 9 & | & 4 \end{bmatrix}$ $3R_1 + R_2 = \begin{bmatrix} 2 & -3 & | & 8 \\ 0 & 0 & | & 28 \end{bmatrix}$

This is a contradiction. R_2 states that $0x + 0y = 28$. There are no pairs, (x, y) for which $0 = 28$. The system is inconsistent and the solution set is $\varnothing$ or $\{\ \}$.

45. $\begin{bmatrix} 1 & 2 & 3 & | & -5 \\ 2 & 1 & 1 & | & 1 \\ 1 & 1 & -1 & | & 8 \end{bmatrix}$ $-2R_1 + R_2$

$= \begin{bmatrix} 1 & 2 & 3 & | & -5 \\ 0 & -3 & -5 & | & 11 \\ 1 & 1 & -1 & | & 8 \end{bmatrix}$ $-R_1 + R_3$

$= \begin{bmatrix} 1 & 2 & 3 & | & -5 \\ 0 & -3 & -5 & | & 11 \\ 0 & -1 & -4 & | & 13 \end{bmatrix}$ $-\dfrac{1}{3}R_2$

$= \begin{bmatrix} 1 & 2 & 3 & | & -5 \\ 0 & 1 & 5/3 & | & -11/3 \\ 0 & -1 & -4 & | & 13 \end{bmatrix}$ $R_2 + R_3$

$= \begin{bmatrix} 1 & 2 & 3 & | & -5 \\ 0 & 1 & 5/3 & | & -11/3 \\ 0 & 0 & -7/3 & | & 28/3 \end{bmatrix}$ $-\dfrac{3}{7}R$

$= \begin{bmatrix} 1 & 2 & 3 & | & -5 \\ 0 & 1 & 5/3 & | & -11/3 \\ 0 & 0 & 1 & | & -4 \end{bmatrix}$

$x + 2y + 3z = -5$
$y + \dfrac{5}{3}z = -\dfrac{11}{3}$
$z = -4$

Back-substitute -4 for z to find y.

$$y + \frac{5}{3}(-4) = -\frac{11}{3}$$

$$y - \frac{20}{3} = -\frac{11}{3}$$

$$y = \frac{9}{3} \text{ or } 3$$

Back-substitute 3 for y and -4 for z to find x.

$$x + 2(3) + 3(-4) = -5$$

$$x + 6 - 12 = -5$$

$$x - 6 = -5$$

$$x = 1$$

The solution is $(1, 3, -4)$.

46.

$$\begin{bmatrix} 1 & -2 & 1 & | & 0 \\ 0 & 1 & -3 & | & -1 \\ 0 & 2 & 5 & | & -2 \end{bmatrix} \quad -2R_2 + R_3 = \begin{bmatrix} 1 & -2 & 1 & | & 0 \\ 0 & 1 & -3 & | & -1 \\ 0 & 0 & 11 & | & 0 \end{bmatrix} \quad \frac{1}{11}R_3 = \begin{bmatrix} 1 & -2 & 1 & | & 0 \\ 0 & 1 & -3 & | & -1 \\ 0 & 0 & 1 & | & 0 \end{bmatrix}$$

$$x - 2y + z = 0$$
$$y - 3z = -1$$
$$z = 0$$

Back-substitute 0 for z to find y.

$$y - 3(0) = -1$$
$$y = -1$$

Back-substitute 1 for y and 0 for z to find x.

$$x - 2(-1) + 0 = 0$$
$$x + 2 = 0$$
$$x = -2$$

The solution is $(-2, -1, 0)$.

47.

$$\begin{vmatrix} 3 & 2 \\ -1 & 5 \end{vmatrix} = 3(5) - (-1)2 = 15 + 2 = 17$$

48.

$$\begin{vmatrix} -2 & -3 \\ -4 & -8 \end{vmatrix} = -2(-8) - (-4)(-3) = 16 - 12 = 4$$

49.

$$\begin{vmatrix} 2 & 4 & -3 \\ 1 & -1 & 5 \\ -2 & 4 & 0 \end{vmatrix} = 2\begin{vmatrix} -1 & 5 \\ 4 & 0 \end{vmatrix} - 1\begin{vmatrix} 4 & -3 \\ 4 & 0 \end{vmatrix} - 2\begin{vmatrix} 4 & -3 \\ -1 & 5 \end{vmatrix}$$

$$= 2\left(-1(0) - 4(5)\right) - 1\left(4(0) - 4(-3)\right) - 2\left(4(5) - (-1)(-3)\right)$$

$$= 2(-20) - 1(12) - 2(20 - 3) = -40 - 12 - 2(17) = -40 - 12 - 34 = -86$$

50.
$$\begin{vmatrix} 4 & 7 & 0 \\ -5 & 6 & 0 \\ 3 & 2 & -4 \end{vmatrix} = 4\begin{vmatrix} 6 & 0 \\ 2 & -4 \end{vmatrix} - (-5)\begin{vmatrix} 7 & 0 \\ 2 & -4 \end{vmatrix} + 3\begin{vmatrix} 7 & 0 \\ 6 & 0 \end{vmatrix}$$
$$= 4\big(6(-4) - 2(0)\big) + 5\big(7(-4) - 2(0)\big) + 3\big(7(0) - 6(0)\big)$$
$$= 4(-24) + 5(-28) + 3(0) = -96 - 140 = -236$$

51.
$$D = \begin{vmatrix} 1 & -2 \\ 3 & 2 \end{vmatrix} = 1(2) - 3(-2) = 2 + 6 = 8$$

$$D_x = \begin{vmatrix} 8 & -2 \\ -1 & 2 \end{vmatrix} = 8(2) - (-1)(-2) = 16 - 2 = 14 \qquad D_y = \begin{vmatrix} 1 & 8 \\ 3 & -1 \end{vmatrix} = 1(-1) - 3(8) = -1 - 24 = -25$$

$$x = \frac{D_x}{D} = \frac{14}{8} = \frac{7}{4} \qquad\qquad\qquad\qquad\qquad y = \frac{D_y}{D} = \frac{-25}{8} = -\frac{25}{8}$$

The solution is $\left(\dfrac{7}{4}, -\dfrac{25}{8}\right)$.

52.
$$D = \begin{vmatrix} 7 & 2 \\ 2 & 1 \end{vmatrix} = 7(1) - 2(2) = 7 - 4 = 3$$

$$D_x = \begin{vmatrix} 0 & 2 \\ -3 & 1 \end{vmatrix} = 0(1) - (-3)(2) = 6 \qquad D_y = \begin{vmatrix} 7 & 0 \\ 2 & -3 \end{vmatrix} = 7(-3) - 2(0) = -21$$

$$x = \frac{D_x}{D} = \frac{6}{3} = 2 \qquad\qquad\qquad y = \frac{D_y}{D} = \frac{-21}{3} = -7$$

The solution is $(2, -7)$ and the solution set is $\{(2, -7)\}$.

53.
$$D = \begin{vmatrix} 1 & 2 & 2 \\ 2 & 4 & 7 \\ -2 & -5 & -2 \end{vmatrix} = 1\begin{vmatrix} 4 & 7 \\ -5 & -2 \end{vmatrix} - 2\begin{vmatrix} 2 & 2 \\ -5 & -2 \end{vmatrix} - 2\begin{vmatrix} 2 & 2 \\ 4 & 7 \end{vmatrix}$$
$$= 1\big(4(-2) - (-5)7\big) - 2\big(2(-2) - (-5)2\big) - 2\big(2(7) - 4(2)\big)$$
$$= 1(-8 + 35) - 2(-4 + 10) - 2(14 - 8) = 1(27) - 2(6) - 2(6) = 27 - 12 - 12 = 3$$

$$D_x = \begin{vmatrix} 5 & 2 & 2 \\ 19 & 4 & 7 \\ 8 & -5 & -2 \end{vmatrix} = 5\begin{vmatrix} 4 & 7 \\ -5 & -2 \end{vmatrix} - 19\begin{vmatrix} 2 & 2 \\ -5 & -2 \end{vmatrix} + 8\begin{vmatrix} 2 & 2 \\ 4 & 7 \end{vmatrix}$$
$$= 5\big(4(-2) - (-5)7\big) - 19\big(2(-2) - (-5)2\big) + 8\big(2(7) - 4(2)\big)$$
$$= 5(-8 + 35) - 19(-4 + 10) + 8(14 - 8) = 5(27) - 19(6) + 8(6) = 135 - 114 + 48 = 69$$

$$D_y = \begin{vmatrix} 1 & 5 & 2 \\ 2 & 19 & 7 \\ -2 & 8 & -2 \end{vmatrix} = 1\begin{vmatrix} 19 & 7 \\ 8 & -2 \end{vmatrix} - 2\begin{vmatrix} 5 & 2 \\ 8 & -2 \end{vmatrix} - 2\begin{vmatrix} 5 & 2 \\ 19 & 7 \end{vmatrix}$$
$$= 1\big(19(-2) - (8)7\big) - 2\big(5(-2) - 8(2)\big) - 2\big(5(7) - 19(2)\big)$$
$$= 1(-38 - 56) - 2(-10 - 16) - 2(35 - 38) = 1(-94) - 2(-26) - 2(-3) = -94 + 52 + 6 = -36$$

$$D_z = \begin{vmatrix} 1 & 2 & 5 \\ 2 & 4 & 19 \\ -2 & -5 & 8 \end{vmatrix} = 1 \begin{vmatrix} 4 & 19 \\ -5 & 8 \end{vmatrix} - 2 \begin{vmatrix} 2 & 5 \\ -5 & 8 \end{vmatrix} - 2 \begin{vmatrix} 2 & 5 \\ 4 & 19 \end{vmatrix}$$

$$= 1(4(8) - (-5)19) - 2(2(8) - (-5)5) - 2(2(19) - 4(5))$$

$$= 1(32 + 95) - 2(16 + 25) - 2(38 - 20) = 1(127) - 2(41) - 2(18) = 127 - 82 - 36 = 9$$

$$x = \frac{D_x}{D} = \frac{69}{3} = 23 \qquad y = \frac{D_y}{D} = \frac{-36}{3} = -12 \qquad z = \frac{D_z}{D} = \frac{9}{3} = 3$$

The solution is $(23, -12, 3)$.

54.   Rewrite the system in $Ax + By + Cz = D$ form.

$$2x + y \qquad\quad = -4$$
$$\qquad y - 2z = \quad 0$$
$$3x \qquad - 2z = -11$$

$$D = \begin{vmatrix} 2 & 1 & 0 \\ 0 & 1 & -2 \\ 3 & 0 & -2 \end{vmatrix} = 2 \begin{vmatrix} 1 & -2 \\ 0 & -2 \end{vmatrix} - 0 \begin{vmatrix} 1 & 0 \\ 0 & -2 \end{vmatrix} + 3 \begin{vmatrix} 1 & 0 \\ 1 & -2 \end{vmatrix} = 2\left(1(-2) - 0(-2)\right) + 3\left(1(-2) - 1(0)\right)$$

$$= 2(-2) + 3(-2) = -4 - 6 = -10$$

$$D_x = \begin{vmatrix} -4 & 1 & 0 \\ 0 & 1 & -2 \\ -11 & 0 & -2 \end{vmatrix} = -4 \begin{vmatrix} 1 & -2 \\ 0 & -2 \end{vmatrix} - 0 \begin{vmatrix} 1 & 0 \\ 0 & -2 \end{vmatrix} - 11 \begin{vmatrix} 1 & 0 \\ 1 & -2 \end{vmatrix} = -4\left(1(-2) - 0(-2)\right) - 11\left(1(-2) - 1(0)\right)$$

$$= -4(-2) - 11(-2) = 8 + 22 = 30$$

$$D_y = \begin{vmatrix} 2 & -4 & 0 \\ 0 & 0 & -2 \\ 3 & -11 & -2 \end{vmatrix} = 2 \begin{vmatrix} 0 & -2 \\ -11 & -2 \end{vmatrix} - 0 \begin{vmatrix} -4 & 0 \\ -11 & -2 \end{vmatrix} + 3 \begin{vmatrix} -4 & 0 \\ 0 & -2 \end{vmatrix}$$

$$= 2\left(0(-2) - (-11)(-2)\right) + 3\left(-4(-2) - 0(0)\right) = 2(-22) + 3(8) = -44 + 24 = -20$$

$$D_z = \begin{vmatrix} 2 & 1 & -4 \\ 0 & 1 & 0 \\ 3 & 0 & -11 \end{vmatrix} = 2 \begin{vmatrix} 1 & 0 \\ 0 & -11 \end{vmatrix} - 0 \begin{vmatrix} 1 & -4 \\ 0 & -11 \end{vmatrix} + 3 \begin{vmatrix} 1 & -4 \\ 1 & 0 \end{vmatrix} = 2\left(1(-11) - 0(0)\right) + 3\left(1(0) - 1(-4)\right)$$

$$= 2(-11) + 3(4) = -22 + 12 = -10$$

$$x = \frac{D_x}{D} = \frac{30}{-10} = -3 \qquad y = \frac{D_y}{D} = \frac{-20}{-10} = 2 \qquad z = \frac{D_z}{D} = \frac{-10}{-10} = 1$$

The solution is $(-3, 2, 1)$.

55. $(x, y) = (20, 400)$ $(x, y) = (40, 150)$ $(x, y) = (60, 400)$

$400 = a(20)^2 + b(20) + c$ $150 = a(40)^2 + b(40) + c$ $400 = a(60)^2 + b(60) + c$

$400 = a(400) + 20b + c$ $150 = a(1600) + 40b + c$ $400 = a(3600) + 60b + c$

$400 = 400a + 20b + c$ $150 = 1600a + 40b + c$ $400 = 3600a + 60b + c$

The system of three equations in three variables is as follows.

$$400a + 20b + c = 400$$
$$1600a + 40b + c = 150$$
$$3600a + 60b + c = 400$$

$$D = \begin{vmatrix} 400 & 20 & 1 \\ 1600 & 40 & 1 \\ 3600 & 60 & 1 \end{vmatrix} = 400\begin{vmatrix} 40 & 1 \\ 60 & 1 \end{vmatrix} - 1600\begin{vmatrix} 20 & 1 \\ 60 & 1 \end{vmatrix} + 3600\begin{vmatrix} 20 & 1 \\ 40 & 1 \end{vmatrix}$$

$$= 400\big(40(1) - 60(1)\big) - 1600\big(20(1) - 60(1)\big) + 3600\big(20(1) - 40(1)\big)$$

$$= 400(40 - 60) - 1600(20 - 60) + 3600(20 - 40) = 400(-20) - 1600(-40) + 3600(-20)$$

$$= -8000 + 64000 - 72000 = -16000$$

$$D_x = \begin{vmatrix} 400 & 20 & 1 \\ 150 & 40 & 1 \\ 400 & 60 & 1 \end{vmatrix} = 400\begin{vmatrix} 40 & 1 \\ 60 & 1 \end{vmatrix} - 150\begin{vmatrix} 20 & 1 \\ 60 & 1 \end{vmatrix} + 400\begin{vmatrix} 20 & 1 \\ 40 & 1 \end{vmatrix}$$

$$= 400\big(40(1) - 60(1)\big) - 150\big(20(1) - 60(1)\big) + 400\big(20(1) - 40(1)\big)$$

$$= 400(40 - 60) - 150(20 - 60) + 400(20 - 40) = 400(-20) - 150(-40) + 400(-20)$$

$$= -8000 + 6000 - 8000 = -10000$$

$$D_y = \begin{vmatrix} 400 & 400 & 1 \\ 1600 & 150 & 1 \\ 3600 & 400 & 1 \end{vmatrix} = 400\begin{vmatrix} 150 & 1 \\ 400 & 1 \end{vmatrix} - 1600\begin{vmatrix} 400 & 1 \\ 400 & 1 \end{vmatrix} + 3600\begin{vmatrix} 400 & 1 \\ 150 & 1 \end{vmatrix}$$

$$= 400\big(150(1) - 400(1)\big) - 1600\big(400(1) - 400(1)\big) + 3600\big(400(1) - 150(1)\big)$$

$$= 400(150 - 400) - 1600(400 - 400) + 3600(400 - 150) = 400(-250) - 1600(0) + 3600(250)$$

$$= 400(-250) + 3600(250) = -100000 + 900000 = 800000$$

$$D_z = \begin{vmatrix} 400 & 20 & 400 \\ 1600 & 40 & 150 \\ 3600 & 60 & 400 \end{vmatrix} = 400\begin{vmatrix} 40 & 150 \\ 60 & 400 \end{vmatrix} - 1600\begin{vmatrix} 20 & 400 \\ 60 & 400 \end{vmatrix} + 3600\begin{vmatrix} 20 & 400 \\ 40 & 150 \end{vmatrix}$$

$$= 400\big(40(400) - 60(150)\big) - 1600\big(20(400) - 60(400)\big) + 3600\big(20(150) - 40(400)\big)$$

$$= 400(16000 - 9000) - 1600(8000 - 24000) + 3600(3000 - 16000)$$

$$= 400(7000) - 1600(-16000) + 3600(-13000) = 2800000 + 25600000 - 46800000 = -18400000$$

$$x = \frac{D_x}{D} = \frac{-10000}{-16000} = \frac{5}{8} \qquad y = \frac{D_y}{D} = \frac{800000}{-16000} = -50 \qquad z = \frac{D_z}{D} = \frac{-18400000}{-16000} = 1150$$

The quadratic function is $f(x) = \dfrac{5}{8}x^2 - 50x + 1150$.

$$f(30) = \frac{5}{8}(30)^2 - 50(30) + 1150 \qquad\qquad f(50) = \frac{5}{8}(50)^2 - 50(50) + 1150$$

$$= \frac{5}{8}(900) - 1500 + 1150 \qquad\qquad\qquad = \frac{5}{8}(2500) - 2500 + 1150$$

$$= 562.5 - 1500 + 1150 = 212.5 \qquad\qquad = 1562.5 - 2500 + 1150 = 212.5$$

Both 30-year-olds and 50-year-olds are involved in approximately 212.5 accidents per day in the United States.

Chapter 8 Test

1. The relation is a function.
    Domain $\{1, 3, 5, 6\}$; Range $\{2, 4, 6\}$

2. The relation is not a function.
    Domain $\{2, 4, 6\}$; Range $\{1, 3, 5, 6\}$

3. $f(a+4)=3(a+4)-2=3a+12-2=3a+10$

4. $f(-2)=4(-2)^2-3(-2)+6$
    $=4(4)+6+6=16+6+6=28$

5.

    g shifts the graph of f up 2 units

6. The vertical line test shows that this is the graph of a function.

7. The vertical line test shows that this is not the graph of a function.

8. $f(6)=-3$

9. When $x=-5$, $f(x)=-6$.

10. Domain of $f = \{x \mid x$ is a real number and $x \neq 10\}$

11. $(f+g)(x)=f(x)+g(x)=(x^2+4x)+(x+2)$
    $=x^2+4x+x+2=x^2+5x+2$
    $(f+g)(3)=(3)^2+5(3)+2=9+15+2=26$

12. $(f-g)(x)=f(x)-g(x)$
    $=(x^2+4x)-(x+2)$
    $=x^2+4x-x-2=x^2+3x-2$
    $(f-g)(-1)=(-1)^2+3(-1)-2$
    $=1-3-2=-4$

13. $f(-5)=(-5)^2+4(-5)=25-20=5$
    $g(-5)=-5+2=-3$
    $(fg)(-5)=f(-5)\cdot g(-5)=5(-3)=-15$

14. $\left(\dfrac{f}{g}\right)(x)=\dfrac{x^2+4x}{x+2}$
    $\left(\dfrac{f}{g}\right)(2)=\dfrac{(2)^2+4(2)}{2+2}=\dfrac{4+8}{4}=\dfrac{12}{4}=3$

15. Domain of $\dfrac{f}{g} = \{x \mid x$ is a real number and $x \neq -2\}$

16. Multiply the first equation by 7 and add to the second equation.
    $$7x+7y+7z = 42$$
    $$\underline{3x+4y-7z = 1}$$
    $$10x+11y = 43$$
    Multiply the first equation by -3 and add to the third equation.
    $$-3x-3y-3z = -18$$
    $$\underline{2x-y+3z = 5}$$
    $$-x-4y = -13$$
    The resulting system is as follows.
    $$10x+11y = 43$$
    $$-x-4y = -13$$
    Multiply the second equation by 10 and solve by addition.
    $$10x+11y = 43$$
    $$\underline{-10x-40y = -130}$$
    $$-29y = -87$$
    $$y = 3$$
    Back-substitute 3 for y to find x.

$$-x - 4(3) = -13$$
$$-x - 12 = -13$$
$$1 = x$$

Back-substitute 1 for x and 3 for y to find z.

$$1 + 3 + z = 6$$
$$4 + z = 6$$
$$z = 2$$

The solution is $(1, 3, 2)$.

17.
$$\begin{bmatrix} 1 & 0 & -4 & \bigm| & 5 \\ 0 & -1 & 26 & \bigm| & -20 \\ 2 & -1 & 4 & \bigm| & -3 \end{bmatrix}$$

18.
$$\begin{bmatrix} 2 & 1 & \bigm| & 6 \\ 3 & -2 & \bigm| & 16 \end{bmatrix} \quad \tfrac{1}{2}R_1$$

$$= \begin{bmatrix} 1 & 1/2 & \bigm| & 3 \\ 3 & -2 & \bigm| & 16 \end{bmatrix} \quad -3R_1 + R_2$$

$$= \begin{bmatrix} 1 & 1/2 & \bigm| & 3 \\ 0 & -7/2 & \bigm| & 7 \end{bmatrix} \quad -\tfrac{2}{7}R_2$$

$$= \begin{bmatrix} 1 & 1/2 & \bigm| & 3 \\ 0 & 1 & \bigm| & -2 \end{bmatrix}$$

$$x + \frac{1}{2}y = 3$$
$$y = -2$$

Back-substitute –2 for y to find x.

$$x + \frac{1}{2}(-2) = 3$$
$$x - 1 = 3$$
$$x = 4$$

The solution is $(4, -2)$.

19.
$$\begin{bmatrix} 1 & -4 & 4 & \bigm| & -1 \\ 2 & -1 & 5 & \bigm| & 6 \\ -1 & 3 & -1 & \bigm| & 5 \end{bmatrix} \quad -2R_1 + R_2$$

$$= \begin{bmatrix} 1 & -4 & 4 & \bigm| & -1 \\ 0 & 7 & -3 & \bigm| & 8 \\ -1 & 3 & -1 & \bigm| & 5 \end{bmatrix} \quad \tfrac{1}{7}R_2$$

$$= \begin{bmatrix} 1 & -4 & 4 & \bigm| & -1 \\ 0 & 1 & -3/7 & \bigm| & 8/7 \\ -1 & 3 & -1 & \bigm| & 5 \end{bmatrix} \quad R_1 + R_2$$

$$= \begin{bmatrix} 1 & -4 & 4 & \bigm| & -1 \\ 0 & 1 & -3/7 & \bigm| & 8/7 \\ 0 & -1 & 3 & \bigm| & 4 \end{bmatrix} \quad R_2 + R_3$$

$$= \begin{bmatrix} 1 & -4 & 4 & \bigm| & -1 \\ 0 & 1 & -3/7 & \bigm| & 8/7 \\ 0 & 0 & 18/7 & \bigm| & 36/7 \end{bmatrix} \quad \frac{7}{18}R_3$$

$$= \begin{bmatrix} 1 & -4 & 4 & \bigm| & -1 \\ 0 & 1 & -3/7 & \bigm| & 8/7 \\ 0 & 0 & 1 & \bigm| & 2 \end{bmatrix}$$

$$x - 4y + 4z = -1$$
$$y - \frac{3}{7}z = \frac{8}{7}$$
$$z = 2$$

Back-substitute 2 for z to find y.

$$y - \frac{3}{7}(2) = \frac{8}{7}$$
$$y - \frac{6}{7} = \frac{8}{7}$$
$$y = \frac{14}{7} \text{ or } 2$$

Back-substitute 2 for y and 2 for z to find x.

$$x - 4(2) + 4(2) = -1$$
$$x - 8 + 8 = -1$$
$$x = -1$$

The solution is $(-1, 2, 2)$.

20. $\begin{vmatrix} -1 & -3 \\ 7 & 4 \end{vmatrix} = -1(4) - 7(-3) = -4 + 21 = 17$

21.
$$\begin{vmatrix} 3 & 4 & 0 \\ -1 & 0 & -3 \\ 4 & 2 & 5 \end{vmatrix}$$

$$= 3\begin{vmatrix} 0 & -3 \\ 2 & 5 \end{vmatrix} - (-1)\begin{vmatrix} 4 & 0 \\ 2 & 5 \end{vmatrix} + 4\begin{vmatrix} 4 & 0 \\ 0 & -3 \end{vmatrix}$$

$$= 3\big(0(5) - 2(-3)\big) - (-1)\big(4(5) - 2(0)\big)$$
$$\qquad + 4\big(4(-3) - 0(0)\big)$$

$$= 3(6) + 1(20) + 4(-12)$$
$$= 18 + 20 - 48 = -10$$

22.

$$D = \begin{vmatrix} 4 & -3 \\ 3 & -1 \end{vmatrix} = 4(-1) - 3(-3) = -4 + 9 = 5$$

$$D_x = \begin{vmatrix} 14 & -3 \\ 3 & -1 \end{vmatrix} = 14(-1) - 3(-3) = -14 + 9 = -5$$

$$D_y = \begin{vmatrix} 4 & 14 \\ 3 & 3 \end{vmatrix} = 4(3) - 3(14) = 12 - 42 = -30$$

$$x = \frac{D_x}{D} = \frac{-5}{5} = -1 \qquad\qquad y = \frac{D_y}{D} = \frac{-30}{5} = -6$$

The solution is $(-1, -6)$.

23.

$$D = \begin{vmatrix} 2 & 3 & 1 \\ 3 & 3 & -1 \\ 1 & -2 & -3 \end{vmatrix} = 2\begin{vmatrix} 3 & -1 \\ -2 & -3 \end{vmatrix} - 3\begin{vmatrix} 3 & 1 \\ -2 & -3 \end{vmatrix} + 1\begin{vmatrix} 3 & 1 \\ 3 & -1 \end{vmatrix}$$

$$= 2(3(-3) - (-2)(-1)) - 3(3(-3) - (-2)1) + 1(3(-1) - 3(1))$$

$$= 2(-9 - 2) - 3(-9 + 2) + 1(-3 - 3) = 2(-11) - 3(-7) + 1(-6) = -22 + 21 - 6 = -7$$

$$D_x = \begin{vmatrix} 2 & 3 & 1 \\ 0 & 3 & -1 \\ 1 & -2 & -3 \end{vmatrix} = 2\begin{vmatrix} 3 & -1 \\ -2 & -3 \end{vmatrix} - 0\begin{vmatrix} 3 & 1 \\ -2 & -3 \end{vmatrix} + 1\begin{vmatrix} 3 & 1 \\ 3 & -1 \end{vmatrix}$$

$$= 2(3(-3) - (-2)(-1)) + 1(3(-1) - 3(1)) = 2(-9 - 2) + 1(-3 - 3) = 2(-11) + 1(-6)$$

$$= -22 - 6 = -28$$

$$D_y = \begin{vmatrix} 2 & 2 & 1 \\ 3 & 0 & -1 \\ 1 & 1 & -3 \end{vmatrix} = 2\begin{vmatrix} 0 & -1 \\ 1 & -3 \end{vmatrix} - 3\begin{vmatrix} 2 & 1 \\ 1 & -3 \end{vmatrix} + 1\begin{vmatrix} 2 & 1 \\ 0 & -1 \end{vmatrix}$$

$$= 2(0(-3) - 1(-1)) - 3(2(-3) - 1(1)) + 1(2(-1) - 0(1))$$

$$= 2(1) - 3(-6 - 1) + 1(-2) = 2 - 3(-7) - 2 = 2 + 21 - 2 = 21$$

$$D_z = \begin{vmatrix} 2 & 3 & 2 \\ 3 & 3 & 0 \\ 1 & -2 & 1 \end{vmatrix} = 2\begin{vmatrix} 3 & 0 \\ -2 & 1 \end{vmatrix} - 3\begin{vmatrix} 3 & 2 \\ -2 & 1 \end{vmatrix} + 1\begin{vmatrix} 3 & 2 \\ 3 & 0 \end{vmatrix}$$

$$= 2(3(1) - (-2)(0)) - 3(3(1) - (-2)2) + 1(3(0) - 3(2))$$

$$= 2(3) - 3(3 + 4) + 1(-6) = 6 - 3(7) - 6 = 6 - 21 - 6 = -21$$

$$x = \frac{D_x}{D} = \frac{-28}{-7} = 4 \qquad y = \frac{D_y}{D} = \frac{21}{-7} = -3 \qquad z = \frac{D_z}{D} = \frac{-21}{-7} = 3$$

The solution is $(4, -3, 3)$.

Cumulative Review Exercises
Chapters 1 -8

1. $2x+3x-5+7=10x+3-6x-4$

$$5x+2=4x-1$$
$$x+2=-1$$
$$x=-3$$

2.
$$2x^2+5x=12$$
$$2x^2+5x-12=0$$
$$(2x-3)(x+4)=0$$
$$2x-3=0 \quad \text{or} \quad x+4=0$$
$$2x=3 \qquad\qquad x=-4$$
$$x=\frac{3}{2}$$

The solutions are -4 and $\dfrac{3}{2}$.

3. $8x-\ 5y=\ -4$
$2x+15y=-66$
Multiply the first equation by 3 and solve by addition.
$$\begin{aligned}24x-15y&=-12\\ \underline{2x+15y}&=\underline{-66}\\ 26x&=-78\\ x&=-3\end{aligned}$$
Back-substitute -3 for x to find y.
$$8(-3)-5y=-4$$
$$-24-5y=-4$$
$$-5y=20$$
$$y=-4$$
The solution is $(-3, -4)$.

4. $\dfrac{15}{x}-4=\dfrac{6}{x}+3$
Multiply both sides of the equation by x.
$$15-4x=6+3x$$
$$15-7x=6$$

$$-7x=-9$$
$$x=\frac{9}{7}$$

5. $-3x-7=8$
$$-3x=15$$
$$x=-5$$

6. $(f-g)(x)=f(x)-g(x)$
$$=2x^2-5x+2-\left(x^2-2x+3\right)$$
$$=2x^2-5x+2-x^2+2x-3$$
$$=x^2-3x-1$$
$$(f-g)(3)=(3)^2-3(3)-1$$
$$=9-9-1=-1$$

7. $\dfrac{8x^3}{-4x^7}=\dfrac{\cancel{4}\cdot 2\cancel{x^3}}{-\cancel{4}\,\cancel{x^3}\cdot x^4}=-\dfrac{2}{x^4}$

8. $6\sqrt{75}-4\sqrt{12}$
$$=6\sqrt{25\cdot3}-4\sqrt{4\cdot3}$$
$$=6\cdot5\sqrt{3}-4\cdot2\sqrt{3}$$
$$=30\sqrt{3}-8\sqrt{3}=22\sqrt{3}$$

9. $\dfrac{\dfrac{1}{x}-\dfrac{1}{2}}{\dfrac{1}{3}-\dfrac{x}{6}}$

$$=\frac{6x}{6x}\cdot\frac{\dfrac{1}{x}-\dfrac{1}{2}}{\dfrac{1}{3}-\dfrac{x}{6}}$$

$$=\frac{6x\cdot\dfrac{1}{x}-6x\cdot\dfrac{1}{2}}{6x\cdot\dfrac{1}{3}-6x\cdot\dfrac{x}{6}}$$

$$=\frac{6-3x}{2x-x^2}$$

$$=\frac{3(2-x)}{x(2-x)}=\frac{3}{x}$$

10.

$$\frac{4-x^2}{3x^2-5x-2}=\frac{(2+x)(2-x)}{(3x+1)(x-2)}$$

$$=\frac{(2+x)\cancel{(2-x)}}{-1(3x+1)\cancel{(x-2)}}$$

$$=-\frac{2+x}{3x+1}$$

11. $-5-(-8)-(4-6)=-5+8-(-2)$

$$=-5+8+2=5$$

12. $x^2-18x+77=(x-7)(x-11)$

13. $x^3-25x=x(x^2-25)=x(x+5)(x-5)$

14. $\dfrac{6x^3-19x^2+16x-4}{x-2}$

$$\begin{array}{r} 6x^2-\ 7x+2 \\ x-2\overline{\smash{\big)}6x^3-19x^2+16x-4} \\ \underline{6x^3-12x^2} \\ -7x^2+16x \\ \underline{-7x^2+14x} \\ 2x-4 \\ \underline{2x-4} \\ 0 \end{array}$$

$$\frac{6x^3-19x^2+16x-4}{x-2}=6x^2-7x+2$$

15.

$$\begin{array}{r} 4x^2+6x+9 \\ \underline{2x-3} \\ 8x^3+12x^2+18x \\ \underline{-12x^2-18x-27} \\ 8x^3\qquad\qquad\ -27 \end{array}$$

16. $\dfrac{3x}{x^2+x-2}-\dfrac{2}{x+2}$

$$=\frac{3x}{(x+2)(x-1)}-\frac{2}{x+2}$$

$$=\frac{3x}{(x+2)(x-1)}-\frac{(x-1)}{(x-1)}\cdot\frac{2}{x+2}$$

$$=\frac{3x}{(x+2)(x-1)}-\frac{2x-2}{(x+2)(x-1)}$$

$$=\frac{3x-2x+2}{(x+2)(x-1)}=\frac{x+2}{(x+2)(x-1)}=\frac{1}{x-1}$$

17. $\dfrac{5x^2-6x+1}{x^2-1}\div\dfrac{16x^2-9}{4x^2+7x+3}$

$$=\frac{5x^2-6x+1}{x^2-1}\cdot\frac{4x^2+7x+3}{16x^2-9}$$

$$=\frac{(5x-1)\cancel{(x-1)}}{\cancel{(x+1)}\cancel{(x-1)}}\cdot\frac{\cancel{(4x+3)}\cancel{(x+1)}}{\cancel{(4x+3)}(4x-3)}$$

$$=\frac{5x-1}{4x-3}$$

18. Add the first and second equations.

$$\begin{array}{r} x+3y-\ z=\ 5 \\ \underline{-x+2y+3z=13} \\ 5y+2z=18 \end{array}$$

Multiply the first equation by -2 and add to the third equation.

$$\begin{array}{r} -2x-6y+2z=-10 \\ \underline{2x-5y-\ z=\ -8} \\ -11y+z=-18 \end{array}$$

The system of two equations in two variables is as follows.

$$5y+2z=\ 18$$
$$-11y+\ z=-18$$

Multiply the second equation by -2 and solve by addition.

$$\begin{array}{r} 5y+2z=18 \\ \underline{22y-2z=36} \\ 27y=54 \\ y=2 \end{array}$$

Back-substitute 2 for y to find z.

$$5(2)+2z=18$$
$$10+2z=18$$
$$2z=8$$
$$z=4$$

Back-substitute 2 for y and 4 for z to find x.
$$x + 3(2) - 4 = 5$$
$$x + 6 - 4 = 5$$
$$x + 2 = 5$$
$$x = 3$$
The solution is $(3, 2, 4)$.

19. $2x - y = 4$
$$-y = -2x + 4$$
$$y = 2x - 4$$
$$m = 2 \qquad y\text{-intercept} = -4$$

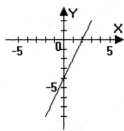

20. $y = -\dfrac{2}{3}x$

$$m = -\dfrac{2}{3} \qquad y\text{-intercept} = 0$$

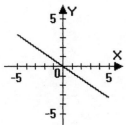

21. $\begin{vmatrix} 0 & 1 & -2 \\ -7 & 0 & -4 \\ 3 & 0 & 5 \end{vmatrix} = 0 \begin{vmatrix} 0 & -4 \\ 0 & 5 \end{vmatrix} - (-7) \begin{vmatrix} 1 & -2 \\ 0 & 5 \end{vmatrix} + 3 \begin{vmatrix} 1 & -2 \\ 0 & -4 \end{vmatrix}$

$= 7\big(1(5) - 0(-2)\big) + 3\big(1(-4) - 0(-2)\big)$

$= 7(5) + 3(-4) = 35 - 12 = 23$

22. $m = \dfrac{5 - (-3)}{-1 - 2} = \dfrac{5 + 3}{-3} = -\dfrac{8}{3}$

23. point-slope form:
$$y - y_1 = m(x - x_1)$$
$$y - (-3) = 5(x - (-2))$$
$$y + 3 = 5(x + 2)$$
slope-intercept form:
$$y + 3 = 5x + 10$$
$$y = 5x + 7$$

24. $\begin{vmatrix} 2 & 3 & -1 & -1 \\ 1 & 2 & 3 & 2 \\ 3 & 5 & -2 & -3 \end{vmatrix} \quad R_1 \leftrightarrow R_2$

$= \begin{vmatrix} 1 & 2 & 3 & 2 \\ 2 & 3 & -1 & -1 \\ 3 & 5 & -2 & -3 \end{vmatrix} \begin{matrix} -2R_1 + R_2 \\ \text{and} \\ -3R_1 + R_3 \end{matrix}$

$= \begin{vmatrix} 1 & 2 & 3 & 2 \\ 0 & -1 & -7 & -5 \\ 0 & -1 & -11 & -9 \end{vmatrix} \quad -R_2$

$= \begin{vmatrix} 1 & 2 & 3 & 2 \\ 0 & 1 & 7 & 5 \\ 0 & -1 & -11 & -9 \end{vmatrix} \quad R_2 + R_3$

$= \begin{vmatrix} 1 & 2 & 3 & 2 \\ 0 & 1 & 7 & 5 \\ 0 & 0 & -4 & -4 \end{vmatrix} \quad -\dfrac{1}{4}R_3$

$= \begin{vmatrix} 1 & 2 & 3 & 2 \\ 0 & 1 & 7 & 5 \\ 0 & 0 & 1 & 1 \end{vmatrix}$

$$x + 2y + 3z = 2$$
$$y + 7z = 5$$
$$z = 1$$
Back-substitute 1 for z to find y.
$$y + 7(1) = 5$$
$$y + 7 = 5$$
$$y = -2$$
Back-substitute -2 for y and 1 for z to find x.
$$x + 2(-2) + 3(1) = 2$$
$$x - 4 + 3 = 2$$
$$x - 1 = 2$$
$$x = 3$$
The solution is $(3, -2, 1)$.

25.

$$D = \begin{vmatrix} 3 & 4 \\ -2 & 1 \end{vmatrix} = 3(1) - (-2)4 = 3 + 8 = 11$$

$$D_x = \begin{vmatrix} -1 & 4 \\ 8 & 1 \end{vmatrix} = -1(1) - 8(4)$$
$$= -1 - 32 = -33$$

$$D_y = \begin{vmatrix} 3 & -1 \\ -2 & 8 \end{vmatrix} = 3(8) - (-2)(-1)$$
$$= 24 - 2 = 22$$

$$x = \frac{D_x}{D} = \frac{-33}{11} = -3 \qquad y = \frac{D_y}{D} = \frac{22}{11} = 2$$

The solution is $(-3, 2)$.

INEQUALITIES AND PROBLEM SOLVING

Interval Notation and Business Applications Using Linear Inequalities

9.1 CHECK POINTS

CHECK POINT 1

a.

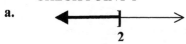

2

b.

-4

c.

2   6

CHECK POINT 2

a. $[-2,5) = \{x|-2 \le x < 5\}$

2   5

b. $[1,3.5] = \{x|1 \le x \le 3.5\}$

1   3.5

c. $(-\infty,-1) = \{x|x < -1\}$

-1

CHECK POINT 3

$-12-8x \le 4(6-x)$

$-12-8x \le 24-4x$

$-12-4x \le 24$

$-4x \le 36$

$x \ge -9$

The solution set is $\{x|x \ge -9\}$ or $[-9,\infty)$.

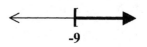

-9

CHECK POINT 4

$$\frac{x-4}{2} > \frac{x-2}{3} + \frac{5}{6}$$

$$6\left(\frac{x-4}{2}\right) > 6\left(\frac{x-2}{3}\right) + 6\left(\frac{5}{6}\right)$$

$$3(x-4) > 2(x-2)+5$$

$$3x-12 > 2x-4+5$$

$$3x-12 > 2x+1$$

$$x-12 > 1$$

$$x > 13$$

The solution set is $\{x|x > 13\}$ or $(13,\infty)$.

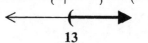

13

CHECK POINT 5

a. $P(x) = R(x) - C(x)$
$= 200x - (160,000 + 75x)$
$= 200x - 160,000 - 75x$
$= 125x - 160,000$

b. $P(x) > 0$
$125x - 160,000 > 0$
$125x > 160,000$
$x > 1280$

More than 1280 units would have to be produced.

CHECK POINT 6

a. $C(x) = 300,000 + 30x$

b. $R(x) = 80x$

c. $P(x) = R(x) - C(x)$
$= 80x - (300,000 + 30x)$

$$= 80x - 300,000 - 30x$$
$$= 50x - 300,000$$

d.
$$P(x) > 0$$
$$50x - 300,000 > 0$$
$$50x > 300,000$$
$$x > 6000$$

More than 6000 pairs of shoes would have to be produced.

EXERCISE SET 9.1

1. $\{x \mid 1 < x \leq 6\}$

3. $\{x \mid -5 \leq x < 2\}$

5. $\{x \mid -3 \leq x \leq 1\}$

7. $\{x \mid x > 2\}$

9. $\{x \mid x \geq -3\}$

11. $\{x \mid x < 3\}$

13. $\{x \mid x < 5.5\}$

15. $5x + 11 < 26$
$$5x < 15$$
$$x < 3$$

The solution set is $\{x \mid x < 3\}$ or $(-\infty, 3)$.

17. $3x - 8 \geq 13$
$$3x \geq 21$$
$$x \geq 7$$

The solution set is $\{x \mid x \geq 7\}$ or $[7, \infty)$.

19. $-9x \geq 36$
$$x \leq -4$$

The solution set is $\{x \mid x \leq -4\}$ or $(-\infty, -4]$.

21. $8x - 11 \leq 3x - 13$
$$5x - 11 \leq -13$$
$$5x \leq -2$$
$$x \leq -\frac{2}{5}$$

The solution set is $\left\{x \mid x \leq -\frac{2}{5}\right\}$ or $\left(-\infty, -\frac{2}{5}\right]$.

23. $4(x+1) + 2 \geq 3x + 6$
$$4x + 4 + 2 \geq 3x + 6$$
$$4x + 6 \geq 3x + 6$$
$$x + 6 \geq 6$$
$$x \geq 0$$

The solution set is $\{x \mid x \geq 0\}$ or $[0, \infty)$.

25. $2x - 11 < -3(x + 2)$
$$2x - 11 < -3x - 6$$
$$5x - 11 < -6$$
$$5x < 5$$
$$x < 1$$

The solution set is $\{x|x<1\}$ or $(-\infty,1)$.

1

27. $1-(x+3)\geq 4-2x$

$1-x-3\geq 4-2x$

$-x-2\geq 4-2x$

$x-2\geq 4$

$x\geq 6$

The solution set is $\{x|x\geq 6\}$ or $[6,\infty)$.

6

29.
$$\frac{x}{4}-\frac{1}{2}\leq\frac{x}{2}+1$$

$$4\left(\frac{x}{4}\right)-4\left(\frac{1}{2}\right)\leq 4\left(\frac{x}{2}\right)+4(1)$$

$$x-2\leq 2x+4$$

$$-x-2\leq 4$$

$$-x\leq 6$$

$$x\geq -6$$

The solution set is $\{x|x\geq -6\}$ or $[-6,\infty)$.

-6

31.
$$1-\frac{x}{2}>4$$

$$2(1)-2\left(\frac{x}{2}\right)>2(4)$$

$$2-x>8$$

$$-x>6$$

$$x<-6$$

The solution set is $\{x|x<-6\}$ or

$(-\infty,-6)$.

-6

33.
$$\frac{x-4}{6}\geq\frac{x-2}{9}+\frac{5}{18}$$

$$18\left(\frac{x-4}{6}\right)\geq 18\left(\frac{x-2}{9}\right)+18\left(\frac{5}{18}\right)$$

$3(x-4)\geq 2(x-2)+5$

$3x-12\geq 2x-4+5$

$3x-12\geq 2x+1$

$x-12\geq 1$

$x\geq 13$

The solution set is $\{x|x\geq 13\}$ or $[13,\infty)$.

13

35. a. $P(x)=R(x)-C(x)$
$$=(32x)-(25,500+15x)$$
$$=32x-25,500-15x$$
$$=17x-25,500$$

b. $P(x)>0$

$17x-25,500>0$

$17x>25,500$

$x>1500$

More than 1500 units will have to be produced.

37. a. $P(x)=R(x)-C(x)$
$$=(245x)-(105x+70,000)$$
$$=245x-105x-70,000$$
$$=140x-70,000$$

b. $P(x)>0$

$140x-70,000>0$

$140x>70,000$

$x>500$

More than 500 units will have to be produced.

39. Playing Sports and Sports Events

41. Exercise, Movies, Gardening, and Amusement Parks

43. Movies and Gardening

45. Gardening, Amusement Parks, and Home Improvement

47. $-0.7x + 80 < 52$

$\qquad -0.7x < -28$

$\qquad\quad x > 40$

This means that in all years after $1965 + 40 = 2005$, fewer than 52% of adults will read the daily newspaper.

49. $\qquad\qquad W < M$

$-0.19t + 57 < -0.15t + 50$

$-0.04t + 57 < 50$

$\qquad -0.04t < -7$

$\qquad\qquad t > 175$

The women's winning time will be less than the men's winning time after $1900 + 175 = 2075$.

51. a. $C(x) = 18,000 + 20x$

b. $R(x) = 80x$

c. $P(x) = R(x) - C(x)$

$\qquad = 80x - (18,000 + 20x)$

$\qquad = 80x - 18,000 - 20x$

$\qquad = 60x - 18,000$

d. $\qquad\quad P(x) > 0$

$\quad 60x - 18,000 > 0$

$\qquad\qquad 60x > 18,000$

$\qquad\qquad\quad x > 300$

More than 300 units will have to be produced.

53. a. $C(x) = 30,000 + 2500x$

b. $R(x) = 3125x$

c. $P(x) = R(x) - C(x)$

$\qquad = 3125x - (30,000 + 2500x)$

$\qquad = 3125x - 30,000 - 2500x$

$\qquad = 625x - 30,000$

d. $\qquad\quad P(x) > 0$

$\quad 625x - 30,000 > 0$

$\qquad\qquad 625x > 30,000$

$\qquad\qquad\quad x > 48$

More than 48 units will have to be produced.

55. Cost: $C = 10,000 + 0.40x$

Revenue: $R = 2x$

$\qquad\qquad C < R$

$10,000 + 0.40x < 2x$

$\quad 10,000 - 1.6x < 0$

$\qquad\quad -1.6x < -10,000$

$\qquad\qquad\quad x > 6250$

More than 6250 tapes must be produced and sold each week.

57. The cost with Plan A is $C_A = 15 + 0.08x$.

The cost with Plan B is $C_B = 3 + 0.12x$.

$\qquad\quad C_A < C_B$

$15 + 0.08x < 3 + 0.12x$

$15 - 0.04x < 3$

$\qquad -0.04x < -12$

$\qquad\qquad x > 300$

Plan A is a better deal when more than 300 minutes of long-distance are used per month.

For Exercises 59-63, answers may vary.

65. Statement **d.** is true.

Statement **a.** is false. The inequality $3x > 6$ is equivalent to $x > 2$.

Statement **b.** is false. $2x > 6$ is equivalent to $x > 3$. The smallest whole number or the smallest integer in the solution set is 4, not the smallest real number.

Statement **c.** is false. If x is at least 7, then $x \geq 7$.

67. We need to find the x-values for which the graph of $3(-x - 5) - 9$ is between 0 and 6.

The x-coordinates of the intersection points of the lines are the endpoints of the region in which the inequality is true. The intersection points are $(-10, 6)$ and $(-8, 0)$. Therefore, the solution set is $\{x | -10 < x < -8\}$ or $(-10, -8)$.

69. $-2(x+4) > 6x+16$

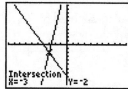

Moving from left to right on the graphing calculator screen, we see that the graph of $-2(x+4)$ is above the graph of $6x+16$ from $-\infty$ to -3. The solution set is $\{x \mid x < -3\}$ or $(-\infty, -3)$.

71. $R(x) = 50x$
$C(x) = 20x + 180$

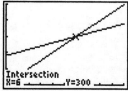

The intersection point, (6, 300), is the break-even point. This means that when 6 units are produced and sold, costs and revenue are the same at approximately $300.

Review Exercises

73. $f(-4) = (-4)^2 - 2(-4) + 5 = 16 + 8 + 5 = 29$

74. Add the first and third equations to eliminate y.

$$\begin{aligned} 2x - y - z &= -3 \\ -x + y + 2z &= 4 \\ \hline x + z &= 1 \end{aligned}$$

Multiply the third equation by 2 and add to the second equation.

$$\begin{aligned} 3x - 2y - 2z &= -5 \\ -2x + 2y + 4z &= 8 \\ \hline x + 2z &= 3 \end{aligned}$$

We now have two equations in two variables.

$x + z = 1$
$x + 2z = 3$

Multiply the second equation by -1 and solve for z.

$$\begin{aligned} x + z &= 1 \\ -x - 2z &= -3 \\ \hline -z &= -2 \\ z &= 2 \end{aligned}$$

Back-substitute 2 for z to find x.
$x + 2 = 1$
$x = -1$

Back-substitute 2 for z and -1 and x to find y.

$$\begin{aligned} 2(-1) - y - 2 &= -3 \\ -2 - y - 2 &= -3 \\ -y - 4 &= -3 \\ 1 &= y \end{aligned}$$

The solution is $(-1, -1, 2)$.

75. $25x^2 - 81 = (5x + 9)(5x - 9)$

Compound Inequalities

9.2 CHECK POINTS

CHECK POINT 1
$\{3, 4, 5, 6, 7\} \cap \{3, 7, 8, 9\} = \{3, 7\}$

CHECK POINT 2

$x + 2 < 5$ and $2x - 4 < -2$
$\quad x < 3 \qquad\qquad 2x < 2$
$\qquad\qquad\qquad\qquad x < 1$

$x < 3$ and $x < 1$

The solution set is $\{x \mid x < 1\}$ or $(-\infty, 1)$.

CHECK POINT 3
$4x - 5 > 7$ and $5x - 2 < 3$
$\quad 4x > 12 \qquad\qquad 5x < 5$
$\quad\; x > 3 \qquad\qquad\; x < 1$

$x > 3$ and $x < 1$

Since the two sets do not intersect, the solution set is $\varnothing$ or $\{\ \ \}$.

CHECK POINT 4
$$1 \le 2x + 3 < 11$$
$$-2 \le 2x < 8$$
$$-1 \le x < 4$$

The solution set is $\{x \mid -1 \le x < 4\}$ or $[-1, 4)$.

CHECK POINT 5
$$\{3,4,5,6,7\} \cup \{3,7,8,9\} = \{3,4,5,6,7,8,9\}$$

CHECK POINT 6
$$3x - 5 \le -2 \quad \text{or} \quad 10 - 2x < 4$$
$$3x \le 3 \qquad\qquad -2x < -6$$
$$x \le 1 \qquad\qquad\quad x > 3$$

$x \le 1$ or $x > 3$

The solution set is $\{x \mid x \le 1 \text{ or } x > 3\}$ or $(-\infty, 1] \cup (3, \infty)$.

CHECK POINT 7
$$2x + 5 \ge 3 \quad \text{or} \quad 2x + 3 < 3$$
$$2x \ge -2 \qquad\qquad 2x < 0$$
$$x \ge -1 \qquad\qquad x < 0$$

$x \ge -1$ or $x < 0$

The solution set is $\mathbb{R}$, $(-\infty, \infty)$ or $\{x \mid x \text{ is a real number}\}$.

EXERCISE SET 9.2

1. $\{1, 2, 3, 4\} \cap \{2, 4, 5\} = \{2, 4\}$

3. $\{1, 3, 5, 7\} \cap \{2, 4, 6, 8, 10\} = \{\ \ \}$
     The empty set is also denoted by $\varnothing$.

5. $x > 3$

     $x > 6$

     $x > 3$ and $x > 6$

     The solution set is $\{x \mid x > 6\}$ or $(6, \infty)$.

7. $x \le 5$

     $x \le 1$

     $x \le 5$ and $x \le 1$

     The solution set is $\{x \mid x \le 1\}$ or $(-\infty, 1]$.

9. $x < 2$

     $x \ge -1$

     $x < 2$ and $x \ge -1$

     The solution set is $\{x \mid -1 \le x < 2\}$ or $[-1, 2)$.

11. $x > 2$

     $x < -1$

     $x > 2$ and $x < -1$

     Since the two sets do not intersect, the solution set is $\varnothing$ or $\{\ \ \}$.

13. $5x < -20$

$x < -4$

$3x > -18$

$x > -6$

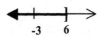

$x < -4$ and $x > -6$

The solution set is $\{x|-6 < x < -4\}$ or $(-6, -4)$.

15. $x - 4 \le 2$ and $3x + 1 > -8$

$x \le 6$ $\qquad 3x > -9$

$\qquad\qquad x > -3$

$x \le 6$

$x > -3$

$x \le 6$ and $x > -3$

The solution set is $\{x|-3 < x \le 6\}$ or $(-3, 6]$.

17. $2x > 5x - 15$ and $7x > 2x + 10$

$-3x > -15$ $\qquad 5x > 10$

$x < 5$ $\qquad\qquad x > 2$

$x < 5$

$x > 2$

$x < 5$ and $x > 2$

The solution set is $\{x|2 < x < 5\}$ or $(2, 5)$.

19. $4(1-x) < -6$ $\qquad \dfrac{x-7}{5} \le -2$

$4 - 4x < -6$

$-4x < -10$ $\qquad x - 7 \le -10$

$x > \dfrac{5}{2}$ $\qquad\qquad x \le -3$

$x > \dfrac{5}{2}$

$x \le -3$

$x > \dfrac{5}{2}$ and $x \le -3$

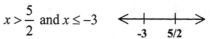

Since the two sets do not intersect, the solution set is $\varnothing$ or $\{\ \}$.

21. $x - 1 \le 7x - 1$ and $4x - 7 < 3 - x$

$-6x - 1 \le -1$ $\qquad 5x - 7 < 3$

$-6x \le 0$ $\qquad\qquad 5x < 10$

$x \ge 0$ $\qquad\qquad x < 2$

$x < 2$

$x \ge 0$

$x < 2$ and $x \ge 0$

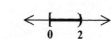

The solution set is $\{x|0 \le x < 2\}$ or $[0, 2)$.

23. $6 < x + 3 < 8$

$3 < x < 5$

The solution set is $\{x|3 < x < 5\}$ or $(3, 5)$.

25. $-3 \le x - 2 < 1$

$-1 \le x < 3$

The solution set is $\{x|-1 \le x < 3\}$ or $[-1,3)$.

27. $-11 < 2x - 1 \le -5$

$-10 < 2x \le -4$

$-5 < x \le -2$

The solution set is $\{x|-5 < x \le -2\}$ or $(-5,-2]$.

29. $-3 \le \dfrac{2x}{3} - 5 < -1$

$2 \le \dfrac{2x}{3} < 4$

$6 \le 2x < 12$

$3 \le x < 6$

The solution set is $\{x|3 \le x < 6\}$ or $[3,6)$.

31. $\{1,2,3,4\} \cup \{2,4,5\} = \{1,2,3,4,5\}$

33. $\{1,3,5,7\} \cup \{2,4,6,8,10\}$
$= \{1,2,3,4,5,6,7,8,10\}$

35. $x > 3$

$x > 6$

$x > 3$ or $x > 6$

The solution set is $\{x|x > 3\}$ or $(3,\infty)$.

37. $x \le 5$

$x \le 1$

$x \le 5$ or $x \le 1$

The solution set is $\{x|x \le 5\}$ or $(-\infty,5]$.

39. $x < 2$

$x \ge -1$

$x < 2$ or $x \ge -1$

The solution set is $\mathbb{R}$, $(-\infty,\infty)$ or $\{x|x$ is a real number$\}$.

41. $x \ge 2$

$x < -1$

$x \ge 2$ or $x < -1$

The solution set is $\{x|x < -1$ or $x \ge 2\}$ or $(-\infty,-1) \cup [2,\infty)$.

43. $3x > 12$ or $2x < -6$
$\quad x > 4 \qquad\qquad x < -3$

$x > 4$

$x < -3$

$x > 4$ or $x < -3$

The solution set is $\{x|x < -3$ or $x > 4\}$ or $(-\infty,-3) \cup (4,\infty)$.

45. $3x + 2 \le 5$ or $5x - 7 \ge 8$
$\quad 3x \le 3 \qquad\qquad 5x \ge 15$
$\quad\ x \le 1 \qquad\qquad\ x \ge 3$

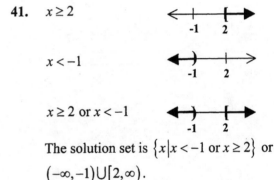

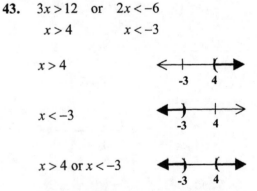

$x \leq 1$

$x \geq 3$

$x \leq 1$ or $x \geq 3$

The solution set is $\left\{x \mid x \leq 1 \text{ or } x \geq 3\right\}$ or $(-\infty, 1] \cup [3, \infty)$.

47. $4x + 3 < -1$ or $2x - 3 \geq -11$

     $4x < -4$ $2x \geq -8$

      $x < -1$ $x \geq -4$

$x < -1$

$x \geq -4$

$x < -1$ or $x \geq -4$

The solution set is $\mathbb{R}$, $(-\infty, \infty)$ or $\left\{x \mid x \text{ is a real number}\right\}$.

49. $-2x + 5 > 7$ or $-3x + 10 > 2x$

     $-2x > 2$ $-5x + 10 > 0$

       $x < -1$ $-5x > -10$

                     $x < 2$

$x < -1$

$x < 2$

$x < -1$ or $x < 2$

The solution set is $\left\{x \mid x < 2\right\}$ or $(-\infty, 2)$.

51.   {toys requested by > 10% of boys}
∩ {toys requested by < 20% of girls}
={toys cars and trucks, sports equipment, spatial-temporal toys} ∩ {toy cars and trucks, sports equipment, spatial-temporal toys, doll houses}
={toys cars and trucks, sports equipment, spatial-temporal toys}

53.   {toys requested by > 10% of boys}
∪ {toys requested by < 20% of girls}
={toys cars and trucks, sports equipment, spatial-temporal toys} ∪ {toy cars and trucks, sports equipment, spatial-temporal toys, doll houses}
={toys cars and trucks, sports equipment, spatial-temporal toys, doll houses}

55.   {toys requested by > 40% of boys}
∩ {toys requested by > 10% of girls}
={toys cars and trucks} ∩ {sports equipment, spatial-temporal toys, dolls, domestic accessories, doll houses}
= { }
No toys were requested by more than 40% of the boys and more than 10% of the girls.

57. $52 \leq 0.01x + 56.7 \leq 57.2$

     $-4.7 \leq 0.01x \leq 0.5$

     $-470 \leq x \leq 50$

The range of years is from 1905 − 470 = 1435 through 1905 + 50 = 1955. Notice, although the inequality tells us that the global mean temperature was at least 52°F and at most 57.2°F as far back as 1435, our model only predicts temperature since 1905.

59.   Let x = the score on the fifth exam

$$80 \leq \frac{70 + 75 + 87 + 92 + x}{5} < 90$$

$$80 \leq \frac{324 + x}{5} < 90$$

$$400 \leq 324 + x < 450$$

$$76 \leq x < 126$$

A grade between 76 and 125 is needed on the fifth exam. (Because the score must be less than 126, we say 125 is the highest possible score. In interval notation, we can use parentheses to exclude the maximum value. The range of scores can be expressed as $[76, 126)$.)

61. Let x = the number of times the bridge is crossed per three month period

$C_3 = 7.50 + 0.50x$

$C_6 = 30$

$2(7.50 + 0.50x) < 30$

$\qquad 15 + x < 30$

$\qquad\qquad x < 15$

We also must consider the cost without purchasing a pass. We need this cost to be less than the cost with a 3-month pass.

$\qquad 3x > 7.50 + 0.50x$

$2.50x > 7.50$

$\qquad x > 3$

The 3-month pass is the best deal when making more than 3 but less than 15 crossings per 3-month period.

For Exercises 63-69, answers may vary.

71. $-7 \leq 8 - 3x \leq 20$ and $-7 < 6x - 1 < 41$

$\quad -15 \leq -3x \leq 12 \qquad\qquad -6 < 6x < 42$

$\qquad 5 \geq x \geq -4 \qquad\qquad\qquad -1 < x < 7$

$\qquad -4 \leq x \leq 5$

$-4 \leq x \leq 5$

$-1 < x < 7$

$-4 \leq x \leq 5$ and $-1 < x < 7$

The solution set is $\{x | -1 < x \leq 5\}$ or $(-1, 5]$.

73. $f(x) = -x + 4$

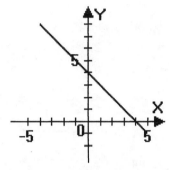

The function falls between 2 and 7 when x is between -3 and 2. The solution set is $\{x | -3 < x < 2\}$ or $(-3, 2)$.

75. The domain of $f = \{x | x \leq 4\}$ or $(-\infty, 4]$.

77. The domain of $f + g = \{x | -1 \leq x \leq 4\}$ or $[-1, 4]$.

79. Let x = the number of nickels

Let $2x - 3$ = the number of dimes

$2x + 2$ = the number of quarters

$3.20 \leq 0.05x + 0.10(2x - 3) + 0.25(2x + 2) \leq 5.45$

$3.20 \leq 0.05x + 0.20x - 0.30 + 0.50x + 0.50 \leq 5.45$

$\qquad\qquad 3.20 \leq 0.75x + 0.20 \leq 5.45$

$\qquad\qquad\quad 3.00 \leq 0.75x \leq 5.25$

$\qquad\qquad\qquad\quad 4 \leq x \leq 7$

The least possible number of nickels is 4 and the greatest possible number of nickels is 7.

81. $-1 < \dfrac{x+4}{2} < 3$

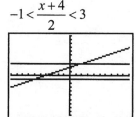

We need to find the range of the x-values of the points lying between the two constant functions. Use the intersection feature to determine the x-values of the endpoints of the range.

The solution set is $\{x \mid -6 < x < 2\}$ or $(-6, 2)$.

83. $2 \le 4 - x \le 7$

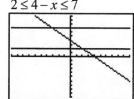

We need to find the range of the x-values of the points lying between the two constant functions. Use the intersection feature to determine the x-values of the endpoints of the range. The solution set is $\{x \mid -3 \le x \le 2\}$ or $[-3, 2]$.

Review Exercises

84. $(g - f)(x) = g(x) - f(x)$

$$= (2x - 5) - (x^2 - 3x + 4)$$
$$= 2x - 5 - x^2 + 3x - 4$$
$$= -x^2 + 5x - 9$$
$$(g - f)(-1) = -(-1)^2 + 5(-1) - 9$$
$$= -1 - 5 - 9 = -15$$

85. $y = -\dfrac{2}{3}x + 4$

slope $= -\dfrac{2}{3}$ y–intercept $= 4$

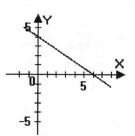

86. $4 - [2(x - 4) - 5] = 4 - [2x - 8 - 5]$
$$= 4 - [2x - 13] = 4 - 2x + 13 = 17 - 2x$$

Equations and Inequalities Involving Absolute Value

9.3 CHECK POINTS

CHECK POINT 1
$|2x - 1| = 5$

$2x - 1 = 5$ or $2x - 1 = -5$
$\quad 2x = 6 \qquad\qquad 2x = -4$
$\quad\; x = 3 \qquad\qquad\; x = -2$

CHECK POINT 2
$|2x - 7| = |x + 3|$

$2x - 7 = x + 3$ or $2x - 7 = -(x + 3)$
$\quad x - 7 = 3 \qquad\qquad 2x - 7 = -x - 3$
$\qquad x = 10 \qquad\qquad 3x - 7 = -3$
$\qquad\qquad\qquad\qquad\quad 3x = 4$
$\qquad\qquad\qquad\qquad\quad\; x = \dfrac{4}{3}$

CHECK POINT 3
$|x - 2| < 5$

$-5 < x - 2 < 5$
$\quad -3 < x < 7$

The solution set is $\{x \mid -3 < x < 7\}$ or $(-3, 7)$.

CHECK POINT 4

$|2x-5| \geq 3$

$2x-5 \leq -3$ or $2x-5 \geq 3$

$\qquad 2x \leq 2 \qquad\qquad\qquad 2x \geq 8$

$\qquad\quad x \leq 1 \qquad\qquad\qquad\quad x \geq 4$

$\qquad\qquad$ 1 $\qquad$ 4

The solution set is $\{x | x \leq 1 \text{ and } x \geq 4\}$ or

$(-\infty, 1] \cup [4, \infty)$.

CHECK POINT 5

$\qquad |x-11| \leq 2.9$

$-2.9 \leq x - 11 \leq 2.9$

$\quad 8.1 \leq x \leq 13.9$

$\qquad$ 8.1 $\quad$ 13.9

The solution set is $\{x | 8.1 \leq x \leq 13.9\}$ or

$[8.1, 13.9]$. The inequality describes the margin of error for children who think that not being able to do everything they want is a bad thing. The percentage of children in the population who think this is between 8.1% and 13.9%, inclusive.

EXERCISE SET 9.3

1. $\qquad |x| = 8$

$\qquad x = 8$ or $x = -8$

3. $\qquad |x-2| = 7$

$\qquad x - 2 = 7$ or $x - 2 = -7$

$\qquad\quad x = 9 \qquad\qquad\quad x = -5$

5. $\qquad |2x-1| = 7$

$\qquad 2x - 1 = 7$ or $2x - 1 = -7$

$\qquad\quad 2x = 8 \qquad\qquad\quad 2x = -6$

$\qquad\quad\;\; x = 4 \qquad\qquad\quad\;\; x = -3$

7. $\qquad \left| \dfrac{4x-2}{3} \right| = 2$

$\qquad \dfrac{4x-2}{3} = 2$ or $\dfrac{4x-2}{3} = -2$

$\qquad 4x - 2 = 3(2) \qquad 4x - 2 = 3(-2)$

$\qquad 4x - 2 = 6 \qquad\quad\; 4x - 2 = -6$

$\qquad\quad\; 4x = 8 \qquad\qquad\quad 4x = -4$

$\qquad\quad\;\; x = 2 \qquad\qquad\qquad x = -1$

9. $\qquad |x| = -8$

The solution set is $\varnothing$ or $\{\ \ \}$. There are no values of x for which the absolute value of x is a negative number.

11. $\qquad |x+3| = 0$

$\qquad x + 3 = 0$

$\qquad\quad x = -3$

13. $\qquad 2|y+6| = 10$

$\qquad\quad |y+6| = 5$

$\qquad y + 6 = 5$ or $y + 6 = -5$

$\qquad\quad\; y = -1 \qquad\qquad y = -11$

15. $\qquad 3|2x-1| = 21$

$\qquad\quad |2x-1| = 7$

$\qquad 2x - 1 = 7$ or $2x - 1 = -7$

$\qquad\quad 2x = 8 \qquad\qquad 2x = -6$

$\qquad\quad\;\; x = 4 \qquad\qquad\;\; x = -3$

17. $\qquad |6y-2| + 4 = 32$

$\qquad\quad\; |6y-2| = 28$

$\qquad 6y - 2 = 28$ or $6y - 2 = -28$

$\qquad\quad 6y = 30 \qquad\qquad 6y = -26$

$\qquad\quad\; y = 5 \qquad\qquad\;\; y = -\dfrac{26}{6} = -\dfrac{13}{3}$

19. $\qquad 7|5x| + 2 = 16$

$\qquad\quad\; 7|5x| = 14$

$\qquad\quad\;\; |5x| = 2$

$5x = 2$ or $5x = -2$

$x = \dfrac{2}{5}$ $\qquad$ $x = -\dfrac{2}{5}$

21. $|x+1|+5=3$

$\qquad |x+1| = -2$

The solution set is $\varnothing$ or $\{\ \}$, since absolute values are always positive.

23. $|4y+1|+10=4$

$\qquad |4y+1| = -6$

The solution set is $\varnothing$ or $\{\ \}$, since absolute values are always positive.

25. $|2x-1|+3=3$

$\qquad |2x-1| = 0$

$2x-1=0$

$\qquad 2x=1$

$\qquad x = \dfrac{1}{2}$

27. $|5x-8| = |3x+2|$

$5x-8=3x+2$ or $5x-8=-3x-2$

$2x-8=2$ $\qquad$ $8x-8=-2$

$\quad 2x=10$ $\qquad$ $\quad 8x=6$

$\qquad x=5$ $\qquad$ $\qquad x = \dfrac{6}{8} = \dfrac{3}{4}$

29. $|2x-4| = |x-1|$

$2x-4=x-1$ or $2x-4=-x+1$

$\;x-4=-1$ $\qquad$ $3x-4=1$

$\qquad x=3$ $\qquad$ $\quad 3x=5$

$\qquad$ $\qquad$ $\qquad x = \dfrac{5}{3}$

31. $|2x-5| = |2x+5|$

$2x-5=2x+5$ or $2x-5=-2x-5$

$\quad -5 \neq 5$ $\qquad$ $4x-5=-5$

$\qquad$ $\qquad$ $\quad 4x=0$

$\qquad$ $\qquad$ $\qquad x=0$

33. $|x-3| = |5-x|$

$x-3=5-x$ or $x-3=-(5-x)$

$2x-3=5$ $\qquad$ $x-3=-5+x$

$\quad 2x=8$ $\qquad$ $\quad -3 \neq -5$

$\qquad x=4$

35. $|2y-6| = |10-2y|$

$2y-6=10-2y$ or $2y-6=-10+2y$

$4y-6=10$ $\qquad$ $\quad -6 \neq -10$

$\quad 4y=16$

$\qquad x=4$

37. $\left|\dfrac{2x}{3}-2\right| = \left|\dfrac{x}{3}+3\right|$

$\dfrac{2x}{3}-2 = \dfrac{x}{3}+3$ or $\dfrac{2x}{3}-2 = -\left(\dfrac{x}{3}+3\right)$

$2x-6=x+9$ $\qquad$ $\dfrac{2x}{3}-2 = -\dfrac{x}{3}-3$

$\;x-6=9$ $\qquad$ $2x-6=-x-9$

$\qquad x=15$ $\qquad$ $3x-6=-9$

$\qquad$ $\qquad$ $\qquad 3x=-3$

$\qquad$ $\qquad$ $\qquad\;\; x=-1$

39. $|x| < 3$

$-3 < x < 3$

The solution set is $\{x|-3 < x < 3\}$ or $(-3,3)$.

41. $|x-2| < 1$

$-1 < x-2 < 1$

$\quad 1 < x < 3$

The solution set is $\{x|1 < x < 3\}$ or $(1,3)$.

43. $|x+2| \leq 1$

$-1 \leq x+2 \leq 1$

$-3 \leq x \leq -1$

The solution set is $\{x|-3 \le x \le -1\}$ or $[-3,-1]$.

45.
$$|2x-6| < 8$$
$$-8 < 2x-6 < 8$$
$$-2 < 2x < 14$$
$$-1 < x < 7$$

The solution set is $\{x|-1 < x < 7\}$ or $(-1,7)$.

47.
$$|x| > 3$$
$$x < -3 \quad \text{or} \quad x > 3$$

The solution set is $\{x|x < -3 \text{ and } x > 3\}$ or $(-\infty,-3) \cup (3,\infty)$.

49.
$$|x+3| > 1$$
$$x+3 < -1 \quad \text{or} \quad x+3 > 1$$
$$x < -4 \qquad\qquad x > -2$$

The solution set is $\{x|x < -4 \text{ and } x > -2\}$ or $(-\infty,-4) \cup (-2,\infty)$.

51.
$$|x-4| \ge 2$$
$$x-4 \le -2 \quad \text{or} \quad x-4 \ge 2$$
$$x \le 2 \qquad\qquad x \ge 6$$

The solution set is $\{x|x \le 2 \text{ and } x \ge 6\}$ or $(-\infty,2] \cup [6,\infty)$.

53.
$$|3x-8| > 7$$
$$3x-8 < -7 \quad \text{or} \quad 3x-8 > 7$$
$$3x < 1 \qquad\qquad 3x > 15$$
$$x < \frac{1}{3} \qquad\qquad x > 5$$

The solution set is $\left\{x \middle| x < \frac{1}{3} \text{ and } x > 5\right\}$ or $\left(-\infty,\frac{1}{3}\right) \cup (5,\infty)$.

55.
$$|2(x-1)+4| \le 8$$
$$|2x-2+4| \le 8$$
$$|2x+2| \le 8$$
$$-8 \le 2x+2 \le 8$$
$$-10 \le 2x \le 6$$
$$-5 \le x \le 3$$

The solution set is $\{x|-5 \le x \le 3\}$ or $[-5,3]$.

57.
$$\left|\frac{2y+6}{3}\right| < 2$$
$$-2 < \frac{2y+6}{3} < 2$$
$$-6 < 2y+6 < 6$$
$$-12 < 2y < 0$$
$$-6 < y < 0$$

The solution set is $\{x|-6 < x < 0\}$ or $(-6,0)$.

59. $\left|\dfrac{2x+2}{4}\right| \geq 2$

$\dfrac{2x+2}{4} \leq -2 \quad$ or $\quad \dfrac{2x+2}{4} \geq 2$

$2x+2 \leq -8 \qquad\qquad 2x+2 \geq 8$

$\qquad 2x \leq -10 \qquad\qquad 2x \geq 6$

$\qquad\quad x \leq -5 \qquad\qquad\quad x \geq 3$

The solution set is $\{x|x \leq -5 \text{ and } x \geq 3\}$ or $(-\infty, -5] \cup [3, \infty)$.

61. $\left|3 - \dfrac{2x}{3}\right| > 5$

$3 - \dfrac{2x}{3} < -5 \quad$ or $\quad 3 - \dfrac{2x}{3} > 5$

$\quad -\dfrac{2x}{3} < -8 \qquad\qquad -\dfrac{2x}{3} > 2$

$\quad -2x < -24 \qquad\qquad -2x > 6$

$\qquad\quad x > 12 \qquad\qquad\quad x < -3$

The solution set is $\{x|x < -3 \text{ and } x > 12\}$ or $(-\infty, -3) \cup (12, \infty)$.

63. $|x-2| < -1$

The solution set is $\varnothing$ or $\{\ \}$. Since all absolute values are positive, there are no values of x that will make the absolute value of the expression less than -1.

65. $|x+6| > -10$

Since all absolute values are positive, we know that when simplified, the left hand side will be a positive number. We also know that any positive number is greater than any negative number. Regardless of the value of x, the left hand side will be greater than the right hand side of the inequality. The solution set is $\{x|x \text{ is a real number}\}$, $\mathbb{R}$ or $(-\infty, \infty)$.

67. $|x+2| + 9 \leq 16$

$|x+2| \leq 7$

$-7 \leq x+2 \leq 7$

$-9 \leq x \leq 5$

The solution set is $\{x|-9 \leq x \leq 5\}$ or $[-9, 5]$.

69. $2|2x-3| + 10 > 12$

$2|2x-3| > 2$

$|2x-3| > 1$

$2x-3 < -1 \quad$ or $\quad 2x-3 > 1$

$2x < 2 \qquad\qquad\quad 2x > 4$

$\quad x < 1 \qquad\qquad\quad x > 2$

The solution set is $\{x|x < 1 \text{ and } x > 2\}$ or $(-\infty, 1) \cup (2, \infty)$.

71. $|x - 60.2| \leq 1.6$

$-1.6 \leq x - 60.2 \leq 1.6$

$58.6 \leq x \leq 61.8$

The percentage of the U.S. population that watched M*A*S*H is between 58.6% and 61.8%, inclusive. The margin of error is 1.6%.

73. $|T - 57| \leq 7$

$-7 \leq T - 57 \leq 7$

$50 \leq T \leq 64$

The monthly average temperature for ranges from 50°F to 64°F, inclusive.

75. $|x - 8.6| \leq 0.01$

$-0.01 \leq x - 8.6 \leq 0.01$

$8.59 \leq x \leq 8.61$

The length of the machine part must be between 8.59 and 8.61 centimeters, inclusive.

77. $\left|\dfrac{h-50}{5}\right| \geq 1.645$

$\dfrac{h-50}{5} \leq -1.645$ or $\dfrac{h-50}{5} \geq 1.645$

$h-50 \leq 5(-1.645)$ $h-50 \geq 5(1.645)$

$h-50 \leq -8.225$ $h-50 \geq 8.225$

$\quad h \leq 41.775$ $h \geq 58.225$

The coin would be considered unfair if the tosses resulted in 41 or less heads, or 59 or more heads.

For Exercises 79-85, answers may vary.

87. The solutions of $|4-x| = 1$ are 3 and 5 and the solution set is $\{3,5\}$. These are the points of intersection of $y = |4-x|$ and $y = 1$.

89. $\quad |p-0.3| \leq 0.2$

$-0.2 \leq p - 0.3 \leq 0.2$

$\quad 0.1 \leq p \leq 0.5$

This means that at least 0.1% and at most 0.5% of the products are defective.
$100,000 \times 0.001 = 100$

$100,000 \times 0.005 = 500$

At least 100 and at most 500 products will be defective. At $5 per refund, the company will be paying out at least $500 and at most $2500.

91. $\quad |x+1| = 5$

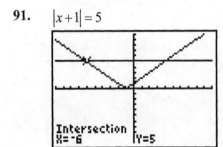

93. $\quad |2x-3| = |9-4x|$

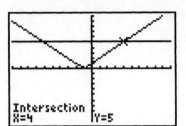

The solutions are –6 and 4.

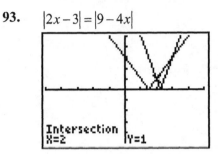

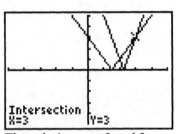

The solutions are 2 and 3.

95. $\quad \left|\dfrac{2x-1}{3}\right| < \dfrac{5}{3}$

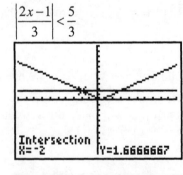

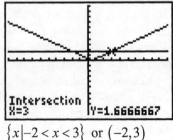

$\{x | -2 < x < 3\}$ or $(-2,3)$

97. $|2x-1|>7$

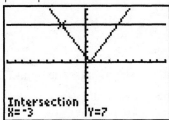

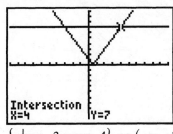

$\{x|x<-3 \text{ or } x>4\}$ or $(-\infty,-3)\cup(4,\infty)$.

99. $|x+4|>-1$

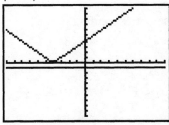

$\{x|x \text{ is a real number}\}$, $\mathbb{R}$, or $(-\infty,\infty)$

Review Exercises

101. $3x-5y=15$
$-5y=-3x+15$
$y=\dfrac{3}{5}x-3$

$y\text{-intercept}=-3 \qquad m=\dfrac{3}{5}$

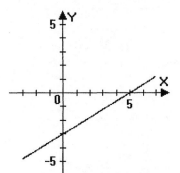

102. $f(x)=-\dfrac{2}{3}x$ or $y=-\dfrac{2}{3}x$

$y\text{-intercept}=0 \qquad m=-\dfrac{2}{3}$

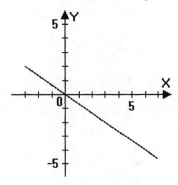

103. $f(x)=-2$ or $y=-2$

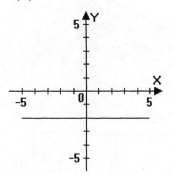

Linear Inequalities in Two Variables

9.4 CHECK POINTS

CHECK POINT 1
$2x - 4y \geq 8$
Graph the line, $2x - 4y = 8$.

x – intercept y – intercept

$2x - 4(0) = 8$ $2(0) - 4y = 8$

    $2x = 8$ $-4y = 8$

     $x = 4$ $y = -2$

Next, use the origin as a test point to determine shading.

$$2(0) - 4(0) \geq 8$$
$$0 \geq 8$$

This is a false statement. This means that the origin will not fall in the shaded half-plane.

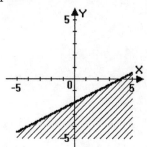

CHECK POINT 2
$y \geq -\dfrac{3}{4}x$

Graph the line, $y = -\dfrac{3}{4}x$.

$m = -\dfrac{3}{4}$ y–intercept $= 0$

Use a test point to determine shading. We cannot use the origin, because it lies on the line. Use the point, $(1,1)$.

$$1 \geq -\dfrac{3}{4}(1)$$
$$1 \geq -\dfrac{3}{4}$$

This is a true statement. The point, $(1,1)$, lies in the shaded half-plane.

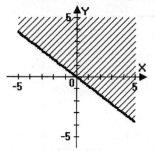

CHECK POINT 3
$x + 2y > 4$
$2x - 3y \leq -6$
Graph the corresponding lines.

$x + 2y = 4$ $2x - 3y = -6$

  $2y = -x + 4$ $-3y = -2x - 6$

   $y = -\dfrac{1}{2}x + 2$ $y = \dfrac{2}{3}x + 2$

$m = -\dfrac{1}{2}$ $m = \dfrac{2}{3}$

y – intercept $= 2$ y – intercept $= 2$

y-intercept $= 2$ slope $= \dfrac{2}{3}$

Graph the inequalities using test points to determine shading. The solution to the system is the intersection of the shaded half-planes.

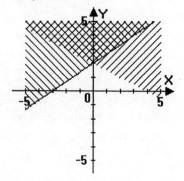

CHECK POINT 4

$x + y < 2$

$-2 \le x < 1$

$y > -3$

Graph the corresponding lines.

$x + y = 2$

$y = -x + 2$

y-intercept $= 2$

slope $= -1$

$-2 \le x < 1$ is equivalent to $x \ge -2$ and $x < 1$. Graph the vertical lines, $x = -2$ and $x = 1$.

For $y > -3$, graph the horizontal line, $y = -3$.

Graph the inequalities using test points to determine shading. The solution to the system is the intersection of the shaded half-planes.

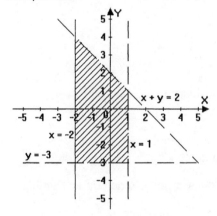

CHECK POINT 5

Show that point B satisfies each of the inequalities.

$T \ge 35$ $5T - 7P \ge 70$

$60 \ge 35$ $5(60) - 7(20) \ge 70$

$300 - 140 \ge 70$

$160 \ge 70$

$3T - 35P \le -140$

$3(60) - 35(20) \le -140$

$180 - 700 \le -140$

$-520 \le -140$

Since point B's coordinates makes each inequality true, it is a solution of the system.

EXERCISE SET 9.4

1. $x + y \ge 3$

Graph the corresponding line.

$x + y = 3$

$y = -x + 3$

y-intercept $= 3$

slope $= -1$

Use a test point to determine shading.

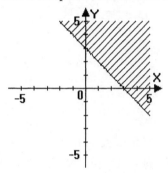

3. $x - y < 5$

Graph the corresponding line.

$x - y = 5$

$-y = -x + 5$

$y = x - 5$

y-intercept $= -5$

slope $= 1$

Use a test point to determine shading.

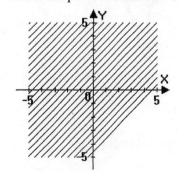

5. $x + 2y > 4$

Graph the corresponding line.

$x + 2y = 4$

$\qquad 2y = -x + 4$

$\qquad y = -\dfrac{1}{2}x + 2$

y-intercept $= 2$

slope $= -\dfrac{1}{2}$

Use a test point to determine shading.

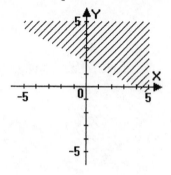

7. $3x - y \le 6$

Graph the corresponding line.

$3x - y = 6$

$\qquad -y = -3x + 6$

$\qquad y = 3x - 6$

y-intercept $= -6$ $m = 3$

Use a test point to determine shading.

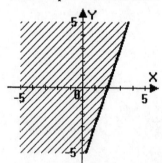

9. $\dfrac{x}{2} + \dfrac{y}{3} < 1$

Graph the corresponding line.

$$\dfrac{x}{2} + \dfrac{y}{3} = 1$$

$$6\left(\dfrac{x}{2}\right) + 6\left(\dfrac{y}{3}\right) = 6(1)$$

$$3x + 2y = 6$$

$$2y = -3x + 6$$

$$y = -\dfrac{3}{2}x + 3$$

y-intercept $= 3$ slope $= -\dfrac{3}{2}$

Use a test point to determine shading.

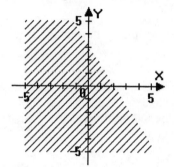

11. $y > \dfrac{1}{3}x$

Consider the corresponding line.

$$y = \dfrac{1}{3}x$$

y-intercept $= 0$ $m = \dfrac{1}{3}$

Use a test point to determine shading.

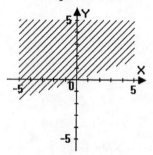

13. $y \le 3x + 2$

Graph the corresponding line.

$y = 3x + 2$

y-intercept $= 2$ $m = 3$

Use a test point to determine shading.

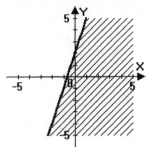

Use a test point to determine shading.

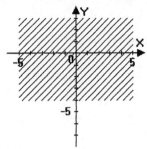

15. $y < -\dfrac{1}{4}x$

Graph the corresponding line.

$y = -\dfrac{1}{4}x$

y–intercept $= 0 \qquad m = -\dfrac{1}{4}$

Use a test point to determine shading.

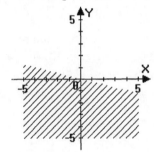

17. $x \le 2$

Graph the corresponding line, $x = 2$.
This is the vertical line positioned at 2.
Use a test point to determine shading.

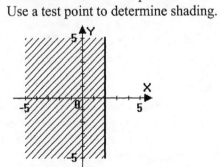

19. $y > -4$

Graph the corresponding line, $y = -4$.
This is the horizontal line positioned at -4.

21. $y \ge 0$

Graph the corresponding line, $y = 0$.
This is the equation of the x–axis.
Use a test point to determine shading.

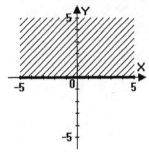

23. $3x + 6y \le 6$

$\qquad 2x + y \le 8$

Graph the equations using the intercepts.

$3x + 6y = 6 \qquad\qquad 2x + y = 8$

$x - \text{intercept} = 2 \qquad x - \text{intercept} = 4$

$y - \text{intercept} = 1 \qquad y - \text{intercept} = 8$

Use the origin as a test point to determine shading.

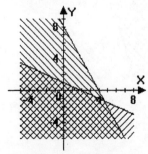

The solution set is the intersection of the shaded half-planes.

25. $2x - 5y \leq 10$

$3x - 2y > 6$

Graph the equations using the intercepts.

$2x - 5y = 10 \qquad 3x - 2y = 6$

$x - \text{intercept} = 5 \qquad x - \text{intercept} = 2$

$y - \text{intercept} = 2 \qquad y - \text{intercept} = -3$

Use the origin as a test point to determine shading.

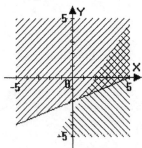

The solution set is the intersection of the shaded half-planes.

27. $y > 2x - 3$

$y < -x + 6$

Graph the equations using the intercepts.

$y = 2x - 3 \qquad\qquad y = -x + 6$

$x - \text{intercept} = \dfrac{3}{2} \qquad x - \text{intercept} = 6$

$y - \text{intercept} = -3 \qquad y - \text{intercept} = 6$

Use the origin as a test point to determine shading.

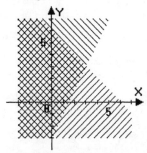

The solution set is the intersection of the shaded half-planes.

29. $x + 2y \leq 4$

$y \geq x - 3$

Graph the equations using the intercepts.

$x + 2y = 4 \qquad\qquad y = x - 3$

$x - \text{intercept} = 4 \qquad x - \text{intercept} = 3$

$y - \text{intercept} = 2 \qquad y - \text{intercept} = -3$

Use the origin as a test point to determine shading.

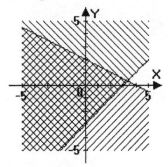

The solution set is the intersection of the shaded half-planes.

31. $x \leq 2$

$y \geq -1$

Graph the vertical line, $x = 2$, and the horizontal line, $y = -1$. Use the origin as a test point to determine shading.

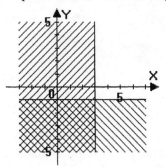

The solution set is the intersection of the shaded half-planes.

33. $-2 \leq x < 5$

Since x lies between -2 and 5, graph the two vertical lines, $x = -2$ and $x = 5$. Since x lies between -2 and 5, shade between the two vertical lines.

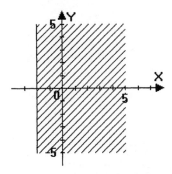

The solution is the shaded region.

35. $x - y \le 1 \qquad x \ge 2$
Graph the equations.
$x - y = 1 \qquad\qquad x = 2$
$x - \text{intercept} = 1 \qquad x - \text{intercept} = 2$
$y - \text{intercept} = -1 \qquad \text{vertical line}$
Use the origin as a test point to determine shading.

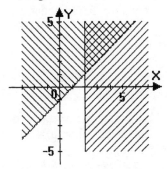

The solution set is the intersection of the shaded half-planes.

37. $x + y > 4 \qquad x + y < -1$
Graph the equations using the intercepts.
$x + y = 4 \qquad\qquad x + y = -1$
$x - \text{intercept} = 4 \quad x - \text{intercept} = -1$
$y - \text{intercept} = 4 \quad y - \text{intercept} = -1$
Use the origin as a test point to determine shading.

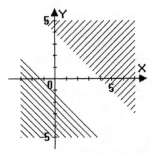

The solution set is the intersection of the shaded half-planes. Since the shaded half-planes do not intersect, there is no solution.

39. $x + y > 4 \qquad x + y > -1$
Graph the equations using the intercepts.
$x + y = 4 \qquad\qquad x + y = -1$
$x - \text{intercept} = 4 \qquad x - \text{intercept} = -1$
$y - \text{intercept} = 4 \qquad y - \text{intercept} = -1$
Use a test point to determine shading.

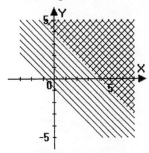

The solution set is the intersection of the shaded half-planes.

41. $x - y \le 2 \qquad x \ge -2 \qquad y \le 3$
Graph the equations using the intercepts.
$x - y = 2 \qquad\qquad y = 3$
$x - \text{intercept} = 2 \qquad y - \text{intercept} = 3$
$y - \text{intercept} = -2 \qquad \text{horizontal line}$

$x = -2$
$x - \text{intercept} = -2$
vertical line

Use a test point to determine shading.

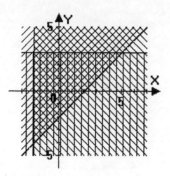

The solution set is the intersection of the shaded half-planes.

43. $x \geq 0$ $2x + 5y \leq 10$

$y \geq 0$ $3x + 4y \leq 12$

Since both x and y are greater than 0, we are concerned only with the first quadrant. Graph the other equations using the intercepts.

$2x + 5y = 10$ $3x + 4y = 12$

$x-\text{intercept} = 5$ $x-\text{intercept} = 4$

$y-\text{intercept} = 2$ $y-\text{intercept} = 3$

Use a test point to determine shading.

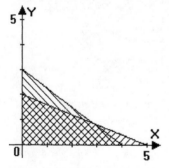

The solution set is the intersection of the shaded half-planes.

45. $3x + y \leq 6$ $x \geq -2$

$2x - y \leq -1$ $y \leq 4$

Graph the equations using the intercepts.

$3x + y = 6$ $x = -2$

$x-\text{intercept} = 2$ $x-\text{intercept} = -2$

$y-\text{intercept} = 6$ vertical line

$2x - y = -1$ $y = 4$

$x-\text{intercept} = -\dfrac{1}{2}$ $y-\text{intercept} = 4$

$y-\text{intercept} = 1$ horizontal line

Use the origin as a test point to determine shading.

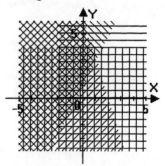

The solution set is the intersection of the shaded half-planes. Because all inequalities are greater than or equal to or less than or equal to, the boundaries of the shaded half-planes are also included in the solution set.

47. a.   The coordinates of point A are $(20,160)$. This means that a 20 year-old person with a pulse rate of 160 beats per minute falls within the target zone.

b. $10 \leq a \leq 70$ $a + p \leq 190$

$10 \leq 20 \leq 70$ $20 + 160 \leq 190$

True $180 \leq 190$

True

$$2a + 3p \geq 450$$
$$2(20) + 3(160) \geq 450$$
$$40 + 480 \geq 450$$
$$520 \geq 450$$
True

Since point A makes all three inequalities true, it is a solution of the system.

49.

$$T \geq 35 \qquad\qquad 5T - 7P \geq 70$$
$$70 \geq 35 \qquad 5(70) - 7(40) \geq 70$$
$$\text{True} \qquad\quad 350 - 280 \geq 70$$
$$70 \geq 70$$
$$\text{True}$$

$$3T - 35P \leq -140$$
$$3(70) - 35(40) \leq -140$$
$$210 - 1400 \leq -140$$
$$-1190 \leq -140$$
$$\text{True}$$

Since the coordinates of the point (70, 40) make each inequality true, it is a solution of the system.

51. The maximum healthy weight for a person who is 6 feet tall is approximately 190 pounds.

53. The border of the underweight region is the line $7w - 25h = -800$. Using a test point, we can determine what inequality symbol should be used. Consider the point (100, 70). Find the value of $7w - 25h$.
$$7w - 25h = 7(100) - 25(70)$$
$$= 700 - 1750 = -1050$$
Since $-1050 < -800$ is a true statement, the inequality should be written $7w - 25h < -800$.

55. The healthy weight region falls between the lines $7w - 25h = -800$ and $w - 5h = -170$. Replace the equal sign in each equation with an inequality sign. Use a test point to determine which sign to use. One point within the region is (150, 70).

$$7w - 25h \qquad\qquad w - 5h$$
$$= 7(150) - 25(70) \qquad = -170 - 5(70)$$
$$= 1050 - 1750 \qquad\quad = -170 - 350$$
$$= -700 \qquad\qquad\quad = -520$$

Since $-700 \geq -800$, we know that $7w - 25h \geq -800$. Also, since

$-520 \leq -170$, we know that $w - 5h \leq -170$.
The system of inequalities that describes the healthy weight region is:
$$7w - 25h \geq -800$$
$$w - 5h \leq -170.$$

For Exercises 57-65, answers may vary.

67. Looking at the graph, we can see the intercepts are (0, -4) and (2,0). First, find the slope.
$$m = \frac{y_2 - y_1}{x_2 - x_1} = \frac{0 - (-4)}{2 - 0} = \frac{4}{2} = 2$$
$$y - 0 = 2(x - 2)$$
$$y = 2x - 4$$
$$y - 2x = -4$$
We need to determine which inequality symbol to use. Use the origin, $(0,0)$, as a test point. Evaluate $y - 2x$.
$$y - 2x = 0 - 2(0) = 0 - 0 = 0$$
Since $0 > -4$, we write the inequality as $y - 2x > -4$.

69. Let x = the amount invested as high risk, high yield,
Let y = the amount invested as low risk, low yield
$$x + y \leq 15,000$$
$$x \geq 2000$$
$$y \geq 3x$$

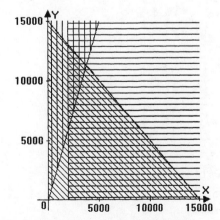

71. $y \le 4x + 4$

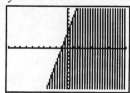

73. $2x + y \le 6$

$y \le -2x + 6$

75. Answers may vary.

77. Answers may vary. For example, verify Exercise 23.

$3x + 6y \le 6$ $\qquad$ $2x + y \le 8$

$\quad 6y \le -3x + 6$ $\qquad$ $\quad y \le -2x + 8$

$$y \le -\frac{1}{2}x + 1$$

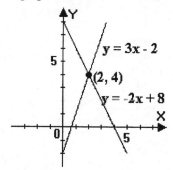

Review Exercises

78. $\begin{bmatrix} 3 & -1 & | & 8 \\ 1 & -5 & | & -2 \end{bmatrix} R_1 \leftrightarrow R_2$

$= \begin{bmatrix} 1 & -5 & | & -2 \\ 3 & -1 & | & 8 \end{bmatrix} -3R_1 + R_2$

$= \begin{bmatrix} 1 & -5 & | & -2 \\ 0 & 14 & | & 14 \end{bmatrix} \frac{1}{14}R_2$

$= \begin{bmatrix} 1 & -5 & | & -2 \\ 0 & 1 & | & 1 \end{bmatrix}$

$x - 5y = -2$

$\qquad y = 1$

Since we know $y = 1$, we can use back-substitution to find x.

$x - 5(1) = -2$

$\quad x - 5 = -2$

$\qquad x = 3$

The solution is $(3,1)$.

79. $y = 3x - 2$

$y = -2x + 8$

Both equations are in slope-intercept form, so use the slopes and y-intercepts to graph the lines.

The solution is the intersection point $(2,4)$.

80. $\begin{vmatrix} 8 & 2 & -1 \\ 3 & 0 & 5 \\ 6 & -3 & 4 \end{vmatrix}$

$= 8 \begin{vmatrix} 0 & 5 \\ -3 & 4 \end{vmatrix} - 3 \begin{vmatrix} 2 & -1 \\ -3 & 4 \end{vmatrix} + 6 \begin{vmatrix} 2 & -1 \\ 0 & 5 \end{vmatrix}$

$= 8 \left(0(4) - (-3(5)) \right) - 3 \left(2(4) - (-3)(-1) \right)$

$\qquad\qquad\qquad + 6 \left(2(5) - 0(-1) \right)$

$= 8(15) - 3(8 - 3) + 6(10)$

$= 120 - 3(5) + 60 = 120 - 15 + 60 = 165$

Linear Programming

9.5 CHECK POINTS

CHECK POINT 1
The objective function is $z = 25x + 55y$.

CHECK POINT 2
Since not more than 80 bookshelves and desks can be manufactured per day, we have $x + y \leq 80$.

CHECK POINT 3
Objective Function:
$z = 25x + 55y$
Constraints:
$x + y \leq 80$
$30 < x < 80$
$10 \leq y \leq 30$

CHECK POINT 4
First, graph the constraints.
$x + y \leq 80$
$30 \leq x \leq 80$
$10 \leq y \leq 30$

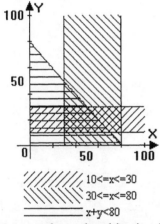

Next, evaluate the objective function at each corner of the region where the constraints intersect.

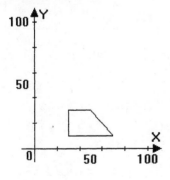

Corner (x, y)	Objective Function $z = 25x + 55y$
(30, 10)	$z = 25(30) + 55(10)$ $= 750 + 550 = 1300$
(30, 30)	$z = 25(30) + 55(30)$ $= 750 + 1150 = 1900$
(50, 30)	$z = 25(50) + 55(30)$ $= 1250 + 1150 = 2400$
(70, 10)	$z = 25(70) + 55(10)$ $= 1750 + 550 = 2300$

The maximum value of z is 2400 and occurs at the point (50, 30). In order to maximize profit, 50 bookshelves and 30 desks must be produced each day for a profit of $2400.

CHECK POINT 5
First, graph the constraints.
$x \geq 0$ $\qquad$ $y \geq 0$
$x + y \geq 1$ $\qquad$ $x + y \leq 6$

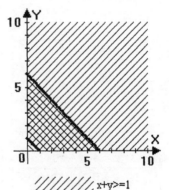

Next, evaluate the objective function at each corner of the region where the constraints intersect.

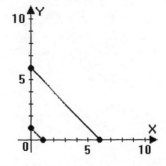

Corner (x, y)	Objective Function $z = 3x + 5y$
(0, 1)	$z = 3(0) + 5(1) = 5$
(1, 0)	$z = 3(1) + 5(0) = 3$
(0, 6)	$z = 3(0) + 5(6) = 30$
(6, 0)	$z = 3(6) + 5(0) = 18$

The maximum value of z occurs at the point (0, 6). At this point, the maximum value is 30.

EXERCISE SET 9.5

1.

Corner (x, y)	Objective Function $z = 5x + 6y$
(1, 2)	$z = 5(1) + 6(2)$ $= 5 + 12 = 17$
(8, 3)	$z = 5(8) + 6(3)$ $= 40 + 18 = 58$
(7, 5)	$z = 5(7) + 6(5)$ $= 35 + 30 = 65$
(2, 10)	$z = 5(2) + 6(10)$ $= 10 + 60 = 70$

The maximum value is 70 and the minimum is 17.

3.

Corner (x, y)	Objective Function $z = 40x + 50y$
(0, 0)	$z = 40(0) + 50(0)$ $= 0 + 0 = 0$
(8, 0)	$z = 40(8) + 50(0) = 320$
(4, 9)	$z = 40(4) + 50(9)$ $= 160 + 450 = 610$
(0, 8)	$z = 40(0) + 50(8) = 400$

The maximum value is 610 and the minimum value is 0.

5. Objective Function: $z = 3x + 2y$
Constraints: $x \geq 0, \; y \geq 0$
                      $2x + y \leq 8$
                      $x + y \geq 4$

a.

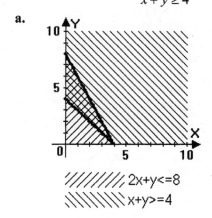

$$/////// \; 2x + y <= 8$$
$$\backslash\backslash\backslash\backslash\backslash\backslash \; x + y >= 4$$

b.

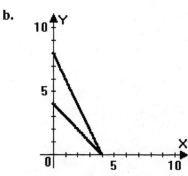

Corner (x, y)	Objective Function $z = 3x + 2y$
(4, 0)	$z = 3(4) + 2(0) = 12$
(0, 8)	$z = 3(0) + 2(8) = 16$
(0, 4)	$z = 3(0) + 2(4) = 8$

c. The maximum value is 16. It occurs at the point (0, 8).

7. Objective Function: $z = 4x + y$
Constraints: $x \geq 0, \; y \geq 0$
                      $2x + 3y \leq 12$
                      $x + y \geq 3$

a.

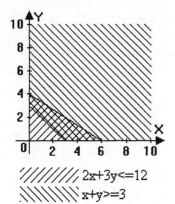

///// $2x+3y<=12$

\\\\\ $x+y>=3$

b.

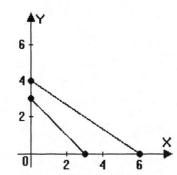

Corner (x, y)	Objective Function $z = 4x + y$
$(3, 0)$	$z = 4(0) + 0 = 0$
$(6, 0)$	$z = 4(6) + 0 = 24$
$(0, 3)$	$z = 4(0) + 3 = 3$

c. The maximum value is 24. It occurs at the point (6, 0).

9. Objective Function: $z = 3x - 2y$

Constraints: $1 \le x \le 5$

$y \ge 2$

$x - y \ge -3$

a.

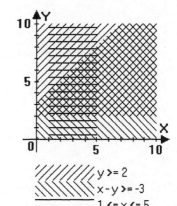

///// $y >= 2$

\\\\\ $x - y >= -3$

——— $1 <= x <= 5$

b.

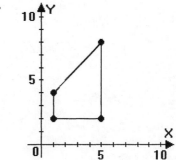

Corner (x, y)	Objective Function $z = 3x - 2y$
$(1, 2)$	$z = 3(1) - 2(2)$ $= 3 - 4 = -1$
$(5, 2)$	$z = 3(5) - 2(2)$ $= 15 - 4 = 11$
$(5, 8)$	$z = 3(5) - 2(8)$ $= 15 - 16 = -1$
$(1, 4)$	$z = 3(1) - 2(4)$ $= 3 - 8 = -5$

c. The maximum value is 11. It occurs at the point (5, 2).

11. Objective Function: $z = 4x + 2y$

Constraints: $x \ge 0, \; y \ge 0$

$2x + 3y \le 12$

$3x + 2y \le 12$

$x + y \ge 2$

a.

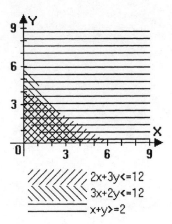

|⁄⁄⁄⁄⁄⁄⁄⁄| 2x+3y<=12
|\\\\\\\\| 3x+2y<=12
|————| x+y>=2

b.

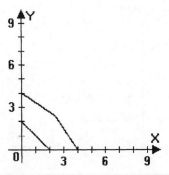

Corner (x, y)	Objective Function $z = 4x + 2y$
(2, 0)	$z = 4(2) + 2(0) = 8$
(4, 0)	$z = 4(4) + 2(0) = 16$
(2.4, 2.4)	$z = 4(2.4) + 2(2.4)$ $= 9.6 + 4.8 = 14.4$
(0, 4)	$z = 4(0) + 2(4) = 8$
(0, 2)	$z = 4(0) + 2(2) = 4$

c.   The maximum value is 16. It occurs at the point (4, 0).

13.   Objective Function: $z = 10x + 12y$

Constraints: $x \ge 0, \quad y \ge 0$

$x + y \le 7$

$2x + y \le 10$

$2x + 3y \le 18$

a.

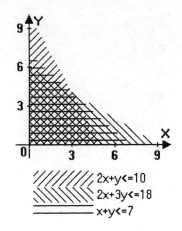

|⁄⁄⁄⁄⁄⁄⁄⁄| 2x+y<=10
|\\\\\\\\| 2x+3y<=18
|————| x+y<=7

b.

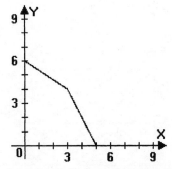

Corner (x, y)	Objective Function $z = 10x + 12y$
(0, 0)	$z = 10(0) + 12(0)$ $= 0 + 0 = 0$
(5, 0)	$z = 10(5) + 12(0) = 50$
(3, 4)	$z = 10(3) + 12(4)$ $= 30 + 48 = 78$
(0, 6)	$z = 10(0) + 12(6) = 72$

c.   The maximum value is 78 and it occurs at the point (3, 4)

15.   a.   The objective function is $z = 125x + 200y$.

b. $x \le 450$

$y \le 200$

$600x + 900y \le 360,000$

c.

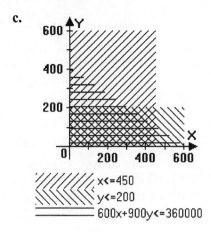

x<=450
y<=200
600x+900y<=360000

d.

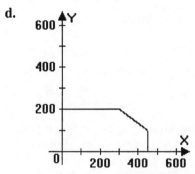

Corner (x, y)	Objective Function $z = 125x + 200y$
(0, 0)	$z = 125(0) + 200(0) = 0$
(0, 200)	$z = 125(0) + 200(200)$ $= 40,000$
(300, 200)	$z = 125(300) + 200(200)$ $= 37,500 + 40,000$ $= 77,500$
(450, 100)	$z = 125(450) + 200(100)$ $= 56,250 + 20,000$ $= 76,250$
(450, 0)	$z = 125(450) + 200(0)$ $= 56,250$

e. The television manufacturer will make the greatest profit by manufacturing 300 console televisions each month and 200 wide screen televisions each month. The maximum monthly profit is $77,500.

17. Let x = the number of model A
Let y = the number of model B
The objective function is $z = 25x + 15y$.
The assembling constraint is
$5x + 4y \le 200$.
The painting constraint is $2x + 3y \le 108$.
We also know that x and y must either be zero or a positive number. We cannot make a negative number of bicycles.

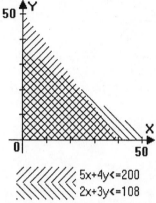

5x+4y<=200
2x+3y<=108

Using the graph, find the value of the objective function at each of the corner points.

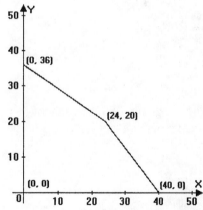

Corner (x, y)	Objective Function $z = 25x + 15y$
(0, 0)	$z = 25(0) + 15(0) = 0$
(40, 0)	$z = 25(40) + 15(0) = 1000$
(24, 20)	$z = 25(24) + 15(20)$ $= 600 + 300 = 900$
(0, 36)	$z = 25(0) + 15(36) = 540$

The maximum of 1000 occurs at the point (40, 0). This means that the company should produce 40 of model A and none of model B each week for a profit of \$1000.

19. Let x = the number of cartons of food
Let y = the number of cartons of clothing
The objective function is $z = 12x + 5y$.
The weight constraint is
$50x + 20y \le 19{,}000$.
The volume constraint is
$20x + 10y \le 8000$.
We also know that x and y must either be zero or a positive number. We cannot have a negative number of cartons of food or clothing.
Next, graph the constraints.

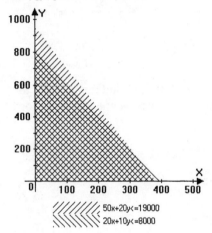

Using the graph, find the value of the objective function at each of the corner points.

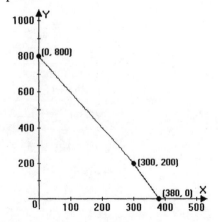

Corner (x, y)	Objective Function $z = 12x + 5y$
(0, 0)	$z = 12(0) + 5(0) = 0$
(380, 0)	$z = 12(380) + 5(0) = 4560$
(300, 200)	$z = 12(300) + 5(200)$ $= 3600 + 1000 = 4600$
(0, 600)	$z = 12(0) + 5(600) = 3000$

The maximum of 4600 occurs at the point (300, 200). This means that to maximize the number of people who are helped, 300 boxes of food and 200 boxes of clothing should be sent.

21. Let x = the number of parents
Let y = the number of students
The objective function is $z = 2x + y$.
The seating constraint is $x + y \le 150$.
The two parents per student constraint is $2x \ge y$.
We also know that x and y must either be zero or a positive number. We cannot have a negative number of parents or students.
Next, graph the constraints.

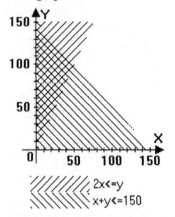

Using the graph, find the value of the objective function at each of the corner points.

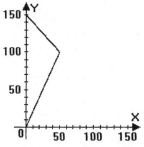

Corner (x, y)	Objective Function $z = 2x + y$
(0, 0)	$z = 2(0) + 0 = 0$
(50, 100)	$z = 2(50) + 100$ $= 100 + 100 = 200$
(0, 150)	$z = 2(0) + 100 = 100$

The maximum of 200 occurs at the point (50, 100). This means that to maximize the amount of money raised, 50 parents and 100 students should attend.

23. Let x = the number of Boeing 727s
Let y = the number of Falcon 20s
The objective function is $z = x + y$.

The hourly operating cost constraint is $1400x + 500y \le 35000$.

The total payload constraint is $42000x + 6000y \ge 672,000$.

The 727 constraint is $x \le 20$.
We also know that x and y must either be zero or a positive number. We cannot have a negative number of aircraft.
Next, graph the constraints.

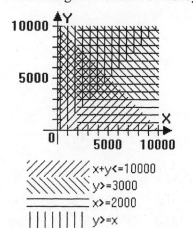

$////$ 1400x+500y<=35000
$\backslash\backslash\backslash$ 42000x+6000y>=672000
——— x<=20

Using the graph, find the value of the objective function at each of the corner points.

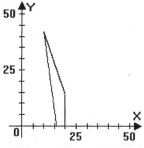

Corner (x, y)	Objective Function $z = x + y$
(16, 0)	$z = 16 + 0 = 16$
(20, 0)	$z = 20 + 0 = 20$
(20, 14)	$z = 20 + 14 = 34$
(10, 42)	$z = 10 + 42 = 52$

The maximum of 52 occurs at the point (10, 42). This means that to maximize the number of aircraft, 10 Boeing 727s and 42 Falcon 20s should be purchased.

For Exercises 25-27, answers may vary.

29. Let x = the amount invested in stocks
Let y = the amount invested in bonds
$z = 0.12x + 0.08y$

$x + y \le 10000$ $y \ge 3000$
$x \ge 2000$ $y \ge x$

We also know that x and y must either be zero or a positive number. We cannot invest a negative amount of money.

$////$ x+y<=10000
$\backslash\backslash\backslash$ y>=3000
——— x>=2000
| | | | | | | | y>=x

Using the graph, find the value of the objective function at each of the corner points.

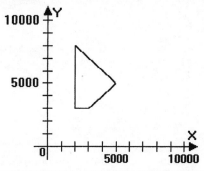

Corner (x, y)	Objective Function $z = 0.12x + 0.08y$
(2000,3000)	$z = 0.12(2000) + 0.08(3000)$ $= 240 + 240 = 480$
(3000,3000)	$z = 0.12(3000) + 0.08(3000)$ $= 360 + 240 = 600$
(5000,5000)	$z = 0.12(5000) + 0.08(5000)$ $= 600 + 400 = 1000$
(2000,8000)	$z = 0.12(2000) + 0.08(8000)$ $= 240 + 640 = 880$

The maximum of 1000 occurs at the point (5000, 5000). This means that to maximize the return on the investment, $5000 should be invested in stocks and $5000 should be invested in bonds.

Review Exercises

31. $x^2 - 12x + 36 = 0$

$$(x - 6)^2 = 0$$

$$x - 6 = 0$$

$$x = 6$$

32. $\dfrac{1}{x^2 - 17x + 30} \div \dfrac{1}{x^2 + 7x - 18}$

$$= \dfrac{1}{x^2 - 17x + 30} \cdot \dfrac{x^2 + 7x - 18}{1}$$

$$= \dfrac{1}{(x - 15)(x - 2)} \cdot \dfrac{(x + 9)(x - 2)}{1} = \dfrac{x + 9}{x - 15}$$

33. $f(-1) = (-1)^3 + 2(-1)^2 - 5(-1) + 4$

$$= -1 + 2(1) + 5 + 4$$

$$= -1 + 2 + 5 + 4 = 10$$

Chapter 9 Review Exercises

1. $\{x | -2 < x \le 3\}$

2. $\{x | -1.5 \le x \le 2\}$

3. $\{x | x > -1\}$

4. $-6x + 3 \le 15$

$$-6x \le 12$$

$$x \ge -2$$

The solution set is $\{x | x \ge -2\}$ or $[2, \infty)$.

5. $6x - 9 \ge -4x - 3$

$$10x - 9 \ge -3$$

$$10x \ge 6$$

$$x \ge \dfrac{6}{10} \text{ or } \dfrac{3}{5}$$

The solution set is $\left\{x \middle| x \ge \dfrac{3}{5}\right\}$ or $\left[\dfrac{3}{5}, \infty\right)$.

6.

$$\frac{x}{3} - \frac{3}{4} - 1 > \frac{x}{2}$$

$$12\left(\frac{x}{3}\right) - 12\left(\frac{3}{4}\right) - 12(1) > 12\left(\frac{x}{2}\right)$$

$$4x - 3(3) - 12 > 6x$$

$$4x - 9 - 12 > 6x$$

$$4x - 21 > 6x$$

$$-2x - 21 > 0$$

$$-2x > 21$$

$$x < -\frac{21}{2}$$

-21/2

The solution set is $\left\{x \middle| x < -\frac{21}{2}\right\}$ or

$\left(-\infty, -\frac{21}{2}\right)$.

7.

$$6x + 5 > -2(x - 3) - 25$$

$$6x + 5 > -2x + 6 - 25$$

$$6x + 5 > -2x - 19$$

$$8x + 5 > -19$$

$$8x > -24$$

$$x > -3$$

-3

The solution set is $\{x | x > -3\}$ or $(-3, \infty)$.

8.

$$3(2x - 1) - 2(x - 4) \geq 7 + 2(3 + 4x)$$

$$6x - 3 - 2x + 8 \geq 7 + 6 + 8x$$

$$4x + 5 \geq 13 + 8x$$

$$-4x + 5 \geq 13$$

$$-4x \geq 8$$

$$x \leq -2$$

-2

The solution set is $\{x | x \leq -2\}$ or

$(-\infty, -2)$.

9. **a.**

$$P(x) = R(x) - C(x)$$

$$= 125x - (40x + 357,000)$$

$$= 125x - 40x - 357,000$$

$$= 85x - 357,000$$

b.

$$P(x) > 0$$

$$85x - 357,000 > 0$$

$$85x > 357,000$$

$$x > 4200$$

More than 4200 units must be sold.

10. $C(x) = 360,000 + 850x$

11. $R(x) = 1150x$

12.

$$P(x) = R(x) - C(x)$$

$$= 1150x - (360,000 + 850x)$$

$$= 1150x - 360,000 - 850x$$

$$= 300x - 360,000$$

13.

$$P(x) > 0$$

$$300x - 360,000 > 0$$

$$300x > 360,000$$

$$x > 1200$$

More than 1200 units must be sold.

14. Let x = the number of checks written per month

$$c_1 = 11 + 0.06x$$

$$c_2 = 4 + 0.20x$$

$$c_1 < c_2$$

$$11 + 0.06x < 4 + 0.20x$$

$$11 - 0.14x < 4$$

$$-0.14x < -7$$

$$x > 50$$

The first method is a better deal when more than 50 checks per month are written.

15. $A \cap B = \{a, c\}$

16. $A \cap C = \{a\}$

17. $A \cup B = \{a,b,c,d,e\}$

18. $A \cup C = \{a,b,c,d,f,g\}$

19. $x \le 3$

$x < 6$

$x \le 3$ and $x < 6$

The solution set is $\{x | x \le 3\}$ or $(-\infty, 3]$.

20. $x \le 3$ or $x < 6$

The solution set is $\{x | x < 6\}$ or $(-\infty, 6)$.

21. $-2x < -12$ and $x - 3 < 5$

$\quad x > 6 \qquad\qquad x < 8$

$x < 8$ and $x > 6$

The solution set is $\{x | 6 < x < 8\}$ or $(6, 8)$.

22. $5x + 3 \le 18$ and $2x - 7 \le -5$

$\quad 5x \le 15 \qquad\qquad 2x \le 2$

$\quad\; x \le 3 \qquad\qquad\; x \le 1$

$x \le 3$ and $x \le 1$

The solution set is $\{x | x \le 1\}$ or $(-\infty, 1]$.

23. $2x - 5 > -1$ and $3x < 3$

$\quad 2x > 4 \qquad\qquad x < 1$

$\quad\; x > 2$

$x > 2$ and $x < 1$

Since the two sets do not intersect, the solution set is $\varnothing$ or $\{\ \ \}$.

24. $2x - 5 > -1$ or $3x < 3$

$\quad 2x > 4 \qquad\qquad x < 1$

$\quad\; x > 2$

$x > 2$ or $x < 1$

The solution set is $\{x | x < 1 \text{ or } x > 2\}$ or $(-\infty, 1) \cup (2, \infty)$.

25. $x + 1 \le -3$ or $-4x + 3 < -5$

$\quad\; x \le -4 \qquad\qquad -4x < -8$

$\qquad\qquad\qquad\qquad\quad x > 2$

$x \le -4$ or $x > 2$

The solution set is $\{x | x \le -4 \text{ and } x > 2\}$ or $(-\infty, -4] \cup (2, \infty)$.

26. $5x - 2 \le -22$ or $-3x - 2 > 4$

$\quad\; 5x \le -20 \qquad\qquad -3x > 6$

$\quad\;\; x \le -4 \qquad\qquad\quad x < -2$

$x \le -4$ or $x < -2$

The solution set is $\{x | x < -2\}$ or $(-\infty, -2)$.

27. $5x + 4 \ge -11$ or $1 - 4x \ge 9$

$\quad\; 5x \ge -15 \qquad\qquad -4x \ge 8$

$\quad\;\; x \ge -3 \qquad\qquad\quad x \le -2$

$x \ge -3$ or $x \le -2$

The solution set is $\mathbb{R}$, $(-\infty, \infty)$ or $\{x | x \text{ is a real number}\}$.

28. $-3 < x + 2 \le 4$

$\quad -5 < x \le 2$

The solution set is $\{x | -5 < x \le 2\}$ or $(-5, 2]$.

29. $-1 \le 4x + 2 \le 6$

$-3 \le 4x \le 4$

$-\dfrac{3}{4} \le x \le 1$

-3/4   1

The solution set is $\left\{ x \middle| -\dfrac{3}{4} \le x \le 1 \right\}$ or

$\left[-\dfrac{3}{4}, 1 \right]$.

30. Let $x =$ the grade on the fifth exam

$80 \le \dfrac{72 + 73 + 94 + 80 + x}{5} < 90$

$80 \le \dfrac{319 + x}{5} < 90$

$400 \le 319 + x < 450$

$81 \le x < 131$

You need to score at least 81 and less than 131 on the exam to receive a B. In interval notation, the range is $[81, 131)$.

31. $|2x + 1| = 7$

$2x + 1 = 7$ or $2x + 1 = -7$

$2x = 6$ $2x = -8$

$x = 3$ $x = -4$

32. $|3x + 2| = -5$

There are no values of x for which the absolute value of $3x + 2$ is a negative number. By definition, absolute values are always positive. The solution set is $\varnothing$ or $\{\ \}$.

33. $2|x - 3| - 7 = 10$

$2|x - 3| = 17$

$|x - 3| = 8.5$

$x - 3 = 8.5$ or $x - 3 = -8.5$

$x = 11.5$ $x = -5.5$

34. $|4x - 3| = |7x + 9|$

$4x - 3 = 7x + 9$ or $4x - 3 = -7x - 9$

$-3x - 3 = 9$ $11x - 3 = -9$

$-3x = 12$ $11x = -6$

$x = -4$ $x = -\dfrac{6}{11}$

35. $|2x + 3| \le 15$

$-15 \le 2x + 3 \le 15$

$-18 \le 2x \le 12$

$-9 \le x \le 6$

-9   6

The solution set is $\{x | -9 \le x \le 6\}$ or $[-9, 6]$.

36. $\left| \dfrac{2x + 6}{3} \right| > 2$

$\dfrac{2x + 6}{3} < -2$ or $\dfrac{2x + 6}{3} > 2$

$2x + 6 < -6$ $2x + 6 > 6$

$2x < -12$ $2x > 0$

$x < -6$ $x > 0$

-6   0

The solution set is $\{x | x < -6 \text{ or } x > 0\}$ or $(-\infty, -6) \cup (0, \infty)$.

37. $|2x + 5| - 7 < -6$

$|2x + 5| < 1$

$-1 < 2x + 5 < 1$

$-6 < 2x < -4$

$-3 < x < -2$

-3   -2

The solution set is $\{x | -3 < x < -2\}$ or $(-3, -2)$.

38. $|2x - 3| + 4 = -10$

$|2x - 3| = -14$

There are no values of x for which the absolute value of $2x - 3$ is a negative number. By definition, absolute values are always positive. The solution set is $\varnothing$ or $\{\ \}$.

39.   Answers may vary.

40. $3x - 4y > 12$
Graph the line, $3x - 4y = 12$.

$x - \text{intercept}$ $y - \text{intercept}$

$3x - 4(0) = 12$ $3(0) - 4y = 12$

$\qquad 3x = 12$ $\qquad -4y = 12$

$\qquad\ x = 4$ $\qquad\quad y = -3$

Use a test point to determine shading.

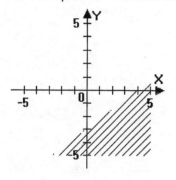

41. $x - 3y \leq 6$
Graph the line, $x - 3y = 6$.

$x - \text{intercept}$ $y - \text{intercept}$

$x - 3(0) = 6$ $0 - 3y = 6$

$\qquad x = 6$ $\qquad -3y = 6$

$\qquad\qquad\qquad\qquad\quad y = -2$

Use a test point to determine shading.

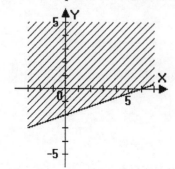

42.
$$y \leq -\frac{1}{2}x + 2$$

Graph the line, $y = -\dfrac{1}{2}x + 2$.

$y\text{–intercept} = 2$ $m = -\dfrac{1}{2}$

Use a test point to determine shading.

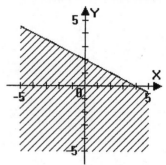

43.
$$y > \frac{3}{5}x$$

Graph the line, $y = \dfrac{3}{5}x$.

$y\text{–intercept} = 0$ $m = \dfrac{3}{5}$

Use a test point to determine shading.

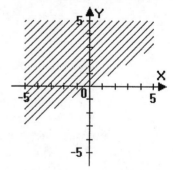

44. $x \leq 2$
Graph the line, $x = 2$. This is the vertical line positioned at 2.
Use a test point to determine shading.

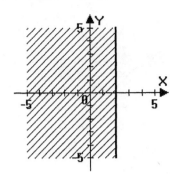

45. $y > -3$

Graph the line, $y = -3$. This is the horizontal line positioned at -3. Use a test point to determine shading.

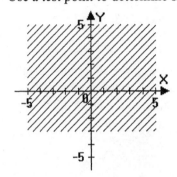

46. $3x - y \leq 6 \qquad x + y \geq 2$

Graph the corresponding lines.

$3x - y = 6 \qquad\qquad x + y = 2$

$-y = -3x + 6 \qquad\qquad y = -x + 2$

$y = 3x - 6 \qquad\qquad y\text{-intercept} = 2$

$y\text{-intercept} = -6 \qquad\qquad m = -1$

$m = 3$

Use test points to determine shading. The solution to the system is the intersection of the shaded half-planes.

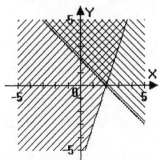

47. $y < -x + 4 \qquad y > x - 4$

Graph the corresponding lines.

$y = -x + 4 \qquad\qquad y = x - 4$

$y\text{-intercept} = 4 \qquad\qquad y\text{-intercept} = -4$

$m = -1 \qquad\qquad m = 1$

Use test points to determine shading. The solution to the system is the intersection of the shaded half-planes.

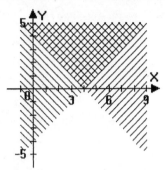

48. $-3 \leq x < 5$

Rewrite the three part inequality as two separate inequalities. We have $-3 \leq x$ and $x < 5$. Graph the corresponding lines, $-3 = x$ and $x = 5$. These are vertical lines positioned at -3 and 5. The shading will be between $x = -3$ and $x = 5$. The solution to the system is the intersection of the shaded half-planes.

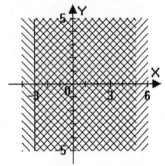

49. $-2 < y \leq 6$

Rewrite the three part inequality as two separate inequalities. We have $-2 < y$ and $y \leq 6$. Graph the corresponding lines, $-2 = y$ and $y = 6$. These are horizontal lines positioned at -2 and 6. The shading will be between $y = -2$ and

$y = 6$. The solution to the system is the intersection of the shaded half-planes.

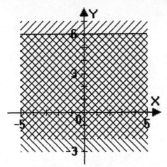

50. $x \geq 3$ $y \leq 0$

Graph the corresponding lines.
$x = 3$ is the vertical line positioned at 3.
$y = 0$ is the equation of the x–axis. Use test points to determine shading. The solution to the system is the intersection of the shaded half-planes.

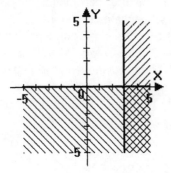

51. $2x - y > -4$ $x \geq 0$

Graph the corresponding lines.

$2x - y = -4$	$x = 0$
$-y = -2x - 4$	vertical line
$y = 2x + 4$	

y-intercept $= 4$
$m = 2$

Use test points to determine shading. The solution to the system is the intersection of the shaded half-planes.

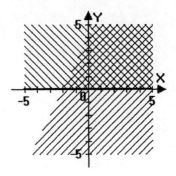

52. $x + y \leq 6$ $y \geq 2x - 3$

Graph the corresponding lines.

$x + y = 6$	$y = 2x - 3$
$y = -x + 6$	y-intercept $= -3$
y-intercept $= 6$	$m = 2$
$m = -1$	

Use test points to determine shading. The solution to the system is the intersection of the shaded half-planes.

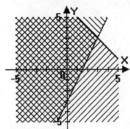

53. $3x + 2y \geq 4$ $x - y \leq 3$

        $x \geq 0$ $y \geq 0$

Graph the corresponding lines.

$3x + 2y = 4$	$x - y = 3$
$2y = -3x + 4$	$-y = -x + 3$
$y = -\dfrac{3}{2}x + 2$	$y = x - 3$

y-intercept $= 2$	y-intercept $= -3$
$m = -\dfrac{3}{2}$	$m = 1$

Use test points to determine shading. The solution to the system is the intersection of the shaded half-planes.

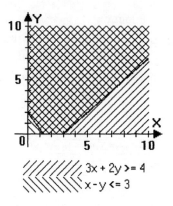

$3x + 2y >= 4$
$x - y <= 3$

54. $2x - y > 2$ $2x - y < -2$

Graph the corresponding lines.

$2x - y = 2$	$2x - y = -2$
$-y = -2x + 2$	$-y = -2x - 2$
$y = 2x - 2$	$y = 2x + 2$
y-intercept $= -2$	y-intercept $= 2$
$m = 2$	$m = 2$

Use test points to determine shading. The solution to the system is the intersection of the shaded half-planes.

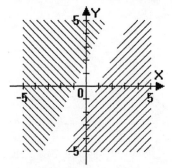

The graphs of the inequalities do not intersect, so there is no solution. The solution set is $\varnothing$ or $\{\ \}$.

55.

Corner (x, y)	Objective Function $z = 2x + 3y$
$(1, 0)$	$z = 2(1) + 3(0) = 2$
$(4, 0)$	$z = 2(4) + 3(0) = 8$
$(2, 2)$	$z = 2(2) + 3(2) = 4 + 6 = 10$

$\left(\dfrac{1}{2}, \dfrac{1}{2}\right)$	$z = 2\left(\dfrac{1}{2}\right) + 3\left(\dfrac{1}{2}\right) = \dfrac{2}{2} + \dfrac{3}{2} = \dfrac{5}{2}$

The maximum value is 10 and the minimum is 2.

56.   Objective Function: $z = 2x + 3y$

Constraints: $x \ge 0, \quad y \ge 0$

$x + y \le 8$

$3x + 2y \ge 6$

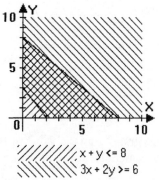

$x + y <= 8$
$3x + 2y >= 6$

Using the graph, find the value of the objective function at each of the corner points.

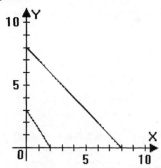

Corner (x, y)	Objective Function $z = 2x + 3y$
$(2, 0)$	$z = 2(2) + 3(0) = 4$
$(8, 0)$	$z = 2(8) + 3(0) = 16$
$(0, 8)$	$z = 2(0) + 3(8) = 24$
$(0, 3)$	$z = 2(0) + 3(3) = 9$

The maximum of 24 occurs at the point $(0, 8)$.

57. Objective Function: $z = x + 4y$

Constraints: $0 \le x \le 5$

$0 \le y \le 7$

$x + y \ge 3$

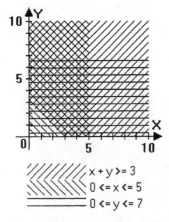

Using the graph, find the value of the objective function at each of the corner points.

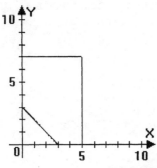

Corner (x, y)	Objective Function $z = x + 4y$
$(3, 0)$	$z = 3 + 4(0) = 3$
$(5, 0)$	$z = 5 + 4(0) = 5$
$(5, 7)$	$z = 5 + 4(7) = 5 + 28 = 33$
$(0, 7)$	$z = 0 + 4(7) = 28$
$(0, 3)$	$z = 0 + 4(3) = 12$

The maximum of 33 occurs at the point $(5, 7)$.

58. Objective Function: $z = 5x + 6y$

Constraints: $x \ge 0,\ \ y \ge 0$

$y \le x$

$2x + y \le 12$

$2x + 3y \ge 6$

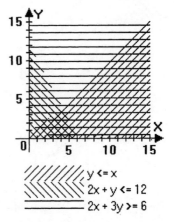

Using the graph, find the value of the objective function at each of the corner points.

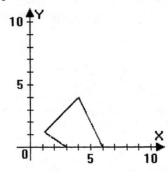

Corner (x, y)	Objective Function $z = 5x + 6y$
$(3, 0)$	$z = 5(3) + 6(0) = 15$
$(6, 0)$	$z = 5(6) + 6(0) = 30$
$(4, 4)$	$z = 5(4) + 6(4)$ $= 20 + 24 = 44$
$(1.2, 1.2)$	$z = 5(1.2) + 6(1.2)$ $= 6 + 7.2 = 13.2$

The maximum of 44 occurs at the point $(4, 4)$.

59. **a.** The objective function is
$z = 500x + 350y$.

b. $x + y \leq 200$

$x \geq 10$

$y \geq 80$

c.

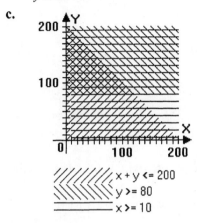

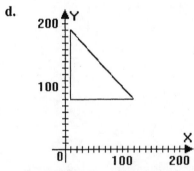

Corner (x, y)	Objective Function $z = 500x + 350y$
(10, 80)	$z = 500(10) + 350(80)$ $= 5000 + 28000 = 33000$
(120, 80)	$z = 500(120) + 350(80)$ $= 60000 + 28000 = 88000$
(10, 190)	$z = 500(10) + 350(190)$ $= 5000 + 66500 = 71500$

e. The company will make the greatest profit by producing <u>120</u> units of writing paper and <u>80</u> units of newsprint each day. The maximum daily profit is $<u>88,000</u>.

60. Let x = the number of model A
Let y = the number of model B

$z = 25x + 40y$

$0.9x + 1.8y \leq 864$

$0.8x + 1.2y \leq 672$

We also know that x and y are either zero or a positive number.

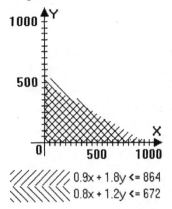

Using the graph, find the value of the objective function at each of the corner points.

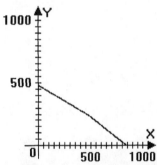

Corner (x, y)	Objective Function $z = 25x + 40y$
(0, 0)	$z = 25(0) + 40(0) = 0$
(840, 0)	$z = 25(840) + 40(0) = 21000$
(480, 240)	$z = 25(480) + 40(240)$ $= 12000 + 9600 = 21600$
(0, 480)	$z = 25(0) + 40(480) = 19200$

The maximum of 21,600 occurs at the point (480, 240). In order to maximize profit, 480 of model A and 240 of model B should be manufactured monthly for a profit of $21,600.

Chapter 9 Test

1. $\{x|-3 \le x < 2\}$

-3   2

2. $\{x|x \le -1\}$

-1

3.
$$3(x+4) \ge 5x - 12$$
$$3x + 12 \ge 5x - 12$$
$$-2x + 12 \ge -12$$
$$-2x \ge -24$$
$$x \le 12$$

12

The solution set is $\{x|x \le 12\}$ or $(-\infty, 12]$.

4.
$$\frac{x}{6} + \frac{1}{8} \le \frac{x}{2} - \frac{3}{4}$$
$$24\left(\frac{x}{6}\right) + 24\left(\frac{1}{8}\right) \le 24\left(\frac{x}{2}\right) - 24\left(\frac{3}{4}\right)$$
$$4x + 3 \le 12x - 6(3)$$
$$4x + 3 \le 12x - 18$$
$$-8x + 3 \le -18$$
$$-8x \le -21$$
$$x \ge \frac{21}{8}$$

21/8

The solution set is $\left\{x \middle| x \ge \frac{21}{8}\right\}$ or $\left[\frac{21}{8}, \infty\right)$.

5. **a.** $C(x) = 60,000 + 200x$

   b. $R(x) = 450x$

c.
$$P(x) = R(x) - C(x)$$
$$= 450x - (60,000 + 200x)$$
$$= 450x - 60,000 - 200x$$
$$= 250x - 60,000$$

d.
$$P(x) > 0$$
$$250x - 60,000 > 0$$
$$250x > 60,000$$
$$x > 240$$
More than 240 desks must be produced and sold.

6. $\{2,4,6,8,10\} \cap \{4,6,12,14\} = \{4,6\}$

7. $\{2,4,6,8,10\} \cup \{4,6,12,14\}$
$$= \{2,4,6,8,10,12,14\}$$

8. $2x + 4 < 2$ and $x - 3 > -5$
        $2x < -2$ $x > -2$
        $x < -1$

$x < -1$ and $x > -2$

-2   -1

The solution set is $\{x|-2 < x < -1\}$ or $(-2, -1)$.

9. $x + 6 \ge 4$ and $2x + 3 \ge -2$
        $x \ge -2$ $2x \ge -5$
                                $x \ge -\frac{5}{2}$

$x \ge -2$ and $x \ge -\frac{5}{2}$

-5/2   -2

The solution set is $\{x|x \ge -2\}$ or $[-2, \infty)$.

10. $2x - 3 < 5$ or $3x - 6 \le 4$
         $2x < 8$ $3x \le 10$
         $x < 4$ $x \le \frac{10}{3}$

$x < 4$ or $x \le \dfrac{10}{3}$ ←|————→ 10/3 4

The solution set is $\{x \mid x < 4\}$ or $(-\infty, 4)$.

11. $x + 3 \le -1$ or $-4x + 3 < -5$

$\qquad x \le -4 \qquad\qquad -4x < -8$

$\qquad\qquad\qquad\qquad\qquad x > 2$

$x \le -4$ or $x > 2$ ←|——(→ -4 2

The solution set is $\{x \mid x \le -4 \text{ or } x > 2\}$

or $(-\infty, -4] \cup (2, \infty)$.

12.

$-3 \le \dfrac{2x + 5}{3} < 6$

$3(-3) \le 3\left(\dfrac{2x + 5}{3}\right) < 3(6)$

$-9 \le 2x + 5 < 18$

$-14 \le 2x < 13$

$-7 \le x < \dfrac{13}{2}$ ←(——)→ -7 13/2

The solution set is $\left\{x \mid -7 \le x < \dfrac{13}{2}\right\}$ or

$\left[-7, \dfrac{13}{2}\right)$.

13. $|5x + 3| = 7$

$5x + 3 = 7$ or $5x + 3 = -7$

$5x = 4 \qquad\qquad 5x = -10$

$x = \dfrac{4}{5} \qquad\qquad x = -2$

14. $|6x + 1| = |4x + 15|$

$6x + 1 = 4x + 15$ or $6x + 1 = -(4x + 15)$

$2x + 1 = 15 \qquad\qquad 6x + 1 = -4x - 15$

$2x = 14 \qquad\qquad 10x + 1 = -15$

$x = 7 \qquad\qquad 10x = -16$

$\qquad\qquad\qquad x = -\dfrac{16}{10} = -\dfrac{8}{5}$

15. $|2x - 1| < 7$

$-7 < 2x - 1 < 7$

$-6 < 2x < 8$

$-3 < x < 4$ ←(——)→ -3 4

The solution set is $\{x \mid -3 < x < 4\}$ or

$(-3, 4)$.

16. $|2x - 3| \ge 5$

$2x - 3 \le -5$ or $2x - 3 \ge 5$

$2x \le -2 \qquad\qquad 2x \ge 8$

$x \le -1 \qquad\qquad x \ge 4$

←|——|→ -1 4

The solution set is $\{x \mid x \le -1 \text{ or } x \ge 4\}$ or

$(-\infty, -1] \cup [4, \infty)$.

17.

$|T - 74| \le 8$

$-8 \le T - 74 \le 8$

$66 \le T \le 82$

The monthly average temperature for Miami, Florida is between 66°F and 82°F, inclusive.

18. $3x - 2y < 6$

Graph the corresponding line,

$3x - 2y = 6$.

x – intercept	y – intercept
$3x - 2(0) = 6$	$3(0) - 2y = 6$
$3x = 6$	$-2y = 6$
$x = 2$	$y = -3$

Use a test point to determine shading.

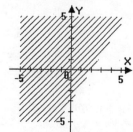

19.

$$y \geq \frac{1}{2}x - 1$$

Graph the corresponding line.

$$y = \frac{1}{2}x - 1$$

y-intercept $= -1$ slope $= \dfrac{1}{2}$

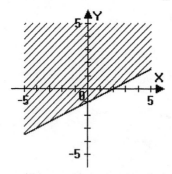

20. $y \leq -1$

Graph the corresponding line, $y = -1$.
This is the horizontal line positioned at
-1. Use a test point to determine
shading.

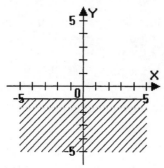

21. $x + y \geq 2$

$x - y \geq 4$

Graph the corresponding lines.

$x + y = 2$ $x - y = 4$

$y = -x + 2$ $-y = -x + 4$

y-intercept $= 2$ $y = x - 4$

$m = -1$ y-intercept $= -4$

$m = 1$

Use test points to determine shading.
The solution to the system is the
intersection of the shaded half-planes.

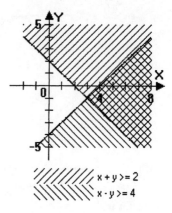

$x + y >= 2$
$x - y >= 4$

22. $3x + y \leq 9$ $2x + 3y \geq 6$

$x \geq 0$ $y \geq 0$

Graph the corresponding lines.

$3x + y = 9$ $2x + 3y = 6$

$y = -3x + 9$ $3y = -2x + 6$

y-intercept $= 9$

$m = -3$ $y = -\dfrac{2}{3}x + 2$

y-intercept $= 2$

$m = -\dfrac{2}{3}$

Since $x \geq 0$ and $y \geq 0$, we know x and y
are both positive and are only concerned
with the first quadrant.
Use test points to determine shading.
The solution to the system is the
intersection of the shaded half-planes.

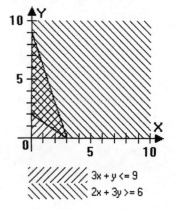

$3x + y <= 9$
$2x + 3y >= 6$

23. $-2 < x \leq 4$

Rewrite the three part inequality as
$-2 < x$ and $x \leq 4$. Graph the

corresponding lines, $-2 = x$ and $x = 4$.
These are the vertical lines positioned at
-2 and 4. Use a test point to determine
shading.

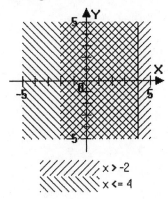

24. Objective Function: $z = 3x + 5y$
    Constraints: $x \geq 0$, $y \geq 0$
    $\qquad\qquad\qquad x + y \leq 6$
    $\qquad\qquad\qquad x \geq 2$

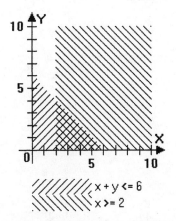

Using the graph, find the value of the
objective function at each of the corner
points.

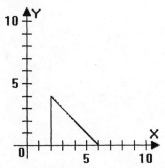

Corner (x, y)	Objective Function $z = 3x + 5y$
$(2, 0)$	$z = 3(2) + 5(0) = 6$
$(6, 0)$	$z = 3(6) + 5(0) = 18$
$(2, 4)$	$z = 3(2) + 5(4) = 6 + 20 = 26$

The maximum of 26 occurs at the point
$(2, 4)$.

25. Let x = the number of regular jet skis
    Let y = the number of deluxe jet skis
    $z = 200x + 250y$
    $x \geq 50$
    $y \geq 75$
    $x + y \leq 150$

    We also know that x and y are either zero
    or positive, since a negative number of
    units cannot be produced.

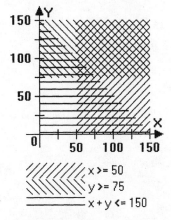

Using the graph, find the value of the
objective function at each of the corner
points.

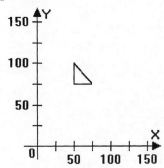

Corner (x, y)	Objective Function $z = 200x + 250y$
(50, 75)	$z = 200(50) + 250(75)$
	$= 10000 + 18750 = 28750$
(75, 75)	$z = 200(75) + 250(75)$
	$= 15000 + 18750 = 33750$
(50, 100)	$z = 200(50) + 250(100)$
	$= 10000 + 25000 = 35000$

The maximum of 35,000 occurs at the point (50, 100). In order to maximize profit at $35,000, 50 regular jet skis and 100 deluxe jet skis should be manufactured weekly.

Cumulative Review Exercises Chapters 1 -9

1. $5(x+1) + 2 = x - 3(2x+1)$

$5x + 5 + 2 = x - 6x - 3$

$5x + 7 = -5x - 3$

$10x + 7 = -3$

$10x = -10$

$x = -1$

2. $\dfrac{2(x+6)}{3} = 1 + \dfrac{4x-7}{3}$

$3\left(\dfrac{2(x+6)}{3}\right) = 3(1) + 3\left(\dfrac{4x-7}{3}\right)$

$2(x+6) = 3 + 4x - 7$

$2x + 12 = 4x - 4$

$-2x + 12 = -4$

$-2x = -16$

$x = 8$

3. $\dfrac{-10x^2 y^4}{15x^7 y^{-3}} = \dfrac{-10}{15} x^{2-7} y^{4-(-3)}$

$= -\dfrac{2}{3} x^{-5} y^7 = -\dfrac{2y^7}{3x^5}$

4. $f(-3) = (-3)^2 - 3(-3) + 4$

$= 9 + 9 + 4 = 22$

$f(2a) = (2a)^2 - 3(2a) + 4$

$= 4a^2 - 6a + 4$

5. $(f - g)(x) = f(x) - g(x)$

$= (3x^2 - 4x + 1) - (x^2 - 5x - 1)$

$= 3x^2 - 4x + 1 - x^2 + 5x + 1$

$= 2x^2 + x + 2$

$(f - g)(2) = 2(2)^2 + 2 + 2$

$= 2(4) + 2 + 2$

$= 8 + 2 + 2 = 12$

6. $y = 2x - 3$

$m = 2$

The slope of the line perpendicular to this line is $m = -\dfrac{1}{2}$.

point-slope form:

$y - 3 = -\dfrac{1}{2}(x - 2)$

slope-intercept form:

$y - 3 = -\dfrac{1}{2}x + 1$

$y = -\dfrac{1}{2}x + 4$

$f(x) = -\dfrac{1}{2}x + 4$

7. $y = 2x + 1$

$\begin{array}{ll} x - \text{intercept} & y - \text{intercept} \\ \;\;0 = 2x + 1 & y = 2(0) + 1 \\ -1 = 2x & y = 1 \\ -\dfrac{1}{2} = x & \end{array}$

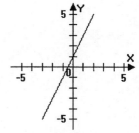

8. $y > 2x$
Graph the corresponding line.
$y = 2x$
$m = 2 \qquad y\text{–intercept} = 0$
Use a test point to determine shading.

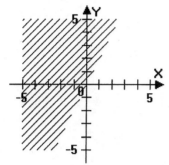

9. $2x - y \geq 6$
Graph the corresponding line.
$2x - y = 6$
$x\text{–intercept} = 3$
$y\text{–intercept} = -6$
Use a test point to determine shading.

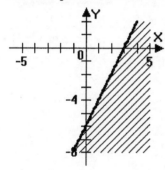

10. $f(x) = -1$ or $y = -1$
This is the horizontal line at $y = -1$.

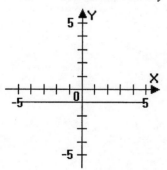

11. Add the first two equations to eliminate z.
$$3x - y + z = -15$$
$$\underline{x + 2y - z = \quad 1}$$
$$4x + y = -14$$
Multiply the first equation by 2 and add to the third equation.
$$6x - 2y + 2z = -30$$
$$\underline{2x + 3y - 2z = \quad 0}$$
$$8x + y = -30$$
The system of two equations in two variables becomes is as follows.
$$4x + y = -14$$
$$8x + y = -30$$
Multiply the first equation by -1 and add to the second equation.
$$-4x - y = \quad 14$$
$$\underline{8x + y = -30}$$
$$4x = -16$$
$$x = -4$$
Back-substitute -4 for x to find y.
$$4(-4) + y = -14$$
$$-16 + y = -14$$
$$y = 2$$
Back-substitute 2 for y and -4 for x to find z.
$$3(-4) - 2 + z = -15$$
$$-12 - 2 + z = -15$$
$$-14 + z = -15$$
$$z = -1$$
The solution is $(-4, 2, -1)$.

12. $\begin{bmatrix} 2 & -1 & | & -4 \\ 1 & 3 & | & 5 \end{bmatrix} \quad R_1 \leftrightarrow R_2$
$= \begin{bmatrix} 1 & 3 & | & 5 \\ 2 & -1 & | & -4 \end{bmatrix} \quad -2R_1 + R_2$
$= \begin{bmatrix} 1 & 3 & | & 5 \\ 0 & -7 & | & -14 \end{bmatrix} \quad -\frac{1}{7}R_2$
$= \begin{bmatrix} 1 & 3 & | & 5 \\ 0 & 1 & | & 2 \end{bmatrix}$

$x + 3y = 5$

$y = 2$

Back-substitute 2 for y to find x.

$x + 3(2) = 5$

$x + 6 = 5$

$x = -1$

The solution is $(-1, 2)$.

13. $\begin{vmatrix} 4 & 3 \\ -1 & -5 \end{vmatrix} = 4(-5) - (-1)3 = -20 + 3 = -17$

14. Let x = the number of rooms with a kitchen
Let y = the number of rooms without a kitchen

$x + y = 60$

$90x + 80y = 5260$

Solve the first equation for y.

$x + y = 60$

$y = 60 - x$

Substitute $60 - x$ for y to find x.

$90x + 80(60 - x) = 5260$

$90x + 4800 - 80x = 5260$

$10x + 4800 = 5260$

$10x = 460$

$x = 46$

Back-substitute 46 for x to find y.

$y = 60 - x = 60 - 46 = 14$

There are 46 rooms with kitchens and 14 rooms without kitchens.

15. Using the vertical line test, we see that graphs **a.** and **b.** are functions.

16.

$$\frac{x}{4} - \frac{3}{4} - 1 \le \frac{x}{2}$$

$$4\left(\frac{x}{4}\right) - 4\left(\frac{3}{4}\right) - 4(1) \le 4\left(\frac{x}{2}\right)$$

$$x - 3 - 4 \le 2x$$

$$x - 7 \le 2x$$

$$x \le 2x + 7$$

$$-x \le 7$$

$$x \ge -7$$

The solution set is $\{x \mid x \ge -7\}$ or $(-7, \infty)$.

17. $2x + 5 \le 11$ and $-3x > 18$

$2x \le 6$ $x < -6$

$x \le 3$

$x \le 3$ and $x < -6$

The solution set is $\{x \mid x < -6\}$ or $(-\infty, -6)$.

18. $x - 4 \ge 1$ or $-3x + 1 \ge -5 - x$

$x \ge 5$ $-2x + 1 \ge -5$

$-2x \ge -6$

$x \le 3$

$x \ge 5$ or $x \le 3$

The solution set is $\{x \mid x \le 3 \text{ or } x \ge 5\}$ or $(-\infty, 3] \cup [5, \infty)$.

19. $|2x + 3| \le 17$

$-17 \le 2x + 3 \le 17$

$-20 \le 2x \le 14$

$-10 \le x \le 7$

The solution set is $\{x \mid -10 \le x \le 7\}$ or $[-10, 7]$.

20. $|3x - 8| > 7$

$3x - 8 < -7$ or $3x - 8 > 7$

$3x < 1$ $3x > 15$

$x < \dfrac{1}{3}$ $x > 5$

$x < \dfrac{1}{3}$ or $x > 5$

The solution set is $\left\{ x \,\middle|\, x < \dfrac{1}{3} \text{ or } x > 5 \right\}$ or

$\left(-\infty, \dfrac{1}{3} \right) \cup \left(5, \infty \right)$.

RADICALS, RADICAL FUNCTIONS, AND RATIONAL EXPONENTS

Radical Expressions and Functions

10.1 CHECK POINTS

CHECK POINT 1

a. $\sqrt{64} = 8$

b. $-\sqrt{49} = -7$

c. $\sqrt{\dfrac{16}{25}} = \dfrac{4}{5}$

d. $\sqrt{0.0081} = 0.09$

e. $\sqrt{9+16} = \sqrt{25} = 5$

f. $\sqrt{9} + \sqrt{16} = 3 + 4 = 7$

CHECK POINT 2

a. $f(3) = \sqrt{12(3)-20} = \sqrt{36-20} = \sqrt{16} = 4$

b. $g(-5) = -\sqrt{9-3(-5)} = -\sqrt{9+15}$
$= -\sqrt{24} \approx -4.90$

CHECK POINT 3
$9x - 27 \geq 0$
$9x \geq 27$
$x \geq 3$
The domain of f is $\{x | x \geq 3\}$ or $[3, \infty)$.

CHECK POINT 4
$f(4) = 6.75\sqrt{4} + 12 = 6.75(2) + 12$
$= 13.5 + 12 = 25.5$
The amount of new student loans is $25.5 billion. The model describes the data very well.

CHECK POINT 5

a. $\sqrt{(-7)^2} = |-7| = 7$

b. $\sqrt{(x+8)^2} = |x+8|$

c. $\sqrt{49x^{10}} = \sqrt{(7x^5)^2} = |7x^5|$

d. $\sqrt{x^2 - 6x + 9} = \sqrt{(x-3)^2} = |x-3|$

CHECK POINT 6

a. $f(33) = \sqrt[3]{33-6} = \sqrt[3]{27} = 3$

b. $g(-5) = \sqrt[3]{2(-5)+2} = \sqrt[3]{-10+2} = \sqrt[3]{-8} = -2$

CHECK POINT 7
$\sqrt[3]{-27x^3} = \sqrt[3]{(-3x)^3} = -3x$

CHECK POINT 8

a. $\sqrt[4]{16} = \sqrt[4]{2^4} = 2$

b. $-\sqrt[4]{16} = -\sqrt[4]{2^4} = -2$

c. $\sqrt[4]{-16}$ is not a real number. The index is even and the radicand is negative.

d. $\sqrt[5]{-1} = \sqrt[5]{(-1)^5} = -1$

CHECK POINT 9

a. $\sqrt[4]{(x+6)^4} = \sqrt[4]{(x+6)^4} = |x+6|$

b. $\sqrt[5]{(3x-2)^5} = \sqrt[5]{(3x-2)^5} = 3x-2$

c. $\sqrt[6]{(-8)^6} = |-8| = 8$

EXERCISE SET 10.1

1. $\sqrt{36} = 6$ because $6^2 = 36$

3. $-\sqrt{36} = -6$ because $6^2 = 36$

5. $\sqrt{-36}$
Not a real number

7. $\sqrt{\dfrac{1}{25}} = \dfrac{1}{5}$ because $\left(\dfrac{1}{5}\right)^2 = \dfrac{1}{25}$

9. $-\sqrt{0.04} = -0.2$ because $(0.2)^2 = 0.04$

11. $\sqrt{25-16} = \sqrt{9} = 3$

13. $\sqrt{25} - \sqrt{16} = 5 - 4 = 1$

15. $\sqrt{16-25} = \sqrt{-9}$ Not a real number

17. $f(18) = \sqrt{18-2} = \sqrt{16} = 4$
$f(3) = \sqrt{3-2} = \sqrt{1} = 1$
$f(2) = \sqrt{2-2} = \sqrt{0} = 0$
$f(-2) = \sqrt{-2-2} = \sqrt{-4}$
Not a real number

19. $g(11) = -\sqrt{2(11)+3} = -\sqrt{22+3}$
$\qquad = -\sqrt{25} = -5$
$g(1) = -\sqrt{2(1)+3} = -\sqrt{2+3}$
$\qquad = -\sqrt{5} \approx -2.24$
$g(-1) = -\sqrt{2(-1)+3} = -\sqrt{-2+3}$
$\qquad = -\sqrt{1} = -1$
$g(-2) = -\sqrt{2(-2)+3} = -\sqrt{-4+3} = -\sqrt{-1}$
$\qquad$ Not a real number

21. $h(5) = \sqrt{(5-1)^2} = \sqrt{(4)^2} = |4| = 4$
$h(3) = \sqrt{(3-1)^2} = \sqrt{(2)^2} = |2| = 2$
$h(0) = \sqrt{(0-1)^2} = \sqrt{(-1)^2} = |-1| = 1$
$h(-5) = \sqrt{(-5-1)^2} = \sqrt{(-6)^2} = |-6| = 6$

23. $x-3 \geq 0$
$\quad x \geq 3$
The domain of f is $\{x | x \geq 3\}$ or $[3,\infty)$.
This corresponds to graph (**c**).

25. $3x+15 \geq 0$
$\quad 3x \geq -15$
$\quad\; x \geq -5$

The domain of f is $\{x | x \geq -5\}$ or $[-5,\infty)$.
This corresponds to graph (**d**).

27. $6-2x \geq 0$
$\quad -2x \geq -6$
$\qquad x \leq 3$
The domain of f is $\{x | x \leq 3\}$ or $(-\infty,3]$.
This corresponds to graph (**e**).

29. $\sqrt{5^2} = 5$

31. $\sqrt{(-4)^2} = |-4| = 4$

33. $\sqrt{(x-1)^2} = |x-1|$

35. $\sqrt{36x^4} = \sqrt{(6x^2)^2} = |6x^2| = 6x^2$

37. $-\sqrt{100x^6} = -\sqrt{(10x^3)^2} = -|10x^3| = -10|x^3|$

39. $\sqrt{x^2+12x+36} = \sqrt{(x+6)^2} = |x+6|$

41. $-\sqrt{x^2-8x+16} = -\sqrt{(x-4)^2} = -|x-4|$

43. $\sqrt[3]{27} = 3$ because $3^3 = 27$

45. $\sqrt[3]{-27} = -3$ because $(-3)^3 = -27$

47. $\sqrt[3]{\dfrac{1}{125}} = \dfrac{1}{5}$ because $\left(\dfrac{1}{5}\right)^3 = \dfrac{1}{125}$

49. $f(28) = \sqrt[3]{28-1} = \sqrt[3]{27} = 3$
$f(9) = \sqrt[3]{9-1} = \sqrt[3]{8} = 2$
$f(0) = \sqrt[3]{0-1} = \sqrt[3]{-1} = -1$
$f(-63) = \sqrt[3]{-63-1} = \sqrt[3]{-64} = -4$

51. $g(2) = -\sqrt[3]{8(2)-8} = -\sqrt[3]{16-8} = -\sqrt[3]{8} = -2$

$$g(1) = -\sqrt[3]{8(1)-8} = -\sqrt[3]{8-8} = -\sqrt[3]{0} = 0$$

$$g(0) = -\sqrt[3]{8(0)-8} = -\sqrt[3]{-8} = -(-2) = 2$$

53. $\sqrt[4]{1} = 1$ because $1^4 = 1$

55. $\sqrt[4]{16} = 2$ because $2^4 = 16$

57. $-\sqrt[4]{16} = -2$ because $2^4 = 16$

59. $\sqrt[4]{-16}$ Not a real number

61. $\sqrt[5]{-1} = -1$ because $(-1)^5 = -1$

63. $\sqrt[6]{-1}$ Not a real number

65. $-\sqrt[4]{256} = -4$ because $4^4 = 256$

67. $\sqrt[6]{64} = 2$ because $2^6 = 64$

69. $-\sqrt[5]{32} = -2$ because $2^5 = 32$

71. $\sqrt[3]{x^3} = x$

73. $\sqrt[4]{y^4} = |y|$

75. $\sqrt[3]{-8x^3} = -2x$

77. $\sqrt[3]{(-5)^3} = -5$

79. $\sqrt[4]{(-5)^4} = |-5| = 5$

81. $\sqrt[4]{(x+3)^4} = |x+3|$

83. $\sqrt[5]{-32(x-1)^5} = -2(x-1)$

85. $f(48) = 2.9\sqrt{48} + 20.1 = 2.9(6.9) + 20.1$
$$= 20.1 + 20.1 \approx 40.2$$

The model predicts the median height of boys who are 48 months old to be 40.1 inches. The model predicts the median height very well. According to the table, the median height is 40.8.

87. $f(245) = \sqrt{20(245)} = \sqrt{4900} = 70$

The officer should not believe the motorist. The model predicts that the motorist's speed was 70 miles per hour. This is well above the 50 miles per hour speed limit.

For Exercises 89-99, answers may vary.

101. Answers will vary. One example is $f(x) = \sqrt{5-x}$.

103.
$$\sqrt{(2x+3)^{10}} = \sqrt{\left((2x+3)^5\right)^2} = \left|(2x+3)^5\right|$$

105. $h(x) = \sqrt{x+3}$

x	$h(x)$
-3	0
-2	1
1	2
6	3

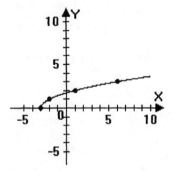

The graph of h is the graph of f shifted three units to the left.

107. $y = \sqrt{x}$ $y = \sqrt{x} + 4$
$$y = \sqrt{x} - 3$$

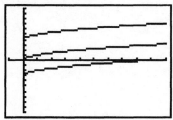

The graphs have the same shape but differ in their orientation on the y-axis.

109.

$$y_1 = \sqrt{x^2} \qquad y_2 = -x$$

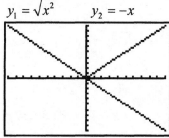

a. $\sqrt{x^2} = -x$ for $\{x \,|\, x \le 0\}$.

b. $\sqrt{x^2} \ne -x$ for $\{x \,|\, x > 0\}$.

Review Exercises

110. $3x - 2\big[x - 3(x+5)\big] = 3x - 2\big[x - 3x - 15\big]$
$$= 3x - 2\big[-2x - 15\big]$$
$$= 7x + 30$$

111. $\left(-3x^{-4}y^3\right)^{-2} = \left(-3\right)^{-2} x^8 y^{-6}$
$$= \frac{x^8}{\left(-3\right)^2 y^6} = \frac{x^8}{9y^6}$$

112. $|3x - 4| > 11$
$$3x - 4 < -11 \quad \text{or} \quad 3x - 4 > 11$$
$$3x < -7 \qquad\qquad 3x > 15$$
$$x < -\frac{7}{3} \qquad\qquad x > 5$$

The solution set is $\left\{ x \,\Big|\, x < -\dfrac{7}{3} \text{ or } x > 5 \right\}$ or

$\left(-\infty, -\dfrac{7}{3}\right) \cup (5, \infty)$.

Rational Exponents

10.2 CHECK POINTS

CHECK POINT 1

a. $25^{1/2} = \sqrt{25} = 5$

b. $(-8)^{1/3} = \sqrt[3]{-8} = -2$

c. $\left(5xy^2\right)^{\frac{1}{4}} = \sqrt[4]{5xy^2}$

CHECK POINT 2

a. $\sqrt[4]{5xy} = (5xy)^{\frac{1}{4}}$

b. $\sqrt[5]{\dfrac{a^3 b}{2}} = \left(\dfrac{a^3 b}{2}\right)^{\frac{1}{5}}$

CHECK POINT 3

a. $27^{\frac{4}{3}} = \left(\sqrt[3]{27}\right)^4 = (3)^4 = 81$

b. $4^{\frac{3}{2}} = \left(\sqrt{4}\right)^3 = (2)^3 = 8$

c. $-16^{\frac{3}{4}} = -\left(\sqrt[4]{16}\right)^3 = -(2)^3 = -8$

CHECK POINT 4

a. $\sqrt[3]{6^4} = 6^{\frac{4}{3}}$

b. $\left(\sqrt[5]{2xy}\right)^7 = (2xy)^{\frac{7}{5}}$

CHECK POINT 5

a. $25^{-\frac{1}{2}} = \dfrac{1}{25^{\frac{1}{2}}} = \dfrac{1}{\sqrt{25}} = \dfrac{1}{5}$

b. $64^{-\frac{1}{3}} = \dfrac{1}{64^{\frac{1}{3}}} = \dfrac{1}{\sqrt[3]{64}} = \dfrac{1}{4}$

c. $32^{-\frac{4}{5}} = \dfrac{1}{32^{\frac{4}{5}}} = \dfrac{1}{\left(\sqrt[5]{32}\right)^4} = \dfrac{1}{2^4} = \dfrac{1}{16}$

d. $(3xy)^{-\frac{5}{9}} = \dfrac{1}{(3xy)^{\frac{5}{9}}}$

CHECK POINT 6

$$S(16) = 63.25(16)^{\frac{1}{4}} = 63.25\sqrt[4]{16}$$
$$= 63.25(2) = 126.5$$

In 1997, the average sale price was \$126.5 thousand or \$126,500.

CHECK POINT 7

a. $7^{\frac{1}{2}} \cdot 7^{\frac{1}{3}} = 7^{\frac{1}{2}+\frac{1}{3}} = 7^{\frac{3}{6}+\frac{2}{6}} = 7^{\frac{5}{6}}$

b. $\dfrac{50x^{\frac{1}{3}}}{10x^{\frac{4}{3}}} = \dfrac{50}{10}x^{\frac{1}{3}-\frac{4}{3}} = 5x^{-\frac{3}{3}} = 5x^{-1} = \dfrac{5}{x}$

c. $\left(9.1^{\frac{2}{5}}\right)^{\frac{3}{4}} = 9.1^{\frac{2}{5}\cdot\frac{3}{4}} = 9.1^{\frac{6}{20}} = 9.1^{\frac{3}{10}}$

d. $\left(x^{-\frac{3}{5}}y^{\frac{1}{4}}\right)^{\frac{1}{3}} = x^{-\frac{3}{5}\cdot\frac{1}{3}}y^{\frac{1}{4}\cdot\frac{1}{3}} = x^{-\frac{1}{5}}y^{\frac{1}{12}} = \dfrac{y^{\frac{1}{12}}}{x^{\frac{1}{5}}}$

CHECK POINT 8

a. $\sqrt[6]{x^3} = x^{\frac{3}{6}} = x^{\frac{1}{2}} = \sqrt{x}$

b. $\sqrt[3]{8a^{12}} = \left(8a^{12}\right)^{\frac{1}{3}} = (8)^{\frac{1}{3}}\left(a^{12}\right)^{\frac{1}{3}} = 2a^{\frac{12}{3}} = 2a^4$

c. $\sqrt[8]{x^4 y^2} = \left(x^4 y^2\right)^{\frac{1}{8}} = \left(x^4\right)^{\frac{1}{8}}\left(y^2\right)^{\frac{1}{8}} = x^{\frac{4}{8}}y^{\frac{2}{8}}$
$$= x^{\frac{2}{4}}y^{\frac{1}{4}} = \left(x^2 y\right)^{\frac{1}{4}} = \sqrt[4]{x^2 y}$$

d. $\dfrac{\sqrt{x}}{\sqrt[3]{x}} = \dfrac{x^{\frac{1}{2}}}{x^{\frac{1}{3}}} = x^{\frac{1}{2}-\frac{1}{3}} = x^{\frac{3}{6}-\frac{2}{6}} = x^{\frac{1}{6}} = \sqrt[6]{x}$

e. $\sqrt{\sqrt[3]{x}} = \sqrt{x^{\frac{1}{3}}} = \left(x^{\frac{1}{3}}\right)^{\frac{1}{2}} = x^{\frac{1}{3}\cdot\frac{1}{2}} = x^{\frac{1}{6}} = \sqrt[6]{x}$

EXERCISE SET 10.2

1. $49^{1/2} = \sqrt{49} = 7$

3. $(-27)^{1/3} = \sqrt[3]{-27} = -3$

5. $-16^{1/4} = -\sqrt[4]{16} = -2$

7. $(xy)^{1/3} = \sqrt[3]{xy}$

9. $\left(2xy^3\right)^{1/5} = \sqrt[5]{2xy^3}$

11. $81^{3/2} = \left(\sqrt{81}\right)^3 = 9^3 = 729$

13. $125^{2/3} = \left(\sqrt[3]{125}\right)^2 = 5^2 = 25$

15. $(-32)^{3/5} = \left(\sqrt[5]{-32}\right)^3 = (-2)^3 = -8$

17. $27^{2/3} + 16^{3/4} = \left(\sqrt[3]{27}\right)^2 + \left(\sqrt[4]{16}\right)^3$
$$= 3^2 + 2^3 = 9 + 8 = 17$$

19. $(xy)^{4/7} = \left(\sqrt[7]{xy}\right)^4$ or $\sqrt[7]{(xy)^4}$

21. $\sqrt{7} = 7^{1/2}$

23. $\sqrt[3]{5} = 5^{1/3}$

25. $\sqrt[5]{11x} = (11x)^{1/5}$

27. $\sqrt{x^3} = x^{3/2}$

29. $\sqrt[5]{x^3} = x^{3/5}$

31. $\sqrt[5]{x^2 y} = \left(x^2 y\right)^{1/5}$

33. $\left(\sqrt{19xy}\right)^3 = (19xy)^{3/2}$

35. $\left(\sqrt[6]{7xy^2}\right)^5 = \left(7xy^2\right)^{5/6}$

37. $2x\sqrt[3]{y^2} = 2xy^{2/3}$

39. $49^{-1/2} = \dfrac{1}{49^{1/2}} = \dfrac{1}{\sqrt{49}} = \dfrac{1}{7}$

41.
$$27^{-1/3} = \frac{1}{27^{1/3}} = \frac{1}{\sqrt[3]{27}} = \frac{1}{3}$$

43.
$$16^{-3/4} = \frac{1}{16^{3/4}} = \frac{1}{\left(\sqrt[4]{16}\right)^3} = \frac{1}{2^3} = \frac{1}{8}$$

45.
$$8^{-2/3} = \frac{1}{8^{2/3}} = \frac{1}{\left(\sqrt[3]{8}\right)^2} = \frac{1}{2^2} = \frac{1}{4}$$

47.
$$\left(\frac{8}{27}\right)^{-1/3} = \left(\frac{27}{8}\right)^{1/3} = \sqrt[3]{\frac{27}{8}} = \frac{3}{2}$$

49.
$$(-64)^{-2/3} = \frac{1}{(-64)^{2/3}} = \frac{1}{\left(\sqrt[3]{-64}\right)^2}$$
$$= \frac{1}{(-4)^2} = \frac{1}{16}$$

51.
$$(2xy)^{-7/10} = \frac{1}{(2xy)^{7/10}}$$
$$= \frac{1}{\sqrt[10]{(2xy)^7}} \text{ or } \frac{1}{\left(\sqrt[10]{2xy}\right)^7}$$

53.
$$5xz^{-1/3} = \frac{5xz^{-1/3}}{1} = \frac{5x}{z^{1/3}}$$

55.
$$3^{3/4} \cdot 3^{1/4} = 3^{(3/4)+(1/4)} = 3^{4/4} = 3^1 = 3$$

57.
$$\frac{16^{3/4}}{16^{1/4}} = 16^{(3/4)-(1/4)} = 16^{2/4} = 16^{1/2} = \sqrt{16} = 4$$

59.
$$x^{1/2} \cdot x^{1/3} = x^{(1/2)+(1/3)} = x^{(3/6)+(2/6)} = x^{5/6}$$

61.
$$\frac{x^{4/5}}{x^{1/5}} = x^{(4/5)-(1/5)} = x^{3/5}$$

63.
$$\frac{x^{1/3}}{x^{3/4}} = x^{(1/3)-(3/4)} = x^{(4/12)-(9/12)}$$
$$= x^{-5/12} = \frac{1}{x^{5/12}}$$

65.
$$\left(5^{\frac{2}{3}}\right)^3 = 5^{\frac{2}{3}\cdot 3} = 5^2 = 25$$

67.
$$\left(y^{-2/3}\right)^{1/4} = y^{(-2/3)\cdot(1/4)} = y^{-2/12} = y^{-1/6} = \frac{1}{y^{1/6}}$$

69.
$$\left(2x^{1/5}\right)^5 = 2^5 x^{(1/5)\cdot 5} = 32x^1 = 32x$$

71.
$$\left(25x^4 y^6\right)^{1/2} = 25^{1/2}\left(x^4\right)^{1/2}\left(y^6\right)^{1/2}$$
$$= \sqrt{25}\,x^{4(1/2)} y^{6(1/2)} = 5x^2 y^3$$

73.
$$\left(x^{1/2} y^{-3/5}\right)^{1/2} = \left(\frac{x^{1/2} y^{-3/5}}{1}\right)^{1/2} = \left(\frac{x^{1/2}}{y^{3/5}}\right)^{1/2}$$
$$= \frac{x^{(1/2)\cdot(1/2)}}{y^{(3/5)\cdot(1/2)}} = \frac{x^{1/4}}{y^{3/10}}$$

75.
$$\frac{3^{1/2} \cdot 3^{3/4}}{3^{1/4}} = 3^{(1/2)+(3/4)-(1/4)} = 3^{(2/4)+(3/4)-(1/4)}$$
$$= 3^{4/4} = 3^1 = 3$$

77.
$$\frac{\left(3y^{1/4}\right)^3}{y^{1/12}} = \frac{3^3 y^{(1/4)\cdot 3}}{y^{1/12}} = \frac{27y^{3/4}}{y^{1/12}} = 27y^{(3/4)-(1/12)}$$
$$= 27y^{(9/12)-(1/12)} = 27y^{8/12} = 27y^{2/3}$$

79.
$$\sqrt[8]{x^2} = x^{2/8} = x^{1/4} = \sqrt[4]{x}$$

81.
$$\sqrt[3]{8a^6} = 8^{1/3} a^{6/3} = 2a^2$$

83.
$$\sqrt[5]{x^{10} y^{15}} = x^{10/5} y^{15/5} = x^2 y^3$$

85.
$$\left(\sqrt[3]{xy}\right)^{18} = (xy)^{18/3} = (xy)^6 = x^6 y^6$$

87.
$$\sqrt[10]{(3y)^2} = (3y)^{2/10} = (3y)^{1/5} = \sqrt[5]{3y}$$

89.
$$\left(\sqrt[6]{2a}\right)^4 = (2a)^{4/6} = (2a)^{2/3}$$
$$= \left(4a^2\right)^{1/3} = \sqrt[3]{4a^2}$$

91.
$$\sqrt[9]{x^6 y^3} = x^{6/9} y^{3/9} = x^{2/3} y^{1/3} = \sqrt[3]{x^2 y}$$

93. $\sqrt{2} \cdot \sqrt[3]{2} = 2^{1/2} \cdot 2^{1/3} = 2^{(1/2)+(1/3)} = 2^{(3/6)+(2/6)}$

$= 2^{5/6} = \sqrt[6]{2^5}$ or $\sqrt[6]{32}$

$= \left(x^3 y^5\right)^{12/4} = \left(x^3 y^5\right)^3$

$= x^{3 \cdot 3} y^{5 \cdot 3} = x^9 y^{15}$

95. $\dfrac{\sqrt[4]{x}}{\sqrt[5]{x}} = \dfrac{x^{1/4}}{x^{1/5}} = x^{(1/4)-(1/5)} = x^{(5/20)-(4/20)}$

$= x^{1/20} = \sqrt[20]{x}$

107. $f(8) = 29(8)^{1/3} = 29\sqrt[3]{8} = 29(2) = 58$

There are 58 plant species on an 8 square mile island.

97. $\dfrac{\sqrt[3]{y^2}}{\sqrt[6]{y}} = \dfrac{y^{2/3}}{y^{1/6}} = y^{(2/3)-(1/6)} = y^{(4/6)-(1/6)}$

$= y^{3/6} = y^{1/2} = \sqrt{y}$

109. $f(9) = 0.07(9)^{3/2} = 0.07\left(\sqrt{9}\right)^3$

$= 0.07(3)^3 = 0.07(27) \approx 1.9$

The duration is approximately 1.9 hours.

99. $\sqrt[4]{\sqrt{x}} = \sqrt[4]{x^{1/2}} = \left(x^{1/2}\right)^{1/4}$

$= x^{(1/2) \cdot (1/4)} = x^{1/8} = \sqrt[8]{x}$

111.

$P(8) = \dfrac{73(8)^{1/3} - 28(8)^{2/3}}{8} = \dfrac{73\sqrt[3]{8} - 28\left(\sqrt[3]{8}\right)^2}{8}$

$= \dfrac{73(2) - 28(2)^2}{8} = \dfrac{146 - 28(4)}{8}$

$= \dfrac{146 - 112}{8} = \dfrac{34}{8} = 4.25$

4.25% of employees tested positive.

101. $\sqrt{\sqrt{x^2 y}} = \sqrt{\left(x^2 y\right)^{1/2}} = \left(\left(x^2 y\right)^{1/2}\right)^{1/2}$

$= \left(x^2 y\right)^{(1/2) \cdot (1/2)} = \left(x^2 y\right)^{1/4} = \sqrt[4]{x^2 y}$

103. $\sqrt[4]{\sqrt[3]{2x}} = \sqrt[4]{(2x)^{1/3}} = \left((2x)^{1/3}\right)^{1/4}$

$= (2x)^{(1/3) \cdot (1/4)} = (2x)^{1/12} = \sqrt[12]{2x}$

113. $f(80) = 70(80)^{3/4} = 70(26.75) = 1872.5$

A person weighing 80 kilograms needs approximately 1872 calories to maintain life.

105. $\left(\sqrt[4]{x^3 y^5}\right)^{12} = \left(\left(x^3 y^5\right)^{1/4}\right)^{12} = \left(x^3 y^5\right)^{(1/4) \cdot 12}$

115. **a.** $L + 1.25 S^{1/2} - 9.8 D^{1/3} \leq 16.296$

b.
$$L + 1.25 S^{1/2} - 9.8 D^{1/3} \leq 16.296$$
$$20.85 + 1.25(276.4)^{1/2} - 9.8(18.55)^{1/3} \leq 16.296$$
$$20.85 + 1.25\sqrt{276.4} - 9.8\sqrt[3]{18.55} \leq 16.296$$
$$20.85 + 1.25(16.625) - 9.8(2.647) \leq 16.296$$
$$20.85 + 20.781 - 25.941 \leq 16.296$$
$$15.69 \leq 16.296$$

The yacht is eligible to enter the America's Cup.

For Exercises 117-125, answers may vary.

127. $2^{5/2} \cdot 2^{3/4} \div 2^{1/4}$

$= 2^{(5/2)+(3/4)-(1/4)} = 2^{(10/4)+(3/4)-(1/4)}$

$= 2^{12/4} = 2^3 = 8$

The son is 8 years old.

129. $\left[3 + \left(27^{2/3} + 32^{2/5}\right)\right]^{3/2} - 9^{1/2}$

$$= \left[3 + \left(\left(\sqrt[3]{27} \right)^2 + \left(\sqrt[5]{32} \right)^2 \right) \right]^{3/2} - \sqrt{9}$$

$$= \left[3 + \left(3^2 + 2^2 \right) \right]^{3/2} - 3 = \left[3 + (9 + 4) \right]^{3/2} - 3$$

$$= \left[3 + (13) \right]^{3/2} - 3 = \left[16 \right]^{3/2} - 3$$

$$= \left(\sqrt{16} \right)^3 - 3 = (4)^3 - 3$$

$$= 64 - 3 = 61$$

131. Consider Exercise 15.

133. **a.** $y_1 = x^{\wedge}(2 \div 3)$

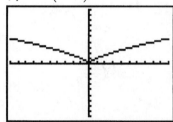

This is the same as the graph shown in Exercise 133. On some calculators only the half of the graph for $x \geq 0$ is displayed. On other calculators, the entire graph is displayed.

b. $y_1 = \left(x^{\wedge}(1 \div 3) \right)^{\wedge} 2$

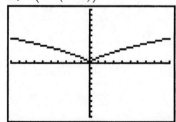

This is the same as the graph shown in Exercise 133.

Review Exercises

135.
$$m = \frac{y_2 - y_1}{x_2 - x_1} = \frac{3 - 1}{4 - 5} = \frac{2}{-1} = -2$$

point-slope form:
$$y - 3 = -2(x - 4)$$

slope-intercept form:
$$y - 3 = -2x + 8$$
$$y = -2x + 11 \text{ or } f(x) = -2x + 11$$

136.
$$y \leq -\frac{3}{2}x + 3$$

Graph the corresponding line,
$$y = -\frac{3}{2}x + 3.$$

$$\text{slope} = -\frac{3}{2} \qquad y\text{–intercept} = 3$$

Use a test point to determine shading.

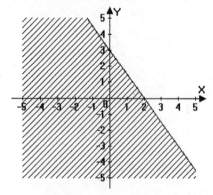

137.
$$D = \begin{vmatrix} 5 & -3 \\ 7 & 1 \end{vmatrix} = 5(1) - 7(-3) = 5 + 21 = 26$$

$$D_x = \begin{vmatrix} 3 & -3 \\ 25 & 1 \end{vmatrix} = 3(1) - 25(-3) = 3 + 75 = 78$$

$$D_y = \begin{vmatrix} 5 & 3 \\ 7 & 25 \end{vmatrix} = 5(25) - 7(3) = 125 - 21 = 104$$

$$x = \frac{D_x}{D} = \frac{78}{26} = 3 \qquad y = \frac{D_y}{D} = \frac{104}{26} = 4$$

The solution is $(3, 4)$.

Multiplying and Simplifying Radical Expressions

10.3 CHECK POINTS

CHECK POINT 1
a. $\sqrt{5}\cdot\sqrt{11}=\sqrt{5\cdot11}=\sqrt{55}$

b. $\sqrt{x+4}\cdot\sqrt{x-4}=\sqrt{(x+4)(x-4)}=\sqrt{x^2-16}$

c. $\sqrt[3]{6}\cdot\sqrt[3]{10}=\sqrt[3]{6\cdot10}=\sqrt[3]{60}$

d. $\sqrt[7]{2x}\cdot\sqrt[7]{6x^3}=\sqrt[7]{2x\cdot6x^3}=\sqrt[7]{12x^4}$

CHECK POINT 2
a. $\sqrt{80}=\sqrt{16\cdot5}=\sqrt{16}\cdot\sqrt{5}=4\sqrt{5}$

b. $\sqrt[3]{40}=\sqrt[3]{8\cdot5}=\sqrt[3]{8}\cdot\sqrt[3]{5}=2\sqrt[3]{5}$

c. $\sqrt[4]{32}=\sqrt[4]{16\cdot2}=\sqrt[4]{16}\cdot\sqrt[4]{2}=2\sqrt[4]{2}$

d. $\sqrt{200x^2y}=\sqrt{100x^2\cdot2y}=\sqrt{100x^2}\cdot\sqrt{2y}$
$=10|x|\sqrt{2y}$

CHECK POINT 3
$f(x)=\sqrt{3x^2-12x+12}=\sqrt{3(x^2-4x+4)}$
$=\sqrt{3(x-2)^2}=|x-2|\sqrt{3}$

CHECK POINT 4
$\sqrt{x^9y^{11}z^3}=\sqrt{x^8\cdot x\cdot y^{10}\cdot y\cdot z^2\cdot z}$
$=\sqrt{x^8y^{10}z^2}\cdot\sqrt{xyz}=x^4y^5z\sqrt{xyz}$

CHECK POINT 5
$\sqrt[3]{40x^{10}y^{14}}=\sqrt[3]{8\cdot5\cdot x^9\cdot x\cdot y^{12}\cdot y^2}$
$=\sqrt[3]{8x^9y^{12}}\cdot\sqrt[3]{5xy^2}=2x^3y^4\sqrt[3]{5xy^2}$

CHECK POINT 6
$\sqrt[5]{32x^{12}y^2z^8}=\sqrt[5]{32\cdot x^{10}\cdot x^2\cdot y^2\cdot z^5\cdot z^3}$
$=\sqrt[5]{32x^{10}z^5}\cdot\sqrt[5]{x^2y^2z^3}=2x^2z\sqrt[5]{x^2y^2z^3}$

CHECK POINT 7
a. $\sqrt{6}\cdot\sqrt{2}=\sqrt{6\cdot2}=\sqrt{12}=\sqrt{4\cdot3}=\sqrt{4}\cdot\sqrt{3}=2\sqrt{3}$

b. $10\sqrt[3]{16}\cdot5\sqrt[3]{2}=50\sqrt[3]{16\cdot2}=50\sqrt[3]{32}$
$=50\sqrt[3]{8\cdot4}=50\sqrt[3]{8}\cdot\sqrt[3]{4}$
$=50\cdot2\cdot\sqrt[3]{4}=100\sqrt[3]{4}$

c. $\sqrt[4]{4x^2y}\cdot\sqrt[4]{8x^6y^3}=\sqrt[4]{4x^2y\cdot8x^6y^3}$
$=\sqrt[4]{32x^8y^4}=\sqrt[4]{16\cdot2\cdot x^8y^4}$
$=\sqrt[4]{16x^8y^4}\cdot\sqrt[4]{2}=2x^2y\sqrt[4]{2}$

EXERCISE SET 10.3

1. $\sqrt{3}\cdot\sqrt{5}=\sqrt{3\cdot5}=\sqrt{15}$

3. $\sqrt[3]{2}\cdot\sqrt[3]{9}=\sqrt[3]{2\cdot9}=\sqrt[3]{18}$

5. $\sqrt[4]{11}\cdot\sqrt[4]{3}=\sqrt[4]{11\cdot3}=\sqrt[4]{33}$

7. $\sqrt{3x}\cdot\sqrt{11y}=\sqrt{3x\cdot11y}=\sqrt{33xy}$

9. $\sqrt[5]{6x^3}\cdot\sqrt[5]{4x}=\sqrt[5]{6x^3\cdot4x}=\sqrt[5]{24x^4}$

11. $\sqrt{x+3}\cdot\sqrt{x-3}=\sqrt{(x+3)(x-3)}=\sqrt{x^2-9}$

13. $\sqrt[6]{x-4}\cdot\sqrt[6]{(x-4)^4}$
$=\sqrt[6]{(x-4)(x-4)^4}=\sqrt[6]{(x-4)^5}$

15. $\sqrt{\dfrac{2x}{3}}\cdot\sqrt{\dfrac{3}{2}}=\sqrt{\dfrac{2x}{3}\cdot\dfrac{3}{2}}=\sqrt{\dfrac{\cancel{12}x}{\cancel{13}}\cdot\dfrac{\cancel{13}}{\cancel{12}}}=\sqrt{x}$

17. $\sqrt[4]{\dfrac{x}{7}}\cdot\sqrt[4]{\dfrac{3}{y}}=\sqrt[4]{\dfrac{x}{7}\cdot\dfrac{3}{y}}=\sqrt[4]{\dfrac{3x}{7y}}$

19. $\sqrt[7]{7x^2y}\cdot\sqrt[7]{11x^3y^2}=\sqrt[7]{7x^2y\cdot11x^3y^2}$
$=\sqrt[7]{7\cdot11x^2x^3yy^2}=\sqrt[7]{77x^5y^3}$

21. $\sqrt{50}=\sqrt{25\cdot2}=\sqrt{25}\cdot\sqrt{2}=5\sqrt{2}$

23. $\sqrt{45}=\sqrt{9\cdot5}=\sqrt{9}\cdot\sqrt{5}=3\sqrt{5}$

25. $\sqrt{75x}=\sqrt{25\cdot3x}=\sqrt{25}\cdot\sqrt{3x}=5\sqrt{3x}$

27. $\sqrt[3]{16} = \sqrt[3]{8 \cdot 2} = \sqrt[3]{8} \cdot \sqrt[3]{2} = 2\sqrt[3]{2}$

29. $\sqrt[3]{27x^3} = \sqrt[3]{27 \cdot x^3} = \sqrt[3]{27} \cdot \sqrt[3]{x^3} = 3x$

31. $\sqrt[3]{-16x^2y^3} = \sqrt[3]{-8 \cdot 2x^2y^3}$
$$= \sqrt[3]{-8y^3} \cdot \sqrt[3]{2x^2} = -2y\sqrt[3]{2x^2}$$

33. $f(x) = \sqrt{36(x+2)^2} = 6|x+2|$

35. $f(x) = \sqrt[3]{32(x+2)^3} = \sqrt[3]{8 \cdot 4(x+2)^3}$
$$= \sqrt[3]{8(x+2)^3} \cdot \sqrt[3]{4} = 2(x+2)\sqrt[3]{4}$$

37. $f(x) = \sqrt{3x^2 - 6x + 3} = \sqrt{3(x^2 - 2x + 1)}$
$$= \sqrt{3(x-1)^2} = |x-1|\sqrt{3}$$

39. $\sqrt{x^7} = \sqrt{x^6 \cdot x} = \sqrt{x^6} \cdot \sqrt{x} = x^3\sqrt{x}$

41. $\sqrt{x^8y^9} = \sqrt{x^8y^8y} = \sqrt{x^8y^8}\sqrt{y} = x^4y^4\sqrt{y}$

43. $\sqrt{48x^3} = \sqrt{16 \cdot 3x^2x} = \sqrt{16x^2} \cdot \sqrt{3x} = 4x\sqrt{3x}$

45. $\sqrt[3]{y^8} = \sqrt[3]{y^6 \cdot y^2} = \sqrt[3]{y^6} \cdot \sqrt[3]{y^2} = y^2\sqrt[3]{y^2}$

47. $\sqrt[3]{x^{14}y^3z} = \sqrt[3]{x^{12}x^2y^3z}$
$$= \sqrt[3]{x^{12}y^3} \cdot \sqrt[3]{x^2z} = x^4y\sqrt[3]{x^2z}$$

49. $\sqrt[3]{81x^8y^6} = \sqrt[3]{27 \cdot 3x^6x^2y^6} = \sqrt[3]{27x^6y^6} \cdot \sqrt[3]{3x^2}$
$$= 3x^2y^2\sqrt[3]{3x^2}$$

51. $\sqrt[3]{(x+y)^5} = \sqrt[3]{(x+y)^3 \cdot (x+y)^2}$
$$= \sqrt[3]{(x+y)^3} \cdot \sqrt[3]{(x+y)^2}$$
$$= (x+y)\sqrt[3]{(x+y)^2}$$

53. $\sqrt[5]{y^{17}} = \sqrt[5]{y^{15} \cdot y^2} = \sqrt[5]{y^{15}} \cdot \sqrt[5]{y^2} = y^3\sqrt[5]{y^2}$

55. $\sqrt[5]{64x^6y^{17}} = \sqrt[5]{32 \cdot 2x^5xy^{15}y^2}$
$$= \sqrt[5]{32x^5y^{15}} \cdot \sqrt[5]{2xy^2} = 2xy^3\sqrt[5]{2xy^2}$$

57. $\sqrt[4]{80x^{10}} = \sqrt[4]{16 \cdot 5x^8x^2} = \sqrt[4]{16x^8} \cdot \sqrt[4]{5x^2}$
$$= 2x^2\sqrt[4]{5x^2}$$

59. $\sqrt[4]{(x-3)^{10}} = \sqrt[4]{(x-3)^8(x-3)^2}$
$$= \sqrt[4]{(x-3)^8} \cdot \sqrt[4]{(x-3)^2}$$
$$= (x-3)^2\sqrt[4]{(x-3)^2}$$

61. $\sqrt{12} \cdot \sqrt{2} = \sqrt{12 \cdot 2} = \sqrt{24}$
$$= \sqrt{4 \cdot 6} = \sqrt{4} \cdot \sqrt{6} = 2\sqrt{6}$$

63. $\sqrt{5x} \cdot \sqrt{10y} = \sqrt{5x \cdot 10y} = \sqrt{50xy}$
$$= \sqrt{25 \cdot 2xy} = 5\sqrt{2xy}$$

65. $\sqrt{12x} \cdot \sqrt{3x} = \sqrt{12x \cdot 3x} = \sqrt{36x^2} = 6x$

67. $\sqrt{50xy} \cdot \sqrt{4xy^2} = \sqrt{50xy \cdot 4xy^2}$
$$= \sqrt{200x^2y^3} = \sqrt{100 \cdot 2x^2y^2y}$$
$$= \sqrt{100x^2y^2} \cdot \sqrt{2y} = 10xy\sqrt{2y}$$

69. $2\sqrt{5} \cdot 3\sqrt{40} = 2 \cdot 3\sqrt{5 \cdot 40} = 6\sqrt{200}$
$$= 6\sqrt{100 \cdot 2} = 6\sqrt{100} \cdot \sqrt{2}$$
$$= 6 \cdot 10\sqrt{2} = 60\sqrt{2}$$

71. $\sqrt[3]{12} \cdot \sqrt[3]{4} = \sqrt[3]{12 \cdot 4} = \sqrt[3]{48} = \sqrt[3]{8 \cdot 6}$
$$= \sqrt[3]{8} \cdot \sqrt[3]{6} = 2\sqrt[3]{6}$$

73. $\sqrt{5x^3} \cdot \sqrt{8x^2}$
$$= \sqrt{5x^3 \cdot 8x^2} = \sqrt{40x^5} = \sqrt{4 \cdot 10x^4x}$$
$$= \sqrt{4x^4} \cdot \sqrt{10x} = 2x^2\sqrt{10x}$$

75. $\sqrt[3]{25x^4y^2} \cdot \sqrt[3]{5xy^{12}} = \sqrt[3]{25x^4y^2 \cdot 5xy^{12}}$
$$= \sqrt[3]{125x^5y^{14}} = \sqrt[3]{125x^3x^2y^{12}y^2}$$
$$= \sqrt[3]{125x^3y^{12}} \cdot \sqrt[3]{x^2y^2} = 5xy^4\sqrt[3]{x^2y^2}$$

77. $\sqrt[4]{8x^2y^3z^6} \cdot \sqrt[4]{2x^4yz} = \sqrt[4]{8x^2y^3z^6 \cdot 2x^4yz}$

$= \sqrt[4]{16x^6y^4z^7} = \sqrt[4]{16x^4x^2y^4z^4z^3}$

$= \sqrt[4]{16x^4y^4z^4} \cdot \sqrt[4]{x^2z^3} = 2xyz\sqrt[4]{x^2z^3}$

79. $\sqrt[5]{8x^4y^6} \cdot \sqrt[5]{8xy^7} = \sqrt[5]{8x^4y^6 \cdot 8xy^7}$

$= \sqrt[5]{64x^5y^{13}} = \sqrt[5]{32 \cdot 2x^5y^{10}y^3}$

$= \sqrt[5]{32x^5y^{10}} \cdot \sqrt[5]{2y^3} = 2xy^2\sqrt[5]{2y^3}$

81. $\sqrt[3]{x-y} \cdot \sqrt[3]{(x-y)^7} = \sqrt[3]{(x-y)\cdot(x-y)^7}$

$= \sqrt[3]{(x-y)^8} = \sqrt[3]{(x-y)^6(x-y)^2}$

$= \sqrt[3]{(x-y)^6} \cdot \sqrt[3]{(x-y)^2} = (x-y)^2\sqrt[3]{(x-y)^2}$

83. $r(8) = 4\sqrt{8} = 4\sqrt{4 \cdot 2} = 4\sqrt{4} \cdot \sqrt{2}$

$= 4 \cdot 2\sqrt{2} = 8\sqrt{2}$

The maximum rate a cyclist should travel around a corner of radius 8 feet is $8\sqrt{2} \approx 8(1.414) \approx 11.3$ miles per hour.

85. $T(320) = \sqrt{\dfrac{320}{16}} = \sqrt{20} = \sqrt{4 \cdot 5}$

$= \sqrt{4} \cdot \sqrt{5} = 2\sqrt{5}$

It will take $2\sqrt{5} \approx 4.5$ seconds for the ball to hit the ground.

87. **a.** $C(32) = \dfrac{7.644}{\sqrt[4]{32}} = \dfrac{7.644}{\sqrt[4]{16 \cdot 2}}$

$= \dfrac{7.644}{2\sqrt[4]{2}} = \dfrac{3.822}{\sqrt[4]{2}}$

The cardiac index of a 32-year-old is $\dfrac{3.822}{\sqrt[4]{2}}$.

b. $\dfrac{3.822}{\sqrt[4]{2}} = \dfrac{3.822}{1.189} = \dfrac{3.822}{1.189} \approx 3.21$

The cardiac index of a 32-year-old is 3.21 liters per minute per square meter. This is shown on the graph as the point (32, 3.21).

For Exercises 89-93, answers may vary.

95. If a number is tripled, its square root is multiplied by $\sqrt{3}$. For example, consider the number 4 and its triple, 12.

$\sqrt{4} = 2 \qquad \sqrt{12} = \sqrt{4 \cdot 3} = 2\sqrt{3}$

Thus, if a number is tripled, its square root is multiplied by $\sqrt{3}$.

97. $(fg)(x) = f(x) \cdot g(x)$

$2x = \sqrt[3]{2x} \cdot g(x)$

$\dfrac{2x}{\sqrt[3]{2x}} = g(x)$

$\dfrac{(2x)^1}{(2x)^{\frac{1}{3}}} = g(x)$

$(2x)^{1-\frac{1}{3}} = g(x)$

$(2x)^{\frac{2}{3}} = g(x)$

$\sqrt[3]{(2x)^2} = g(x)$

$g(x) = \sqrt[3]{4x^2}$

99. Consider Exercise 21.

```
√(50)
          7.071067812
5√(2)
          7.071067812
■
```

101. $\sqrt{8x^2} = 4x\sqrt{2}$

The graphs do not coincide. Correct the simplification.

$\sqrt{8x^2} = \sqrt{4 \cdot 2x^2} = 2x\sqrt{2}$

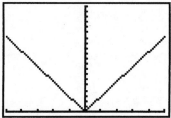

The graphs coincide, so the simplification is correct.

103. $\sqrt[3]{2x} \cdot \sqrt[3]{4x^2} = 4x$

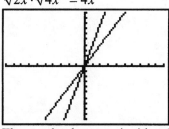

The graphs do not coincide. Correct the simplification.

$$\sqrt[3]{2x} \cdot \sqrt[3]{4x^2} = \sqrt[3]{2x \cdot 4x^2} = \sqrt[3]{8x^3} = 2x$$

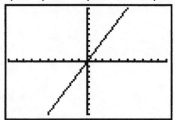

The graphs coincide. The simplification is correct.

Review Exercises

104.
$$
\begin{array}{ll}
2x-1 \le 21 & \text{and} \quad 2x+2 \ge 12 \\
2x \le 22 & \qquad 2x \ge 10 \\
x \le 11 & \qquad x \ge 5
\end{array}
$$

The solution set is $\{x | 5 \le x \le 11\}$ or $[5, 11]$.

105. Multiply the first equation by –3, and the second equation by 2.
$$
\begin{array}{r}
-15x - 6y = -6 \\
8x + 6y = -8 \\
\hline
-7x = -14 \\
x = 2
\end{array}
$$

Back-substitute 2 for x to find y.
$$
\begin{aligned}
5(2) + 2y &= 2 \\
10 + 2y &= 2 \\
2y &= -8 \\
y &= -4
\end{aligned}
$$
The solution is $(2, -4)$.

106.
$$
\begin{aligned}
64x^3 - 27 &= (4x)^3 - (3)^3 \\
&= (4x - 3)\left((4x)^2 + 4x \cdot 3 + 3^2\right) \\
&= (4x - 3)(16x^2 + 12x + 9)
\end{aligned}
$$

Adding, Subtracting, and Dividing Radical Expressions

10.4 CHECK POINTS

CHECK POINT 1

a. $8\sqrt{13} + 2\sqrt{13} = (8+2)\sqrt{13} = 10\sqrt{13}$

b.
$$
\begin{aligned}
9\sqrt[3]{7} - 6x\sqrt[3]{7} + 12\sqrt[3]{7} &= (9 - 6x + 12)\sqrt[3]{7} \\
&= (21 - 6x)\sqrt[3]{7}
\end{aligned}
$$

c.
$$
\begin{aligned}
7\sqrt[4]{3x} - 2\sqrt[4]{3x} + 2\sqrt[3]{3x} &= \left(7\sqrt[4]{3x} - 2\sqrt[4]{3x}\right) + 2\sqrt[3]{3x} \\
&= \left((7-2)\sqrt[4]{3x}\right) + 2\sqrt[3]{3x} = 5\sqrt[4]{3x} + 2\sqrt[3]{3x}
\end{aligned}
$$

CHECK POINT 2

a.
$$
\begin{aligned}
3\sqrt{20} + 5\sqrt{45} &= 3\sqrt{4 \cdot 5} + 5\sqrt{9 \cdot 5} \\
&= 3 \cdot 2\sqrt{5} + 5 \cdot 3\sqrt{5} = 6\sqrt{5} + 15\sqrt{5} \\
&= (6 + 15)\sqrt{5} = 21\sqrt{5}
\end{aligned}
$$

b.
$$
\begin{aligned}
3\sqrt{12x} - 6\sqrt{27x} &= 3\sqrt{4 \cdot 3x} - 6\sqrt{9 \cdot 3x} \\
&= 3 \cdot 2\sqrt{3x} - 6 \cdot 3\sqrt{3x} = 6\sqrt{3x} - 18\sqrt{3x} \\
&= (6 - 18)\sqrt{3x} = -12\sqrt{3x}
\end{aligned}
$$

c. $8\sqrt{5} - 6\sqrt{2}$
Cannot be simplified.

CHECK POINT 3

a.
$$
\begin{aligned}
3\sqrt[3]{24} - 5\sqrt[3]{81} &= 3\sqrt[3]{8 \cdot 3} - 5\sqrt[3]{27 \cdot 3} \\
&= 3 \cdot 2\sqrt[3]{3} - 5 \cdot 3\sqrt[3]{3} = 6\sqrt[3]{3} - 15\sqrt[3]{3} \\
&= (6 - 15)\sqrt[3]{3} = -9\sqrt[3]{3}
\end{aligned}
$$

b.
$$5\sqrt[3]{x^2 y} + \sqrt[3]{27x^5 y^4} = 5\sqrt[3]{x^2 y} + \sqrt[3]{27x^3 x^2 y^3 y}$$
$$= 5\sqrt[3]{x^2 y} + \sqrt[3]{27x^3 y^3 \cdot x^2 y}$$
$$= 5\sqrt[3]{x^2 y} + 3xy\sqrt[3]{x^2 y}$$
$$= (5 + 3xy)\sqrt[3]{x^2 y}$$

CHECK POINT 4

a. $\sqrt[3]{\dfrac{24}{125}} = \dfrac{\sqrt[3]{24}}{\sqrt[3]{125}} = \dfrac{\sqrt[3]{8 \cdot 3}}{5} = \dfrac{2\sqrt[3]{3}}{5}$

b. $\sqrt{\dfrac{9x^3}{y^{10}}} = \dfrac{\sqrt{9x^3}}{\sqrt{y^{10}}} = \dfrac{\sqrt{9x^2 \cdot x}}{y^5} = \dfrac{3x\sqrt{x}}{y^5}$

c. $\sqrt[3]{\dfrac{8y^7}{x^{12}}} = \dfrac{\sqrt[3]{8y^7}}{\sqrt[3]{x^{12}}} = \dfrac{\sqrt[3]{8y^6 y}}{x^4} = \dfrac{2x^2\sqrt[3]{y}}{x^4}$

CHECK POINT 5

a. $\dfrac{\sqrt{40x^5}}{\sqrt{2x}} = \sqrt{\dfrac{40x^5}{2x}} = \sqrt{20x^4} = \sqrt{4 \cdot 5x^4}$
$$= \sqrt{4x^4 \cdot 5} = 2x^2\sqrt{5}$$

b. $\dfrac{\sqrt{50xy}}{2\sqrt{2}} = \dfrac{1}{2} \cdot \sqrt{\dfrac{50xy}{2}} = \dfrac{1}{2} \cdot \sqrt{25xy} = \dfrac{1}{2} \cdot 5\sqrt{xy}$
$$= \dfrac{5}{2}\sqrt{xy} \text{ or } \dfrac{5\sqrt{xy}}{2}$$

c. $\dfrac{\sqrt[3]{48x^7 y}}{\sqrt[3]{6xy^{-2}}} = \sqrt[3]{\dfrac{48x^7 y}{6xy^{-2}}} = \sqrt[3]{8x^6 y^3} = 2x^2 y$

EXERCISE SET 10.4

1. $8\sqrt{5} + 3\sqrt{5} = (8 + 3)\sqrt{5} = 11\sqrt{5}$

3. $9\sqrt[3]{6} - 2\sqrt[3]{6} = (9 - 2)\sqrt[3]{6} = 7\sqrt[3]{6}$

5. $4\sqrt[5]{2} + 3\sqrt[5]{2} - 5\sqrt[5]{2} = (4 + 3 - 5)\sqrt[5]{2} = 2\sqrt[5]{2}$

7. $3\sqrt{13} - 2\sqrt{5} - 2\sqrt{13} + 4\sqrt{5}$
$$= 3\sqrt{13} - 2\sqrt{13} - 2\sqrt{5} + 4\sqrt{5}$$
$$= (3 - 2)\sqrt{13} + (-2 + 4)\sqrt{5} = \sqrt{13} + 2\sqrt{5}$$

9. $3\sqrt{5} - \sqrt[3]{x} + 4\sqrt{5} + 3\sqrt[3]{x}$
$$= 3\sqrt{5} + 4\sqrt{5} - \sqrt[3]{x} + 3\sqrt[3]{x}$$
$$= (3 + 4)\sqrt{5} + (-1 + 3)\sqrt[3]{x} = 7\sqrt{5} + 2\sqrt[3]{x}$$

11. $\sqrt{3} + \sqrt{27} = \sqrt{3} + \sqrt{9 \cdot 3} = \sqrt{3} + 3\sqrt{3}$
$$= (1 + 3)\sqrt{3} = 4\sqrt{3}$$

13. $7\sqrt{12} + \sqrt{75} = 7\sqrt{4 \cdot 3} + \sqrt{25 \cdot 3}$
$$= 7 \cdot 2\sqrt{3} + 5\sqrt{3} = 14\sqrt{3} + 5\sqrt{3}$$
$$= (14 + 5)\sqrt{3} = 19\sqrt{3}$$

15. $3\sqrt{32x} - 2\sqrt{18x} = 3\sqrt{16 \cdot 2x} - 2\sqrt{9 \cdot 2x}$
$$= 3 \cdot 4\sqrt{2x} - 2 \cdot 3\sqrt{2x}$$
$$= 12\sqrt{2x} - 6\sqrt{2x} = 6\sqrt{2x}$$

17. $5\sqrt[3]{16} + \sqrt[3]{54} = 5\sqrt[3]{8 \cdot 2} + \sqrt[3]{27 \cdot 2}$
$$= 5 \cdot 2\sqrt[3]{2} + 3\sqrt[3]{2} = 10\sqrt[3]{2} + 3\sqrt[3]{2}$$
$$= (10 + 3)\sqrt[3]{2} = 13\sqrt[3]{2}$$

19. $3\sqrt{45x^3} + \sqrt{5x} = 3\sqrt{9 \cdot 5x^2 x} + \sqrt{5x}$
$$= 3 \cdot 3x\sqrt{5x} + \sqrt{5x}$$
$$= 9x\sqrt{5x} + \sqrt{5x} = (9x + 1)\sqrt{5x}$$

21. $\sqrt[3]{54xy^3} + y\sqrt[3]{128x} = \sqrt[3]{27 \cdot 2xy^3} + y\sqrt[3]{64 \cdot 2x}$
$$= 3y\sqrt[3]{2x} + 4y\sqrt[3]{2x}$$
$$= (3y + 4y)\sqrt[3]{2x} = 7y\sqrt[3]{2x}$$

23. $\sqrt[3]{54x^4} - \sqrt[3]{16x} = \sqrt[3]{27 \cdot 2x^3 x} - \sqrt[3]{8 \cdot 2x}$
$$= 3x\sqrt[3]{2x} - 2\sqrt[3]{2x}$$
$$= (3x - 2)\sqrt[3]{2x}$$

25. $\sqrt{9x - 18} + \sqrt{x - 2} = \sqrt{9(x - 2)} + \sqrt{x - 2}$
$$= 3\sqrt{x - 2} + \sqrt{x - 2}$$
$$= (3 + 1)\sqrt{x - 2} = 4\sqrt{x - 2}$$

27.
$$2\sqrt[3]{x^4 y^2} + 3x\sqrt[3]{xy^2} = 2\sqrt[3]{x^3 xy^2} + 3x\sqrt[3]{xy^2}$$
$$= 2x\sqrt[3]{xy^2} + 3x\sqrt[3]{xy^2}$$
$$= (2x + 3x)\sqrt[3]{xy^2}$$
$$= 5x\sqrt[3]{xy^2}$$

29.
$$\sqrt{\frac{11}{4}} = \frac{\sqrt{11}}{\sqrt{4}} = \frac{\sqrt{11}}{2}$$

31.
$$\sqrt[3]{\frac{19}{27}} = \frac{\sqrt[3]{19}}{\sqrt[3]{27}} = \frac{\sqrt[3]{19}}{3}$$

33.
$$\sqrt{\frac{x^2}{36y^8}} = \frac{\sqrt{x^2}}{\sqrt{36y^8}} = \frac{x}{6y^4}$$

35.
$$\sqrt{\frac{8x^3}{25y^6}} = \frac{\sqrt{8x^3}}{\sqrt{25y^6}} = \frac{\sqrt{4 \cdot 2x^2 x}}{5y^3} = \frac{2x\sqrt{2x}}{5y^3}$$

37.
$$\sqrt[3]{\frac{x^4}{8y^3}} = \frac{\sqrt[3]{x^4}}{\sqrt[3]{8y^3}} = \frac{\sqrt[3]{x^3 x}}{2y} = \frac{x\sqrt[3]{x}}{2y}$$

39.
$$\sqrt[3]{\frac{50x^8}{27y^{12}}} = \frac{\sqrt[3]{50x^8}}{\sqrt[3]{27y^{12}}} = \frac{\sqrt[3]{50x^6 x^2}}{3y^4} = \frac{x^2\sqrt[3]{50x^2}}{3y^4}$$

39.
$$\sqrt[3]{\frac{50x^8}{27y^{12}}} = \frac{\sqrt[3]{50x^8}}{\sqrt[3]{27y^{12}}} = \frac{\sqrt[3]{50x^6 x^2}}{3y^4} = \frac{x^2\sqrt[3]{50x^2}}{3y^4}$$

41.
$$\sqrt[4]{\frac{9y^6}{x^8}} = \frac{\sqrt[4]{9y^6}}{\sqrt[4]{x^8}} = \frac{\sqrt[4]{9y^4 y^2}}{x^2} = \frac{y\sqrt[4]{9y^2}}{x^2}$$

43.
$$\sqrt[5]{\frac{64x^{13}}{y^{20}}} = \frac{\sqrt[5]{64x^{13}}}{\sqrt[5]{y^{20}}} = \frac{\sqrt[5]{32 \cdot 2x^{10} x^3}}{y^4} = \frac{2x^2\sqrt[5]{2x^3}}{y^4}$$

45.
$$\frac{\sqrt{40}}{\sqrt{5}} = \sqrt{\frac{40}{5}} = \sqrt{8} = \sqrt{4 \cdot 2} = 2\sqrt{2}$$

47.
$$\frac{\sqrt[3]{48}}{\sqrt[3]{6}} = \sqrt[3]{\frac{48}{6}} = \sqrt[3]{8} = 2$$

49.
$$\frac{\sqrt{54x^3}}{\sqrt{6x}} = \sqrt{\frac{54x^3}{6x}} = \sqrt{9x^2} = 3x$$

51.
$$\frac{\sqrt{x^5 y^3}}{\sqrt{xy}} = \sqrt{\frac{x^5 y^3}{xy}} = \sqrt{x^4 y^2} = x^2 y$$

53.
$$\frac{\sqrt{200x^3}}{\sqrt{10x^{-1}}} = \sqrt{\frac{200x^3}{10x^{-1}}} = \sqrt{20x^{3-(-1)}}$$
$$= \sqrt{20x^4} = \sqrt{4 \cdot 5x^4} = 2x^2\sqrt{5}$$

55.
$$\frac{\sqrt{72xy}}{2\sqrt{2}} = \frac{1}{2}\sqrt{\frac{72xy}{2}} = \frac{1}{2}\sqrt{36xy}$$
$$= \frac{1}{2} \cdot 6\sqrt{xy} = 3\sqrt{xy}$$

57.
$$\frac{\sqrt[3]{24x^3 y^5}}{\sqrt[3]{3y^2}} = \sqrt[3]{\frac{24x^3 y^5}{3y^2}} = \sqrt[3]{8x^3 y^3} = 2xy$$

59.
$$\frac{\sqrt[4]{32x^{10} y^8}}{\sqrt[4]{2x^2 y^{-2}}} = \sqrt[4]{\frac{32x^{10} y^8}{2x^2 y^{-2}}} = \sqrt[4]{16x^8 y^{8-(-2)}}$$
$$= \sqrt[4]{16x^8 y^{10}} = \sqrt[4]{16x^8 y^8 y^2}$$
$$= 2x^2 y^2 \sqrt[4]{y^2}$$

61.
$$\frac{\sqrt[3]{x^2 + 5x + 6}}{\sqrt[3]{x+2}} = \sqrt[3]{\frac{x^2 + 5x + 6}{x+2}}$$
$$= \sqrt[3]{\frac{(x+2)(x+3)}{x+2}} = \sqrt[3]{x+3}$$

63. a.
$$R_f \frac{\sqrt{c^2 - v^2}}{\sqrt{c^2}} = R_f \sqrt{\frac{c^2 - v^2}{c^2}} = R_f \sqrt{\frac{c^2}{c^2} - \frac{v^2}{c^2}}$$
$$= R_f \sqrt{1 - \left(\frac{v}{c}\right)^2}$$

b.
$$R_f \sqrt{1 - \left(\frac{v}{c}\right)^2} = R_f \sqrt{1 - \left(\frac{c}{c}\right)^2}$$
$$= R_f \sqrt{1 - (1)^2} = R_f \sqrt{1-1}$$
$$= R_f \sqrt{0} = R_f \cdot 0 = 0$$

Your aging rate is zero. This means that a person moving close to the speed of light does not age relative to a friend on Earth.

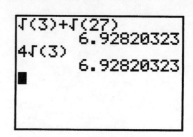

65.
$$P = 2l + 2w = 2\left(2\sqrt{20}\right) + 2\left(\sqrt{125}\right)$$
$$= 4\sqrt{20} + 2\sqrt{125} = 4\sqrt{4 \cdot 5} + 2\sqrt{25 \cdot 5}$$
$$= 4 \cdot 2\sqrt{5} + 2 \cdot 5\sqrt{5} = 8\sqrt{5} + 10\sqrt{5}$$
$$= (8 + 10)\sqrt{5} = 18\sqrt{5}$$

The perimeter is $18\sqrt{5}$ feet.
$$A = lw = 2\sqrt{20} \cdot \sqrt{125} = 2\sqrt{20 \cdot 125}$$
$$= 2\sqrt{2500} = 2 \cdot 50 = 100$$
The area is 100 square feet.

For Exercises 67-71, answers may vary.

73. Statement **d.** is true.
Statement **a.** is false.
$$\sqrt{5} + \sqrt{5} = 2\sqrt{5}$$
Statement **b.** is false. $4\sqrt{3} + 5\sqrt{3} = 9\sqrt{3}$
Statement **c.** is false. In order for two radical expressions to be combined, both the index and the radicand must be the same. Just because two radical expressions are completely simplified does guarantee that the index and radicands match.

75.
$$\frac{\sqrt{20}}{3} + \frac{\sqrt{45}}{4} - \sqrt{80}$$
$$= \frac{\sqrt{4 \cdot 5}}{3} + \frac{\sqrt{9 \cdot 5}}{4} - \sqrt{16 \cdot 5}$$
$$= \frac{2\sqrt{5}}{3} + \frac{3\sqrt{5}}{4} - 4\sqrt{5} = \frac{2}{3}\sqrt{5} + \frac{3}{4}\sqrt{5} - 4\sqrt{5}$$
$$= \left(\frac{2}{3} + \frac{3}{4} - 4\right)\sqrt{5} = \left(\frac{2}{3} \cdot \frac{4}{4} + \frac{3}{4} \cdot \frac{3}{3} - \frac{4}{1} \cdot \frac{12}{12}\right)\sqrt{5}$$
$$= \left(\frac{8}{12} + \frac{9}{12} - \frac{48}{12}\right)\sqrt{5} = -\frac{31}{12}\sqrt{5} \text{ or } -\frac{31\sqrt{5}}{12}$$

77. Answers will vary. For example, consider Exercise 11.

79. $\sqrt{16x} - \sqrt{9x} = \sqrt{7x}$

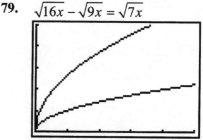

The graphs do not coincide.
Correct the simplification.
$$\sqrt{16x} - \sqrt{9x} = 4\sqrt{x} - 3\sqrt{x}$$
$$= (4 - 3)\sqrt{x} = \sqrt{x}$$

Review Exercises

81.
$$2(3x - 1) - 4 = 2x - (6 - x)$$
$$6x - 2 - 4 = 2x - 6 + x$$
$$6x - 6 = x - 6$$
$$5x = 0$$
$$x = 0$$

82. $x^2 - 8xy + 12y^2 = (x - 6y)(x - 2y)$

83.
$$\frac{2}{x^2 + 5x + 6} + \frac{3x}{x^2 + 6x + 9}$$
$$= \frac{2}{(x + 3)(x + 2)} + \frac{3x}{(x + 3)^2}$$
$$= \frac{2(x + 3)}{(x + 3)^2(x + 2)} + \frac{3x(x + 2)}{(x + 3)^2(x + 2)}$$

$$= \frac{2(x+3)+3x(x+2)}{(x+3)^2(x+2)}$$

$$= \frac{2x+6+3x^2+6x}{(x+3)^2(x+2)} = \frac{3x^2+8x+6}{(x+3)^2(x+2)}$$

Multiplying with More Than One Term and Rationalizing Denominators

10.5 CHECK POINTS

CHECK POINT 1

a.
$$\sqrt{6}\left(x+\sqrt{10}\right)=\sqrt{6}\cdot x+\sqrt{6}\cdot\sqrt{10}=x\sqrt{6}+\sqrt{60}$$
$$=x\sqrt{6}+\sqrt{4\cdot15}=x\sqrt{6}+2\sqrt{15}$$

b. $\sqrt[3]{y}\left(\sqrt[3]{y^2}-\sqrt[3]{7}\right)=\sqrt[3]{y}\cdot\sqrt[3]{y^2}-\sqrt[3]{y}\cdot\sqrt[3]{7}$
$$=\sqrt[3]{y^3}-\sqrt[3]{7y}=y-\sqrt[3]{7y}$$

c. $\left(6\sqrt{5}+3\sqrt{2}\right)\left(2\sqrt{5}-4\sqrt{2}\right)$
$$=12\sqrt{25}+\left(-24\sqrt{10}\right)+6\sqrt{10}+\left(-12\sqrt{4}\right)$$
$$=12\cdot5+\left(-24+6\right)\sqrt{10}+\left(-12\cdot2\right)$$
$$=60-18\sqrt{10}-24=36-18\sqrt{10}$$

CHECK POINT 2

a. $\left(\sqrt{5}+\sqrt{6}\right)^2=\left(\sqrt{5}\right)^2+2\cdot\sqrt{5}\cdot\sqrt{6}+\left(\sqrt{6}\right)^2$
$$=5+2\sqrt{30}+6=11+2\sqrt{30}$$

b. $\left(\sqrt{6}+\sqrt{5}\right)\left(\sqrt{6}-\sqrt{5}\right)=\left(\sqrt{6}\right)^2-\left(\sqrt{5}\right)^2$
$$=6-5=1$$

c. $\left(\sqrt{a}-\sqrt{7}\right)\left(\sqrt{a}+\sqrt{7}\right)=\left(\sqrt{a}\right)^2-\left(\sqrt{7}\right)^2=a-7$

CHECK POINT 3

a. $\dfrac{\sqrt{3}}{\sqrt{7}}=\dfrac{\sqrt{3}}{\sqrt{7}}\cdot\dfrac{\sqrt{7}}{\sqrt{7}}=\dfrac{\sqrt{21}}{\sqrt{49}}=\dfrac{\sqrt{21}}{7}$

b. $\sqrt[3]{\dfrac{2}{9}}=\dfrac{\sqrt[3]{2}}{\sqrt[3]{9}}=\dfrac{\sqrt[3]{2}}{\sqrt[3]{3^2}}=\dfrac{\sqrt[3]{2}}{\sqrt[3]{3^2}}\cdot\dfrac{\sqrt[3]{3}}{\sqrt[3]{3}}=\dfrac{\sqrt[3]{6}}{\sqrt[3]{3^3}}=\dfrac{\sqrt[3]{6}}{3}$

CHECK POINT 4

a.
$$\sqrt{\dfrac{2x}{7y}}=\dfrac{\sqrt{2x}}{\sqrt{7y}}=\dfrac{\sqrt{2x}}{\sqrt{7y}}\cdot\dfrac{\sqrt{7y}}{\sqrt{7y}}=\dfrac{\sqrt{14xy}}{7y}$$

b.
$$\dfrac{\sqrt[3]{x}}{\sqrt[3]{9y}}=\dfrac{\sqrt[3]{x}}{\sqrt[3]{3^2 y}}\cdot\dfrac{\sqrt[3]{3y^2}}{\sqrt[3]{3y^2}}=\dfrac{\sqrt[3]{3xy^2}}{\sqrt[3]{3^3 y^3}}=\dfrac{\sqrt[3]{3xy^2}}{3y}$$

c.
$$\dfrac{6x}{\sqrt[5]{8x^2y^4}}=\dfrac{6x}{\sqrt[5]{2^3x^2y^4}}\cdot\dfrac{\sqrt[5]{2^2x^3y}}{\sqrt[5]{2^2x^3y}}$$
$$=\dfrac{6x\sqrt[5]{2^2x^3y}}{\sqrt[5]{2^5x^5y^5}}=\dfrac{6x\sqrt[5]{4x^3y}}{2xy}=\dfrac{3\sqrt[5]{4x^3y}}{y}$$

CHECK POINT 5

$$\dfrac{18}{2\sqrt{3}+3}=\dfrac{18}{2\sqrt{3}+3}\cdot\dfrac{2\sqrt{3}-3}{2\sqrt{3}-3}$$
$$=\dfrac{18\left(2\sqrt{3}-3\right)}{\left(2\sqrt{3}+3\right)\left(2\sqrt{3}-3\right)}=\dfrac{18\left(2\sqrt{3}-3\right)}{\left(2\sqrt{3}\right)^2-3^2}$$
$$=\dfrac{18\left(2\sqrt{3}-3\right)}{4\cdot3-9}=\dfrac{18\left(2\sqrt{3}-3\right)}{12-9}=\dfrac{\overset{6}{\cancel{18}}\left(2\sqrt{3}-3\right)}{\underset{1}{\cancel{3}}}$$
$$=6\left(2\sqrt{3}-3\right)=12\sqrt{3}-18$$

CHECK POINT 6

$$\dfrac{3+\sqrt{7}}{\sqrt{5}-\sqrt{2}}=\dfrac{3+\sqrt{7}}{\sqrt{5}-\sqrt{2}}\cdot\dfrac{\sqrt{5}+\sqrt{2}}{\sqrt{5}+\sqrt{2}}$$
$$=\dfrac{3\sqrt{5}+3\sqrt{2}+\sqrt{7}\sqrt{5}+\sqrt{7}\sqrt{2}}{\left(\sqrt{5}\right)^2-\left(\sqrt{2}\right)^2}$$
$$=\dfrac{3\sqrt{5}+3\sqrt{2}+\sqrt{35}+\sqrt{14}}{5-2}$$
$$=\dfrac{3\sqrt{5}+3\sqrt{2}+\sqrt{35}+\sqrt{14}}{3}$$

CHECK POINT 7

$$\dfrac{\sqrt{x+3}-\sqrt{x}}{3}=\dfrac{\sqrt{x+3}-\sqrt{x}}{3}\cdot\dfrac{\sqrt{x+3}+\sqrt{x}}{\sqrt{x+3}+\sqrt{x}}$$
$$=\dfrac{\left(\sqrt{x+3}\right)^2-\left(\sqrt{x}\right)^2}{3\left(\sqrt{x+3}+\sqrt{x}\right)}=\dfrac{x+3-x}{3\left(\sqrt{x+3}+\sqrt{x}\right)}$$

$$=\frac{3}{3\left(\sqrt{x+3}+\sqrt{x}\right)}=\frac{1}{\sqrt{x+3}+\sqrt{x}}$$

EXERCISE SET 10.5

1. $\sqrt{2}\left(x+\sqrt{7}\right)=\sqrt{2}\cdot x+\sqrt{2}\sqrt{7}=x\sqrt{2}+\sqrt{14}$

3. $\sqrt{6}\left(7-\sqrt{6}\right)=\sqrt{6}\cdot7-\sqrt{6}\sqrt{6}$
$$=7\sqrt{6}-\sqrt{36}=7\sqrt{6}-6$$

5. $\sqrt{3}\left(4\sqrt{6}-2\sqrt{3}\right)=\sqrt{3}\cdot4\sqrt{6}-\sqrt{3}\cdot2\sqrt{3}$
$$=4\sqrt{18}-2\sqrt{9}=4\sqrt{9\cdot2}-2\cdot3$$
$$=4\cdot3\sqrt{2}-6=12\sqrt{2}-6$$

7. $\sqrt[3]{2}\left(\sqrt[3]{6}+4\sqrt[3]{5}\right)=\sqrt[3]{2}\cdot\sqrt[3]{6}+\sqrt[3]{2}\cdot4\sqrt[3]{5}$
$$=\sqrt[3]{12}+4\sqrt[3]{10}$$

9. $\sqrt[3]{x}\left(\sqrt[3]{16x^2}-\sqrt[3]{x}\right)=\sqrt[3]{x}\cdot\sqrt[3]{16x^2}-\sqrt[3]{x}\cdot\sqrt[3]{x}$
$$=\sqrt[3]{x}\cdot\sqrt[3]{8\cdot2x^2}-\sqrt[3]{x^2}=\sqrt[3]{8\cdot2x^3}-\sqrt[3]{x^2}$$
$$=2x\sqrt[3]{2}-\sqrt[3]{x^2}$$

11. $\left(5+\sqrt{2}\right)\left(6+\sqrt{2}\right)=5\cdot6+5\sqrt{2}+6\sqrt{2}+\sqrt{2}\sqrt{2}$
$$=30+(5+6)\sqrt{2}+2=32+11\sqrt{2}$$

13. $\left(6+\sqrt{5}\right)\left(9-4\sqrt{5}\right)$
$$=6\cdot9-6\cdot4\sqrt{5}+9\sqrt{5}-4\sqrt{5}\sqrt{5}$$
$$=54-24\sqrt{5}+9\sqrt{5}-4\cdot5$$
$$=54+(-24+9)\sqrt{5}-20$$
$$=34+(-15)\sqrt{5}=34-15\sqrt{5}$$

15. $\left(6-3\sqrt{7}\right)\left(2-5\sqrt{7}\right)$
$$=6\cdot2-6\cdot5\sqrt{7}-2\cdot3\sqrt{7}+3\sqrt{7}\cdot5\sqrt{7}$$
$$=12-30\sqrt{7}-6\sqrt{7}+15\cdot7$$
$$=12+(-30-6)\sqrt{7}+105$$
$$=117+(-36)\sqrt{7}=117-36\sqrt{7}$$

17. $\left(\sqrt{2}+\sqrt{7}\right)\left(\sqrt{3}+\sqrt{5}\right)$
$$=\sqrt{2}\sqrt{3}+\sqrt{2}\sqrt{5}+\sqrt{7}\sqrt{3}+\sqrt{7}\sqrt{5}$$
$$=\sqrt{6}+\sqrt{10}+\sqrt{21}+\sqrt{35}$$

19. $\left(\sqrt{2}-\sqrt{7}\right)\left(\sqrt{3}-\sqrt{5}\right)$
$$=\sqrt{2}\sqrt{3}-\sqrt{2}\sqrt{5}-\sqrt{7}\sqrt{3}+\sqrt{7}\sqrt{5}$$
$$=\sqrt{6}-\sqrt{10}-\sqrt{21}+\sqrt{35}$$

21. $\left(3\sqrt{2}-4\sqrt{3}\right)\left(2\sqrt{2}+5\sqrt{3}\right)$
$$=3\sqrt{2}\left(2\sqrt{2}\right)+3\sqrt{2}\left(5\sqrt{3}\right)$$
$$-4\sqrt{3}\left(2\sqrt{2}\right)-4\sqrt{3}\left(5\sqrt{3}\right)$$
$$=6\cdot2+15\sqrt{6}-8\sqrt{6}-20\cdot3=12+7\sqrt{6}-60$$
$$=7\sqrt{6}\quad48\ \text{or}\ -48+7\sqrt{6}$$

23. $\left(\sqrt{3}+\sqrt{5}\right)^2=\left(\sqrt{3}\right)^2+2\sqrt{3}\sqrt{5}+\left(\sqrt{5}\right)^2$
$$=3+2\sqrt{15}+5=8+2\sqrt{15}$$

25. $\left(\sqrt{3x}-\sqrt{y}\right)^2=\left(\sqrt{3x}\right)^2-2\sqrt{3x}\sqrt{y}+\left(\sqrt{y}\right)^2$
$$=3x-2\sqrt{3xy}+y$$

27. $\left(\sqrt{5}+7\right)\left(\sqrt{5}-7\right)=\sqrt{5}\sqrt{5}-7\sqrt{5}+7\sqrt{5}-7\cdot7$
$$=5-7\sqrt{5}+7\sqrt{5}-49$$
$$=5-49=-44$$

29. $\left(2-5\sqrt{3}\right)\left(2+5\sqrt{3}\right)$
$$=2\cdot2+2\cdot5\sqrt{3}-2\cdot5\sqrt{3}-5\sqrt{3}\cdot5\sqrt{3}$$
$$=4+10\sqrt{3}-10\sqrt{3}-25\cdot3=4-75=-71$$

31. $\left(3\sqrt{2}+2\sqrt{3}\right)\left(3\sqrt{2}-2\sqrt{3}\right)$
$$=3\sqrt{2}\cdot3\sqrt{2}-3\sqrt{2}\cdot2\sqrt{3}$$
$$+3\sqrt{2}\cdot2\sqrt{3}-2\sqrt{3}\cdot2\sqrt{3}$$
$$=9\cdot2-6\sqrt{6}+6\sqrt{6}-4\cdot3=18-12=6$$

33. $\left(3-\sqrt{x}\right)\left(2-\sqrt{x}\right)$
$$=3\cdot2-3\sqrt{x}-2\sqrt{x}+\sqrt{x}\sqrt{x}$$

$$= 6 + (-3 - 2)\sqrt{x} + x$$
$$= 6 + (-5)\sqrt{x} + x = 6 - 5\sqrt{x} + x$$

35. $\left(\sqrt[3]{x} - 4\right)\left(\sqrt[3]{x} + 5\right) = \sqrt[3]{x}\sqrt[3]{x} + 5\sqrt[3]{x} - 4\sqrt[3]{x} - 4 \cdot 5$

$$= \sqrt[3]{x^2} + (5 - 4)\sqrt[3]{x} - 20 = \sqrt[3]{x^2} + \sqrt[3]{x} - 20$$

37. $\left(x + \sqrt[3]{y^2}\right)\left(2x - \sqrt[3]{y^2}\right)$

$$= x \cdot 2x - x\sqrt[3]{y^2} + 2x\sqrt[3]{y^2} - \sqrt[3]{y^2}\sqrt[3]{y^2}$$
$$= 2x^2 + (-x + 2x)\sqrt[3]{y^2} - \sqrt[3]{y^4}$$
$$= 2x^2 + x\sqrt[3]{y^2} - \sqrt[3]{y^3 y} = 2x^2 + x\sqrt[3]{y^2} - y\sqrt[3]{y}$$

39. $\dfrac{\sqrt{2}}{\sqrt{5}} = \dfrac{\sqrt{2}}{\sqrt{5}} \cdot \dfrac{\sqrt{5}}{\sqrt{5}} = \dfrac{\sqrt{2 \cdot 5}}{\sqrt{5 \cdot 5}} = \dfrac{\sqrt{10}}{5}$

41. $\sqrt{\dfrac{11}{x}} = \dfrac{\sqrt{11}}{\sqrt{x}} = \dfrac{\sqrt{11}}{\sqrt{x}} \cdot \dfrac{\sqrt{x}}{\sqrt{x}} = \dfrac{\sqrt{11x}}{\sqrt{x^2}} = \dfrac{\sqrt{11x}}{x}$

43. $\dfrac{9}{\sqrt{3y}} = \dfrac{9}{\sqrt{3y}} \cdot \dfrac{\sqrt{3y}}{\sqrt{3y}} = \dfrac{9\sqrt{3y}}{\sqrt{3y \cdot 3y}}$

$$= \dfrac{\overset{3}{\cancel{9}}\sqrt{3y}}{\underset{1}{\cancel{3}} y} = \dfrac{3\sqrt{3y}}{y}$$

45. $\dfrac{1}{\sqrt[3]{2}} = \dfrac{1}{\sqrt[3]{2}} \cdot \dfrac{\sqrt[3]{2^2}}{\sqrt[3]{2^2}} = \dfrac{\sqrt[3]{2^2}}{\sqrt[3]{2^3}} = \dfrac{\sqrt[3]{4}}{2}$

47. $\dfrac{6}{\sqrt[3]{4}} = \dfrac{6}{\sqrt[3]{4}} \cdot \dfrac{\sqrt[3]{4^2}}{\sqrt[3]{4^2}} = \dfrac{6\sqrt[3]{4^2}}{\sqrt[3]{4}\sqrt[3]{4^2}} = \dfrac{6\sqrt[3]{16}}{\sqrt[3]{4^3}}$

$$= \dfrac{6\sqrt[3]{8 \cdot 2}}{4} = \dfrac{6 \cdot 2\sqrt[3]{2}}{4} = \dfrac{\overset{3}{\cancel{12}}\sqrt[3]{2}}{\underset{1}{\cancel{4}}} = 3\sqrt[3]{2}$

49. $\sqrt[3]{\dfrac{2}{3}} = \dfrac{\sqrt[3]{2}}{\sqrt[3]{3}} = \dfrac{\sqrt[3]{2}}{\sqrt[3]{3}} \cdot \dfrac{\sqrt[3]{3^2}}{\sqrt[3]{3^2}} = \dfrac{\sqrt[3]{2 \cdot 3^2}}{\sqrt[3]{3^3}}$

$$= \dfrac{\sqrt[3]{2 \cdot 9}}{3} = \dfrac{\sqrt[3]{18}}{3}$$

51. $\dfrac{4}{\sqrt[3]{x}} = \dfrac{4}{\sqrt[3]{x}} \cdot \dfrac{\sqrt[3]{x^2}}{\sqrt[3]{x^2}} = \dfrac{4\sqrt[3]{x^2}}{\sqrt[3]{x}\sqrt[3]{x^2}} = \dfrac{4\sqrt[3]{x^2}}{\sqrt[3]{x^3}} = \dfrac{4\sqrt[3]{x^2}}{x}$

53. $\sqrt[3]{\dfrac{2}{y^2}} = \dfrac{\sqrt[3]{2}}{\sqrt[3]{y^2}} = \dfrac{\sqrt[3]{2}}{\sqrt[3]{y^2}} \cdot \dfrac{\sqrt[3]{y}}{\sqrt[3]{y}} = \dfrac{\sqrt[3]{2y}}{\sqrt[3]{y^3}} = \dfrac{\sqrt[3]{2y}}{y}$

55. $\dfrac{7}{\sqrt[3]{2x^2}} = \dfrac{7}{\sqrt[3]{2x^2}} \cdot \dfrac{\sqrt[3]{2^2 x}}{\sqrt[3]{2^2 x}} = \dfrac{7\sqrt[3]{2^2 x}}{\sqrt[3]{2x^2}\sqrt[3]{2^2 x}}$

$$= \dfrac{7\sqrt[3]{4x}}{\sqrt[3]{2^3 x^3}} = \dfrac{7\sqrt[3]{4x}}{2x}$$

57. $\sqrt[3]{\dfrac{2}{xy^2}} = \dfrac{\sqrt[3]{2}}{\sqrt[3]{xy^2}} = \dfrac{\sqrt[3]{2}}{\sqrt[3]{xy^2}} \cdot \dfrac{\sqrt[3]{x^2 y}}{\sqrt[3]{x^2 y}}$

$$= \dfrac{\sqrt[3]{2}\sqrt[3]{x^2 y}}{\sqrt[3]{xy^2}\sqrt[3]{x^2 y}} = \dfrac{\sqrt[3]{2x^2 y}}{\sqrt[3]{x^3 y^3}} = \dfrac{\sqrt[3]{2x^2 y}}{xy}$

59. $\dfrac{3}{\sqrt[4]{x}} = \dfrac{3}{\sqrt[4]{x}} \cdot \dfrac{\sqrt[4]{x^3}}{\sqrt[4]{x^3}} = \dfrac{3\sqrt[4]{x^3}}{\sqrt[4]{xx^3}} = \dfrac{3\sqrt[4]{x^3}}{\sqrt[4]{x^4}} = \dfrac{3\sqrt[4]{x^3}}{x}$

61. $\dfrac{6}{\sqrt[5]{8x^3}} = \dfrac{6}{\sqrt[5]{2^3 x^3}} \cdot \dfrac{\sqrt[5]{2^2 x^2}}{\sqrt[5]{2^2 x^2}} = \dfrac{6\sqrt[5]{4x^2}}{\sqrt[5]{2^5 x^5}}$

$$= \dfrac{6\sqrt[5]{4x^2}}{2x} = \dfrac{3\sqrt[5]{4x^2}}{x}$$

63. $\dfrac{2x^2 y}{\sqrt[5]{4x^2 y^4}} = \dfrac{2x^2 y}{\sqrt[5]{2^2 x^2 y^4}} \cdot \dfrac{\sqrt[5]{2^3 x^3 y}}{\sqrt[5]{2^3 x^3 y}} = \dfrac{2x^2 y\sqrt[5]{8x^3 y}}{\sqrt[5]{2^5 x^5 y^5}}$

$$= \dfrac{\cancel{2}x^{\cancel{2}} \cancel{y}\sqrt[5]{8x^3 y}}{\cancel{2}\,\cancel{x}\,\cancel{y}} = x\sqrt[5]{8x^3 y}$$

65. $\dfrac{8}{\sqrt{5} + 2} = \dfrac{8}{\sqrt{5} + 2} \cdot \dfrac{\sqrt{5} - 2}{\sqrt{5} - 2}$

$$= \dfrac{8\sqrt{5} - 8 \cdot 2}{\sqrt{5}\sqrt{5} - 2\sqrt{5} + 2\sqrt{5} - 2 \cdot 2}$$

$$= \dfrac{8\sqrt{5} - 16}{5 - 2\cancel{\sqrt{5}} + 2\cancel{\sqrt{5}} - 4}$$

$$= \dfrac{8\sqrt{5} - 16}{5 - 4} = \dfrac{8\sqrt{5} - 16}{1} = 8\sqrt{5} - 16$$

67.
$$\frac{13}{\sqrt{11}-3} = \frac{13}{\sqrt{11}-3}\cdot\frac{\sqrt{11}+3}{\sqrt{11}+3}$$
$$= \frac{13(\sqrt{11}+3)}{(\sqrt{11}-3)(\sqrt{11}+3)}$$
$$= \frac{13\sqrt{11}+13\cdot 3}{\sqrt{11}\cdot\sqrt{11}+3\sqrt{11}-3\sqrt{11}-3\cdot 3}$$
$$= \frac{13\sqrt{11}+39}{11+3\sqrt{11}-3\sqrt{11}-9}$$
$$= \frac{13\sqrt{11}+39}{11-9} = \frac{13\sqrt{11}+39}{2}$$

69.
$$\frac{6}{\sqrt{5}+\sqrt{3}} = \frac{6}{\sqrt{5}+\sqrt{3}}\cdot\frac{\sqrt{5}-\sqrt{3}}{\sqrt{5}-\sqrt{3}}$$
$$= \frac{6(\sqrt{5}-\sqrt{3})}{(\sqrt{5}+\sqrt{3})(\sqrt{5}-\sqrt{3})}$$
$$= \frac{6\sqrt{5}-6\sqrt{3}}{\sqrt{5}\sqrt{5}-\sqrt{3}\sqrt{5}+\sqrt{3}\sqrt{5}-\sqrt{3}\sqrt{3}}$$
$$= \frac{6\sqrt{5}-6\sqrt{3}}{5-\sqrt{15}+\sqrt{15}-3}$$
$$= \frac{6\sqrt{5}-6\sqrt{3}}{5-3} = \frac{6\sqrt{5}-6\sqrt{3}}{2}$$
$$= \frac{2(3\sqrt{5}-3\sqrt{3})}{2} = 3\sqrt{5}-3\sqrt{3}$$

71.
$$\frac{\sqrt{a}}{\sqrt{a}-\sqrt{b}}$$
$$= \frac{\sqrt{a}}{\sqrt{a}-\sqrt{b}}\cdot\frac{\sqrt{a}+\sqrt{b}}{\sqrt{a}+\sqrt{b}} = \frac{\sqrt{a}(\sqrt{a}+\sqrt{b})}{(\sqrt{a}-\sqrt{b})(\sqrt{a}+\sqrt{b})}$$
$$= \frac{\sqrt{a}\sqrt{a}+\sqrt{a}\sqrt{b}}{\sqrt{a}\sqrt{a}+\sqrt{a}\sqrt{b}-\sqrt{a}\sqrt{b}-\sqrt{b}\sqrt{b}} = \frac{a+\sqrt{ab}}{a-b}$$

73.
$$\frac{25}{5\sqrt{2}-3\sqrt{5}} = \frac{25}{5\sqrt{2}-3\sqrt{5}}\cdot\frac{5\sqrt{2}+3\sqrt{5}}{5\sqrt{2}+3\sqrt{5}}$$
$$= \frac{25(5\sqrt{2}+3\sqrt{5})}{(5\sqrt{2}-3\sqrt{5})(5\sqrt{2}+3\sqrt{5})}$$

$$= \frac{125\sqrt{2}+75\sqrt{5}}{5\cdot 5\sqrt{2\cdot 2}+5\cdot 3\sqrt{2\cdot 5}-5\cdot 3\sqrt{2\cdot 5}-3\cdot 3\sqrt{5\cdot 5}}$$
$$= \frac{125\sqrt{2}+75\sqrt{5}}{25\cdot 2-9\cdot 5} = \frac{125\sqrt{2}+75\sqrt{5}}{50-45}$$
$$= \frac{125\sqrt{2}+75\sqrt{5}}{5} = \frac{5(25\sqrt{2}+15\sqrt{5})}{5}$$
$$= 25\sqrt{2}+15\sqrt{5}$$

75.
$$\frac{\sqrt{5}+\sqrt{3}}{\sqrt{5}-\sqrt{3}}$$
$$= \frac{\sqrt{5}+\sqrt{3}}{\sqrt{5}-\sqrt{3}}\cdot\frac{\sqrt{5}+\sqrt{3}}{\sqrt{5}+\sqrt{3}} = \frac{(\sqrt{5}+\sqrt{3})^2}{(\sqrt{5}-\sqrt{3})(\sqrt{5}+\sqrt{3})}$$
$$= \frac{(\sqrt{5})^2+2\sqrt{5}\sqrt{3}+(\sqrt{3})^2}{\sqrt{5}\cdot\sqrt{5}+\sqrt{5}\cdot\sqrt{3}-\sqrt{5}\cdot\sqrt{3}-\sqrt{3}\sqrt{3}}$$
$$= \frac{5+2\sqrt{15}+3}{5+\sqrt{15}-\sqrt{15}-3} = \frac{8+2\sqrt{15}}{5-3}$$
$$= \frac{2(4+\sqrt{15})}{2} = 4+\sqrt{15}$$

77.
$$\frac{\sqrt{x}+1}{\sqrt{x}+3} = \frac{\sqrt{x}+1}{\sqrt{x}+3}\cdot\frac{\sqrt{x}-3}{\sqrt{x}-3}$$
$$= \frac{\sqrt{x}\cdot\sqrt{x}-3\sqrt{x}+1\sqrt{x}-3\cdot 1}{\sqrt{x}\cdot\sqrt{x}-3\sqrt{x}+3\sqrt{x}-3\cdot 3}$$
$$= \frac{\sqrt{x^2}+(-3+1)\sqrt{x}-3}{\sqrt{x^2}-9}$$
$$= \frac{x+(-2)\sqrt{x}-3}{x-9} = \frac{x-2\sqrt{x}-3}{x-9}$$

79.
$$\frac{5\sqrt{3}-3\sqrt{2}}{3\sqrt{2}-2\sqrt{3}}$$
$$= \frac{5\sqrt{3}-3\sqrt{2}}{3\sqrt{2}-2\sqrt{3}}\cdot\frac{3\sqrt{2}+2\sqrt{3}}{3\sqrt{2}+2\sqrt{3}}$$
$$= \frac{5\sqrt{3}\cdot 3\sqrt{2}+5\sqrt{3}\cdot 2\sqrt{3}-3\sqrt{2}\cdot 3\sqrt{2}-3\sqrt{2}\cdot 2\sqrt{3}}{3\sqrt{2}\cdot 3\sqrt{2}+3\sqrt{2}\cdot 2\sqrt{3}-3\sqrt{2}\cdot 2\sqrt{3}-2\sqrt{3}\cdot 2\sqrt{3}}$$
$$= \frac{15\sqrt{6}+10\cdot 3-9\cdot 2-6\sqrt{6}}{9\cdot 2+6\sqrt{6}-6\sqrt{6}-4\cdot 3}$$

$$= \frac{15\sqrt{6}+30-18-6\sqrt{6}}{18-12} = \frac{9\sqrt{6}+12}{6}$$

$$= \frac{\cancel{3}\left(3\sqrt{6}+4\right)}{\cancel{3}\cdot 2} = \frac{3\sqrt{6}+4}{2}$$

81.
$$\frac{2\sqrt{x}+\sqrt{y}}{\sqrt{y}-2\sqrt{x}} = \frac{2\sqrt{x}+\sqrt{y}}{\sqrt{y}-2\sqrt{x}}\cdot\frac{\sqrt{y}+2\sqrt{x}}{\sqrt{y}+2\sqrt{x}}$$

$$= \frac{2\sqrt{x}\sqrt{y}+2\sqrt{x}\cdot 2\sqrt{x}+\sqrt{y}\sqrt{y}+2\sqrt{x}\sqrt{y}}{\sqrt{y}\sqrt{y}+2\sqrt{x}\sqrt{y}-2\sqrt{x}\sqrt{y}-2\sqrt{x}\cdot 2\sqrt{x}}$$

$$= \frac{2\sqrt{xy}+4\sqrt{x^2}+\sqrt{y^2}+2\sqrt{xy}}{\sqrt{y^2}+2\cancel{\sqrt{xy}}-2\cancel{\sqrt{xy}}-4\sqrt{x^2}}$$

$$= \frac{2\sqrt{xy}+4x+y+2\sqrt{xy}}{y-4x} = \frac{4\sqrt{xy}+4x+y}{y-4x}$$

83.
$$\sqrt{\frac{3}{2}} = \frac{\sqrt{3}}{\sqrt{2}}\cdot\frac{\sqrt{3}}{\sqrt{3}} = \frac{\sqrt{3}\sqrt{3}}{\sqrt{2}\sqrt{3}} = \frac{3}{\sqrt{6}}$$

85.
$$\frac{\sqrt[3]{4x}}{\sqrt[3]{y}} = \frac{\sqrt[3]{4x}}{\sqrt[3]{y}}\cdot\frac{\sqrt[3]{4^2 x^2}}{\sqrt[3]{4^2 x^2}} = \frac{\sqrt[3]{4^3 x^3}}{\sqrt[3]{4^2 x^2 y}}$$

$$= \frac{4x}{\sqrt[3]{16x^2 y}} = \frac{4x}{\sqrt[3]{8\cdot 2x^2 y}} = \frac{4x}{2\sqrt[3]{2x^2 y}} = \frac{2x}{\sqrt[3]{2x^2 y}}$$

87.
$$\frac{\sqrt{x}+3}{\sqrt{x}} = \frac{\sqrt{x}+3}{\sqrt{x}}\cdot\frac{\sqrt{x}-3}{\sqrt{x}-3}$$

$$= \frac{\sqrt{x}\cdot\sqrt{x}-3\sqrt{x}+3\sqrt{x}-3\cdot 3}{\sqrt{x}\cdot\sqrt{x}-3\sqrt{x}}$$

$$= \frac{\sqrt{x^2}-9}{\sqrt{x^2}-3\sqrt{x}} = \frac{x-9}{x-3\sqrt{x}}$$

89.
$$\frac{\sqrt{a}+\sqrt{b}}{\sqrt{a}-\sqrt{b}} = \frac{\sqrt{a}+\sqrt{b}}{\sqrt{a}-\sqrt{b}}\cdot\frac{\sqrt{a}-\sqrt{b}}{\sqrt{a}-\sqrt{b}}$$

$$= \frac{\sqrt{a}\cdot\sqrt{a}-\sqrt{a}\sqrt{b}+\sqrt{a}\sqrt{b}-\sqrt{b}\sqrt{b}}{\sqrt{a}\cdot\sqrt{a}-\sqrt{a}\sqrt{b}-\sqrt{a}\sqrt{b}+\sqrt{b}\sqrt{b}}$$

$$= \frac{\sqrt{a^2}-\cancel{\sqrt{ab}}+\cancel{\sqrt{ab}}-\sqrt{b^2}}{\sqrt{a^2}-\sqrt{ab}-\sqrt{ab}+\sqrt{b^2}}$$

$$= \frac{a-b}{a-2\sqrt{ab}+b}$$

91.
$$\frac{\sqrt{x+5}-\sqrt{x}}{5} = \frac{\sqrt{x+5}-\sqrt{x}}{5}\cdot\frac{\sqrt{x+5}+\sqrt{x}}{\sqrt{x+5}+\sqrt{x}}$$

$$= \frac{\left(\sqrt{x+5}\right)^2+\sqrt{x+5}\cdot\sqrt{x}-\sqrt{x+5}\cdot\sqrt{x}-\left(\sqrt{x}\right)^2}{5\left(\sqrt{x+5}+\sqrt{x}\right)}$$

$$= \frac{x+5+\sqrt{x(x+5)}-\sqrt{x(x+5)}-x}{5\left(\sqrt{x+5}+\sqrt{x}\right)}$$

$$= \frac{5}{5\left(\sqrt{x+5}+\sqrt{x}\right)} = \frac{1}{\sqrt{x+5}+\sqrt{x}}$$

93.
$$\frac{\sqrt{x}+\sqrt{y}}{x^2-y^2} = \frac{\sqrt{x}+\sqrt{y}}{x^2-y^2}\cdot\frac{\sqrt{x}-\sqrt{y}}{\sqrt{x}-\sqrt{y}}$$

$$= \frac{\left(\sqrt{x}\right)^2-\cancel{\sqrt{xy}}+\cancel{\sqrt{xy}}-\left(\sqrt{y}\right)^2}{x^2\sqrt{x}-x^2\sqrt{y}-y^2\sqrt{x}+y^2\sqrt{y}}$$

$$= \frac{x-y}{x^2\left(\sqrt{x}-\sqrt{y}\right)-y^2\left(\sqrt{x}-\sqrt{y}\right)}$$

$$= \frac{x-y}{\left(\sqrt{x}-\sqrt{y}\right)\left(x^2-y^2\right)}$$

$$= \frac{\cancel{x-y}}{\left(\sqrt{x}-\sqrt{y}\right)(x+y)\cancel{(x-y)}}$$

$$= \frac{1}{\left(\sqrt{x}-\sqrt{y}\right)(x+y)}$$

95.
$$P(4) = 6.85\sqrt{4}+19 = 6.85\cdot 2+19$$
$$= 13.7+19 = 32.7$$

Approximately 33% of U.S. households are online. This model predicts the number of households extremely well. The actual percentage shown on the graph is 33%.

97.
$$\frac{\text{change in percent}}{\text{change in time}} = \frac{33-19}{2001-1997} = \frac{14}{4} = 3.5$$

The average yearly increase from 1997 to 2001 is 3.5%

99.

$$6.85\left(\frac{\sqrt{t+h}-\sqrt{t}}{h}\right)=6.85\left(\frac{\sqrt{0+4}-\sqrt{0}}{4}\right)$$

$$=6.85\left(\frac{\sqrt{4}}{4}\right)=6.85\left(\frac{2}{4}\right)=6.85\left(\frac{1}{2}\right)\approx 3.4$$

The model predicts the yearly increase in percentage very well. The average yearly increase predicted in Exercise 97 is 3.5%. This is very close to 3.4% found here.

101. a.

$$6.85\left(\frac{\sqrt{t+h}-\sqrt{t}}{h}\right)$$

$$=6.85\left(\frac{\sqrt{t+h}-\sqrt{t}}{h}\cdot\frac{\sqrt{t+h}+\sqrt{t}}{\sqrt{t+h}+\sqrt{t}}\right)$$

$$=6.85\left(\frac{\left(\sqrt{t+h}\right)^2-\left(\sqrt{t}\right)^2}{h\sqrt{t+h}+h\sqrt{t}}\right)$$

$$=6.85\left(\frac{t+h-t}{h\sqrt{t+h}+h\sqrt{t}}\right)$$

$$=6.85\left(\frac{h}{h\left(\sqrt{t+h}+\sqrt{t}\right)}\right)$$

$$=6.85\left(\frac{1}{\sqrt{t+h}+\sqrt{t}}\right)=\frac{6.85}{\sqrt{t+h}+\sqrt{t}}$$

b.

$$\frac{6.85}{\sqrt{t+h}+\sqrt{t}}=\frac{6.85}{\sqrt{t+0}+\sqrt{t}}$$

$$=\frac{6.85}{\sqrt{t}+\sqrt{t}}=\frac{6.85}{2\sqrt{t}}=\frac{3.425}{\sqrt{t}}$$

c.

$$\frac{3.425}{\sqrt{t}}=\frac{3.425}{\sqrt{4}}=\frac{3.425}{2}=1.7125$$

The rate of change in percentage in 2001 was approximately 1.7%.

103. a.

$$P(25)=\frac{25\left(13+\sqrt{25}\right)}{5\sqrt{25}}$$

$$=\frac{25(13+5)}{5\cdot 5}=\frac{25(18)}{25}=18$$

18% of 25-year-olds must pay more taxes.

b.

$$p(x)=\frac{x\left(13+\sqrt{x}\right)}{5\sqrt{x}}=\frac{13x+x\sqrt{x}}{5\sqrt{x}}\cdot\frac{\sqrt{x}}{\sqrt{x}}$$

$$=\frac{\sqrt{x}\left(13x+x\sqrt{x}\right)}{5\sqrt{x}\cdot\sqrt{x}}$$

$$=\frac{13x\sqrt{x}+x\left(\sqrt{x}\right)^2}{5x}$$

$$=\frac{13x\sqrt{x}+x\cdot x}{5x}$$

$$=\frac{x\left(13\sqrt{x}+x\right)}{5x}=\frac{13\sqrt{x}+x}{5}$$

105. Perimeter $=2l+2w$

$$=2\left(\sqrt{8}+1\right)+2\left(\sqrt{8}-1\right)$$

$$=2\sqrt{8}+2+2\sqrt{8}-2$$

$$=(2+2)\sqrt{8}=4\sqrt{8}$$

$$=4\sqrt{4\cdot 2}=4\cdot 2\sqrt{2}=8\sqrt{2}$$

The perimeter is $8\sqrt{2}$ inches.

Area $=lw=\left(\sqrt{8}+1\right)\left(\sqrt{8}-1\right)$

$$=\left(\sqrt{8}\right)^2-\sqrt{8}+\sqrt{8}-1$$

$$=8-1=7$$

The area is 7 square inches.

107.

$$\frac{7\sqrt{2\cdot 2\cdot 3}}{6}=\frac{7\cdot 2\sqrt{3}}{6}=\frac{7\cdot 2\sqrt{3}}{2\cdot 3}=\frac{7}{3}\sqrt{3}$$

For Exercises 109–117, answers may vary.

119. Statement **c.** is true.

$$\frac{4\sqrt{x}}{\sqrt{x}-y}=\frac{4\sqrt{x}}{\sqrt{x}-y}\cdot\frac{\sqrt{x}+y}{\sqrt{x}+y}$$

$$=\frac{4\sqrt{x}\sqrt{x}+4\sqrt{x}\cdot y}{\left(\sqrt{x}\right)^2-y\sqrt{x}+y\sqrt{x}-y^2}$$

$$=\frac{4x+4y\sqrt{x}}{x-y^2}=\frac{4\left(x+y\sqrt{x}\right)}{x-y^2}$$

Statement **a.** is false.

$$\frac{\sqrt{3}+7}{\sqrt{3}-2} = \frac{\sqrt{3}+7}{\sqrt{3}-2} \cdot \frac{\sqrt{3}+2}{\sqrt{3}+2}$$

$$= \frac{\left(\sqrt{3}\right)^2 + 2\sqrt{3} + 7\sqrt{3} + 14}{\left(\sqrt{3}\right)^2 - 2^2}$$

$$= \frac{3 + 9\sqrt{3} + 14}{3 - 4} = \frac{17 + 9\sqrt{3}}{-1}$$

$$= -\left(17 + 9\sqrt{3}\right) = -17 - 9\sqrt{3}$$

Statement **b.** is false.

$$\frac{4}{\sqrt{x+y}} = \frac{4}{\sqrt{x+y}} \cdot \frac{\sqrt{x+y}}{\sqrt{x+y}} = \frac{4\sqrt{x+y}}{x+y}$$

Statement **d.** is false.

$$\left(\sqrt{x}-7\right)^2 = \left(\sqrt{x}\right)^2 + 2 \cdot \sqrt{x} \cdot (-7) + (-7)^2$$

$$= x - 14\sqrt{x} + 49$$

121.

$$\left(\sqrt{2+\sqrt{3}} + \sqrt{2-\sqrt{3}}\right)^2$$

$$= \left(\sqrt{2+\sqrt{3}}\right)^2 + 2\sqrt{2+\sqrt{3}}\sqrt{2-\sqrt{3}} + \left(\sqrt{2-\sqrt{3}}\right)^2$$

$$= 2 + \sqrt{3} + 2\sqrt{\left(2+\sqrt{3}\right)\left(2-\sqrt{3}\right)} + 2 - \sqrt{3}$$

$$= 2 + \cancel{\sqrt{3}} + 2\sqrt{4 - 2\cancel{\sqrt{3}} + 2\cancel{\sqrt{3}} - 3} + 2 - \cancel{\sqrt{3}}$$

$$= 4 + 2\sqrt{4-3} = 4 + 2\sqrt{1} = 4 + 2 = 6$$

123.

$$3x^2 + 2 = 6x$$

$$3\left(\frac{3+\sqrt{3}}{3}\right)^2 + 2 = 6\left(\frac{3+\sqrt{3}}{3}\right)$$

$$3\left(\frac{3^2 + 2 \cdot 3\sqrt{3} + \left(\sqrt{3}\right)^2}{9}\right) + 2 = 2\left(3+\sqrt{3}\right)$$

$$\cancel{3}\left(\frac{12+6\sqrt{3}}{3 \cdot \cancel{3}}\right) + 2 = 6 + 2\sqrt{3}$$

$$\frac{12+6\sqrt{3}}{3} + 2 = 6 + 2\sqrt{3}$$

$$\frac{\cancel{3}\left(4+2\sqrt{3}\right)}{\cancel{3}} + 2 = 6 + 2\sqrt{3}$$

$$4 + 2\sqrt{3} + 2 = 6 + 2\sqrt{3}$$

$$6 + 2\sqrt{3} = 6 + 2\sqrt{3}$$

$$\frac{3+\sqrt{3}}{3} \text{ is a solution.}$$

125. $\left(\sqrt{x}+2\right)\left(\sqrt{x}-2\right) = x^2 - 4 \quad$ for $x \geq 0$

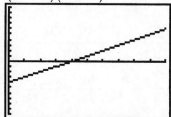

The graphs do not coincide. Correct the simplification.

$$\left(\sqrt{x}+2\right)\left(\sqrt{x}-2\right) = x - 4 \quad \text{for } x \geq 0$$

The graphs coincide. The new simplification is correct.

127. $\dfrac{3}{\sqrt{x+3}-\sqrt{x}} = \sqrt{x+3} + \sqrt{x}$

The graphs coincide, so the simplification is correct.

Review Exercises

128. $4x + 3y = 18$
$5x - 9y = 48$

$$D = \begin{vmatrix} 4 & 3 \\ 5 & -9 \end{vmatrix} = 4(-9) - 5(3)$$
$$= -36 - 15 = -51$$

$$D_x = \begin{vmatrix} 18 & 3 \\ 48 & -9 \end{vmatrix} = 18(-9) - 48(3)$$
$$= -162 - 144 = -306$$

$$D_y = \begin{vmatrix} 4 & 18 \\ 5 & 48 \end{vmatrix} = 4(48) - 5(18)$$
$$= 192 - 90 = 102$$

$$x = \frac{D_x}{D} = \frac{-306}{-51} = 6$$

$$y = \frac{D_y}{D} = \frac{102}{-51} = -2$$

The solution is $(6, -2)$.

129.
$$\frac{6x}{x^2 - 4} - \frac{3}{x+2} = \frac{6x}{(x+2)(x-2)} - \frac{3}{x+2}$$

$$= \frac{6x}{(x+2)(x-2)} - \frac{3(x-2)}{(x+2)(x-2)}$$

$$= \frac{6x - 3(x-2)}{(x+2)(x-2)} = \frac{6x - 3x + 6}{(x+2)(x-2)}$$

$$= \frac{3x + 6}{(x+2)(x-2)} = \frac{3(x+2)}{(x+2)(x-2)} = \frac{3}{x-2}$$

130.
$$2x^3 - 16x^2 + 30x = 2x(x^2 - 8x + 15)$$
$$= 2x(x-5)(x-3)$$

Radical Equations

10.6 CHECK POINTS

CHECK POINT 1
$$\sqrt{3x+4} = 8$$
$$\left(\sqrt{3x+4}\right)^2 = 8^2$$
$$3x + 4 = 64$$
$$3x = 60$$
$$x = 20$$
The solution checks.

CHECK POINT 2
$$\sqrt{x-1} + 7 = 2$$
$$\sqrt{x-1} = -5$$
$$\left(\sqrt{x-1}\right)^2 = (-5)^2$$
$$x - 1 = 25$$
$$x = 26$$
The solution does not check. 26 is an extraneous solution. There is no solution. The solution set is $\varnothing$ or $\{\ \}$.

CHECK POINT 3
$$\sqrt{6x+7} - x = 2$$
$$\sqrt{6x+7} = x + 2$$
$$\left(\sqrt{6x+7}\right)^2 = (x+2)^2$$
$$6x + 7 = x^2 + 4x + 4$$
$$0 = x^2 - 2x - 3$$
$$0 = (x-3)(x+1)$$
$$x - 3 = 0 \quad \text{or} \quad x + 1 = 0$$
$$x = 3 \quad\quad\quad x = -1$$
The solutions check.

CHECK POINT 4
$$\sqrt{x+5} - \sqrt{x-3} = 2$$
$$\sqrt{x+5} = \sqrt{x-3} + 2$$
$$\left(\sqrt{x+5}\right)^2 = \left(\sqrt{x-3} + 2\right)^2$$
$$\cancel{x} + 5 = \cancel{x} - 3 + 4\sqrt{x-3} + 4$$
$$4 = 4\sqrt{x-3}$$
$$\frac{4}{4} = \frac{4\sqrt{x-3}}{4}$$
$$1 = \sqrt{x-3}$$
$$1^2 = \left(\sqrt{x-3}\right)^2$$
$$1 = x - 3$$
$$4 = x$$
The solution checks.

CHECK POINT 5
$$(2x-3)^{\frac{1}{3}} + 3 = 0$$
$$\sqrt[3]{2x-3} + 3 = 0$$

$$\sqrt[3]{2x-3} = -3$$
$$\left(\sqrt[3]{2x-3}\right)^3 = (-3)^3$$
$$2x-3 = -27$$
$$2x = -24$$
$$x = -12$$
The solution checks.

CHECK POINT 6

$$\frac{1}{10} \cdot 280 = 28 \text{ million Americans}$$

$$28 = 2.6\sqrt{x} + 11$$
$$17 = 2.6\sqrt{x}$$
$$\frac{17}{2.6} = \sqrt{x}$$
$$\left(\frac{17}{2.6}\right)^2 = \left(\sqrt{x}\right)^2$$
$$42.75 \approx x$$

This means that $\frac{1}{10}$ of the total population or 28 million Americans will live alone approximately 43 years after 1970 in the year $1970 + 43 = 2013$.

EXERCISE SET 10.6

1.
$$\sqrt{3x-2} = 4$$
$$\left(\sqrt{3x-2}\right)^2 = 4^2$$
$$3x-2 = 16$$
$$3x = 18$$
$$x = 6$$
The solution checks.

3.
$$\sqrt{5x-4} - 9 = 0$$
$$\sqrt{5x-4} = 9$$
$$\left(\sqrt{5x-4}\right)^2 = 9^2$$
$$5x-4 = 81$$
$$5x = 85$$
$$x = 17$$
The solution checks.

5.
$$\sqrt{3x+7} + 10 = 4$$
$$\sqrt{3x+7} = -6$$

Since the square root of a number is always positive, the solution set is $\{ \ \}$ or $\varnothing$.

7.
$$x = \sqrt{7x+8}$$
$$x^2 = \left(\sqrt{7x+8}\right)^2$$
$$x^2 = 7x+8$$
$$x^2 - 7x - 8 = 0$$
$$(x-8)(x+1) = 0$$
$$x-8 = 0 \qquad x+1 = 0$$
$$x = 8 \qquad x = -1$$
We disregard –1 because square roots are always positive. The solution is 8.

9.
$$\sqrt{5x+1} = x+1$$
$$\left(\sqrt{5x+1}\right)^2 = (x+1)^2$$
$$5x + \cancel{1} = x^2 + 2x + \cancel{1}$$
$$0 = x^2 - 3x$$
$$0 = x(x-3)$$
$$x = 0 \qquad x-3 = 0$$
$$x = 3$$
Both solutions check.

11.
$$x = \sqrt{2x-2} + 1$$
$$x-1 = \sqrt{2x-2}$$
$$(x-1)^2 = \left(\sqrt{2x-2}\right)^2$$
$$x^2 - 2x + 1 = 2x - 2$$
$$x^2 - 4x + 3 = 0$$
$$(x-3)(x-1) = 0$$
$$x-3 = 0 \qquad x-1 = 0$$
$$x = 3 \qquad x = 1$$
Both solutions check.

13.
$$x - 2\sqrt{x-3} = 3$$
$$x - 3 = 2\sqrt{x-3}$$

$$(x-3)^2 = \left(2\sqrt{x-3}\right)^2$$
$$x^2 - 6x + 9 = 4(x-3)$$
$$x^2 - 6x + 9 = 4x - 12$$
$$x^2 - 10x + 21 = 0$$
$$(x-7)(x-3) = 0$$
$$x - 7 = 0 \qquad x - 3 = 0$$
$$x = 7 \qquad\quad x = 3$$
Both solutions check.

15.
$$\sqrt{2x-5} = \sqrt{x+4}$$
$$\left(\sqrt{2x-5}\right)^2 = \left(\sqrt{x+4}\right)^2$$
$$2x - 5 = x + 4$$
$$x - 5 = 4$$
$$x = 9$$
The solution checks.

17.
$$\sqrt[3]{2x+11} = 3$$
$$\left(\sqrt[3]{2x+11}\right)^3 = 3^3$$
$$2x + 11 = 27$$
$$2x = 16$$
$$x = 8$$
The solution checks.

19.
$$\sqrt[3]{2x-6} - 4 = 0$$
$$\sqrt[3]{2x-6} = 4$$
$$\left(\sqrt[3]{2x-6}\right)^3 = 4^3$$
$$2x - 6 = 64$$
$$2x = 70$$
$$x = 35$$
The solution checks.

21.
$$\sqrt{x-7} = 7 - \sqrt{x}$$
$$\left(\sqrt{x-7}\right)^2 = \left(7 - \sqrt{x}\right)^2$$
$$\cancel{x} - 7 = 49 - 14\sqrt{x} + \cancel{x}$$
$$-56 = -14\sqrt{x}$$
$$4 = \sqrt{x}$$
$$4^2 = \left(\sqrt{x}\right)^2$$
$$16 = x$$
The solution checks.

23.
$$\sqrt{x+2} + \sqrt{x-1} = 3$$
$$\sqrt{x+2} = 3 - \sqrt{x-1}$$
$$\left(\sqrt{x+2}\right)^2 = \left(3 - \sqrt{x-1}\right)^2$$
$$\cancel{x} + 2 = 9 - 6\sqrt{x-1} + \cancel{x} - 1$$
$$-6 = -6\sqrt{x-1}$$
$$1 = \sqrt{x-1}$$
$$1^2 = \left(\sqrt{x-1}\right)^2$$
$$1 = x - 1$$
$$2 = x$$
The solution checks.

25.
$$(2x+3)^{1/3} + 4 = 6$$
$$(2x+3)^{1/3} = 2$$
$$\left((2x+3)^{1/3}\right)^3 = 2^3$$
$$2x + 3 = 8$$
$$2x = 5$$
$$x = \frac{5}{2}$$
The solution checks.

27.
$$(3x+1)^{1/4} + 7 = 9$$
$$(3x+1)^{1/4} = 2$$
$$\left((3x+1)^{1/4}\right)^4 = 2^4$$
$$3x + 1 = 16$$
$$3x = 15$$
$$x = 5$$
The solution checks.

29.
$$(x+2)^{1/2} + 8 = 4$$
$$(x+2)^{1/2} = -4$$
$$\sqrt{x+2} = -4$$
The square root of a number must be positive. The solution set is $\varnothing$.

31.
$$\sqrt{2x-3} - \sqrt{x-2} = 1$$
$$\sqrt{2x-3} = \sqrt{x-2} + 1$$
$$\left(\sqrt{2x-3}\right)^2 = \left(\sqrt{x-2} + 1\right)^2$$
$$2x - 3 = x - 2 + 2\sqrt{x-2} + 1$$

$$2x-3=x-1+2\sqrt{x-2}$$
$$x-2=2\sqrt{x-2}$$
$$(x-2)^2=\left(2\sqrt{x-2}\right)^2$$
$$x^2-4x+4=4(x-2)$$
$$x^2-4x+4=4x-8$$
$$x^2-8x+12=0$$
$$(x-6)(x-2)=0$$
$$x-6=0 \qquad x-2=0$$
$$x=6 \qquad\quad x=2$$

Both solutions check.

33.
$$3x^{1/3}=\left(x^2+17x\right)^{1/3}$$
$$\left(3x^{1/3}\right)^3=\left(\left(x^2+17x\right)^{1/3}\right)^3$$
$$3^3x=x^2+17x$$
$$27x=x^2+17x$$
$$0=x^2-10x$$
$$0=x(x-10)$$
$$x=0 \qquad x-10=0$$
$$\qquad\qquad x=10$$

Both solutions check.

35.
$$(x+8)^{1/4}=(2x)^{1/4}$$
$$\left((x+8)^{1/4}\right)^4=\left((2x)^{1/4}\right)^4$$
$$x+8=2x$$
$$8=x$$

The solution checks.

37.
$$304=4\sqrt{x}+280$$
$$24=4\sqrt{x}$$
$$6=\sqrt{x}$$
$$6^2=\left(\sqrt{x}\right)^2$$
$$36=x$$

The average score will return to 304 thirty-six years after 1982 in 2018.

39.
$$32.25=6.75\sqrt{x}+12$$
$$20.25=6.75\sqrt{x}$$
$$3=\sqrt{x}$$

$$3^2=\left(\sqrt{x}\right)^2$$
$$9=x$$

The loan amount will reach $32.25 billion 9 years after 1993 in the year 2002.

41.
$$40000=5000\sqrt{100-x}$$
$$8=\sqrt{100-x}$$
$$8^2=\left(\sqrt{100-x}\right)^2$$
$$64=100-x$$
$$-36=-x$$
$$36=x$$

40,000 people in the group will survive to age 36. This is shown on the graph as the point $(36,\ 40{,}000)$.

43.
$$87=29x^{1/3}$$
$$3=x^{1/3}$$
$$3^3=\left(x^{1/3}\right)^3$$
$$27=x$$

A Galápagos island with an area of 27 square miles will have 87 plant species.

45.
$$365=0.2x^{1/3}$$
$$1825=x^{1/3}$$
$$1825^3=\left(x^{1/3}\right)^3$$
$$6{,}078{,}390{,}625=x$$

The average distance of the Earth from the sun is approximately 6078 million or 6,078,000,000 kilometers.

For Exercises 47-53, answers may vary.

55.
$$\left(\sqrt{x-7}\right)^2+\left(\sqrt{x}\right)^2=\left(1+\sqrt{x}\right)^2$$
$$\cancel{x}-7+x=1+2\sqrt{x}+\cancel{x}$$
$$-7+x=1+2\sqrt{x}$$
$$-8+x=2\sqrt{x}$$
$$(-8+x)^2=\left(2\sqrt{x}\right)^2$$
$$64-16x+x^2=4x$$

$$x^2 - 16x + 64 = 4x$$

$$x^2 - 20x + 64 = 0$$

$$(x-16)(x-4) = 0$$

$$x - 16 = 0 \qquad x - 4 = 0$$

$$x = 16 \qquad \cancel{x = 4}$$

We disregard 4. If $x = 4$, one of the legs becomes $\sqrt{4-7} = \sqrt{-3}$

The legs of the triangle are:

$$\sqrt{x-7} = \sqrt{16-7} = \sqrt{9} = 3$$

$$\sqrt{x} = \sqrt{16} = 4, \text{ and}$$

$$1 + \sqrt{x} = 1 + \sqrt{16} = 1 + 4 = 5.$$

57.
$$\sqrt{\sqrt{x} + \sqrt{x+9}} = 3$$

$$\left(\sqrt{\sqrt{x} + \sqrt{x+9}}\right)^2 = 3^2$$

$$\sqrt{x} + \sqrt{x+9} = 9$$

$$\sqrt{x+9} = 9 - \sqrt{x}$$

$$\left(\sqrt{x+9}\right)^2 = \left(9 - \sqrt{x}\right)^2$$

$$\cancel{x} + 9 = 81 - 18\sqrt{x} + \cancel{x}$$

$$9 = 81 - 18\sqrt{x}$$

$$-72 = -18\sqrt{x}$$

$$4 = \sqrt{x}$$

$$4^2 = \left(\sqrt{x}\right)^2$$

$$16 = x$$

59. $\sqrt{2x+2} = \sqrt{3x-5}$

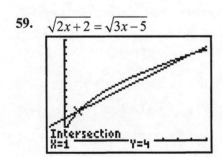

The solutions are 1 and 9.

61. $\sqrt{x^2+3} = x+1$

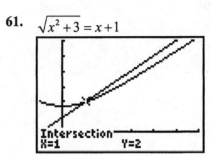

The solution set is $\{1\}$.

63. $\sqrt{x} + 4 = 2$

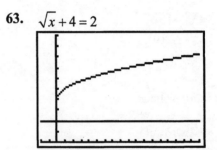

The graphs do not intersect. This means that the solution set is $\varnothing$.

Review Exercises

64.

$$\begin{array}{r|rrrrr} -3 & 4 & -3 & 2 & -1 & -1 \\ & & -12 & 45 & -141 & 426 \\ \hline & 4 & -15 & 47 & -142 & 425 \end{array}$$

$$\frac{4x^4 - 3x^3 + 2x^2 - x - 1}{x+3}$$

$$= 4x^3 - 15x^2 + 47x - 142 + \frac{425}{x+3}$$

65. $\dfrac{3x^2 - 12}{x^2 + 2x - 8} \div \dfrac{6x+18}{x+4}$

$$=\frac{3x^2-12}{x^2+2x-8}\cdot\frac{x+4}{6x+18}$$

$$=\frac{3(x^2-4)}{(x+4)(x-2)}\cdot\frac{x+4}{6(x+3)}$$

$$=\frac{3(x+2)(x-2)}{(x-2)}\cdot\frac{1}{6(x+3)}$$

$$=\frac{3(x+2)}{1}\cdot\frac{1}{6(x+3)}=\frac{3(x+2)}{6(x+3)}=\frac{x+2}{2(x+3)}$$

66. $64x^3-x=x(64x^2-1)$

$$=x(8x+1)(8x-1)$$

Complex Numbers

10.7 CHECK POINTS

CHECK POINT 1

a. $\sqrt{-16}=\sqrt{16(-1)}=\sqrt{16}\sqrt{-1}=4i$

b. $\sqrt{-5}=\sqrt{5(-1)}=\sqrt{5}\sqrt{-1}=\sqrt{5}i$

c. $\sqrt{-50}=\sqrt{50(-1)}=\sqrt{25\cdot2}\sqrt{-1}=5\sqrt{2}i$

CHECK POINT 2

a. $(5-2i)+(3+3i)=5-2i+3+3i=5+3-2i+3i$

$$=(5+3)+(-2i+3i)$$

$$=8+(-2+3)i=8+1i=8+i$$

b. $(2+6i)-(12-4i)=2+6i-12+4i$

$$=2-12+6i+4i$$

$$=(2-12)+(6i+4i)$$

$$=-10+(6+4)i=-10+10i$$

CHECK POINT 3

a. $7i(2-9i)=7i\cdot2-7i\cdot9i=14i-63i^2$

$$=14i-63(-1)=63+14i$$

b. $(5+4i)(6-7i)=30-35i+24i-28i^2$

$$=30-11i-28(-1)$$

$$=30-11i+28=58-11i$$

CHECK POINT 4

$$\sqrt{-5}\cdot\sqrt{-7}=\sqrt{5}\sqrt{-1}\cdot\sqrt{7}\sqrt{-1}=\sqrt{5}i\cdot\sqrt{7}i$$

$$=\sqrt{35}i^2=\sqrt{35}(-1)=-\sqrt{35}$$

CHECK POINT 5

$$\frac{6+2i}{4-3i}=\frac{6+2i}{4-3i}\cdot\frac{4+3i}{4+3i}=\frac{24+18i+8i+6i^2}{4^2-(3i)^2}$$

$$=\frac{24+26i+6(-1)}{16-9i^2}=\frac{24+26i-6}{16-9(-1)}$$

$$=\frac{18+26i}{16+9}=\frac{18+26i}{25}=\frac{18}{25}+\frac{26}{25}i$$

CHECK POINT 6

$$\frac{3-2i}{4i}=\frac{3-2i}{4i}\cdot\frac{i}{i}=\frac{3i-2i^2}{4i^2}=\frac{3i-2(-1)}{4(-1)}$$

$$=\frac{2+3i}{-4}=\frac{2}{-4}+\frac{3i}{-4}=-\frac{1}{2}-\frac{3}{4}i$$

CHECK POINT 7

a. $i^{16}=(1^2)^8=(-1)^8=1$

b. $i^{25}=i^{24}\cdot i=(i^2)^{12}i=(-1)^{12}i=1i=i$

c. $i^{35}=i^{34}i=(i^2)^{17}\cdot i=(-1)^{17}\cdot i=(-1)\cdot i=-i$

EXERCISE SET 10.7

1. $\sqrt{-49}=\sqrt{49\cdot-1}=\sqrt{49}\cdot\sqrt{-1}=7i$

3. $\sqrt{-17}=\sqrt{17\cdot-1}=\sqrt{17}\cdot\sqrt{-1}=\sqrt{17}\,i$

5. $\sqrt{-75}=\sqrt{25\cdot3\cdot-1}=\sqrt{25}\cdot\sqrt{3}\cdot\sqrt{-1}=5\sqrt{3}\,i$

7. $\sqrt{-28}=\sqrt{4\cdot7\cdot-1}=\sqrt{4}\cdot\sqrt{7}\cdot\sqrt{-1}=2\sqrt{7}\,i$

9. $-\sqrt{-150}=-\sqrt{25\cdot6\cdot-1}$

$$=-\sqrt{25}\cdot\sqrt{6}\cdot\sqrt{-1}=-5\sqrt{6}\,i$

11. $7+\sqrt{-16}=7+\sqrt{16\cdot-1}=7+\sqrt{16}\cdot\sqrt{-1}=7+4i$

13. $5+\sqrt{-5}=5+\sqrt{5\cdot-1}=5+\sqrt{5}\cdot\sqrt{-1}=5+\sqrt{5}\,i$

15. $6-\sqrt{-18}=6-\sqrt{9\cdot2\cdot-1}=6-\sqrt{9}\cdot\sqrt{2}\cdot\sqrt{-1}$
$=6-3\sqrt{2}\ i$

17. $(3+2i)+(5+i)=3+2i+5+i=3+5+2i+i$
$=(3+5)+(2+1)i=8+3i$

19. $(7+2i)+(1-4i)=7+2i+1-4i=7+1+2i-4i$
$=(7+1)+(2-4)i=8-2i$

21. $(10+7i)-(5+4i)$
$=10+7i-5-4i=10-5+7i-4i$
$=(10-5)+(7-4)i=5+3i$

23. $(9-4i)-(10+3i)$
$=9-4i-10-3i=9-10-4i-3i$
$=(9-10)+(-4-3)i=-1+(-7)i=-1-7i$

25. $(3+2i)-(5-7i)$
$=3+2i-5+7i=3-5+2i+7i$
$=(3-5)+(2+7)i=-2+9i$

27. $(-5+4i)-(-13-11i)$
$=-5+4i+13+11i=-5+13+4i+11i$
$=(-5+13)+(4+11)i=8+15i$

29. $8i-(14-9i)=8i-14+9i=-14+8i+9i$
$=-14+(8+9)i=-14+17i$

31. $\left(2+\sqrt{3}\ i\right)+\left(7+4\sqrt{3}\ i\right)$
$=2+\sqrt{3}\ i+7+4\sqrt{3}\ i=2+7+\sqrt{3}\ i+4\sqrt{3}\ i$
$=(2+7)+\left(\sqrt{3}+4\sqrt{3}\right)i=9+5\sqrt{3}\ i$

33. $2i(5+3i)=2i\cdot5+2i\cdot3i=10i+6i^2$
$=10i+6(-1)=-6+10i$

35. $3i(7i-5)=3i\cdot7i-3i\cdot5=21i^2-15i$
$=21(-1)-15i=-21-15i$

37. $-7i(2-5i)=-7i\cdot2-(-7i)5i=-14i+35i^2$
$=-14i+35(-1)=-35-14i$

39. $(3+i)(4+5i)=12+15i+4i+5i^2$
$=12+15i+4i+5(-1)$
$=12-5+15i+4i=7+19i$

41. $(7-5i)(2-3i)=14-21i-10i+15i^2$
$=14-21i-10i+15(-1)$
$=14-15-21i-10i=-1-31i$

43. $(6-3i)(-2+5i)=-12+30i+6i-15i^2$
$=-12+30i+6i-15(-1)$
$=-12+15+30i+6i=3+36i$

45. $(3+5i)(3-5i)=9-\cancel{15i}+\cancel{15i}-25i^2$
$=9-25(-1)=9+25=34=34+0i$

47. $(-5+3i)(-5-3i)=25+\cancel{15i}-\cancel{15i}-9i^2$
$=25-9(-1)=25+9$
$=34=34+0i$

49. $\left(3-\sqrt{2}\ i\right)\left(3+\sqrt{2}\ i\right)=9+\cancel{3\sqrt{2}\ i}-\cancel{3\sqrt{2}\ i}-2i^2$
$=9-2(-1)=9+2=11=11+0i$

51. $(2+3i)^2=4+2\cdot6i+9i^2=4+12i+9(-1)$
$=4-9+12i=-5+12i$

53. $(5-2i)^2=25-2\cdot10i+4i^2=25-20i+4(-1)$
$=25-4-20i=21-20i$

55. $\sqrt{-7}\cdot\sqrt{-2}=\sqrt{7}\sqrt{-1}\cdot\sqrt{2}\sqrt{-1}=\sqrt{7}\ i\cdot\sqrt{2}\ i$
$=\sqrt{14}\ i^2=\sqrt{14}(-1)=-\sqrt{14}=-\sqrt{14}+0i$

57. $\sqrt{-9}\cdot\sqrt{-4}=\sqrt{9}\sqrt{-1}\cdot\sqrt{4}\sqrt{-1}=3i\cdot2i=6i^2$
$=6(-1)=-6=-6+0i$

59. $\sqrt{-7}\cdot\sqrt{-25}=\sqrt{7}\sqrt{-1}\cdot\sqrt{25}\sqrt{-1}=\sqrt{7}\ i\cdot5i$
$=5\sqrt{7}\ i^2=5\sqrt{7}(-1)=-5\sqrt{7}=-5\sqrt{7}+0i$

61. $\sqrt{-8}\cdot\sqrt{-3}=\sqrt{4\cdot 2}\sqrt{-1}\cdot\sqrt{3}\sqrt{-1}=2\sqrt{2}\ i\cdot\sqrt{3}\ i$

$=2\sqrt{6}\ i^2=2\sqrt{6}(-1)=-2\sqrt{6}=-2\sqrt{6}+0i$

63. $\dfrac{2}{3+i}=\dfrac{2}{3+i}\cdot\dfrac{3-i}{3-i}=\dfrac{6-2i}{3^2-i^2}=\dfrac{6-2i}{9-(-1)}$

$=\dfrac{6-2i}{9+1}=\dfrac{6-2i}{10}=\dfrac{6}{10}-\dfrac{2i}{10}=\dfrac{3}{5}-\dfrac{1}{5}i$

65. $\dfrac{2i}{1+i}=\dfrac{2i}{1+i}\cdot\dfrac{1-i}{1-i}=\dfrac{2i-2i^2}{1^2-i^2}=\dfrac{2i-2(-1)}{1-(-1)}$

$=\dfrac{2+2i}{1+1}=\dfrac{2+2i}{2}=\dfrac{2}{2}+\dfrac{2i}{2}=1+i$

67. $\dfrac{7}{4-3i}=\dfrac{7}{4-3i}\cdot\dfrac{4+3i}{4+3i}=\dfrac{28+21i}{4^2-(3i)^2}$

$=\dfrac{28+21i}{16-9i^2}=\dfrac{28+21i}{16-9(-1)}=\dfrac{28+21i}{16+9}$

$=\dfrac{28+21i}{25}=\dfrac{28}{25}+\dfrac{21}{25}i$

69. $\dfrac{6i}{3-2i}=\dfrac{6i}{3-2i}\cdot\dfrac{3+2i}{3+2i}=\dfrac{18i+12i^2}{3^2-(2i)^2}$

$=\dfrac{18i+12(-1)}{9-4i^2}=\dfrac{-12+18i}{9-4(-1)}=\dfrac{-12+18i}{9+4}$

$=\dfrac{-12+18i}{13}=-\dfrac{12}{13}+\dfrac{18}{13}i$

71. $\dfrac{1+i}{1-i}=\dfrac{1+i}{1-i}\cdot\dfrac{1+i}{1+i}=\dfrac{1+2i+i^2}{1^2-i^2}$

$=\dfrac{1+2i+(-1)}{1-(-1)}=\dfrac{2i}{2}=i$ or $0+i$

73. $\dfrac{2-3i}{3+i}=\dfrac{2-3i}{3+i}\cdot\dfrac{3-i}{3-i}=\dfrac{6-2i-9i+3i^2}{3^2-i^2}$

$=\dfrac{6-11i+3(-1)}{9-(-1)}=\dfrac{6-3-11i}{9+1}$

$=\dfrac{3-11i}{10}=\dfrac{3}{10}-\dfrac{11}{10}i$

75. $\dfrac{5-2i}{3+2i}=\dfrac{5-2i}{3+2i}\cdot\dfrac{3-2i}{3-2i}$

$=\dfrac{15-10i-6i+4i^2}{3^2-(2i)^2}=\dfrac{15-10i-6i+4i^2}{3^2-(2i)^2}$

$=\dfrac{15-16i+4(-1)}{9-4i^2}=\dfrac{15-4-16i}{9-4(-1)}$

$=\dfrac{11-16i}{9+4}=\dfrac{11-16i}{13}=\dfrac{11}{13}-\dfrac{16}{13}i$

77. $\dfrac{4+5i}{3-7i}=\dfrac{4+5i}{3-7i}\cdot\dfrac{3+7i}{3+7i}=\dfrac{12+28i+15i+35i^2}{3^2-(7i)^2}$

$=\dfrac{12+43i+35(-1)}{9-49i^2}=\dfrac{12-35+43i}{9-49(-1)}$

$=\dfrac{-23+43i}{9+49}=\dfrac{-23+43i}{58}=-\dfrac{23}{58}+\dfrac{43}{58}i$

79. $\dfrac{7}{3i}=\dfrac{7}{3i}\cdot\dfrac{-3i}{-3i}=\dfrac{-21i}{-9i^2}=\dfrac{-21i}{-9(-1)}$

$=\dfrac{-21i}{9}=-\dfrac{7}{3}i$ or $0-\dfrac{7}{3}i$

81. $\dfrac{8-5i}{2i}=\dfrac{8-5i}{2i}\cdot\dfrac{-2i}{-2i}=\dfrac{-16i+10i^2}{-4i^2}$

$=\dfrac{-16i+10(-1)}{-4(-1)}=\dfrac{-10-16i}{4}$

$=-\dfrac{10}{4}-\dfrac{16}{4}i=-\dfrac{5}{2}-4i$

83. $\dfrac{4+7i}{-3i}=\dfrac{4+7i}{-3i}\cdot\dfrac{3i}{3i}=\dfrac{12i+21i^2}{-9i^2}$

$=\dfrac{12i+21(-1)}{-9(-1)}=\dfrac{-21+12i}{9}$

$=-\dfrac{21}{9}+\dfrac{12}{9}i=-\dfrac{7}{3}+\dfrac{4}{3}i$

85. $i^{10}=\left(i^2\right)^5=(-1)^5=-1$

87. $i^{11}=\left(i^2\right)^5 i=(-1)^5 i=-i$

89. $i^{22}=\left(i^2\right)^{11}=(-1)^{11}=-1$

91. $i^{200} = \left(i^2\right)^{100} = (-1)^{100} = 1$

93. $i^{17} = \left(i^2\right)^8 i = (-1)^8 i = i$

95. $(-i)^4 = (-1)^4 i^4 = i^4 = \left(i^2\right)^2 = (-1)^2 = 1$

97. $(-i)^9 = (-1)^9 i^9 = (-1)\left(i^2\right)^4 i$
$= (-1)(-1)^4 i = (-1)i = -i$

99. $i^{24} + i^2 = \left(i^2\right)^{12} + (-1) = (-1)^{12} + (-1)$
$= 1 + (-1) = 0$

101. $E = IR = (4-5i)(3+7i)$
$= 12 + 28i - 15i - 35i^2$
$= 12 + 13i - 35(-1)$
$= 12 + 35 + 13i = 47 + 13i$
The voltage of the circuit is
$(47 + 13i)$ volts.

103. Sum:
$\left(5+\sqrt{15}\,i\right)+\left(5-\sqrt{15}\,i\right)$
$= 5 + \sqrt{15}\,i + 5 - \sqrt{15}\,i = 5+5 = 10$
Product:
$\left(5+\sqrt{15}\,i\right)\left(5-\sqrt{15}\,i\right)$
$= 25 - 5\sqrt{15}\,i + 5\sqrt{15}\,i - 15i^2$
$= 25 - 15(-1) = 25 + 15 = 40$

For Exercises 105-117, answers may vary.

119. Statement **d.** is true.
$(x+yi)(x-yi)$
$= x^2 - xyi + xyi - y^2 i^2$
$= x^2 - y^2(-1) = x^2 + y^2$
Statement **a.** is false. All irrational numbers are complex numbers.
Statement **b.** is false.

$(3+7i)(3-7i) = 3^2 - (7i)^2 = 9 - 49i^2$
$= 9 - 49(-1) = 9 + 49 = 58$
Statement **c.** is false.
$\dfrac{7+3i}{5+3i} = \dfrac{7+3i}{5+3i}\cdot\dfrac{5-3i}{5-3i} = \dfrac{35-21i+15i-9i^2}{5^2-(3i)^2}$
$= \dfrac{35-6i-9(-1)}{25-9i^2} = \dfrac{35-6i+9}{25-9(-1)} = \dfrac{44-6i}{25+9}$
$= \dfrac{44-6i}{34} = \dfrac{44}{34} - \dfrac{6}{34}i = \dfrac{22}{17} - \dfrac{3}{17}i$

121. $\dfrac{4}{(2+i)(3-i)} = \dfrac{4}{6-2i+3i-i^2} = \dfrac{4}{6+i-(-1)}$
$= \dfrac{4}{6+1+i} = \dfrac{4}{7+i}\cdot\dfrac{7-i}{7-i} = \dfrac{28-4i}{7^2-i^2}$
$= \dfrac{28-4i}{49-(-1)} = \dfrac{28-4i}{50} = \dfrac{28}{50} - \dfrac{4}{50}i = \dfrac{14}{25} - \dfrac{2}{25}i$

123. $x^2 - 2x + 2 = (1+i)^2 - 2(1+i) + 2$
$= 1 + 2i + i^2 - 2 - 2i + 2$
$= 1 + (-1) = 0$

Review Exercises

124. $2x - 1 = x^2 - 4x + 4$
$0 = x^2 - 6x + 5$
$0 = (x-5)(x-1)$
$x - 5 = 0 \quad \text{and} \quad x - 1 = 0$
$x = 5 \qquad\qquad x = 1$

125. $\left(2x^2\right)^{-3} = \dfrac{1}{\left(2x^2\right)^3} = \dfrac{1}{8x^6}$

126. $\dfrac{x^2-6x+9}{12}\cdot\dfrac{3}{x^2-9} = \dfrac{(x-3)^2}{3\cdot4}\cdot\dfrac{3}{(x+3)(x-3)}$
$= \dfrac{(x-3)}{4}\cdot\dfrac{1}{(x+3)} = \dfrac{x-3}{4(x+3)}$

Chapter 10 Review Exercises

1. $\sqrt{81} = 9$ because $9^2 = 81$

2. $-\sqrt{\dfrac{1}{100}} = -\dfrac{1}{10}$ because $\left(\dfrac{1}{10}\right)^2 = \dfrac{1}{100}$

3. $\sqrt[3]{-27} = -3$ because $(-3)^3 = -27$

4. $\sqrt[4]{-16}$
Not a real number - The index is even and the radicand is negative.

5. $\sqrt[5]{-32} = -2$ because $(-2)^5 = -32$

6. $f(15) = \sqrt{2(15)-5} = \sqrt{30-5} = \sqrt{25} = 5$
$f(4) = \sqrt{2(4)-5} = \sqrt{8-5} = \sqrt{3}$
$f\left(\dfrac{5}{2}\right) = \sqrt{2\left(\dfrac{5}{2}\right)-5} = \sqrt{5-5} = \sqrt{0} = 0$
$f(1) = \sqrt{2(1)-5} = \sqrt{2-5} = \sqrt{-3}$
Not a real number

7. $g(4) = \sqrt[3]{4(4)-8} = \sqrt[3]{16-8} = \sqrt[3]{8} = 2$
$g(0) = \sqrt[3]{4(0)-8} = \sqrt[3]{-8} = -2$
$g(-14) = \sqrt[3]{4(-14)-8} = \sqrt[3]{-56-8} = \sqrt[3]{-64} = -4$

8. $x-2 \geq 0$
$x \geq 2$
The domain of f is $\{x | x \geq 2\}$ or $[2, \infty)$.

9. $100 - 4x \geq 0$
$-4x \geq -100$
$x \leq 25$
The domain of g is $\{x | x \leq 25\}$ or $(-\infty, 25]$.

10. $\sqrt{25x^2} = 5|x|$

11. $\sqrt{(x+14)^2} = |x+14|$

12. $\sqrt{x^2-8x+16} = \sqrt{(x-4)^2} = |x-4|$

13. $\sqrt[3]{64x^3} = 4x$

14. $\sqrt[4]{16x^4} = 2|x|$

15. $\sqrt[5]{-32(x+7)^5} = -2(x+7)$

16. $(5xy)^{\frac{1}{3}} = \sqrt[3]{5xy}$

17. $16^{\frac{3}{2}} = \left(\sqrt{16}\right)^3 = (4)^3 = 64$

18. $32^{\frac{4}{5}} = \left(\sqrt[5]{32}\right)^4 = (2)^4 = 16$

19. $\sqrt{7x} = (7x)^{\frac{1}{2}}$

20. $\left(\sqrt[3]{19xy}\right)^5 = (19xy)^{\frac{5}{3}}$

21. $8^{-\frac{2}{3}} = \dfrac{1}{8^{\frac{2}{3}}} = \dfrac{1}{\left(\sqrt[3]{8}\right)^2} = \dfrac{1}{(2)^2} = \dfrac{1}{4}$

22. $3x(ab)^{-\frac{4}{5}} = \dfrac{3x}{(ab)^{\frac{4}{5}}} = \dfrac{3x}{\left(\sqrt[5]{ab}\right)^4}$ or $\dfrac{3x}{\sqrt[5]{(ab)^4}}$

23. $x^{\frac{1}{3}} \cdot x^{\frac{1}{4}} = x^{\frac{1}{3}+\frac{1}{4}} = x^{\frac{4}{12}+\frac{3}{12}} = x^{\frac{7}{12}}$

24. $\dfrac{5^{\frac{1}{2}}}{5^{\frac{1}{3}}} = 5^{\frac{1}{2}-\frac{1}{3}} = 5^{\frac{3}{6}-\frac{2}{6}} = 5^{\frac{1}{6}}$

25. $\left(8x^6 y^3\right)^{\frac{1}{3}} = 8^{\frac{1}{3}} x^{6 \cdot \frac{1}{3}} y^{3 \cdot \frac{1}{3}} = 2x^2 y$

26.
$$\left(x^{-\frac{2}{3}}y^{\frac{1}{4}}\right)^{\frac{1}{2}} = x^{-\frac{2}{3}\cdot\frac{1}{2}}y^{\frac{1}{4}\cdot\frac{1}{2}} = x^{-\frac{1}{3}}y^{\frac{1}{8}} = \frac{y^{\frac{1}{8}}}{x^{\frac{1}{3}}}$$

27.
$$\sqrt[3]{x^9 y^{12}} = \left(x^9 y^{12}\right)^{\frac{1}{3}} = x^{9\cdot\frac{1}{3}} y^{12\cdot\frac{1}{3}} = x^3 y^4$$

28.
$$\sqrt[9]{x^3 y^9} = \left(x^3 y^9\right)^{\frac{1}{9}} = x^{3\cdot\frac{1}{9}} y^{9\cdot\frac{1}{9}} = x^{\frac{1}{3}} y = y\sqrt[3]{x}$$

29.
$$\sqrt{x}\cdot\sqrt[3]{x} = x^{\frac{1}{2}} x^{\frac{1}{3}} = x^{\frac{1}{2}+\frac{1}{3}} = x^{\frac{3}{6}+\frac{2}{6}} = x^{\frac{5}{6}} = \sqrt[6]{x^5}$$

30.
$$\frac{\sqrt[3]{x^2}}{\sqrt[4]{x^2}} = \frac{x^{\frac{2}{3}}}{x^{\frac{2}{4}}} = x^{\frac{2}{3}-\frac{2}{4}} = x^{\frac{4}{6}-\frac{3}{6}} = x^{\frac{1}{6}} = \sqrt[6]{x}$$

31.
$$\sqrt[5]{\sqrt[3]{x}} = \sqrt[5]{x^{\frac{1}{3}}} = \left(x^{\frac{1}{3}}\right)^{\frac{1}{5}} = x^{\frac{1}{3}\cdot\frac{1}{5}} = x^{\frac{1}{15}} = \sqrt[15]{x}$$

32.
$$f(27) = 350(27)^{\frac{2}{3}} = 350\left(\sqrt[3]{27}\right)^2$$
$$= 350(3)^2 = 350(9) = 3150$$

Expenditures will be $3150 million or $3,150,000,000 in the year 2012.

33.
$$\sqrt{3x}\cdot\sqrt{7y} = \sqrt{21xy}$$

34.
$$\sqrt[5]{7x^2}\cdot\sqrt[5]{11x} = \sqrt[5]{77x^3}$$

35.
$$\sqrt[6]{x-5}\cdot\sqrt[6]{(x-5)^4} = \sqrt[6]{(x-5)^5}$$

36.
$$f(x) = \sqrt{7x^2-14x+7} = \sqrt{7(x^2-2x+1)}$$
$$= \sqrt{7(x-1)^2} = \sqrt{7}\,|x-1|$$

37.
$$\sqrt{20x^3} = \sqrt{4\cdot5\cdot x^2\cdot x} = \sqrt{4x^2\cdot5x} = 2x\sqrt{5x}$$

38.
$$\sqrt[3]{54x^8 y^6} = \sqrt[3]{27\cdot2\cdot x^6\cdot x^2 y^6}$$
$$= \sqrt[3]{27x^6 y^6\cdot2x^2} = 3x^2 y^2\sqrt[3]{2x^2}$$

39.
$$\sqrt[4]{32x^3 y^{11}} = \sqrt[4]{16\cdot2\cdot x^3 y^8\cdot y^3}$$
$$= \sqrt[4]{16y^8\cdot2x^3 y^3} = 2y^2\sqrt[4]{2x^3 y^3}$$

40.
$$\sqrt{6x^3}\cdot\sqrt{4x^2} = \sqrt{24x^5} = \sqrt{4\cdot6\cdot x^4\cdot x}$$
$$= \sqrt{4x^4\cdot6x} = 2x^2\sqrt{6x}$$

41.
$$\sqrt[3]{4x^2 y}\cdot\sqrt[3]{4xy^4} = \sqrt[3]{16x^3 y^5} = \sqrt[3]{8\cdot2\cdot x^3\cdot y^3\cdot y^2}$$
$$= \sqrt[3]{8x^3 y^3\cdot2y^2} = 2xy\sqrt[3]{2y^2}$$

42.
$$\sqrt[5]{2x^4 y^3}\cdot\sqrt[5]{8xy^6} = \sqrt[5]{16x^5 y^9} = \sqrt[5]{16\cdot x^5\cdot y^5\cdot y^4}$$
$$= \sqrt[5]{x^5 y^5\cdot16y^4} = xy\sqrt[5]{16y^4}$$

43.
$$\sqrt{x+1}\cdot\sqrt{x-1} = \sqrt{(x+1)(x-1)} = \sqrt{x^2-1}$$

44.
$$6\sqrt[3]{3} + 2\sqrt[3]{3} = (6+2)\sqrt[3]{3} = 8\sqrt[3]{3}$$

45.
$$5\sqrt{18} - 3\sqrt{8} = 5\sqrt{9\cdot2} - 3\sqrt{4\cdot2}$$
$$= 5\cdot3\sqrt{2} - 3\cdot2\sqrt{2} = 15\sqrt{2} - 6\sqrt{2}$$
$$= (15-6)\sqrt{2} = 9\sqrt{2}$$

46.
$$\sqrt[3]{27x^4} + \sqrt[3]{xy^6} = \sqrt[3]{27x^3 x} + \sqrt[3]{xy^6}$$
$$= 3x\sqrt[3]{x} + y^2\sqrt[3]{x} = \left(3x + y^2\right)\sqrt[3]{x}$$

47.
$$2\sqrt[3]{6} - 5\sqrt[3]{48} = 2\sqrt[3]{6} - 5\sqrt[3]{8\cdot6}$$
$$= 2\sqrt[3]{6} - 5\cdot2\sqrt[3]{6} = 2\sqrt[3]{6} - 10\sqrt[3]{6}$$
$$= (2-10)\sqrt[3]{6} = -8\sqrt[3]{6}$$

48.
$$\sqrt[3]{\frac{16}{125}} = \sqrt[3]{\frac{8\cdot2}{125}} = \frac{2}{5}\sqrt[3]{2}$$

49.
$$\sqrt{\frac{x^3}{100y^4}} = \sqrt{\frac{x^2\cdot x}{100y^4}} = \frac{x}{10y^2}\sqrt{x} \text{ or } \frac{x\sqrt{x}}{10y^2}$$

50.
$$\sqrt[4]{\frac{3y^5}{16x^{20}}} = \sqrt[4]{\frac{y^4\cdot3y}{16x^{20}}} = \frac{y}{2x^5}\sqrt[4]{3y} \text{ or } \frac{y\sqrt[4]{3y}}{2x^5}$$

51. $\dfrac{\sqrt{48}}{\sqrt{2}} = \sqrt{\dfrac{48}{2}} = \sqrt{24} = \sqrt{4 \cdot 6} = 2\sqrt{6}$

52. $\dfrac{\sqrt[3]{32}}{\sqrt[3]{2}} = \sqrt[3]{\dfrac{32}{2}} = \sqrt[3]{16} = \sqrt[3]{8 \cdot 2} = 2\sqrt[3]{2}$

53. $\dfrac{\sqrt[4]{64x^7}}{\sqrt[4]{2x^2}} = \sqrt[4]{\dfrac{64x^7}{2x^2}} = \sqrt[4]{32x^5} = \sqrt[4]{16 \cdot 2 \cdot x^4 \cdot x}$

$\qquad = \sqrt[4]{16x^4 \cdot 2x} = 2x\sqrt[4]{2x}$

54. $\dfrac{\sqrt{200x^3y^2}}{\sqrt{2x^{-2}y}} = \sqrt{\dfrac{200x^3y^2}{2x^{-2}y}} = \sqrt{100x^5 y}$

$\qquad = \sqrt{100x^4 xy} = 10x^2\sqrt{xy}$

55. $\sqrt{3}\left(2\sqrt{6} + 4\sqrt{15}\right)$

$\quad = 2\sqrt{18} + 4\sqrt{45} = 2\sqrt{9 \cdot 2} + 4\sqrt{9 \cdot 5}$

$\quad = 2 \cdot 3\sqrt{2} + 4 \cdot 3\sqrt{5} = 6\sqrt{2} + 12\sqrt{5}$

56. $\sqrt[3]{5}\left(\sqrt[3]{50} - \sqrt[3]{2}\right) = \sqrt[3]{250} - \sqrt[3]{10}$

$\quad = \sqrt[3]{125 \cdot 2} - \sqrt[3]{10} = 5\sqrt[3]{2} - \sqrt[3]{10}$

57. $\left(\sqrt{7} - 3\sqrt{5}\right)\left(\sqrt{7} + 6\sqrt{5}\right)$

$\quad = 7 + 6\sqrt{35} - 3\sqrt{35} - 18 \cdot 5 = 7 + 3\sqrt{35} - 90$

$\quad = 3\sqrt{35} - 83 \ \text{ or } \ -83 + 3\sqrt{35}$

58. $\left(\sqrt{x} - \sqrt{11}\right)\left(\sqrt{y} - \sqrt{11}\right)$

$\quad = \sqrt{xy} - \sqrt{11x} - \sqrt{11y} + 11$

59. $\left(\sqrt{5} + \sqrt{8}\right)^2 = 5 + 2 \cdot \sqrt{5} \cdot \sqrt{8} + 8$

$\quad = 13 + 2\sqrt{40} = 13 + 2\sqrt{4 \cdot 10}$

$\quad = 13 + 2 \cdot 2\sqrt{10} = 13 + 4\sqrt{10}$

60. $\left(2\sqrt{3} - \sqrt{10}\right)^2 = 4 \cdot 3 - 2 \cdot 2\sqrt{3} \cdot \sqrt{10} + 10$

$\qquad = 12 - 4\sqrt{30} + 10 = 22 - 4\sqrt{30}$

61. $\left(\sqrt{7} + \sqrt{13}\right)\left(\sqrt{7} - \sqrt{13}\right) = \left(\sqrt{7}\right)^2 - \left(\sqrt{13}\right)^2$

$\qquad = 7 - 13 = -6$

62. $\left(7 - 3\sqrt{5}\right)\left(7 + 3\sqrt{5}\right) = 7^2 - \left(3\sqrt{5}\right)^2$

$\qquad = 49 - 9 \cdot 5 = 49 - 45 = 4$

63. $\dfrac{4}{\sqrt{6}} = \dfrac{4}{\sqrt{6}} \cdot \dfrac{\sqrt{6}}{\sqrt{6}} = \dfrac{4\sqrt{6}}{6} = \dfrac{2\sqrt{6}}{3}$

64. $\sqrt{\dfrac{2}{7}} = \dfrac{\sqrt{2}}{\sqrt{7}} = \dfrac{\sqrt{2}}{\sqrt{7}} \cdot \dfrac{\sqrt{7}}{\sqrt{7}} = \dfrac{\sqrt{14}}{7}$

65. $\dfrac{12}{\sqrt[3]{9}} = \dfrac{12}{\sqrt[3]{3^2}} \cdot \dfrac{\sqrt[3]{3}}{\sqrt[3]{3}} = \dfrac{12\sqrt[3]{3}}{\sqrt[3]{3^3}} = \dfrac{12\sqrt[3]{3}}{3} = 4\sqrt[3]{3}$

66. $\sqrt{\dfrac{2x}{5y}} = \dfrac{\sqrt{2x}}{\sqrt{5y}} \cdot \dfrac{\sqrt{5y}}{\sqrt{5y}} = \dfrac{\sqrt{10xy}}{\sqrt{5^2 y^2}} = \dfrac{\sqrt{10xy}}{5y}$

67. $\dfrac{14}{\sqrt[3]{2x^2}} = \dfrac{14}{\sqrt[3]{2x^2}} \cdot \dfrac{\sqrt[3]{2^2 x}}{\sqrt[3]{2^2 x}} = \dfrac{14\sqrt[3]{2^2 x}}{\sqrt[3]{2^3 x^3}}$

$\qquad = \dfrac{14\sqrt[3]{4x}}{2x} = \dfrac{7\sqrt[3]{4x}}{x}$

68. $\sqrt[4]{\dfrac{7}{3x}} = \dfrac{\sqrt[4]{7}}{\sqrt[4]{3x}} = \dfrac{\sqrt[4]{7}}{\sqrt[4]{3x}} \cdot \dfrac{\sqrt[4]{3^3 x^3}}{\sqrt[4]{3^3 x^3}}$

$\qquad = \dfrac{\sqrt[4]{7 \cdot 3^3 x^3}}{\sqrt[4]{3^4 x^4}} = \dfrac{\sqrt[4]{7 \cdot 27 x^3}}{3x} = \dfrac{\sqrt[4]{189x^3}}{3x}$

69. $\dfrac{5}{\sqrt[5]{32x^4 y}} = \dfrac{5}{\sqrt[5]{2^5 x^4 y}} \cdot \dfrac{\sqrt[5]{xy^4}}{\sqrt[5]{xy^4}}$

$\qquad = \dfrac{5\sqrt[5]{xy^4}}{\sqrt[5]{2^5 x^5 y^5}} = \dfrac{5\sqrt[5]{xy^4}}{2xy}$

70.
$$\frac{6}{\sqrt{3}-1} = \frac{6}{\sqrt{3}-1} \cdot \frac{\sqrt{3}+1}{\sqrt{3}+1}$$
$$= \frac{6\left(\sqrt{3}+1\right)}{\left(\sqrt{3}\right)^2 - 1^2} = \frac{6\left(\sqrt{3}+1\right)}{3-1}$$
$$= \frac{6\left(\sqrt{3}+1\right)}{2} = 3\left(\sqrt{3}+1\right) = 3\sqrt{3}+3$$

71.
$$\frac{\sqrt{7}}{\sqrt{5}+\sqrt{3}} = \frac{\sqrt{7}}{\sqrt{5}+\sqrt{3}} \cdot \frac{\sqrt{5}-\sqrt{3}}{\sqrt{5}-\sqrt{3}} = \frac{\sqrt{35}-\sqrt{21}}{\left(\sqrt{5}\right)^2 - \left(\sqrt{3}\right)^2}$$
$$= \frac{\sqrt{35}-\sqrt{21}}{5-3} = \frac{\sqrt{35}-\sqrt{21}}{2}$$

72.
$$\frac{10}{2\sqrt{5}-3\sqrt{2}} = \frac{10}{2\sqrt{5}-3\sqrt{2}} \cdot \frac{2\sqrt{5}+3\sqrt{2}}{2\sqrt{5}+3\sqrt{2}}$$
$$= \frac{10\left(2\sqrt{5}+3\sqrt{2}\right)}{\left(2\sqrt{5}\right)^2 - \left(3\sqrt{2}\right)^2} = \frac{10\left(2\sqrt{5}+3\sqrt{2}\right)}{4\cdot5 - 9\cdot2}$$
$$= \frac{10\left(2\sqrt{5}+3\sqrt{2}\right)}{20-18} = \frac{10\left(2\sqrt{5}+3\sqrt{2}\right)}{2}$$
$$= 5\left(2\sqrt{5}+3\sqrt{2}\right) = 10\sqrt{5}+15\sqrt{2}$$

73.
$$\frac{\sqrt{x}+5}{\sqrt{x}-3} = \frac{\sqrt{x}+5}{\sqrt{x}-3} \cdot \frac{\sqrt{x}+3}{\sqrt{x}+3}$$
$$= \frac{x+3\sqrt{x}+5\sqrt{x}+15}{\left(\sqrt{x}\right)^2 - 3^2} = \frac{x+8\sqrt{x}+15}{x-9}$$

74.
$$\frac{\sqrt{7}+\sqrt{3}}{\sqrt{7}-\sqrt{3}} = \frac{\sqrt{7}+\sqrt{3}}{\sqrt{7}-\sqrt{3}} \cdot \frac{\sqrt{7}+\sqrt{3}}{\sqrt{7}+\sqrt{3}}$$
$$= \frac{7+2\cdot\sqrt{7}\cdot\sqrt{3}+3}{\left(\sqrt{7}\right)^2 - \left(\sqrt{3}\right)^2} = \frac{10+2\sqrt{21}}{7-3}$$
$$= \frac{10+2\sqrt{21}}{4} = \frac{2\left(5+\sqrt{21}\right)}{4} = \frac{5+\sqrt{21}}{2}$$

75.
$$\frac{2\sqrt{3}+\sqrt{6}}{2\sqrt{6}+\sqrt{3}} = \frac{2\sqrt{3}+\sqrt{6}}{2\sqrt{6}+\sqrt{3}} \cdot \frac{2\sqrt{6}-\sqrt{3}}{2\sqrt{6}-\sqrt{3}}$$

$$= \frac{4\sqrt{18}-2\cdot3+2\cdot6-\sqrt{18}}{\left(2\sqrt{6}\right)^2 - \left(\sqrt{3}\right)^2} = \frac{3\sqrt{18}-6+12}{4\cdot6-3}$$
$$= \frac{3\sqrt{9\cdot2}+6}{24-3} = \frac{3\cdot3\sqrt{2}+6}{21} = \frac{9\sqrt{2}+6}{21}$$
$$= \frac{3\left(3\sqrt{2}+2\right)}{21} = \frac{3\sqrt{2}+2}{7}$$

76.
$$\sqrt{\frac{2}{7}} = \frac{\sqrt{2}}{\sqrt{7}} = \frac{\sqrt{2}}{\sqrt{7}} \cdot \frac{\sqrt{2}}{\sqrt{2}} = \frac{2}{\sqrt{14}}$$

77.
$$\frac{\sqrt[3]{3x}}{\sqrt[3]{y}} = \frac{\sqrt[3]{3x}}{\sqrt[3]{y}} \cdot \frac{\sqrt[3]{3^2 x^2}}{\sqrt[3]{3^2 x^2}} = \frac{\sqrt[3]{3^3 x^3}}{\sqrt[3]{3^2 x^2 y}} = \frac{3x}{\sqrt[3]{9x^2 y}}$$

78.
$$\frac{\sqrt{7}}{\sqrt{5}+\sqrt{3}} = \frac{\sqrt{7}}{\sqrt{5}+\sqrt{3}} \cdot \frac{\sqrt{7}}{\sqrt{7}} = \frac{7}{\sqrt{35}+\sqrt{21}}$$

79.
$$\frac{\sqrt{7}+\sqrt{3}}{\sqrt{7}-\sqrt{3}} = \frac{\sqrt{7}+\sqrt{3}}{\sqrt{7}-\sqrt{3}} \cdot \frac{\sqrt{7}-\sqrt{3}}{\sqrt{7}-\sqrt{3}}$$
$$= \frac{\left(\sqrt{7}\right)^2 - \left(\sqrt{3}\right)^2}{7-2\sqrt{7}\sqrt{3}+3} = \frac{7-3}{10-2\sqrt{21}}$$
$$= \frac{4}{10-2\sqrt{21}} = \frac{4}{2\left(5-\sqrt{21}\right)} = \frac{2}{5-\sqrt{21}}$$

80.
$$\sqrt{2x+4} = 6$$
$$\left(\sqrt{2x+4}\right)^2 = 6^2$$
$$2x+4 = 36$$
$$2x = 32$$
$$x = 16$$
The solution checks.

81.
$$\sqrt{x-5}+9 = 4$$
$$\sqrt{x-5} = -5$$
The square root of a number is always positive. The solution set is $\varnothing$ or $\{\ \ \}$.

82.
$$\sqrt{2x-3}+x=3$$
$$\sqrt{2x-3}=3-x$$
$$\left(\sqrt{2x-3}\right)^2=(3-x)^2$$
$$2x-3=9-6x+x^2$$
$$0=12-8x+x^2$$
$$0=x^2-8x+12$$
$$0=(x-6)(x-2)$$
$$x-6=0 \qquad x-2=0$$
$$x=6 \qquad x=2$$

6 is an extraneous solution. The solution is 2.

83.
$$\sqrt{x-4}+\sqrt{x+1}=5$$
$$\sqrt{x-4}=5-\sqrt{x+1}$$
$$\left(\sqrt{x-4}\right)^2=\left(5-\sqrt{x+1}\right)^2$$
$$x-4=25-10\sqrt{x+1}+x+1$$
$$-30=-10\sqrt{x+1}$$
$$3=\sqrt{x+1}$$
$$3^2=\left(\sqrt{x+1}\right)^2$$
$$9=x+1$$
$$8=x$$
The solution checks.

84.
$$\left(x^2+6x\right)^{\frac{1}{3}}+2=0$$
$$\left(x^2+6x\right)^{\frac{1}{3}}=-2$$
$$\sqrt[3]{x^2+6x}=-2$$
$$\left(\sqrt[3]{x^2+6x}\right)^3=(-2)^3$$
$$x^2+6x=-8$$
$$x^2+6x+8=0$$
$$(x+4)(x+2)=0$$
$$x+4=0 \qquad x+2=0$$
$$x=-4 \qquad x=-2$$
Both solutions check.

85.
$$4=\sqrt{\frac{x}{16}}$$
$$4^2=\left(\sqrt{\frac{x}{16}}\right)^2$$
$$16=\frac{x}{16}$$
$$256=x$$
The hammer was dropped from a height of 256 feet.

86.
$$20{,}000=5000\sqrt{100-x}$$
$$4=\sqrt{100-x}$$
$$4^2=\left(\sqrt{100-x}\right)^2$$
$$16=100-x$$
$$-84=-x$$
$$84=x$$
20,000 people in the group will survive to 84 years old.

87. $\sqrt{-81}=\sqrt{81\cdot-1}=\sqrt{81}\sqrt{-1}=9i$

88. $\sqrt{-63}=\sqrt{9\cdot7\cdot-1}=\sqrt{9}\sqrt{7}\sqrt{-1}=3\sqrt{7}i$

89. $-\sqrt{-8}=-\sqrt{4\cdot2\cdot-1}=-\sqrt{4}\sqrt{2}\sqrt{-1}=-2\sqrt{2}i$

90. $(7+12i)+(5-10i)$
$=7+12i+5-10i=12+2i$

91. $(8-3i)-(17-7i)=8-3i-17+7i=-9+4i$

92. $4i(3i-2)=4i\cdot3i-4i\cdot2=12i^2-8i$
$=12(-1)-8i=-12-8i$

93. $(7-5i)(2+3i)=14+21i-10i-15i^2$
$=14+11i-15(-1)=14+11i+15=29+11i$

94. $(3-4i)^2=3^2-2\cdot3\cdot4i+(4i)^2$
$=9-24i+16i^2=9-24i+16(-1)$
$=9-24i-16=-7-24i$

95. $(7+8i)(7-8i)=7^2-(8i)^2=49-64i^2$

$=49-64(-1)=49+64=113=113+0i$

96. $\sqrt{-8}\cdot\sqrt{-3}=\sqrt{4\cdot2\cdot-1}\cdot\sqrt{3\cdot-1}=2\sqrt{2}i\cdot\sqrt{3}i$

$=2\sqrt{6}i^2=2\sqrt{6}(-1)=-2\sqrt{6}=-2\sqrt{6}+0i$

97. $\dfrac{6}{5+i}=\dfrac{6}{5+i}\cdot\dfrac{5-i}{5-i}=\dfrac{30-6i}{25-i^2}=\dfrac{30-6i}{25-(-1)}$

$=\dfrac{30-6i}{25+1}=\dfrac{30-6i}{26}=\dfrac{30}{26}-\dfrac{6}{26}i=\dfrac{15}{13}-\dfrac{3}{13}i$

98. $\dfrac{3+4i}{4-2i}=\dfrac{3+4i}{4-2i}\cdot\dfrac{4+2i}{4+2i}=\dfrac{12+6i+16i+8i^2}{16-4i^2}$

$=\dfrac{12+22i+8(-1)}{16-4(-1)}=\dfrac{12+22i-8}{16+4}$

$=\dfrac{4+22i}{20}=\dfrac{4}{20}+\dfrac{22}{20}i=\dfrac{1}{5}+\dfrac{11}{10}i$

99. $\dfrac{5+i}{3i}=\dfrac{5+i}{3i}\cdot\dfrac{i}{i}=\dfrac{5i+i^2}{3i^2}=\dfrac{5i+(-1)}{3(-1)}$

$=\dfrac{5i-1}{-3}=\dfrac{-1}{-3}+\dfrac{5}{-3}i=\dfrac{1}{3}-\dfrac{5}{3}i$

100. $i^{16}=\left(i^2\right)^8=(-1)^8=1$

101. $i^{23}=i^{22}\cdot i=\left(i^2\right)^{11}i=(-1)^{11}i=(-1)i=-i$

Chapter 10 Test

1.   **a.** $f(-14)=\sqrt{8-2(-14)}$

$=\sqrt{8+28}=\sqrt{36}=6$

     b.   To find the domain, set the radicand greater than or equal to zero and solve the resulting inequality.

$8-2x\geq0$

$-2x\geq-8$

$x\leq4$

The domain of f is $\{x\mid x\leq4\}$ or $(-\infty,4]$.

2. $27^{-\frac{4}{3}}=\dfrac{1}{27^{\frac{4}{3}}}=\dfrac{1}{\left(\sqrt[3]{27}\right)^4}=\dfrac{1}{(3)^4}=\dfrac{1}{81}$

3. $\left(25x^{-\frac{1}{2}}y^{\frac{1}{4}}\right)^{\frac{1}{2}}=25^{\frac{1}{2}}x^{-\frac{1}{4}}y^{\frac{1}{8}}=5x^{-\frac{1}{4}}y^{\frac{1}{8}}$

$=\dfrac{5y^{\frac{1}{8}}}{x^{\frac{1}{4}}}=\dfrac{5\sqrt[8]{y}}{\sqrt[4]{x}}$

4. $\sqrt[8]{x^4}=\left(x^4\right)^{\frac{1}{8}}=x^{4\cdot\frac{1}{8}}=x^{\frac{1}{2}}=\sqrt{x}$

5. $\sqrt[4]{x}\cdot\sqrt[5]{x}=x^{\frac{1}{4}}\cdot x^{\frac{1}{5}}=x^{\frac{1}{4}+\frac{1}{5}}=x^{\frac{5}{20}+\frac{4}{20}}=x^{\frac{9}{20}}=\sqrt[20]{x^9}$

6. $\sqrt{75x^2}=\sqrt{25\cdot3x^2}=5|x|\sqrt{3}$

7. $\sqrt{x^2-10x+25}=\sqrt{(x-5)^2}=|x-5|$

8. $\sqrt[3]{16x^4y^8}=\sqrt[3]{8\cdot2\cdot x^3\cdot x\cdot y^6\cdot y^2}$

$=\sqrt[3]{8x^3y^6\cdot2xy^2}=2xy^2\sqrt[3]{2xy^2}$

9. $\sqrt[5]{-\dfrac{32}{x^{10}}}=\sqrt[5]{-\dfrac{2^5}{\left(x^2\right)^5}}=-\dfrac{2}{x^2}$

10. $\sqrt[3]{5x^2}\cdot\sqrt[3]{10y}=\sqrt[3]{50x^2y}$

11. $\sqrt[4]{8x^3y}\cdot\sqrt[4]{4xy^2}=\sqrt[4]{32x^4y^3}=\sqrt[4]{16\cdot2\cdot x^4\cdot y^3}$

$=\sqrt[4]{16x^4\cdot2y^3}=2x\sqrt[4]{2y^3}$

12. $3\sqrt{18}-4\sqrt{32}=3\sqrt{9\cdot2}-4\sqrt{16\cdot2}$

$=3\cdot3\sqrt{2}-4\cdot4\sqrt{2}=9\sqrt{2}-16\sqrt{2}=-7\sqrt{2}$

13. $\sqrt[3]{8x^4}+\sqrt[3]{xy^6}=\sqrt[3]{8x^3\cdot x}+\sqrt[3]{xy^6}$

$=2x\sqrt[3]{x}+y^2\sqrt[3]{x}=\left(2x+y^2\right)\sqrt[3]{x}$

14. $\dfrac{\sqrt[3]{16x^8}}{\sqrt[3]{2x^4}} = \sqrt[3]{\dfrac{16x^8}{2x^4}} = \sqrt[3]{8x^4} = \sqrt[3]{8x^3 \cdot 2} = 2x\sqrt[3]{2}$

15. $\sqrt{3}\left(4\sqrt{6} - \sqrt{5}\right) = \sqrt{3} \cdot 4\sqrt{6} - \sqrt{3} \cdot \sqrt{5}$

$= 4\sqrt{18} - \sqrt{15} = 4\sqrt{9 \cdot 2} - \sqrt{15}$

$= 4 \cdot 3\sqrt{2} - \sqrt{15} = 12\sqrt{2} - \sqrt{15}$

16. $\left(5\sqrt{6} - 2\sqrt{2}\right)\left(\sqrt{6} + \sqrt{2}\right)$

$= 5 \cdot 6 + 5\sqrt{12} - 2\sqrt{12} - 2 \cdot 2$

$= 30 + 3\sqrt{12} - 4 = 26 + 3\sqrt{4 \cdot 3}$

$= 26 + 3 \cdot 2\sqrt{3} = 26 + 6\sqrt{3}$

17. $\left(7 - \sqrt{3}\right)^2 = 49 - 2 \cdot 7 \cdot \sqrt{3} + 3 = 52 - 14\sqrt{3}$

18. $\sqrt{\dfrac{5}{x}} = \dfrac{\sqrt{5}}{\sqrt{x}} \cdot \dfrac{\sqrt{x}}{\sqrt{x}} = \dfrac{\sqrt{5x}}{x}$

19. $\dfrac{5}{\sqrt[3]{5x^2}} = \dfrac{5}{\sqrt[3]{5x^2}} \cdot \dfrac{\sqrt[3]{5^2 x}}{\sqrt[3]{5^2 x}} = \dfrac{5\sqrt[3]{5^2 x}}{\sqrt[3]{5^3 x^3}} = \dfrac{5\sqrt[3]{25x}}{5x} = \dfrac{\sqrt[3]{25x}}{x}$

20. $\dfrac{\sqrt{2} - \sqrt{3}}{\sqrt{2} + \sqrt{3}} = \dfrac{\sqrt{2} - \sqrt{3}}{\sqrt{2} + \sqrt{3}} \cdot \dfrac{\sqrt{2} - \sqrt{3}}{\sqrt{2} - \sqrt{3}}$

$= \dfrac{2 - 2\sqrt{2}\sqrt{3} + 3}{2 - 3} = \dfrac{5 - 2\sqrt{6}}{-1} = -5 + 2\sqrt{6}$

21. $3 + \sqrt{2x - 3} = x$

$\sqrt{2x - 3} = x - 3$

$\left(\sqrt{2x - 3}\right)^2 = (x - 3)^2$

$2x - 3 = x^2 - 6x + 9$

$0 = x^2 - 8x + 12$

$0 = (x - 6)(x - 2)$

$x - 6 = 0 \qquad x - 2 = 0$

$x = 6 \qquad\quad x = 2$

2 is an extraneous solution. The solution is 6.

22. $\sqrt{x + 9} - \sqrt{x - 7} = 2$

$\sqrt{x + 9} = 2 + \sqrt{x - 7}$

$\left(\sqrt{x + 9}\right)^2 = \left(2 + \sqrt{x - 7}\right)^2$

$x + 9 = 4 + 2 \cdot 2 \cdot \sqrt{x - 7} + x - 7$

$x + 9 = 4\sqrt{x - 7} + x - 3$

$12 = 4\sqrt{x - 7}$

$3 = \sqrt{x - 7}$

$3^2 = \left(\sqrt{x - 7}\right)^2$

$9 = x - 7$

$16 = x$

23. $(11x + 6)^{\frac{1}{3}} + 3 = 0$

$(11x + 6)^{\frac{1}{3}} = -3$

$\sqrt[3]{11x + 6} = -3$

$\left(\sqrt[3]{11x + 6}\right)^3 = (-3)^3$

$11x + 6 = -27$

$11x = -33$

$x = -3$

24. $40.4 = 2.9\sqrt{x} + 20.1$

$20.3 = 2.9\sqrt{x}$

$7 = \sqrt{x}$

$7^2 = \left(\sqrt{x}\right)^2$

$49 = x$

Boys who are 49 months of age have an average height of 40.4 inches.

25. $\sqrt{-75} = \sqrt{25 \cdot 3 \cdot -1} = \sqrt{25} \cdot \sqrt{3} \cdot \sqrt{-1} = 5\sqrt{3}i$

26. $(5 - 3i) - (6 - 9i) = 5 - 3i - 6 + 9i$

$= 5 - 6 - 3i + 9i = -1 + 6i$

27. $(3 - 4i)(2 + 5i) = 6 + 15i - 8i - 20i^2$

$= 6 + 7i - 20(-1) = 6 + 7i + 20 = 26 + 7i$

28. $\sqrt{-9} \cdot \sqrt{-4} = \sqrt{9 \cdot -1} \cdot \sqrt{4 \cdot -1}$

$= \sqrt{9} \cdot \sqrt{-1} \cdot \sqrt{4} \cdot \sqrt{-1} = 3 \cdot i \cdot 2 \cdot i = 6i^2$

$= 6(-1) = -6 \quad \text{or} \quad -6 + 0i$

29.
$$\frac{3+i}{1-2i} = \frac{3+i}{1-2i} \cdot \frac{1+2i}{1+2i} = \frac{3+6i+i+2i^2}{1-4i^2}$$
$$= \frac{3+7i+2(-1)}{1-4(-1)} = \frac{3+7i-2}{1+4}$$
$$= \frac{1+7i}{5} = \frac{1}{5} + \frac{7}{5}i$$

30. $i^{35} = i^{34} \cdot i = \left(i^2\right)^{17} \cdot i = (-1)^{17} \cdot i = (-1)i = -i$

Cumulative Review Exercises
Chapters 1 -10

1.   Add the first and third equations to eliminate y.
$$2x - y + z = -5$$
$$\underline{x + y - 2z = 1}$$
$$3x \qquad - z = -4$$
Multiply the third equation by 2 and add to the second equation.
$$x - 2y - 3z = 6$$
$$\underline{2x + 2y - 4z = 2}$$
$$3x \qquad - 7z = 8$$
We now have a system of two equations in two variables.
$$3x - z = -4$$
$$3x - 7z = 8$$
Multiply the first equation by -1 and add to the second equation.
$$-3x + z = 4$$
$$\underline{3x - 7z = 8}$$
$$-6z = 12$$
$$z = -2$$
Back-substitute -2 for z to find x.
$$-3x + z = 4$$
$$-3x - 2 = 4$$
$$-3x = 6$$
$$x = -2$$
Back-substitute -2 for x and z in one of the original equations to find y.

$$2x - y + z = -5$$
$$2(-2) - y - 2 = -5$$
$$-4 - y - 2 = -5$$
$$-y - 6 = -5$$
$$-y = 1$$
$$y = -1$$
The solution is $(-2, -1, -2)$.

2.
$$3x^2 - 11x = 4$$
$$3x^2 - 11x - 4 = 0$$
$$(3x + 1)(x - 4) = 0$$
$$3x + 1 = 0 \qquad x - 4 = 0$$
$$3x = -1 \qquad\quad x = 4$$
$$x = -\frac{1}{3}$$

3. $2(x + 4) < 5x + 3(x + 2)$
$$2x + 8 < 5x + 3x + 6$$
$$2x + 8 < 8x + 6$$
$$-6x + 8 < 6$$
$$-6x < -2$$
$$\frac{-6x}{-6} > \frac{-2}{-6}$$
$$x > \frac{1}{3}$$

The solution set is $\left\{ x \,\middle|\, x > \frac{1}{3} \right\}$ or $\left(\frac{1}{3}, \infty \right)$.

4.
$$\frac{1}{x+2} + \frac{15}{x^2 - 4} = \frac{5}{x-2}$$
$$\frac{1}{x+2} + \frac{15}{(x+2)(x-2)} = \frac{5}{x-2}$$
Multiply both sides of the equation by $(x+2)(x-2)$.
$$x - 2 + 15 = 5x + 10$$
$$x + 13 = 5x + 10$$
$$-4x + 13 = 10$$
$$-4x = -3$$
$$x = \frac{3}{4}$$

5.
$$\sqrt{x+2} - \sqrt{x+1} = 1$$
$$\sqrt{x+2} = 1 + \sqrt{x+1}$$
$$\left(\sqrt{x+2}\right)^2 = \left(1+\sqrt{x+1}\right)^2$$
$$x+2 = 1 + 2\sqrt{x+1} + x + 1$$
$$x+2 = 2 + 2\sqrt{x+1} + x$$
$$0^2 = \left(2\sqrt{x+1}\right)^2$$
$$0 = 4(x+1)$$
$$0 = 4x+4$$
$$-4 = 4x$$
$$-1 = x$$

6.
$$x+2y < 2$$
$$2y-x > 4$$

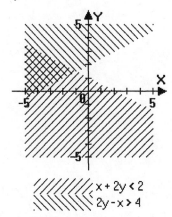

$$x+2y < 2$$
$$2y-x > 4$$

7.
$$\frac{8x^2}{3x^2-12} \div \frac{40}{x-2} = \frac{8x^2}{3(x^2-4)} \cdot \frac{x-2}{40}$$
$$= \frac{8x^2}{3(x+2)(x-2)} \cdot \frac{x-2}{40}$$
$$= \frac{x^2}{3\cdot 5(x+2)} = \frac{x^2}{15(x+2)}$$

8.
$$\frac{x+\dfrac{1}{y}}{y+\dfrac{1}{x}} = \frac{xy}{xy} \cdot \frac{x+\dfrac{1}{y}}{y+\dfrac{1}{x}} = \frac{x^2y+x}{xy^2+y}$$
$$= \frac{x(xy+1)}{y(xy+1)} = \frac{x}{y}$$

9.
$$\begin{array}{r} 4x^2 - 5x - 2 \\ 2x-3 \\ \hline 8x^3 - 10x^2 - 4x \\ -12x^2 + 15x + 6 \\ \hline 8x^3 - 22x^2 + 11x + 6 \end{array}$$

10.
$$\frac{7x}{x^2-2x-15} - \frac{2}{x-5} = \frac{7x}{(x-5)(x+3)} - \frac{2}{x-5}$$
$$= \frac{7x}{(x-5)(x+3)} - \frac{2(x+3)}{(x-5)(x+3)}$$
$$= \frac{7x-2x-6}{(x-5)(x+3)} = \frac{5x-6}{(x-5)(x+3)}$$

11.
$$7(8-10)^3 - 7 + 3 \div (-3)$$
$$= 7(-2)^3 - 7 + 3 \div (-3)$$
$$= 7(-8) - 7 + 3 \div (-3)$$
$$= -56 - 7 + (-1) = -64$$

12.
$$\sqrt{80x} - 5\sqrt{20x} + 2\sqrt{45x}$$
$$= \sqrt{16\cdot 5x} - 5\sqrt{4\cdot 5x} + 2\sqrt{9\cdot 5x}$$
$$= 4\sqrt{5x} - 5\cdot 2\sqrt{5x} + 2\cdot 3\sqrt{5x}$$
$$= 4\sqrt{5x} - 10\sqrt{5x} + 6\sqrt{5x} = 0$$

13.
$$\frac{\sqrt{3}-2}{2\sqrt{3}+5} = \frac{\sqrt{3}-2}{2\sqrt{3}+5} \cdot \frac{2\sqrt{3}-5}{2\sqrt{3}-5}$$
$$= \frac{2\cdot 3 - 5\sqrt{3} - 4\sqrt{3} + 10}{4\cdot 3 - 25}$$
$$= \frac{6 - 9\sqrt{3} + 10}{12 - 25} = \frac{16 - 9\sqrt{3}}{-13}$$
$$= -\frac{16 - 9\sqrt{3}}{13}$$

14.
$$\begin{array}{r} 2x^2 + x + 5 \\ x-2 \overline{)\ 2x^3 - 3x^2 + 3x - 4} \\ \underline{2x^3 - 4x^2} \\ x^2 + 3x \\ \underline{x^2 - 2x} \\ 5x - 4 \\ \underline{5x - 10} \\ 6 \end{array}$$

$$\frac{2x^3 - 3x^2 + 3x - 4}{x-2} = 2x^2 + x + 5 + \frac{6}{x-2}$$

15. $\left(2\sqrt{3} + 5\sqrt{2}\right)\left(\sqrt{3} - 4\sqrt{2}\right)$

$$= 2 \cdot 3 - 8\sqrt{6} + 5\sqrt{6} - 20 \cdot 2$$
$$= 6 - 3\sqrt{6} - 40 = -34 - 3\sqrt{6}$$

16. $24x^2 + 10x - 4 = 2\left(12x^2 + 5x - 2\right)$
$$= 2\left(3x + 2\right)\left(4x - 1\right)$$

17. $16x^4 - 1 = \left(4x^2 + 1\right)\left(4x^2 - 1\right)$
$$= \left(4x^2 + 1\right)\left(2x + 1\right)\left(2x - 1\right)$$

18.
$$l = \frac{k}{d^2}$$
$$120 = \frac{k}{10^2}$$
$$120 = \frac{k}{100}$$
$$12,000 = k$$
$$l = \frac{12,000}{15^2} = \frac{12,000}{225} \approx 53.3$$

At a distance of 15 feet, approximately 53 lumens are provided.

19. Let x = the amount invested at 7%,
Let y = the amount invested at 9%
$$x + \quad y = 6000$$
$$0.07x + 0.09y = \ 510$$
Solve the first equation for y.
$$x + y = 6000$$
$$y = 6000 - x$$
Substitute and solve.
$$0.07x + 0.09\left(6000 - x\right) = 510$$
$$0.07x + 540 - 0.09x = 510$$
$$540 - 0.02x = 510$$
$$-0.02x = -30$$
$$x = 1500$$
Back-substitute 1500 for x to find y.
$$y = 6000 - x$$
$$y = 6000 - 1500$$
$$y = 4500$$

$1500 was invested at 7% and $4500 was invested at 9%.

20. Let x = the number of students enrolled last year
$$x - 0.12x = 2332$$
$$0.88x = 2332$$
$$x = 2650$$
There were 2650 students enrolled last year.

Chapter 11

QUADRATIC EQUATIONS AND FUNCTIONS

The Square Root Property and Completing the Square

11.1 CHECK POINTS

CHECK POINT 1
$5x^2 = 15$
$x^2 = 3$
$x = \sqrt{3}$ or $x = -\sqrt{3}$
The solutions check.

CHECK POINT 2
$2x^2 - 5 = 0$
$2x^2 = 5$
$x^2 = \dfrac{5}{2}$
$x = \sqrt{\dfrac{5}{2}}$ or $x = -\sqrt{\dfrac{5}{2}}$

Because the proposed solutions are opposites, rationalize both denominators at once.
$x = \pm\sqrt{\dfrac{5}{2}} = \pm\dfrac{\sqrt{5}}{\sqrt{2}}\cdot\dfrac{\sqrt{2}}{\sqrt{2}} = \pm\dfrac{\sqrt{10}}{2}$

CHECK POINT 3
$4x^2 + 9 = 0$
$4x^2 = -9$
$x^2 = -\dfrac{9}{4}$
$x = \sqrt{-\dfrac{9}{4}}$ or $x = -\sqrt{-\dfrac{9}{4}}$
$x = \sqrt{\dfrac{9}{4}}\sqrt{-1}$ $\quad x = -\sqrt{\dfrac{9}{4}}\sqrt{-1}$
$x = \dfrac{3}{2}i$ $\quad\quad x = -\dfrac{3}{2}i$

CHECK POINT 4
$(x-2)^2 = 7$

$x - 2 = \sqrt{7}$ or $x - 2 = -\sqrt{7}$
$x = 2 + \sqrt{7}$ $\quad x = 2 - \sqrt{7}$

CHECK POINT 5

a. $\left(\dfrac{b}{2}\right)^2 = \left(\dfrac{10}{2}\right)^2 = (5)^2 = 25$
$x^2 + 10x + 25 = (x+5)^2$

b. $\left(\dfrac{b}{2}\right)^2 = \left(\dfrac{-3}{2}\right)^2 = \dfrac{9}{4}$
$x^2 - 3x + \dfrac{9}{4} = \left(x - \dfrac{3}{2}\right)^2$

c. $\left(\dfrac{b}{2}\right)^2 = \left(\dfrac{3}{4}\div 2\right)^2 = \left(\dfrac{3}{4}\cdot\dfrac{1}{2}\right)^2 = \left(\dfrac{3}{8}\right)^2 = \dfrac{9}{64}$
$x^2 + \dfrac{3}{4}x + \dfrac{9}{64} = \left(x + \dfrac{3}{8}\right)^2$

CHECK POINT 6
$\left(\dfrac{b}{2}\right)^2 = \left(\dfrac{-10}{2}\right)^2 = (-5)^2 = 25$
$x^2 - 10x + 25 = -18 + 25$
$(x-5)^2 = 7$
$x - 5 = \pm\sqrt{7}$
$x = 5 \pm \sqrt{7}$

CHECK POINT 7
$2x^2 - 10x - 1 = 0$
$x^2 - 5x - \dfrac{1}{2} = 0$
$x^2 - 5x = \dfrac{1}{2}$
$x^2 - 5x + \dfrac{25}{4} = \dfrac{1}{2} + \dfrac{25}{4}$
$\left(x - \dfrac{5}{2}\right)^2 = \dfrac{27}{4}$

$$x - \frac{5}{2} = \pm\sqrt{\frac{27}{4}}$$

$$x - \frac{5}{2} = \pm\frac{\sqrt{27}}{2}$$

$$x - \frac{5}{2} = \pm\frac{\sqrt{9 \cdot 3}}{2}$$

$$x - \frac{5}{2} = \pm\frac{3\sqrt{3}}{2}$$

$$x = \frac{5}{2} \pm \frac{3\sqrt{3}}{2}$$

$$x = \frac{5 \pm 3\sqrt{3}}{2}$$

CHECK POINT 8

$$A = P(1 + r)^t$$

$$4320 = 3000(1 + r)^2$$

$$\frac{4320}{3000} = (1 + r)^2$$

$$1.44 = (1 + r)^2$$

$$1 + r = \sqrt{1.44} \quad \text{or} \quad 1 + r = -\sqrt{1.44}$$

$$1 + r = 1.2 \qquad\qquad 1 + r = -1.2$$

$$r = 0.2 \qquad\qquad\quad r = -2.2$$

We reject –2.2 because we cannot have a negative interest rate. The solution is 0.2 and we conclude that the annual interest rate is 20%.

CHECK POINT 9

$$x^2 + 20^2 = 50^2$$

$$x^2 + 400 = 2500$$

$$x^2 = 2100$$

$$x = \pm\sqrt{2100}$$

$$x = \pm\sqrt{21 \cdot 100}$$

$$x = \pm 10\sqrt{21}$$

We reject $-10\sqrt{21}$ because we cannot have a negative length measurement. The solution is $10\sqrt{21}$ feet or $10\sqrt{21} \approx 45.8$ feet. The wire is attached approximately 45.8 feet from the base of the antenna.

EXERCISE SET 11.1

1. $3x^2 = 75$

$$x^2 = 25$$

$$x = \pm\sqrt{25}$$

$$x = \pm 5$$

3. $7x^2 = 42$

$$x^2 = 6$$

$$x = \pm\sqrt{6}$$

5. $16x^2 = 25$

$$x^2 = \frac{25}{16}$$

$$x = \pm\sqrt{\frac{25}{16}}$$

$$x = \pm\frac{5}{4}$$

7. $3x^2 - 2 = 0$

$$3x^2 = 2$$

$$x^2 = \frac{2}{3}$$

$$x = \pm\sqrt{\frac{2}{3}}$$

Rationalize the denominator.

$$x = \pm\sqrt{\frac{2}{3}} = \pm\frac{\sqrt{2}}{\sqrt{3}} \cdot \frac{\sqrt{3}}{\sqrt{3}} = \pm\frac{\sqrt{6}}{3}$$

9. $25x^2 + 16 = 0$

$$25x^2 = -16$$

$$x^2 = -\frac{16}{25}$$

$$x = \pm\sqrt{-\frac{16}{25}}$$

$$x = \pm\sqrt{\frac{16}{25}}\sqrt{-1}$$

$$x = \pm\frac{4}{5}i = 0 \pm \frac{4}{5}i$$

11. $(x+7)^2 = 9$

$\quad x+7 = \sqrt{9}$ or $x+7 = -\sqrt{9}$

$\quad x+7 = 3 \qquad\quad x+7 = -3$

$\qquad\quad x = -4 \qquad\qquad x = -10$

13. $(x-3)^2 = 5$

$\quad x-3 = \pm\sqrt{5}$

$\qquad x = 3 \pm \sqrt{5}$

15. $(x+2)^2 = 8$

$\quad x+2 = \pm\sqrt{8}$

$\quad x+2 = \pm\sqrt{4 \cdot 2}$

$\quad x+2 = \pm 2\sqrt{2}$

$\qquad x = -2 \pm 2\sqrt{2}$

17. $(x-5)^2 = -9$

$\quad x-5 = \pm\sqrt{-9}$

$\quad x-5 = \pm 3i$

$\qquad x = 5 \pm 3i$

19. $\left(x+\dfrac{3}{4}\right)^2 = \dfrac{11}{16}$

$\quad x+\dfrac{3}{4} = \pm\sqrt{\dfrac{11}{16}}$

$\quad x+\dfrac{3}{4} = \pm\dfrac{\sqrt{11}}{4}$

$\qquad x = -\dfrac{3}{4} \pm \dfrac{\sqrt{11}}{4} = \dfrac{-3 \pm \sqrt{11}}{4}$

21. $x^2 - 6x + 9 = 36$

$\quad (x-3)^2 = 36$

$\quad x-3 = \sqrt{36}$ or $x-3 = -\sqrt{36}$

$\quad x-3 = 6 \qquad\qquad x-3 = -6$

$\qquad x = 9 \qquad\qquad\quad x = -3$

23. $\left(\dfrac{b}{2}\right)^2 = \left(\dfrac{2}{2}\right)^2 = (1)^2 = 1$

$\quad x^2 + 2x + 1 = (x+1)^2$

25. $\left(\dfrac{b}{2}\right)^2 = \left(\dfrac{-14}{2}\right)^2 = (-7)^2 = 49$

$\quad x^2 - 14x + 49 = (x-7)^2$

27. $\left(\dfrac{b}{2}\right)^2 = \left(\dfrac{7}{2}\right)^2 = \dfrac{49}{4}$

$\quad x^2 + 7x + \dfrac{49}{4} = \left(x+\dfrac{7}{2}\right)^2$

29. $\left(\dfrac{b}{2}\right)^2 = \left(\dfrac{-1}{2} \div 2\right)^2 = \left(\dfrac{-1}{2} \cdot \dfrac{1}{2}\right)^2 = \left(\dfrac{-1}{4}\right)^2 = \dfrac{1}{16}$

$\quad x^2 - \dfrac{1}{2}x + \dfrac{1}{16} = \left(x-\dfrac{1}{4}\right)^2$

31. $\left(\dfrac{b}{2}\right)^2 = \left(\dfrac{4}{3} \div 2\right)^2 = \left(\dfrac{4}{3} \cdot \dfrac{1}{2}\right)^2 = \left(\dfrac{2}{3}\right)^2 = \dfrac{4}{9}.$

$\quad x^2 + \dfrac{4}{3}x + \dfrac{4}{9} = \left(x+\dfrac{2}{3}\right)^2$

33. $\left(\dfrac{b}{2}\right)^2 = \left(-\dfrac{9}{4} \div 2\right)^2 = \left(-\dfrac{9}{4} \cdot \dfrac{1}{2}\right)^2 = \left(-\dfrac{9}{8}\right)^2 = \dfrac{81}{64}$

$\quad x^2 - \dfrac{9}{4}x + \dfrac{81}{64} = \left(x-\dfrac{9}{8}\right)^2$

35. $\qquad x^2 + 6x = -8$

$\quad x^2 + 6x \qquad = -8$

$\quad x^2 + 6x + 9 = -8 + 9$

$\qquad (x+3)^2 = 1$

$\quad x+3 = \sqrt{1}$ or $x+3 = -\sqrt{1}$

$\quad x+3 = 1 \qquad\qquad x+3 = -1$

$\qquad x = -2 \qquad\qquad\quad x = -4$

37. $\qquad x^2 + 6x = -2$

$\quad x^2 + 6x \qquad = -2$

$\quad x^2 + 6x + 9 = -2 + 9$

$\qquad (x+3)^2 = 7$

$\qquad x+3 = \pm\sqrt{7}$

$\qquad\quad x = -3 \pm \sqrt{7}$

39.
$$x^2 + 4x + 1 = 0$$
$$x^2 + 4x = -1$$
$$x^2 + 4x \qquad = -1$$
$$x^2 + 4x + 4 = -1 + 4$$
$$(x+2)^2 = 3$$
$$x + 2 = \pm\sqrt{3}$$
$$x = -2 \pm \sqrt{3}$$

41.
$$x^2 + 2x + 2 = 0$$
$$x^2 + 2x = -2$$
$$x^2 + 2x \qquad = -2$$
$$x^2 + 2x + 1 = -2 + 1$$
$$(x+1)^2 = -1$$
$$x + 1 = +\sqrt{-1}$$
$$x + 1 = \pm i$$
$$x = -1 \pm i$$

43.
$$x^2 + 3x - 1 = 0$$
$$x^2 + 3x = 1$$
$$x^2 + 3x \qquad = 1$$
$$x^2 + 3x + \frac{9}{4} = 1 + \frac{9}{4}$$
$$\left(x + \frac{3}{2}\right)^2 = \frac{13}{4}$$
$$x + \frac{3}{2} = \pm\sqrt{\frac{13}{4}}$$
$$x + \frac{3}{2} = \pm\frac{\sqrt{13}}{2}$$
$$x = -\frac{3}{2} \pm \frac{\sqrt{13}}{2} = \frac{-3 \pm \sqrt{13}}{2}$$

45.
$$x^2 = 7x - 3$$
$$x^2 - 7x = -3$$
$$x^2 - 7x \qquad = -3$$
$$x^2 - 7x + \frac{49}{4} = -3 + \frac{49}{4}$$
$$\left(x - \frac{7}{2}\right)^2 = -\frac{12}{4} + \frac{49}{4}$$
$$\left(x - \frac{7}{2}\right)^2 = \frac{37}{4}$$

$$x - \frac{7}{2} = \pm\sqrt{\frac{37}{4}}$$
$$x - \frac{7}{2} = \pm\frac{\sqrt{37}}{2}$$
$$x = \frac{7}{2} \pm \frac{\sqrt{37}}{2} = \frac{7 \pm \sqrt{37}}{2}$$

47.
$$x^2 + x - 1 = 0$$
$$x^2 + x = 1$$
$$x^2 + x \qquad = 1$$
$$x^2 + x + \frac{1}{4} = 1 + \frac{1}{4}$$
$$\left(x + \frac{1}{2}\right)^2 = \frac{5}{4}$$
$$x + \frac{1}{2} = \pm\sqrt{\frac{5}{4}}$$
$$x + \frac{1}{2} = \pm\frac{\sqrt{5}}{2}$$
$$x = -\frac{1}{2} \pm \frac{\sqrt{5}}{2} = \frac{-1 \pm \sqrt{5}}{2}$$

49.
$$2x^2 - 3x + 1 = 0$$
$$x^2 - \frac{3}{2}x + \frac{1}{2} = 0$$
$$x^2 - \frac{3}{2}x = -\frac{1}{2}$$
$$x^2 - \frac{3}{2}x \qquad = -\frac{1}{2}$$
$$x^2 - \frac{3}{2}x + \frac{9}{16} = -\frac{1}{2} + \frac{9}{16}$$
$$\left(x - \frac{3}{4}\right)^2 = -\frac{8}{16} + \frac{9}{16}$$
$$\left(x - \frac{3}{4}\right)^2 = \frac{1}{16}$$
$$x - \frac{3}{4} = \pm\sqrt{\frac{1}{16}}$$
$$x - \frac{3}{4} = \pm\frac{1}{4}$$
$$x = \frac{3}{4} \pm \frac{1}{4}$$
$$x = \frac{3}{4} + \frac{1}{4} \ \text{ or } \ \frac{3}{4} - \frac{1}{4}$$

$$x = \frac{4}{4} \text{ or } \frac{2}{4}$$

$$x = 1 \text{ or } \frac{1}{2}$$

51. $2x^2 + 10x + 11 = 0$

$$x^2 + 5x + \frac{11}{2} = 0$$

$$x^2 + 5x = -\frac{11}{2}$$

$$x^2 + 5x \quad = -\frac{11}{2}$$

$$x^2 + 5x + \frac{25}{4} = -\frac{11}{2} + \frac{25}{4}$$

$$\left(x + \frac{5}{2}\right)^2 = -\frac{22}{4} + \frac{25}{4}$$

$$\left(x + \frac{5}{2}\right)^2 = \frac{3}{4}$$

$$x + \frac{5}{2} = \pm\sqrt{\frac{3}{4}}$$

$$x + \frac{5}{2} = \pm\frac{\sqrt{3}}{2}$$

$$x = -\frac{5}{2} \pm \frac{\sqrt{3}}{2} = \frac{-5 \pm \sqrt{3}}{2}$$

53. $3x^2 - 2x - 4 = 0$

$$x^2 - \frac{2}{3}x - \frac{4}{3} = 0$$

$$x^2 - \frac{2}{3}x = \frac{4}{3}$$

$$x^2 - \frac{2}{3}x \quad = \frac{4}{3}$$

$$x^2 - \frac{2}{3}x + \frac{1}{9} = \frac{4}{3} + \frac{1}{9}$$

$$\left(x - \frac{1}{3}\right)^2 = \frac{12}{9} + \frac{1}{9}$$

$$\left(x - \frac{1}{3}\right)^2 = \frac{13}{9}$$

$$x - \frac{1}{3} = \pm\sqrt{\frac{13}{9}}$$

$$x - \frac{1}{3} = \pm\frac{\sqrt{13}}{3}$$

$$x = \frac{1}{3} \pm \frac{\sqrt{13}}{3} = \frac{1 \pm \sqrt{13}}{3}$$

55. $8x^2 - 4x + 1 = 0$

$$x^2 - \frac{1}{2}x + \frac{1}{8} = 0$$

$$x^2 - \frac{1}{2}x = -\frac{1}{8}$$

$$x^2 - \frac{1}{2}x \quad = -\frac{1}{8}$$

$$x^2 - \frac{1}{2}x + \frac{1}{16} = -\frac{1}{8} + \frac{1}{16}$$

$$\left(x - \frac{1}{4}\right)^2 = -\frac{2}{16} + \frac{1}{16}$$

$$\left(x - \frac{1}{4}\right)^2 = -\frac{1}{16}$$

$$x - \frac{1}{4} = \pm\sqrt{-\frac{1}{16}}$$

$$x - \frac{1}{4} = \pm\frac{1}{4}i$$

$$x = \frac{1}{4} \pm \frac{1}{4}i$$

57. $2880 = 2000(1+r)^2$

$$\frac{2880}{2000} = (1+r)^2$$

$$1.44 = (1+r)^2$$

$$1 + r = \pm\sqrt{1.44}$$

$$1 + r = \pm 1.2$$

$$r = -1 \pm 1.2$$

$$r = -1 + 1.2 \text{ or } -1 - 1.2$$

$$r = 0.2 \text{ or } -2.2$$

We reject –2.2 because we cannot have a negative interest rate. The solution is 0.2 and we conclude that the annual interest rate is 20%.

59. $3360 = 3125(1+r)^2$

$$\frac{3360}{3125} = (1+r)^2$$

$$1.0752 = (1+r)^2$$

$$1+r = \pm\sqrt{1.0752}$$
$$1+r = \pm 1.0369$$
$$r = -1 \pm 1.0369$$
$$r = -1+1.0369 \quad \text{or} \quad -1-1.0369$$
$$r = 0.0369 \quad \text{or} \quad -2.0369$$

We reject -2.0369 because we cannot have a negative interest rate. The solution is 0.0369 and we conclude that the annual interest rate is 3.69%.

61.
$$20 = 0.4x^2 + 0.5$$
$$19.5 = 0.4x^2$$
$$\frac{19.5}{0.4} = x^2$$
$$48.75 = x^2$$
$$x = \pm\sqrt{48.75} = \pm 6.98 \approx \pm 7$$

We disregard -7 because we can't have a negative number of years. The solution is 7 and we conclude that there will be 20 million cable-TV modem users in the year $1996 + 7 = 2003$.

63.
$$4800 = 16t^2$$
$$\frac{4800}{16} = t^2$$
$$300 = t^2$$
$$t = \pm\sqrt{300} = \pm\sqrt{100 \cdot 3}$$
$$t = \pm 10\sqrt{3} \approx \pm 17.3$$

We disregard -17.3 because we can't have a negative time measurement. The solution is 17.3 and we conclude that the skydiver was in a free fall for $10\sqrt{3}$ or approximately 17.3 seconds.

65.

$$6^2 + 3^2 = x^2$$
$$36 + 9 = x^2$$
$$45 = x^2$$
$$x = \pm\sqrt{45} = \pm\sqrt{9 \cdot 5} = \pm 3\sqrt{5}$$

We disregard $-3\sqrt{5}$ because we can't have a negative length measurement. The solution is $3\sqrt{5}$ and we conclude that the pedestrian route is $3\sqrt{5}$ or approximately 6.7 miles long.

67.
$$x^2 + 15^2 = 20^2$$
$$x^2 + 225 = 400$$
$$x^2 = 175$$
$$x = \pm\sqrt{175} = \pm\sqrt{25 \cdot 7} = \pm 5\sqrt{7}$$

We disregard $-5\sqrt{7}$ because we can't have a negative length measurement. The solution is $5\sqrt{7}$ and we conclude that the ladder reaches $5\sqrt{7}$ or approximately 13.2 feet up the house.

69.

$$50^2 + 50^2 = x^2$$
$$2500 + 2500 = x^2$$
$$5000 = x^2$$
$$x = \pm\sqrt{5000} = \pm\sqrt{2500 \cdot 2}$$
$$x = \pm 50\sqrt{2} \approx \pm 70.7$$

Disregard -70.7 because length measurements must be positive. The solution is 70.7. A supporting wire of $50\sqrt{2}$ or approximately 70.7 feet is required.

71.
$$E = mc^2$$
$$\frac{E}{m} = c^2$$
$$\pm\sqrt{\frac{E}{m}} = c$$

Rationalize the denominator.
$$c = \pm\frac{\sqrt{E}}{\sqrt{m}} \cdot \frac{\sqrt{m}}{\sqrt{m}} = \pm\frac{\sqrt{Em}}{m}$$

Because the speed of light is positive, we disregard the negative solution.

$$c = \sqrt{\frac{E}{m}} \text{ or } \frac{\sqrt{Em}}{m}$$

73. $A = lw$

$$144 = (x+2+2)(x+2+2)$$

$$144 = (x+4)(x+4)$$

$$144 = x^2 + 8x + 16$$

$$0 = x^2 + 8x - 128$$

$$0 = (x+16)(x-8)$$

$$x + 16 = 0 \qquad x - 8 = 0$$

$$x = -16 \qquad x = 8$$

We disregard -16 because we can't have a negative length measurement. The solution is 8 and we conclude that the length of the original square is 8 meters.

For Exercises 75-83, answers may vary.

85. $\dfrac{x^2}{a^2} + \dfrac{y^2}{b^2} = 1$

$$\frac{y^2}{b^2} = 1 - \frac{x^2}{a^2}$$

$$y^2 = b^2\left(1 - \frac{x^2}{a^2}\right)$$

$$\sqrt{y^2} = \pm\sqrt{b^2\left(1 - \frac{x^2}{a^2}\right)}$$

$$y = \pm b\sqrt{1 - \frac{x^2}{a^2}}$$

$$y = \pm b\sqrt{\frac{a^2}{a^2} - \frac{x^2}{a^2}}$$

$$y = \pm b\sqrt{\frac{a^2 - x^2}{a^2}} = \pm\frac{b\sqrt{a^2 - x^2}}{a}$$

87. $x^2 + bx + c = 0$

$$x^2 + bx \qquad = -c$$

$$x^2 + bx + \frac{b^2}{4} = -c + \frac{b^2}{4}$$

$$\left(x + \frac{b}{2}\right)^2 = -c + \frac{b^2}{4}$$

$$x + \frac{b}{2} = \pm\sqrt{-c + \frac{b^2}{4}}$$

$$x = -\frac{b}{2} \pm \sqrt{-\frac{4c}{4} + \frac{b^2}{4}}$$

$$x = -\frac{b}{2} \pm \sqrt{\frac{-4c + b^2}{4}}$$

$$x = -\frac{b}{2} \pm \frac{\sqrt{-4c + b^2}}{2}$$

$$x = \frac{-b \pm \sqrt{b^2 - 4c}}{2}$$

89. $4 - (x+1)^2 = 0$

The solutions are -3 and 1.

91. Answers will vary.
For example, Exercise 35.

$$x^2 + 6x = -8$$

$$x^2 + 6x + 8 = 0$$

The solutions are -4 and -2. These are the same solutions as obtained in Exercise 35.

Review Exercises

92. $4x - 2 - 3\left[4 - 2(3 - x)\right]$

$$= 4x - 2 - 3\left[4 - 6 + 2x\right]$$

$$= 4x - 2 - 3\left[-2 + 2x\right]$$

$$= 4x - 2 + 6 - 6x = 4 - 2x$$

93. $1 - 8x^3 = 1^3 - (2x)^3 = (1 - 2x)(1 + 2x + 4x^2)$

94.

$$\underline{3|}\ \begin{array}{rrrrr} 1 & -5 & 2 & 0 & -6 \\ & 3 & -6 & -12 & -36 \\ \hline 1 & -2 & -4 & -12 & -42 \end{array}$$

$$(x^4 - 5x^3 + 2x^2 - 6) \div (x - 3)$$

$$= x^3 - 2x^2 - 4x - 12 - \frac{42}{x - 3}$$

The Quadratic Formula

11.2 CHECK POINTS

CHECK POINT 1

$a = 2 \quad b = 9 \quad c = -5$

$$x = \frac{-9 \pm \sqrt{9^2 - 4(2)(-5)}}{2(2)}$$

$$= \frac{-9 \pm \sqrt{81 - (-40)}}{4}$$

$$= \frac{-9 \pm \sqrt{121}}{4} = \frac{-9 \pm 11}{4}$$

$$x = \frac{-9 + 11}{4} \quad \text{or} \quad x = \frac{-9 - 11}{4}$$

$$x = \frac{2}{4} = \frac{1}{2} \qquad\qquad x = \frac{-20}{4} = -5$$

CHECK POINT 2

$$2x^2 = 6x - 1$$

$$2x^2 - 6x + 1 = 0$$

$a = 2 \quad b = -6 \quad c = 1$

$$x = \frac{-(-6) \pm \sqrt{(-6)^2 - 4(2)(1)}}{2(2)}$$

$$= \frac{6 \pm \sqrt{36 - 8}}{4} = \frac{6 \pm \sqrt{28}}{4}$$

$$= \frac{6 \pm \sqrt{4 \cdot 7}}{4} = \frac{6 \pm 2\sqrt{7}}{4}$$

$$= \frac{2(3 \pm \sqrt{7})}{4} = \frac{3 \pm \sqrt{7}}{2}$$

CHECK POINT 3

$$3x^2 + 5 = -6x$$

$$3x^2 + 6x + 5 = 0$$

$a = 3 \quad b = 6 \quad c = 5$

$$x = \frac{-6 \pm \sqrt{6^2 - 4(3)(5)}}{2(3)} = \frac{-6 \pm \sqrt{36 - 60}}{6}$$

$$= \frac{-6 \pm \sqrt{-24}}{6} = \frac{-6 \pm \sqrt{4 \cdot 6(-1)}}{6}$$

$$= \frac{-6 \pm 2\sqrt{6}i}{6} = \frac{-6}{6} \pm \frac{2\sqrt{6}i}{6} = -1 \pm \frac{\sqrt{6}}{3}i$$

CHECK POINT 4

a. $\quad x^2 + 6x + 9 = 0$

$a = 1 \quad b = 6 \quad c = 9$

$$b^2 - 4ac = 6^2 - 4(1)(9)$$

$$= 36 - 36 = 0$$

Since the discriminant is zero, there is one real solution.

b. $\qquad 2x^2 - 7x - 4 = 0$

$a = 2 \quad b = -7 \quad c = -4$

$$b^2 - 4ac = (-7)^2 - 4(2)(-4) = 49 - (-32) = 81$$

Since the discriminant is greater than zero, there are two unequal real solutions. Also, since the discriminant is a perfect square, the solutions are rational.

c. $\qquad 3x^2 - 2x + 4 = 0$

$a = 3 \quad b = -2 \quad c = 4$

$$b^2 - 4ac = (-2)^2 - 4(3)(4) = 4 - 48 = -44$$

Since the discriminant is less than zero, there is no solution. There are two imaginary solutions that are complex conjugates.

CHECK POINT 5

a.

$$x = -\frac{3}{5} \quad \text{or} \quad x = \frac{1}{4}$$

$$x + \frac{3}{5} = 0 \qquad\qquad x - \frac{1}{4} = 0$$

$$5x + 3 = 0 \qquad\qquad 4x - 1 = 0$$

$$(5x+3)(4x-1) = 0$$
$$20x^2 - 5x + 12x - 3 = 0$$
$$20x^2 + 7x - 3 = 0$$

b. $x = 7i$ or $x = -7i$
$x - 7i = 0$ $x + 7i = 0$
$$(x-7i)(x+7i) = 0$$
$$x^2 + \cancel{7i} - \cancel{7i} - 49i^2 = 0$$
$$x^2 - 49(-1) = 0$$
$$x^2 + 49 = 0$$

CHECK POINT 6
$$f(x) = -1.65x^2 + 51.8x + 111.44$$
$$330 = -1.65x^2 + 51.8x + 111.44$$
$$0 = -1.65x^2 + 51.8x - 218.56$$
$$a = -1.65 \quad b = 51.8 \quad c = -218.56$$
$$x = \frac{-51.8 \pm \sqrt{(51.8)^2 - 4(-1.65)(-218.56)}}{2(-1.65)}$$
$$= \frac{-51.8 \pm \sqrt{2683.24 - 1442.496}}{-3.3}$$
$$= \frac{-51.8 \pm \sqrt{1240.744}}{-3.3} = \frac{-51.8 \pm 35.224}{-3.3}$$
$$= \frac{-51.8 + 35.224}{-3.3} \quad \text{or} \quad \frac{-51.8 - 35.224}{-3.3}$$
$$\approx -26.37 \text{ or } 5.02$$

We disregard –26.37 because we can't have a negative number of years. The solution is 5.02. This means that approximately 5 years after 1990 in 1995, there were 330,000 U.S. AIDS deaths. The actual number of deaths was approximately 340,000. The function describes the data very well for that year.

EXERCISE SET 11.2

1.
$$x = \frac{-8 \pm \sqrt{8^2 - 4(1)(12)}}{2(1)}$$
$$= \frac{-8 \pm \sqrt{64 - 48}}{2} = \frac{-8 \pm \sqrt{16}}{2} = \frac{-8 \pm 4}{2}$$

$$x = \frac{-8 - 4}{2} \qquad \text{or} \qquad x = \frac{-8 + 4}{2}$$
$$x = \frac{-12}{2} = -6 \qquad x = \frac{-4}{2} = -2$$

3. $2x^2 - 7x = -5$
$$2x^2 - 7x + 5 = 0$$
$$a = 2 \quad b = -7 \quad c = 5$$
$$x = \frac{-(-7) \pm \sqrt{(-7)^2 - 4(2)(5)}}{2(2)}$$
$$= \frac{7 \pm \sqrt{49 - 40}}{4} = \frac{7 \pm \sqrt{9}}{4} = \frac{7 \pm 3}{4}$$
$$x = \frac{7-3}{4} \quad \text{or} \quad x = \frac{7+3}{4}$$
$$x = \frac{4}{4} = 1 \qquad x = \frac{10}{4} = \frac{5}{2}$$

5. $a = 1 \quad b = 3 \quad c = -20$
$$x = \frac{-3 \pm \sqrt{3^2 - 4(1)(-20)}}{2(1)}$$
$$= \frac{-3 \pm \sqrt{9 - (-80)}}{2} = \frac{-3 \pm \sqrt{89}}{2}$$

7. $3x^2 - 7x = 3$
$$3x^2 - 7x - 3 = 0$$
$$a = 3 \quad b = -7 \quad c = -3$$
$$x = \frac{-(-7) \pm \sqrt{(-7)^2 - 4(3)(-3)}}{2(3)}$$
$$= \frac{7 \pm \sqrt{49 - (-36)}}{6} = \frac{7 \pm \sqrt{85}}{6}$$

9. $6x^2 = 2x + 1$
$$6x^2 - 2x - 1 = 0$$
$$a = 6 \quad b = -2 \quad c = -1$$
$$x = \frac{-(-2) \pm \sqrt{(-2)^2 - 4(6)(-1)}}{2(6)}$$

$$= \frac{2 \pm \sqrt{4-(-24)}}{12} = \frac{2 \pm \sqrt{28}}{12}$$

$$= \frac{2 \pm \sqrt{4 \cdot 7}}{12} = \frac{2 \pm 2\sqrt{7}}{12}$$

$$= \frac{2\left(1 \pm \sqrt{7}\right)}{12} = \frac{1 \pm \sqrt{7}}{6}$$

11.
$$4x^2 - 3x = -6$$
$$4x^2 - 3x + 6 = 0$$
$$a = 4 \quad b = -3 \quad c = 6$$
$$x = \frac{-(-3) \pm \sqrt{(-3)^2 - 4(4)(6)}}{2(4)}$$
$$= \frac{3 \pm \sqrt{9 - 96}}{8} = \frac{3 \pm \sqrt{-87}}{8}$$
$$= \frac{3 \pm \sqrt{87(-1)}}{8} = \frac{3 \pm \sqrt{87}i}{8} = \frac{3}{8} \pm \frac{\sqrt{87}}{8}i$$

13.
$$x^2 - 4x + 8 = 0$$
$$a = 1 \quad b = -4 \quad c = 8$$
$$x = \frac{-(-4) \pm \sqrt{(-4)^2 - 4(1)(8)}}{2(1)}$$
$$= \frac{4 \pm \sqrt{16 - 32}}{2} = \frac{4 \pm \sqrt{-16}}{2}$$
$$= \frac{4 \pm 4i}{2} = \frac{4}{2} \pm \frac{4}{2}i = 2 \pm 2i$$

15.
$$3x^2 = 8x - 7$$
$$3x^2 - 8x + 7 = 0$$
$$a = 3 \quad b = -8 \quad c = 7$$
$$x = \frac{-(-8) \pm \sqrt{(-8)^2 - 4(3)(7)}}{2(3)}$$
$$= \frac{8 \pm \sqrt{64 - 84}}{6} = \frac{8 \pm \sqrt{-20}}{6}$$
$$= \frac{8 \pm \sqrt{4 \cdot 5(-1)}}{6} = \frac{8 \pm 2\sqrt{5}i}{6}$$
$$= \frac{8}{6} \pm \frac{2}{6}\sqrt{5}i = \frac{4}{3} \pm \frac{\sqrt{5}}{3}i$$

17.
$$x^2 + 8x + 3 = 0$$
$$a = 1 \quad b = 8 \quad c = 3$$
$$b^2 - 4ac = 8^2 - 4(1)(3)$$
$$= 64 - 12 = 50$$
Since the discriminant is positive and not a perfect square, there are two irrational solutions.

19.
$$x^2 + 6x + 8 = 0$$
$$a = 1 \quad b = 6 \quad c = 8$$
$$b^2 - 4ac = (6)^2 - 4(1)(8)$$
$$= 36 - 32 = 4$$
Since the discriminant is greater than zero, there are two unequal real solutions. Also, since the discriminant is a perfect square, the solutions are rational.

21.
$$2x^2 + x + 3 = 0$$
$$a = 2 \quad b = 1 \quad c = 3$$
$$b^2 - 4ac = 1^2 - 4(2)(3)$$
$$= 1 - 24 = -23$$
Since the discriminant is negative, there are no real solutions. There are two imaginary solutions that are complex conjugates.

23.
$$2x^2 + 6x = 0$$
$$a = 2 \quad b = 6 \quad c = 0$$
$$b^2 - 4ac = (6)^2 - 4(1)(0)$$
$$= 36 - 0 = 36$$
Since the discriminant is greater than zero, there are two unequal real solutions. Also, since the discriminant is a perfect square, the solutions are rational.

25.
$$5x^2 + 3 = 0$$
$$a = 5 \quad b = 0 \quad c = 3$$
$$b^2 - 4ac = 0^2 - 4(5)(3)$$
$$= 0 - 60 = -60$$
Since the discriminant is negative, there are no real solutions. There are two imaginary solutions that are complex conjugates.

27.
$$9x^2 = 12x - 4$$
$$9x^2 - 12x + 4 = 0$$
$$a = 9 \quad b = -12 \quad c = 4$$
$$b^2 - 4ac = (-12)^2 - 4(9)(4)$$
$$= 144 - 144 = 0$$
Since the discriminant is zero, there is one repeated rational solution.

29.
$$3x^2 - 4x = 4$$
$$3x^2 - 4x - 4 = 0$$
$$(3x + 2)(x - 2) = 0$$
$$3x + 2 = 0 \quad \text{or} \quad x - 2 = 0$$
$$3x = -2 \qquad\qquad x = 2$$
$$x = -\frac{2}{3}$$

31.
$$x^2 - 2x = 1$$
$$x^2 - 2x + 1 = 1 + 1$$
$$(x - 1)^2 = 2$$
$$x - 1 = \pm\sqrt{2}$$
$$x = 1 \pm \sqrt{2}$$

33.
$$(2x - 5)(x + 1) = 2$$
$$2x^2 + 2x - 5x - 5 = 2$$
$$2x^2 - 3x - 5 = 2$$
$$2x^2 - 3x - 7 = 0$$
$$a = 2 \quad b = -3 \quad c = -7$$
$$x = \frac{-(-3) \pm \sqrt{(-3)^2 - 4(2)(-7)}}{2(2)}$$
$$= \frac{3 \pm \sqrt{9 - (-56)}}{4} = \frac{3 \pm \sqrt{65}}{4}$$

35.
$$(3x - 4)^2 = 16$$
$$3x - 4 = \sqrt{16} \quad \text{or} \quad 3x - 4 = -\sqrt{16}$$
$$3x - 4 = 4 \qquad\qquad 3x - 4 = -4$$
$$3x = 8 \qquad\qquad\quad 3x = 0$$
$$x = \frac{8}{3} \qquad\qquad\qquad x = 0$$

37.
$$\frac{x^2}{2} + 2x + \frac{2}{3} = 0$$
Multiply both sides of the equation by 6 to clear fractions.
$$3x^2 + 12x + 4 = 0$$
$$a = 3 \quad b = 12 \quad c = 4$$
$$x = \frac{-12 \pm \sqrt{12^2 - 4(3)(4)}}{2(3)}$$
$$= \frac{-12 \pm \sqrt{144 - 48}}{6} = \frac{-12 \pm \sqrt{96}}{6}$$
$$= \frac{-12 \pm \sqrt{16 \cdot 6}}{6} = \frac{-12 \pm 4\sqrt{6}}{6}$$
$$= \frac{2(-6 \pm 2\sqrt{6})}{6} = \frac{-6 \pm 2\sqrt{6}}{3}$$

39.
$$(3x - 2)^2 = 10$$
$$3x - 2 = \pm\sqrt{10}$$
$$3x = 2 \pm \sqrt{10}$$
$$x = \frac{2 \pm \sqrt{10}}{3}$$

41.
$$\frac{1}{x} + \frac{1}{x + 2} = \frac{1}{3}$$
$$3x(x + 2)\left(\frac{1}{x} + \frac{1}{x + 2}\right) = 3x(x + 2)\left(\frac{1}{3}\right)$$
$$3(x + 2) + 3x = x(x + 2)$$
$$3x + 6 + 3x = x^2 + 2x$$
$$6 + 6x = x^2 + 2x$$
$$0 = x^2 - 4x - 6$$
$$a = 1 \quad b = -4 \quad c = -6$$
$$x = \frac{-(-4) \pm \sqrt{(-4)^2 - 4(1)(-6)}}{2(1)}$$
$$= \frac{4 \pm \sqrt{16 - (-24)}}{2} = \frac{4 \pm \sqrt{40}}{2}$$
$$= \frac{4 \pm \sqrt{4 \cdot 10}}{2} = \frac{4 \pm 2\sqrt{10}}{2}$$
$$= \frac{2(2 \pm 1\sqrt{10})}{2} = 2 \pm \sqrt{10}$$

43.
$$(2x-6)(x+2)=5(x-1)-12$$
$$2x^2+4x-6x-12=5x-5-12$$
$$2x^2-2x-12=5x-17$$
$$2x^2-7x+5=0$$
$$(2x-5)(x-1)=0$$
$$2x-5=0 \quad \text{or} \quad x-1=0$$
$$2x=5 \qquad\qquad x=1$$
$$x=\frac{5}{2}$$

45.
$$x=-3 \quad \text{or} \qquad x=5$$
$$x+3=0 \qquad\quad x-5=0$$
$$(x+3)(x-5)=0$$
$$x^2-5x+3x-15=0$$
$$x^2-2x-15=0$$

47.
$$x=-\frac{2}{3} \quad \text{or} \quad x=\frac{1}{4}$$
$$x+\frac{2}{3}=0 \qquad 4x-1=0$$
$$3x+2=0$$
$$(3x+2)(4x-1)=0$$
$$12x^2-3x+8x-2=0$$
$$12x^2+5x-2=0$$

49.
$$x=6i \quad \text{or} \quad x=-6i$$
$$x-6i=0 \qquad x+6i=0$$

$$(x-6i)(x+6i)=0$$
$$x^2+\cancel{6i}-\cancel{6i}-36i^2=0$$
$$x^2-36(-1)=0$$
$$x^2+36=0$$

51.
$$x=\sqrt{2} \quad \text{or} \quad x=-\sqrt{2}$$
$$x-\sqrt{2}=0 \qquad x+\sqrt{2}=0$$
$$\left(x-\sqrt{2}\right)\left(x+\sqrt{2}\right)=0$$
$$x^2+\cancel{x\sqrt{2}}-\cancel{x\sqrt{2}}-2=0$$
$$x^2-2=0$$

53.
$$x=2\sqrt{5} \quad \text{or} \qquad x=-2\sqrt{5}$$
$$x-2\sqrt{5}=0 \qquad x+2\sqrt{5}=0.$$
$$\left(x-2\sqrt{5}\right)\left(x+2\sqrt{5}\right)=0$$
$$x^2+\cancel{2x\sqrt{5}}-\cancel{2x\sqrt{5}}-4\cdot 5=0$$
$$x^2-20=0$$

55.
$$x=1+i \quad \text{or} \qquad x=1-i$$
$$x-(1+i)=0 \qquad x-(1-i)=0.$$
$$\left(x-(1+i)\right)\left(x-(1-i)\right)=0$$
$$x^2-x(1-i)-x(1+i)+(1+i)(1-i)=0$$
$$x^2-x+\cancel{xi}-x-\cancel{xi}+1-i^2=0$$
$$x^2-x-x+1-(-1)=0$$
$$x^2-2x+2=0$$

57.
$$x=1+\sqrt{2} \quad \text{or} \qquad x=1-\sqrt{2}$$
$$x-\left(1+\sqrt{2}\right)=0 \qquad x-\left(1-\sqrt{2}\right)=0.$$
$$\left(x-\left(1+\sqrt{2}\right)\right)\left(x-\left(1-\sqrt{2}\right)\right)=0$$
$$x^2-x\left(1-\sqrt{2}\right)-x\left(1+\sqrt{2}\right)+\left(1+\sqrt{2}\right)\left(1-\sqrt{2}\right)=0$$
$$x^2-x+\cancel{x\sqrt{2}}-x-\cancel{x\sqrt{2}}+1-2=0$$
$$x^2-2x-1=0$$

59.
$$f(x) = 23.4x^2 - 259.1x + 815.8$$
$$1000 = 23.4x^2 - 259.1x + 815.8$$
$$0 = 23.4x^2 - 259.1x - 184.2$$
$$a = 23.4 \quad b = -259.1 \quad c = -184.2$$
$$x = \frac{-(-259.1) \pm \sqrt{(-259.1)^2 - 4(23.4)(-184.2)}}{2(23.4)}$$
$$= \frac{259.1 \pm \sqrt{67132.81 - (-17241.12)}}{46.8}$$
$$= \frac{259.1 \pm \sqrt{84373.93}}{46.8} \approx \frac{259.1 \pm 290.47}{46.8}$$
$$\approx 11.7 \text{ or } -0.67$$

We disregard –0.67 because can't have a negative number of policemen. The solution is approximately 12 and we conclude that in the year 1990 + 12 = 2002, there will be 1000 police officers convicted of felonies.

61.
$$f(x) = 0.013x^2 - 1.19x + 28.24$$
$$10 = 0.013x^2 - 1.19x + 28.24$$
$$0 = 0.013x^2 - 1.19x + 18.24$$
$$a = 0.013 \quad b = -1.19 \quad c = 18.24$$
$$x = \frac{-(-1.19) \pm \sqrt{(-1.19)^2 - 4(0.013)(18.24)}}{2(0.013)}$$
$$= \frac{1.19 \pm \sqrt{1.4161 - 0.94848}}{0.026}$$
$$= \frac{1.19 \pm \sqrt{0.46762}}{0.026} \approx \frac{1.19 \pm 0.68383}{0.026}$$

Evaluate the expression to obtain two solutions.

$$x = \frac{1.19 + 0.68383}{0.026} \quad \text{or} \quad x = \frac{1.19 - 0.68383}{0.026}$$
$$x = \frac{1.87383}{0.026} \qquad\qquad x = \frac{0.50617}{0.026}$$
$$x \approx 72.1 \qquad\qquad x \approx 19$$

Drivers of approximately age 19 and age 72 are expected to be involved in 10 fatal crashes per 100 million miles driven. The model doesn't seem to predict the number of accidents very well. The model overestimates the crashes.

63.
$$f(t) = -16t^2 + 60t + 4$$
$$0 = -16t^2 + 60t + 4$$
$$a = -16 \quad b = 60 \quad c = 4$$
$$x = \frac{-60 \pm \sqrt{60^2 - 4(-16)(4)}}{2(-16)}$$
$$= \frac{-60 \pm \sqrt{3600 - (-256)}}{-32}$$
$$= \frac{-60 \pm \sqrt{3856}}{-32} \approx \frac{-60 \pm 62.1}{-32}$$
$$\approx -0.07 \text{ or } 3.8$$

We disregard –0.07 because we can't have a negative time measurement. The solution is 3.8. The ball will hit the ground in approximately 3.8 seconds.

65. Let x = the width
Let $x + 3$ = the length
$$A = lw$$
$$36 = x(x + 3)$$
$$36 = x^2 + 3x$$
$$0 = x^2 + 3x - 36$$
$$a = 1 \quad b = 3 \quad c = -36$$
$$x = \frac{-3 \pm \sqrt{3^2 - 4(1)(-36)}}{2(1)}$$
$$= \frac{-3 \pm \sqrt{9 - (-144)}}{2}$$
$$= \frac{-3 \pm \sqrt{153}}{2} \approx \frac{-3 \pm 12.4}{2}$$

Evaluate the expression to obtain two solutions.

$$x = \frac{-3 + 12.4}{2} \quad \text{or} \quad x = \frac{-3 - 12.4}{2}$$
$$x = \frac{9.4}{2} = 4.7 \qquad x = \frac{-15.4}{2} = -7.7$$

We disregard –7.7 because we can't have a negative length measurement. The solution is 4.7 and we conclude that the rectangle's dimensions are 4.7 meters by 4.7 + 3 = 7.7 meters.

67. Let x = the length of the one leg

Let $x + 1$ = the length of the other leg

$$x^2 + (x+1)^2 = 4^2$$
$$x^2 + x^2 + 2x + 1 = 16$$
$$2x^2 + 2x + 1 = 16$$
$$2x^2 + 2x - 15 = 0$$

$a = 2 \quad b = 2 \quad c = -15$

$$x = \frac{-2 \pm \sqrt{2^2 - 4(2)(-15)}}{2(2)}$$

$$= \frac{-2 \pm \sqrt{4 - (-120)}}{4}$$

$$= \frac{-2 \pm \sqrt{124}}{4} \approx \frac{-2 \pm 11.1}{4}$$

Evaluate the expression to obtain two solutions.

$$x = \frac{-2 + 11.1}{4} \quad \text{or} \quad x = \frac{-2 - 11.1}{4}$$

$$x = \frac{9.1}{4} \qquad\qquad x = \frac{-13.1}{4}$$

$$x = 2.275 \qquad\qquad x = -3.275$$

We disregard –3.275 because we can't have a negative length measurement. The solution is 2.275 and we conclude that the triangle's legs are approximately 2.3 feet and 2.3 + 1 = 3.3 feet.

69.
$$x(20 - 2x) = 13$$
$$20x - 2x^2 = 13$$
$$0 = 2x^2 - 20x + 13$$

$a = 2 \quad b = -20 \quad c = 13$

$$x = \frac{-(-20) \pm \sqrt{(-20)^2 - 4(2)(13)}}{2(2)}$$

$$= \frac{20 \pm \sqrt{400 - 104}}{4} = \frac{20 \pm \sqrt{296}}{4}$$

$$\approx \frac{20 + 17.2}{4} \quad \text{or} \quad \frac{20 - 17.2}{4}$$

$$\approx \frac{37.2}{4} \quad \text{or} \quad \frac{2.8}{4} \approx 9.3 \text{ or } 0.7$$

A gutter with depth 9.3 or 0.7 inches will have a cross-sectional area of 13 square inches.

For Exercises 71-77, answers may vary.

79. Statement **d.** is true. Any quadratic equation that can be solved by completing the square can be solved by the quadratic formula.

Statement **a.** is false. The quadratic equation is developed by completing the square and the zero product principle.

Statement **b.** is false. Before using the quadratic equation to solve $5x^2 = 2x - 7$, the equation must be rewritten in standard form.
$$5x^2 = 2x - 7$$
$$5x^2 - 2x + 7 = 0$$
We now have, $a = 5$, $b = -2$ and $c = 7$.

Statement **c.** is false. The quadratic equation can be used to solve $x^2 - 9 = 0$, with $a = 1$, $b = 0$ and $c = -9$. (It would be easier, however, to factor or use the square root property.)

81.
$$10^{-4}x^2 + 2 \cdot 10^{-3}x + 10^{-2} = 0$$
$$\frac{10^{-4}x^2 + 2 \cdot 10^{-3}x + 10^{-2}}{10^{-4}} = \frac{0}{10^{-4}}$$
$$\frac{10^{-4}x^2}{10^{-4}} + \frac{2 \cdot 10^{-3}x}{10^{-4}} + \frac{10^{-2}}{10^{-4}} = 0$$
$$x^2 + 2 \cdot 10x + 10^2 = 0$$
$$x^2 + 20x + 100 = 0$$
$$(x + 10)^2 = 0$$
$$x + 10 = 0$$
$$x = -10$$

83. Let x = the number in the diving group
$$x(10 - 0.10(x - 20)) = 323.90$$
$$x(10 - 0.10x + 2) = 323.90$$
$$x(12 - 0.10x) = 323.90$$

$$-0.10x^2 + 12x - 323.90 = 0$$

$$a = -0.10 \quad b = 12 \quad c = -323.90$$

$$x = \frac{-12 \pm \sqrt{12^2 - 4(-0.10)(-323.90)}}{2(-0.10)}$$

$$= \frac{-12 \pm \sqrt{144 - 129.56}}{-0.2} = \frac{-12 \pm \sqrt{14.44}}{-0.2}$$

$$\approx \frac{-12 \pm 3.8}{-0.2}$$

$$x = \frac{-12 + 3.8}{-0.2} \quad \text{or} \quad x = \frac{-12 - 3.8}{-0.2}$$

$$x = \frac{-8.2}{-0.2} \qquad\qquad x = \frac{-15.8}{-0.2}$$

$$x = 41 \qquad\qquad x = 79$$

We disregard 79 because the diving boat can hold at most 70 people. The solution is 41 and we conclude that when 41 people are in the diving group the total cost will be $323.90.

85. Answers will vary. For example, consider Exercise 63.

$$f(t) = -16t^2 + 60t + 4$$

The ball will hit the ground in 3.8 seconds. This is the same answer obtained in Exercise 63.

Review Exercises

87. $|5x + 2| = |4 - 3x|$

$$5x + 2 = 4 - 3x \quad \text{or} \quad 5x + 2 = -(4 - 3x)$$

$$8x + 2 = 4 \qquad\qquad 5x + 2 = -4 + 3x$$

$$8x = 2 \qquad\qquad\quad 2x + 2 = -4$$

$$x = \frac{1}{4} \qquad\qquad\qquad 2x = -6$$

$$\qquad\qquad\qquad\qquad\quad x = -3$$

88. $\sqrt{2x - 5} - \sqrt{x - 3} = 1$

$$\sqrt{2x - 5} = \sqrt{x - 3} + 1$$

$$\left(\sqrt{2x - 5}\right)^2 = \left(\sqrt{x - 3} + 1\right)^2$$

$$2x - 5 = x - 3 + 2\sqrt{x - 3} + 1$$

$$2x - 5 = x - 2 + 2\sqrt{x - 3}$$

$$x - 3 = 2\sqrt{x - 3}$$

$$(x - 3)^2 = \left(2\sqrt{x - 3}\right)^2$$

$$x^2 - 6x + 9 = 4(x - 3)$$

$$x^2 - 6x + 9 = 4x - 12$$

$$x^2 - 10x + 21 = 0$$

$$(x - 7)(x - 3) = 0$$

$$x - 7 = 0 \quad \text{or} \quad x - 3 = 0$$

$$x = 7 \qquad\qquad x = 3$$

Both solutions check.

89.

$$\frac{5}{\sqrt{3} + x} = \frac{5}{\sqrt{3} + x} \cdot \frac{\sqrt{3} - x}{\sqrt{3} - x}$$

$$= \frac{5\left(\sqrt{3} - x\right)}{3 - x^2} = \frac{5\sqrt{3} - 5x}{3 - x^2}$$

Quadratic Functions and Their Graphs

11.3 CHECK POINTS

CHECK POINT 1

$$f(x) = -(x - 1)^2 + 4$$

Since $a = -1$ is negative, the parabola opens downward. The vertex of the parabola is $(h, k) = (1, 4)$. Replace $f(x)$ with 0 to find x– intercepts.

$$0 = -(x - 1)^2 + 4$$

$$-4 = -(x - 1)^2$$

$$4 = (x - 1)^2$$

Apply the square root property.

$x - 1 = \sqrt{4}$ or $x - 1 = -\sqrt{4}$
$x - 1 = 2$ $x - 1 = -2$
$x = 3$ $x = -1$

The x–intercepts are –1 and 3. Set $x = 0$ and solve for y to obtain the y–intercept.

$y = -(0 - 1)^2 + 4 = -(-1)^2 + 4$
$\quad = -(1) + 4 = 3$

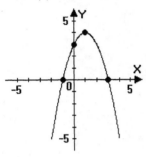

CHECK POINT 2

$f(x) = (x - 2)^2 + 1$

Since $a = 1$ is positive, the parabola opens upward. The vertex of the parabola is $(h, k) = (2, 1)$. Replace $f(x)$ with 0 to find x–intercepts.

$0 = (x - 2)^2 + 1$
$-1 = (x - 2)^2$

Apply the square root property.

$x - 2 = \sqrt{-1}$ or $x - 2 = -\sqrt{-1}$
$x - 2 = i$ $x - 2 = -i$
$\quad x = 2 + i$ $\quad x = 2 - i$

Because this solution has no real solutions, the parabola has no x–intercepts. Set $x = 0$ and solve for y to obtain the y–intercept.

$y = (0 - 2)^2 + 1 = (-2)^2 + 1 = 4 + 1 = 5$

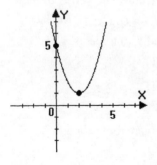

CHECK POINT 3

$f(x) = x^2 - 2x - 3$

Since $a = 1$ is positive, the parabola opens upward. The x–coordinate of the vertex of the parabola is $-\dfrac{b}{2a} = -\dfrac{-2}{2(1)} = -\dfrac{-2}{2} = 1$

and the y–coordinate of the vertex of the parabola is

$f\left(-\dfrac{b}{2a}\right) = f(1) = (1)^2 - 2(1) - 3$
$\qquad\qquad = 1 - 2 - 3 = -4.$

The vertex is $(1, -4)$. Replace $f(x)$ with 0 to find x–intercepts.

$0 = x^2 - 2x - 3$
$0 = (x - 3)(x + 1)$

Apply the zero product principle.

$x - 3 = 0$ or $x + 1 = 0$
$\quad x = 3$ $\quad x = -1$

The x–intercepts are –1 and 3.
Set $x = 0$ and solve for y to obtain the y–intercept.

$y = (0)^2 - 2(0) - 3 = -3$

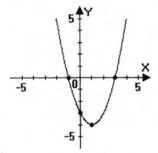

CHECK POINT 4

$f(x) = 0.4x^2 - 36x + 1000$

Since $a = 0.4$ is positive, we know the function opens upward and has a minimum

at $x = -\dfrac{b}{2a} = -\dfrac{-36}{2(0.4)} = -\dfrac{-36}{0.8} = 45.$

Drivers of age 45 have the least number of accidents per 50 million miles driven. At this age, the number of accidents drivers have is

$$f(45) = 0.4(45)^2 - 36(45) + 1000$$
$$= 0.4(2025) - 1620 + 1000$$
$$= 810 - 1620 + 1000 = 190.$$

The minimum number of accidents is 190 per 50 million miles driven.

CHECK POINT 5

Maximize the area of a rectangle constructed with 120 feet of fencing.

Let x = the length of the rectangle

Let y = the width of the rectangle

Since we need an equation in one variable, use the perimeter to express y in terms of x.

$$2x + 2y = 120$$
$$2y = 120 - 2x$$
$$y = \frac{120 - 2x}{2}$$
$$y = 60 - x$$

We need to maximize $A = xy = x(60 - x)$.

Rewrite A as a function of x.

$$A(x) = x(60 - x) = -x^2 + 60x$$

Since $a = -1$ is negative, we know the function opens downward and has a maximum at

$$x = -\frac{b}{2a} = -\frac{60}{2(-1)} = -\frac{60}{-2} = 30.$$

When the length x is 30, the width y is $y = 60 - x = 60 - 30 = 30$. The dimensions of the rectangular region with maximum area are 30 feet by 30 feet for an area of 90 square feet.

EXERCISE SET 11.3

1. The vertex is the point $(-1, -1)$. The equation is $f(x) = (x - (-1))^2 - 1$
$$= (x + 1)^2 - 1.$$

3. The vertex is the point $(-1, 1)$. The equation is
$$g(x) = (x - (-1))^2 + 1 = (x + 1)^2 + 1.$$

5. The vertex is the point $(0, -1)$. The equation is $f(x) = (x - 0)^2 - 1 = x^2 - 1$.

7. The vertex is the point $(1, 0)$. The equation is $f(x) = (x - 1)^2 + 0 = (x - 1)^2$.

9. The vertex is $(3, 1)$.

11. The vertex is $(-1, 5)$.

13. $-\dfrac{b}{2a} = -\dfrac{-8}{2(2)} = -\dfrac{-8}{4} = 2$

$$f(2) = 2(2)^2 - 8(2) + 3$$
$$= 2(4) - 16 + 3 = 8 - 16 + 3 = -5$$

The vertex is $(2, -5)$.

15. $-\dfrac{b}{2a} = -\dfrac{-2}{2(-1)} = -\dfrac{-2}{-2} = -1$

$$f(-1) = -(-1)^2 - 2(-1) + 8 = -1 + 2 + 8 = 9$$

The vertex is $(-1, 9)$.

17. Vertex: $(h, k) = (4, -1)$

x–intercepts:
$$0 = (x - 4)^2 - 1$$
$$1 = (x - 4)^2$$
$$x - 4 = \sqrt{1} \quad \text{or} \quad x - 4 = -\sqrt{1}$$
$$x - 4 = 1 \qquad\qquad x - 4 = -1$$
$$x = 5 \qquad\qquad\quad x = 3$$

y–intercept:
$$y = (0 - 4)^2 - 1 = (-4)^2 - 1 = 16 - 1 = 15$$

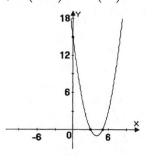

Axis of symmetry: $x = 4$

19. Vertex: $(h,k) = (1,2)$

x–intercepts:

$$0 = (x-1)^2 + 2$$
$$-2 = (x-1)^2$$

Because the solutions are imaginary, there are no x–intercepts.

y–intercept:

$$y = (0-1)^2 + 2 = (-1)^2 + 2$$
$$= 1 + 2 = 3$$

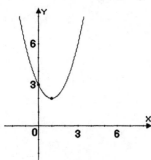

Axis of symmetry: $x = 1$

21.
$$y - 1 = (x-3)^2$$
$$y = (x-3)^2 + 1$$

Vertex: $(h,k) = (3,1)$

x–intercepts:

$$0 = (x-3)^2 + 1$$
$$-1 = (x-3)^2$$

Because the solutions are imaginary, there are no x–intercepts.

y–intercept:

$$y = (0-3)^2 + 1 = (-3)^2 + 1$$
$$= 9 + 1 = 10$$

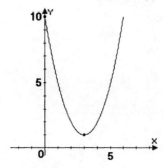

Axis of symmetry: $x = 3$

23. Vertex: $(h,k) = (-2,-1)$

x–intercepts:

$$0 = 2(x+2)^2 - 1$$
$$1 = 2(x+2)^2$$
$$\frac{1}{2} = (x+2)^2$$
$$x + 2 = \pm\sqrt{\frac{1}{2}} = -2 \pm \sqrt{\frac{1}{2}}$$
$$x \approx -2 - \sqrt{\frac{1}{2}} \quad \text{or} \quad -2 + \sqrt{\frac{1}{2}}$$
$$x \approx -2.7 \quad \text{or} \quad -1.3$$

The x–intercepts are -1.3 and -2.7.

y–intercept:

$$y = 2(0+2)^2 - 1 = 2(2)^2 - 1$$
$$= 2(4) - 1 = 8 - 1 = 7$$

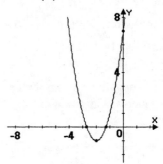

Axis of symmetry: $x = -2$

25.
$$f(x) = 4 - (x-1)^2$$
$$f(x) = -(x-1)^2 + 4$$

Vertex: $(h,k) = (1,4)$

x–intercepts:

$$0 = -(x-1)^2 + 4$$
$$-4 = -(x-1)^2$$
$$4 = (x-1)^2$$
$$\sqrt{4} = x-1 \quad \text{or} \quad -\sqrt{4} = x-1$$
$$2 = x-1 \qquad\qquad -2 = x-1$$
$$3 = x \qquad\qquad\quad -1 = x$$

y–intercept:

$$y = -(0-1)^2 + 4 = -(-1)^2 + 4 = -1 + 4 = 3$$

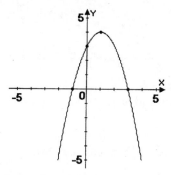

Axis of symmetry: $x = 1$

27. Vertex:

$$-\frac{b}{2a} = -\frac{2}{2(1)} = -\frac{2}{2} = -1$$

$$f(-1) = (-1)^2 + 2(-1) - 3 = 1 - 2 - 3 = -4$$

The vertex is $(-1, -4)$.

x–intercepts:

$$0 = x^2 + 2x - 3$$

$$0 = (x+3)(x-1)$$

$$x + 3 = 0 \quad \text{or} \quad x - 1 = 0$$
$$x = -3 \qquad\qquad x = 1$$

y–intercept:

$$y = (0)^2 + 2(0) - 3$$

$$y = -3$$

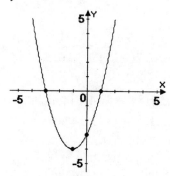

Axis of symmetry: $x = -1$

29. Vertex:

$$-\frac{b}{2a} = -\frac{3}{2(1)} = -\frac{3}{2}$$

$$f\left(-\frac{3}{2}\right) = \left(-\frac{3}{2}\right)^2 + 3\left(-\frac{3}{2}\right) - 10$$

$$= \frac{9}{4} - \frac{9}{2} - 10 = \frac{9}{4} - \frac{18}{4} - \frac{40}{4} = -\frac{49}{4}$$

The vertex is $\left(-\frac{3}{2}, -\frac{49}{4}\right)$.

x–intercepts:

$$0 = x^2 + 3x - 10$$

$$0 = (x+5)(x-2)$$

$$x + 5 = 0 \quad \text{or} \quad x - 2 = 0$$
$$x = -5 \qquad\qquad x = 2$$

y–intercept:

$$y = 0^2 + 3(0) - 10 = -10$$

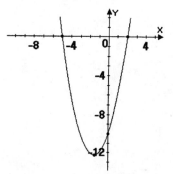

Axis of symmetry: $x = -2$

31. $f(x) = 2x - x^2 + 3$

$f(x) = -x^2 + 2x + 3$

Vertex:

$$-\frac{b}{2a} = -\frac{2}{2(-1)} = -\frac{2}{-2} = 1$$

$$f(1) = -(1)^2 + 2(1) + 3 = -1 + 2 + 3 = 4$$

The vertex is $(1, 4)$.

x–intercepts:

$$0 = -x^2 + 2x + 3$$

$$0 = x^2 - 2x - 3$$

$$0 = (x-3)(x+1)$$

$$x - 3 = 0 \quad \text{or} \quad x + 1 = 0$$
$$x = 3 \qquad\qquad x = -1$$

y–intercept:

$$y = -(0)^2 + 2(0) + 3 = 3$$

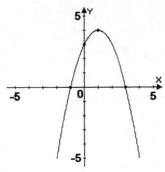

Axis of symmetry: $x = 1$

33. $f(x) = 2x - x^2 - 2$
$f(x) = -x^2 + 2x - 2$
Vertex:
$$-\frac{b}{2a} = -\frac{2}{2(-1)} = -\frac{2}{-2} = 1$$
$$f(1) = -(1)^2 + 2(1) - 2 = -1 + 2 - 2 = -1$$
The vertex is $(1, -1)$.
x–intercepts:
$$0 = -x^2 + 2x - 2$$
$$x^2 - 2x = -2$$
$$x^2 - 2x + 1 = -2 + 1$$
$$(x - 1)^2 = -1$$
Because the solutions are imaginary, there are no x–intercepts.
y–intercept:
$$y = 2(0) - 0^2 - 2 = -2$$

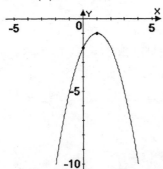

Axis of symmetry: $x = 1$

35.   Since $a = 3$, the parabola opens upward and has a minimum.

$$-\frac{b}{2a} = -\frac{-12}{2(3)} = -\frac{-12}{6} = 2$$
$$f(2) = 3(2)^2 - 12(2) - 1 = 3(4) - 24 - 1$$
$$= 12 - 24 - 1 = -13$$
The minimum is $(2, -13)$.

37.   Since $a = -4$, the parabola opens downward and has a maximum.
$$-\frac{b}{2a} = -\frac{8}{2(-4)} = -\frac{8}{-8} = 1$$
$$f(1) = -4(1)^2 + 8(1) - 3$$
$$= -4(1) + 8 - 3 = -4 + 8 - 3 = 1$$
The maximum is $(1, 1)$.

39.   Since $a = 5$, the parabola opens upward and has a minimum.
$$-\frac{b}{2a} = -\frac{-5}{2(5)} = -\frac{-5}{10} = \frac{1}{2}$$
$$f\left(\frac{1}{2}\right) = 5\left(\frac{1}{2}\right)^2 - 5\left(\frac{1}{2}\right) = 5\left(\frac{1}{4}\right) - \frac{5}{2}$$
$$= \frac{5}{4} - \frac{10}{4} = -\frac{5}{4}$$
The minimum is $\left(\frac{1}{2}, -\frac{5}{4}\right)$.

41. $$x = -\frac{b}{2a} = -\frac{51.5}{2(-3.1)} = -\frac{51.5}{-6.2} \approx 8.3$$
$$1960 + 8 = 1968$$
$$f(8) = -3.1(8)^2 + 51.4(8) + 4024.5$$
$$= -3.1(64) + 411.2 + 4024.5$$
$$= -198.4 + 411.2 + 4024.5 = 4237.3.$$
The maximum consumption was approximately 4237 cigarettes.

43.   The x-coordinate of the minimum is
$$x = -\frac{-1501.5}{2(104.5)} = -\frac{-1501.5}{209} \approx 7.2.$$
$$f(7.2) = 104.5(7.2)^2 - 1501.5(7.2) + 6016$$
$$= 104.5(51.84) - 10810.8 + 6016$$
$$= 622.48$$

The minimum death rate is approximately 622 per year per 100,000 males among U.S. men who average 7.2 hours of sleep per night.

45. a.
$$t = -\frac{64}{2(-16)} = -\frac{64}{-32} = 2$$

$$s(2) = -16(2)^2 + 64(2) + 160$$
$$= -16(4) + 128 + 160$$
$$= -64 + 128 + 160 = 224$$

The ball reaches a maximum height of 244 feet 2 seconds after it is thrown.

b.
$$0 = -16t^2 + 64t + 160$$
$$0 = t^2 - 4t - 10$$
$$a = 1 \quad b = -4 \quad c = -10$$

$$t = \frac{-(-4) \pm \sqrt{(-4)^2 - 4(1)(-10)}}{2(1)}$$

$$= \frac{4 \pm \sqrt{16 + 40}}{2} = \frac{4 \pm \sqrt{56}}{2}$$

$$\approx \frac{4 \pm 7.48}{2}$$

$$x = \frac{4 + 7.48}{2} \quad \text{or} \quad x = \frac{4 - 7.48}{2}$$

$$x = \frac{11.48}{2} \qquad\qquad x = \frac{-3.48}{2}$$

$$x = 5.74 \qquad\qquad x = -1.74$$

We disregard –1.74 because we can't have a negative time measurement. The solution is 5.74 and we conclude that the ball will hit the ground in approximately 5.7 seconds.

c.
$$s(0) = -16(0)^2 + 64(0) + 160 = 160$$

At $t = 0$, the ball has not yet been thrown and is at a height of 160 feet. This is the height of the building.

d.

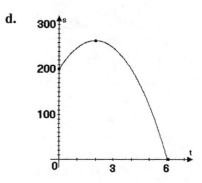

47. The vertex is (15, 41.1). The year is defined as the number of years after 1920, so the first coordinate represents 1920 + 15 = 1935. This means that the Consumer Price Index was 41.1 in the year 1935. What cost $100 in 1967 cost $41.10 in 1935.

49. Let x = the length of the rectangle
Let y = the width of the rectangle
$$x + 2y = 120$$
$$2y = 120 - x$$
$$y = \frac{120 - x}{2} = 60 - \frac{1}{2}x$$

$$A = xy = x\left(60 - \frac{1}{2}x\right)$$

Rewrite A as a function of x.

$$A(x) = x\left(60 - \frac{1}{2}x\right) = 60x - \frac{1}{2}x^2$$
$$= -\frac{1}{2}x^2 + 60x$$

Since $a = -\frac{1}{2}$ is negative, we know the function opens downward and has a maximum at

$$x = -\frac{b}{2a} = -\frac{60}{2\left(-\frac{1}{2}\right)} = -\frac{60}{-1} = 60.$$

When the length, x, is 60, the width, y, is

$$y = 60 - \frac{1}{2}(60) = 60 - 30 = 30.$$

The dimensions of the rectangular plot with maximum area are 60 feet by 30 feet for an area of 1800 ft^2.

51. Let $x =$ one of the numbers
Let $16 - x =$ the other number
$$P(x) = x(16-x) = 16x - x^2 = -x^2 + 16x$$
The maximum is
$$x = -\frac{b}{2a} = -\frac{16}{2(-1)} = -\frac{16}{-2} = 8.$$
The other number is $16 - x = 16 - 8 = 8$.
The numbers that maximize the product are 8 and 8. The maximum product is $8 \cdot 8 = 64$.

53. Let $x =$ one of the numbers
Let $x - 10 =$ the other number
$$P(x) = x(x-10) = x^2 - 10x$$
The maximum is
$$x = -\frac{b}{2a} = -\frac{-10}{2(1)} = -\frac{-10}{2} = 5.$$
The other number is $x - 10 = 5 - 10 = -5$.
The numbers that minimize the product are 5 and –5. The minimum product is $5(-5) = -25$.

55. Let $x =$ the length of the rectangle
Let $y =$ the width of the rectangle
$$2x + 2y = 50$$
$$2y = 50 - 2x$$
$$y = \frac{50 - 2x}{2}$$
$$y = 25 - x$$
$$A = xy = x(25 - x).$$
Rewrite A as a function of x.
$$A(x) = x(25-x) = -x^2 + 25x$$
Since $a = -1$ is negative, we know the function opens downward and has a maximum at
$$x = -\frac{b}{2a} = -\frac{25}{2(-1)} = -\frac{25}{-2} = 12.5.$$
When the length x is 12.5, the width y is $y = 25 - x = 25 - 12.5 = 12.5$.
The dimensions of the rectangular region with maximum area are 12.5 yards by 12.5 yards. This gives an area of $12.5 \cdot 12.5 = 156.25$ square feet.

57. $A(x) = x(20-2x) = 20x - 2x^2 = -2x^2 + 20x$
Since $a = -2$ is negative, we know the function opens downward and has a maximum at
$$x = -\frac{b}{2a} = -\frac{20}{2(-2)} = -\frac{20}{-4} = 5.$$
When the height x is 5, the width is
$20 - 2x = 20 - 2(5) = 20 - 10 = 10$.
$$A(5) = -2(5)^2 + 20(5) = -2(25) + 100$$
$$= -50 + 100 = 50$$
The maximum cross-sectional area is 50 square inches. This occurs when the gutter is 5 inches deep and 10 inches wide.

59. **a.** $C(x) = 525 + 0.55x$

b. $P(x) = R(x) - C(x)$
$$= (-0.001x^2 + 3x) - (525 + 0.55x)$$
$$= -0.001x^2 + 3x - 525 - 0.55x$$
$$= -0.001x^2 + 2.45x - 525$$

c. $P(x) = R(x) - C(x)$
$$= (-0.001x^2 + 3x) - (525 + 0.55x)$$
$$= -0.001x^2 + 3x - 525 - 0.55x$$
$$= -0.001x^2 + 2.45x - 525$$
Since $a = -0.001$ is negative, we know the function opens downward and has a maximum at
$$x - \frac{2.45}{2(-0.001)} = -\frac{2.45}{-0.002} = 1225.$$
When the number of units x is 1225, the profit is
$$P(1225) = -0.001(1225)^2 + 2.45(1225) - 525$$
$$= -0.001(1500625) + 3001.25 - 525$$
$$= -1500.625 + 3001.25 - 525$$
$$= 975.625.$$
The store maximizes its weekly profit when 1225 roast beef sandwiches are produced and sold. This results in a profit of \$975.63.

For Exercises 61-67, answers may vary.

69. $f(x) = 3(x+2)^2 - 5$

Since the vertex is $(-2, -5)$, we know that the axis of symmetry is $x = -2$. The point $(-1, -2)$ is on the parabola and lies one unit to the right of the axis of symmetry. This means that the point $(-3, -2)$ will also lie on the parabola since it lies one unit to the left of the axis of symmetry.

71.
$$P = 3x + 4y$$
$$1000 = 3x + 4y$$
$$1000 - 3x = 4y$$
$$\frac{1000 - 3x}{4} = y$$
$$A(x) = x\left(\frac{1000 - 3x}{4}\right)$$
$$= 250x - \frac{3}{4}x^2 = -\frac{3}{4}x^2 + 250x.$$
$$-\frac{b}{2a} = -\frac{250}{2\left(-\dfrac{3}{4}\right)} = -\frac{250}{-1.5} \approx 166.7$$
$$y = \frac{1000 - 3x}{4} = \frac{1000 - 3(166.7)}{4}$$
$$= \frac{1000 - 500.1}{4} = \frac{499.9}{4} \approx 125 \text{ feet}$$

The enclosed area is
$A = xy = 166.7(125) \approx 20{,}838.$

The dimensions of the enclosed area are approximately 166.7 feet by 125 feet with an enclosed area of 20,838 square feet.

73. Answers will vary. For example, consider Exercise 18.
$$f(x) = (x-1)^2 - 2$$

This is the same graph obtained in Exercise 18.

75.
$$-\frac{b}{2a} = -\frac{40}{2(-0.25)} = -\frac{40}{-0.5} = 80$$
$$f\left(-\frac{b}{2a}\right) = f(80) = -0.25(80)^2 + 40(80)$$
$$= -0.25(6400) + 3200$$
$$= -1600 + 3200 = 1600$$

The vertex is $(80, 1600)$. Using the viewing window $[0, 160, 10]$ by $[1000, 2000, 100]$, we have the following.

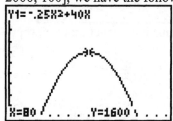

77.
$$-\frac{b}{2a} = -\frac{40}{2(5)} = -\frac{40}{10} = -4$$
$$f\left(-\frac{b}{2a}\right) = f(-4) = 5(-4)^2 + 40(-4) + 600$$
$$= 5(16) - 160 + 600$$
$$= 80 - 160 + 600 = 520$$

The vertex is $(-4, 520)$. Using the viewing window $[-50, 50, 10]$ by $[0, 1000, 100]$, we have the following.

79. a.

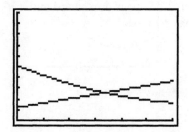

b. Since 1970, the yearly consumption of whole milk has been decreasing while the yearly consumption of low-fat milk has been increasing.

81. a.

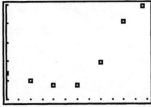

A quadratic function is appropriate for this data because the values of y decrease, then increase.

b.

The quadratic function is
$y = 0.006x^2 - 0.192x + 14.929$.

c. $-\dfrac{b}{2a} = -\dfrac{-0.192}{2(0.006)} = -\dfrac{-0.192}{0.012} = 16$

$f(16) = 0.006(16)^2 - 0.192(16) + 14.929$

$= 0.006(256) - 3.072 + 14.929$

$= 1.536 - 3.072 + 14.929 = 13.393$

The minimum is (16, 13.393). This means that the worst year for automobile efficiency was 1940 + 16 = 1956. The average number of miles per gallon was 13.393.

d.

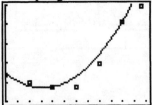

Review Exercises

82. $\dfrac{2}{x+5} + \dfrac{1}{x-5} = \dfrac{16}{x^2-25}$

$\dfrac{2}{x+5} + \dfrac{1}{x-5} = \dfrac{16}{(x+5)(x-5)}$

Multiply both sides of the equation by $(x+5)(x-5)$.

$(x-5)(2) + (x+5)(1) = 16$

$2x - 10 + x + 5 = 16$

$3x - 5 = 16$

$3x = 21$

$x = 7$

83. $\dfrac{x^2-x-6}{3x-3} \div \dfrac{x^2-4}{x-1} = \dfrac{x^2-x-6}{3x-3} \cdot \dfrac{x-1}{x^2-4}$

$= \dfrac{(x-3)(x+2)}{3(x-1)} \cdot \dfrac{x-1}{(x+2)(x-2)}$

$= \dfrac{(x-3)}{3} \cdot \dfrac{1}{(x-2)} = \dfrac{x-3}{3(x-2)}$

84. $2x + 3y = 6$
$x - 4y = 14$

$D = \begin{vmatrix} 2 & 3 \\ 1 & -4 \end{vmatrix} = 2(-4) - 1(3) = -8 - 3 = -11$

$D_x = \begin{vmatrix} 6 & 3 \\ 14 & -4 \end{vmatrix} = 6(-4) - 14(3)$

$= -24 - 42 = -66$

$D_y = \begin{vmatrix} 2 & 6 \\ 1 & 14 \end{vmatrix} = 2(14) - 1(6) = 28 - 6 = 22$

$x = \dfrac{D_x}{D} = \dfrac{-66}{-11} = 6 \qquad y = \dfrac{D_y}{D} = \dfrac{22}{-11} = -2$

The solution is $(6, -2)$.

Equations Quadratic in Form

11.4 CHECK POINTS

CHECK POINT 1
Let $t = x^2$.

$x^4 - 17x^2 + 16 = 0$

$(x^2)^2 - 17x^2 + 16 = 0$

$$t^2 - 17t + 16 = 0$$
$$(t - 16)(t - 1) = 0$$
$$t - 16 = 0 \quad \text{or} \quad t - 1 = 0$$
$$t = 16 \qquad\qquad t = 1$$

Replace t by x^2.

$$x^2 = 16 \quad \text{or} \quad x^2 = 1$$
$$x = \pm 4 \qquad\qquad x = \pm 1$$

CHECK POINT 2
Let $t = \sqrt{x}$.

$$x - 2\sqrt{x} - 8 = 0$$
$$\left(\sqrt{x}\right)^2 - 2\sqrt{x} - 8 = 0$$
$$t^2 - 2t - 8 = 0$$
$$(t - 4)(t + 2) = 0$$
$$t - 4 = 0 \quad \text{or} \quad t + 2 = 0$$
$$t = 4 \qquad\qquad t = -2$$

Replace t by $\sqrt{x}$.

$$\sqrt{x} = 4 \quad \text{or} \quad \cancel{\sqrt{x} = -2}$$
$$x = 4^2$$
$$x = 16$$

We disregard -2 because the square root of x cannot be a negative number. The solution, 16, checks.

CHECK POINT 3
Let $t = x^2 - 4$.

$$\left(x^2 - 4\right)^2 + \left(x^2 - 4\right) - 6 = 0$$
$$t^2 + t - 6 = 0$$
$$t^2 + t - 6 = 0$$
$$(t + 3)(t - 2) = 0$$
$$t + 3 = 0 \quad \text{or} \quad t - 2 = 0$$
$$t = -3 \qquad\qquad t = 2$$

Replace t by $x^2 - 4$.

$$x^2 - 4 = -3 \quad \text{or} \quad x^2 - 4 = 2$$
$$x^2 = 1 \qquad\qquad x^2 = 6$$
$$x = \pm 1 \qquad\qquad x = \pm\sqrt{6}$$

CHECK POINT 4
Let $t = x^{-1}$.

$$2x^{-2} + x^{-1} - 1 = 0$$
$$2\left(x^{-1}\right)^2 + x^{-1} - 1 = 0$$
$$2t^2 + t - 1 = 0$$
$$(2t - 1)(t + 1) = 0$$
$$2t - 1 = 0 \quad \text{or} \quad t + 1 = 0$$
$$2t = 1 \qquad\qquad t = -1$$
$$t = \frac{1}{2}$$

Replace t by x^{-1}.

$$x^{-1} = \frac{1}{2} \quad \text{or} \quad x^{-1} = -1$$
$$\frac{1}{x} = \frac{1}{2} \qquad\qquad \frac{1}{x} = -1$$
$$x = 2 \qquad\qquad x = -1$$

CHECK POINT 5
Let $t = x^{\frac{1}{3}}$.

$$3x^{\frac{2}{3}} - 11x^{\frac{1}{3}} - 4 = 0$$
$$3\left(x^{\frac{1}{3}}\right)^2 - 11x^{\frac{1}{3}} - 4 = 0$$
$$3t^2 - 11t - 4 = 0$$
$$(3t + 1)(t - 4) = 0$$
$$3t + 1 = 0 \quad \text{or} \quad t - 4 = 0$$
$$3t = -1 \qquad\qquad t = 4$$
$$t = -\frac{1}{3}$$

Replace t by $x^{\frac{1}{3}}$.

$$x^{\frac{1}{3}} = -\frac{1}{3} \quad \text{or} \quad x^{\frac{1}{3}} = 4$$
$$\left(x^{\frac{1}{3}}\right)^3 = \left(-\frac{1}{3}\right)^3 \qquad \left(x^{\frac{1}{3}}\right)^3 = (4)^3$$
$$x = -\frac{1}{27} \qquad\qquad x = 64$$

EXERCISE SET 11.4

1.   Let $t = x^2$.
$$x^4 - 5x^2 + 4 = 0$$
$$\left(x^2\right)^2 - 5x^2 + 4 = 0$$
$$t^2 - 5t + 4 = 0$$
$$(t-4)(t-1) = 0$$
$$t - 4 = 0 \quad \text{or} \quad t - 1 = 0$$
$$t = 4 \qquad\qquad t = 1$$
Replace t by x^2.
$$x^2 = 4 \quad \text{or} \quad x^2 = 1$$
$$x = \pm 2 \qquad\quad x = \pm 1$$

3.   Let $t = x^2$.
$$x^4 - 11x^2 + 18 = 0$$
$$\left(x^2\right)^2 - 11x^2 + 18 = 0$$
$$t^2 - 11t + 18 = 0$$
$$(t-9)(t-2) = 0$$
$$t - 9 = 0 \quad \text{or} \quad t - 2 = 0$$
$$t = 9 \qquad\qquad t = 2$$
Replace t by x^2.
$$x^2 = 9 \quad \text{or} \quad x^2 = 2$$
$$x = \pm 3 \qquad\quad x = \pm\sqrt{2}$$

5.   Let $t = x^2$.
$$x^4 + 2x^2 = 8$$
$$x^4 + 2x^2 - 8 = 0$$
$$\left(x^2\right)^2 + 2x^2 - 8 = 0$$
$$t^2 + 2t - 8 = 0$$
$$(t+4)(t-2) = 0$$
$$t + 4 = 0 \quad \text{or} \quad t - 2 = 0$$
$$t = -4 \qquad\qquad t = 2$$
Replace t by x^2.
$$x^2 = -4 \quad \text{or} \quad x^2 = 2$$
$$x = \pm\sqrt{-4} \qquad x = \pm\sqrt{2}$$
$$x = \pm 2i$$

7.   Let $t = \sqrt{x}$.
$$x + \sqrt{x} - 2 = 0$$
$$\left(\sqrt{x}\right)^2 + \sqrt{x} - 2 = 0$$
$$t^2 + t - 2 = 0$$
$$(t+2)(t-1) = 0$$
$$t + 2 = 0 \quad \text{or} \quad t - 1 = 0$$
$$t = -2 \qquad\qquad t = 1$$
Replace t by $\sqrt{x}$.
$$\cancel{\sqrt{x} = -2} \quad \text{or} \quad \sqrt{x} = 1$$
$$x = 1$$
We disregard -2 because the square root of x cannot be a negative number. The solution, 1, checks.

9.   Let $t = x^{\frac{1}{2}}$.
$$x - 4x^{\frac{1}{2}} - 21 = 0$$
$$\left(x^{\frac{1}{2}}\right)^2 - 4x^{\frac{1}{2}} - 21 = 0$$
$$t^2 - 4t - 21 = 0$$
$$(t-7)(t+3) = 0$$
$$t - 7 = 0 \quad \text{or} \quad t + 3 = 0$$
$$t = 7 \qquad\qquad t = -3$$
Replace t by $x^{\frac{1}{2}}$.
$$x^{\frac{1}{2}} = 7 \quad \text{or} \quad x^{\frac{1}{2}} = -3$$
$$\sqrt{x} = 7 \qquad\quad \cancel{\sqrt{x} = -3}$$
$$x = 49$$
We disregard -2 because the square root of x cannot be a negative number. The solution, 49, checks.

11.   Let $t = \sqrt{x}$.
$$x - 13\sqrt{x} + 40 = 0$$
$$\left(\sqrt{x}\right)^2 - 13\sqrt{x} + 40 = 0$$
$$t^2 - 13t + 40 = 0$$
$$(t-5)(t-8) = 0$$

$t - 5 = 0$ or $t - 8 = 0$

$t = 5$ $t = 8$

Replace t by $\sqrt{x}$.

$\sqrt{x} = 5$ or $\sqrt{x} = 8$

$x = 25$ $x = 64$

Both solutions check.

13. Let $t = x - 5$.

$(x - 5)^2 - 4(x - 5) - 21 = 0$

$t^2 - 4t - 21 = 0$

$(t - 7)(t + 3) = 0$

$t - 7 = 0$ or $t + 3 = 0$

$t = 7$ $t = -3$

Replace t by $x - 5$.

$x - 5 = 7$ or $x - 5 = -3$

$x = 12$ $x = 2$

15. Let $t = x^2 - 1$.

$(x^2 - 1)^2 - (x^2 - 1) = 2$

$(x^2 - 1)^2 - (x^2 - 1) - 2 = 0$

$t^2 - t - 2 = 0$

$(t - 2)(t + 1) = 0$

$t - 2 = 0$ or $t + 1 = 0$

$t = 2$ $t = -1$

Replace t by $x^2 - 1$.

$x^2 - 1 = 2$ or $x^2 - 1 = -1$

$x^2 = 3$ $x^2 = 0$

$x = \pm\sqrt{3}$ $x = 0$

17. Let $t = x^2 + 3x$.

$(x^2 + 3x)^2 - 8(x^2 + 3x) - 20 = 0$

$t^2 - 8t - 20 = 0$

$(t - 10)(t + 2) = 0$

$t - 10 = 0$ or $t + 2 = 0$

$t = 10$ $t = -2$

Replace t by $x^2 + 3x$.

First, consider $t = 10$.

$x^2 + 3x = 10$

$x^2 + 3x - 10 = 0$

$(x + 5)(x - 2) = 0$

$x + 5 = 0$ or $x - 2 = 0$

$x = -5$ $x = 2$

Next, consider $t = -2$.

$x^2 + 3x = -2$

$x^2 + 3x + 2 = 0$

$(x + 2)(x + 1) = 0$

$x + 2 = 0$ or $x + 1 = 0$

$x = -2$ $x = -1$

The solutions are $-5, -2, -1,$ and 2.

19. Let $t = x^{-1}$.

$x^{-2} - x^{-1} - 20 = 0$

$(x^{-1})^2 - x^{-1} - 20 = 0$

$t^2 - t - 20 = 0$

$(t - 5)(t + 4) = 0$

$t - 5 = 0$ or $t + 4 = 0$

$t = 5$ $t = -4$

Replace t by x^{-1}.

$x^{-1} = 5$ or $x^{-1} = -4$

$\dfrac{1}{x} = 5$ $\dfrac{1}{x} = -4$

$5x = 1$ $-4x = 1$

$x = \dfrac{1}{5}$ $x = -\dfrac{1}{4}$

21. Let $t = x^{-1}$.

$2x^{-2} - 7x^{-1} + 3 = 0$

$2(x^{-1})^2 - 7x^{-1} + 3 = 0$

$2t^2 - 7t + 3 = 0$

$(2t - 1)(t - 3) = 0$

$2t - 1 = 0$ or $t - 3 = 0$

$2t = 1$ $t = 3$

$t = \dfrac{1}{2}$

Replace t by x^{-1}.

$x^{-1} = \dfrac{1}{2}$ or $x^{-1} = 3$

$\dfrac{1}{x} = \dfrac{1}{2}$ $\dfrac{1}{x} = 3$

$x = 2$ $3x = 1$

$x = \dfrac{1}{3}$

23.   Let $t = x^{-1}$.

$x^{-2} - 4x^{-1} = 3$

$x^{-2} - 4x^{-1} - 3 = 0$

$\left(x^{-1}\right)^2 - 4x^{-1} - 3 = 0$

$t^2 - 4t - 3 = 0$

$a = 1$ $b = -4$ $c = -3$

$t = \dfrac{-(-4) \pm \sqrt{(-4)^2 - 4(1)(-3)}}{2(1)}$

$= \dfrac{4 \pm \sqrt{16 + 12}}{2} = \dfrac{4 \pm \sqrt{28}}{2}$

$= \dfrac{4 \pm 2\sqrt{7}}{2} = \dfrac{2\left(2 \pm \sqrt{7}\right)}{2} = 2 \pm \sqrt{7}$

Replace t by x^{-1}.

$x^{-1} = 2 \pm \sqrt{7}$

$\dfrac{1}{x} = 2 \pm \sqrt{7}$

$\left(2 \pm \sqrt{7}\right)x = 1$

$x = \dfrac{1}{2 \pm \sqrt{7}}$

Rationalize the denominator.

$x = \dfrac{1}{2 \pm \sqrt{7}} \cdot \dfrac{2 \mp \sqrt{7}}{2 \mp \sqrt{7}} = \dfrac{2 \mp \sqrt{7}}{2^2 - \left(\sqrt{7}\right)^2}$

$= \dfrac{2 \mp \sqrt{7}}{4 - 7} = \dfrac{2 \mp \sqrt{7}}{-3} = \dfrac{-2 \pm \sqrt{7}}{3}$

25.   Let $t = x^{\frac{1}{3}}$.

$x^{\frac{2}{3}} - x^{\frac{1}{3}} - 6 = 0$

$\left(x^{\frac{1}{3}}\right)^2 - x^{\frac{1}{3}} - 6 = 0$

$t^2 - t - 6 = 0$

$(t - 3)(t + 2) = 0$

$t - 3 = 0$ or $t + 2 = 0$

$t = 3$ $t = -2$

Replace t by $x^{\frac{1}{3}}$.

$x^{\frac{1}{3}} = 3$ or $x^{\frac{1}{3}} = -2$

$\left(x^{\frac{1}{3}}\right)^3 = 3^3$ $\left(x^{\frac{1}{3}}\right)^3 = (-2)^3$

$x = 27$ $x = -8$

27.   Let $t = x^{\frac{1}{5}}$.

$x^{\frac{2}{5}} + x^{\frac{1}{5}} - 6 = 0$

$\left(x^{\frac{1}{5}}\right)^2 + x^{\frac{1}{5}} - 6 = 0$

$t^2 + t - 6 = 0$

$(t + 3)(t - 2) = 0$

$t + 3 = 0$ or $t - 2 = 0$

$t = -3$ $t = 2$

Replace t by $x^{\frac{1}{5}}$.

$x^{\frac{1}{5}} = -3$ or $x^{\frac{1}{5}} = 2$

$\left(x^{\frac{1}{5}}\right)^5 = (-3)^5$ $\left(x^{\frac{1}{5}}\right)^5 = (2)^5$

$x = -243$ $x = 32$

29.   Let $t = x^{\frac{1}{4}}$.

$2x^{\frac{1}{2}} - x^{\frac{1}{4}} = 1$

$2\left(x^{\frac{1}{4}}\right)^2 - x^{\frac{1}{4}} - 1 = 0$

$2t^2 - t - 1 = 0$

$(2t + 1)(t - 1) = 0$

$2t + 1 = 0 \quad$ or $\quad t - 1 = 0$

$\qquad 2t = -1 \qquad\qquad t = 1$

$\qquad t = -\dfrac{1}{2}$

Replace t by $x^{\frac{1}{4}}$.

$x^{\frac{1}{4}} = -\dfrac{1}{2} \qquad$ or $\qquad x^{\frac{1}{4}} = 1$

$\left(x^{\frac{1}{4}}\right)^4 = \left(-\dfrac{1}{2}\right)^4 \qquad \left(x^{\frac{1}{4}}\right)^4 = 1^4$

$\qquad\qquad\qquad\qquad\qquad x = 1$

$x = \dfrac{1}{16}$

Since both sides of the equations were raised to an even power, the solutions must be checked. The solution, $\dfrac{1}{16}$, does not check. The solution is 1.

31.

Let $t = x - \dfrac{8}{x}$.

$\left(x - \dfrac{8}{x}\right)^2 + 5\left(x - \dfrac{8}{x}\right) - 14 = 0$

$\qquad\qquad t^2 + 5t - 14 = 0$

$\qquad\qquad (t + 7)(t - 2) = 0$

$t + 7 = 0 \quad$ or $\quad t - 2 = 0$

$\quad t = -7 \qquad\qquad t = 2$

Replace t by $x - \dfrac{8}{x}$.

First, consider $t = -7$.

$x - \dfrac{8}{x} = -7$

$x\left(x - \dfrac{8}{x}\right) = x(-7)$

$x^2 - 8 = -7x$

$x^2 + 7x - 8 = 0$

$(x + 8)(x - 1) = 0$

$x + 8 = 0 \quad$ or $\quad x - 1 = 0$

$\quad x = -8 \qquad\qquad x = 1$

Next, consider $t = 2$.

$x - \dfrac{8}{x} = 2$

$x\left(x - \dfrac{8}{x}\right) = x(2)$

$x^2 - 8 = 2x$

$x^2 - 2x - 8 = 0$

$(x - 4)(x + 2) = 0$

$x - 4 = 0 \quad$ or $\quad x + 2 = 0$

$\quad x = 4 \qquad\qquad x = -2$

The solutions are -8, -2, 1, and 4.

33.

$0 = x^4 - 5x^2 + 4$

Let $t = x^2$.

$x^4 - 5x^2 + 4 = 0$

$\left(x^2\right)^2 - 5x^2 + 4 = 0$

$t^2 - 5t + 4 = 0$

$(t - 4)(t - 1) = 0$

$t - 1 = 0 \quad$ or $\quad t - 4 = 0$

$\quad t = 1 \qquad\qquad t = 4$

Substitute x^2 for t.

$x^2 = 1 \quad$ or $\quad x^2 = 4$

$x = \pm 1 \qquad\qquad x = \pm 2$

The intercepts are ± 1 and ± 2. The corresponding graph is graph **c.**

35.

$0 = x^{\frac{1}{3}} + 2x^{\frac{1}{6}} - 3$

Let $t = x^{\frac{1}{6}}$.

$x^{\frac{1}{3}} + 2x^{\frac{1}{6}} - 3 = 0$

$\left(x^{\frac{1}{6}}\right)^2 + 2x^{\frac{1}{6}} - 3 = 0$

$\qquad t^2 + 2t - 3 = 0$

$\qquad (t + 3)(t - 1) = 0$

$t + 3 = 0 \quad$ or $\quad t - 1 = 0$

$\quad t = -3 \qquad\qquad t = 1$

Substitute $x^{\frac{1}{6}}$ for t.

$$x^{\frac{1}{6}} = -3 \qquad \text{or} \qquad x^{\frac{1}{6}} = 1$$

$$\left(x^{\frac{1}{6}}\right)^6 = (-3)^6 \qquad \left(x^{\frac{1}{6}}\right)^6 = (1)^6$$

$$x = 729 \qquad\qquad x = 1$$

Since both sides of the equations were raised to an even power, the solutions must be checked. The solution, 729, does not check. The intercept is 1. The corresponding graph is graph **e.**

37. $(x+2)^2 - 9(x+2) + 20 = 0$

Let $t = x + 2$.

$$t^2 - 9t + 20 = 0$$

$$(t-5)(t-4) = 0$$

Substitute $x + 2$ for t.

$$x + 2 = 5 \quad \text{or} \quad x + 2 = 4$$

$$x = 3 \qquad\qquad x = 2$$

The intercepts are 2 and 3. The corresponding graph is graph **f.**

39. $P(x) = 0.04(x+40)^2 - 3(x+40) + 104$

$$60 = 0.04(x+40)^2 - 3(x+40) + 104$$

$$0 = 0.04(x+40)^2 - 3(x+40) + 44$$

Let $t = x + 40$.

$$0.04(x+40)^2 - 3(x+40) + 44 = 0$$

$$0.04t^2 - 3t + 44 = 0$$

$$a = 0.04 \quad b = -3 \quad c = 44$$

$$t = \frac{-(-3) \pm \sqrt{(-3)^2 - 4(0.04)(44)}}{2(0.04)}$$

$$= \frac{3 \pm \sqrt{9 - 7.04}}{0.08} = \frac{3 \pm \sqrt{1.96}}{0.08}$$

$$= \frac{3 + 1.4}{0.08} \quad \text{or} \quad \frac{3 - 1.4}{0.08} = 55 \text{ or } 20$$

The ages at which 60% of us feel that having a clean house is very important are 20 and 55. From the graph, we see that at 20, 58%, and at 55, 52% feel that a clean house if very important. The function models the data fairly well.

For Exercises 41-42, answers may vary.

45. $x^4 - 5x^2 - 2 = 0$

Let $t = x^2$.

$$x^4 - 5x^2 - 2 = 0$$

$$\left(x^2\right)^2 - 5x^2 - 2 = 0$$

$$t^2 - 5t - 2 = 0$$

$$a = 1 \quad b = -5 \quad c = -2$$

$$t = \frac{-(-5) \pm \sqrt{(-5)^2 - 4(1)(-2)}}{2(1)}$$

$$= \frac{5 \pm \sqrt{25 + 8}}{2} = \frac{5 \pm \sqrt{33}}{2}$$

Substitute x^2 for t.

$$x^2 = \frac{5 \pm \sqrt{33}}{2}$$

$$x = \pm\sqrt{\frac{5 \pm \sqrt{33}}{2}} = \pm\frac{\sqrt{5 \pm \sqrt{33}}}{\sqrt{2}} \cdot \frac{\sqrt{2}}{\sqrt{2}}$$

$$x = \pm\frac{\sqrt{2(5 \pm \sqrt{33})}}{2} = \pm\frac{\sqrt{10 \pm 2\sqrt{33}}}{2}$$

47.

$$\sqrt{\frac{x+4}{x-1}} + \sqrt{\frac{x-1}{x+4}} = \frac{5}{2}$$

$$\sqrt{\frac{x+4}{x-1}} + \left(\sqrt{\frac{x+4}{x-1}}\right)^{-1} = \frac{5}{2}$$

Let $t = \sqrt{\frac{x+4}{x-1}}$.

$$\sqrt{\frac{x+4}{x-1}} + \left(\sqrt{\frac{x+4}{x-1}}\right)^{-1} = \frac{5}{2}$$

$$t + t^{-1} = \frac{5}{2}$$

$$t + \frac{1}{t} = \frac{5}{2}$$

$$t\left(t + \frac{1}{t}\right) = t\left(\frac{5}{2}\right)$$

$$t^2 + 1 = \frac{5}{2}t$$

$$t^2 - \frac{5}{2}t + 1 = 0$$

$$a = 1 \quad b = -\frac{5}{2} = -2.5 \quad c = 1$$

$$t = \frac{-(-2.5) \pm \sqrt{(-2.5)^2 - 4(1)(1)}}{2(1)}$$

$$= \frac{2.5 \pm \sqrt{6.25 - 4}}{2} = \frac{2.5 \pm \sqrt{2.25}}{2}$$

$$= \frac{2.5 \pm 1.5}{2} = \frac{2.5 - 1.5}{2} \quad \text{or} \quad \frac{2.5 + 1.5}{2}$$

$$= \frac{1}{2} \quad \text{or} \quad \frac{4}{2} = \frac{1}{2} \quad \text{or} \quad 2$$

Substitute $\sqrt{\dfrac{x+4}{x-1}}$ for t.

$$\sqrt{\frac{x+4}{x-1}} = \frac{1}{2} \qquad\qquad \sqrt{\frac{x+4}{x-1}} = 2$$

$$2\sqrt{x+4} = \sqrt{x-1} \qquad \sqrt{x+4} = 2\sqrt{x-1}$$

$$4(x+4) = x-1 \qquad\quad x+4 = 4(x-1)$$

$$4x+16 = x-1 \qquad\quad x+4 = 4x-4$$

$$3x+16 = -1 \qquad\quad -3x+4 = -4$$

$$3x = -17 \qquad\qquad -3x = -8$$

$$x = -\frac{17}{3} \qquad\qquad x = \frac{8}{3}$$

49. $x^6 - 7x^3 - 8 = 0$

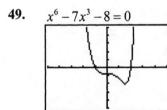

The solutions are –1 and 2. Check each solution by substituting it into the original equation.

51. $x^4 - 10x^2 + 9 = 0$

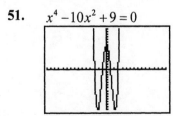

The solutions are –3, –1, 1 and 3.

Check each solution by substituting it into the original equation.

53.
$$2(x+1)^2 = 5(x+1)+3$$

$$2(x+1)^2 - 5(x+1)-3 = 0$$

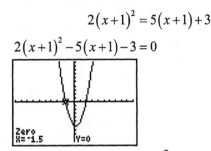

The solutions are $-1.5 = -\dfrac{3}{2}$ and 2.

Because $-\dfrac{3}{2}$ is not an integer, the calculate zero feature was used to determine the intercept. Check each solution by substituting it into the original equation.

55.
$$x^{\frac{1}{2}} + 4x^{\frac{1}{4}} = 5$$

$$x^{\frac{1}{2}} + 4x^{\frac{1}{4}} - 5 = 0$$

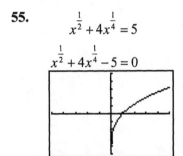

The solution is 1. Check each solution by substituting it into the original equation.

Review Exercises

57. $\dfrac{2x^2}{10x^3 - 2x^2} = \dfrac{2x^2}{2x^2(5x-1)} = \dfrac{1}{5x-1}$

58. $\dfrac{2+i}{1-i} = \dfrac{2+i}{1-i} \cdot \dfrac{1+i}{1+i} = \dfrac{2+2i+i+i^2}{1^2 - i^2}$

$$= \frac{2+3i-1}{1-(-1)} = \frac{1+3i}{2} = \frac{1}{2} + \frac{3}{2}i$$

59. $\begin{bmatrix} 2 & 1 & | & 6 \\ 1 & -2 & | & 8 \end{bmatrix} \quad R_1 \leftrightarrow R_2$

$$= \begin{bmatrix} 1 & -2 & | & 8 \\ 2 & 1 & | & 6 \end{bmatrix} \quad -2R_1 + R_2$$

$$= \begin{bmatrix} 1 & -2 & | & 8 \\ 0 & 5 & | & -10 \end{bmatrix} \quad \frac{1}{5}R_2$$

$$= \begin{bmatrix} 1 & -2 & | & 8 \\ 0 & 1 & | & -2 \end{bmatrix}$$

$$x - 2y = 8$$
$$y = -2$$

Back-substitute -2 for y to find x.

$$x - 2(-2) = 8$$
$$x + 4 = 8$$
$$x = 4$$

The solution is $(4, -2)$.

Quadratic and Rational Inequalities

11.5 CHECK POINTS

CHECK POINT 1
Solve the related quadratic equation.

$$x^2 + 2x - 3 = 0$$
$$(x + 3)(x - 1) = 0$$
$$x + 3 = 0 \quad \text{or} \quad x - 1 = 0$$
$$x = -3 \qquad\qquad x = 1$$

The boundary points are -3 and 1.

Test Interval	Test Number	Test	Conclusion
$(-\infty, -3)$	-4	$(-4)^2 + 2(-4) - 3 < 0$ $5 < 0, \quad$ false	$(-\infty, -3)$ does not belong to the solution set.
$(-3, 1)$	0	$0^2 + 2(0) - 3 < 0$ $-3 < 0, \quad$ true	$(-3, 1)$ belongs to the solution set.
$(1, \infty)$	2	$2^2 + 2(2) - 3 < 0$ $5 < 0,$ false	$(1, \infty)$ does not belong to the solution set.

The solution set is $(1, \infty)$ or $\{x | -3 < x < 1\}$.

-3   1

CHECK POINT 2

$$x^2 - x \ge 20$$

$$x^2 - x - 20 \ge 0$$

Solve the related quadratic equation.

$$x^2 - x - 20 = 0$$
$$(x - 5)(x + 4) = 0$$
$$x - 5 = 0 \quad \text{or} \quad x + 4 = 0$$
$$x = 5 \qquad\qquad x = -4$$

The boundary points are -4 and 5.

Test Interval	Test Number	Test	Conclusion
$(-\infty, -4]$	-5	$(-5)^2 - (-5) \ge 20$ $30 \ge 20$, true	$(-\infty, -4]$ belongs to the solution set.
$[-4, 5]$	0	$0^2 - 0 \ge 20$ $0 \ge 20$, false	$[-4, 5]$ does not belong to the solution set.
$[5, \infty)$	6	$6^2 - 6 \ge 20$ $30 \ge 20$, true	$[5, \infty)$ belongs to the solution set.

The solution set is $(-\infty, -4] \cup [5, \infty)$ or $\{x | x \le -4 \text{ or } x \ge 5\}$.

CHECK POINT 3

$x - 5 = 0 \qquad x + 2 = 0$

$\quad x = 5 \qquad\quad x = -2$

The boundary points are –2 and 5.

Test Interval	Test Number	Test	Conclusion
$(-\infty, -2)$	-3	$\dfrac{-3-5}{-3+2} > 0$ $8 > 0$, true	$(-\infty, -2)$ belongs to the solution set.
$(-2, 5)$	0	$\dfrac{0-5}{0+2} > 0$ $-\dfrac{5}{2} > 0$, false	$(-2, 5)$ does not belong to the solution set.
$(5, \infty)$	6	$\dfrac{6-5}{6+2} > 0$ $\dfrac{1}{8} > 0$, true	$(5, \infty)$ belongs to the solution set.

The solution set is $(-\infty, -2) \cup (5, \infty)$ or $\{x | x < -2 \text{ or } x > 5\}$.

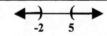

CHECK POINT 4

$$\frac{2x}{x+1} \le 1$$

$$\frac{2x}{x+1} - 1 \le 0$$

$$\frac{2x}{x+1} - \frac{x+1}{x+1} \le 0$$

$$\frac{2x - x - 1}{x+1} \le 0$$

$$\frac{x-1}{x+1} \le 0$$

$x - 1 = 0 \qquad x + 1 = 0$

$\quad x = 1 \qquad\quad x = -1$

The boundary points are –1 and 1.

Test Interval	Test Number	Test	Conclusion
$(-\infty, -1)$	-2	$\dfrac{2(-2)}{-2+1} \leq 1$ $4 \leq 1$, true	$(-\infty, -1)$ does not belong to the solution set.
$(-1, 1]$	0	$\dfrac{2(0)}{0+1} \leq 1$ $0 \leq 1$, true	$(-1, 1]$ belongs to the solution set.
$[1, \infty)$	2	$\dfrac{2(2)}{2+1} \leq 1$ $\dfrac{4}{3} \leq 1$, false	$[1, \infty)$ does not belong to the solution set.

The solution set is $(-1, 1]$ or $\{x | -1 < x \leq 1\}$.

CHECK POINT 5

Solve the related quadratic equation.

$$-16t^2 + 80t = 64$$
$$-16t^2 + 80t - 64 = 0$$
$$t^2 - 5t + 4 = 0$$
$$(t-4)(t-1) = 0$$
$$t - 4 = 0 \quad \text{or} \quad t - 1 = 0$$
$$t = 4 \qquad\qquad t = 1$$

The boundary points are 1 and 4.

Test Interval	Test Number	Test	Conclusion
$(1, 4)$	2	$-16(2)^2 + 80(2) > 64$ $96 > 64$, true	$(1, 4)$ belongs to the solution set.
$(4, \infty)$	5	$-16(5)^2 + 80(5) > 64$ $0 > 64$, false	$(4, \infty)$ does not belong to the solution set.

The ball will be more than 64 feet above the ground between 1 and 4 seconds.

EXERCISE SET 11.5

1.   Solve the related quadratic equation.

$$(x-4)(x+2) = 0$$
$$x - 4 = 0 \quad \text{or} \quad x + 2 = 0$$
$$x = 4 \qquad\qquad x = -2$$

The boundary points are –2 and 4.

Test Interval	Test Number	Test	Conclusion
$(-\infty, -2)$	-3	$(-3-4)(-3+2) > 0$ $7 > 0$, true	$(-\infty, -2)$ belongs to the solution set.

$(-2,4)$	0	$(0-4)(0+2)>0$ $-8>0$, false	$(-2,4)$ does not belong to the solution set.
$(4,\infty)$	5	$(5-4)(5+2)>0$ $7>0$, true	$(4,\infty)$ belongs to the solution set.

The solution set is $(-\infty,-2)\cup(4,\infty)$ or $\{x\mid x<-2 \text{ or } x>4\}$.

3. Solve the related quadratic equation.

$(x-7)(x+3)=0$

$x-7=0$ or $x+3=0$

$x=7$ $\qquad x=-3$

The boundary points are –3 and 7.

Test Interval	Test Number	Test	Conclusion
$(-\infty,-3]$	-4	$(-4-7)(-4+3)\le 0$ $11\le 0$, false	$(-\infty,-3]$ does not belong to the solution set.
$[-3,7]$	0	$(0-7)(0+3)\le 0$ $-21\le 0$, true	$[-3,7]$ belongs to the solution set.
$[7,\infty)$	8	$(8-7)(8+3)\le 0$ $11\le 0$, false	$[7,\infty)$ does not belong to the solution set.

The solution set is $[-3,7]$ or $\{x\mid -3\le x\le 7\}$.

5. Solve the related quadratic equation.

$x^2-5x+4=0$

$(x-4)(x-1)=0$

$x-4=0$ or $x-1=0$

$x=4$ $\qquad x=1$

The boundary points are 1 and 4.

Test Interval	Test Number	Test	Conclusion
$(-\infty,1)$	0	$0^2-5(0)+4>0$ $4>0$, true	$(-\infty,1)$ belongs to the solution set.
$(1,4)$	2	$2^2-5(2)+4>0$ $-2>0$, false	$(1,4)$ does not belong to the solution set.
$(4,\infty)$	5	$5^2-5(5)+4>0$ $4>0$, true	$(4,\infty)$ belongs to the solution set.

The solution set is $(-\infty,1)\cup(4,\infty)$ or $\{x\mid x<1 \text{ or } x>4\}$.

7. Solve the related quadratic equation.

$x^2+5x+4=0$

$(x+4)(x+1)=0$

$$x + 4 = 0 \quad \text{or} \quad x + 1 = 0$$
$$\quad x = -4 \qquad\qquad x = -1$$

The boundary points are –1 and –4.

Test Interval	Test Number	Test	Conclusion
$(-\infty, -4)$	-5	$(-5)^2 + 5(-5) + 4 > 0$ $4 > 0$, true	$(-\infty, -4)$ belongs to the solution set.
$(-4, -1)$	-2	$(-2)^2 + 5(-2) + 4 > 0$ $-2 > 0$, false	$(-4, -1)$ does not belong to the solution set.
$(-1, \infty)$	0	$0^2 + 5(0) + 4 > 0$ $4 > 0$, true	$(-1, \infty)$ belongs to the solution set.

The solution set is $(-\infty, -4) \cup (-1, \infty)$ or $\{x | x < -4 \text{ or } x > -1\}$.

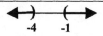

9.   Solve the related quadratic equation.

$$x^2 - 6x + 8 = 0$$
$$(x - 4)(x - 2) = 0$$
$$x - 4 = 0 \quad \text{or} \quad x - 2 = 0$$
$$\quad x = 4 \qquad\qquad x = 2$$

The boundary points are 2 and 4.

Test Interval	Test Number	Test	Conclusion
$(-\infty, 2]$	0	$0^2 - 6(0) + 8 \le 0$ $8 \le 0$, false	$(-\infty, 2]$ does not belong to the solution set.
$[2, 4]$	3	$3^2 - 6(3) + 8 \le 0$ $-1 \le 0$, true	$[2, 4]$ belongs to the solution set.
$[4, \infty)$	5	$5^2 - 6(5) + 8 \le 0$ $3 \le 0$, false	$[4, \infty)$ does not belong to the solution set.

The solution set is $[2, 4]$ or $\{x | 2 \le x \le 4\}$.

11.   Solve the related quadratic equation.

$$3x^2 + 10x - 8 = 0$$
$$(3x - 2)(x + 4) = 0$$
$$3x - 2 = 0 \quad \text{or} \quad x + 4 = 0$$
$$\quad 3x = 2 \qquad\qquad x = -4$$
$$\quad x = \frac{2}{3}$$

The boundary points are –4 and $\frac{2}{3}$.

Test Interval	Test Number	Test	Conclusion
$(-\infty, -4]$	-5	$3(-5)^2 + 10(-5) - 8 \le 0$ $17 \le 0$, false	$(-\infty, -4]$ does not belong to the solution set.

$\left[-4,\dfrac{2}{3}\right]$	0	$3(0)^2+10(0)-8\le 0$ $-8\le 0,\ \text{true}$	$\left[-4,\dfrac{2}{3}\right]$ belongs to the solution set.
$\left[\dfrac{2}{3},\infty\right)$	1	$3(1)^2+10(1)-8\le 0$ $5\le 0,\ \text{false}$	$\left[\dfrac{2}{3},\infty\right)$ does not belong to the solution set.

The solution set is $\left[-4,\dfrac{2}{3}\right]$ or $\left\{x\middle|-4\le x\le \dfrac{2}{3}\right\}$.

13. $\qquad 2x^2+x<15$

$2x^2+x-15<0$

Solve the related quadratic equation.

$\qquad 2x^2+x-15=0$

$(2x-5)(x+3)=0$

$2x-5=0 \quad\text{or}\quad x+3=0$

$\qquad 2x=5 \qquad\qquad x=-3$

$\qquad\quad x=\dfrac{5}{2}$

The boundary points are -3 and $\dfrac{5}{2}$.

Test Interval	Test Number	Test	Conclusion
$(-\infty,-3)$	-4	$2(-4)^2+(-4)<15$ $28<15,\ \text{false}$	$(-\infty,-3)$ does not belong to the solution set.
$\left(-3,\dfrac{5}{2}\right)$	0	$2(0)^2+0<15$ $0<15,\ \text{true}$	$\left(-3,\dfrac{5}{2}\right)$ belongs to the solution set.
$\left(\dfrac{5}{2},\infty\right)$	3	$2(3)^2+3<15$ $21<15,\ \text{false}$	$\left(\dfrac{5}{2},\infty\right)$ does not belong to the solution set.

The solution set is $\left(-3,\dfrac{5}{2}\right)$ or $\left\{x\middle|-3<x<\dfrac{5}{2}\right\}$.

15. $\qquad 4x^2+7x<-3$

$4x^2+7x+3<0$

Solve the related quadratic equation.

$\qquad 4x^2+7x+3=0$

$(4x+3)(x+1)=0$

$$4x + 3 = 0 \quad \text{or} \quad x + 1 = 0$$
$$4x = -3 \qquad\qquad x = -1$$
$$x = -\frac{3}{4}$$

The boundary points are -1 and $-\frac{3}{4}$.

Test Interval	Test Number	Test	Conclusion
$(-\infty, -1)$	-2	$4(-2)^2 + 7(-2) < -3$ $2 < -3$, false	$(-\infty, -1)$ does not belong to the solution set.
$\left(-1, -\frac{3}{4}\right)$	$-\frac{7}{8}$	$4\left(-\frac{7}{8}\right)^2 + 7\left(-\frac{7}{8}\right) < -3$ $-3\frac{1}{16} < -3$, true	$\left(-1, -\frac{3}{4}\right)$ belongs to the solution set.
$\left(-\frac{3}{4}, \infty\right)$	0	$4(0)^2 + 7(0) < -3$ $0 < -3$, false	$\left(-\frac{3}{4}, \infty\right)$ does not belong to the solution set.

The solution set is $\left(-1, -\frac{3}{4}\right)$ or $\left\{ x \middle| -1 < x < -\frac{3}{4} \right\}$.
-1   -3/4

17. $x^2 - 4x \geq 0$
Solve the related quadratic equation.
$$x^2 - 4x = 0$$
$$x(x - 4) = 0$$
$$x = 0 \quad \text{or} \quad x - 4 = 0$$
$$x = 4$$
The boundary points are 0 and 4.

Test Interval	Test Number	Test	Conclusion
$(-\infty, 0]$	-1	$(-1)^2 - 4(-1) \geq 0$ $5 \geq 0$, true	$(-\infty, 0]$ belongs to the solution set.
$[0, 4]$	1	$(1)^2 - 4(1) \geq 0$ $-3 \geq 0$, false	$[0, 4]$ does not belong to the solution set.
$[4, \infty)$	5	$(5)^2 - 4(5) \geq 0$ $5 \geq 0$, true	$[4, \infty)$ belongs to the solution set.

The solution set is $(-\infty, 0] \cup [4, \infty)$ or $\{ x \mid x \leq 0 \text{ or } x \geq 4 \}$.

0   4

19. Solve the related quadratic equation.
$$2x^2 + 3x = 0$$
$$x(2x + 3) = 0$$

$$x = 0 \quad \text{or} \quad 2x + 3 = 0$$
$$2x = -3$$
$$x = -\frac{3}{2}$$

The boundary points are $-\frac{3}{2}$ and 0.

Test Interval	Test Number	Test	Conclusion
$\left(-\infty, -\frac{3}{2}\right)$	-2	$2(-2)^2 + 3(-2) > 0$ $2 > 0$, true	$\left(-\infty, -\frac{3}{2}\right)$ belongs to the solution set.
$\left(-\frac{3}{2}, 0\right)$	-1	$2(-1)^2 + 3(-1) > 0$ $-1 > 0$, false	$\left(-\frac{3}{2}, 0\right)$ does not belong to the solution set.
$(0, \infty)$	1	$2(1)^2 + 3(1) > 0$ $5 > 0$, true	$(0, \infty)$ belongs to the solution set.

The solution set is $\left(-\infty, -\frac{3}{2}\right) \cup (0, \infty)$ or $\left\{x \mid x < -\frac{3}{2} \text{ or } x > 0\right\}$.

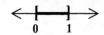

-3/2   0

21. Solve the related quadratic equation.
$$-x^2 + x = 0$$
$$-x(x - 1) = 0$$
$$-x = 0 \quad \text{or} \quad x - 1 = 0$$
$$x = 0 \qquad\qquad x = 1$$

The boundary points are 0 and 1.

Test Interval	Test Number	Test	Conclusion
$(-\infty, 0]$	-1	$-(-1)^2 + (-1) \geq 0$ $-2 \geq 0$, false	$(-\infty, 0]$ does not belong to the solution set.
$[0, 1]$	$\frac{1}{2}$	$-\left(\frac{1}{2}\right)^2 + \frac{1}{2} \geq 0$ $\frac{1}{4} \geq 0$, true	$[0, 1]$ belongs to the solution set.
$[1, \infty)$	2	$-(2)^2 + 2 \geq 0$ $-2 \geq 0$, false	$[1, \infty)$ does not belong to the solution set.

The solution set is $[0, 1]$ or $\{x \mid 0 \leq x \leq 1\}$.

0   1

23.
$$x^2 \leq 4x - 2$$
$$x^2 - 4x + 2 \leq 0$$
Solve the related quadratic equation, using the quadratic formula.
$$x^2 - 4x + 2 = 0$$

$$a = 1 \quad b = -4 \quad c = 2$$

$$x = \frac{-(-4) \pm \sqrt{(-4)^2 - 4(1)(2)}}{2(1)} = \frac{4 \pm \sqrt{16-8}}{2} = \frac{4 \pm \sqrt{8}}{2} = \frac{4 \pm \sqrt{4 \cdot 2}}{2} = \frac{4 \pm 2\sqrt{2}}{2} = \frac{2\left(2 \pm \sqrt{2}\right)}{2} = 2 \pm \sqrt{2}$$

The boundary points are $2 - \sqrt{2}$ and $2 + \sqrt{2}$.

Test Interval	Test Number	Test	Conclusion
$\left(-\infty, 2-\sqrt{2}\,\right]$	0	$0^2 \le 4(0) - 2$ $0 \le -2$, false	$\left(-\infty, 2-\sqrt{2}\,\right]$ does not belong to the solution set.
$\left[2-\sqrt{2}, 2+\sqrt{2}\,\right]$	2	$2^2 \le 4(2) - 2$ $4 \le 6$, true	$\left[2-\sqrt{2}, 2+\sqrt{2}\,\right]$ belongs to the solution set.
$\left[2+\sqrt{2}, \infty\right)$	4	$4^2 \le 4(4) - 2$ $16 \le 14$, false	$\left[2+\sqrt{2}, \infty\right)$ does not belong to the solution set.

The solution set is $\left[2-\sqrt{2}, 2+\sqrt{2}\,\right]$ or $\left\{x \mid 2-\sqrt{2} \le x \le 2+\sqrt{2}\right\}$.

$$2-\sqrt{2} \qquad 2+\sqrt{2}$$

25.   Solve the related quadratic equation.

$$x^2 - 6x + 9 = 0$$

$$(x-3)^2 = 0$$

$$x - 3 = 0$$

$$x = 3$$

The boundary point is 3.

Test Interval	Test Number	Test	Conclusion
$(-\infty, 3)$	0	$0^2 - 6(0) + 9 < 0$ $9 < 0$, false	$(-\infty, 3)$ does not belong to the solution set.
$(3, \infty)$	4	$4^2 - 6(4) + 9 < 0$ $1 < 0$, false	$(3, \infty)$ does not belong to the solution set.

There is no solution. The solution set is $\varnothing$ or $\{\ \ \}$.

27. $x - 4 = 0 \qquad x + 3 = 0$

$\quad\quad\ x = 4 \qquad\quad x = -3$

The boundary points are -3 and 4. We exclude -3 from the solution set, since this would make the denominator zero.

Test Interval	Test Number	Test	Conclusion
$(-\infty, -3)$	-4	$\dfrac{-4-4}{-4+3} > 0$ $8 > 0$, true	$(-\infty, -3)$ belongs to the solution set.

| $(-3,4)$ | 0 | $\dfrac{0-4}{0+3}>0$ $\dfrac{-4}{3}>0$, false | $(-3,4)$ does not belong to the solution set. |
| $(4,\infty)$ | 5 | $\dfrac{5-4}{5+3}>0$ $\dfrac{1}{8}>0$, true | $(4,\infty)$ belongs to the solution set. |

The solution set is $(-\infty,-3)\cup(4,\infty)$ or $\{x\,|\,x<-3 \text{ or } x>4\}$.

29. $x+3=0 \qquad x+4=0$

$\qquad x=-3 \qquad\quad x=-4$

The boundary points are –4 and –3.

Test Interval	Test Number	Test	Conclusion
$(-\infty,-4)$	-5	$\dfrac{-5+3}{-5+4}<0$ $2<0$, false	$(-\infty,-4)$ does not belong to the solution set.
$(-4,-3)$	-3.5	$\dfrac{-3.5+3}{-3.5+4}<0$ $-1<0$, true	$(-4,-3)$ belongs to the solution set.
$(-3,\infty)$	0	$\dfrac{0+3}{0+4}<0$ $\dfrac{3}{4}<0$, false	$(-3,\infty)$ does not belong to the solution set.

The solution set is $(-4,-3)$ or $\{x\,|-4<x<-3\}$.

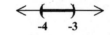

31. $-x+2=0 \quad$ and $\quad x-4=0$

$\qquad 2=x \qquad\qquad x=4$

The boundary points are 2 and 4. We exclude 4 from the solution set because 4 would make the denominator zero.

Test Interval	Test Number	Test	Conclusion
$(-\infty,2]$	0	$\dfrac{-0+2}{0-4}\geq 0$ $-\dfrac{1}{2}\geq 0$, false	$(-\infty,2]$ does not belong to the solution set.
$[2,4)$	3	$\dfrac{-3+2}{3-4}\geq 0$ $1\geq 0$, true	$[2,4)$ belongs to the solution set.
$(4,\infty)$	5	$\dfrac{-5+2}{5-4}\geq 0$ $-3\geq 0$, false	$(4,\infty)$ does not belong to the solution set.

The solution set is $[2,4)$ or $\{x|2 \le x < 4\}$.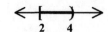

33. $4 - 2x = 0$ and $3x + 4 = 0$

$\qquad$ $-2x = -4$ $\qquad\qquad$ $3x = -4$

$\qquad$ $x = 2$ $\qquad\qquad\qquad$ $x = -\dfrac{4}{3}$

The boundary points are $-\dfrac{4}{3}$ and 2. We exclude $-\dfrac{4}{3}$ from the solution set because $-\dfrac{4}{3}$ would make the denominator zero.

Test Interval	Test Number	Test	Conclusion
$\left(-\infty, -\dfrac{4}{3}\right)$	-2	$\dfrac{4-2(-2)}{3(-2)+4} \le 0$ $-4 \le 0$, true	$\left(-\infty, -\dfrac{4}{3}\right)$ belongs to the solution set.
$\left(-\dfrac{4}{3}, 2\right]$	0	$\dfrac{4-2(0)}{3(0)+4} \le 0$ $1 \le 0$, false	$\left(-\dfrac{4}{3}, 2\right]$ does not belong to the solution set.
$[2, \infty)$	3	$\dfrac{4-2(3)}{3(3)+4} \le 0$ $-\dfrac{2}{13} \le 0$, true	$[2, \infty)$ belongs to the solution set.

The solution set is $\left(-\infty, -\dfrac{4}{3}\right) \cup [2, \infty)$ or $\left\{x \middle| x < -\dfrac{4}{3} \text{ and } x \ge 2\right\}$.

35. $x = 0$ and $x - 3 = 0$

$\qquad\qquad\qquad\qquad$ $x = 3$

The boundary points are 0 and 3.

Test Interval	Test Number	Test	Conclusion
$(-\infty, 0)$	-1	$\dfrac{-1}{-1-3} > 0$ $\dfrac{1}{4} > 0$, true	$\left(-\infty, -\dfrac{4}{3}\right)$ belongs to the solution set.
$(0, 3)$	1	$\dfrac{1}{1-3} > 0$ $-\dfrac{1}{2} > 0$, false	$(0, 3)$ does not belong to the solution set.
$(3, \infty)$	4	$\dfrac{4}{4-3} > 0$ $4 > 0$, true	$(3, \infty)$ belongs to the solution set.

The solution set is $(-\infty, 0) \cup (3, \infty)$ or $\{x|x < 0 \text{ and } x > 3\}$.

37.
$$\frac{x+1}{x+3} < 2$$

$$\frac{x+1}{x+3} - 2 < 0$$

$$\frac{x+1}{x+3} - \frac{2(x+3)}{x+3} < 0$$

$$\frac{x+1-2(x+3)}{x+3} < 0$$

$$\frac{x+1-2x-6}{x+3} < 0$$

$$\frac{-x-5}{x+3} < 0$$

Find the values of x that make the numerator and denominator zero.

$$-x-5 = 0 \qquad x+3 = 0$$

$$-x = 5 \qquad\qquad x = -3$$

$$x = -5$$

The boundary points are –5 and –3.

Test Interval	Test Number	Test	Conclusion
$(-\infty,-5)$	-6	$\dfrac{-6+1}{-6+3} < 2$ $\dfrac{5}{3} < 2$, true	$(-\infty,-5)$ belongs to the solution set.
$(-5,-3)$	-4	$\dfrac{-4+1}{-4+3} < 2$ $3 < 2$, false	$(-5,-3)$ does not belong to the solution set.
$(-3,\infty)$	0	$\dfrac{0+1}{0+3} < 2$ $\dfrac{1}{3} < 2$, true	$(-3,\infty)$ belongs to the solution set.

The solution set is $(-\infty,-5)\cup(-3,\infty)$ or $\{x\,|\,x < -5 \text{ and } x > -3\}$.

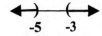

-5   **-3**

39.
$$\frac{x+4}{2x-1} \le 3$$

$$\frac{x+4}{2x-1} - 3 \le 0$$

$$\frac{x+4}{2x-1} - \frac{3(2x-1)}{2x-1} \le 0$$

$$\frac{x+4-3(2x-1)}{2x-1} \le 0$$

$$\frac{x+4-6x+3}{2x-1} \le 0$$

$$\frac{-5x+7}{2x-1} \leq 0$$

Find the values of x that make the numerator and denominator zero.

$$-5x+7=0 \qquad 2x-1=0$$
$$-5x=-7 \qquad 2x=1$$
$$x=\frac{7}{5} \qquad x=\frac{1}{2}$$

The boundary points are $\frac{1}{2}$ and $\frac{7}{5}$. We exclude $\frac{1}{2}$ from the solution set because $\frac{1}{2}$ would make the denominator zero.

Test Interval	Test Number	Test	Conclusion
$\left(-\infty,\frac{1}{2}\right)$	0	$\frac{0+4}{2(0)-1}\leq 3$ $-4\leq 3$, true	$\left(-\infty,\frac{1}{2}\right)$ belongs to the solution set.
$\left(\frac{1}{2},\frac{7}{5}\right]$	1	$\frac{1+4}{2(1)-1}\leq 3$ $5\leq 3$, false	$\left(\frac{1}{2},\frac{7}{5}\right]$ does not belong to the solution set.
$\left[\frac{7}{5},\infty\right)$	2	$\frac{2+4}{2(2)-1}\leq 3$ $2\leq 3$, true	$\left[\frac{7}{5},\infty\right)$ belongs to the solution set.

The solution set is $\left(-\infty,\frac{1}{2}\right)\cup\left[\frac{7}{5},\infty\right)$ or $\left\{x\,\middle|\,x<\frac{1}{2} \text{ and } x\geq\frac{7}{5}\right\}$.

41.
$$\frac{x-2}{x+2}\leq 2$$
$$\frac{x-2}{x+2}-2\leq 0$$
$$\frac{x-2}{x+2}-\frac{2(x+2)}{x+2}\leq 0$$
$$\frac{x-2-2(x+2)}{x+2}\leq 0$$
$$\frac{x-2-2x-4}{x+2}\leq 0$$
$$\frac{-x-6}{x+2}\leq 0$$

Find the values of x that make the numerator and denominator zero.

$$-x-6=0 \qquad x+2=0$$
$$-x=6 \qquad x=-2$$
$$x=-6$$

The boundary points are -6 and -2. We exclude -2 from the solution set because -2 would make the denominator zero.

Test Interval	Test Number	Test	Conclusion
$(-\infty,-6]$	-7	$\dfrac{-7-2}{-7+2} \le 2$ $\dfrac{9}{5} \le 2$, true	$(-\infty,-6]$ belongs to the solution set.
$[-6,-2)$	-3	$\dfrac{-3-2}{-3+2} \le 2$ $5 \le 2$, false	$[-6,-2)$ does not belong to the solution set.
$(-2,\infty)$	0	$\dfrac{0-2}{0+2} \le 2$ $-1 \le 2$, true	$(-2,\infty)$ belongs to the solution set.

The solution set is $(-\infty,-6]\cup(-2,\infty)$ or $\{x \mid x \le -6 \text{ and } x > -2\}$.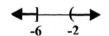

-6   -2

43. $-16t^2 + 48t + 160 > 160$
Solve the related quadratic equation.
$$-16t^2 + 48t + 160 = 160$$
$$-16t^2 + 48t = 0$$
$$t^2 - 3t = 0$$
$$t(t-3) = 0$$
$$t = 0 \quad \text{or} \quad t-3 = 0$$
$$t = 3$$
The boundary points are 0 and 3.

Test Interval	Test Number	Test	Conclusion
$(0,3)$	1	$-16(1)^2 + 48(1) + 160 > 160$ $192 > 160$, true	$(0,3)$ belongs to the solution set.
$(3,\infty)$	4	$-16(4)^2 + 48(4) + 160 > 160$ $96 > 160$, true	$(3,\infty)$ does not belong to the solution set.

The solution set is $(0,3)$. This means that the ball exceeds the height of the building between 0 and 3 seconds.

45. $f(8) = 27(8) + 163 = 216 + 163 = 379$

$g(8) = 1.2(8)^2 + 15.2(8) + 181.4 = 1.2(64) + 121.6 + 181.4 = 76.8 + 121.6 + 181.4 = 379.8$

Since the graph indicates that Medicare spending will reach \$379 billion, we conclude that both functions model the data quite well.

47. $1.2x^2 + 15.2x + 181.4 > 536.6$
Solve the related quadratic equation using the quadratic formula.
$$1.2x^2 + 15.2x + 181.4 = 536.6$$
$$1.2x^2 + 15.2x - 355.2 = 0$$
$$a = 1.2 \quad b = 15.2 \quad c = -355.2$$

$$x = \frac{-15.2 \pm \sqrt{15.2^2 - 4(1.2)(-355.2)}}{2(1.2)} = \frac{-15.2 \pm \sqrt{231.04 + 1704.96}}{2.4}$$

$$= \frac{-15.2 \pm \sqrt{1936}}{2.4} = \frac{-15.2 \pm 44}{2.4} = \frac{-15.2 - 44}{2.4} \text{ or } \frac{-15.2 + 44}{2.4} = -24\frac{2}{3} \text{ or } 12$$

We disregard $-24\frac{2}{3}$ since x represents the number of years after 1995 and cannot be negative.

The boundary point is 12.

Test Interval	Test Number	Test	Conclusion
$(0,12)$	1	$1.2(1)^2 + 15.2(1) + 181.4 > 536.6$ $197.8 > 536.6$, false	$(0,12)$ does not belong to the solution set.
$(12,\infty)$	13	$1.2(13)^2 + 15.2(13) + 181.4 > 536.6$ $581.8 > 536.6$, true	$(12,\infty)$ belongs to the solution set.

The solution set is $(12,\infty)$. This means that spending will exceed \$536.6 billion after $1995 + 12 = 2007$.

49. $f(18) = 1.3(18)^2 + 32(18) + 303 = 1.3(324) + 576 + 303 = 421.2 + 576 + 303 = 1300.2$

The function predicts that there will be 1300.2 thousand or 1,300,200 inmates. The function models the actual number for 1998 very well.

51. $1.3x^2 + 32x + 303 > 2433$

Solve the related quadratic equation using the quadratic formula.

$$1.3x^2 + 32x + 303 = 2433$$

$$1.3x^2 + 32x - 2130 = 0$$

$$a = 1.3 \quad b = 32 \quad c = -2130$$

$$x = \frac{-32 \pm \sqrt{32^2 - 4(1.3)(-2130)}}{2(1.3)} = \frac{-32 \pm \sqrt{1024 + 11076}}{2.6} = \frac{-32 \pm \sqrt{12100}}{2.6} = \frac{-32 \pm 110}{2.6}$$

$$= \frac{-32 - 110}{2.6} \text{ or } \frac{-32 + 110}{2.6} = -54\frac{8}{13} \text{ or } 30$$

We disregard $-54\frac{8}{13}$ since x represents the number of years after 1980 and cannot be negative.

The boundary point is 30.

Test Interval	Test Number	Test	Conclusion
$(0,30)$	1	$1.3(1)^2 + 32(1) + 303 > 2433$ $336.3 > 2433$, false	$(0,30)$ does not belong to the solution set.
$(30,\infty)$	31	$1.3(31)^2 + 32(31) + 303 > 2433$ $2544.3 > 2433$, true	$(30,\infty)$ belongs to the solution set.

The solution set is $(30,\infty)$. This means the number of inmates will exceed 2433 thousand or 2,433,000 after the year $1980 + 30 = 2010$.

53.

$$\frac{500,000+400x}{x} \le 425$$

$$\frac{500,000+400x}{x} - 425 \le 0$$

$$\frac{500,000+400x}{x} - \frac{425x}{x} \le 0$$

$$\frac{500,000+400x-425x}{x} \le 0$$

$$\frac{500,000-25x}{x} \le 0$$

Find the values of x that make the numerator and denominator zero.

$$500,000 - 25x = 0 \qquad x = 0$$
$$500,000 = 25x$$
$$20,000 = x$$

The boundary points are 0 and 20,000.

Test Interval	Test Number	Test	Conclusion
$[0, 20000]$	1	$\dfrac{500,000+400(1)}{1} \le 425$ $500,400 \le 425$, false	$[0, 20000]$ does not belong to the solution set.
$[20000, \infty)$	25,000	$\dfrac{500,000+400(25,000)}{25,000} \le 425$ $420 \le 425$, true	$[20000, \infty)$ belongs to the solution set.

The solution set is $[20000, \infty)$. This means that the company's production level will have to be at least 20,000 wheelchairs per week. The boundary corresponds to the point (20,000, 425) on the graph. When production is 20,000 or more per month, the average cost is $425 or less.

For Exercises 55-57, answers may vary.

59. Statement **d.** is true.

Statement **a.** is false.
$x^2 > 25$

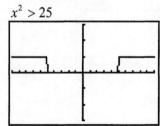

The solution set is $\{x | x < -5 \text{ or } x > 5\}$ or $(-\infty, -5) \cup (5, \infty)$.

Statement **b.** is false. The inequality cannot be solved by multiplying both sides by $x + 3$. We do not know if $x + 3$ is positive or negative. Thus, we do not know whether or not to reverse the sense of the inequality.

Statement **c.** is false. The solution sets are not the same.

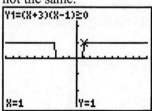

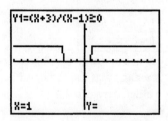

The value, 1, is included in the domain of the first inequality, but not included in the domain of the second inequality.

61. Answers will vary. An example is $\dfrac{x-3}{x+4} \geq 0.$

63. $(x-2)^2 \leq 0$

Since the left hand side of the inequality is a square, we know it cannot be negative. In addition, the inequality calls for a number that is less than or equal to zero. The only possible solution is for the left hand side to equal zero. The left hand side of the inequality is zero when x is 2. Hence, the solution set is $\{2\}$.

65. $\dfrac{1}{(x-2)^2} > 0$

Since the denominator in the inequality is a square, we know it cannot be negative. Additionally, because the numerator is 1, the fraction will never be negative. As a result, x can be any real number except one that makes the denominator zero. Since 2 is the only value that makes the denominator zero, the solution set is $\{x | x \text{ is a real number and } x \neq 2\}$ or $(-\infty, 2) \cup (2, \infty)$.

67. Write an inequality stating that the radicand must be greater than or equal to zero.

$27 - 3x^2 \geq 0$

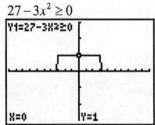

The inequality is true for values between 3 and –3. This means that the radicand is positive for values between 3 and –3, and

the domain of the function is $\{x | -3 \leq x \leq 3\}$ or $[-3, 3]$.

69. $2x^2 + 5x - 3 \leq 0$

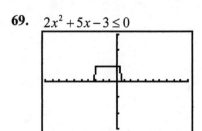

The solution set is $\left\{x \middle| -3 \leq x \leq \dfrac{1}{2}\right\}$ or $\left[-3, \dfrac{1}{2}\right]$.

71. $\dfrac{x+2}{x-3} \leq 2$

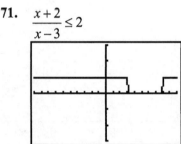

The solution set is $\{x | x < 3 \text{ or } x \geq 8\}$ or $(-\infty, 3) \cup [8, \infty)$.

73. $x^3 + 2x^2 - 5x - 6 > 0$

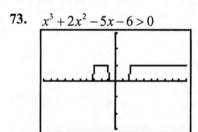

The solution set is $\{x | -3 < x < -1 \text{ or } x > 2\}$ or $(-3, -1) \cup (2, \infty)$.

Review Exercises

74. $\left|\dfrac{x-5}{3}\right| < 8$

$-8 < \dfrac{x-5}{3} < 8$

$$-24 < x - 5 < 24$$
$$-19 < x < 29$$

The solution set is $\{x | -19 < x < 29\}$ or $(-19, 29)$.

75.

$$\frac{2x+6}{x^2+8x+16} \div \frac{x^2-9}{x^2+3x-4}$$

$$= \frac{2x+6}{x^2+8x+16} \cdot \frac{x^2+3x-4}{x^2-9}$$

$$= \frac{2(x+3)}{(x+4)(x+4)} \cdot \frac{(x+4)(x-1)}{(x+3)(x-3)}$$

$$= \frac{2(x-1)}{(x+4)(x-3)}$$

76. $x^4 - 16y^4 = (x^2 + 4y^2)(x^2 - 4y^2)$
$$= (x^2 + 4y^2)(x + 2y)(x - 2y)$$

Chapter 11 Review Exercises

1.
$$2x^2 - 3 = 125$$
$$2x^2 = 128$$
$$x^2 = 64$$
$$x = \pm 8$$

2.
$$3x^2 - 150 = 0$$
$$3x^2 = 150$$
$$x^2 = 50$$
$$x = \pm\sqrt{50}$$
$$x = \pm\sqrt{25 \cdot 2} = \pm 5\sqrt{2}$$

3.
$$3x^2 - 2 = 0$$
$$3x^2 = 2$$
$$x^2 = \frac{2}{3}$$
$$x = \pm\sqrt{\frac{2}{3}}$$

Rationalize the denominator.

$$x = \pm\frac{\sqrt{2}}{\sqrt{3}} \cdot \frac{\sqrt{3}}{\sqrt{3}} = \pm\frac{\sqrt{6}}{3}$$

4.
$$(x-4)^2 = 18$$
$$x - 4 = \pm\sqrt{18}$$
$$x = 4 \pm \sqrt{9 \cdot 2} = 4 \pm 3\sqrt{2}$$

5.
$$(x+7)^2 = -36$$
$$x + 7 = \pm\sqrt{-36}$$
$$x = -7 \pm 6i$$

6.
$$\left(\frac{b}{2}\right)^2 = \left(\frac{20}{2}\right)^2 = (10)^2 = 100$$
$$x^2 + 20x + 100 = (x+10)^2$$

7.
$$\left(\frac{b}{2}\right)^2 = \left(\frac{3}{2}\right)^2 = \frac{9}{4}$$
$$x^2 - 3x + \frac{9}{4} = \left(x - \frac{3}{2}\right)^2$$

8.
$$\left(\frac{b}{2}\right)^2 = \left(\frac{-12}{2}\right)^2 = (-6)^2 = 36$$
$$x^2 - 12x + 27 = 0$$
$$x^2 - 12x + 36 = -27 + 36$$
$$(x-6)^2 = 9$$
$$x - 6 = 3 \qquad x - 6 = -3$$
$$x = 9 \qquad\quad x = 3$$

9.
$$\left(\frac{b}{2}\right)^2 = \left(\frac{-7}{2}\right)^2 = \frac{49}{4}$$
$$x^2 - 7x + \frac{49}{4} = 1 + \frac{49}{4}$$
$$\left(x - \frac{7}{2}\right)^2 = \frac{4}{4} + \frac{49}{4}$$
$$\left(x - \frac{7}{2}\right)^2 = \frac{53}{4}$$
$$x - \frac{7}{2} = \pm\sqrt{\frac{53}{4}}$$

$$x = \frac{7}{2} \pm \frac{\sqrt{53}}{2} = \frac{7 \pm \sqrt{53}}{2}$$

10.
$$2x^2 + 3x - 4 = 0$$
$$x^2 + \frac{3}{2}x - 2 = 0$$
$$x^2 + \frac{3}{2}x \quad = 2$$
$$x^2 + \frac{3}{2}x + \frac{9}{16} = 2 + \frac{9}{16}$$
$$\left(x + \frac{3}{4}\right)^2 = \frac{32}{16} + \frac{9}{16}$$
$$\left(x + \frac{3}{4}\right)^2 = \frac{41}{16}$$
$$x + \frac{3}{4} = \pm\sqrt{\frac{41}{16}}$$
$$x = -\frac{3}{4} \pm \frac{\sqrt{41}}{4} = \frac{-3 \pm \sqrt{41}}{4}$$

11.
$$A = P(1 + r)^t$$
$$2916 = 2500(1 + r)^2$$
$$\frac{2916}{2500} = (1 + r)^2$$
$$1 + r = \pm\sqrt{\frac{2916}{2500}}$$
$$r = -1 \pm \sqrt{1.1664} = -1 \pm 1.08$$

The solutions are $-1 - 1.08 = -2.08$ and $-1 + 1.08 = 0.08$. We disregard -2.08 since we cannot have a negative interest rate. The interest rate is 0.08 or 8%.

12.
$$W(t) = 3t^2$$
$$1200 = 3t^2$$
$$400 = t^2$$
$$t = \pm\sqrt{400} = \pm 20$$

The solutions are -20 and 20. We disregard -20, because we cannot have a negative time measurement. The fetus will weigh 1200 grams after 20 weeks.

13.

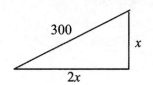

$$(2x)^2 + x^2 = 300^2$$
$$4x^2 + x^2 = 90,000$$
$$5x^2 = 90,000$$
$$x^2 = 18,000$$
$$x = \pm\sqrt{18,000}$$
$$x = \pm\sqrt{3600 \cdot 5} = \pm 60\sqrt{5}$$

The solutions are $\pm 60\sqrt{5}$ meters. We disregard $-60\sqrt{5}$ meters, because we can't have a negative length measurement. Therefore, the building is $60\sqrt{5}$ or approximately 134.2 meters high.

14.
$$x^2 = 2x + 4$$
$$x^2 - 2x - 4 = 0$$
$$a = 1 \quad b = -2 \quad c = -4$$
$$x = \frac{-(-2) \pm \sqrt{(-2)^2 - 4(1)(-4)}}{2(1)}$$
$$= \frac{2 \pm \sqrt{4 + 16}}{2} = \frac{2 \pm \sqrt{20}}{2}$$
$$= \frac{2 \pm \sqrt{4 \cdot 5}}{2} = \frac{2 \pm 2\sqrt{5}}{2}$$
$$= \frac{2(1 \pm \sqrt{5})}{2} = 1 \pm \sqrt{5}$$

15.
$$x^2 - 2x + 19 = 0$$
$$a = 1 \quad b = -2 \quad c = 19$$
$$x = \frac{-(-2) \pm \sqrt{(-2)^2 - 4(1)(19)}}{2(1)}$$
$$= \frac{2 \pm \sqrt{4 - 76}}{2} = \frac{2 \pm \sqrt{-72}}{2}$$
$$= \frac{2 \pm \sqrt{-36 \cdot 2}}{2} = \frac{2 \pm 6\sqrt{2}i}{2}$$
$$= \frac{2(1 \pm 3\sqrt{2}i)}{2} = 1 \pm 3\sqrt{2}i$$

16.
$$2x^2 = 3 - 4x$$
$$2x^2 + 4x - 3 = 0$$
$$a = 2 \quad b = 4 \quad c = -3$$
$$x = \frac{-4 \pm \sqrt{4^2 - 4(2)(-3)}}{2(2)}$$
$$= \frac{-4 \pm \sqrt{16 + 24}}{4} = \frac{-4 \pm \sqrt{40}}{4}$$
$$= \frac{-4 \pm \sqrt{4 \cdot 10}}{4} = \frac{-4 \pm 2\sqrt{10}}{4}$$
$$= \frac{2(-2 \pm \sqrt{10})}{4} = \frac{-2 \pm \sqrt{10}}{2}$$

17.
$$x^2 - 4x + 13 = 0$$
$$a = 1 \quad b = -4 \quad c = 13$$
Find the discriminant.
$$b^2 - 4ac = (-4)^2 - 4(1)(13)$$
$$= 16 - 52 = -36$$

Since the discriminant is negative, there are two imaginary solutions that are complex conjugates.

18.
$$9x^2 = 2 - 3x$$
$$9x^2 + 3x - 2 = 0$$
$$a = 9 \quad b = 3 \quad c = -2$$
Find the discriminant.
$$b^2 - 4ac = 3^2 - 4(9)(-2) = 9 + 72 = 81$$
Since the discriminant is greater than zero, there are two unequal real solutions. Also, since the discriminant is a perfect square, the solutions are rational.

19.
$$2x^2 + 4x = 3$$
$$2x^2 + 4x - 3 = 0$$
$$a = 2 \quad b = 4 \quad c = -3$$
Find the discriminant.
$$b^2 - 4ac = 4^2 - 4(2)(-3) = 16 + 24 = 40$$
Since the discriminant is greater than zero, there are two unequal real solutions.

20.
$$2x^2 - 11x + 5 = 0$$
$$(2x - 1)(x - 5) = 0$$

$$2x - 1 = 0 \quad \text{and} \quad x - 5 = 0$$
$$2x = 1 \qquad\qquad x = 5$$
$$x = \frac{1}{2}$$

21.
$$(3x + 5)(x - 3) = 5$$
$$3x^2 - 9x + 5x - 15 = 5$$
$$3x^2 - 4x - 15 = 5$$
$$3x^2 - 4x - 20 = 0$$
$$a = 3 \quad b = -4 \quad c = -20$$
$$x = \frac{-(-4) \pm \sqrt{(-4)^2 - 4(3)(-20)}}{2(3)}$$
$$= \frac{4 \pm \sqrt{16 + 240}}{6} = \frac{4 \pm \sqrt{256}}{6}$$
$$= \frac{4 \pm 16}{6} = \frac{4 - 16}{6} \quad \text{or} \quad \frac{4 + 16}{6}$$
$$= \frac{-12}{6} \quad \text{or} \quad \frac{20}{6} = -2 \text{ or } \frac{10}{3}$$

22.
$$3x^2 - 7x + 1 = 0$$
$$a = 3 \quad b = -7 \quad c = 1$$
$$x = \frac{-(-7) \pm \sqrt{(-7)^2 - 4(3)(1)}}{2(3)}$$
$$= \frac{7 \pm \sqrt{49 - 12}}{6} = \frac{7 \pm \sqrt{37}}{6}$$

23.
$$x^2 - 9 = 0$$
$$x^2 = 9$$
$$x = \pm 3$$

24.
$$(x - 3)^2 - 8 = 0$$
$$(x - 3)^2 = 8$$
$$x - 3 = \pm\sqrt{8}$$
$$x = 3 \pm \sqrt{4 \cdot 2} = 3 \pm 2\sqrt{2}$$

25.
$$3x^2 - x + 2 = 0$$
$$a = 3 \quad b = -1 \quad c = 2$$
$$x = \frac{-(-1) \pm \sqrt{(-1)^2 - 4(3)(2)}}{2(3)}$$
$$= \frac{1 \pm \sqrt{1 - 24}}{6} = \frac{1 \pm \sqrt{-23}}{6} = \frac{1}{6} \pm \frac{\sqrt{23}}{6}i$$

26.

$$\frac{5}{x+1}+\frac{x-1}{4}=2$$

$$4(x+1)\left(\frac{5}{x+1}+\frac{x-1}{4}\right)=4(x+1)(2)$$

$$20+(x+1)(x-1)=8x+8$$

$$20+x^2-1=8x+8$$

$$x^2-8x+11=0$$

$$a=1 \quad b=-8 \quad c=11$$

$$x=\frac{-(-8)\pm\sqrt{(-8)^2-4(1)(11)}}{2(1)}$$

$$=\frac{8\pm\sqrt{64-44}}{2}=\frac{8\pm\sqrt{20}}{2}=\frac{8\pm\sqrt{4\cdot 5}}{2}$$

$$=\frac{8\pm 2\sqrt{5}}{2}=\frac{2(4\pm\sqrt{5})}{2}=4\pm\sqrt{5}$$

27.

$$x=-\frac{1}{3} \quad \text{or} \quad x=\frac{3}{5}$$

$$x+\frac{1}{3}=0 \qquad x-\frac{3}{5}=0$$

$$3x+1=0 \qquad 5x-3=0$$

$$(3x+1)(5x-3)=0$$

$$15x^2-9x+5x-3=0$$

$$15x^2-4x-3=0$$

28.

$$x=-9i \quad \text{or} \quad x=9i$$

$$x+9i=0 \qquad x-9i=0$$

$$(x+9i)(x-9i)=0$$

$$x^2-81i^2=0$$

$$x^2-81(-1)=0$$

$$x^2+81=0$$

29.

$$x=-4\sqrt{3} \quad \text{or} \quad x=4\sqrt{3}$$

$$x+4\sqrt{3}=0 \qquad x-4\sqrt{3}=0$$

$$(x+4\sqrt{3})(x-4\sqrt{3})=0$$

$$x^2-(4\sqrt{3})^2=0$$

$$x^2-16\cdot 3=0$$

$$x^2-48=0$$

30.

$$13=0.2x^2-1.2x+2$$

$$0=0.2x^2-1.2x-11$$

$$a=0.2 \quad b=-1.2 \quad c=-11$$

$$x=\frac{-(-1.2)\pm\sqrt{(-1.2)^2-4(0.2)(-11)}}{2(0.2)}$$

$$=\frac{1.2\pm\sqrt{1.44+8.8}}{0.4}=\frac{1.2\pm\sqrt{10.24}}{0.4}$$

$$=\frac{1.2\pm 3.2}{0.4}=\frac{1.2-3.2}{0.4} \quad \text{or} \quad \frac{1.2+3.2}{0.4}$$

$$=\frac{-2}{0.4} \quad \text{or} \quad \frac{4.4}{0.4}=-5 \text{ or } 11$$

We disregard –5 because we cannot have a negative time measurement. The solution is 11 and we conclude that the infection rate will be 11 PCs per month for every 1000 PCs in the year 1990 + 11 = 2001.

31.

$$0=-16t^2+140t+3$$

$$a=-16 \quad b=140 \quad c=3$$

$$=\frac{-140\pm\sqrt{19,600+192}}{-32}$$

$$=\frac{-140\pm\sqrt{19,792}}{-32}=\frac{-140\pm 140.7}{-32}$$

$$=\frac{-140-140.7}{-32} \quad \text{or} \quad \frac{-140+140.7}{-32}$$

$$=\frac{-280.7}{-32} \quad \text{or} \quad \frac{0.7}{-32}=8.8 \text{ or } -0.02$$

We disregard –0.02 because we cannot have a negative time measurement. The solution is 8.8 and we conclude that the ball will hit the ground in 8.8 seconds.

32. Vertex: $(h,k)=(-1,4)$

Axis of symmetry: $x=-1$

x–intercepts:

$$0=-(x+1)^2+4$$

$$-4=-(x+1)^2$$

$$4=(x+1)^2$$

$$x+1=\sqrt{4} \quad \text{or} \quad x+1=-\sqrt{4}$$

$$x+1=2 \qquad x+1=-2$$

$$x=1 \qquad x=-3$$

y–intercept:

$$y=-(0+1)^2+4=-(1)^2+4=-1+4=3$$

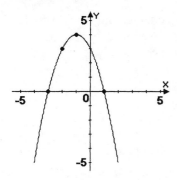

33. Vertex: $(h,k) = (-4,-2)$

Axis of symmetry: $x = -4$

x–intercepts:

$0 = (x+4)^2 - 2$

$2 = (x+4)^2$

$x + 4 = \sqrt{2}$ or $x + 4 = -\sqrt{2}$

$\quad x = -4 + \sqrt{2}$ $\qquad x = -4 - \sqrt{2}$

y–intercept:

$y = (0+4)^2 - 2 = 4^2 - 2 = 16 - 2 = 14$

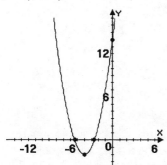

34. Vertex:

$-\dfrac{b}{2a} = -\dfrac{2}{2(-1)} = -\dfrac{2}{-2} = 1$

$f(1) = -1^2 + 2(1) + 3 = -1 + 2 + 3 = 4$

The vertex is (1, 4).

x–intercepts:

$0 = -x^2 + 2x + 3$

$0 = x^2 - 2x - 3$

$0 = (x-3)(x+1)$

$x - 3 = 0$ or $x + 1 = 0$

$\quad x = 3$ $\qquad\quad x = -1$

y–intercept:

$y = -0^2 + 2(0) + 3 = 0 + 0 + 3 = 3$

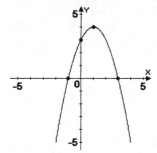

35. Vertex:

$-\dfrac{b}{2a} = -\dfrac{-4}{2(2)} = -\dfrac{-4}{4} = 1$

$f(1) = 2(1)^2 - 4(1) - 6 = 2(1) - 4 - 6$

$\qquad = 2 - 4 - 6 = -8$

The vertex is $(1,-8)$.

x–intercepts:

$0 = 2x^2 - 4x - 6$

$0 = x^2 - 2x - 3$

$0 = (x-3)(x+1)$

$x - 3 = 0$ or $x + 1 = 0$

$\quad x = 3$ $\qquad\quad x = -1$

y–intercept:

$y = 2(0)^2 - 4(0) - 6 = 2(0) - 0 - 6$

$\qquad = 0 - 0 - 6 = -6$

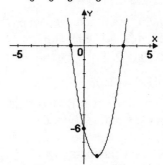

36. $x = -\dfrac{b}{2a} = -\dfrac{1}{2(-0.02)} = -\dfrac{1}{-0.04} = 25$

The maximum growth occurs when 25 inches of rain falls. The maximum growth is

$$f(25) = -0.02(25)^2 + 25 + 1$$
$$= -0.02(625) + 25 + 1$$
$$= -12.5 + 25 + 1 = 13.5.$$

A maximum yearly growth of 13.5 inches occurs when 25 inches of rainfalls per year.

37. $x = -\dfrac{b}{2a} = -\dfrac{400}{2(-16)} = -\dfrac{400}{-32} = 12.5$

At 12.5 seconds, the rocket reaches its maximum height. The maximum height is

$$s(12.5) = -16(12.5)^2 + 400(12.5) + 40$$
$$= -16(156.25) + 5000 + 40$$
$$= -2500 + 5000 + 40 = 2540.$$

The rocket reaches a maximum height of 2540 feet in 12.5 seconds.

38. According to the graph, the maximum is (20, 5.4). This means that the maximum divorce rate of 5.4 divorces per 1000 people occurred in the year $1960 + 20 = 1980$.

39. $A(x) = x(100 - 2x) = -2x^2 + 100x$

Since $a = -2$ is negative, we know the function opens downward and has a maximum at

$$x = -\frac{b}{2a} = -\frac{100}{2(-2)} = -\frac{100}{-4} = 25.$$

The maximum area is achieved when the width is 25 yards. The maximum area is

$$A(25) = 25(100 - 2(25)) = 25(100 - 50)$$
$$= 25(50) = 1250.$$

The area is maximized at 1250 square yards when the width is 25 yards.

40. Let x = one of the numbers
Let $14 + x$ = the other number
$$P(x) = x(14 + x) = 14x + x^2 = x^2 + 14x.$$
The minimum is at
$$x = -\frac{b}{2a} = -\frac{14}{2(1)} = -\frac{14}{2} = -7.$$
The other number is $14 + x = 14 + (-7) = 7.$

The numbers that minimize the product are -7 and 7. The minimum product is $-7 \cdot 7 = -49.$

41. Let $t = x^2$.
$$x^4 - 6x^2 + 8 = 0$$
$$(x^2)^2 - 6x^2 + 8 = 0$$
$$t^2 - 6t + 8 = 0$$
$$(t - 4)(t - 2) = 0$$
$$t - 4 = 0 \quad \text{or} \quad t - 2 = 0$$
$$t = 4 \qquad\qquad t = 2$$
Replace t by x^2.
$$x^2 = 4 \quad \text{or} \quad x^2 = 2$$
$$x = \pm 2 \qquad x = \pm\sqrt{2}$$

42. Let $t = \sqrt{x}$.
$$x + 7\sqrt{x} - 8 = 0$$
$$(\sqrt{x})^2 + 7\sqrt{x} - 8 = 0$$
$$t^2 + 7t - 8 = 0$$
$$(t + 8)(t - 1) = 0$$
$$t + 8 = 0 \quad \text{or} \quad t - 1 = 0$$
$$t = -8 \qquad\qquad t = 1$$
Replace t by $\sqrt{x}$.
$$\cancel{\sqrt{x} = -8} \quad \text{or} \quad \sqrt{x} = 1$$
$$x = 1$$

We disregard -8 because the square root of x cannot be a negative number. The solution, 1, checks.

43. Let $t = x^2 + 2x$.
$$(x^2 + 2x)^2 - 14(x^2 + 2x) = 15$$
$$(x^2 + 2x)^2 - 14(x^2 + 2x) - 15 = 0$$
$$t^2 - 14t - 15 = 0$$
$$(t - 15)(t + 1) = 0$$
$$t - 15 = 0 \quad \text{or} \quad t + 1 = 0$$
$$t = 15 \qquad\qquad t = -1$$
Replace t by $x^2 + 2x$.
First, consider $t = 15$.

$$x^2 + 2x = 15$$
$$x^2 + 2x - 15 = 0$$
$$(x+5)(x-3) = 0$$
$$x+5 = 0 \quad \text{or} \quad x-3 = 0$$
$$x = -5 \qquad\qquad x = 3$$

Next, consider $t = -1$.

$$x^2 + 2x = -1$$
$$x^2 + 2x + 1 = 0$$
$$(x+1)^2 = 0$$
$$x+1 = 0$$
$$x = -1$$

The solutions are $-5, -1,$ and 3.

44. Let $t = x^{-1}$.

$$x^{-2} + x^{-1} - 56 = 0$$
$$\left(x^{-1}\right)^2 + x^{-1} - 56 = 0$$
$$t^2 + t - 56 = 0$$
$$(t+8)(t-7) = 0$$
$$t+8 = 0 \quad \text{or} \quad t-7 = 0$$
$$t = -8 \qquad\qquad t = 7$$

Replace t by x^{-1}.

$$x^{-1} = -8 \quad \text{or} \quad x^{-1} = 7$$
$$\frac{1}{x} = -8 \qquad\qquad \frac{1}{x} = 7$$
$$-8x = 1 \qquad\qquad 7x = 1$$
$$x = -\frac{1}{8} \qquad\qquad x = \frac{1}{7}$$

45. Let $t = x^{\frac{1}{3}}$.

$$x^{\frac{2}{3}} - x^{\frac{1}{3}} - 12 = 0$$
$$\left(x^{\frac{1}{3}}\right)^2 - x^{\frac{1}{3}} - 12 = 0$$
$$t^2 - t - 12 = 0$$
$$(t-4)(t+3) = 0$$

$$t-4 = 0 \quad \text{or} \quad t+3 = 0$$
$$t = 4 \qquad\qquad t = -3$$

Replace t by $x^{\frac{1}{3}}$.

$$x^{\frac{1}{3}} = 4 \quad \text{or} \quad x^{\frac{1}{3}} = -3$$
$$\left(x^{\frac{1}{3}}\right)^3 = 4^3 \qquad \left(x^{\frac{1}{3}}\right)^3 = (-3)^3$$
$$x = 64 \qquad\qquad x = -27$$

46. Let $t = x^{\frac{1}{4}}$.

$$x^{\frac{1}{2}} + 3x^{\frac{1}{4}} - 10 = 0$$
$$\left(x^{\frac{1}{4}}\right)^2 + 3x^{\frac{1}{4}} - 10 = 0$$
$$t^2 + 3t - 10 = 0$$
$$(t+5)(t-2) = 0$$
$$t+5 = 0 \quad \text{or} \quad t-2 = 0$$
$$t = -5 \qquad\qquad t = 2$$

Replace t by $x^{\frac{1}{4}}$.

$$x^{\frac{1}{4}} = -5 \quad \text{or} \quad x^{\frac{1}{4}} = 2$$
$$\cancel{\sqrt[4]{x} = -5} \qquad \left(x^{\frac{1}{4}}\right)^4 = 2^4$$
$$x = 16$$

We disregard -5 because the fourth root of x cannot be a negative number.
We need to check the solution, 16, because both sides of the equation were raised to an even power. The solution checks.

47. Solve the related quadratic equation.

$$2x^2 + 5x - 3 = 0$$
$$(2x-1)(x+3) = 0$$

$$2x - 1 = 0 \quad \text{or} \quad x + 3 = 0$$
$$2x = 1 \qquad\qquad x = -3$$
$$x = \frac{1}{2}$$

The boundary points are -3 and $\dfrac{1}{2}$.

Test Interval	Test Number	Test	Conclusion
$(-\infty,-3)$	-4	$2(-4)^2+5(-4)-3<0$ $9<0,$ false	$(-\infty,-3)$ does not belong to the solution set.
$\left(-3,\dfrac{1}{2}\right)$	0	$2(0)^2+5(0)-3<0$ $-3<0,$ true	$\left(-3,\dfrac{1}{2}\right)$ belongs to the solution set.
$\left(\dfrac{1}{2},\infty\right)$	1	$2(1)^2+5(1)-3<0$ $4<0,$ false	$\left(\dfrac{1}{2},\infty\right)$ does not belong to the solution set.

The solution set is $\left(-3,\dfrac{1}{2}\right)$ or $\left\{x\middle|-3<x<\dfrac{1}{2}\right\}$.

48. Solve the related quadratic equation.
$$2x^2+9x+4=0$$
$$(2x+1)(x+4)=0$$
$$2x+1=0 \quad \text{or} \quad x+4=0$$
$$2x=-1 \qquad\qquad x=-4$$
$$x=-\dfrac{1}{2}$$

The boundary points are -4 and $-\dfrac{1}{2}$.

Test Interval	Test Number	Test	Conclusion
$(-\infty,-4]$	-5	$2(-5)^2+9(-5)+4\geq0$ $9\geq0,$ true	$(-\infty,-4]$ belongs to the solution set.
$\left[-4,-\dfrac{1}{2}\right]$	-1	$2(-1)^2+9(-1)+4\geq0$ $-3\geq0,$ false	$\left[-4,-\dfrac{1}{2}\right]$ does not belong to the solution set.
$\left[-\dfrac{1}{2},\infty\right)$	0	$2(0)^2+9(0)+4\geq0$ $4\geq0,$ true	$\left[-\dfrac{1}{2},\infty\right)$ belongs to the solution set.

The solution set is $(-\infty,-4]\cup\left[-\dfrac{1}{2},\infty\right)$ or $\left\{x\middle|x\leq-4 \text{ or } x\geq-\dfrac{1}{2}\right\}$.

49. $\dfrac{x-6}{x+2}>0$
$$x-6=0 \qquad x+2=0$$
$$x=6 \qquad\quad x=-2$$
The boundary points are -2 and 6.

Test Interval	Test Number	Test	Conclusion
$(-\infty, -2)$	-3	$\dfrac{-3-6}{-3+2} > 0$ $9 > 0$, true	$(-\infty, -2)$ belongs to the solution set.
$(-2, 6)$	0	$\dfrac{0-6}{0+2} > 0$ $-3 > 0$, false	$(-2, 6)$ does not belong to the solution set.
$(6, \infty)$	7	$\dfrac{7-6}{7+2} > 0$ $\dfrac{1}{9} > 0$, true	$(6, \infty)$ belongs to the solution set.

The solution set is $(-\infty, -2) \cup (6, \infty)$ or $\{x | x < -2 \text{ or } x > 6\}$.

50.
$$\frac{x+3}{x-4} \le 5$$

$$\frac{x+3}{x-4} - 5 \le 0$$

$$\frac{x+3}{x-4} - \frac{5(x-4)}{x-4} \le 0$$

$$\frac{x+3-5(x-4)}{x-4} \le 0$$

$$\frac{x+3-5x+20}{x-4} \le 0$$

$$\frac{-4x+23}{x-4} \le 0$$

Find the values of x that make the numerator and denominator zero.

$-4x + 23 = 0 \quad$ and $\quad x - 4 = 0$

$\quad -4x = -23 \qquad\qquad x = 4$

$\quad x = \dfrac{23}{4}$

The boundary points are 4 and $\dfrac{23}{4}$.

Test Interval	Test Number	Test	Conclusion
$(-\infty, 4)$	0	$\dfrac{0+3}{0-4} \le 5$ $\dfrac{3}{-4} \le 5$, true	$(-\infty, 4)$ belongs to the solution set.
$\left(4, \dfrac{23}{4}\right]$	5	$\dfrac{5+3}{5-4} \le 5$ $8 \le 5$, false	$\left(4, \dfrac{23}{4}\right]$ does not belong to the solution set.

$\left[\dfrac{23}{4},\infty\right)$	6	$\dfrac{6+3}{6-4}\le 5$ $\dfrac{9}{2}\le 5$, true	$\left[\dfrac{23}{4},\infty\right)$ belongs to the solution set.

The solution set is $\left(-\infty,4\right)\cup\left[\dfrac{23}{4},\infty\right)$ or $\left\{x\,\middle|\,x<4 \text{ or } x\ge\dfrac{23}{4}\right\}$.

51. $-16t^2+48t>32$

Solve the related quadratic equation.

$$-16t^2+48t=32$$
$$-16t^2+48t-32=0$$
$$t^2-3t+2=0$$
$$(t-2)(t-1)=0$$
$$t-2=0 \quad \text{or} \quad t-1=0$$
$$t=2 \qquad\qquad t=1$$

The boundary points are 1 and 2.

Test Interval	Test Number	Test	Conclusion
$(0,1)$	0.5	$-16(0.5)^2+48(0.5)>32$ $20>32$, false	$(0,1)$ does not belong to the solution set.
$(1,2)$	1.5	$-16(1.5)^2+48(1.5)>32$ $36>32$, true	$(1,2)$ belongs to the solution set.
$(2,\infty)$	3	$-16(3)^2+48(3)>32$ $0>32$, false	$(2,\infty)$ does not belong to the solution set.

The solution set is $(1,2)$. This means that the ball will be more than 32 feet above the graph between 1 and 2 seconds.

52. a. $H(0)=\dfrac{15}{8}(0)^2-30(0)+200=\dfrac{15}{8}(0)-0+200=0-0+200=200$

The heart rate is 200 beats per minute immediately following the workout.

b.
$$\dfrac{15}{8}x^2-30x+200>110$$
$$\dfrac{15}{8}x^2-30x+90>0$$
$$\dfrac{8}{15}\left(\dfrac{15}{8}x^2-30x+90\right)>\dfrac{8}{15}(0)$$
$$x^2-\dfrac{8}{15}(30x)+\dfrac{8}{15}(90)>0$$
$$x^2-16x+48>0$$

$$(x-12)(x-4)>0$$
$$x-12=0 \quad \text{or} \quad x-4=0$$
$$x=12 \qquad x=4$$

The boundary points are 4 and 12.

Test Interval	Test Number	Test	Conclusion
$(0,4)$	1	$\dfrac{15}{8}(1)^2-30(1)+200>110$ $171\dfrac{7}{8}>110$, true	$(0,4)$ belongs to the solution set.
$(4,12)$	5	$\dfrac{15}{8}(5)^2-30(5)+200>110$ $96\dfrac{7}{8}>110$, false	$(4,\infty)$ does not belong to the solution set.
$(12,\infty)$	13	$\dfrac{15}{8}(13)^2-30(13)+200>110$ $126\dfrac{7}{8}>110$, false	$(12,\infty)$ does not belong to the solution set.

The solution set is $(0,4)\cup(12,\infty)$. This means that the heart rate exceeds 110 beats per minute between 0 and 4 minutes and more than 12 minutes after the workout. Between 0 and 4 minutes provides a more realistic answer since it is unlikely that the heart rate will begin to climb again without further exertion. Model breakdown occurs for the interval $(12,\infty)$.

Chapter 11 Test

1.
$$2x^2-5=0$$
$$2x^2=5$$
$$x^2=\frac{5}{2}$$
$$x=\pm\sqrt{\frac{5}{2}}$$

Rationalize the denominators.
$$x=\pm\frac{\sqrt{5}}{\sqrt{2}}\cdot\frac{\sqrt{2}}{\sqrt{2}}=\pm\frac{\sqrt{10}}{2}$$

2.
$$(x-3)^2=20$$
$$x-3=\pm\sqrt{20}$$
$$x=3\pm\sqrt{4\cdot5}=3\pm2\sqrt{5}$$

3.
$$\left(\frac{b}{2}\right)^2=\left(\frac{-16}{2}\right)^2=(-8)^2=64$$
$$x^2-16x+64=(x-8)^2$$

4.
$$\left(\frac{b}{2}\right)^2=\left(\frac{\frac{2}{5}}{2}\right)^2=\left(\frac{2}{5}\div2\right)^2$$
$$=\left(\frac{2}{5}\cdot\frac{1}{2}\right)^2=\left(\frac{1}{5}\right)^2=\frac{1}{25}$$
$$x^2+\frac{2}{5}x+\frac{1}{25}=\left(x+\frac{1}{5}\right)^2$$

5.
$$x^2-6x+7=0$$
$$x^2-6x=-7$$
$$x^2-6x+9=-7+9$$
$$(x-3)^2=2$$
$$x-3=\pm\sqrt{2}$$
$$x=3\pm\sqrt{2}$$

6.
$$50^2 + 50^2 = x^2$$
$$2500 + 2500 = x^2$$
$$5000 = x^2$$
$$\pm\sqrt{5000} = x$$
$$\pm\sqrt{2500 \cdot 2} = x$$
$$\pm 50\sqrt{2} = x$$

The solutions are $\pm 50\sqrt{2}$ feet. We disregard $-50\sqrt{2}$ feet because we can't have a negative length measurement. The width of the pond is $50\sqrt{2}$ feet.

7. $a = 3$ $b = 4$ $c = -2$
$$b^2 - 4ac = 4^2 - 4(3)(-2) = 16 + 24 = 40$$
Since the discriminant is greater than zero, there are two unequal real solutions.

8.
$$x^2 = 4x - 8$$
$$x^2 - 4x + 8 = 0$$
$$a = 1 \quad b = -4 \quad c = 8$$
$$b^2 - 4ac = (-4)^2 - 4(1)(8)$$
$$= 16 - 32 = -16$$
Since the discriminant is negative, there are two imaginary solutions that are complex conjugates.

9.
$$2x^2 + 9x = 5$$
$$2x^2 + 9x - 5 = 0$$
$$(2x - 1)(x + 5) = 0$$
$$2x - 1 = 0 \quad \text{and} \quad x + 5 = 0$$
$$2x = 1 \qquad\qquad x = -5$$
$$x = \frac{1}{2}$$

10. $a = 1$ $b = 8$ $c = 5$
$$x = \frac{-8 \pm \sqrt{8^2 - 4(1)(5)}}{2(1)}$$
$$= \frac{-8 \pm \sqrt{64 - 20}}{2} = \frac{-8 \pm \sqrt{44}}{2}$$
$$= \frac{-8 \pm \sqrt{4 \cdot 11}}{2} = \frac{-8 \pm 2\sqrt{11}}{2}$$
$$= \frac{2\left(-4 \pm \sqrt{11}\right)}{2} = -4 \pm \sqrt{11}$$

11.
$$(x + 2)^2 + 25 = 0$$
$$(x + 2)^2 = -25$$
$$x + 2 = \pm\sqrt{-25}$$
$$x = -2 \pm 5i$$

12. $a = 2$ $b = -6$ $c = 5$
$$x = \frac{-(-6) \pm \sqrt{(-6)^2 - 4(2)(5)}}{2(2)}$$
$$= \frac{6 \pm \sqrt{36 - 40}}{4} = \frac{6 \pm \sqrt{-4}}{4}$$
$$= \frac{6 \pm 2i}{4} = \frac{2(3 \pm i)}{4}$$
$$= \frac{3 \pm i}{2} = \frac{3}{2} \pm \frac{1}{2}i$$

13. $x = -3$ or $x = 7$
$$x + 3 = 0 \qquad x - 7 = 0$$
$$(x + 3)(x - 7) = 0$$
$$x^2 - 7x + 3x - 21 = 0$$
$$x^2 - 4x - 21 = 0$$

14. $x = -10i$ or $x = 10i$
$$x + 10i = 0 \qquad x - 10i = 0$$
$$(x + 10i)(x - 10i) = 0$$
$$x^2 - 100i^2 = 0$$
$$x^2 - 100(-1) = 0$$
$$x^2 + 100 = 0$$

15.
$$20 = -0.5x^2 + 4x + 19$$
$$0 = -0.5x^2 + 4x - 1$$
$$a = -0.5 \quad b = 4 \quad c = -1$$
$$x = \frac{-4 \pm \sqrt{4^2 - 4(-0.5)(-1)}}{2(-0.5)}$$
$$= \frac{-4 \pm \sqrt{16 - 2}}{-1} = \frac{-4 \pm \sqrt{14}}{-1}$$
$$= \frac{-4 - \sqrt{14}}{-1} \text{ or } \frac{-4 + \sqrt{14}}{-1}$$
$$= \frac{-4 - 3.7}{-1} \text{ or } \frac{-4 + 3.7}{-1}$$

$$= \frac{-7.7}{-1} \text{ or } \frac{-0.3}{-1} = 7.7 \text{ or } 0.3$$

$$\approx 8 \text{ or } 0$$

In the years 1900 and 1998, 20 million people received food stamps.

16. Vertex: $(h,k) = (-1,4)$

Axis of symmetry: $x = -1$

x–intercepts:

$$0 = (x+1)^2 + 4$$
$$-4 = (x+1)^2$$

Since the solution are complex, there are no x–intercepts.

y–intercept:

$$y = (0+1)^2 + 4 = (1)^2 + 4 = 1 + 4 = 5$$

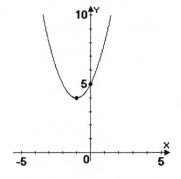

17. Vertex:

$$-\frac{b}{2a} = -\frac{-2}{2(1)} = -\frac{-2}{2} = 1$$

$$f(1) = 1^2 - 2(1) - 3 = 1 - 2 - 3 = -4$$

The vertex is $(1,-4)$.

x–intercepts:

$$0 = x^2 - 2x - 3$$
$$0 = (x-3)(x+1)$$
$$x - 3 = 0 \quad \text{or} \quad x + 1 = 0$$
$$x = 3 \qquad\qquad x = -1$$

The x–intercepts are -1 and 3.

y–intercept:

$$y = 0^2 - 2(0) - 3 = 0 - 0 - 3 = -3$$

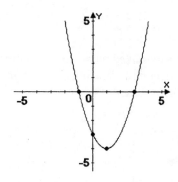

18. Since $a = -16$ is negative, we know the function opens downward and has a maximum at

$$x = -\frac{b}{2a} = -\frac{64}{2(-16)} = -\frac{64}{-32} = 2.$$

The ball reaches its maximum height a two seconds. The maximum height is

$$s(2) = -16(2)^2 + 64(2) + 5$$
$$= -16(4) + 128 + 5 = -64 + 128 + 5 = 69.$$

The baseball reaches a maximum height of 69 feet after 2 seconds.

19. $0 = -16t^2 + 64t + 5$

$$a = -16 \quad b = 64 \quad c = 5$$

$$x = \frac{-64 \pm \sqrt{64^2 - 4(-16)(5)}}{2(-16)}$$

$$= \frac{-64 \pm \sqrt{4096 + 320}}{-32} = \frac{-64 \pm \sqrt{4416}}{-32}$$

$$= \frac{-64 - 66.5}{-32} \quad \text{or} \quad \frac{-64 + 66.5}{-32}$$

$$= \frac{-130.5}{-32} \quad \text{or} \quad \frac{2.5}{-32} \approx 4.1 \text{ or } -0.1$$

We disregard -0.1 since we cannot have a negative time measurement. The solution is 4.1 and we conclude that the baseball hits the ground in approximately 4.1 seconds.

20. Since $a = -1$ is negative, we know the function opens downward and has a maximum at

$$x = -\frac{b}{2a} = -\frac{46}{2(-1)} = -\frac{46}{-2} = 23.$$

Profit is maximized when 23 computers are manufactured. The maximum profit is

$$f(23) = -23^2 + 46(23) - 360$$
$$= -529 + 1058 - 360 = 169.$$

23 computers should be manufactured each day. This produces a profit of 169 hundreds or $16,900.

21. Let $t = 2x - 5$.
$$(2x-5)^2 + 4(2x-5) + 3 = 0$$
$$t^2 + 4t + 3 = 0$$
$$(t+3)(t+1) = 0$$
$$t + 3 = 0 \quad \text{or} \quad t + 1 = 0$$
$$t = -3 \qquad\qquad t = -1$$
Replace t by $2x - 5$.
$$2x - 5 = -3 \quad \text{or} \quad 2x - 5 = -1$$
$$2x = 2 \qquad\qquad 2x = 4$$
$$x = 1 \qquad\qquad x = 2$$

22. Let $t = x^2$.
$$x^4 - 13x^2 + 36 = 0$$
$$(x^2)^2 - 13x^2 + 36 = 0$$
$$t^2 - 13t + 36 = 0$$
$$(t-9)(t-4) = 0$$
$$t - 9 = 0 \quad \text{or} \quad t - 4 = 0$$
$$t = 9 \qquad\qquad t = 4$$
Replace t by x^2.
$$x^2 = 9 \quad \text{or} \quad x^2 = 4$$
$$x = \pm 3 \qquad\qquad x = \pm 2$$

23. Let $t = x^{1/3}$.
$$x^{2/3} - 9x^{1/3} + 8 = 0$$
$$(x^{1/3})^2 - 9x^{1/3} + 8 = 0$$
$$t^2 - 9t + 8 = 0$$
$$(t-8)(t-1) = 0$$
$$t - 8 = 0 \quad \text{or} \quad t - 1 = 0$$
$$t = 8 \qquad\qquad t = 1$$
Replace t by $x^{1/3}$.
$$x^{1/3} = 8 \quad \text{or} \quad x^{1/3} = 1$$
$$(x^{1/3})^3 = 8^3 \qquad (x^{1/3})^3 = 1^3$$
$$x = 512 \qquad\qquad x = 1$$

24. Solve the related quadratic equation.
$$x^2 - x - 12 - 0$$
$$(x-4)(x+3) = 0$$
$$x - 4 = 0 \quad \text{or} \quad x + 3 = 0$$
$$x = 4 \qquad\qquad x = -3$$
The boundary points are −3 and 4.

Test Interval	Test Number	Test	Conclusion
$(-\infty, -3)$	-4	$(-4)^2 - (-4) - 12 < 0$ $8 < 0$, false	$(-\infty, -3)$ does not belong to the solution set.
$(-3, 4)$	0	$0^2 - 0 - 12 < 0$ $-12 < 0$, true	$(-3, 4)$ belongs to the solution set.
$(4, \infty)$	5	$5^2 - 5 - 12 < 0$ $8 < 0$, false	$(4, \infty)$ does not belong to the solution set.

The solution set is $(-3, 4)$ or $\{x | -3 < x < 4\}$.

-3   4

25.

$$\frac{2x+1}{x-3} \le 3$$

$$\frac{2x+1}{x-3} - 3 \le 0$$

$$\frac{2x+1}{x-3} - \frac{3(x-3)}{x-3} \le 0$$

$$\frac{2x+1-3(x-3)}{x-3} \le 0$$

$$\frac{2x+1-3x+9}{x-3} \le 0$$

$$\frac{-x+10}{x-3} \le 0$$

Find the values of x that make the numerator and denominator zero.

$$-x+10=0 \quad \text{and} \quad x-3=0$$
$$-x=-10 \qquad\qquad x=3$$
$$x=10$$

The boundary points are 3 and 10. We exclude 3 from the solution set(s), since this would make the denominator zero.

Test Interval	Test Number	Test	Conclusion
$(-\infty,3)$	0	$\dfrac{2(0)+1}{0-3} \le 3$ $-\dfrac{1}{3} \le 3$, true	$(-\infty,3)$ belongs to the solution set.
$(3,10]$	4	$\dfrac{2(4)+1}{4-3} \le 3$ $9 \le 3$, false	$(3,10]$ does not belong to the solution set.
$[10,\infty)$	11	$\dfrac{2(10)+1}{10-3} \le 3$ $3 \le 3$, true	$[10,\infty)$ belongs to the solution set.

The solution set is $(-\infty,3)\cup[10,\infty)$ or $\{x|x<3 \text{ or } x\ge 10\}$.

Cumulative Review Exercises
Chapters 1-11

1.
$$8-(4x-5)=x-7$$
$$8-4x+5=x-7$$
$$13-4x=x-7$$
$$13=5x-7$$
$$20=5x$$
$$4=x$$

2. Multiply the first equation by 2 and solve by addition.

$$10x+8y= \ \ 44$$
$$\underline{3x-8y=-18}$$
$$13x=26$$
$$x=2$$

Back-substitute 2 for x to find y.

$$5(2)+4y=22$$
$$10+4y=22$$

$$4y = 12$$
$$y = 3$$

The solution is $(2,3)$.

3. Multiply the second equation by 2 and add to the first equation to eliminate y.

$$-3x + 2y + 4z = 6$$
$$\underline{14x - 2y + 6z = 46}$$
$$11x + 10z = 52$$

Multiply the second equation by 3 and add to the second equation to eliminate y.

$$21x - 3y + 9z = 69$$
$$\underline{2x + 3y + z = 7}$$
$$23x + 10z = 76$$

The system of two variables in two equations is as follows.

$$11x + 10z = 52$$
$$23x + 10z = 76$$

Multiply the first equation by -1 and add to the second equation.

$$-11x - 10z = -52$$
$$\underline{23x + 10z = 76}$$
$$12x = 24$$
$$x = 2$$

Back-substitute 2 for x to find z.

$$11(2) + 10z = 52$$
$$22 + 10z = 52$$
$$10z = 30$$
$$z = 3$$

Back-substitute 2 for x and 3 for z to find y.

$$-3(2) + 2y + 4(3) = 6$$
$$-6 + 2y + 12 = 6$$
$$2y + 6 = 6$$
$$2y = 0$$
$$y = 0$$

The solution is $(2,0,3)$.

4. $|x - 1| > 3$

$$x - 1 < -3 \quad \text{or} \quad x - 1 > 3$$
$$x < -2 \qquad\qquad x > 4$$

The solution set is $\{x | x < -2 \ \text{and} \ x > 4\}$ or $(-\infty, -2) \cup (4, \infty)$.

5. $\sqrt{x+4} - \sqrt{x-4} = 2$

$$\sqrt{x+4} = 2 + \sqrt{x-4}$$
$$\left(\sqrt{x+4}\right)^2 = \left(2 + \sqrt{x-4}\right)^2$$
$$x + 4 = 4 + 4\sqrt{x-4} + x - 4$$
$$\cancel{x} + 4 = 4\sqrt{x-4} + \cancel{x}$$
$$4 = 4\sqrt{x-4}$$
$$1 = \sqrt{x-4}$$
$$1^2 = \left(\sqrt{x-4}\right)^2$$
$$1 = x - 4$$
$$5 = x$$

6. $x - 4 \geq 0 \quad \text{and} \quad -3x \leq -6$

$$x \geq 4 \qquad\qquad x \geq 2$$

$$x \geq 4 \quad \text{and} \quad x \geq 2$$

The solution set is $\{x | x \geq 4\}$ or $[4, \infty)$.

7. $$2x^2 = 3x - 2$$
$$2x^2 - 3x + 2 = 0$$
$$a = 2 \qquad b = -3 \qquad c = 2$$
$$x = \frac{-(-3) \pm \sqrt{(-3)^2 - 4(2)(2)}}{2(2)}$$
$$= \frac{3 \pm \sqrt{9 - 16}}{4} = \frac{3 \pm \sqrt{-7}}{4}$$
$$= \frac{3 \pm \sqrt{7}i}{4} = \frac{3}{4} \pm \frac{\sqrt{7}}{4}i$$

8. $3x = 15 + 5y$

x–intercept	y–intercept
$3x = 15 + 5(0)$	$3(0) = 15 + 5y$
$3x = 15$	$0 = 15 + 5y$
$x = 5$	$-15 = 5y$
	$-3 = y$

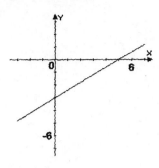

9. $2x - 3y > 6$

Graph the corresponding line,
$2x - 3y = 6$.

x–intercept	y–intercept
$2x - 3(0) = 6$	$2(0) - 3y = 6$
$2x = 6$	$-3y = 6$
$x = 3$	$y = -2$

Use a test point to determine shading.

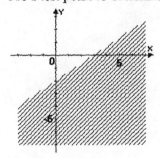

10. $f(x) = -\dfrac{1}{2}x + 1$

$m = -\dfrac{1}{2}$ $y - \text{intercept} = 1$

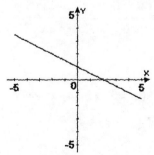

Vertex:

$-\dfrac{b}{2a} = -\dfrac{6}{2(1)} = -\dfrac{6}{2} = -3$

$f(-3) = (-3)^2 + 6(-3) + 8$
$= 9 - 18 + 8 = -1$

The vertex is $(-3, -1)$.

x–intercepts:
$0 = x^2 + 6x + 8$
$0 = (x + 4)(x + 2)$

$x + 4 = 0$ or $x + 2 = 0$
$x = -4$ $x = -2$

The x–intercepts are -4 and -2.

y–intercept:
$y = 0^2 + 6(0) + 8 = 0 + 0 + 8 = 8$

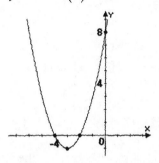

12. Vertex: $(h, k) = (3, -4)$

Axis of symmetry is $x = 3$
x–intercepts:
$0 = (x - 3)^2 - 4$
$4 = (x - 3)^2$

$x - 3 = -2$ and $x - 3 = 2$
$x = 1$ $x = 5$

The x–intercepts are 1 and 5.
y–intercept:
$y = (0 - 3)^2 - 4 = (-3)^2 - 4 = 9 - 4 = 5$

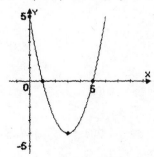

13.
$$\begin{vmatrix} 3 & 1 & 0 \\ 0 & 5 & -6 \\ -2 & -1 & 0 \end{vmatrix}$$

$$= 3\begin{vmatrix} 5 & -6 \\ -1 & 0 \end{vmatrix} - 0\begin{vmatrix} 1 & 0 \\ -1 & 0 \end{vmatrix} + (-2)\begin{vmatrix} 1 & 0 \\ 5 & -6 \end{vmatrix}$$

$$= 3\big(5(0) - (-1)(-6)\big) + (-2)\big(1(-6) - 5(0)\big)$$

$$= 3(-6) + (-2)(-6) = -18 + 12 = -6$$

14.
$$\frac{x - \dfrac{1}{3}}{3 - \dfrac{1}{x}} = \frac{3x}{3x} \cdot \frac{x - \dfrac{1}{3}}{3 - \dfrac{1}{x}} = \frac{3x \cdot x - 3x \cdot \dfrac{1}{3}}{3x \cdot 3 - 3x \cdot \dfrac{1}{x}}$$

$$= \frac{3x^2 - x}{9x - 3} = \frac{x(3x - 1)}{3(3x - 1)} = \frac{x}{3}$$

15. $2x + y = 10$
$$\qquad y = -2x + 10$$

$m = -2$

Since the lines are perpendicular, the slope

will be $\dfrac{1}{2}$.

point-slope form:

$$y - 4 = \frac{1}{2}\big(x - (-2)\big)$$

$$y - 4 = \frac{1}{2}(x + 2)$$

slope-intercept form:

$$y - 4 = \frac{1}{2}x + 1$$

$$y = \frac{1}{2}x + 5$$

$$f(x) = \frac{1}{2}x + 5$$

16. $\dfrac{-5x^3 y^7}{15x^4 y^{-2}} = \dfrac{-y^7 y^2}{3x} = \dfrac{-y^9}{3x} = -\dfrac{y^9}{3x}$

17. $\big(4x^2 - 5y\big)^2 = \big(4x^2\big)^2 + 2\big(4x^2\big)(-5y) + (-5y)^2$
$$= 16x^4 - 40x^2 y + 26y^2$$

18.
$$\begin{array}{r} x^2 - 5x + 1 \\ 5x+1{\overline{\smash{\big)}\,5x^3 - 24x^2 + 0x + 9}} \end{array}$$
$$\underline{5x^3 + \ \ x^2}$$
$$-25x^2 + 0x$$
$$\underline{-25x^2 - 5x}$$
$$5x + 9$$
$$\underline{5x + 1}$$
$$8$$

$$\frac{5x^3 - 24x^2 + 9}{5x + 1} = x^2 - 5x + 1 + \frac{8}{5x + 1}$$

19.
$$\frac{\sqrt[3]{32xy^{10}}}{\sqrt[3]{2xy^2}} = \sqrt[3]{\frac{32xy^{10}}{2xy^2}} = \sqrt[3]{16y^8}$$

$$= \sqrt[3]{8 \cdot 2y^6 y^2} = 2y^2 \sqrt[3]{2y^2}$$

20.
$$\frac{x+2}{x^2 - 6x + 8} + \frac{3x - 8}{x^2 - 5x + 6}$$

$$= \frac{x+2}{(x-4)(x-2)} + \frac{3x-8}{(x-2)(x-3)}$$

$$= \frac{(x+2)(x-3)}{(x-4)(x-2)(x-3)} + \frac{(3x-8)(x-4)}{(x-4)(x-2)(x-3)}$$

$$= \frac{(x+2)(x-3) + (3x-8)(x-4)}{(x-4)(x-2)(x-3)}$$

$$= \frac{x^2 - 3x + 2x - 6 + 3x^2 - 12x - 8x + 32}{(x-4)(x-2)(x-3)}$$

$$= \frac{4x^2 - 21x + 26}{(x-4)(x-2)(x-3)}$$

$$= \frac{(4x-13)(x-2)}{(x-4)(x-2)(x-3)} = \frac{4x-13}{(x-4)(x-3)}$$

21. $x^4 - 4x^3 + 8x - 32$
$$= x^3(x-4) + 8(x-4) = (x-4)\big(x^3 + 8\big)$$
$$= (x-4)(x+2)\big(x^2 - 2x + 4\big)$$

22. $2x^2 + 12xy + 18y^2 = 2\big(x^2 + 6xy + 9y^2\big)$
$$= 2(x+3y)^2$$

23. Let x = the width of the carpet
Let $2x + 4$ = the length of the carpet
$$x(2x + 4) = 48$$
$$2x^2 + 4x = 48$$
$$2x^2 + 4x - 48 = 0$$
$$x^2 + 2x - 24 = 0$$
$$(x + 6)(x - 4) = 0$$
$$x + 6 = 0 \quad \text{and} \quad x - 4 = 0$$
$$x = -6 \qquad\qquad x = 4$$

We disregard –6 because we can't have a negative length measurement. The width of the carpet is 4 feet and the length of the carpet is $2x + 4 = 2(4) + 4 = 8 + 4 = 12$ feet.

$$\frac{20}{15 + x} = \frac{10}{15 - x}$$
$$20(15 - x) = 10(15 + x)$$
$$300 - 20x = 150 + 10x$$
$$300 = 150 + 30x$$
$$150 = 30x$$
$$5 = x$$

The rate of the current is 5 miles per hour.

24.

	Part Done in 1 Hour	Time Working Together	Part Done in x Hours
You	$\dfrac{1}{2}$	x	$\dfrac{x}{2}$
Your Sister	$\dfrac{1}{3}$	x	$\dfrac{x}{3}$

$$\frac{x}{2} + \frac{x}{3} = 1$$
$$6\left(\frac{x}{2}\right) + 6\left(\frac{x}{3}\right) = 6(1)$$
$$3x + 2x = 6$$
$$5x = 6$$
$$x = \frac{6}{5}$$

If you and your sister work together, it will take $\dfrac{6}{5}$ hours or 1 hour and 12 minutes to clean the house.

25.

	d	r	$t = \dfrac{d}{r}$
Down Stream	20	$15 + x$	$\dfrac{20}{15 + x}$
Up Stream	10	$15 - x$	$\dfrac{10}{15 - x}$

EXPONENTIAL AND LOGARITHMIC FUNCTIONS

Exponential Functions

12.1 CHECK POINTS

CHECK POINT 1

$$f(60) = 13.49(0.967)^{60} - 1$$
$$= 13.49(0.13353) - 1 \approx 0.8$$

Approximately one O-ring is expected to fail.

CHECK POINT 2

x	$f(x)$
-3	$3^{-3} = \dfrac{1}{3^3} = \dfrac{1}{27}$
-2	$3^{-2} = \dfrac{1}{3^2} = \dfrac{1}{9}$
-1	$3^{-1} = \dfrac{1}{3^1} = \dfrac{1}{3}$
0	$3^0 = 1$
1	$3^1 = 3$
2	$3^2 = 9$
3	$3^3 = 27$

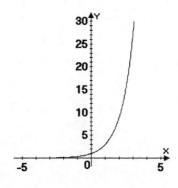

CHECK POINT 3

$$f(x) = \left(\frac{1}{3}\right)^x$$

x	$f(x) = \left(\dfrac{1}{3}\right)^x$ or 3^{-x}
-3	$3^{-(-3)} = 3^3 = 27$
-2	$3^{-(-2)} = 3^2 = 9$
-1	$3^{-(-1)} = 3^1 = 3$
0	$3^{-(0)} = 3^0 = 1$
1	$3^{-(1)} = 3^{-1} = \dfrac{1}{3}$
2	$3^{-(2)} = 3^{-2} = \dfrac{1}{3^2} = \dfrac{1}{9}$
3	$3^{-(3)} = 3^{-3} = \dfrac{1}{3^3} = \dfrac{1}{27}$

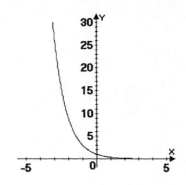

CHECK POINT 4

$$f(x) = 3^x \text{ and } g(x) = 3^{x-1}$$

x	$f(x)$	$g(x)$
-2	$\dfrac{1}{9}$	$\dfrac{1}{27}$
-1	$\dfrac{1}{3}$	$\dfrac{1}{9}$
0	1	$\dfrac{1}{3}$
1	3	1
2	9	3

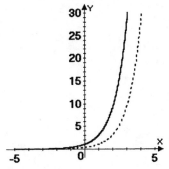

The graph of g is the graph of f shifted 1 unit to the right.

CHECK POINT 5

$f(x) = 2^x$ and $g(x) = 2^x + 3$

x	$f(x)$	$g(x)$
-2	$\dfrac{1}{4}$	$3\dfrac{1}{4}$
-1	$\dfrac{1}{2}$	$3\dfrac{1}{2}$
0	1	4
1	2	5
2	4	7

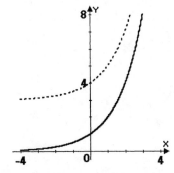

The graph of g is the graph of f shifted up 3 units.

CHECK POINT 6

$f(50) = 6e^{0.013(50)} = 6e^{0.65} \approx 11.49$

In 2050, the world population will be approximately 11.49 billion.

CHECK POINT 7

a.
$$A = 10,000\left(1 + \frac{0.08}{4}\right)^{4(5)}$$
$$= 10,000(1 + 0.02)^{20}$$

$$= 10,000(1.02)^{20} = 14859.47$$

The balance in the account is \$14859.47 after 5 years of quarterly compounding.

b. $A = 10,000e^{0.08(5)} = 10,000e^{0.4} = 14918.25$

The balance in the account is \$14918.25 after 5 years of continuous compounding.

EXERCISE SET 12.1

1. $2^{3.4} = 10.556$

3. $3^{\sqrt{5}} = 11.665$

5. $4^{-1.5} = 0.125$

7. $e^{2.3} = 9.974$

9. $e^{-0.95} = 0.387$

11. $f(x) = 3^x$

x	$f(x)$
-2	$3^{-2} = \dfrac{1}{3^2} = \dfrac{1}{9}$
-1	$3^{-1} = \dfrac{1}{3^1} = \dfrac{1}{3}$
0	$3^0 = 1$
1	$3^1 = 3$
2	$3^2 = 9$

This functions matches graph (**d**).

13. $f(x) = 3^x - 1$

x	$f(x)$
-2	$3^{-2} - 1 = \dfrac{1}{3^2} - 1 = \dfrac{1}{9} - 1 = -\dfrac{8}{9}$
-1	$3^{-1} - 1 = \dfrac{1}{3^1} - 1 = \dfrac{1}{3} - 1 = -\dfrac{2}{3}$
0	$3^0 - 1 = 1 - 1 = 0$
1	$3^1 - 1 = 3 - 1 = 2$
2	$3^2 - 1 = 9 - 1 = 8$

This functions matches graph (**e**).

15. $f(x) = 3^{-x}$

x	$f(x)$
-2	$3^{-(-2)} = 3^2 = 9$

-1	$3^{-(-1)} = 3^1 = 3$
0	$3^{-(0)} = 3^0 = 1$
1	$3^{-(1)} = 3^{-1} = \dfrac{1}{3}$
2	$3^{-(2)} = 3^{-2} = \dfrac{1}{3^2} = \dfrac{1}{9}$

This functions matches graph (**f**).

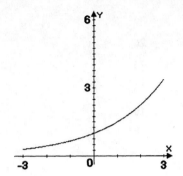

17. $f(x) = 4^x$

x	$f(x)$
-2	$4^{-2} = \dfrac{1}{4^2} = \dfrac{1}{16}$
-1	$4^{-1} = \dfrac{1}{4^1} = \dfrac{1}{4}$
0	$4^0 = 1$
1	$4^1 = 4$
2	$4^2 = 16$

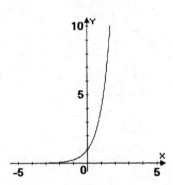

21. $h(x) = \left(\dfrac{1}{2}\right)^x$

x	$h(x)$
-2	$\left(\dfrac{1}{2}\right)^{-2} = \left(\dfrac{2}{1}\right)^2 = \dfrac{4}{1} = 4$
-1	$\left(\dfrac{1}{2}\right)^{-1} = \left(\dfrac{2}{1}\right)^1 = \dfrac{2}{1} = 2$
0	$\left(\dfrac{1}{2}\right)^0 = 1$
1	$\left(\dfrac{1}{2}\right)^1 = \dfrac{1}{2}$
2	$\left(\dfrac{1}{2}\right)^2 = \dfrac{1}{4}$

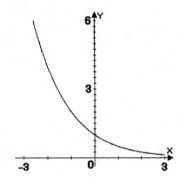

19. $g(x) = \left(\dfrac{3}{2}\right)^x$

x	$g(x)$
-2	$\left(\dfrac{3}{2}\right)^{-2} = \left(\dfrac{2}{3}\right)^2 = \dfrac{4}{9}$
-1	$\left(\dfrac{3}{2}\right)^{-1} = \left(\dfrac{2}{3}\right)^1 = \dfrac{2}{3}$
0	$\left(\dfrac{3}{2}\right)^0 = 1$
1	$\left(\dfrac{3}{2}\right)^1 = \dfrac{3}{2}$
2	$\left(\dfrac{3}{2}\right)^2 = \dfrac{9}{4}$

23. $f(x) = (0.6)^x = \left(\dfrac{6}{10}\right)^x = \left(\dfrac{3}{5}\right)^x$

x	$f(x)$
-2	$\left(\dfrac{3}{5}\right)^{-2} = \left(\dfrac{5}{3}\right)^2 = \dfrac{25}{9}$
-1	$\left(\dfrac{3}{5}\right)^{-1} = \left(\dfrac{5}{3}\right)^1 = \dfrac{5}{3}$
0	$\left(\dfrac{3}{5}\right)^0 = 1$

| 1 | $\left(\dfrac{3}{5}\right)^1 = \dfrac{3}{5}$ |
| 2 | $\left(\dfrac{3}{5}\right)^2 = \dfrac{9}{25}$ |

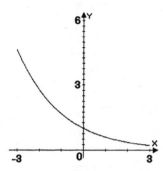

25. $f(x) = 2^x$ and $g(x) = 2^{x+1}$

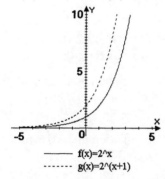

The graph of g is the graph of f shifted 1 unit to the left.

27. $f(x) = 2^x$ and $g(x) = 2^{x-2}$

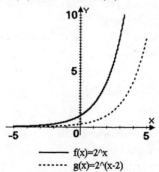

The graph of g is the graph of f shifted 2 units to the right.

29. $f(x) = 2^x$ and $g(x) = 2^x + 1$

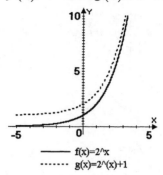

The graph of g is the graph of f shifted up 1 unit.

31. $f(x) = 2^x$ and $g(x) = 2^x - 2$

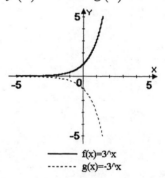

The graph of g is the graph of f shifted down 2 units.

33. $f(x) = 3^x$ and $g(x) = -3^x$

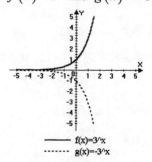

The graph of g is the graph of f reflected across the x–axis.

35. $f(x) = 2^x$ and $g(x) = 2^{x+1} - 1$

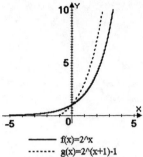

     —— f(x)=2^x
     ······· g(x)=2^(x+1)-1

The graph of g is the graph of f shifted 1 unit down and 1 unit to the left.

37. $f(x) = 3^x$ and $g(x) = \dfrac{1}{3} \cdot 3^x$

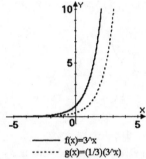

     —— f(x)=3^x
     ······· g(x)=(1/3)(3^x)

The graph of g is the graph of f compressed vertically by $\dfrac{1}{3}$.

39.   **a.**
$$A = 10,000\left(1 + \frac{0.055}{2}\right)^{2(5)}$$
$$= 10,000(1 + 0.0275)^{10}$$
$$= 10,000(1.0275)^{10} = 13116.51$$

The balance in the account is $13,116.51 after 5 years of semiannual compounding.

     b.
$$A = 10,000\left(1 + \frac{0.055}{12}\right)^{12(5)}$$
$$= 10,000(1 + 0.0046)^{60}$$
$$= 10,000(1.0046)^{60} = 13157.04$$

The balance in the account is $13,157.04 after 5 years of monthly compounding.

c.
$$A = Pe^{rt} = 10,000e^{0.055(5)}$$
$$= 10,000e^{0.275} = 13165.31$$

The balance in the account is $13,165.31 after 5 years of continuous compounding.

41.   Monthly Compounding
$$A = 12,000\left(1 + \frac{0.07}{12}\right)^{12(3)}$$
$$= 10,000(1 + 0.0058)^{36}$$
$$= 10,000(1.0058)^{36} = 12329.24$$

Continuous Compounding
$$A = 12,000e^{0.0685(3)}$$
$$= 10,000e^{0.2055} = 12281.39$$

Monthly compounding at 7% yields the greatest return.

43.   **a.** $f(0) = 67.38(1.026)^0$
$$= 67.38(1) = 67.38$$

Mexico's population in 1980 was 67.38 million.

     b. $f(27) = 67.38(1.026)^{27} \approx 134.74$ Mexico's population in 2007 will be 134.74 million.

     c. $f(54) = 67.38(1.026)^{54} \approx 269.46$ Mexico's population in 2034 will be 269.46 million.

     d. $f(81) = 67.38(1.026)^{81} \approx 538.85$ Mexico's population in 2061 will be 538.85 million.

     e.   Mexico's population doubles every 27 years.

45. $S = 65,000(1 + 0.06)^{10}$
$$= 65,000(1.06)^{10} = 116,405.10$$

In 10 years, the house will be worth $116,405.10.

47. $2^{1.7} = 3.249009585$
$$2^{1.73} = 3.317278183$$
$$2^{1.732} = 3.321880096$$

$2^{1.73205} = 3.321995226$

$2^{1.7320508} = 3.321997068$

$2^{\sqrt{3}} = 3.321997085$

As the number of decimal places in the approximation of $\sqrt{3}$ in the exponent increases, the value of the expression approaches $2^{\sqrt{3}}$.

49. $f(11) = 24000e^{0.21(11)} = 24000e^{2.31}$
$\qquad = 241786.1917$

Eleven years after 1989, in the year 2000, there were approximately 241,786 cases of AIDS in the US among intravenous drug users.

51. **a.** $f(0) = 80e^{-0.5(0)} + 20$
$\qquad = 80e^0 + 20 = 80(1) + 20$
$\qquad = 80 + 20 = 100$

100% of information is remembered at the moment it is first learned.

b. $f(1) = 80e^{-0.5(1)} + 20 = 80e^{-0.5} + 20$
$\qquad = 48.522 + 20 = 68.522$

Approximately 68.5% of information is remembered after one week.

c. $f(4) = 80e^{-0.5(4)} + 20 = 80e^{-2} + 20$
$\qquad = 10.827 + 20 = 30.827$

Approximately 30.8% of information is remembered after four weeks.

d. $f(52) = 80e^{-0.5(52)} + 20 = 80e^{-26} + 20$
$\qquad = (4.087 \times 10^{-10}) + 20 \approx 20$

Approximately 20% of information is remembered after one year.
(4.087×10^{-10} will be eliminated in rounding.)

53. $f(30) = \dfrac{90}{1 + 270e^{-0.122(30)}}$
$\qquad = \dfrac{90}{1 + 270e^{-3.66}} = \dfrac{90}{1 + 6.948}$
$\qquad = \dfrac{90}{7.948} \approx 11.3$

Approximately 11.3% of 30-year-olds have some coronary heart disease.

55. **a.** $N(0) = \dfrac{30,000}{1 + 20e^{-1.5(0)}} = \dfrac{30,000}{1 + 20e^0}$
$\qquad = \dfrac{30,000}{1 + 20(1)} = \dfrac{30,000}{1 + 20}$
$\qquad = \dfrac{30,000}{21} \approx 1428.6$

Approximately 1429 people became ill with the flu when the epidemic began.

b. $N(3) = \dfrac{30,000}{1 + 20e^{-1.5(3)}} = \dfrac{30,000}{1 + 20e^{-4.5}}$
$\qquad = \dfrac{30,000}{1 + .22218} = \dfrac{30,000}{1.22218}$
$\qquad \approx 24546$

Approximately 24,546 people became ill with the flu by the end of the third week.

c. The epidemic cannot grow indefinitely because there are a limited number of people that can become ill. Because there are 30,000 people in the town, the limit is 30,000.

For Exercises 57-61, answers may vary.

63.

Graph **(a)** is $y = \left(\dfrac{1}{3}\right)^x$.

Graph **(b)** is $y = \left(\dfrac{1}{5}\right)^x$.

Graph **(c)** is $y = 5^x$.

Graph **(d)** is $y = 3^x$.

Answers will vary. A base between 0 and 1 will rise to the left and a base greater than 1 will rise to the right.

65.

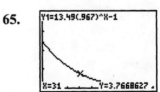

At 31°F, the number of O-rings expected to fail is between 3 and 4. It is extremely unlikely that NASA would have allowed the launch if they had been using the model.

67. a.

$$Q(t) = 10000\left(1 + \frac{0.05}{4}\right)^{4t}$$

$$M(t) = 10000\left(1 + \frac{0.045}{12}\right)^{12t}$$

b.

The bank paying 5% compounded quarterly offers a better return.

Review Exercises

69.

$$\frac{2x+3}{x^2 - 7x + 12} - \frac{2}{x-3}$$

$$= \frac{2x+3}{(x-3)(x-4)} - \frac{2}{x-3}$$

$$= \frac{2x+3}{(x-3)(x-4)} - \frac{2(x-4)}{(x-3)(x-4)}$$

$$= \frac{(2x+3) - 2(x-4)}{(x-3)(x-4)} = \frac{2x+3-2x+8}{(x-3)(x-4)}$$

$$= \frac{11}{(x-3)(x-4)}$$

70.

$$\begin{vmatrix} 3 & -2 \\ 7 & -5 \end{vmatrix} = 3(-5) - 7(-2) = -15 + 14 = -1$$

71.

$$x(x-3) = 10$$
$$x^2 - 3x = 10$$
$$x^2 - 3x - 10 = 0$$
$$(x-5)(x+2) = 0$$
$$x - 5 = 0 \quad \text{or} \quad x + 2 = 0$$
$$x = 5 \qquad\qquad x = -2$$

Composite and Inverse Functions

12.2 CHECK POINTS

CHECK POINT 1

a.
$$(f \circ g)(x) = f(g(x)) = f(x^2 - 1)$$
$$= 5(x^2 - 1) + 6 = 5x^2 - 5 + 6$$
$$= 5x^2 + 1$$

b.
$$(g \circ f)(x) = g(f(x))$$
$$= g(5x + 6) = (5x + 6)^2 - 1$$
$$= 25x^2 + 60x + 36 - 1$$
$$= 25x^2 + 60x + 35$$

CHECK POINT 2

$$f(g(x)) = f\left(\frac{x}{7}\right) = 7\left(\frac{x}{7}\right) = x$$

$$g(f(x)) = g(7x) = \frac{7x}{7} = x$$

The functions are inverses.

CHECK POINT 3

$$f(g(x)) = f\left(\frac{x+7}{4}\right) = 4\left(\frac{x+7}{4}\right) - 7$$
$$= (x+7) - 7 = x + 7 - 7 = x$$

$$g(f(x)) = g(4x - 7) = \frac{(4x-7)+7}{4}$$
$$= \frac{4x - 7 + 7}{4} = \frac{4x}{4} = x$$

The functions are inverses.

CHECK POINT 4

$$y = 2x + 7$$

Interchange x and y.

$$x = 2y + 7$$
$$x - 7 = 2y$$
$$\frac{x-7}{2} = y$$
$$f^{-1}(x) = \frac{x-7}{2}$$

CHECK POINT 5

$y = 4x^3 - 1$

Interchange x and y.

$$x = 4y^3 - 1$$

$$x + 1 = 4y^3$$

$$\frac{x+1}{4} = y^3$$

$$\sqrt[3]{\frac{x+1}{4}} = y$$

CHECK POINT 6

Graphs (**b**) and (**c**) satisfy the horizontal line test and have inverse functions.

CHECK POINT 7

Since the points $(-2,1), (0,0)$ and $(1,-1)$ lie on the graph of the function, the points $(1,-2), (0,0)$ and $(-1,1)$ lie on the inverse function.

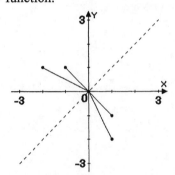

EXERCISE SET 12.2

1.   **a.** $(f \circ g)(x)$

        $= f(g(x)) = f(x + 7)$

        $= 2(x + 7) = 2x + 14$

   b. $(g \circ f)(x) = g(f(x)) = g(2x)$

                $= 2x + 7$

   c. $(f \circ g)(2) = 2(2) + 14$

               $= 4 + 14 = 18$

3.   **a.** $(f \circ g)(x) = f(g(x)) = f(2x + 1)$

             $= (2x + 1) + 4 = 2x + 5$

b. $(g \circ f)(x) = g(f(x))$

     $= g(x + 4) = 2(x + 4) + 1$

     $= 2x + 8 + 1 = 2x + 9$

c. $(f \circ g)(2) = 2(2) + 5 = 4 + 5 = 9$

5.   **a.** $(f \circ g)(x) = f(g(x))$

        $= f(5x^2 - 2) = 4(5x^2 - 2) - 3$

        $= 20x^2 - 8 - 3 = 20x^2 - 11$

   b. $(g \circ f)(x) = g(f(x))$

        $= g(4x - 3) = 5(4x - 3)^2 - 2$

        $= 5(16x^2 - 24x + 9) - 2$

        $= 80x^2 - 120x + 45 - 2$

        $= 80x^2 - 120x + 43$

   c. $(f \circ g)(2) = 20(2)^2 - 11$

        $= 20(4) - 11 = 80 - 11 = 69$

7.   **a.** $(f \circ g)(x) = f(g(x))$

        $= f(x^2 - 2) = (x^2 - 2)^2 + 2$

        $= x^4 - 4x^2 + 4 + 2 = x^4 - 4x^2 + 6$

   b. $(g \circ f)(x) = g(f(x))$

        $= g(x^2 + 2) = (x^2 + 2)^2 - 2$

        $= x^4 + 4x^2 + 4 - 2 = x^4 + 4x^2 + 2$

   c. $(f \circ g)(2) = 2^4 - 4(2)^2 + 6$

        $= 16 - 4(4) + 6 = 16 - 16 + 6 = 6$

9.   **a.** $(f \circ g)(x) = f(g(x))$

              $= f(x - 1) = \sqrt{x - 1}$

   b. $(g \circ f)(x) = g(f(x))$

              $= g(\sqrt{x}) = \sqrt{x} - 1$

   c. $(f \circ g)(2) = \sqrt{2 - 1} = \sqrt{1} = 1$

11. **a.**

    $(f \circ g)(x) = f(g(x)) = f\left(\dfrac{x+3}{2}\right)$

    $= 2\left(\dfrac{x+3}{2}\right) - 3 = x + 3 - 3 = x$

b. $(g \circ f)(x) = g(f(x)) = g(2x - 3)$

$= \dfrac{(2x-3)+3}{2} = \dfrac{2x-3+3}{2} = \dfrac{2x}{2} = x$

c. $(f \circ g)(2) = 2$

13. a. $(f \circ g)(x) = f(g(x)) = f\left(\dfrac{1}{x}\right)$

$= \dfrac{1}{\dfrac{1}{x}} = 1 \div \dfrac{1}{x} = 1 \cdot \dfrac{x}{1} = x$

b. $(g \circ f)(x) = g(f(x)) = g\left(\dfrac{1}{x}\right)$

$= \dfrac{1}{\dfrac{1}{x}} = 1 \div \dfrac{1}{x} = 1 \cdot \dfrac{x}{1} = x$

c. $(f \circ g)(2) = 2$

15. $f(g(x)) = f\left(\dfrac{x}{4}\right) = 4\left(\dfrac{x}{4}\right) = x$

$g(f(x)) = g(4x) = \dfrac{4x}{4} = x$

The functions are inverses.

17. $f(g(x)) = f\left(\dfrac{x-8}{3}\right) = 3\left(\dfrac{x-8}{3}\right) + 8$

$= x - 8 + 8 = x$

$g(f(x)) = g(3x+8) = \dfrac{(3x+8)-8}{3}$

$= \dfrac{3x+8-8}{3} = \dfrac{3x}{3} = x$

The functions are inverses.

19. $f(g(x)) = f\left(\dfrac{x+5}{9}\right) = 5\left(\dfrac{x+5}{9}\right) - 9$

$= \dfrac{5x+25}{9} - \dfrac{81}{9} = \dfrac{5x+25-81}{9} = \dfrac{5x-56}{9}$

Since $f(g(x)) \neq x$, we conclude the functions are not inverses.

21. $f(g(x)) = f\left(\dfrac{3}{x} + 4\right) = \dfrac{3}{\left(\dfrac{3}{x}+4\right)-4}$

$= \dfrac{3}{\dfrac{3}{x}+4-4} = \dfrac{3}{\dfrac{3}{x}} = 3 \div \dfrac{3}{x}$

$= 3 \cdot \dfrac{x}{3} = x$

$g(f(x)) = g\left(\dfrac{3}{x-4}\right) = \dfrac{3}{\dfrac{3}{x-4}} + 4$

$= 3 \div \dfrac{3}{x-4} + 4 = 3 \cdot \dfrac{x-4}{3} + 4$

$= x - 4 + 4 = x$

The functions are inverses.

23. $f(g(x)) = f(-x) = -(-x) = x$

$g(f(x)) = g(-x) = -(-x) = x$

The functions are inverses.

25. a. $y = x + 3$

Interchange x and y.

$x = y + 3$

$x - 3 = y$

$f^{-1}(x) = x - 3$

b. $f(f^{-1}(x)) = f(x-3) = (x-3) + 3$

$= x - 3 + 3 = x$

$f^{-1}(f(x)) = f(x+3) = (x+3) - 3$

$= x + 3 - 3 = x$

27. a. $y = 2x$

Interchange x and y.

$x = 2y$

$\dfrac{x}{2} = y$

$f^{-1}(x) = \dfrac{x}{2}$

b. $f(f^{-1}(x)) = f\left(\dfrac{x}{2}\right) = 2\left(\dfrac{x}{2}\right) = x$

$f^{-1}(f(x)) = f(2x) = \dfrac{2x}{2} = x$

29. a. $y = 2x + 3$

Interchange x and y.

$$x = 2y + 3$$
$$x - 3 = 2y$$
$$\frac{x-3}{2} = y$$
$$f^{-1}(x) = \frac{x-3}{2}$$

b.
$$f\left(f^{-1}(x)\right) = f\left(\frac{x-3}{2}\right)$$
$$= 2\left(\frac{x-3}{2}\right) + 3$$
$$= x - 3 + 3 = x$$
$$f^{-1}\left(f(x)\right) = f^{-1}(2x+3)$$
$$= \frac{(2x+3)-3}{2}$$
$$= \frac{2x+3-3}{2} = \frac{2x}{2} = x$$

31. a. $y = x^3 + 2$
Interchange x and y.
$$x = y^3 + 2$$
$$x - 2 = y^3$$
$$\sqrt[3]{x-2} = y$$
$$f^{-1}(x) = \sqrt[3]{x-2}$$

b.
$$f\left(f^{-1}(x)\right) = f\left(\sqrt[3]{x-2}\right)$$
$$= \left(\sqrt[3]{x-2}\right)^3 + 2$$
$$= x - 2 + 2 = x$$
$$f^{-1}\left(f(x)\right) = f^{-1}\left(x^3 + 2\right)$$
$$= \sqrt[3]{(x^3+2)-2}$$
$$= \sqrt[3]{x^3+2-2} = \sqrt[3]{x^3} = x$$

33. a. $y = (x+2)^3$
Interchange x and y.
$$x = (y+2)^3$$
$$\sqrt[3]{x} = \sqrt[3]{(y+2)^3}$$
$$\sqrt[3]{x} = y + 2$$
$$\sqrt[3]{x} - 2 = y$$
$$f^{-1}(x) = \sqrt[3]{x} - 2$$

b.
$$f\left(f^{-1}(x)\right) = f\left(\sqrt[3]{x} - 2\right)$$
$$= \left(\left(\sqrt[3]{x} - 2\right) + 2\right)^3$$
$$= \left(\sqrt[3]{x} - 2 + 2\right)^3$$
$$= \left(\sqrt[3]{x}\right)^3 = x$$
$$f^{-1}\left(f(x)\right) = f^{-1}\left((x+2)^3\right)$$
$$= \sqrt[3]{(x+2)^3} - 2$$
$$= x + 2 - 2 = x$$

35. a. $y = \frac{1}{x}$
Interchange x and y.
$$x = \frac{1}{y}$$
$$xy = 1$$
$$y = \frac{1}{x}$$
$$f^{-1}(x) = \frac{1}{x}$$

b.
$$f\left(f^{-1}(x)\right) = f\left(\frac{1}{x}\right) = \frac{1}{\frac{1}{x}}$$
$$= 1 \div \frac{1}{x} = 1 \cdot \frac{x}{1} = x$$
$$f^{-1}\left(f(x)\right) = f^{-1}\left(\frac{1}{x}\right) = \frac{1}{\frac{1}{x}}$$
$$= 1 \div \frac{1}{x} = 1 \cdot \frac{x}{1} = x$$

37. a. $y = \sqrt{x}$
Interchange x and y.
$$x = \sqrt{y}$$
$$x^2 = y$$
$$f^{-1}(x) = x^2$$

b.
$$f\left(f^{-1}(x)\right) = f\left(x^2\right) = \sqrt{x^2} = x$$
$$f^{-1}\left(f(x)\right) = f^{-1}\left(\sqrt{x}\right) = \left(\sqrt{x}\right)^2 = x$$

39. a. $y = x^2 + 1$
Interchange x and y.

$$x = y^2 + 1$$
$$x - 1 = y^2$$
$$\sqrt{x-1} = y$$
$$f^{-1}(x) = \sqrt{x-1}$$

b. $f\left(f^{-1}(x)\right) = f\left(\sqrt{x-1}\right)$

$$= \left(\sqrt{x-1}\right)^2 + 1$$
$$= x - 1 + 1 = x$$
$$f^{-1}(f(x)) = f^{-1}(x^2 + 1)$$
$$= \sqrt{(x^2 + 1) - 1}$$
$$= \sqrt{x^2 + 1 - 1} = \sqrt{x^2} = x$$

41. a. $y = \dfrac{2x+1}{x-3}$

Interchange x and y.

$$x = \frac{2y+1}{y-3}$$
$$x(y-3) = 2y+1$$
$$xy - 3x = 2y + 1$$
$$xy - 2y = 3x + 1$$
$$(x-2)y = 3x+1$$
$$y = \frac{3x+1}{x-2}$$
$$f^{-1}(x) = \frac{3x+1}{x-2}$$

b. $f\left(f^{-1}(x)\right) = f\left(\dfrac{3x+1}{x-2}\right)$

$$= \frac{2\left(\dfrac{3x+1}{x-2}\right)+1}{\left(\dfrac{3x+1}{x-2}\right)-3}$$
$$= \frac{x-2}{x-2} \cdot \frac{2\left(\dfrac{3x+1}{x-2}\right)+1}{\left(\dfrac{3x+1}{x-2}\right)-3}$$
$$= \frac{2(3x+1)+1(x-2)}{(3x+1)-3(x-2)}$$
$$= \frac{6x+2+x-2}{3x+1-3x+6}$$
$$= \frac{7x}{7} = x$$

$$f^{-1}(f(x)) = f^{-1}\left(\frac{2x+1}{x-3}\right)$$
$$= \frac{3\left(\dfrac{2x+1}{x-3}\right)+1}{\left(\dfrac{2x+1}{x-3}\right)-2}$$
$$= \frac{x-3}{x-3} \cdot \frac{3\left(\dfrac{2x+1}{x-3}\right)+1}{\left(\dfrac{2x+1}{x-3}\right)-2}$$
$$= \frac{3(2x+1)+1(x-3)}{(2x+1)-2(x-3)}$$
$$= \frac{6x+3+x-3}{2x+1-2x+6}$$
$$= \frac{7x}{7} = x$$

43. a. $y = \sqrt[3]{x-4} + 3$

Interchange x and y.

$$x = \sqrt[3]{y-4} + 3$$
$$x - 3 = \sqrt[3]{y-4}$$
$$(x-3)^3 = y - 4$$
$$(x-3)^3 + 4 = y$$
$$f^{-1}(x) = (x-3)^3 + 4$$

b. $f\left(f^{-1}(x)\right) = f\left((x-3)^3 + 4\right)$

$$= \sqrt[3]{\left((x-3)^3 + 4\right) - 4} + 3$$
$$= \sqrt[3]{(x-3)^3 + 4 - 4} + 3$$
$$= \sqrt[3]{(x-3)^3} + 3$$
$$= x - 3 + 3 = x$$

$$f^{-1}(f(x)) = f^{-1}\left(\sqrt[3]{x-4} + 3\right)$$
$$= \left(\left(\sqrt[3]{x-4} + 3\right) - 3\right)^3 + 4$$
$$= \left(\sqrt[3]{x-4} + 3 - 3\right)^3 + 4$$
$$= \left(\sqrt[3]{x-4}\right)^3 + 4$$
$$= x - 4 + 4 = x$$

45. The graph does not satisfy the horizontal line test so the function does not have an inverse.

47. The graph does not satisfy the horizontal line test so the function does not have an inverse.

49. The graph satisfies the horizontal line test so the function has an inverse.

51.

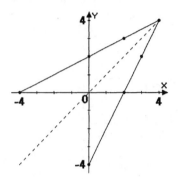

53.

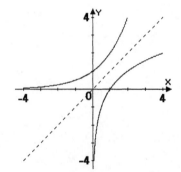

55. **a.** f is the regular price of the computer less $400.
g is 75% of the regular price of the computer.

b. $(f \circ g)(x) = f(g(x))$
$= f(0.75x) = 0.75x - 400$
$f \circ g$ represents 75% f the regular price of the computer less $400.

c. $(g \circ f)(x)$
$= g(f(x)) = g(x - 400)$
$= 0.75(x - 400) = 0.75x - 300$
$g \circ f$ represents 75% of the regular price of the computer less $300.

d. $f \circ g$ models the greater discount. It is a savings of $100 over $g \circ f$.

e. $y = x - 400$
Interchange x and y.
$x = y - 400$
$x + 400 = y$
$f^{-1}(x) = x + 400$
f^{-1} models the regular price of the computer plus $400.

57. **a.** We know that f has an inverse because it satisfies the horizontal line test.

b. $f^{-1}(0.25)$ or 15 represents the number of people who must be in a room so that the probability of 2 sharing a birthday would be 25%.
$f^{-1}(0.5)$ or 23 represents the number of people who must be in a room so that the probability of 2 sharing a birthday would be 50%.
$f^{-1}(0.7)$ or 30 represents the number of people who must be in a room so that the probability of 2 sharing a birthday would be 70%.

59. Because the graph does not satisfy the vertical line test, it does not have an inverse function. This means that we cannot use age at first marriage to predict year.

For Exercises 61-67, answers may vary.

69. Answers will vary. One example is $f(x) = \sqrt{x+5}$ and $g(x) = 3x^2$.

71. $f(x) = \dfrac{3x-2}{5x-3}$

$y = \dfrac{3x-2}{5x-3}$

Interchange x and y.

$$x = \frac{3y-2}{5y-3}$$

$$x(5y-3) = 3y-2$$

$$5xy-3x = 3y-2$$

$$5xy-3y = 3x-2$$

$$y(5x-3) = 3x-2$$

$$y = \frac{3x-2}{5x-3}$$

$$f^{-1}(x) = \frac{3x-2}{5x-3}$$

73. $f(x) = x^2 - 1$

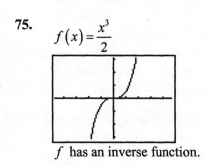

f does not have an inverse function.

75. $f(x) = \dfrac{x^3}{2}$

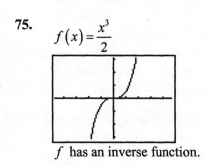

f has an inverse function.

77. $f(x) = |x-2|$

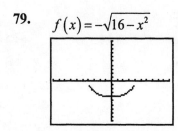

f does not have an inverse function.

79. $f(x) = -\sqrt{16-x^2}$

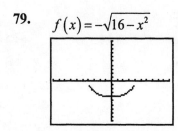

f does not have an inverse function.

81. $f(x) = 4x+4$ $g(x) = 0.25x - 1$

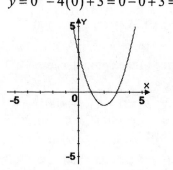

f and g are inverses.

83. $f(x) = \sqrt[3]{x} - 2$ $g(x) = (x+2)^3$

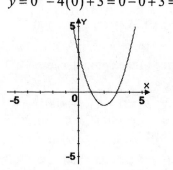

f and g are inverses.

Review Exercises

84.
$$\frac{4.3 \times 10^5}{8.6 \times 10^{-4}} = \frac{4.3}{8.6} \times \frac{10^5}{10^{-4}} = 0.5 \times 10^9$$
$$= 5 \times 10^{-1} \times 10^9 = 5 \times 10^8$$

85.
Vertex: $-\dfrac{b}{2a} = -\dfrac{-4}{2(1)} = -\dfrac{-4}{2} = 2$

$$f(2) = 2^2 - 4(2) + 3 = 4 - 8 + 3 = -1$$

The vertex is at $(2, -1)$.

x–intercepts:
$$0 = x^2 - 4x + 3$$
$$0 = (x-3)(x-1)$$
$$x - 3 = 0 \quad \text{or} \quad x - 1 = 0$$
$$x = 3 \qquad\qquad x = 1$$

y–intercept:
$$y = 0^2 - 4(0) + 3 = 0 - 0 + 3 = 3$$

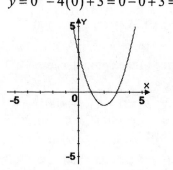

86.
$$\sqrt{x+4}-\sqrt{x-1}=1$$
$$\sqrt{x+4}=\sqrt{x-1}+1$$
$$\left(\sqrt{x+4}\right)^2=\left(\sqrt{x-1}+1\right)^2$$
$$x+4=x-1+2\sqrt{x-1}+1$$
$$x+4=x+2\sqrt{x-1}$$
$$4=2\sqrt{x-1}$$
$$2=\sqrt{x-1}$$
$$2^2=\left(\sqrt{x-1}\right)^2$$
$$4=x-1$$
$$5=x$$

Logarithmic Functions

12.3 CHECK POINTS

CHECK POINT 1
a. $7^3=x$
b. $b^2=25$
c. $4^y=26$

CHECK POINT 2
a. $5=\log_2 x$
b. $3=\log_b 27$
c. $y=\log_e 33$

CHECK POINT 3
a. $\log_{10}100=2$ because $10^2=100$
b. $\log_3 3=1$ because $3^1=3$
c. $\log_{36}6=\dfrac{1}{2}$ because $36^{\frac{1}{2}}=6$

CHECK POINT 4
a. $\log_9 9=1$ because $\log_b b=1$
b. $\log_8 1=0$ because $\log_b 1=0$

CHECK POINT 5
a. $\log_7 7^8=8$ because $\log_b b^x=x$
b. $3^{\log_3 17}=17$ because $b^{\log_b x}=x$

CHECK POINT 6

x	-2	-1	0	1	2	3
$f(x)$	$\dfrac{1}{9}$	$\dfrac{1}{3}$	1	3	9	27

x	$\dfrac{1}{9}$	$\dfrac{1}{3}$	1	3	9	27
$g(x)$	-2	-1	0	1	2	3

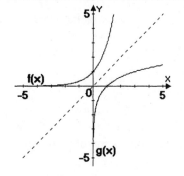

CHECK POINT 7
The domain of $h(x)=\log_4(x-5)$ is all values of x for which $x-5>0$.
$$x-5>0$$
$$x>5$$
The domain of h is $\{x|x>5\}$ or $(5,\infty)$.

CHECK POINT 8
$$h(10)=29+48.8\log(10+1)$$
$$=29+48.8\log 11\approx 79.8$$
A boy has reached approximately 80% of his adult height by age 10.

CHECK POINT 9
$$R=\log\frac{I}{I_0}=\log\frac{10,000I_0}{I_0}$$
$$=\log 10,000=\log 10^4=4$$
The magnitude on the Richter scale is 4.

CHECK POINT 10
a.
$$4-x>0$$
$$-x>-4$$
$$x<4$$
The domain of f is $\{x|x<4\}$ or $(-\infty,4)$.

b. The domain of g is all real numbers for which $x^2 > 0$. The only number that must be excluded is 0. The domain of f is $\{x \mid x \neq 0\}$ or $(-\infty, 0) \cup (0, \infty)$.

CHECK POINT 11

a. Because $\ln e^x = x$, we conclude that $\ln e^{25x} = 25x$.

b. Because $e^{\ln x} = x$, we conclude that $e^{\ln \sqrt{x}} = \sqrt{x}$.

CHECK POINT 12

$W = 0.35 \ln P + 2.74$

$\quad = 0.35 \ln 197 + 2.74 \approx 4.6$

The average walking speed in Jackson, Mississippi is approximately 4.6 feet per second.

EXERCISE SET 12.3

1. $4 = \log_2 16$

$\quad 2^4 = 16$

3. $2 = \log_3 x$

$\quad 3^2 = x$

5. $5 = \log_b 32$

$\quad b^5 = 32$

7. $\log_6 216 = y$

$\quad 6^y = 216$

9. $2^3 = 8$

$\quad \log_2 8 = 3$

11. $2^{-4} = \dfrac{1}{16}$

$\quad \log_2 \dfrac{1}{16} = -4$

13. $\sqrt[3]{8} = 2$

$\quad 8^{\frac{1}{3}} = 2$

$\log_8 2 = \dfrac{1}{3}$

15. $13^2 = x$

$\quad \log_{13} x = 2$

17. $b^3 = 1000$

$\quad \log_b 1000 = 3$

19. $7^y = 200$

$\quad \log_7 200 = y$

21. $\log_4 16 = y$

$\quad 4^y = 16$

$\quad 4^y = 4^2$

$\quad y = 2$

23. $\log_2 64 = y$

$\quad 2^y = 64$

$\quad 2^y = 2^6$

$\quad y = 6$

25. $\log_7 \sqrt{7} = y$

$\quad 7^y = \sqrt{7}$

$\quad 7^y = 7^{\frac{1}{2}}$

$\quad y = \dfrac{1}{2}$

27. $\log_2 \dfrac{1}{8} = y$

$\quad 2^y = \dfrac{1}{8}$

$\quad 2^y = \dfrac{1}{2^3}$

$\quad 2^y = 2^{-3}$

$\quad y = -3$

29. $\log_{64} 8 = y$

$\quad 64^y = 8$

$\quad 64^y = 64^{\frac{1}{2}}$

$\quad y = \dfrac{1}{2}$

31. $\log_5 5 = y$
$$5^y = 5^1$$
$$y = 1$$

33. $\log_4 1 = y$
$$4^y = 1$$
$$4^y = 4^0$$
$$y = 0$$

35. $\log_5 5^7 = y$
$$5^y = 5^7$$
$$y = 7$$

37. Since $b^{\log_b x} = x$, $8^{\log_8 19} = 19$.

39. $f(x) = 4^x$
$g(x) = \log_4 x$

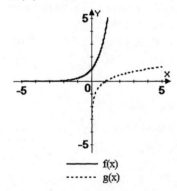

    ——— f(x)
    ······· g(x)

41. $f(x) = 5^x$
$g(x) = \log_5 x$

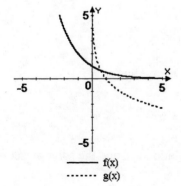

    ——— f(x)
    ······· g(x)

43. $x + 4 > 0$
$$x > -4$$
The domain of f is $\{x | x > -4\}$ or $(-4, \infty)$.

45. $2 - x > 0$
$$-x > -2$$
$$x < 2$$
The domain of f is $\{x | x < 2\}$ or $(-\infty, 2)$.

47. The domain of g is all real numbers for which $(x - 2)^2 > 0$. The only number that must be excluded is 2. The domain of f is $\{x | x \neq 2\}$ or $(-\infty, 2) \cup (2, \infty)$.

49. $\log 100 = y$
$$10^y = 100$$
$$10^y = 10^2$$
$$y = 2$$

51. $\log 10^7 = y$
$$10^y = 10^7$$
$$y = 7$$

53. Since $10^{\log x} = x$, $10^{\log 33} = 33$.

55. $\ln 1 = y$
$$e^y = 1$$
$$e^y = e^0$$
$$y = 0$$

57. Since $\ln e^x = x$, $\ln e^6 = 6$.

59. $\ln \dfrac{1}{e^6} = \ln e^{-6}$
Since $\ln e^x = x$, $\ln e^{-6} = -6$.

61. Since $e^{\ln x} = x$, $e^{\ln 125} = 125$.

63. Since $\ln e^x = x$, $\ln e^{9x} = 9x$.

65. Since $e^{\ln x} = x$, $e^{\ln 5x^2} = 5x^2$.

67. Since $10^{\log x} = x$, $10^{\log \sqrt{x}} = \sqrt{x}$.

69. $f(13) = 62 + 35\log(13 - 4)$
$= 62 + 35\log(9) \approx 95.4$

A 13-year-old girl is approximately 95.4% of her adult height.

71. $f(16) = 2.05 + 1.3\ln 16 \approx 5.7$

In 2000, approximately \$5.7 billion was spent on admission on spectator sports.

73. $D = 10\log\left(10^{12}\left(6.3 \times 10^{6}\right)\right)$
$= 10\log\left(6.3 \times 10^{18}\right) \approx 188.0$

The decibel level of a blue whale is approximately 188 decibels. At close range, the sound could rupture the human ear drum.

75.   a. $f(0) = 88 - 15\ln(0 + 1) = 88 - 15\ln(1) \approx 88$

The score on the original exam was 88%.

b. $f(2) = 88 - 15\ln(2 + 1)$
$= 88 - 15\ln(3) \approx 71.5$
$f(4) = 88 - 15\ln(4 + 1)$
$= 88 - 15\ln(5) \approx 63.9$
$f(6) = 88 - 15\ln(6 + 1)$
$= 88 - 15\ln(7) \approx 58.8$
$f(8) = 88 - 15\ln(8 + 1)$
$= 88 - 15\ln(9) \approx 55.0$
$f(10) = 88 - 15\ln(10 + 1)$
$= 88 - 15\ln(11) \approx 52.0$
$f(12) = 88 - 15\ln(12 + 1)$
$= 88 - 15\ln(13) \approx 49.5$

c.

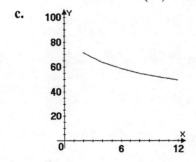

The students remembered less of the material over time.

For Exercises 77-83, answers may vary.

85. Statement **d.** is true. Recall: $b^{\log_b x} = x$.

Statement **a.** is false. To evaluate $\dfrac{\log_2 8}{\log_2 4}$, evaluate each term independently.

$\begin{array}{ll} \log_2 8 = y & \log_2 4 = y \\ \quad 2^y = 8 & \quad 2^y = 4 \\ \quad 2^y = 2^3 & \quad 2^y = 2^2 \\ \quad\; y = 3 & \quad\; y = 2 \end{array}$

Now substitute these values in the original expression.

$\dfrac{\log_2 8}{\log_2 4} = \dfrac{3}{2}$

Statement **b.** is false. We cannot take the log of a negative number.
Statement **c.** is false. The domain of $f(x) = \log_2 x$ is $(0, \infty)$.

87. $\log_4\left[\log_3\left(\log_2 x\right)\right] = 0$

Let $t = \log_3\left(\log_2 x\right)$.
$\log_4[t] = 0$
$\quad 4^0 = t$
$\quad\; 1 = t$

We now have $\log_3\left(\log_2 x\right) = 1$.

Let $u = \log_2 x$.
$\log_3(u) = 1$
$\quad 3^1 = u$
$\quad\; 3 = u$

We now have $\log_2 x = 3$.
$\log_2 x = 3$
$\quad 2^3 = x$
$\quad\; 8 = x$

The solution is 8 and the solution set is $\{8\}$.

89. $f(x) = \ln x \qquad g(x) = \ln(x+3)$

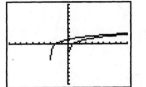

The graph of g is the graph of f shifted 3 units to the left.

91. $f(x) = \log x \qquad g(x) = -\log x$

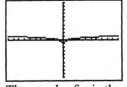

The graph of g is the graph of f reflected across the x–axis.

93. $f(t) = 75 - 10\log(t+1)$

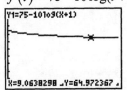

After approximately 9 months, the average score falls below 65.

95.

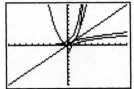

Use the trace function to compare how quickly the functions increase. In order from slowest to fastest, the functions are: $y = \ln x$, $y = \sqrt{x}$, $y = x$, $y = x^2$, $y = e^x$, and $y = x^x$.

Review Exercises

96. Rewrite the equations in $Ax + By = C$ form.

$2x + 5y = 11$
$3x - 2y = -12$

Multiply the first equation by 2 and the second equation by 5 and solve by addition.

$$4x + 10y = 22$$
$$15x - 10y = -60$$

$$19x = -38$$
$$x = -2$$

Back-substitute –2 for x to find y.

$$2(-2) + 5y = 11$$
$$-4 + 5y = 11$$
$$5y = 15$$
$$y = 3$$

The solution is $(-2, 3)$.

97. $6x^2 - 8xy + 2y^2 = 2(3x^2 - 4xy + y^2)$
$ = 2(3x - y)(x - y)$

98. $x + 3 \leq -4 \quad$ or $\quad 2 - 7x \leq 16$
$ x \leq -7 \qquad\qquad -7x \leq 14$
$ x \geq -2$

The solution set is $\{x | x \leq -7 \text{ or } x \geq -2\}$ or $(-\infty, -7] \cup [-2, \infty)$.

Properties of Exponents

12.4 CHECK POINTS

CHECK POINT 1

a. $\log_6(7 \cdot 11) = \log_6 7 + \log_6 11$

b. $\log(100x) = \log 100 + \log x = 2 + \log x$

CHECK POINT 2

a. $\log_8\left(\dfrac{23}{x}\right) = \log_8 23 - \log_8 x$

b. $\ln\left(\dfrac{e^5}{11}\right) = \ln e^5 - \ln 11 = 5 - \ln 11$

CHECK POINT 3

a. $\log_6 8^9 = 9\log_6 8$

b. $\ln \sqrt[3]{x} = \ln x^{\frac{1}{3}} = \dfrac{1}{3}\ln x$

CHECK POINT 4

a.
$$\log_b x^4 \sqrt[3]{y} = \log_b x^4 + \log_b \sqrt[3]{y}$$
$$= 4\log_b x + \log_b y^{\frac{1}{3}}$$
$$= 4\log_b x + \frac{1}{3}\log_b y$$

b.
$$\log_5\left(\frac{\sqrt{x}}{25y^3}\right)$$
$$= \log_5 \sqrt{x} - \log_5 25y^3$$
$$= \log_5 x^{\frac{1}{2}} - \left(\log_5 25 + \log_5 y^3\right)$$
$$= \frac{1}{2}\log_5 x - \log_5 5^2 - 3\log_5 y$$
$$= \frac{1}{2}\log_5 x - 2 - 3\log_5 y$$

CHECK POINT 5

a. $\log 25 + \log 4 = \log(25 \cdot 4) = \log 100 = 2$

b.
$$\log(7x+6) - \log x = \log\left(\frac{7x+6}{x}\right)$$

CHECK POINT 6

a.
$$2\ln x + \frac{1}{3}\ln(x+5) = \ln x^2 + \ln(x+5)^{\frac{1}{3}}$$
$$= \ln x^2(x+5)^{\frac{1}{3}}$$
$$= \ln x^2 \sqrt[3]{x+5}$$

b.
$$2\log(x-3) - \log x = \log(x-3)^2 - \log x$$
$$= \log\frac{(x-3)^2}{x}$$

CHECK POINT 7
$$\log_7 2506 = \frac{\log 2506}{\log 7} \approx 4.02$$

CHECK POINT 8
$$\ln_7 2506 = \frac{\ln 2506}{\ln 7} \approx 4.02$$

EXERCISE SET 12.4

1. $\log_5(7 \cdot 3) = \log_5 7 + \log_5 3$

3.
$$\log_7(7x) = \log_7 7 + \log_7 x$$
$$= 1 + \log_7 x$$

5. $\log(1000x) = \log 1000 + \log x = 3 + \log x$

7.
$$\log_7\left(\frac{7}{x}\right) = \log_7 7 - \log_7 x = 1 - \log_7 x$$

9.
$$\log\left(\frac{x}{100}\right) = \log x - \log 100 = \log x - 2$$

11.
$$\log_4\left(\frac{64}{y}\right) = \log_4 64 - \log_4 y = 3 - \log_4 y$$

13.
$$\ln\left(\frac{e^2}{5}\right) = \ln e^2 - \ln 5 = 2 - \ln 5$$

15. $\log_b x^3 = 3\log_b x$

17. $\log N^{-6} = -6\log N$

19.
$$\ln \sqrt[5]{x} = \ln x^{\frac{1}{5}} = \frac{1}{5}\ln x$$

21.
$$\log_b x^2 y = \log_b x^2 + \log_b y$$
$$= 2\log_b x + \log_b y$$

23.
$$\log_4\left(\frac{\sqrt{x}}{64}\right) = \log_4 \sqrt{x} - \log_4 64$$
$$= \log_4 x^{\frac{1}{2}} - 3 = \frac{1}{2}\log_4 x - 3$$

25.
$$\log_6\left(\frac{36}{\sqrt{x+1}}\right) = \log_6 36 - \log_6 \sqrt{x+1}$$
$$= 2 - \log_6(x+1)^{\frac{1}{2}}$$
$$= 2 - \frac{1}{2}\log_6(x+1)$$

27.
$$\log_b\left(\frac{x^2 y}{z^2}\right) = \log_b x^2 y - \log_b z^2$$

29.
$$\log\sqrt{100x} = \log(100x)^{\frac{1}{2}}$$
$$= \frac{1}{2}\log(100x)$$

$$= \frac{1}{2}(\log 100 + \log x)$$

$$= \frac{1}{2}(2 + \log x)$$

$$= 1 + \frac{1}{2}\log x$$

31.
$$\log \sqrt[3]{\frac{x}{y}} = \log\left(\frac{x}{y}\right)^{\frac{1}{3}} = \frac{1}{3}\log\left(\frac{x}{y}\right)$$

$$= \frac{1}{3}(\log x - \log y)$$

$$= \frac{1}{3}\log x - \frac{1}{3}\log y$$

33. $\log 5 + \log 2 = \log(5 \cdot 2) = \log 10 = 1$

35. $\ln x + \ln 7 = \ln(x \cdot 7) = \ln(7x)$

37. $\log_2 96 - \log_2 3 = \log_2 \frac{96}{3} = \log_2 32 = 5$

39. $\log(2x+5) - \log x = \log\left(\frac{2x+5}{x}\right)$

41. $\log x + 3\log y = \log x + \log y^3 = \log xy^3$

43.
$$\frac{1}{2}\ln x + \ln y = \ln x^{\frac{1}{2}} + \ln y$$

$$= \ln x^{\frac{1}{2}}y = \ln y\sqrt{x}$$

45. $2\log_b x + 3\log_b y = \log_b x^2 + \log_b y^3$
$$= \log_b x^2 y^3$$

47. $5\ln x - 2\ln y = \ln x^5 - \ln y^2 = \ln\frac{x^5}{y^2}$

49.
$$3\ln x - \frac{1}{3}\ln y = \ln x^3 - \ln y^{\frac{1}{3}}$$

$$= \ln\frac{x^3}{y^{\frac{1}{3}}} = \ln\frac{x^3}{\sqrt[3]{y}}$$

51. $4\ln(x+6) - 3\ln x = \ln(x+6)^4 - \ln x^3$
$$= \ln\frac{(x+6)^4}{x^3}$$

53. $\log_5 13 = \frac{\log 13}{\log 5} \approx 1.5937$

55. $\log_{14} 87.5 = \frac{\log 87.5}{\log 14} \approx 1.6944$

57. $\log_{0.1} 17 = \frac{\log 17}{\log 0.1} \approx -1.2304$

59. $\log_\pi 63 = \frac{\log 63}{\log \pi} \approx 3.6193$

61. a.
$$D = 10(\log I - \log I_0) = 10\left(\log\frac{I}{I_0}\right)$$

b.
$$D = 10\left(\log\frac{100}{1}\right) = 10(\log 100)$$
$$= 10(2) = 20$$

The sound is 20 decibels louder on the decibel scale.

For Exercises 63-69, answers may vary.

71. Statement **d.** is true.
$$\ln\sqrt{2} = \ln 2^{\frac{1}{2}} = \frac{1}{2}\ln 2 = \frac{\ln 2}{2}$$

Statement **a.** is false.
$$\frac{\log_7 49}{\log_7 7} = \frac{\log_7 49}{1} = \log_7 49 = 2$$

Statement **b.** is false.

$\log_b(x^3 + y^3)$ cannot be simplified. If we were taking the logarithm of a product and not a sum, we would have been able to simplify as follows.
$$\log_b(x^3 y^3) = \log_b x^3 + \log_b y^3$$
$$= 3\log_b x + 3\log_b y$$

Statement **c.** is false.

$$\log_b(xy)^5 = 5\log_b(xy) = 5(\log_b x + \log_b y)$$
$$= 5\log_b x + 5\log_b y$$

73.
$$\log_7 9 = \frac{\log 9}{\log 7} = \frac{\log 3^2}{\log 7} = \frac{2\log 3}{\log 7} = \frac{2A}{B}$$

75.   **a.**
$$y = \log_3 x = \frac{\log x}{\log 3}$$

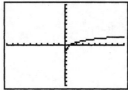

b. $y = 2 + \log_3 x$ $y = -\log_3 x$

$y = \log_3(x+2)$ $y = \log_3 x$

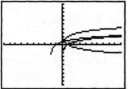

The graph of $y = 2 + \log_3 x$ is the graph of $y = \log_3 x$ shifted up two units.

The graph of $y = \log_3(x+2)$ is the graph of $y = \log_3 x$ shifted 2 units to the left.

The graph of $y = -\log_3 x$ is the graph of $y = \log_3 x$ reflected about the x–axis.

77. $y = \log_3 x$ $y = \log_{25} x$

$y = \log_{100} x$

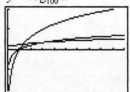

a.   Change the window to focus on the (0, 1) interval.

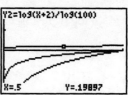

$y = \log_{100} x$ is on top.

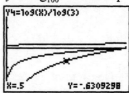

$y = \log_3 x$ is on the bottom.

b.   Change the window to focus on the (1, 10) interval.

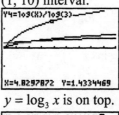

$y = \log_3 x$ is on top.

$y = \log_{100} x$ is on the bottom.

c.   If $y = \log_b x$ is graphed for varying values of b, the graph of the one with the largest base will be on top in the interval (0, 1) and the one with the smallest base will be on top in the interval $(1, \infty)$. Conversely, If $y = \log_b x$ is graphed for varying values of b, the graph of the one with the smallest base will be on the bottom in the interval (0, 1) and the one with the largest base will be on the bottom in the interval $(1, \infty)$.

79.   To verify that $\log\dfrac{x}{y} = \dfrac{\log x}{\log y}$, let $y = 3$.

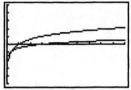

The graphs do not coincide, so the expressions are not equivalent.

81. To verify that $\ln(xy) = (\ln x)(\ln y)$, let $y = 3$.

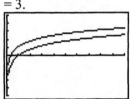

The graphs do not coincide, so the expressions are not equivalent.

Review Exercises

83. $5x - 2y > 10$

Graph the corresponding line,
$5x - 2y = 10$.

x–intercept $\qquad$ y–intercept
$5x - 2(0) = 10 \qquad 5(0) - 2y = 10$
$\qquad 5x = 10 \qquad\qquad -2y = 10$
$\qquad\quad x = 2 \qquad\qquad\quad y = -5$

Use a test point to determine shading.

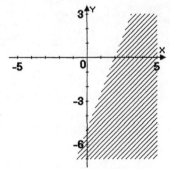

84. $x - 2(3x - 2) > 2x - 3$
$x - 6x + 4 > 2x - 3$
$-5x + 4 > 2x - 3$
$-7x + 4 > -3$
$-7x > -7$
$x < 1$

85.
$$\frac{\sqrt[3]{40x^2y^6}}{\sqrt[3]{5xy}} = \sqrt[3]{\frac{40x^2y^6}{5xy}} = \sqrt[3]{8xy^5}$$
$$= \sqrt[3]{8xy^3y^2} = 2y\sqrt[3]{xy^2}$$

Exponential and Logarithmic Equations

12.5 CHECK POINTS

CHECK POINT 1

a. $5^{3x-6} = 125$
$5^{3x-6} = 5^3$
$3x - 6 = 3$
$3x = 9$
$x = 3$

b. $4^x = 32$
$2^{2x} = 2^5$
$2x = 5$
$x = \dfrac{5}{2}$

CHECK POINT 2

$5^x = 134$
$\ln 5^x = \ln 134$
$x \ln 5 = \ln 134$
$x = \dfrac{\ln 134}{\ln 5} \approx 3.04$

CHECK POINT 3

$7e^{2x} = 63$
$e^{2x} = 9$
$\ln e^{2x} = \ln 9$
$2x = \ln 9$
$x = \dfrac{\ln 9}{2} \approx 1.10$

CHECK POINT 4

$\log_2(x - 4) = 3$
$2^3 = x - 4$
$8 = x - 4$
$12 = x$

CHECK POINT 5

$\log x + \log(x-3) = 1$

$\log(x(x-3)) = 1$

$10^1 = (x(x-3))$

$10 = x^2 - 3x$

$0 = x^2 - 3x - 10$

$0 = (x-5)(x+2)$

$x - 5 = 0 \quad \text{and} \quad x + 3 = 0$

$x = 5 \qquad\qquad x = -3$

We disregard –3 because it would result in taking the logarithm of a negative number. The solution is 5.

CHECK POINT 6

$\log_5(x+1) - \log_5 x = 2$

$\log_5 \dfrac{(x+1)}{x} = 2$

$5^2 = \dfrac{x+1}{x}$

$25 = \dfrac{x+1}{x}$

$25x = x + 1$

$24x = 1$

$x = \dfrac{1}{24}$

CHECK POINT 7

$4\ln 3x = 8$

$\ln 3x = 2$

$e^{\ln 3x} = e^2$

$3x = e^2$

$x = \dfrac{e^2}{3}$

CHECK POINT 8

$R = 6e^{12.77x}$

$6e^{12.77x} = 7$

$\ln e^{12.77x} = \ln \dfrac{7}{6}$

$12.77x = \ln \dfrac{7}{6}$

$x = \dfrac{\ln \dfrac{7}{6}}{12.77} \approx 0.01$

There is a 7% risk of a car accident when the blood alcohol concentration is 0.01.

CHECK POINT 9

$3600 = 1000\left(1 + \dfrac{0.08}{4}\right)^{4t}$

$1000(1+0.02)^{4t} = 3600$

$1000(1.02)^{4t} = 3600$

$\ln(1.02)^{4t} = \ln 3.6$

$4t \ln 1.02 = \ln 3.6$

$t = \dfrac{\ln 3.6}{4\ln 1.02} \approx 16.2$

It will take approximately 16.2 years for $1000 to grow to $3600.

CHECK POINT 10

$461.87 + 299.4\ln x = 2000$

$299.4\ln x = 1538.13$

$\ln x = \dfrac{1538.13}{299.4}$

$e^{\ln x} = e^{\frac{1538.13}{299.4}}$

$x = e^{\frac{1538.13}{299.4}} \approx 170.2$

Approximately 170 years after 1979, in the year 2149, there will be two million U.S. workers in the environmental industry.

EXERCISE SET 12.5

1. $2^x = 64$

$2^x = 2^6$

$x = 6$

3. $5^x = 125$

$5^x = 5^3$

$x = 3$

5. $2^{2x-1} = 32$

$2^{2x-1} = 2^5$

$2x - 1 = 5$

$2x = 6$

$x = 3$

7.
$$4^{2x-1} = 64$$
$$4^{2x-1} = 4^3$$
$$2x - 1 = 3$$
$$2x = 4$$
$$x = 2$$

9.
$$32^x = 8$$
$$\left(2^5\right)^x = 2^3$$
$$2^{5x} = 2^3$$
$$5x = 3$$
$$x = \frac{3}{5}$$

11.
$$9^x = 27$$
$$\left(3^2\right)^x = 3^3$$
$$3^{2x} = 3^3$$
$$2x = 3$$
$$x = \frac{3}{2}$$

13.
$$10^x = 3.91$$
$$\ln 10^x = \ln 3.91$$
$$x \ln 10 = \ln 3.91$$
$$x = \frac{\ln 3.91}{\ln 10} \approx 0.59$$

15.
$$e^x = 5.7$$
$$\ln e^x = \ln 5.7$$
$$x = \ln 5.7 \approx 1.74$$

17.
$$5^x = 17$$
$$\ln 5^x = \ln 17$$
$$x \ln 5 = \ln 17$$
$$x = \frac{\ln 17}{\ln 5} \approx 1.76$$

19.
$$5e^x = 25$$
$$e^x = 5$$
$$\ln e^x = \ln 5$$
$$x = \ln 5 \approx 1.61$$

21.
$$3e^{5x} = 1977$$
$$e^{5x} = 659$$
$$\ln e^{5x} = \ln 659$$
$$5x = \ln 659$$

$$x = \frac{\ln 659}{5} \approx 1.30$$

23.
$$e^{0.7x} = 13$$
$$\ln e^{0.7x} = \ln 13$$
$$0.7x = \ln 13$$
$$x = \frac{\ln 13}{0.7} \approx 3.66$$

25.
$$1250e^{0.055x} = 3750$$
$$e^{0.055x} = 3$$
$$\ln e^{0.055x} = \ln 3$$
$$0.055x = \ln 3$$
$$x = \frac{\ln 3}{0.055} \approx 19.97$$

27.
$$30 - \left(1.4\right)^x = 0$$
$$-1.4^x = -30$$
$$1.4^x = 30$$
$$\ln 1.4^x = \ln 30$$
$$x \ln 1.4 = \ln 30$$
$$x = \frac{\ln 30}{\ln 1.4} \approx 10.11$$

29.
$$e^{1-5x} = 793$$
$$\ln e^{1-5x} = \ln 793$$
$$1 - 5x = \ln 793$$
$$-5x = \ln 793 - 1$$
$$x = \frac{-\left(\ln 793 - 1\right)}{5}$$
$$x = \frac{1 - \ln 793}{5} \approx -1.14$$

31.
$$7^{x+2} = 410$$
$$\ln 7^{x+2} = \ln 410$$
$$\left(x + 2\right)\ln 7 = \ln 410$$
$$x + 2 = \frac{\ln 410}{\ln 7}$$
$$x = \frac{\ln 410}{\ln 7} - 2 \approx 1.09$$

33.
$$2^{x+1} = 5^x$$
$$\ln 2^{x+1} = \ln 5^x$$
$$\left(x + 1\right)\ln 2 = x \ln 5$$
$$x \ln 2 + \ln 2 = x \ln 5$$
$$x \ln 2 = x \ln 5 - \ln 2$$
$$x \ln 2 - x \ln 5 = -\ln 2$$

$$x(\ln 2 - \ln 5) = -\ln 2$$
$$x = \frac{-\ln 2}{\ln 2 - \ln 5}$$
$$x = \frac{\ln 2}{\ln 5 - \ln 2} \approx 0.76$$

35. $\log_3 x = 4$
$$x = 3^4$$
$$x = 81$$

37. $\log_2 x = -4$
$$x = 2^{-4}$$
$$x = \frac{1}{2^4} = \frac{1}{16}$$

39. $\log_9 x = \frac{1}{2}$
$$x = 9^{\frac{1}{2}}$$
$$x = \sqrt{9} = 3$$

41. $\log x = 2$
$$x = 10^2$$
$$x = 100$$

43. $\ln x = -3$
$$x = e^{-3}$$
$$x = \frac{1}{e^3}$$

45. $\log_4(x + 5) = 3$
$$x + 5 = 4^3$$
$$x + 5 = 64$$
$$x = 59$$

47. $\log_3(x - 4) = -3$
$$x - 4 = 3^{-3}$$
$$x - 4 = \frac{1}{3^3}$$
$$x - 4 = \frac{1}{27}$$
$$x = \frac{1}{27} + 4$$
$$x = \frac{1}{27} + \frac{108}{27} = \frac{109}{27}$$

49. $\log_4(3x + 2) = 3$
$$3x + 2 = 4^3$$
$$3x + 2 = 64$$
$$3x = 62$$
$$x = \frac{62}{3}$$

51. $\log_5 x + \log_5(4x - 1) = 1$
$$\log_5(x(4x - 1)) = 1$$
$$x(4x - 1) = 5^1$$
$$4x^2 - x = 5$$
$$4x^2 - x - 5 = 0$$
$$(4x - 5)(x + 1) = 0$$
$$4x - 5 = 0 \quad \text{and} \quad x + 1 = 0$$
$$4x = 5 \qquad\qquad x = -1$$
$$x = \frac{5}{4}$$

We disregard -1 because it would result in taking the logarithm of a negative number.

The solution is $\frac{5}{4}$.

53. $\log_3(x - 5) + \log_3(x + 3) = 2$
$$\log_3((x - 5)(x + 3)) = 2$$
$$(x - 5)(x + 3) = 3^2$$
$$x^2 - 2x - 15 = 9$$
$$x^2 - 2x - 24 = 0$$
$$(x - 6)(x + 2) = 0$$
$$x - 6 = 0 \quad \text{and} \quad x + 2 = 0$$
$$x = 6 \qquad\qquad x = -2$$

We disregard -2 because it would result in taking the logarithm of a negative number. The solution is 6.

55. $\log_2(x + 2) - \log_2(x - 5) = 3$
$$\log_2 \frac{x + 2}{x - 5} = 3$$
$$\frac{x + 2}{x - 5} = 2^3$$
$$\frac{x + 2}{x - 5} = 8$$
$$x + 2 = 8(x - 5)$$
$$x + 2 = 8x - 40$$

$$-7x + 2 = -40$$
$$-7x = -42$$
$$x = 6$$

57. $\log(3x - 5) - \log(5x) = 2$

$$\log\frac{3x-5}{5x} = 2$$

$$\frac{3x-5}{5x} = 10^2$$

$$\frac{3x-5}{5x} = 100$$

$$3x - 5 = 500x$$

$$-5 = 497x$$

$$-\frac{5}{497} = x$$

We disregard $-\dfrac{5}{497}$ because it would result in taking the logarithm of a negative number. There is no solution. The solution set is $\varnothing$ or $\{\ \}$.

59. $\ln x = 2$

$$e^{\ln x} = e^2$$

$$x = e^2 \approx 7.39$$

61. $5\ln 2x = 20$

$$\ln 2x = 4$$

$$e^{\ln 2x} = e^4$$

$$2x = e^4$$

$$x = \frac{e^4}{2} \approx 27.30$$

63. $6 + 2\ln x = 5$

$$2\ln x = -1$$

$$e^{\ln x} = e^{-\frac{1}{2}}$$

$$x = e^{-\frac{1}{2}} \approx 0.61$$

65. $\ln\sqrt{x+3} = 1$

$$\ln(x+3)^{\frac{1}{2}} = 1$$

$$\frac{1}{2}\ln(x+3) = 1$$

$$\ln(x+3) = 2$$

$$e^{\ln(x+3)} = e^2$$

$$x + 3 = e^2$$

$$x = e^2 - 3 \approx 4.39$$

67.
$$R = 6e^{12.77x}$$

$$6e^{12.77x} = 100$$

$$e^{12.77x} = \frac{100}{6}$$

$$\ln e^{12.77x} = \ln\frac{100}{6}$$

$$12.77x = \ln\frac{100}{6}$$

$$x = \frac{\ln\dfrac{100}{6}}{12.77} \approx 0.22$$

A blood alcohol concentration of 0.22 corresponds to a 100% risk.

69. a. $f(0) = 18.2e^{0.001(0)}$

$$= 18.2e^0 = 18.2(1) = 18.2$$

The population of New York was 18.2 million in 1984.

b. $18.5 = 18.2e^{0.001t}$

$$e^{0.001t} = \frac{18.5}{18.2}$$

$$\ln e^{0.001t} = \ln\frac{18.5}{18.2}$$

$$0.001t = \ln\frac{18.5}{18.2}$$

$$t = \frac{\ln\dfrac{18.5}{18.2}}{0.001} \approx 16.3$$

The population of New York will reach 18.5 million approximately 16 years after 1994 in the year 2010.

71.
$$20000 = 12500\left(1 + \frac{0.0575}{4}\right)^{4t}$$

$$20000 = 12500(1 + 0.014375)^{4t}$$

$$20000 = 12500(1.014375)^{4t}$$

$$\frac{20000}{12500} = (1.014375)^{4t}$$

$$1.6 = (1.014375)^{4t}$$
$$\ln 1.6 = \ln (1.014375)^{4t}$$
$$\ln 1.6 = 4t \ln 1.014375$$
$$t = \frac{\ln 1.6}{4 \ln 1.014375} \approx 8.2$$

It will take approximately 8.2 years.

73.
$$1400 = 1000\left(1 + \frac{r}{360}\right)^{360(2)}$$
$$1.4 = \left(1 + \frac{r}{360}\right)^{720}$$
$$\ln 1.4 = \ln\left(1 + \frac{r}{360}\right)^{720}$$
$$\ln 1.4 = 720 \ln\left(1 + \frac{r}{360}\right)$$
$$\frac{\ln 1.4}{720} = \ln\left(1 + \frac{r}{360}\right)$$
$$e^{\frac{\ln 1.4}{720}} = e^{\ln\left(1 + \frac{r}{360}\right)}$$
$$e^{\frac{\ln 1.4}{720}} = 1 + \frac{r}{360}$$
$$1 + \frac{r}{360} = e^{\frac{\ln 1.4}{720}}$$
$$\frac{r}{360} = e^{\frac{\ln 1.4}{720}} - 1$$
$$r = 360\left(e^{\frac{\ln 1.4}{720}} - 1\right) \approx 0.168$$

The annual interest rate is approximately 16.8%.

75.
$$16000 = 8000e^{0.08t}$$
$$2 = e^{0.08t}$$
$$\ln 2 = \ln e^{0.08t}$$
$$\ln 2 = 0.08t$$
$$t = \frac{\ln 2}{0.08} \approx 8.7$$

It will take approximately 8.7 years to double the money.

77.
$$7050 = 2350e^{r7}$$
$$3 = e^{7r}$$
$$\ln 3 = \ln e^{7r}$$
$$\ln 3 = 7r$$

$$r = \frac{\ln 3}{7} \approx 15.7$$

The annual interest rate would have to be 15.7% to triple the money.

79.
$$25000 = 15557 + 5259 \ln x$$
$$9443 = 5259 \ln x$$
$$\ln x = \frac{9443}{5259}$$
$$e^{\ln x} = e^{\frac{9443}{5259}}$$
$$x = e^{\frac{9443}{5259}} \approx 6.0$$

The average price of a new car was $25,000 6 years after 1989 in 1995.

81.
$$50 = 95 - 30 \log_2 x$$
$$-45 = -30 \log_2 x$$
$$\log_2 x = \frac{3}{2}$$
$$x = 2^{\frac{3}{2}} \approx 2.8$$

After approximately 2.8 days, only half the students recall the important features of the lecture. This is represented by the point (2.8, 50).

83.
$$\text{pH} = -\log x$$
$$2.4 = -\log x$$
$$-2.4 = \log x$$
$$x = 10^{-2.4} \approx .004$$

The hydrogen ion concentration is $10^{-2.4}$ or approximately 0.004 moles per liter.

For Exercises 85-91, answers may vary.

93.
$$A_{4000} = 4000\left(1 + \frac{0.03}{1}\right)^{1t}$$
$$A_{2000} = 2000\left(1 + \frac{0.05}{1}\right)^{1t}$$
$$4000\left(1 + \frac{0.03}{1}\right)^{1t} = 2000\left(1 + \frac{0.05}{1}\right)^{1t}$$
$$4000(1 + 0.03)^t = 2000(1 + 0.05)^t$$
$$2(1.03)^t = (1.05)^t$$

$$\ln 2(1.03)^t = \ln(1.05)^t$$
$$\ln 2 + \ln(1.03)^t = t\ln(1.05)$$
$$\ln 2 + t\ln(1.03) = t\ln(1.05)$$
$$\ln 2 = t\ln(1.05) - t\ln(1.03)$$
$$\ln 2 = t(\ln(1.05) - \ln(1.03))$$
$$t = \frac{\ln 2}{\ln(1.05) - \ln(1.03)}$$
$$t \approx 36.0$$

In approximately 36 years, the two accounts will have the same balance.

95. $(\log x)(2\log x + 1) = 6$

Let $t = \log x$.

$$(t)(2t + 1) = 6$$
$$2t^2 + t = 6$$
$$2t^2 + t - 6 = 0$$
$$(2t - 3)(t + 2) = 0$$
$$2t - 3 = 0 \quad \text{and} \quad t + 2 = 0$$
$$2t = 3 \qquad\qquad t = -2$$
$$t = \frac{3}{2}$$

Substitute $\log x$ for t.

$$t = \frac{3}{2} \quad \text{and} \quad t = -2$$
$$\qquad\qquad\qquad \log x = -2$$
$$\log x = \frac{3}{2} \qquad\qquad x = 10^{-2}$$
$$x = 10^{\frac{3}{2}}$$

97. $2^{x+1} = 8$

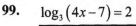

The solution is 2 and the solution set is $\{2\}$. Verify the solution algebraically.

99. $\log_3(4x - 7) = 2$

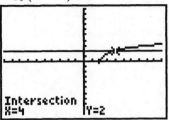

The solution is 4 and the solution set is $\{4\}$. Verify the solution.

101. $\log(x + 3) + \log x = 1$

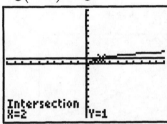

The solution is 2 and the solution set is $\{2\}$. Verify the solution.

103. $3^x = 2x + 3$

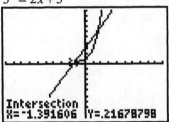

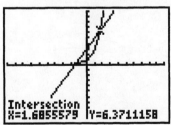

The solutions are -1.39 and 1.69 and the solution set is $\{-1.39, 1.69\}$. Verify the solutions.

105. $29 = 0.48\ln(x+1)+27$

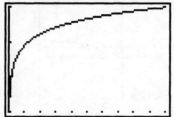

The barometric pressure increases as distance from the eye increases. It increases quickly at first, and the more slowly over time.

107. $P(t) = 145e^{-0.092t}$

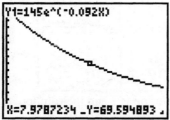

The runner's pulse will be 70 beats per minute after approximately 8.0 minutes.

Review Exercises

109.
$$\sqrt{x+4} - \sqrt{x-1} = 1$$
$$\sqrt{x+4} = 1 + \sqrt{x-1}$$
$$\left(\sqrt{x+4}\right)^2 = \left(1+\sqrt{x-1}\right)^2$$
$$x+4 = 1 + 2\sqrt{x-1} + x - 1$$
$$4 = 2\sqrt{x-1}$$
$$2 = \sqrt{x-1}$$
$$2^2 = \left(\sqrt{x-1}\right)^2$$
$$4 = x-1$$
$$5 = x$$

110.
$$\frac{3}{x+1} - \frac{5}{x} = \frac{19}{x^2+x}$$
$$\frac{3}{x+1} - \frac{5}{x} = \frac{19}{x(x+1)}$$
$$x(x+1)\left(\frac{3}{x+1}-\frac{5}{x}\right) = x(x+1)\left(\frac{19}{x(x+1)}\right)$$

$$x(3) - 5(x+1) = 19$$
$$3x - 5x - 5 = 19$$
$$-2x - 5 = 19$$
$$-2x = 24$$
$$x = -12$$

111.
$$\begin{array}{l} x^2 + xy + y^2 \\ \overline{\hspace{1cm}} \\ x-y\,\overline{)\,x^3 + x^2y + xy^2} \\ \underline{-x^2y - xy^2 - y^3} \\ x^3 - y^3 \end{array}$$

Exponential Growth and Decay; Modeling Data

12.6 CHECK POINTS

CHECK POINT 1

a.
$$643 = 491e^{k10}$$
$$\frac{643}{491} = e^{10k}$$
$$\ln\frac{643}{491} = \ln e^{10k}$$
$$\ln\frac{643}{491} = 10k$$
$$k = \frac{\ln\dfrac{643}{491}}{10} \approx 0.027$$

The exponential growth function is $A = A_0 e^{0.027t}$.

b.
$$1000 = 491e^{0.027t}$$
$$\frac{1000}{491} = e^{0.027t}$$
$$\ln\frac{1000}{491} = \ln e^{0.027t}$$
$$\ln\frac{1000}{491} = 0.027t$$
$$t = \frac{\ln\dfrac{1000}{491}}{0.027} \approx 26.3$$

The population will reach one billion approximately 26 years after 1980 in the year 2006.

CHECK POINT 2

a.
$$\frac{1}{2} = 1e^{k\,28}$$

$$\ln\frac{1}{2} = \ln e^{28k}$$

$$\ln\frac{1}{2} = 28k$$

$$k = \frac{\ln\frac{1}{2}}{28} \approx -0.0248$$

The exponential growth function is $A = A_0 e^{-0.0248t}$.

b.
$$10 = 60e^{-0.0248t}$$

$$\frac{1}{6} = e^{-0.0248t}$$

$$\ln\frac{1}{6} = \ln e^{-0.0248t}$$

$$\ln\frac{1}{6} = -0.0248t$$

$$t = \frac{\ln\frac{1}{6}}{-0.0248} \approx 72.2$$

The strontium-90 will decay from 60 grams to 10 grams in 72.2 years.

EXERCISE SET 12.6

1.
$$A = 208e^{0.008t} = 208e^{0.008(0)}$$
$$= 208e^0 = 208(1) = 208$$

In 1970, the population was 208 million.

3.
$$300 = 208e^{0.008t}$$

$$\frac{300}{208} = e^{0.008t}$$

$$\ln\frac{300}{208} = \ln e^{0.008t}$$

$$\ln\frac{300}{208} = 0.008t$$

$$t = \frac{\ln\frac{300}{208}}{0.008} \approx 45.8$$

The population will reach 300 million approximately 46 years after 1970 in the year 2016.

5. Since $k = 0.026$, each year the population will increase by 2.6%.

7.
$$1624 = 574e^{0.026t}$$

$$\frac{1624}{574} = e^{0.026t}$$

$$\ln\frac{1624}{574} = \ln e^{0.026t}$$

$$\ln\frac{1624}{574} = 0.026t$$

$$t = \frac{\ln\frac{1624}{574}}{0.026} \approx 40.0$$

The population will be 1624 million 40 years after 1974 in the year 2014.

9.
$$V = 140e^{0.068t} = 140e^{0.068(0)}$$
$$= 140e^0 = 140(1) = 140$$

You paid $140 thousand, or $140,000 for the house.

11.
$$200 = 140e^{0.068t}$$

$$\frac{200}{140} = e^{0.068t}$$

$$\ln\frac{10}{7} = \ln e^{0.068t}$$

$$\ln\frac{10}{7} = 0.068t$$

$$t = \frac{\ln\frac{10}{7}}{0.068} \approx 5.2$$

The house will be worth $200,000 approximately 5 years after 2000 in the year 2005.

13.
$$680 = 200e^{k7}$$

$$\frac{680}{200} = e^{7k}$$

$$\ln\frac{17}{5} = \ln e^{7k}$$

$\ln \dfrac{17}{5} = 7k$

$k = \dfrac{\ln \dfrac{17}{5}}{7} \approx 0.175$

The exponential growth model is $A = 200e^{0.175t}$. Since $k = 0.175$, the number of AIDS cases is increasing by 17.5% each year.

15. $A = 16e^{-0.000121t} = 16e^{-0.000121(5715)}$
$= 16e^{-0.691515} \approx 8.01$

Approximately 8 grams of carbon-14 will be present in 5715 years.

17.

10 seconds: $16 \cdot \dfrac{1}{2} = 8$ grams

20 seconds: $8 \cdot \dfrac{1}{2} = 4$ grams

30 seconds: $4 \cdot \dfrac{1}{2} = 2$ grams

40 seconds: $2 \cdot \dfrac{1}{2} = 1$ grams

50 seconds: $1 \cdot \dfrac{1}{2} = \dfrac{1}{2}$ gram

19.

$15 = 100e^{-0.000121t}$

$\dfrac{15}{100} = e^{-0.000121t}$

$\ln 0.15 = \ln e^{-0.000121t}$

$\ln 0.15 = -0.000121t$

$t = \dfrac{\ln 0.15}{-0.000121} \approx 15{,}679$

The paintings are approximately 15,679 years old.

21. a.

$\dfrac{1}{2} = 1e^{k1.31}$

$\ln \dfrac{1}{2} = \ln e^{1.31k}$

$\ln \dfrac{1}{2} = 1.31k$

$k = \dfrac{\ln \dfrac{1}{2}}{1.31} \approx -0.52912$

The exponential model is given by $A = A_0 e^{-0.52912t}$.

b. $0.945A_0 = A_0 e^{-0.52912t}$

$0.945 = e^{-0.52912t}$

$\ln 0.945 = \ln e^{-0.52912t}$

$\ln 0.945 = -0.52912t$

$t = \dfrac{\ln 0.945}{-0.52912} \approx 0.1069$

The age of the dinosaur ones is approximately 0.1069 billion or 106,900,000 years old.

23. $2A_0 = A_0 e^{kt}$

$2 = e^{kt}$

$\ln 2 = \ln e^{kt}$

$\ln 2 = kt$

$t = \dfrac{\ln 2}{k}$

The population will double in $t = \dfrac{\ln 2}{k}$ years.

25. $t = \dfrac{\ln 2}{k} = \dfrac{\ln 2}{0.011} \approx 63.0$

China's population will double in approximately 63 years.

For Exercises 27-33, answers may vary.

35. Answers may vary.

37.

```
ExpReg
 y=a*b^x
 a=1.73989839
 b=1.037252402
 r²=.9426534978
 r=.9709034441
■
```

The exponential model is $y = 1.740(1.037)^x$. Since $r = 0.97$, the model fits the data very well.

39.

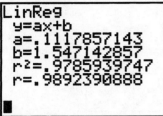

The linear model is $y = 0.112x + 1.547$. Since $r = 0.99$, the model fits the data very well.

41. Using r, the model of best fit is $y = 0.112x + 1.547$. Substitute 7.50 for y.

$7.50 = 0.112x + 1.547$

$5.953 = 0.112x$

$x \approx 53$

The minimum wage will be \$7.50 53 years after 1970 in the year 2023. Answers will vary based on model chosen.

Review Exercises

43.

$$\frac{x^2 - 9}{2x^2 + 7x + 3} \div \frac{x^2 - 3x}{2x^2 + 11x + 5}$$

$$= \frac{x^2 - 9}{2x^2 + 7x + 3} \cdot \frac{2x^2 + 11x + 5}{x^2 - 3x}$$

$$= \frac{\cancel{(x+3)}\,\cancel{(x-3)}}{\cancel{(2x+1)}\,\cancel{(x+3)}} \cdot \frac{\cancel{(2x+1)}\,(x+5)}{x\cancel{(x-3)}}$$

$$= \frac{x+5}{x}$$

44. $x^{\frac{2}{3}} + 2x^{\frac{1}{3}} - 3 = 0$

Let $t = x^{\frac{1}{3}}$.

$$\left(x^{\frac{1}{3}}\right)^2 + 2x^{\frac{1}{3}} - 3 = 0$$

$$t^2 + 2t - 3 = 0$$

$$(t + 3)(t - 1) = 0$$

$t + 3 = 0 \quad$ and $\quad t - 1 = 0$

$\quad t = -3 \qquad\qquad t = 1$

Substitute $x^{\frac{1}{3}}$ for t.

$$x^{\frac{1}{3}} = -3 \qquad \text{and} \qquad x^{\frac{1}{3}} = 1$$

$$\left(x^{\frac{1}{3}}\right)^3 = (-3)^3 \qquad \left(x^{\frac{1}{3}}\right)^3 = (1)^3$$

$$x = -27 \qquad\qquad x = 1$$

45. $6\sqrt{2} - 2\sqrt{50} + 3\sqrt{98}$

$= 6\sqrt{2} - 2\sqrt{25 \cdot 2} + 3\sqrt{49 \cdot 2}$

$= 6\sqrt{2} - 2 \cdot 5\sqrt{2} + 3 \cdot 7\sqrt{2}$

$= 6\sqrt{2} - 10\sqrt{2} + 21\sqrt{2} = 17\sqrt{2}$

Chapter 12 Review Exercises

1. $f(x) = 4^x$

x	$f(x)$
-2	$4^{-2} = \dfrac{1}{16}$
-1	$4^{-1} = \dfrac{1}{4}$
0	$4^0 = 1$
1	$4^1 = 4$
2	$4^2 = 16$

The coordinates match graph **d**.

2. $f(x) = 4^{-x}$

x	$f(x)$
-2	$4^{-(-2)} = 16$
-1	$4^{-(-1)} = 4$
0	$4^{-0} = 1$
1	$4^{-1} = \dfrac{1}{4}$
2	$4^{-2} = \dfrac{1}{16}$

The coordinates match graph **a.**

3. $f(x) = -4^{-x}$

x	$f(x)$
-2	$-4^{-(-2)} = -16$
-1	$-4^{-(-1)} = -4$

0	$-4^{-0} = -1$
1	$-4^{-1} = -\dfrac{1}{4}$
2	$-4^{-2} = -\dfrac{1}{16}$

The coordinates match graph **b.**

4. $f(x) = -4^{-x} + 3$

x	$f(x)$
-2	$-4^{-(-2)} + 3 = -13$
-1	$-4^{-(-1)} + 3 = -1$
0	$-4^{-0} + 3 = 2$
1	$-4^{-1} + 3 = \dfrac{11}{4}$
2	$-4^{-2} + 3 = \dfrac{47}{16}$

The coordinates match graph **c.**

5. $f(x) = 2^x$ and $g(x) = 2^{x-1}$

x	$f(x)$	$g(x)$
-2	$\dfrac{1}{4}$	$\dfrac{1}{8}$
-1	$\dfrac{1}{2}$	$\dfrac{1}{4}$
0	1	$\dfrac{1}{2}$
1	2	1
2	4	2

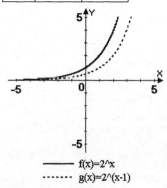

──── f(x)=2^x
······ g(x)=2^(x-1)

The graph of g is the graph of f shifted 1 unit to the right.

6. $f(x) = 2^x$ and $g(x) = \left(\dfrac{1}{2}\right)^x$

x	$f(x)$	$g(x)$
-2	$\dfrac{1}{4}$	4
-1	$\dfrac{1}{2}$	2
0	1	1
1	2	$\dfrac{1}{2}$
2	4	$\dfrac{1}{4}$

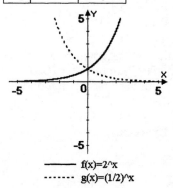

──── f(x)=2^x
······ g(x)=(1/2)^x

The graph of g is the graph of f reflected across the y–axis.

7. $f(x) = 3^x$ and $g(x) = 3^x - 1$

x	$f(x)$	$g(x)$
-2	$\dfrac{1}{9}$	$-\dfrac{8}{9}$
-1	$\dfrac{1}{3}$	$-\dfrac{2}{3}$
0	1	0
1	3	2
2	9	8

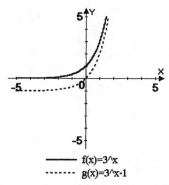

f(x)=3^x
g(x)=3^x-1

The graph of g is the graph of f shifted down 1 unit.

8. $f(x)=3^x$ and $g(x)=-3^x$

x	$f(x)$	$g(x)$
-2	$\dfrac{1}{9}$	$-\dfrac{1}{9}$
-1	$\dfrac{1}{3}$	$-\dfrac{1}{3}$
0	1	-1
1	3	-3
2	9	-9

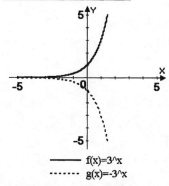

f(x)=3^x
g(x)=-3^x

The graph of g is the graph of f reflected across the x–axis.

9. 5.5% Compounded Semiannually:

$$A=5000\left(1+\frac{0.055}{2}\right)^{2\cdot5}=5000(1+0.0275)^{10}$$

$$=5000(1.0275)^{10}\approx6558.26$$

5.25% Compounded Monthly:

$$A=5000\left(1+\frac{0.0525}{12}\right)^{12\cdot5}=5000(1+0.004375$$

$$=5000(1.004375)^{60}\approx6497.16$$

5.5% compounded semiannually yields the greater return.

10. 7.0% Compounded Monthly:

$$A=14000\left(1+\frac{0.07}{12}\right)^{12\cdot10}=14000\left(1+\frac{7}{1200}\right)^{120}$$

$$=14000\left(\frac{1207}{1200}\right)^{120}\approx28135.26$$

6.85% Compounded Continuously:
$$A=14000e^{0.0685\cdot10}=14000e^{0.685}\approx27772.81$$
7.0% compounded monthly yields the greater return.

11. a. The coffee was 200°F when it was first taken out of the microwave.
b. After 20 minutes, the temperature is approximately 119°F.
c. The coffee will cool to a low of 70°F. This means that the temperature of the room is 70°F.

12. a. $(f\circ g)(x)=f(g(x))=f(4x-1)$
$$=(4x-1)^2+3=16x^2-8x+1+3$$
$$=16x^2-8x+4$$

b. $(g\circ f)(x)=g(f(x))=g(x^2+3)$
$$=4(x^2+3)-1=4x^2+12-1=4x^2+11$$

c. $(f\circ g)(3)=16(3)^2-8(3)+4$
$$=16(9)-24+4=144-24+4=124$$

13. a. $(f\circ g)(x)=f(g(x))=f(x+1)$
$$=\sqrt{x+1}$$

b. $(g\circ f)(x)=g(f(x))=g(\sqrt{x})$
$$=\sqrt{x}+1$$

c. $(f\circ g)(3)=\sqrt{3+1}=\sqrt{4}=2$

14.
$$f(g(x)) = f\left(\frac{5}{3}x - 2\right) = \frac{3}{5}\left(\frac{5}{3}x - 2\right) + \frac{1}{2}$$
$$= \frac{3}{5}\left(\frac{5}{3}x\right) - \left(\frac{3}{5}\right)2 + \frac{1}{2}$$
$$= x - \frac{6}{5} + \frac{1}{2} = x - \frac{7}{10}$$
$$g(f(x)) = g\left(\frac{3}{5}x + \frac{1}{2}\right) = \frac{5}{3}\left(\frac{3}{5}x + \frac{1}{2}\right) - 2$$
$$= \frac{5}{3}\left(\frac{3}{5}x\right) + \left(\frac{5}{3}\right)\frac{1}{2} - 2$$
$$= x + \frac{5}{6} - 2 = x - \frac{7}{6}$$
The functions are not inverses.

15.
$$f(g(x)) = f\left(\frac{2-x}{5}\right) = 2 - 5\left(\frac{2-x}{5}\right)$$
$$= 2 - (2 - x) = 2 - 2 + x = x$$
$$g(f(x)) = g(2 - 5x) = \frac{2 - (2 - 5x)}{5}$$
$$= \frac{2 - 2 + 5x}{5} = \frac{5x}{5} = x$$
The functions are inverses.

16. $y = 4x - 3$
Interchange x and y.
$$x = 4y - 3$$
$$x + 3 = 4y$$
$$\frac{x+3}{4} = y$$
$$f^{-1}(x) = \frac{x+3}{4}$$

16. a. $y = 4x - 3$
Interchange x and y.
$$x = 4y - 3$$
$$x + 3 = 4y$$
$$\frac{x+3}{4} = y$$
$$f^{-1}(x) = \frac{x+3}{4}$$

b.
$$f(f^{-1}(x)) = f\left(\frac{x+3}{4}\right) = 4\left(\frac{x+3}{4}\right) - 3$$
$$= x + 3 - 3 = x$$
$$f^{-1}(f(x)) = f(4x - 3) = \frac{(4x - 3) + 3}{4}$$
$$= \frac{4x - 3 + 3}{4} = \frac{4x}{4} = x$$

17. a. $y = \sqrt{x + 2}$
Interchange x and y.
$$x = \sqrt{y + 2}$$
$$x^2 = y + 2$$
$$x^2 - 2 = y$$
$$f^{-1}(x) = x^2 - 2 \text{ for } x \geq 0$$

b.
$$f(f^{-1}(x)) = f(\sqrt{x+2}) = (\sqrt{x+2})^2 - 2$$
$$= x + 2 - 2 = x$$
$$f^{-1}(f(x)) = f(x^2 - 2) = \sqrt{(x^2 - 2) + 2}$$
$$= \sqrt{x^2 - 2 + 2} = \sqrt{x^2} = x$$

18. a. $y = 8x^3 + 1$
Interchange x and y.
$$x = 8y^3 + 1$$
$$x - 1 = 8y^3$$
$$\frac{x-1}{8} = y^3$$
$$\sqrt[3]{\frac{x-1}{8}} = y$$
$$\frac{\sqrt[3]{x-1}}{2} = y$$
$$f^{-1}(x) = \frac{\sqrt[3]{x-1}}{2}$$

b.
$$f(f^{-1}(x)) = f\left(\frac{\sqrt[3]{x-1}}{2}\right) = 8\left(\frac{\sqrt[3]{x-1}}{2}\right)^3 + 1$$
$$= 8\left(\frac{x-1}{8}\right) + 1 = x - 1 + 1 = x$$
$$f^{-1}(f(x)) = f(8x^3 + 1) = \frac{\sqrt[3]{(8x^3 + 1) - 1}}{2}$$

$$= \frac{\sqrt[3]{8x^3+1-1}}{2} = \frac{\sqrt[3]{8x^3}}{2} = \frac{2x}{2} = x$$

19. It has an inverse function.

20. It does not have an inverse function.

21. It has an inverse function.

22. It does not have an inverse function.

23. Since the points $(-3,-1), (0,0)$ and $(2,4)$ lie on the graph of the function, the points $(-1,-3)$, $(0,0)$ and $(4,2)$ lie on the inverse function.

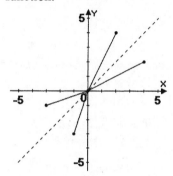

24.
$$\frac{1}{2} = \log_{49} 7$$
$$49^{\frac{1}{2}} = 7$$

25. $3 = \log_4 x$
$$4^3 = x$$

26. $\log_3 81 = y$
$$3^y = 81$$

27. $6^3 = 216$
$$\log_6 216 = 3$$

28. $b^4 = 625$
$$\log_b 625 = 4$$

29. $13^y = 874$
$$\log_{13} 874 = y$$

30. $\log_4 64 = y$
$$4^y = 64$$
$$4^y = 4^3$$
$$y = 3$$

31.
$$\log_5 \frac{1}{25} = y$$
$$5^y = \frac{1}{25}$$
$$5^y = 5^{-2}$$
$$y = -2$$

32. $\log_3(-9)$

This logarithm cannot be evaluated because -9 is not in the domain of $y = \log_3(-9)$.

33. $\log_{16} 4 = y$
$$16^y = 4$$
$$16^y = 16^{\frac{1}{2}}$$
$$y = \frac{1}{2}$$

34. $\log_{17} 17 = 1$ because $17^1 = 17$.

35. $\log_3 3^8 = 8$ because $\log_b b^x = x$.

36. Because $\ln e^x = x$, we conclude that $\ln e^5 = 5$.

37. Since $\log_8 8 = 1$, we have
$$\log_3(\log_8 8) = \log_3 1.$$ Now, evaluate $\log_3 1$.
$$\log_3 1 = y$$
$$3^y = 1$$
$$3^y = 3^0$$
$$y = 0$$
Therefore $\log_3(\log_8 8) = 0$.

38. $f(x) = 2^x$ $\qquad$ $g(x) = \log_2 x$

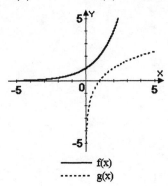

39. $f(x) = 2^x$ $\qquad$ $g(x) = \log_2 x$

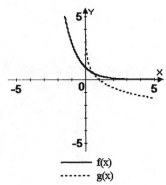

40. $x + 5 > 0$
$\quad x > -5$
The domain of f is $\{x | x > -5\}$ or $(-5, \infty)$.

41. $3 - x > 0$
$\quad -x > -3$
$\quad x < 3$
The domain of f is $\{x | x < 3\}$ or $(-\infty, 3)$.

42. The domain of g is all real numbers for which $(x - 1)^2 > 0$. The only number that must be excluded is 1. The domain of f is $\{x | x \neq 1\}$ or $(-\infty, 1) \cup (1, \infty)$.

43. Since $\ln e^x = x$, $\ln e^{6x} = 6x$.

44. Since $e^{\ln x} = x$, $e^{\ln \sqrt{x}} = \sqrt{x}$.

45. Since $10^{\log x} = x$, $10^{\log 4x^2} = 4x^2$.

46.
$$R = \log \frac{I}{I_0}$$
$$R = \log \frac{1000 I_0}{I_0}$$
$$R = \log 1000$$
$$10^R = 1000$$
$$10^R = 10^3$$
$$R = 3$$
The magnitude on the Richter scale is 3.

47. a. $f(0) = 76 - 18 \log(0 + 1)$
$\qquad = 76 - 18 \log(1)$
$\qquad = 76 - 18(0) = 76 - 0 = 76$

The average score when the exam was first given was 76.

b. $f(2) = 76 - 18 \log(2 + 1)$
$\qquad = 76 - 18 \log(3) \approx 67.4$
$f(4) = 76 - 18 \log(4 + 1)$
$\qquad = 76 - 18 \log(5) \approx 63.4$
$f(6) = 76 - 18 \log(6 + 1)$
$\qquad = 76 - 18 \log(7) \approx 60.8$
$f(8) = 76 - 18 \log(8 + 1)$
$\qquad = 76 - 18 \log(9) \approx 58.8$
$f(12) = 76 - 18 \log(12 + 1)$
$\qquad = 76 - 18 \log(13) \approx 55.9$

c.

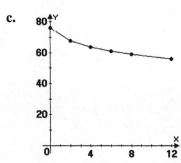

The students retain less material over time.

48. $t = \dfrac{1}{0.06}\ln\left(\dfrac{12}{12-5}\right) = \dfrac{1}{0.06}\ln\left(\dfrac{12}{7}\right) \approx 9.0$

It will take approximately 9 weeks for the man to run 5 miles per hour.

49. $\log_6\left(36x^3\right) = \log_6 36 + \log_6 x^3$

$\qquad\qquad = 2 + 3\log_6 x$

50. $\log_4 \dfrac{\sqrt{x}}{64} = \log_4 \sqrt{x} - \log_4 64 = \log_4 x^{\frac{1}{2}} - 3$

$\qquad\qquad = \dfrac{1}{2}\log_4 x - 3$

51. $\log_2\left(\dfrac{xy^2}{64}\right) = \log_2 xy^2 - \log_2 64$

$\qquad\qquad\qquad = \log_2 x + \log_2 y^2 - 6$

$\qquad\qquad\qquad = \log_2 x + 2\log_2 y - 6$

52. $\ln\sqrt[3]{\dfrac{x}{e}} = \ln\left(\dfrac{x}{e}\right)^{\frac{1}{3}} = \dfrac{1}{3}\ln\left(\dfrac{x}{e}\right) = \dfrac{1}{3}\left(\ln x - \ln e\right)$

$\qquad\qquad = \dfrac{1}{3}\left(\ln x - 1\right) = \dfrac{1}{3}\ln x - \dfrac{1}{3}$

53. $\log_b 7 + \log_b 3 = \log_b\left(7 \cdot 3\right) = \log_b 21$

54. $\log 3 - 3\log x = \log 3 - \log x^3 = \log\dfrac{3}{x^3}$

55. $3\ln x + 4\ln y = \ln x^3 + \ln y^4 = \ln\left(x^3 y^4\right)$

56. $\dfrac{1}{2}\ln x - \ln y = \ln x^{\frac{1}{2}} - \ln y = \ln\sqrt{x} - \ln y$

$\qquad\qquad = \ln\dfrac{\sqrt{x}}{y}$

57. $\log_6 72,348 = \dfrac{\log 72,348}{\log 6} \approx 6.2448$

58. $\log_4 0.863 = \dfrac{\log 0.863}{\log 4} \approx -0.1063$

59. $2^{4x-2} = 64$

$2^{4x-2} = 2^6$

$4x - 2 = 6$

$4x = 8$

$x = 2$

60. $125^x = 25$

$\left(5^3\right)^x = 5^2$

$5^{3x} = 5^2$

$3x = 2$

$x = \dfrac{2}{3}$

61. $9^x = \dfrac{1}{27}$

$\left(3^2\right)^x = 3^{-3}$

$3^{2x} = 3^{-3}$

$2x = -3$

$x = -\dfrac{3}{2}$

62. $8^x = 12,143$

$\ln 8^x = \ln 12,143$

$x\ln 8 = \ln 12,143$

$x = \dfrac{\ln 12,143}{\ln 8} \approx 4.52$

63. $9e^{5x} = 1269$

$e^{5x} = \dfrac{1269}{9}$

$\ln e^{5x} = \ln 141$

$5x = \ln 141$

$x = \dfrac{\ln 141}{5} \approx 0.99$

64. $30e^{0.045x} = 90$

$e^{0.045x} = 3$

$\ln e^{0.045x} = \ln 3$

$0.045x = \ln 3$

$x = \dfrac{\ln 3}{0.045} \approx 24.41$

65. $\log_5 x = -3$

$$x = 5^{-3} = \frac{1}{125}$$

66. $\log x = 2$

$$x = 10^2 = 100$$

67. $\log_4(3x-5) = 3$

$$3x - 5 = 4^3$$
$$3x - 5 = 64$$
$$3x = 69$$
$$x = 23$$

68. $\log_2(x+3) + \log_2(x-3) = 4$

$$\log_2((x+3)(x-3)) = 4$$
$$\log_2(x^2 - 9) = 4$$
$$x^2 - 9 = 2^4$$
$$x^2 - 9 = 16$$
$$x^2 = 25$$
$$x = \pm 5$$

We disregard –5 because it would result in taking the logarithm of a negative number. The solution is 5.

69. $\log_3(x-1) - \log_3(x+2) = 2$

$$\log_3 \frac{x-1}{x+2} = 2$$
$$\frac{x-1}{x+2} = 3^2$$
$$\frac{x-1}{x+2} = 9$$
$$x - 1 = 9(x+2)$$
$$x - 1 = 9x + 18$$
$$-8x - 1 = 18$$
$$-8x = 19$$
$$x = -\frac{19}{8}$$

We disregard $-\dfrac{19}{8}$ because it would result in taking the logarithm of a negative number. There is no solution. The solution set is $\varnothing$ or $\{\ \}$.

70. $\ln x = -1$

$$x = e^{-1} = \frac{1}{e}$$

71. $3 + 4\ln 2x = 15$

$$4\ln 2x = 12$$
$$\ln 2x = 3$$
$$2x = e^3$$
$$x = \frac{e^3}{2}$$

72. $13 = 10.1 e^{0.005t}$

$$\frac{13}{10.1} = e^{0.005t}$$
$$\ln\frac{13}{10.1} = \ln e^{0.005t}$$
$$\ln\frac{13}{10.1} = 0.005t$$
$$t = \frac{\ln\dfrac{13}{10.1}}{0.005} \approx 50$$

If the growth rate continues, the population will reach 13 million approximately 50 years after 1992 in the year 2042.

73. $560 = 364(1.005)^t$

$$\frac{560}{364} = (1.005)^t$$
$$\ln\frac{560}{364} = \ln(1.005)^t$$
$$\ln\frac{560}{364} = t\ln 1.005$$
$$t = \frac{\ln\dfrac{560}{364}}{\ln 1.005} \approx 86.4$$

The carbon dioxide concentration will double the pre-industrial level approximately 86 years after the year 2000 in the year 2086.

74. $30{,}000 = 15{,}557 + 5259\ln x$

$14{,}443 = 5259\ln x$

$\dfrac{14{,}443}{5259} = \ln x$

$e^{\frac{14{,}443}{5259}} = e^{\ln x}$

$x = e^{\frac{14{,}443}{5259}} \approx 15.6$

The average cost of a new car will be $30,000 approximately 16 years after 1989 in the year 2005.

75.

$$20{,}000 = 12{,}500\left(1 + \frac{0.065}{4}\right)^{4t}$$

$$20{,}000 = 12{,}500(1 + 0.01625)^{4t}$$

$$20{,}000 = 12{,}500(1.01625)^{4t}$$

$$1.6 = (1.01625)^{4t}$$

$$\ln 1.6 = \ln(1.01625)^{4t}$$

$$\ln 1.6 = 4t\ln 1.01625$$

$$t = \frac{\ln 1.6}{4\ln 1.01625} \approx 7.3$$

It will take approximately 7.3 years.

76. $3(50{,}000) = 50{,}000e^{0.075t}$

$3 = e^{0.075t}$

$\ln 3 = \ln e^{0.075t}$

$\ln 3 = 0.075t$

$t = \dfrac{\ln 3}{0.075} \approx 14.6$

The money will triple in approximately 14.6 years.

77. $3 = e^{r5}$

$\ln 3 = \ln e^{5r}$

$\ln 3 = 5r$

$r = \dfrac{\ln 3}{5} \approx 0.220$

The money will triple in 5 years if the interest rate is approximately 22%.

78. a. $29.3 = 14.6e^{k17}$

$\dfrac{29.3}{14.6} = e^{17k}$

$\ln\dfrac{29.3}{14.6} = \ln e^{17k}$

$\ln\dfrac{29.3}{14.6} = 17k$

$k = \dfrac{\ln\dfrac{29.3}{14.6}}{17} \approx 0.041$

b. $A = 14.6e^{0.041(25)} = 14.6e^{1.025} \approx 40.7$

The population will reach approximately 40.7 million in the year 2005.

c. $50 = 14.6e^{0.041t}$

$\dfrac{50}{14.6} = e^{0.041t}$

$\ln\dfrac{50}{14.6} = \ln e^{0.041t}$

$\ln\dfrac{50}{14.6} = 0.041t$

$t = \dfrac{\ln\dfrac{50}{14.6}}{0.041} \approx 30.0$

The population will reach 50 million approximately 30 years after 1980 in the year 2010.

79. $15 = 100e^{-0.000121t}$

$\dfrac{15}{100} = e^{-0.000121t}$

$\ln\dfrac{3}{20} = \ln e^{-0.000121t}$

$\ln\dfrac{3}{20} = -0.000121t$

$t = \dfrac{\ln\dfrac{3}{20}}{-0.000121} \approx 15{,}679$

The paintings are approximately 15,679 years old.

80. Answers may vary.

Chapter 12 Test

1. $f(x) = 2^x$

    $g(x) = 2^{x+1}$

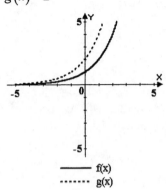

———— f(x)

········ g(x)

2. Semiannual Compounding:

    $A = 3000\left(1 + \dfrac{0.065}{2}\right)^{2(10)} = 3000(1 + 0.0325)^{20}$

    $= 3000(1.0325)^{20} \approx 5687.51$

    Continuous Compounding:

    $A = 3000e^{0.06(10)} = 3000e^{0.6} \approx 5466.36$

    Semiannual compounding at 6.5% yields a greater return. The difference in the yields is $221.

3. $(f \circ g)(x) = f(g(x)) = f(3x - 1)$

    $= (3x - 1)^2 + (3x - 1)$

    $= 9x^2 - 6x + 1 + 3x - 1 = 9x^2 - 3x$

    $(g \circ f)(x) = g(f(x)) = g(x^2 + x)$

    $= 3(x^2 + x) - 1 = 3x^2 + 3x - 1$

4. $f(x) = 5x - 7$

    $y = 5x - 7$

    Interchange x and y.

    $x = 5y - 7$

    $x + 7 = 5y$

    $\dfrac{x + 7}{5} = y$

$f^{-1}(x) = \dfrac{x + 7}{5}$

5. a. Because the line satisfies the vertical line test, we know its inverse is a function.

    b. $f(80) = 2000$

    c. $f^{-1}(2000)$ represents the income, $80,000, of a family that gives $2000 to charity.

6. $\log_5 125 = 3$

    $5^3 = 125$

7. $\sqrt{36} = 6$

    $36^{\frac{1}{2}} = 6$

    $\log_{36} 6 = \dfrac{1}{2}$

8. $f(x) = 3^x \qquad g(x) = \log_3 x$

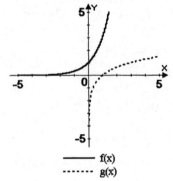

———— f(x)

········ g(x)

9. Since $\ln e^x = x$, $\ln e^{5x} = 5x$.

10. $\log_b b = 1$ because $b^1 = b$.

11. $\log_6 1 = 0$ because $6^0 = 1$.

12. $x - 7 > 0$

    $x > 7$

    The domain of f is $\{x \mid x > 7\}$ or $(7, \infty)$.

13.
$$D = 10\log\frac{I}{I_0} = 10\log\frac{10^{12}I_0}{I_0}$$
$$= 10\log 10^{12} = 10(12) = 120$$

The sound has a loudness of 120 decibels.

14. $\log_4\left(64x^5\right) = \log_4 64 + \log_4 x^5 = 3 + 5\log_4 x$

15.
$$\log_3\frac{\sqrt[3]{x}}{81} = \log_3\sqrt[3]{x} - \log_3 81 = \log_3 x^{\frac{1}{3}} - 4$$
$$= \frac{1}{3}\log_3 x - 4$$

16. $6\log x + 2\log y = \log x^6 + \log y^2 = \log x^6 y^2$

17. $\ln 7 - 3\ln x = \ln 7 - \ln x^3 = \ln\frac{7}{x^3}$

18. $\log_{15} 71 = \frac{\log 71}{\log 15} \approx 1.5741$

19.
$$3^{x-2} = 81$$
$$3^{x-2} = 3^4$$
$$x - 2 = 4$$
$$x = 6$$

20.
$$5^x = 1.4$$
$$\ln 5^x = \ln 1.4$$
$$x\ln 5 = \ln 1.4$$
$$x = \frac{\ln 1.4}{\ln 5} \approx 0.21$$

21.
$$400e^{0.005x} = 1600$$
$$e^{0.005x} = 4$$
$$\ln e^{0.005x} = \ln 4$$
$$0.005x = \ln 4$$
$$x = \frac{\ln 4}{0.005} \approx 277.26$$

22.
$$\log_{25} x = \frac{1}{2}$$
$$x = 25^{\frac{1}{2}} = \sqrt{25} = 5$$

23.
$$\log_6(4x-1) = 3$$
$$4x - 1 = 6^3$$
$$4x - 1 = 216$$
$$4x = 217$$
$$x = \frac{217}{4}$$

24.
$$\log x + \log(x+15) = 2$$
$$\log(x(x+15)) = 2$$
$$x(x+15) = 10^2$$
$$x^2 + 15 = 100$$
$$x^2 + 15 - 100 = 0$$
$$(x+20)(x-5) = 0$$
$$x + 20 = 0 \quad \text{and} \quad x - 5 = 0$$
$$x = -20 \qquad\qquad x = 5$$

We disregard −20 because it would result in taking the logarithm of a negative number.

25.
$$2\ln 3x = 8$$
$$\ln 3x = \frac{8}{2}$$
$$e^{\ln 3x} = e^4$$
$$3x = e^4$$
$$x = \frac{e^4}{3}$$

26. a. $P(0) = 89.18e^{-0.004(0)} = 89.18e^0 = 89.18$ In 1959, 89.18% of married men were employed.

b. The percentage of married men who are employed is decreasing. We know this since the growth rate, k, is negative.

c.
$$77 = 89.18e^{-0.004t}$$
$$\frac{77}{89.18} = e^{-0.004t}$$
$$\ln\frac{77}{89.18} = \ln e^{-0.004t}$$

$$\ln\frac{77}{89.18} = -0.004t$$

$$t = \frac{\ln\dfrac{77}{89.18}}{-0.004} \approx 36.7$$

77% of married men were employed approximately 37 years after 1959 in the year 1996.

27.
$$8000 = 4000\left(1 + \frac{0.05}{4}\right)^{4t}$$

$$2 = (1 + 0.0125)^{4t}$$

$$2 = (1.0125)^{4t}$$

$$\ln 2 = \ln(1.0125)^{4t}$$

$$\ln 2 = 4t\ln(1.0125)$$

$$t = \frac{\ln 2}{4\ln(1.0125)} \approx 13.9$$

It will take approximately 13.9 years for the money to grow to $8000.

28.
$$2 = 1e^{r10}$$

$$2 = e^{10r}$$

$$\ln 2 = \ln e^{10r}$$

$$\ln 2 = 10r$$

$$r = \frac{\ln 2}{10} \approx 0.069$$

The money will double in 10 years with an interest rate of approximately 6.9%.

29.
$$509 = 484e^{k(10)}$$

$$\frac{509}{484} = e^{10k}$$

$$\ln\frac{509}{484} = \ln e^{10k}$$

$$\ln\frac{509}{484} = 10k$$

$$k = \frac{\ln\dfrac{509}{484}}{10} \approx 0.005$$

The exponential growth function is
$A = 484e^{0.005t}$.

30.
$$5 = 100e^{-0.000121t}$$

$$\frac{5}{100} = e^{-0.000121t}$$

$$\ln 0.05 = \ln e^{-0.000121t}$$

$$\ln 0.05 = -0.000121t$$

$$t = \frac{\ln 0.05}{-0.000121} \approx 24758$$

The man died approximately 24,758 years ago.

Cumulative Review Exercises
Chapters 1–12

1.
$$\sqrt{2x+5} - \sqrt{x+3} = 2$$

$$\sqrt{2x+5} = 2 + \sqrt{x+3}$$

$$2x+5 = 4 + 4\sqrt{x+3} + x + 3$$

$$2x+5 = 7 + 4\sqrt{x+3} + x$$

$$x - 2 = 4\sqrt{x+3}$$

$$x^2 - 4x + 4 = 16(x+3)$$

$$x^2 - 4x + 4 = 16x + 48$$

$$x^2 - 20x - 44 = 0$$

$$(x-22)(x+2)=0$$
$$x-22=0 \quad \text{and} \quad x+2=0$$
$$x=22 \qquad \cancel{x=-2}$$

The solution, -2, does not check.

2.

$$(x-5)^2 = -49$$
$$\sqrt{(x-5)^2} = \pm\sqrt{-49}$$
$$x-5 = \pm 7i$$
$$x = 5 \pm 7i$$

3.

$$x^2 + x > 6$$
$$x^2 + x - 6 > 0$$

Solve the related quadratic equation.

$$x^2 + x - 6 = 0$$
$$(x+3)(x-2) = 0$$
$$x+3=0 \quad \text{or} \quad x-2=0$$
$$x=-3 \qquad x=2$$

Test Interval	Test Number	Test	Conclusion
$(-\infty,-3)$	-4	$(-4)^2 + (-4) > 6$ true	$(-\infty,-3)$ belongs to the solution set.
$(-3,2)$	0	$0^2 + 0 > 6$ false	$(-3,2)$ does not belong to the solution set.
$(2,\infty)$	3	$3^2 + 3 > 6$ true	$(2,\infty)$ does not belong to the solution set.

The solution set is $(-\infty,-3) \cup (2,\infty)$ or $\{x | x < -3 \text{ and } x > 2\}$.

4.

$$6x - 3(5x+2) = 4(1-x)$$
$$6x - 15x - 6 = 4 - 4x$$
$$-9x - 6 = 4 - 4x$$
$$-5x = 10$$
$$x = -2$$

5.

$$\frac{2}{x-3} - \frac{3}{x+3} = \frac{12}{x^2-9}$$
$$\frac{2}{x-3} - \frac{3}{x+3} = \frac{12}{(x+3)(x-3)}$$
$$(x+3)(x-3)\left(\frac{2}{x-3} - \frac{3}{x+3}\right) = (x+3)(x-3)\left(\frac{12}{(x+3)(x-3)}\right)$$
$$2(x+3) - 3(x-3) = 12$$
$$2x + 6 - 3x + 9 = 12$$

$$-x+15=12$$
$$-x=-3$$
$$x=3$$

We disregard 3 since it would make one or more of the denominators in the original equation zero. There is no solution. The solution set is $\varnothing$ or $\{\ \}$.

6. $3x+2<4$ and $4-x>1$
  $3x<2$ $\qquad$ $-x>-3$
  $x<\dfrac{2}{3}$ $\qquad$ $x<3$

The solution set is $\left\{x\middle|x<\dfrac{2}{3}\right\}$ or $\left(-\infty,\dfrac{2}{3}\right)$.

⟵————)——|——⟶
       2/3   3

7. Add the first two equations to eliminate z.
$$3x-2y+\ z=\ 7$$
$$\underline{2x+3y-\ z=\ 13}$$
$$5x+y=20$$

Multiply the second equation by 2 and add to the third equation.
$$4x+6y-2z=26$$
$$\underline{x-\ y+2z=-6}$$
$$5x+5y=20$$

The system is as follows.
$$5x+\ y=20$$
$$5x+5y=20$$

Multiply the first equation by -1 and add to the second equation.
$$-5x-\ y=-20$$
$$\underline{5x+5y=\ \ 20}$$
$$4y=0$$
$$y=0$$

Back-substitute 0 for y to find x.
$$5x \mid 0=20$$
$$5x=20$$
$$x=4$$

Back-substitute 4 for x and 0 for y to find z.
$$3(4)-2(0)+z=7$$
$$12+z=7$$
$$z=-5$$

The solution is $(4,0,-5)$.

8. $\log_9 x+\log_9\left(x-8\right)=1$
  $\log_9\left(x(x-8)\right)=1$
  $\left(x(x-8)\right)=9^1$
  $x^2-8x=9$
  $x^2-8x-9=0$
  $(x-9)(x+1)=0$
  $x-9=0$ and $x+1=0$
  $x=9$ $\qquad$ $x=-1$

We disregard -1 because it would result in taking the logarithm of a negative number.

9. $f(x)=(x+2)^2-4$

The vertex of the parabola is $(h,k)=(-2,-4)$. The x–intercepts are -4 and 0. The y–intercept is 0.

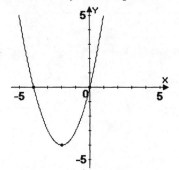

10. $y<-3x+5$

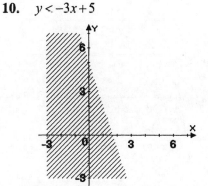

11. $f(x) = 3^{x-2}$

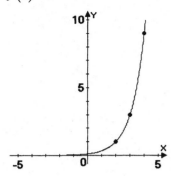

12.
$$\frac{2x+1}{x-5} - \frac{4}{x^2-3x-10} = \frac{2x+1}{x-5} - \frac{4}{(x-5)(x+2)}$$
$$= \frac{(2x+1)(x+2)}{(x-5)(x+2)} - \frac{4}{(x-5)(x+2)}$$
$$= \frac{(2x+1)(x+2)-4}{(x-5)(x+2)} = \frac{2x^2+5x+2-4}{(x-5)(x+2)}$$
$$= \frac{2x^2+5x-2}{(x-5)(x+2)}$$

13.
$$\frac{\frac{1}{x-1}+1}{\frac{1}{x+1}-1} = \frac{(x-1)(x+1)}{(x-1)(x+1)} \cdot \frac{\frac{1}{x-1}+1}{\frac{1}{x+1}-1}$$
$$= \frac{(x+1)+(x-1)(x+1)}{(x-1)-(x-1)(x+1)}$$
$$= \frac{x+1+x^2-1}{x-1-(x^2-1)} = \frac{x+x^2}{x-1-x^2+1}$$
$$= \frac{x^2+x}{x-x^2} = \frac{x(x+1)}{x(1-x)} = \frac{x+1}{1-x} \text{ or } -\frac{x+1}{x-1}$$

14.
$$\frac{6}{\sqrt{5}-\sqrt{2}} = \frac{6}{\sqrt{5}-\sqrt{2}} \cdot \frac{\sqrt{5}+\sqrt{2}}{\sqrt{5}+\sqrt{2}}$$
$$= \frac{6(\sqrt{5}+\sqrt{2})}{5-2} = \frac{6(\sqrt{5}+\sqrt{2})}{3}$$
$$= 2(\sqrt{5}+\sqrt{2}) = 2\sqrt{5}+2\sqrt{2}$$

15.
$$8\sqrt{45}+2\sqrt{5}-7\sqrt{20}$$
$$= 8\sqrt{9\cdot5}+2\sqrt{5}-7\sqrt{4\cdot5}$$
$$= 8\cdot3\sqrt{5}+2\sqrt{5}-7\cdot2\sqrt{5}$$
$$= 24\sqrt{5}+2\sqrt{5}-14\sqrt{5}=12\sqrt{5}$$

16.
$$\frac{5}{\sqrt[3]{2x^2y}} = \frac{5}{\sqrt[3]{2x^2y}} \cdot \frac{\sqrt[3]{2^2xy^2}}{\sqrt[3]{2^2xy^2}}$$
$$= \frac{5\sqrt[3]{4xy^2}}{\sqrt[3]{2^3x^3y^3}} = \frac{5\sqrt[3]{4xy^2}}{2xy}$$

17.
$$5ax+5ay-4bx-4by = 5a(x+y)-4b(x+y)$$
$$= (x+y)(5a-4b)$$

18.
$$5\log x - \frac{1}{2}\log y = \log x^5 - \log y^{\frac{1}{2}}$$
$$= \log\frac{x^5}{y^{\frac{1}{2}}} = \log\frac{x^5}{\sqrt{y}}$$

19. $0.00397 = 3.97 \times 10^{-3}$

20.
$$x^2+2x-15=0$$
$$(x+5)(x-3)=0$$
$$x+5=0 \quad \text{and} \quad x-3=0$$
$$x=-5 \qquad\qquad x=3$$

The domain is $\{x \mid x$ is a real number and $x \neq -5$ and $x \neq 3\}$ or $(-\infty,-5) \cup (-5,3) \cup (3,\infty)$.

21.
$$2x-6 \geq 0$$
$$2x \geq 6$$
$$x \geq 3$$

The domain is $\{x \mid x \geq 3\}$ or $[3,\infty)$.

22.
$$1-x > 0$$
$$-x > -1$$
$$x < 1$$

The domain is $\{x \mid x < 1\}$ or $(-\infty,1)$.

23. Let x = the width of the garden
Let $2x + 2$ = the length of the garden
$$2x+2(2x+2)=22$$
$$2x+4x+4=22$$
$$6x+4=22$$
$$6x=18$$
$$x=3$$
The width is 3 feet and the length
$2x+2 = 2(3)+2 = 6+2=8$ feet.

24. Let x = the salary before the raise
$$x+0.06x=19,610$$
$$1.06x=19,610$$
$$x=\frac{19,610}{1.06}=18,500$$
The salary before the raise is \$18,500.

25. $F(t)=1-k\ln(t+1)$
$$\frac{1}{2}=1-k\ln(3+1)$$
$$-\frac{1}{2}=-k\ln 4$$
$$k\ln 4=\frac{1}{2}$$
$$k=\frac{1}{2\ln 4}\approx 0.3607$$

$F(t)=1-0.3607\ln(t+1)$

$F(6)=1-0.3607\ln(6+1)$
$\quad =1-0.3607\ln 7\approx 0.298$
After 6 hours, 0.298 or $\frac{298}{1000}$ people will
remember all the words.

Chapter 13

CONIC SECTIONS AND SYSTEMS OF NONLINEAR EQUATIONS

Distance and Midpoint Formulas; Circles

13.1 CHECK POINTS

CHECK POINT 1
$$d = \sqrt{(x_2 - x_1)^2 + (y_2 - y_1)^2}$$
$$= \sqrt{(5-2)^2 + (2-(-2))^2}$$
$$= \sqrt{3^2 + 4^2} = \sqrt{9+16} = \sqrt{25} = 5$$

CHECK POINT 2
$$\text{Midpoint} = \left(\frac{x_1 + x_2}{2}, \frac{y_1 + y_2}{2}\right)$$
$$= \left(\frac{1+7}{2}, \frac{2+(-3)}{2}\right)$$
$$= \left(\frac{8}{2}, \frac{-1}{2}\right) = \left(4, -\frac{1}{2}\right)$$

CHECK POINT 3
$$(x-h)^2 + (y-k)^2 = r^2$$
$$(x-0)^2 + (y-0)^2 = 4^2$$
$$x^2 + y^2 = 16$$

CHECK POINT 4
$$(x-h)^2 + (y-k)^2 = r^2$$
$$(x-5)^2 + (y-(-6))^2 = 10^2$$
$$(x-5)^2 + (y+6)^2 = 100$$

CHECK POINT 5
$$(x+3)^2 + (y-1)^2 = 4$$
$$(x-(-3))^2 + (y-1)^2 = 2^2$$
The center is $(-3,1)$ and the radius is 2 units.

CHECK POINT 6
$$x^2 + y^2 + 4x - 4y - 1 = 0$$
$$(x^2 + 4x \quad) + (y^2 - 4y \quad) = 1$$
$$(x^2 + 4x + 4) + (y^2 - 4y + 4) = 1 + 4 + 4$$
$$(x+2)^2 + (y-2)^2 = 9$$

EXERCISE SET 13.1

1.
$$d = \sqrt{(14-2)^2 + (8-3)^2} = \sqrt{12^2 + 5^2}$$
$$= \sqrt{144 + 25} = \sqrt{169} = 13$$

3.
$$d = \sqrt{(6-4)^2 + (3-1)^2} = \sqrt{2^2 + 2^2}$$
$$= \sqrt{4+4} = \sqrt{8} = \sqrt{4 \cdot 2} = 2\sqrt{2} \approx 2.83$$

5.
$$d = \sqrt{(-3-0)^2 + (4-0)^2} = \sqrt{(-3)^2 + 4^2}$$
$$= \sqrt{9+16} = \sqrt{25} = 5$$

7.
$$d = \sqrt{(3-(-2))^2 + (-4-(-6))^2}$$
$$= \sqrt{5^2 + 2^2} = \sqrt{25 + 4} = \sqrt{29} \approx 5.39$$

9.
$$d = \sqrt{(4-0)^2 + (1-(-3))^2} = \sqrt{4^2 + 4^2}$$
$$= \sqrt{16+16} = \sqrt{32} = \sqrt{16 \cdot 2} = 4\sqrt{2} \approx 5.66$$

11.
$$d = \sqrt{(3.5-(-0.5))^2 + (8.2-6.2)^2}$$
$$= \sqrt{4^2 + 2^2} = \sqrt{16 + 4}$$
$$= \sqrt{20} = \sqrt{4 \cdot 5} = 2\sqrt{5} \approx 4.47$$

13.
$$d = \sqrt{(\sqrt{5}-0)^2 + (0-(-\sqrt{3}))^2}$$
$$= \sqrt{(\sqrt{5})^2 + (\sqrt{3})^2} = \sqrt{5+3}$$
$$= \sqrt{8} = \sqrt{4 \cdot 2} = 2\sqrt{2} \approx 2.83$$

15.
$$d = \sqrt{(3\sqrt{3}-(-\sqrt{3}))^2 + (\sqrt{5}-4\sqrt{5})^2}$$

$$=\sqrt{\left(4\sqrt{3}\right)^2+\left(-3\sqrt{5}\right)^2}=\sqrt{16\cdot3+9\cdot5}$$
$$=\sqrt{48+45}=\sqrt{93}\approx9.64$$

17.
$$d=\sqrt{\left(\frac{7}{3}-\frac{1}{3}\right)^2+\left(\frac{1}{5}-\frac{6}{5}\right)^2}=\sqrt{\left(\frac{6}{3}\right)^2+\left(-\frac{5}{5}\right)^2}$$
$$=\sqrt{2^2+\left(-1\right)^2}=\sqrt{4+1}=\sqrt{5}\approx2.24$$

19.
$$\text{Midpoint}=\left(\frac{6+2}{2},\frac{8+4}{2}\right)=\left(\frac{8}{2},\frac{12}{2}\right)=\left(4,6\right)$$

21.
$$\text{Midpoint}=\left(\frac{-2+\left(-6\right)}{2},\frac{-8+\left(-2\right)}{2}\right)$$
$$=\left(\frac{-8}{2},\frac{-10}{2}\right)=\left(-4,-5\right)$$

23.
$$\text{Midpoint}=\left(\frac{-3+6}{2},\frac{-4+\left(-8\right)}{2}\right)$$
$$=\left(\frac{3}{2},\frac{-12}{2}\right)=\left(\frac{3}{2},-6\right)$$

25.
$$\text{Midpoint}=\left(\frac{-\frac{7}{2}+\left(-\frac{5}{2}\right)}{2},\frac{\frac{3}{2}+\left(-\frac{11}{2}\right)}{2}\right)$$
$$=\left(\frac{-\frac{12}{2}}{2},\frac{-\frac{8}{2}}{2}\right)=\left(-\frac{12}{2}\cdot\frac{1}{2},-\frac{8}{2}\cdot\frac{1}{2}\right)$$
$$=\left(-\frac{12}{4},-\frac{8}{4}\right)=\left(-3,-2\right)$$

27.
$$\text{Midpoint}=\left(\frac{8+\left(-6\right)}{2},\frac{3\sqrt{5}+7\sqrt{5}}{2}\right)$$
$$=\left(\frac{2}{2},\frac{10\sqrt{5}}{2}\right)=\left(1,5\sqrt{5}\right)$$

29.
$$\text{Midpoint}=\left(\frac{\sqrt{18}+\sqrt{2}}{2},\frac{-4+4}{2}\right)$$
$$=\left(\frac{\sqrt{9\cdot2}+\sqrt{2}}{2},\frac{0}{2}\right)=\left(\frac{3\sqrt{2}+\sqrt{2}}{2},0\right)$$
$$=\left(\frac{4\sqrt{2}}{2},0\right)=\left(2\sqrt{2},0\right)$$

31.
$$\left(x-h\right)^2+\left(y-k\right)^2=r^2$$
$$\left(x-0\right)^2+\left(y-0\right)^2=7^2$$
$$x^2+y^2=49$$

33.
$$\left(x-h\right)^2+\left(y-k\right)^2=r^2$$
$$\left(x-3\right)^2+\left(y-2\right)^2=5^2$$
$$\left(x-3\right)^2+\left(y-2\right)^2=25$$

35.
$$\left(x-h\right)^2+\left(y-k\right)^2=r^2$$
$$\left(x-\left(-1\right)\right)^2+\left(y-4\right)^2=2^2$$
$$\left(x+1\right)^2+\left(y-4\right)^2=4$$

37.
$$\left(x-h\right)^2+\left(y-k\right)^2=r^2$$
$$\left(x-\left(-3\right)\right)^2+\left(y-\left(-1\right)\right)^2=\left(\sqrt{3}\right)^2$$
$$\left(x+3\right)^2+\left(y+1\right)^2=3$$

39.
$$\left(x-h\right)^2+\left(y-k\right)^2=r^2$$
$$\left(x-\left(-4\right)\right)^2+\left(y-0\right)^2=10^2$$
$$\left(x+4\right)^2+y^2=100$$

41.
$$x^2+y^2=16$$
$$\left(x-0\right)^2+\left(y-0\right)^2=4^2$$
The center is $\left(0,0\right)$ and the radius is 4 units.

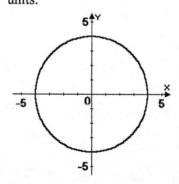

43.
$$\left(x-3\right)^2+\left(y-1\right)^2=36$$
$$\left(x-3\right)^2+\left(y-1\right)^2=6^2$$
The center is $\left(3,1\right)$ and the radius is 6 units.

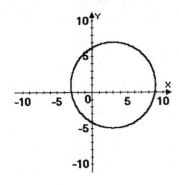

45.
$$(x+3)^2 + (y-2)^2 = 4$$
$$(x-(-3))^2 + (y-2)^2 = 2^2$$
The center is $(-3,2)$ and the radius is 2 units.

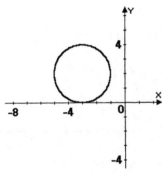

47.
$$(x+2)^2 + (y+2)^2 = 4$$
$$(x-(-2))^2 + (y-(-2))^2 = 2^2$$
The center is $(-2,-2)$ and the radius is 2 units.

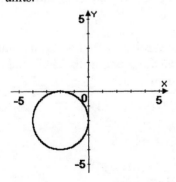

49.
$$x^2 + y^2 + 6x + 2y + 6 = 0$$
$$(x^2 + 6x \quad) + (y^2 + 2y \quad) = -6$$

$$(x^2 + 6x + 9) + (y^2 + 2y + 1) = -6 + 9 + 1$$
$$(x+3)^2 + (y+1)^2 = 4$$
The center is $(-3,-1)$ and the radius is 2 units.

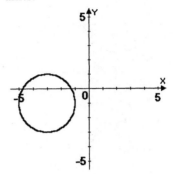

51.
$$x^2 + y^2 - 10x - 6y - 30 = 0$$
$$(x^2 - 10x \quad) + (y^2 - 6y \quad) = 30$$
$$(x^2 - 10x + 25) + (y^2 - 6y + 9) = 30 + 25 + 9$$
$$(x-5)^2 + (y-3)^2 = 64$$
The center is $(5,3)$ and the radius is 8 units.

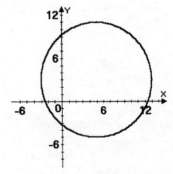

53.
$$x^2 + y^2 + 8x - 2y - 8 = 0$$
$$(x^2 + 8x \quad) + (y^2 - 2y \quad) = 8$$
$$(x^2 + 8x + 16) + (y^2 - 2y + 1) = 8 + 16 + 1$$
$$(x+4)^2 + (y-1)^2 = 25$$
The center is $(-4,1)$ and the radius is 5 units.

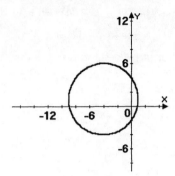

55.

$$x^2 - 2x + y^2 - 15 = 0$$

$$\left(x^2 - 2x \quad\right) + y^2 = 15$$

$$\left(x^2 - 2x + 1\right) + y^2 = 15 + 1$$

$$(x - 1)^2 + y^2 = 16$$

The center is $(1, 0)$ and the radius is 4 units.

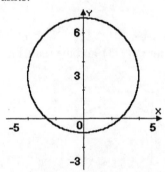

57.

$$d = \sqrt{\left(65 - (-115)\right)^2 + (70 - 170)^2}$$

$$= \sqrt{180^2 + (-100)^2} = \sqrt{32400 + 10000}$$

$$= \sqrt{42400} \approx 205.9$$

The distance is approximately 205.9 miles.

$$t = \frac{d}{r} = \frac{205.9}{400} \approx 0.5$$

It will take approximately 0.5 hours or 30 minutes to make the flight.

59.   The center of the circle is $(0, 68 + 14)$ or $(0, 82)$. The radius of the Ferris wheel is 68 feet. The equation of the circular wheel is:

$$x^2 + (y - 82)^2 = 68^2$$

$$x^2 + (y - 82)^2 = 4624.$$

For Exercises 61-67, answers may vary.

69.   Distance from A to B:

$$d = \sqrt{(3 - 1)^2 + \left((3 + d) - (1 + d)\right)^2}$$

$$= \sqrt{(2)^2 + (3 + d - 1 - d)^2} = \sqrt{4 + (2)^2}$$

$$= \sqrt{4 + 4} = \sqrt{8} = \sqrt{4 \cdot 2} = 2\sqrt{2}$$

Distance from B to C:

$$d = \sqrt{(6 - 3)^2 + \left((6 + d) - (3 + d)\right)^2}$$

$$= \sqrt{(3)^2 + (6 + d - 3 - d)^2} = \sqrt{9 + (3)^2}$$

$$= \sqrt{9 + 9} = \sqrt{18} = \sqrt{9 \cdot 2} = 3\sqrt{2}$$

Distance from A to C.

$$d = \sqrt{(6 - 1)^2 + \left((6 + d) - (1 + d)\right)^2}$$

$$= \sqrt{(5)^2 + (6 + d - 1 - d)^2} = \sqrt{25 + (5)^2}$$

$$= \sqrt{25 + 25} = \sqrt{50} = \sqrt{25 \cdot 2} = 5\sqrt{2}$$

If the points are collinear,

$$d_{AB} + d_{BC} = d_{AC}.$$

$$d_{AB} + d_{BC} = 2\sqrt{2} + 3\sqrt{2} = 5\sqrt{2}$$

Since this is the same as the distance from A to C, we know that the points are collinear.

71.   Find the radius by finding the distance between the center of the circle and the point on the circle.

$$d = \sqrt{\left(3 - (-2)\right)^2 + (-5 - 1)^2}$$

$$= \sqrt{(5)^2 + (-6)^2}$$

$$= \sqrt{25 + 36} = \sqrt{61}$$

Standard Form:

$$\left(x - 3\right)^2 + \left(y - (-5)\right)^2 = \left(\sqrt{61}\right)^2$$

$$(x - 3)^2 + (y + 5)^2 = 61$$

General Form:
$$(x-3)^2 + (y+5)^2 = 61$$
$$x^2 - 6x + 9 + y^2 + 10y + 25 = 61$$
$$x^2 + y^2 - 6x + 10y + 34 = 61$$
$$x^2 + y^2 - 6x + 10y - 27 = 0$$

73. Since the circles have the same center, we can subtract the area of the smaller circle from the area of the larger circle to find the area of the bounded region. Using $A = \pi r^2$ to find the area, we need the radius of each circle. The radius of the larger circle is $\sqrt{36} = 6$ and the radius of the smaller circle is $\sqrt{25} = 5$.
$$A_{larger} - A_{smaller} = \pi(6)^2 - \pi(5)^2 = 36\pi - 25\pi$$
$$= 11\pi \approx 34.6$$
The area of the bounded region is 11π or 34.6 square units.

75. $x^2 + y^2 = 25$
$$y^2 = 25 - x^2$$
$$y = \pm\sqrt{25 - x^2}$$

77. $x^2 + 10x + y^2 - 4y - 20 = 0$
$$(x^2 + 10x \quad) + (y^2 - 4y \quad) = 20$$
Complete the squares.
$$\left(\frac{b}{2}\right)^2 = \left(\frac{10}{2}\right)^2 = (5)^2 = 25$$
$$\left(\frac{b}{2}\right)^2 = \left(\frac{4}{2}\right)^2 = (2)^2 = 4$$
$$(x^2 + 10x + 25) + (y^2 - 4y + 4) = 20 + 25 + 4$$
$$(x+5)^2 + (y-2)^2 = 49$$

$$(y-2)^2 = 49 - (x+5)^2$$
$$y - 2 = \pm\sqrt{49 - (x+5)^2}$$
$$y = 2 \pm\sqrt{49 - (x+5)^2}$$

Review Exercises

78. $f(g(x)) = f(3x+4) = (3x+4)^2 - 2$
$$= 9x^2 + 24x + 16 - 2 = 9x^2 + 24x + 14$$
$$g(f(x)) = g(x^2 - 2) = 3(x^2 - 2) + 4$$
$$= 3x^2 - 6 + 4 = 3x^2 - 2$$

79.
$$2x = \sqrt{7x-3} + 3$$
$$2x - 3 = \sqrt{7x-3}$$
$$(2x-3)^2 = 7x-3$$
$$4x^2 - 12x + 9 = 7x - 3$$
$$4x^2 - 19x + 12 = 0$$
$$(4x-3)(x-4) = 0$$
$$4x - 3 = 0 \qquad x - 4 = 0$$
$$4x = 3 \qquad x = 4$$
$$x = \frac{3}{4}$$

$\frac{3}{4}$ does not check. The solution is 4.

80.
$$|2x - 5| < 10$$
$$-10 < 2x - 5 < 10$$
$$-10 + 5 < 2x - 5 + 5 < 10 + 5$$
$$-5 < 2x < 15$$
$$-\frac{5}{2} < x < \frac{15}{2}$$

The solution set is $\left\{x \left| -\frac{5}{2} < x < \frac{15}{2}\right.\right\}$ or $\left(-\frac{5}{2}, \frac{15}{2}\right)$.

The Ellipse

13.2 CHECK POINTS

CHECK POINT 1

The major axis is horizontal. The vertices
are $(-6,0)$ and $(6,0)$. The endpoints of
the minor axis are $(0,-3)$ and $(0,3)$.

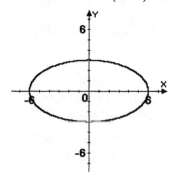

CHECK POINT 2

$$16x^2 + 9y^2 = 144$$

$$\frac{16x^2}{144} + \frac{9y^2}{144} = \frac{144}{144}$$

$$\frac{x^2}{9} + \frac{y^2}{16} = 1$$

The major axis is vertical. The vertices are
$(0,-4)$ and $(0,4)$. The endpoints of the
minor axis are $(-3,0)$ and $(3,0)$.

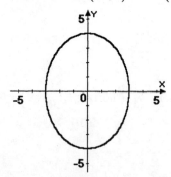

CHECK POINT 3

The center of the ellipse is $(-1,2)$. The
vertices lie 3 units to the left and right of
the center. The endpoints of the minor axis

lie two units above and below the center.

Center	Vertices	Endpoints of Minor Axis
$(-1,2)$	$(-1-3,2)$ $=(-4,2)$	$(-1,2-2)$ $=(-1,0)$
	$(-1+3,2)$ $=(2,2)$	$(-1,2+2)$ $=(-1,4)$

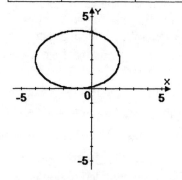

CHECK POINT 4

$$\frac{6^2}{400} + \frac{y^2}{100} = 1$$

$$\frac{36}{400} + \frac{y^2}{100} = 1$$

$$\frac{9}{100} + \frac{y^2}{100} = 1$$

$$100\left(\frac{9}{100} + \frac{y^2}{100}\right) = 100(1)$$

$$9 + y^2 = 100$$

$$y^2 = 91$$

$$y = \sqrt{91} \approx 9.54$$

The height of the archway 6 feet from the
center is approximately 9.54 feet. Since
the truck is 9 feet high, the truck will clear
the archway.

EXERCISE SET 13.2

1.   The major axis is horizontal. The vertices
are $(-4,0)$ and $(4,0)$. The endpoints of
the minor axis are $(0,-2)$ and $(0,2)$.

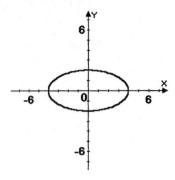

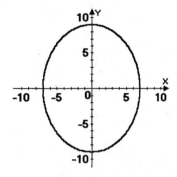

3. The major axis is vertical. The vertices are $(0,-6)$ and $(0,6)$. The endpoints of the minor axis are $(-3,0)$ and $(3,0)$.

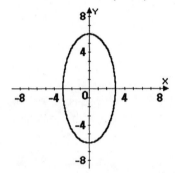

5. The major axis is vertical. The vertices are $(0,-8)$ and $(0,8)$. The endpoints of the minor axis are $(-5,0)$ and $(5,0)$.

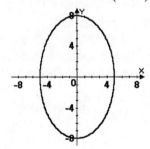

7. The major axis is vertical. The vertices are $(0,-9)$ and $(0,9)$. The endpoints of the minor axis are $(-7,0)$ and $(7,0)$.

9.
$$25x^2 + 4y^2 = 100$$
$$\frac{25x^2}{100} + \frac{4y^2}{100} = \frac{100}{100}$$
$$\frac{x^2}{4} + \frac{y^2}{25} = 1$$
The major axis is vertical. The vertices are $(0,-5)$ and $(0,5)$. The endpoints of the minor axis are $(-2,0)$ and $(2,0)$.

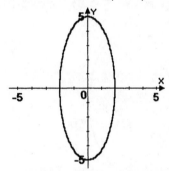

11.
$$4x^2 + 16y^2 = 64$$
$$\frac{4x^2}{64} + \frac{16y^2}{64} = \frac{64}{64}$$
$$\frac{x^2}{16} + \frac{y^2}{4} = 1$$
The major axis is horizontal. The vertices are $(-4,0)$ and $(4,0)$. The endpoints of the minor axis are $(0,-2)$ and $(0,2)$.

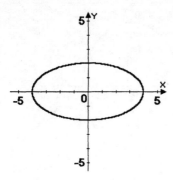

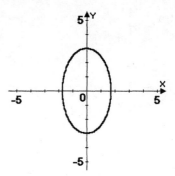

13. $25x^2 + 9y^2 = 225$

$$\frac{25x^2}{225} + \frac{9y^2}{225} = \frac{225}{225}$$

$$\frac{x^2}{9} + \frac{y^2}{25} = 1$$

The major axis is vertical. The vertices are $(0,-3)$ and $(0,3)$. The endpoints of the minor axis are $(-5,0)$ and $(5,0)$.

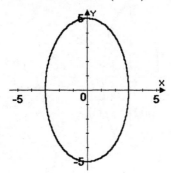

15. $x^2 + 2y^2 = 8$

$$\frac{x^2}{8} + \frac{2y^2}{8} = \frac{8}{8}$$

$$\frac{x^2}{8} + \frac{y^2}{4} = 1$$

The major axis is horizontal. The vertices are $\left(-2\sqrt{2},0\right)$ and $\left(2\sqrt{2},0\right)$.

The endpoints of the minor axis are $(0,-2)$ and $(0,2)$.

17. The center of the ellipse is the origin, the major axis is horizontal with $a = 2$, and $b = 1$.

$$\frac{x^2}{2^2} + \frac{y^2}{1^2} = 1$$

$$\frac{x^2}{4} + \frac{y^2}{1} = 1$$

19. The center of the ellipse is the origin, the major axis is vertical with $a = 2$, and $b = 1$.

$$\frac{x^2}{1^2} + \frac{y^2}{2^2} = 1$$

$$\frac{x^2}{1} + \frac{y^2}{4} = 1$$

21. The center of the ellipse is $(2,1)$.

The major axis is horizontal.
The vertices lie 3 units to the left and right of the center. The endpoints of the minor axis lie two units above and below the center.

Center	Vertices	Endpoints of Minor Axis
$(2,1)$	$(2-3,1)$ $=(-1,1)$	$(2,1-2)$ $=(2,-1)$
	$(2+3,1)$ $=(5,1)$	$(2,1+2)$ $=(2,3)$

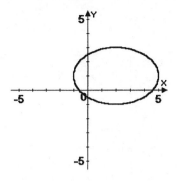

Center	Vertices	Endpoints Minor Axis
$(4,-2)$	$(4,-2-5)$ $=(4,-7)$	$(4-3,-2)$ $=(1,-2)$
	$(4,-2+5)$ $=(4,3)$	$(4+3,-2)$ $=(7,-2)$

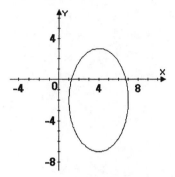

23. $(x+3)^2 + 4(y-2)^2 = 16$

$$\frac{(x+3)^2}{16} + \frac{4(y-2)^2}{16} = \frac{16}{16}$$

$$\frac{(x+3)^2}{16} + \frac{(y-2)^2}{4} = 1$$

The center of the ellipse is $(-3,2)$. The major axis is horizontal. The vertices lie 4 units to the left and right of the center. The endpoints of the minor axis lie two units above and below the center.

Center	Vertices	Endpoints of Minor Axis
$(-3,2)$	$(-3-4,2)$ $=(-7,2)$	$(-3,2-2)$ $=(-3,0)$
	$(-3+4,2)$ $=(1,2)$	$(-3,2+2)$ $=(-3,4)$

27. The center of the ellipse is $(0,2)$. The major axis is vertical. The vertices lie 6 units to the above and below the center. The endpoints of the minor axis lie 5 units to the left and right of the center.

Center	Vertices	Endpoint Minor Axis
$(0,2)$	$(0,2-6)$ $=(0,-4)$	$(0-5,2)$ $=(-5,2)$
	$(0,2+6)$ $=(0,8)$	$(0+5,2)$ $=(5,2)$

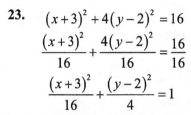

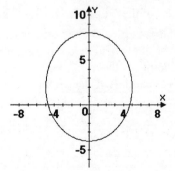

25. The center of the ellipse is $(4,-2)$. The major axis is vertical. The vertices lie 5 units to the above and below the center. The endpoints of the minor axis lie 3 units to the right and left of the center.

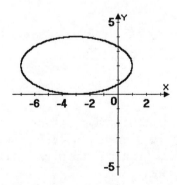

29. $\dfrac{(x+3)^2}{9} + (y-2)^2 = 1$

$$\frac{(x+3)^2}{9} + \frac{(y-2)^2}{1} = 1$$

The center of the ellipse is $(-3, 2)$. The major axis is horizontal. The vertices lie 3 units to the left and right of the center. The endpoints of the minor axis lie two units above and below the center.

Center	Vertices	Endpoints of Minor Axis
$(-3, 2)$	$(-3+3, 2)$ $= (0, 2)$	$(-3, 2-1)$ $= (-3, 1)$
	$(-3-3, 2)$ $= (-6, 2)$	$(-3, 2+1)$ $= (-3, 3)$

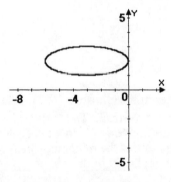

31.
$$9(x-1)^2 + 4(y+3)^2 = 36$$
$$\frac{9(x-1)^2}{36} + \frac{4(y+3)^2}{36} = \frac{36}{36}$$
$$\frac{(x-1)^2}{4} + \frac{(y+3)^2}{9} = 1$$

The center of the ellipse is $(1, -3)$. The major axis is vertical. The vertices lie 3 units to the above and below the center. The endpoints of the minor axis lie 3 units to the right and left of the center.

Center	Vertices	Endpoints of Minor Axis
$(1, -3)$	$(1, -3-3)$ $= (1, -6)$	$(1-3, -3)$ $= (-2, -3)$
	$(1, -3+3)$ $= (1, 0)$	$(1+3, -3)$ $= (4, -3)$

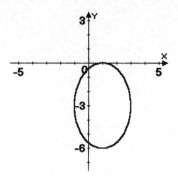

33. From the figure, we see that the major axis is horizontal with $a = 15$, and $b = 10$.
$$\frac{x^2}{15^2} + \frac{y^2}{10^2} = 1$$
$$\frac{x^2}{225} + \frac{y^2}{100} = 1$$

Since the truck is 8 feet wide, determine the height of the archway at $\frac{8}{2} = 4$ feet from the center.
$$\frac{4^2}{225} + \frac{y^2}{100} = 1$$
$$\frac{16}{225} + \frac{y^2}{100} = 1$$
$$900\left(\frac{16}{225} + \frac{y^2}{100}\right) = 900(1)$$
$$4(16) + 9y^2 = 900$$
$$64 + 9y^2 = 900$$
$$9y^2 = 836$$
$$y^2 = \frac{836}{9}$$
$$y = \sqrt{\frac{836}{9}} \approx 9.64$$

The height of the archway 4 feet from the center is approximately 9.64 feet. Since the truck is 7 feet high, the truck will clear the archway.

35. a.
$$\frac{x^2}{48^2} + \frac{y^2}{23^2} = 1$$
$$\frac{x^2}{2304} + \frac{y^2}{529} = 1$$

b.
$$c^2 = a^2 - b^2$$
$$c^2 = 48^2 - 23^2$$
$$c^2 = 2304 - 529$$
$$c^2 = 1775$$
$$c = \sqrt{1775} \approx 42.1$$

The desk was situated approximately 42 feet from the center of the ellipse.

For Exercises 37-41, answers may vary.

43. The center of the ellipse is at the origin and the major axis is vertical. We have $a = 6$.

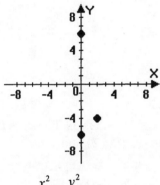

$$\frac{x^2}{b^2} + \frac{y^2}{a^2} = 1$$

$$\frac{2^2}{b^2} + \frac{(-4)^2}{6^2} = 1$$

$$\frac{4}{b^2} + \frac{16}{36} = 1$$

$$36b^2 \left(\frac{4}{b^2} + \frac{16}{36} \right) = 36b^2 (1)$$

$$36(4) + 16b^2 = 36b^2$$

$$144 + 16b^2 = 36b^2$$

$$144 = 20b^2$$

$$\frac{144}{20} = b^2$$

$$\frac{36}{5} = b^2$$

The equation ellipse in standard form is

$$\frac{x^2}{36} + \frac{y^2}{\frac{36}{5}} = 1.$$

45.
$$4x^2 + 9y^2 - 32x + 36y + 64 = 0$$
$$\left(4x^2 - 32x \quad \right) + \left(9y^2 + 36y \quad \right) = -64$$
$$4\left(x^2 - 8x \quad \right) + 9\left(y^2 + 4y \quad \right) = -64$$
$$4\left(x^2 - 8x + 16 \right) + 9\left(y^2 + 4y + 4 \right)$$
$$= -64 + 4(16) + 9(4)$$
$$4(x-4)^2 + 9(y+2)^2 = -64 + 64 + 36$$
$$4(x-4)^2 + 9(y+2)^2 = 36$$
$$\frac{4(x-4)^2}{36} + \frac{9(y+2)^2}{36} = \frac{36}{36}$$
$$\frac{(x-4)^2}{9} + \frac{(y+2)^2}{4} = 1$$
$$\frac{(x-4)^2}{9} + \frac{(y+2)^2}{4} = 1$$

47. The ellipse's vertices lie on the larger circle. This means that a is the radius of the circle. The equation of the larger circle is $x^2 + y^2 = 25$. The endpoints of the ellipse's minor axis lie on the smaller circle. This means that b is the radius of the smaller circle. The equation of the smaller circle is $x^2 + y^2 = 9$.

49. Answers will vary. For example, Exercise 1.

$$\frac{x^2}{16} + \frac{y^2}{4} = 1$$

$$16\left(\frac{x^2}{16} + \frac{y^2}{4} \right) = 16(1)$$

$$x^2 + 4y^2 = 16$$

$$4y^2 = 16 - x^2$$

$$y^2 = \frac{16 - x^2}{4}$$

$$y = \pm \sqrt{\frac{16 - x^2}{4}}$$

$$y = \pm \frac{1}{2} \sqrt{16 - x^2}$$

Review Exercises

51.
$$x^3 + 2x^2 - 4x - 8 = x^2(x+2) - 4(x+2)$$
$$= (x+2)(x^2 - 4)$$
$$= (x+2)(x+2)(x-2)$$
$$= (x+2)^2(x-2)$$

52. $\sqrt[3]{40x^4y^7} = \sqrt[3]{8 \cdot 5x^3xy^6y} = 2xy^2\sqrt[3]{5xy}$

53.
$$\frac{2}{x+2} + \frac{4}{x-2} = \frac{x-1}{x^2-4}$$
$$\frac{2}{x+2} + \frac{4}{x-2} = \frac{x-1}{(x+2)(x-2)}$$

Multiply both sides of the equation by $(x+2)(x-2)$.

$$2(x-2) + 4(x+2) = x-1$$
$$2x - 4 + 4x + 8 = x-1$$
$$6x + 4 = x-1$$
$$5x = -5$$
$$x = -1$$

The solution is –1 and the solution set is $\{-1\}$.

The Hyperbola

13.3 CHECK POINTS

CHECK POINT 1

a. The transverse axis lies along the x–axis and the vertices lie 5 units to the left and right of the origin at $(-5,0)$ and $(5,0)$.

b. The transverse axis lies along the y–axis and the vertices lie 5 units above and below the origin at $(0,-5)$ and $(0,5)$.

CHECK POINT 2

$$\frac{x^2}{36} - \frac{y^2}{9} = 1$$

The transverse axis lies on the x-axis and the vertices are $(-6,0)$ and $(6,0)$.

Construct a rectangle using –6 and 6 on the x–axis, and –3 and 3 on the y–axis. Draw extended diagonals to obtain the asymptotes.

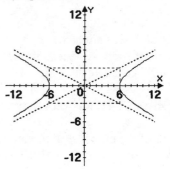

CHECK POINT 3

$$y^2 - 4x^2 = 4$$
$$\frac{y^2}{4} - \frac{4x^2}{4} = \frac{4}{4}$$
$$\frac{y^2}{4} - \frac{x^2}{1} = 1$$

The transverse axis lies on the y-axis and the vertices are $(0,-2)$ and $(0,2)$. Construct a rectangle using –1 and 1 on the x–axis, and –2 and 2 on the y–axis. Draw extended diagonals to obtain the asymptotes.

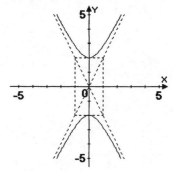

EXERCISE SET 13.3

1. The transverse axis lies along the x–axis. The vertices are $(-2,0)$ and $(2,0)$. This corresponds to graph **(b)**.

3.   The transverse axis lies along the y–axis. The vertices are $(0,-2)$ and $(0,2)$. This corresponds to graph (**a**).

5.   The transverse axis lies on the x-axis and the vertices are $(-3,0)$ and $(3,0)$.

Construct a rectangle using -3 and 3 on the x–axis, and -5 and 5 on the y–axis. Draw extended diagonals to obtain the asymptotes.

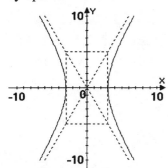

7.   The transverse axis lies on the x-axis and the vertices are $(-10,0)$ and $(10,0)$.

Construct a rectangle using -10 and 10 on the x–axis, and -8 and 8 on the y–axis. Draw extended diagonals to obtain the asymptotes.

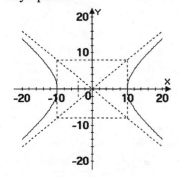

9.   The transverse axis lies on the y-axis and the vertices are $(0,-4)$ and $(0,4)$.

Construct a rectangle using -4 and 4 on the x–axis, and -6 and 6 on the y–axis. Draw extended diagonals to obtain the asymptotes.

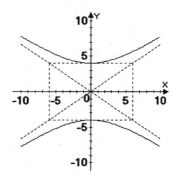

11.   The transverse axis lies on the y-axis and the vertices are $(0,-6)$ and $(0,6)$.

Construct a rectangle using -5 and 5 on the x–axis, and -6 and 6 on the y–axis. Draw extended diagonals to obtain the asymptotes.

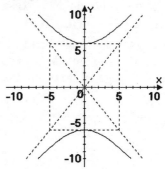

13. $$9x^2 - 4y^2 = 36$$
$$\frac{9x^2}{36} - \frac{4y^2}{36} = \frac{36}{36}$$
$$\frac{x^2}{4} - \frac{y^2}{9} = 1$$

The transverse axis lies on the x-axis and the vertices are $(-2,0)$ and $(2,0)$.

Construct a rectangle using -2 and 2 on the x–axis, and -3 and 3 on the y–axis. Draw extended diagonals to obtain the asymptotes.

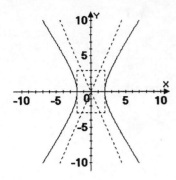

15. $9y^2 - 25x^2 = 225$

$$\frac{9y^2}{225} - \frac{25x^2}{225} = \frac{225}{225}$$

$$\frac{y^2}{25} - \frac{x^2}{9} = 1$$

The transverse axis lies on the y-axis and the vertices are $(0,-5)$ and $(0,5)$.

Construct a rectangle using -3 and 3 on the x-axis, and -5 and 5 on the y-axis. Draw extended diagonals to obtain the asymptotes.

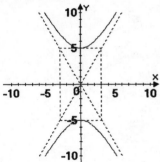

17. $4x^2 = 4 + y^2$

$$4x^2 - y^2 = 4$$

$$\frac{4x^2}{4} - \frac{y^2}{4} = \frac{4}{4}$$

$$\frac{x^2}{1} - \frac{y^2}{4} = 1$$

The transverse axis lies on the x-axis and the vertices are $(-1,0)$ and $(1,0)$.

Construct a rectangle using -1 and 1 on the x-axis, and -2 and 2 on the y-axis. Draw extended diagonals to obtain the asymptotes.

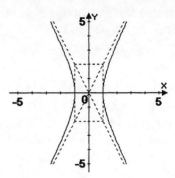

19. The transverse axis lies along the x-axis and the vertices are $(-3,0)$ and $(3,0)$.

This means that $a = 3$. We also see that $b = 5$.

$$\frac{x^2}{a^2} - \frac{y^2}{b^2} = 1$$

$$\frac{x^2}{3^2} - \frac{y^2}{5^2} = 1$$

$$\frac{x^2}{9} - \frac{y^2}{25} = 1$$

21. The transverse axis lies along the y-axis and the vertices are $(0,-2)$ and $(0,2)$.

This means that $a = 2$. We also see that $b = 3$.

$$\frac{y^2}{a^2} - \frac{x^2}{b^2} = 1$$

$$\frac{y^2}{2^2} - \frac{x^2}{3^2} = 1$$

$$\frac{y^2}{4} - \frac{x^2}{9} = 1$$

23. $625y^2 - 400x^2 = 250,000$

$$\frac{625y^2}{250,000} - \frac{400x^2}{250,000} = \frac{250,000}{250,000}$$

$$\frac{y^2}{400} - \frac{x^2}{625} = 1$$

Since the houses at the vertices of the hyperbola will be closest, find the distance between the vertices. Since $a^2 = 400$, $a = 20$. The houses are $20 + 20 = 40$ yards apart.

For Exercises 25-29, answers may vary.

31. $\dfrac{(x-2)^2}{16} - \dfrac{(y-3)^2}{9} = 1$

This is the equation of a hyperbola with center $(2,3)$. The transverse axis is horizontal and the vertices lie 4 units to the right and left of $(2,3)$ at

$(2-4,3) = (-2,3)$ and $(2+4,3) = (6,3)$.

Construct two sides of a rectangle using –2 and 6 on the x–axis. The remaining two sides of the rectangle are constructed 3 units above and 3 units below the center at $3-3 = 0$ and $3+3 = 6$. Draw extended diagonals to obtain the asymptotes.

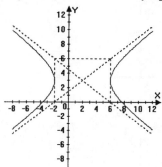

33. $(x-3)^2 - 4(y+3)^2 = 4$

$\dfrac{(x-3)^2}{4} - \dfrac{4(y+3)^2}{4} = \dfrac{4}{4}$

$\dfrac{(x-3)^2}{4} - \dfrac{(y+3)^2}{1} = 1$

This is the equation of a hyperbola with center $(3,-3)$. The transverse axis is horizontal and the vertices lie 2 units to the right and left of $(3,-3)$ at $(3-2,-3)$

$= (1,-3)$ and $(3+2,-3) = (5,-3)$.

Construct two sides of a rectangle using 1 and 5 on the x–axis. The remaining two sides of the rectangle are constructed 1 unit above and below center at $-3-1 = -4$ and $-3+1 = -2$. Draw extended diagonals to obtain the asymptotes.

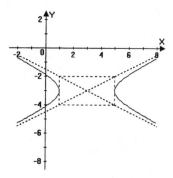

35. Since the vertices are $(6,0)$ and $(-6,0)$, we know that the transverse axis lies along the x–axis and $a = 6$. Use the equation of the asymptote, $y = 4x$, to find b.

$y = 4x = 4(6) = 24$

This means that $b = \pm 24$.

$\dfrac{x^2}{6^2} - \dfrac{y^2}{24^2} = 1$

$\dfrac{x^2}{36} - \dfrac{y^2}{576} = 1$

37.

39. Answers will vary. Consider $a = 3$ and $b = 2$.

$\dfrac{x^2}{9} - \dfrac{y^2}{4} = 1$

$36\left(\dfrac{x^2}{9} - \dfrac{y^2}{4}\right) = 36(1)$

$4x^2 - 9y^2 = 36$

$-9y^2 = -4x^2 + 36$

$9y^2 = 4x^2 - 36$

$y^2 = \dfrac{1}{9}(4x^2 - 36)$

$y = \pm\sqrt{\dfrac{1}{9}(4x^2 - 36)} = \pm\dfrac{1}{3}\sqrt{4x^2 - 36}$

$$\frac{x^2}{9} - \frac{y^2}{4} = -1$$

$$36\left(\frac{x^2}{9} - \frac{y^2}{4}\right) = 36(-1)$$

$$4x^2 - 9y^2 = -36$$

$$-9y^2 = -4x^2 - 36$$

$$9y^2 = 4x^2 + 36$$

$$y^2 = \frac{1}{9}\left(4x^2 + 36\right)$$

$$y = \pm\sqrt{\frac{1}{9}\left(4x^2 + 36\right)} = \pm\frac{1}{3}\sqrt{4x^2 + 36}$$

Both graphs can be drawn using the same rectangle. They differ only in their transverse axes.

40. Vertex:

$$-\frac{b}{2a} = -\frac{-4}{2(-1)} = -2$$

$$f(-2) = -(-2)^2 - 4(-2) + 5$$
$$= -4 + 8 + 5 = 9$$

The vertex is at $(-2, 9)$.

x–intercepts:

$$0 = -x^2 - 4x + 5$$
$$0 = x^2 + 4x - 5$$
$$0 = (x + 5)(x - 1)$$
$$x + 5 = 0 \quad \text{or} \quad x - 1 = 0$$
$$x = -5 \qquad\qquad x = 1$$

y–intercept:

$$y = -0^2 - 4(0) + 5 = 5$$

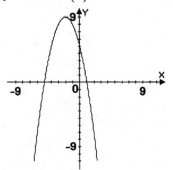

41. Solve the related quadratic equation.

$$3x^2 - 11x - 4 = 0 \qquad\qquad 3x + 1 = 0 \quad \text{or} \quad x - 4 = 0$$
$$(3x + 1)(x - 4) = 0 \qquad\qquad 3x = -1 \qquad\qquad x = 4$$
$$x = -\frac{1}{3}$$

The boundary points are $-\frac{1}{3}$ and 4.

Test Interval	Test Number	Substitution	Conclusion
$\left(-\infty, -\frac{1}{3}\right]$	-1	$3(-1)^2 - 11(-1) - 4 \geq 0$ $10 \geq 0$, true	$\left(-\infty, -\frac{1}{3}\right]$ belongs in the solution set
$\left[-\frac{1}{3}, 4\right]$	0	$3(0)^2 - 11(0) - 4 \geq 0$ $-4 \geq 0$, false	$\left[-\frac{1}{3}, 4\right]$ does not belong in the solution set.
$[4, \infty)$	5	$3(5)^2 - 11(5) - 4 \geq 0$ $16 \geq 0$, true	$[4, \infty)$ belongs in the solution set.

The solution set is $\left(-\infty, -\dfrac{1}{3}\right] \cup [4, \infty)$ or

$\left\{ x \middle| x \le -\dfrac{1}{3} \text{ or } x \ge 4 \right\}$.

42. $\log_4 (3x+1) = 3$

$3x + 1 = 4^3$

$3x + 1 = 64$

$3x = 63$

$x = 21$

The Parabola; Identifying Conic Sections

13.4 CHECK POINTS

CHECK POINT 1

Vertex: $(1, 2)$

x–intercept:

$x = -(0-2)^2 + 1 = -(-2)^2 + 1$

$\quad = -4 + 1 = -3$

y–intercepts:

$0 = -(y-2)^2 + 1$

$0 = -(y^2 - 4y + 4) + 1$

$0 = -y^2 + 4y - 4 + 1$

$0 = -y^2 + 4y - 3$

$0 = y^2 - 4y + 3$

$0 = (y-3)(y-1)$

$y - 3 = 0 \quad \text{and} \quad y - 1 = 0$

$\quad y = 3 \qquad\qquad y = 1$

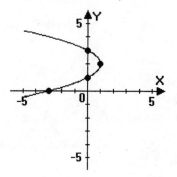

CHECK POINT 2

Vertex:

$-\dfrac{b}{2a} = -\dfrac{8}{2(1)} = -\dfrac{8}{2} = -4$

$x = (-4)^2 + 8(-4) + 7 = 16 - 32 + 7 = -9$

x–intercept:

$x = 0^2 + 8(0) + 7 = 0 + 0 + 7 = 7$

y–intercepts:

$0 = y^2 + 8y + 7$

$0 = (y+7)(y+1)$

$y + 7 = 0 \quad \text{and} \quad y + 1 = 0$

$\quad y = -7 \qquad\qquad y = -1$

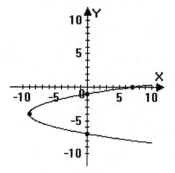

CHECK POINT 3

a. $\qquad x^2 = 4y^2 + 16$

$x^2 - 4y^2 = 16$

Because x^2 and y^2 have opposite signs, the equation's graph is a hyperbola.

b. $\qquad x^2 = 16 - 4y^2$

$x^2 + 4y^2 = 16$

Because x^2 and y^2 have different positive coefficients, the equation's graph is an ellipse.

c. $\qquad 4x^2 = 16 - 4y^2$

$4x^2 + 4y^2 = 16$

Because x^2 and y^2 have the same positive coefficient, the equation's graph is a circle.

d. $\quad x = -4y^2 + 16y$

Since only one variable is squared, the graph of the equation is a parabola.

EXERCISE SET 13.4

1.   a. Since $a = 1$, the parabola opens to the right.
  b. The vertex of the parabola is $(-1,2)$.
  c. Graph **b.** is the equation's graph.

3.   a. Since $a = 1$, the parabola opens to the right.
  b. The vertex of the parabola is $(1,-2)$.
  c. Graph **f** .is the equation's graph.

5.   a. Since $a = -1$, the parabola opens to the left.
  b. The vertex of the parabola is $(1,2)$.
  c. Graph **a.** is the equation's graph. Either graph a or graph e will match this. One will be changed to open to the left.

7. $x = 2y^2$
  $x = 2(y-0)^2 + 0$
  The vertex is the point $(0,0)$.

9. $x = (y-2)^2 + 3$
  The vertex is the point $(3,2)$.

11. $x = -4(y+2)^2 - 1$
  The vertex is the point $(-1,-2)$.

13. $x = 2(y-6)^2$
  $x = 2(y-6)^2 + 0$
  The vertex is the point $(0,6)$.

15. $x = y^2 - 6y + 6$
  The y–coordinate of the vertex is
  $$-\frac{b}{2a} = -\frac{-6}{2(1)} = -\frac{-6}{2} = 3.$$
  The x–coordinate of the vertex is
  $f(3) = 3^2 - 6(3) + 6 = 9 - 18 + 6 = -3.$
  The vertex is the point $(-3,3)$.

17. $x = 3y^2 + 6y + 7$
  The y–coordinate of the vertex is
  $$-\frac{b}{2a} = -\frac{6}{2(3)} = -\frac{6}{6} = -1.$$
  The x–coordinate of the vertex is
  $f(-1) = 3(-1)^2 + 6(-1) + 7$
  $\qquad = 3(1) - 6 + 7 = 3 - 6 + 7 = 4.$
  The vertex is the point $(4,-1)$.

19.   Since $a = 1$ is positive, the parabola opens to the right.
  Vertex: $(-4,2)$
  Axis of symmetry: $y = 2$
  x–intercept:
  $x = (0-2)^2 - 4 = 4 - 4 = 0$
  y–intercepts:
  $0 = (y-2)^2 - 4$
  $0 = y^2 - 4y + 4 - 4$
  $0 = y^2 - 4y$
  $0 = y(y-4)$
  $y = 0 \quad$ and $\quad y - 4 = 0$
  $\qquad\qquad\qquad\qquad y = 4$

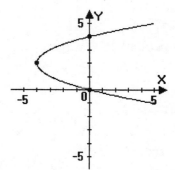

21.   Since $a = 1$ is positive, the parabola opens to the right.
  Vertex: $(-5,3)$
  Axis of symmetry: $y = 3$
  x–intercept:
  $x = (0-3)^2 - 5 = (-3)^2 - 5 = 9 - 5 = 4$
  y–intercepts:
  $0 = (y-3)^2 - 5$
  $0 = y^2 - 6y + 9 - 5$

$0 = y^2 - 6y + 4$

$x = \dfrac{-(-6) \pm \sqrt{(-6)^2 - 4(1)4}}{2(1)} = \dfrac{6 \pm \sqrt{36 - 16}}{2}$

$= \dfrac{6 \pm \sqrt{20}}{2} = \dfrac{6 \pm 2\sqrt{5}}{2} = 3 \pm \sqrt{5}$

The y–intercepts are $3 - \sqrt{5}$ and $3 + \sqrt{5}$.

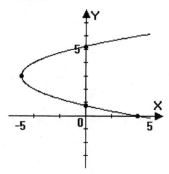

23. Vertex: $(4, 5)$

Axis of symmetry: $y = 5$
x–intercept:
$x = -(0 - 5)^2 + 4 = -(-5)^2 + 4$
$\quad = -25 + 4 = -21$
The x–intercept is -21.
y–intercepts:
$0 = -(y - 5)^2 + 4$
$0 = -(y^2 - 10y + 25) + 4$
$0 = -y^2 + 10y - 25 + 4$
$0 = -y^2 + 10y - 21$
$0 = y^2 - 10y + 21$
$0 = (y - 7)(y - 3)$
$y - 7 = 0 \quad$ and $\quad y - 3 = 0$
$\quad y = 7 \qquad\qquad y = 3$

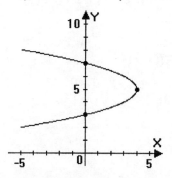

25. Vertex: $(1, 4)$

Axis of symmetry: $y = 4$
x–intercept:
$x = (0 - 4)^2 + 1 = (-4)^2 + 1 = 16 + 1 = 17$
y–intercepts:
$0 = (y - 4)^2 + 1$
$0 = y^2 - 8y + 16 + 1$
$0 = y^2 - 8y + 17$
$y = \dfrac{-(-8) \pm \sqrt{(-8)^2 - 4(1)(17)}}{2(1)}$
$= \dfrac{8 \pm \sqrt{64 - 68}}{2} = \dfrac{8 \pm \sqrt{-4}}{2}$
$= \dfrac{8 \pm 2i}{2} = 4 \pm i$

The solutions are complex, so there are no y–intercepts.

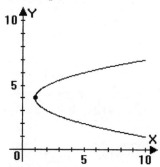

27. Vertex: $(3, 5)$

Axis of symmetry: $y = 5$
x–intercept:
$x = -3(0 - 5)^2 + 3 = -3(-5)^2 + 3$
$\quad = -3(25) + 3 = -75 + 3 = -72$
y–intercepts:
$0 = -3(y - 5)^2 + 3$
$0 = -3(y^2 - 10y + 25) + 3$
$0 = -3y^2 + 30y - 75 + 3$
$0 = -3y^2 + 30y - 72$
$0 = y^2 - 10y + 24$
$0 = (y - 6)(y - 4)$
$y - 6 = 0 \quad$ and $\quad y - 4 = 0$
$\quad y = 6 \qquad\qquad y = 4$

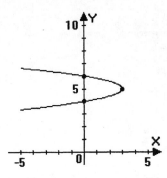

29. Vertex: $(-1, -3)$

Axis of symmetry: $y = -3$

x–intercept:

$x = -2(0+3)^2 - 1 = -2(3)^2 - 1$
$= -2(9) - 1 = -18 - 1 = -19$

y–intercepts:

$0 = -2(y+3)^2 - 1$
$0 = -2(y^2 + 6x + 9) - 1$
$0 = -2y^2 - 12x - 18 - 1$
$0 = -2y^2 - 12x - 19$
$0 = 2y^2 + 12x + 19$

$y = \dfrac{-12 \pm \sqrt{12^2 - 4(2)(19)}}{2(2)}$

$= \dfrac{-12 \pm \sqrt{144 - 152}}{4} = \dfrac{-12 \pm \sqrt{-8}}{4}$

Since the solutions will be complex, there are no y–intercepts.

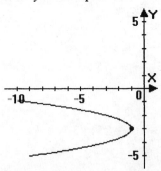

31. Vertex: $(1, -2)$

Axis of symmetry: $y = -2$

x–intercept:

$x = \dfrac{1}{2}(0+2)^2 + 1 = \dfrac{1}{2}(4) + 1 = 2 + 1 = 3$

y–intercepts:

$0 = \dfrac{1}{2}(y+2)^2 + 1$

$0 = \dfrac{1}{2}(y^2 + 2y + 4) + 1$

$0 = \dfrac{1}{2}y^2 + y + 2 + 1$

$0 = \dfrac{1}{2}y^2 + y + 3$

$0 = y^2 + 2y + 6$

$y = \dfrac{-2 \pm \sqrt{2^2 - 4(1)(6)}}{2(1)}$

$= \dfrac{-2 \pm \sqrt{4 - 24}}{2} = \dfrac{-2 \pm \sqrt{-20}}{2}$

Since the solutions will be complex, there are no y–intercepts.

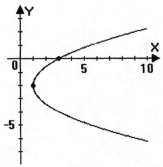

33. Vertex:

$-\dfrac{b}{2a} = -\dfrac{2}{2(1)} = -\dfrac{2}{2} = -1$

$x = (-1)^2 + 2(-1) - 3 = 1 - 2 - 3 = -4$

The vertex of the parabola is $(-4, -1)$.

Axis of symmetry: $y = -1$

x–intercept:

$x = 0^2 + 2(0) - 3 = 0 + 0 - 3 = -3$

y–intercepts:

$0 = y^2 + 2y - 3$
$0 = (y+3)(y-1)$
$y + 3 = 0 \quad$ and $\quad y - 1 = 0$
$\qquad y = -3 \qquad\qquad\quad y = 1$

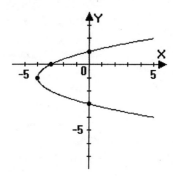

x–intercept:
$$x = 0^2 + 6(0) = 0$$
y–intercepts:
$$0 = y^2 + 6y$$
$$0 = y(y + 6)$$
$$y = 0 \quad \text{and} \quad y + 6 = 0$$
$$y = -6$$

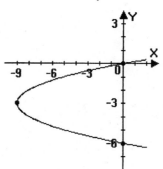

35. Vertex:
$$-\frac{b}{2a} = -\frac{-4}{2(-1)} = -\frac{-4}{-2} = -2$$

$$x = -(-2)^2 - 4(-2) + 5 = -4 + 8 + 5 = 9$$
The vertex of the parabola is $(9, -2)$.
Axis of symmetry: $y = -2$
x–intercept:
$$x = -0^2 - 4(0) + 5 = 0 - 0 + 5 = 5$$
y–intercepts:
$$0 = -y^2 - 4y + 5$$
$$0 = y^2 + 4y - 5$$
$$0 = (y + 5)(y - 1)$$
$$y + 5 = 0 \quad \text{and} \quad y - 1 = 0$$
$$y = -5 \qquad\qquad y = 1$$

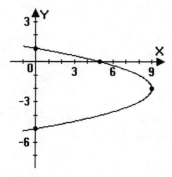

39. Vertex:
$$-\frac{b}{2a} = -\frac{-4}{2(-2)} = -\frac{-4}{-4} = -1$$

$$x = -2(-1)^2 - 4(-1) = -2(1) + 4$$
$$= -2 + 4 = 2$$
The vertex of the parabola is $(2, -1)$.
Axis of symmetry: $y = -1$
x–intercept:
$$x = -2(0)^2 - 4(0) = -2(0) - 0 = 0$$
y–intercepts:
$$0 = -2y^2 - 4y$$
$$0 = y^2 + 2y$$
$$0 = y(y + 2)$$
$$y = 0 \quad \text{and} \quad y + 2 = 0$$
$$y = -2$$

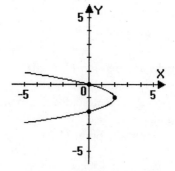

37. Vertex:
$$-\frac{b}{2a} = -\frac{6}{2(1)} = -\frac{6}{2} = -3$$

$$x = (-3)^2 + 6(-3) = 9 - 18 = -9$$
The vertex of the parabola is $(-9, -3)$.
Axis of symmetry: $y = -3$

41.
Vertex: $-\dfrac{b}{2a} = -\dfrac{-4}{2(-2)} = -\dfrac{-4}{-4} = -1$

$x = -2(-1)^2 - 4(-1) + 1 = -2(1) + 4 + 1$
$\qquad = -2 + 4 + 1 = 3$

The vertex of the parabola is $(3, -1)$. Axis of symmetry: $y = -1$

x–intercept:
$x = -2(0)^2 - 4(0) + 1 = -2(0) - 0 + 1$
$\qquad = 0 - 0 + 1 = 1$

y–intercepts:
$0 = -2y^2 - 4y + 1$

$y = \dfrac{-(-4) \pm \sqrt{(-4)^2 - 4(-2)(1)}}{2(-2)}$

$\quad = \dfrac{4 \pm \sqrt{16+8}}{-4} = \dfrac{4 \pm \sqrt{24}}{-4} = \dfrac{4 \pm 2\sqrt{6}}{-4}$

$\quad = \dfrac{2(2 \pm \sqrt{6})}{-4} = \dfrac{2 \pm \sqrt{6}}{-2} = \dfrac{-(2 \pm \sqrt{6})}{2}$

$\quad = \dfrac{-2 \pm \sqrt{6}}{2}$

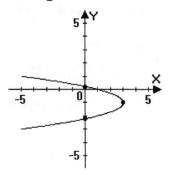

43.
  a. Since the squared term is y, the parabola is horizontal.
  b. Since $a = 2$ is positive, the parabola opens to the right.
  c. The vertex is the point $(2, 1)$.

45.
  a. Since the squared term is x, the parabola is vertical.
  b. Since $a = 2$ is positive, the parabola opens up.
  c. The vertex is the point $(1, 2)$.

47.
  a. Since the squared term is x, the parabola is vertical.
  b. Since $a = -1$ is negative, the parabola opens down.
  c. The vertex is the point $(-3, 4)$.

49.
  a. Since the squared term is y, the parabola is horizontal.
  b. Since $a = -1$ is negative, the parabola opens to the left.
  c. The vertex is the point $(4, -3)$.

51.
  a. Since the squared term is x, the parabola is vertical.
  b. Since $a = 1$ is positive, the parabola opens up.
  c. $-\dfrac{b}{2a} = -\dfrac{-4}{2(1)} = -\dfrac{-4}{2} = 2$

$\quad f(2) = 2^2 - 4(2) - 1 = 4 - 8 - 1 = -5$
The vertex is the point $(2, -5)$.

53.
  a. Since the squared term is y, the parabola is horizontal.
  b. Since $a = -1$ is negative, the parabola opens to the left.
  c. $-\dfrac{b}{2a} = -\dfrac{4}{2(-1)} = -\dfrac{4}{-2} = 2$

$\quad f(2) = -(2)^2 + 4(2) + 1 = -4 + 8 + 1 = 5$
The vertex is the point $(5, 2)$.

55. $x - 7 - 8y = y^2$
Since only one variable is squared, the graph of the equation is a parabola.

57. $\quad 4x^2 = 36 - y^2$
$\quad 4x^2 + y^2 = 36$
Because x^2 and y^2 have different positive coefficients, the graph is an ellipse.

59. $\quad x^2 = 36 + 4y^2$
$\quad x^2 - 4y^2 = 36$
Because x^2 and y^2 have opposite signs, the equation's graph is a hyperbola.

61.
$$3x^2 = 12 - 3y^2$$
$$3x^2 + 3y^2 = 12$$
Because x^2 and y^2 have the same positive coefficient, the equation's graph is a circle.

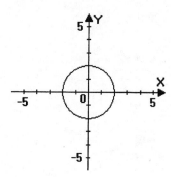

63.
$$3x^2 = 12 + 3y^2$$
$$3x^2 - 3y^2 = 12$$
Because x^2 and y^2 have opposite signs, the equation's graph is a hyperbola.

65. $x^2 - 4y^2 = 16$
$$\frac{x^2}{16} - \frac{4y^2}{16} = \frac{16}{16}$$
$$\frac{x^2}{16} - \frac{y^2}{4} = 1$$
The transverse axis lies on the x-axis and the vertices are $(-4,0)$ and $(4,0)$.

Construct a rectangle using –4 and 4 on the x–axis, and –2 and 2 on the y–axis. Draw extended diagonals to obtain the asymptotes.

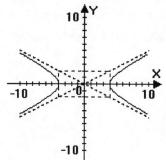

67. $4x^2 + 4y^2 = 16$
$$\frac{4x^2}{4} + \frac{4y^2}{4} = \frac{16}{4}$$
$$x^2 + y^2 = 4$$
The center is $(0,0)$ and the radius is 2 units.

69. $x^2 + 4y^2 = 16$
$$\frac{x^2}{16} + \frac{4y^2}{16} = \frac{16}{16}$$
$$\frac{x^2}{16} + \frac{y^2}{4} = 1$$
The major axis is horizontal. The vertices are $(-4,0)$ and $(4,0)$. The endpoints of the minor axis are $(0,-2)$ and $(0,2)$.

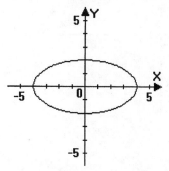

71. $x = (y-1)^2 - 4$
Since only one variable is squared, the graph of the equation is a parabola.
Vertex: $(-4,1)$
Axis of symmetry: $y = 1$
x–intercept:
$$x = (0-1)^2 - 4 = (-1)^2 - 4 = 1 - 4 = -3$$
y–intercepts:
$$0 = (y-1)^2 - 4$$
$$0 = y^2 - 2y + 1 - 4$$
$$0 = y^2 - 2y - 3$$
$$0 = (y-3)(y+1)$$

$$y - 3 = 0 \quad \text{and} \quad y + 1 = 0$$
$$y = 3 \qquad\qquad y = -1$$

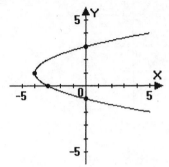

73. $(x-2)^2 + (y+1)^2 = 16$

The center is $(2,-1)$ and the radius is 4 units.

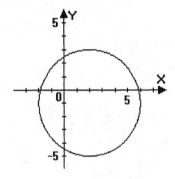

75. **a.**
$$y = ax^2$$
$$316 = a(1750)^2$$
$$316 = a(3062500)$$
$$0.0001032 = a$$
The equation is $y = 0.0001032x^2$.

b. $x = 1750 - 1000 = 750$
$$y = 0.0001032(750)^2$$
$$= 0.0001032(562,500) = 58.05$$
The height of the cable is 58.05 feet.

77. **a.**
$$y = ax^2$$
$$2 = a(6)^2$$
$$2 = a(36)$$
$$a = \frac{2}{36} = \frac{1}{18}$$

The equation is $y = \frac{1}{18}x^2$.

b.
$$a = \frac{1}{4p}$$
$$\frac{1}{18} = \frac{1}{4p}$$
$$4p = 18$$
$$p = \frac{18}{4} = 4.5$$
The receiver should be placed 4.5 feet from the base of the dish.

For Exercises 79-85, answers may vary.

87. Statement **b.** is true. Since $a > 0$, the parabola will open to the right. If the vertex is (3, 2) and the parabola opens to the right, it will not have a y–intercept.
Statement **a.** is false. Because $a = -1$, the parabola will open to the left.
Statement **c.** is false. If a parabola defines y as a function of x, it will open up or down.
Statement **d.** is false. $x = a(y-k)+h$ is not a parabola. There is no squared variable.

89.
$$y = ax^2$$
$$-50 = a(100)^2$$
$$-50 = a(10,000)$$
$$a = -\frac{50}{10,000} = -\frac{1}{200}$$
The equation of the parabola is
$$y = -\frac{1}{200}x^2.$$
$$y = -\frac{1}{200}(30)^2 = -\frac{1}{200}(900) = -4.5$$
The height of the arch is 50 feet. The archway comes down 4.5 feet, so the height of the arch 20 feet from the center is 50 – 4.5 = 45.5 feet.

91.
$$y^2 + 10y - x + 25 = 0$$
$$y^2 + 10y + (-x + 25) = 0$$
$$a = 1 \qquad b = 10 \qquad c = -x + 25$$
$$x - 3 = 0 \quad \text{or} \quad x + 1 = 0$$
$$x = 3 \qquad\qquad x = -1$$

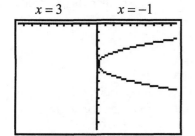

Review Exercises

93. $f(x) = 2^{1-x}$

x	$f(x)$
-2	8
-1	4
0	2
1	1
2	$\dfrac{1}{2}$

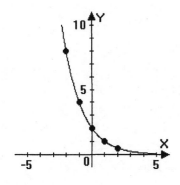

94.
$$y = \frac{1}{3}x - 5$$
Interchange x and y.
$$x = \frac{1}{3}y - 5$$
$$x + 5 = \frac{1}{3}y$$
$$3x + 15 = y$$
$$f^{-1}(x) = 3x + 15$$

95.
$$\frac{x - \dfrac{1}{3}}{3 - \dfrac{1}{x}} = \frac{3x}{3x} \cdot \frac{x - \dfrac{1}{3}}{3 - \dfrac{1}{x}} = \frac{3x \cdot x - 3x \cdot \dfrac{1}{3}}{3x \cdot 3 - 3x \cdot \dfrac{1}{x}}$$
$$= \frac{3x^2 - x}{9x - 3} = \frac{x(3x - 1)}{3(3x - 1)} = \frac{x}{3}$$

Systems of Nonlinear Equations in Two Variables

13.5 CHECK POINTS

CHECK POINT 1
Solve the first equation for y.
$$x^2 = y - 1$$
$$x^2 + 1 = y$$
Substitute $x^2 + 1$ for y and solve for x.
$$4x - (x^2 + 1) = -1$$
$$4x - x^2 - 1 = -1$$
$$4x - x^2 = 0$$
$$x(4 - x) = 0$$
$$x = 0 \quad \text{or} \quad 4 - x = 0$$
$$4 = x$$
Substitute 0 and 4 for x to find y.

$x = 0$	or	$x = 4$
$y = x^2 + 1$		$y = x^2 + 1$
$y = 0^2 + 1$		$y = 4^2 + 1$
$y = 1$		$y = 16 + 1$
		$y = 17$

The solutions are $(0,1)$ and $(4,17)$.

CHECK POINT 2
Solve the first equation for x.
$$x + 2y = 0$$
$$x = -2y$$
Substitute $-2y$ for x in the second equation and solve for y.
$$(-2y - 1)^2 + (y - 1)^2 = 5$$
$$4y^2 + 4y + 1 + y^2 - 2y + 1 = 5$$
$$5y^2 + 2y + 2 = 5$$

$$5y^2 + 2y - 3 = 0$$
$$(5y - 3)(y + 1) = 0$$
$$5y - 3 = 0 \quad \text{or} \quad y + 1 = 0$$
$$5y = 3 \qquad\qquad y = -1$$
$$y = \frac{3}{5}$$

Substitute -1 and $\frac{3}{5}$ for y to find x.

$$x = -2(-1) = 2 \quad \text{or} \quad x = -2\left(\frac{3}{5}\right) = -\frac{6}{5}$$

The solutions are $(2, -1)$ and $\left(-\frac{6}{5}, \frac{3}{5}\right)$.

CHECK POINT 3

Multiply the first equation by -3 and the second equation by 2.

$$-9x^2 - 6y^2 = -105$$
$$\underline{8x^2 + 6y^2 = 96}$$
$$-x^2 = -9$$
$$x^2 = 9$$
$$x = \pm 3$$

Back substitute ± 3 for x to find y.

$$x = \pm 3$$
$$3(\pm 3)^2 + 2y^2 = 35$$
$$3(9) + 2y^2 = 35$$
$$27 + 2y^2 = 35$$
$$2y^2 = 8$$
$$y^2 = 4$$
$$y = \pm 2$$

The solutions are $(3, 2), (3, -2),$
$(-3, 2)$ and $(-3, -2)$.

CHECK POINT 4

Rewrite the equations to solve by addition.

$$-x^2 + y = 5$$
$$\underline{x^2 + y^2 = 25}$$
$$y^2 + y = 30$$
$$y^2 + y - 30 = 0$$
$$(y + 6)(y - 5) = 0$$
$$y + 6 = 0 \quad \text{or} \quad y - 5 = 0$$
$$y = -6 \qquad\qquad y = 5$$

Substitute -6 and 5 for y to find x.

$$-6 = x^2 + 5 \quad \text{or} \quad 5 = x^2 + 5$$
$$\cancel{-11 = x^2} \qquad\qquad 0 = x^2$$
$$0 = x$$

We disregard $y = -6$, there is no value of x for which x^2 is a negative number. The solution is $(0, 5)$.

CHECK POINT 5

Let $x =$ the length of the rectangle
Let $y =$ the width of the rectangle
Perimeter: $\quad 2x + 2y = 20$
Area: $\qquad\qquad\quad xy = 21$
Solve the second equation for y.

$$xy = 21$$
$$y = \frac{21}{x}$$

Substitute $\frac{21}{x}$ for y in the first equation and solve for x.

$$2x + 2\left(\frac{21}{x}\right) = 20$$
$$2x + \frac{42}{x} = 20$$
$$x\left(2x + \frac{42}{x}\right) = x(20)$$
$$2x^2 + 42 = 20x$$
$$2x^2 - 20x + 42 = 0$$
$$x^2 - 10x + 21 = 0$$
$$(x - 7)(x - 3) = 0$$
$$x - 7 = 0 \quad \text{or} \quad x - 3 = 0$$
$$x = 7 \qquad\qquad x = 3$$

Substitute 3 and 7 for x to find y.

$$y = \frac{21}{7} = 3 \quad \text{or} \quad y = \frac{21}{3} = 7$$

The dimensions of the rectangle are 3 feet by 7 feet.

EXERCISE SET 13.5

1.   Substitute $x^2 + 4$ for y in the first equation and solve for x.

$$x + \left(x^2 - 4\right) = 2$$
$$x + x^2 - 4 = 2$$
$$x^2 + x - 6 = 0$$
$$(x+3)(x-2) = 0$$
$$x + 3 = 0 \quad \text{or} \quad x - 2 = 0$$
$$x = -3 \qquad\qquad x = 2$$

Substitute −3 and 2 for x in the second equation to find y.

$$y = (-3)^2 - 4 \quad \text{or} \quad y = 2^2 - 4$$
$$y = 9 - 4 \qquad\qquad y = 4 - 4$$
$$y = 5 \qquad\qquad\quad y = 0$$

The solutions are $(-3, 5)$ and $(2, 0)$.

3. Substitute $x^2 - 4x + 4$ for y in the first equation and solve for x.

$$x + x^2 - 4x + 4 = 2$$
$$x^2 - 3x + 4 = 2$$
$$x^2 - 3x + 2 = 0$$
$$(x-2)(x-1) = 0$$
$$x - 2 = 0 \quad \text{or} \quad x - 1 = 0$$
$$x = 2 \qquad\qquad x = 1$$

Substitute 1 and 2 for x to find y.

$$x + y = 2 \quad \text{or} \quad x + y = 2$$
$$2 + y = 2 \qquad\qquad 1 + y = 2$$
$$y = 0 \qquad\qquad\quad y = 1$$

The solutions are $(2, 0)$ and $(1, 1)$.

5. Substitute $-x^2 - 2x + 14$ for y in the first equation and solve for x.

$$-x^2 - 2x + 14 = x^2 - 4x - 10$$
$$0 = 2x^2 - 2x - 24$$
$$0 = x^2 - x - 12$$
$$0 = (x-4)(x+3)$$
$$x - 4 = 0 \quad \text{or} \quad x + 3 = 0$$
$$x = 4 \qquad\qquad x = -3$$

Substitute 3 and 4 for x to find y.

$$y = 4^2 - 4(4) - 10 = 16 - 16 - 10 = -10$$
$$y = (-3)^2 - 4(-3) - 10 = 9 + 12 - 10 = 11$$

The solutions are $(4, -10)$ and $(-3, 11)$.

7. Solve the second equation for x.
$$x - y = 1$$
$$x = y + 1$$

Substitute $y + 1$ for x to find y.

$$(y+1)^2 + y^2 = 25$$
$$y^2 + 2y + 1 + y^2 = 25$$
$$2y^2 + 2y + 1 = 25$$
$$2y^2 + 2y - 24 = 0$$
$$y^2 + y - 12 = 0$$
$$(y+4)(y-3) = 0$$
$$y + 4 = 0 \quad \text{or} \quad y - 3 = 0$$
$$y = -4 \qquad\qquad y = 3$$

Substitute −4 and 3 for y to find x.

$$x = -4 + 1 = -3 \qquad x = 3 + 1 = 4$$

The solutions are $(-3, -4)$ and $(4, 3)$.

9. Solve the first equation for y.
$$xy = 6$$
$$y = \frac{6}{x}$$

Substitute $\frac{6}{x}$ for y in the second equation and solve for x.

$$2x - \frac{6}{x} = 1$$
$$x\left(2x - \frac{6}{x}\right) = x(1)$$
$$2x^2 - 6 = x$$
$$2x^2 - x - 6 = 0$$
$$(2x+3)(x-2) = 0$$
$$x - 2 = 0 \quad \text{or} \quad 2x + 3 = 0$$
$$x = 2 \qquad\qquad 2x = -3$$
$$\qquad\qquad\qquad x = -\frac{3}{2}$$

Substitute 2 and $-\frac{3}{2}$ for x to find y.

$$2y = 6 \quad \text{or} \quad -\frac{3}{2}y = 6$$
$$y = 3$$
$$y = \left(-\frac{2}{3}\right)6 = -4$$

The solutions are $(2, 3)$ and $\left(-\frac{3}{2}, -4\right)$.

11. Solve the second equation for x.
$$2y = x - 3$$
$$2y + 3 = x$$
Substitute $2y + 3$ for x to find y.
$$y^2 = (2y + 3)^2 - 9$$
$$y^2 = 4y^2 + 12y + 9 - 9$$
$$y^2 = 4y^2 + 12y$$
$$0 = 3y^2 + 12y$$
$$0 = 3y(y + 4)$$
$$3y = 0 \quad \text{or} \quad y + 4 = 0$$
$$y = 0 \qquad\qquad y = -4$$
Substitute –4 and 0 for y to find x.
$$2(0) + 3 = x \quad \text{or} \quad 2(-4) + 3 = x$$
$$3 = x \qquad\qquad\quad -8 + 3 = x$$
$$-5 = x$$
The solutions are $(3, 0)$ and $(-5, -4)$.

13. Solve the first equation for y.
$$xy = 3$$
$$y = \frac{3}{x}$$
Substitute $\frac{3}{x}$ for y to find x.
$$x^2 + \left(\frac{3}{x}\right)^2 = 10$$
$$x^2 + \frac{9}{x^2} = 10$$
$$x^2 \left(x^2 + \frac{9}{x^2}\right) = x^2 (10)$$
$$x^4 + 9 = 10x^2$$
$$x^4 - 10x^2 + 9 = 0$$
$$(x^2 - 9)(x^2 - 1) = 0$$
$$(x + 3)(x - 3)(x + 1)(x - 1) = 0$$
$$x + 3 = 0 \qquad x - 3 = 0$$
$$x = -3 \qquad\quad x = 3$$

$$x + 1 = 0 \qquad x - 1 = 0$$
$$x = -1 \qquad\quad x = 1$$
Substitute ± 1 and ± 3 for x to find y.

$$y = \frac{3}{-3} = -1 \qquad\qquad y = \frac{3}{3} = 1$$

$$y = \frac{3}{-1} = -3 \qquad\qquad y = \frac{3}{1} = 3$$
The solutions are $(-3, -1), (-1, -3)$, $(1, 3)$ and $(3, 1)$.

15. Solve the first equation for y.
$$x + y = 1$$
$$y = -x + 1$$
Substitute $-x + 1$ for y and solve for x.
$$x^2 + x(-x + 1) - (-x + 1)^2 = -5$$
$$x^2 - x^2 + x - (x^2 - 2x + 1) = -5$$
$$x^2 - x^2 + x - x^2 + 2x - 1 = -5$$
$$-x^2 + 3x - 1 = -5$$
$$-x^2 + 3x + 4 = 0$$
$$x^2 - 3x - 4 = 0$$
$$(x - 4)(x + 1) = 0$$
$$x - 4 = 0 \quad \text{or} \quad x + 1 = 0$$
$$x = 4 \qquad\qquad x = -1$$
Substitute –1 and 4 for x to find y.
$$y = -4 + 1 \quad \text{or} \quad y = -(-1) + 1$$
$$y = -3 \qquad\qquad y = 1 + 1$$
$$y = 2$$
The solutions are $(4, -3)$ and $(-1, 2)$.

17. Solve the first equation for y.
$$x + y = 1$$
$$y = -x + 1$$
Substitute $-x + 1$ for y to find x.
$$(x - 1)^2 + ((-x + 1) + 2)^2 = 10$$
$$(x - 1)^2 + (-x + 1 + 2)^2 = 10$$
$$(x - 1)^2 + (-x + 3)^2 = 10$$
$$x^2 - 2x + 1 + x^2 - 6x + 9 = 10$$
$$2x^2 - 8x + 10 = 10$$
$$2x^2 - 8x = 0$$
$$2x(x - 4) = 0$$
$$2x = 0 \quad \text{or} \quad x - 4 = 0$$
$$x = 0 \qquad\qquad x = 4$$

Substitute 0 and 4 for x to find y.

$y = -0 + 1$ or $y = -4 + 1$
$y = 1$ $y = -3$

The solutions are $(0, 1)$ and $(4, -3)$.

19. Solve the system by addition.

$$\begin{array}{r} x^2 + y^2 = 13 \\ \underline{x^2 - y^2 = 5} \\ 2x^2 = 18 \\ x^2 = 9 \\ x = \pm 3 \end{array}$$

Substitute ± 3 for x to find y.

$$(\pm 3)^2 + y^2 = 13$$
$$9 + y^2 = 13$$
$$y^2 = 4$$
$$y = \pm 2$$

The solutions are $(-3, -2), (-3, 2),$
$(3, -2)$ and $(3, 2)$.

21. Multiply the first equation by -3 and add to the second equation.

$$\begin{array}{r} -3x^2 + 12y^2 = 21 \\ \underline{3x^2 + y^2 = 31} \\ 13y^2 = 52 \\ y^2 = 4 \\ y = \pm 2 \end{array}$$

Substitute -2 and 2 for y to find x.

$$3x^2 + (\pm 2)^2 = 31$$
$$3x^2 + 4 = 31$$
$$3x^2 = 27$$
$$x^2 = 9$$
$$x = \pm 3$$

The solutions are $(-3, -2), (-3, 2),$
$(3, -2)$ and $(3, 2)$.

23. Multiply the first equation by 3 and the second equation by 4 and solve by addition.

25. Multiply the first equation by -1 and solve by addition.

$$\begin{array}{r} 9x^2 + 12y^2 - 48 = 0 \\ \underline{8x^2 - 12y^2 - 20 = 0} \\ 17x^2 - 68 = 0 \\ 17x^2 = 68 \\ x^2 = 4 \\ x = \pm 2 \end{array}$$

Substitute ± 2 for x to find y.

$$2(\pm 2)^2 - 3y^2 - 5 = 0$$
$$2(4) - 3y^2 - 5 = 0$$
$$8 - 3y^2 - 5 = 0$$
$$3 - 3y^2 = 0$$
$$3 = 3y^2$$
$$1 = y^2$$
$$\pm 1 = y$$

The solutions are $(-2, -1), (-2, 1),$
$(2, -1)$ and $(2, 1)$.

25. Multiply the first equation by -1 and solve by addition.

$$\begin{array}{r} -x^2 - y^2 = -25 \\ \underline{(x - 8)^2 + y^2 = 41} \\ -x^2 + (x - 8)^2 = 16 \end{array}$$

$$-x^2 + x^2 - 16x + 64 = 16$$
$$-16x + 64 = 16$$
$$-16x = -48$$
$$x = 3$$

Substitute 3 for x to find y.

$$3^2 + y^2 = 25$$
$$6 + y^2 = 25$$
$$y^2 = 16$$
$$y = \pm 4$$

The solutions are $(3, -4)$ and $(3, 4)$.

27. Multiply the first equation by -1 and solve by addition.

$$\begin{array}{r} -y^2 + x = -4 \\ \underline{x^2 + y^2 = 4} \\ x^2 + x = 0 \\ x(x + 1) = 0 \end{array}$$

$$x = 0 \quad \text{or} \quad x + 1 = 0$$
$$x = -1$$

Substitute -1 and 0 for x to find y.

$$y^2 - 0 = 4 \quad \text{or} \quad y^2 - (-1) = 4$$
$$y^2 = 4 \qquad\qquad y^2 + 1 = 4$$
$$y = \pm 2 \qquad\qquad y^2 = 3$$
$$\qquad\qquad\qquad y = \pm\sqrt{3}$$

The solutions are $(0, -2), (0, 2),$
$\left(-1, -\sqrt{3}\right)$ and $\left(-1, \sqrt{3}\right).$

29. Multiply the first equation by -2 and the second equation by 3 and solve by addition.

$$-6x^2 - 8y^2 = -32$$
$$\underline{6x^2 - 9y^2 = 15}$$
$$-17y^2 = -17$$
$$y^2 = 1$$
$$y = \pm 1$$

Substitute ± 1 for y to find x.

$$3x^2 + 4(\pm 1)^2 = 16$$
$$3x^2 + 4(1) = 16$$
$$3x^2 + 4 = 16$$
$$3x^2 = 12$$
$$x^2 = 4$$
$$x = \pm 2$$

The solutions are $(-2, 1), (2, 1), \ (-2, -1)$ and $(2, -1).$

31. Solve the second equation for y.

$$xy = 4$$
$$y = \frac{4}{x}$$

Substitute $\dfrac{4}{x}$ for y in the second equation and solve for x.

$$2x^2 + \left(\frac{4}{x}\right)^2 = 18$$
$$2x^2 + \frac{16}{x^2} = 18$$
$$x^2\left(2x^2 + \frac{16}{x^2}\right) = x^2(18)$$
$$2x^4 + 16 = 18x^2$$

$$2x^4 - 18x^2 + 16 = 0$$
$$x^4 - 9x^2 + 8 = 0$$
$$\left(x^2 - 8\right)\left(x^2 - 1\right) = 0$$
$$\left(x^2 - 8\right)(x + 1)(x - 1) = 0$$
$$x^2 - 8 = 0 \qquad x + 1 = 0 \qquad x - 1 = 0$$
$$x^2 = 8 \qquad\qquad x = -1 \qquad x = 1$$
$$x = \pm\sqrt{8}$$
$$x = \pm 2\sqrt{2}$$

Substitute $\pm 2\sqrt{2}$ and ± 1 for x to find y.

$$y = \frac{4}{1} = 4 \qquad\qquad y = \frac{4}{-1} = -4$$

$$x = \pm 2\sqrt{2}$$
$$y = \frac{4}{\pm 2\sqrt{2}}$$
$$y = \pm\frac{2}{\sqrt{2}} \cdot \frac{\sqrt{2}}{\sqrt{2}}$$
$$y = \pm\frac{2\sqrt{2}}{2} = \pm\sqrt{2}$$

The solutions are $\left(2\sqrt{2}, \sqrt{2}\right),$
$\left(-2\sqrt{2}, -\sqrt{2}\right), \ (1, 4)$ and $(-1, -4).$

33. Solve the second equation for x.

$$x + 2y = 6$$
$$x = 6 - 2y$$

Substitute $6 - 2y$ for x to find y.

$$(6 - 2y)^2 + 4y^2 = 20$$
$$36 - 24y + 4y^2 + 4y^2 = 20$$
$$36 - 24y + 8y^2 = 20$$
$$8y^2 - 24y + 16 = 0$$
$$y^2 - 3y + 2 = 0$$
$$(y - 2)(y - 1) = 0$$
$$y - 2 = 0 \quad \text{or} \quad y - 1 = 0$$
$$y = 2 \qquad\qquad y = 1$$

Substitute 1 and 2 for y to find x.

$$x = 6 - 2(2) = 6 - 4 = 2$$
$$x = 6 - 2(1) = 6 - 2 = 4$$

The solutions are $(2, 2)$ and $(4, 1).$

35. Eliminate y by adding the two equations.
$$x^3 + y = 0$$
$$\underline{x^2 - y = 0}$$
$$x^3 + x^2 = 0$$
$$x^2(x+1) = 0$$

$x^2 = 0$ or $x+1 = 0$
$x = 0$ $\qquad x = -1$

Substitute -1 and 0 for x to find y.
$0^2 - y = 0$ or $(-1)^2 - y = 0$
$\quad -y = 0 \qquad\qquad 1 - y = 0$
$\quad\; y = 0 \qquad\qquad\; -y = -1$
$\qquad\qquad\qquad\qquad\quad y = 1$

The solutions are $(0,0)$ and $(-1,1)$.

37. Solve the second equation for x^2.
$$x^2 - 2y = 0$$
$$x^2 = 2y$$

Substitute $2y$ for x^2 in the first equation and solve for y.
$$2y + (y-2)^2 = 4$$
$$2y + y^2 - 4y + 4 = 4$$
$$y^2 - 2y + 4 = 4$$
$$y^2 - 2y = 0$$
$$y(y-2) = 0$$

$y = 0$ or $y - 2 = 0$
$\qquad\qquad\quad\; y = 2$

Substitute 0 and 2 for y to find x.
$x^2 = 2(0)$ or $x^2 = 2(2)$
$x^2 = 0 \qquad\qquad x^2 = 4$
$x = 0 \qquad\qquad\; x = \pm 2$

The solutions are $(0,0), (-2,2)$ and $(2,2)$.

39. Substitute $(x+3)^2$ for y in the second equation.
$$x + 2(x+3)^2 = -2$$
$$x + 2(x^2 + 6x + 9) = -2$$
$$x + 2x^2 + 12x + 18 = -2$$

$$2x^2 + 13x + 18 = -2$$
$$2x^2 + 13x + 20 = 0$$
$$(2x+5)(x+4) = 0$$

$2x + 5 = 0$ or $x + 4 = 0$
$\quad 2x = -5 \qquad\qquad x = -4$
$\qquad x = -\dfrac{5}{2}$

Substitute $-\dfrac{5}{2}$ and -4 for x to find y.

$-\dfrac{5}{2} + 2y = -2$ or $-4 + 2y = -2$
$\quad -5 + 4y = -4 \qquad\qquad 2y = 2$
$\qquad\quad 4y = 1 \qquad\qquad\quad y = 1$
$\qquad\quad\; y = \dfrac{1}{4}$

The solutions are $\left(-\dfrac{5}{2}, \dfrac{1}{4}\right)$ and $(-4,1)$.

41. Solve the second equation for y.
$$2x + y = -1$$
$$y = -2x - 1$$

Substitute $-2x - 1$ for y to find x.
$$x^2 + (-2x-1)^2 + 3(-2x-1) = 22$$
$$x^2 + 4x^2 + 4x + 1 - 6x - 3 = 22$$
$$5x^2 - 2x - 2 = 22$$
$$5x^2 - 2x - 24 = 0$$
$$(5x-12)(x+2) = 0$$

$5x - 12 = 0$ or $x + 2 = 0$
$\quad 5x = 12 \qquad\qquad x = -2$
$\qquad x = \dfrac{12}{5}$

Substitute -2 and $\dfrac{12}{5}$ for x to find y.

$y = -2\left(\dfrac{12}{5}\right) - 1 = -\dfrac{24}{5} - \dfrac{5}{5} = -\dfrac{29}{5}$
$y = -2(-2) - 1 = 4 - 1 = 3$

The solutions are $\left(\dfrac{12}{5}, -\dfrac{29}{5}\right)$ and $(-2,3)$.

43. Let x = one of the numbers
Let y = the other number
$$x + y = 10$$
$$xy = 24$$
Solve the second equation for y.

$$xy = 24$$
$$y = \frac{24}{x}$$

Substitute $\frac{24}{x}$ for y in the first equation

and solve for x.

$$x + \frac{24}{x} = 10$$
$$x\left(x + \frac{24}{x}\right) = x(10)$$
$$x^2 + 24 = 10x$$
$$x^2 - 10x + 24 = 0$$
$$(x-6)(x-4) = 0$$
$$x - 6 = 0 \quad \text{or} \quad x - 4 = 0$$
$$x = 6 \qquad\qquad x = 4$$

Substitute 6 and 4 for x to find y.

$$y = \frac{24}{6} = 4$$
$$y = \frac{24}{4} = 6$$

The numbers are 4 and 6.

45. Let x = one of the numbers
Let y = the other number

$$x^2 - y^2 = 3$$
$$\underline{2x^2 + y^2 = 9}$$
$$3x^2 = 12$$
$$x^2 = 4$$
$$x = \pm 2$$

Substitute ± 2 for x to find y.

$$(\pm 2)^2 - y^2 = 3$$
$$4 - y^2 = 3$$
$$-y^2 = -1$$
$$y^2 = 1$$
$$y = \pm 1$$

The numbers are either 2 and –1, 2.

47. Solve the second equation for x^2.

$$y = x^2 - 4$$
$$y + 4 = x^2$$

Substitute $x^2 - 4$ for y in the first equation and solve for x.

$$16(y+4) + 4y^2 = 64$$
$$16y + 64 + 4y^2 = 64$$
$$16y + 4y^2 = 0$$
$$4y(4+y) = 0$$
$$4y = 0 \quad \text{or} \quad 4 + y = 0$$
$$y = 0 \qquad\qquad y = -4$$

Substitute 0 and 4 for y to find x.

$$0 = x^2 - 4 \quad \text{or} \quad -4 = x^2 - 4$$
$$4 = x^2 \qquad\qquad 0 = x^2$$
$$\pm 2 = x \qquad\qquad 0 = x$$

The comet intersects the planet's orbit at the points $(2,0), (-2,0)$ and $(0,-4)$.

49. Let x = the length of the rectangle
Let y = the width of the rectangle
Perimeter: $2x + 2y = 36$
Area: $xy = 77$

Solve the second equation for y.

$$xy = 77$$
$$y = \frac{77}{x}$$

Substitute $\frac{77}{x}$ for y in the first equation

and solve for x.

$$2x + 2\left(\frac{77}{x}\right) = 36$$
$$2x + \frac{154}{x} = 36$$
$$x\left(2x + \frac{154}{x}\right) = x(36)$$
$$2x^2 + 154 = 36x$$
$$2x^2 - 36x + 154 = 0$$
$$x^2 - 18x + 77 = 0$$
$$(x-7)(x-11) = 0$$
$$x - 7 = 0 \quad \text{or} \quad x - 11 = 0$$
$$x = 7 \qquad\qquad x = 11$$

Substitute 7 and 11 for x to find y.

$$y = \frac{77}{7} = 11$$
$$y = \frac{77}{11} = 7$$

The dimensions of the rectangle are 7 feet by 11 feet.

51. Let x = the length of the screen
Let y = the width of the screen
$$x^2 + y^2 = 10^2$$
$$xy = 48$$
Solve the second equation for y.
$$xy = 48$$
$$y = \frac{48}{x}$$
Substitute $\frac{48}{x}$ for y to find x.
$$x^2 + \left(\frac{48}{x}\right)^2 = 10^2$$
$$x^2 + \frac{2304}{x^2} = 100$$
$$x^2\left(x^2 + \frac{2304}{x^2}\right) = x^2(100)$$
$$x^4 + 2304 = 100x^2$$
$$x^4 - 100x^2 + 2304 = 0$$
$$(x^2 - 64)(x^2 - 36) = 0$$
$$(x+8)(x-8)(x+6)(x-6) = 0$$

$$x+8 = 0 \qquad x-8 = 0$$
$$x = -8 \qquad\quad x = 8$$

$$x+6 = 0 \qquad x+6 = 0$$
$$x = -6 \qquad\quad x = -6$$

We disregard -8 and -6 because we cannot have a negative length. Substitute 8 and 6 for x to find y.
$$y = \frac{48}{8} = 6$$
$$y = \frac{48}{6} = 8$$
The dimensions of the screen are 8 inches by 6 inches.

53. $x^2 - y^2 = 21$
$4x + 2y = 24$
Solve for y in the second equation.
$$4x + 2y = 24$$
$$2y = 24 - 4x$$
$$y = 12 - 2x$$
Substitute $12 - 2x$ for y and solve for x.

$$x^2 - (12-2x)^2 = 21$$
$$x^2 - (144 - 48x + 4x^2) = 21$$
$$x^2 - 144 + 48x - 4x^2 = 21$$
$$-3x^2 + 48x - 144 = 21$$
$$-3x^2 + 48x - 165 = 0$$
$$x^2 - 16x + 55 = 0$$
$$(x-5)(x-11) = 0$$
$$x - 5 = 0 \quad \text{or} \quad x - 11 = 0$$
$$x = 5 \qquad\qquad x = 11$$
Substitute 5 and 11 for x to find y.
$$y = 12 - 2(5) = 12 - 10 = 2$$
$$y = 12 - 2(11) = 12 - 22 = -10$$
We disregard -10 because we can't have a negative length measurement. The larger square is 5 meters by 5 meters and the smaller square to be cut out is 2 meters by 2 meters.

For Exercises 55-57, answers may vary.

59. Statement **b.** is true. A parabola and a circle can intersect in at most four points, and therefore, has at most four real solutions.

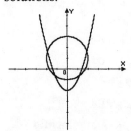

Statement **a.** is false. A circle and a line can intersect in at most two points, and therefore has at most two real solutions.

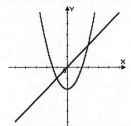

Statement **c.** is false. It is possible that a system of two equations in two variables whose graphs represent circles do not intersect, or intersect in a single point. This means that the system would have no solution, or a single solution, respectively.

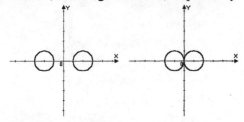

Statement **d.** is false. A circle and a parabola can intersect in one point, and therefore have only one real solution.

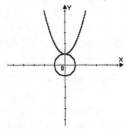

61. Rewrite the equations.
$$y^3 = x$$
$$y^5 = 4x$$

Substitute y^3 for x in the second equation and solve for y.
$$y^5 = 4y^3$$
$$y^5 - 4y^3 = 0$$
$$y^3(y^2 - 4) = 0$$
$$y^3(y + 2)(y - 2) = 0$$

Apply the zero product principle.
$$y^3 = 0 \qquad y + 2 = 0 \qquad y - 2 = 0$$
$$y = 0 \qquad y = -2 \qquad y = 2$$

We disregard 0 and -2 because the base of a logarithm must be greater than zero. Substitute 2 for y to find x.
$$2^3 = x$$
$$8 = x$$
The solution is $(8, 2)$.

63. Answers will vary. For example, consider Exercise 1.

$$x + y = 2 \qquad\qquad y = x^2 - 4$$
$$y = -x + 2$$

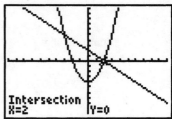

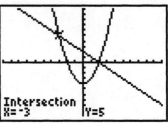

The solutions are $(2, 0)$ and $(-3, 5)$. This is the same answer obtained in Exercise 1.

Review Exercises

65. $3x - 2y \le 6$
Graph the corresponding line,
$3x - 2y = 6$.

x–intercept	y–intercept
$3x - 2(0) = 6$	$3(0) - 2y = 6$
$3x = 6$	$-2y = 6$
$x = 2$	$y = -3$

Use a test point to determine shading.

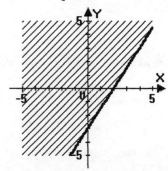

66. $m = \dfrac{y_2 - y_1}{x_2 - x_1} = \dfrac{5 - (-3)}{1 - (-2)} = \dfrac{5 + 3}{1 + 2} = \dfrac{8}{3}$

67.
$$2x^2 - 4x + 3$$
$$\underline{3x - 2}$$
$$6x^3 - 12x^2 + 9x$$
$$\underline{-4x^2 + 8x - 6}$$
$$6x^3 - 16x^2 + 17x - 6$$

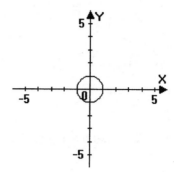

Chapter 13 Review Exercises

1.
$$d = \sqrt{\left(3-(-2)\right)^2 + \left(9-(-3)\right)^2}$$
$$= \sqrt{(3+2)^2 + (9+3)^2} = \sqrt{5^2 + 12^2}$$
$$= \sqrt{25 + 144} = \sqrt{169} = 13$$

2.
$$d = \sqrt{\left(-2-(-4)\right)^2 + (5-3)^2}$$
$$= \sqrt{(-2+4)^2 + 2^2} = \sqrt{2^2 + 4}$$
$$= \sqrt{4+4} = \sqrt{8} = \sqrt{4 \cdot 2} = 2\sqrt{2} \approx 2.83$$

3.
$$M = \left(\frac{2+(-12)}{2}, \frac{6+4}{2}\right) = \left(\frac{-10}{2}, \frac{10}{2}\right) = (-5,5)$$

4.
$$M = \left(\frac{4+(-15)}{2}, \frac{-6+2}{2}\right) = \left(\frac{-11}{2}, \frac{-4}{2}\right)$$
$$= \left(-\frac{11}{2}, -2\right)$$

5.
$$(x-0)^2 + (y-0)^2 = 3^2$$
$$x^2 + y^2 = 9$$

6.
$$\left(x-(-2)\right)^2 + (y-4)^2 = 6^2$$
$$(x+2)^2 + (y-4)^2 = 36$$

7.
$$x^2 + y^2 = 1$$
$$(x-0)^2 + (y-0)^2 = 1^2$$
The center is $(0,0)$ and the radius is 1 unit.

8.
$$(x+2)^2 + (y-3)^2 = 9$$
$$\left(x-(-2)\right)^2 + (y-3)^2 = 3^2$$
The center is $(-2,3)$ and the radius is 3 units.

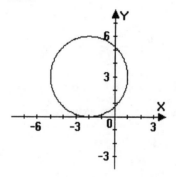

9.
$$x^2 + y^2 - 4x + 2y - 4 = 0$$
$$\left(x^2 - 4x \right) + \left(y^2 + 2y \right) = 4$$
$$\left(x^2 - 4x + 4\right) + \left(y^2 + 2y + 1\right) = 4 + 4 + 1$$
$$(x-2)^2 + (y+1)^2 = 9$$
$$(x-2)^2 + \left(y-(-1)\right)^2 = 3^2$$
The center is $(2,-1)$ and the radius is 3 units.

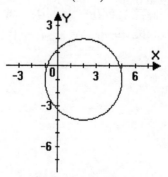

10.
$$x^2 + y^2 - 4y = 0$$
$$x^2 + (y^2 - 4y \quad) = 0$$
$$x^2 + (y^2 - 4y + 4) = 0 + 4$$
$$(x-0)^2 + (y-2)^2 = 4$$
$$(x-0)^2 + (y-2)^2 = 2^2$$

The center is $(0,2)$ and the radius is 2 units.

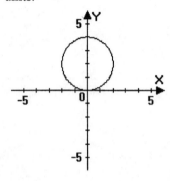

11. The vertices are $(-6,0)$ and $(6,0)$. The endpoints of the minor axis are $(0,-5)$ and $(0,5)$.

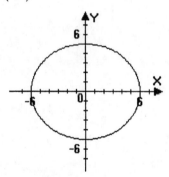

12. The vertices are $(-5,0)$ and $(5,0)$. The endpoints of the minor axis are $(0,-4)$ and $(0,4)$.

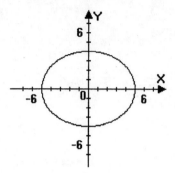

13.
$$4x^2 + y^2 = 16$$
$$\frac{4x^2}{16} + \frac{y^2}{16} = \frac{16}{16}$$
$$\frac{x^2}{4} + \frac{y^2}{16} = 1$$

The vertices are $(0,-4)$ and $(0,4)$. The endpoints of the minor axis are $(-2,0)$ and $(2,0)$.

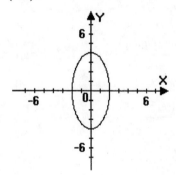

14.
$$4x^2 + 9y^2 = 36$$
$$\frac{4x^2}{36} + \frac{9y^2}{36} = \frac{36}{36}$$
$$\frac{x^2}{9} + \frac{y^2}{4} = 1$$

The vertices are $(-3,0)$ and $(3,0)$. The endpoints of the minor axis are $(0,-2)$ and $(0,2)$.

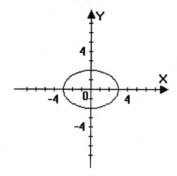

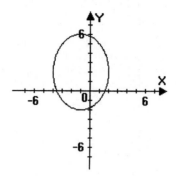

15.
$$\frac{(x-1)^2}{16}+\frac{(y+2)^2}{9}=1$$

The center of the ellipse is $(1,-2)$. The vertices lie 4 units to the left and right of the center. The endpoints of the minor axis lie 3 units above and below the center.

Center	Vertices	Endpoints of Minor Axis
$(1,-2)$	$(1-4,-2)$	$(1,-2-3)$
	$=(-3,-2)$	$=(1,-5)$
	$(1+4,-2)$	$(1,-2+3)$
	$=(5,-2)$	$=(1,1)$

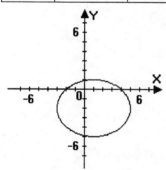

16. The center of the ellipse is $(-1,2)$. The vertices lie 4 units above and below the center. The endpoints of the minor axis lie 3 units to the left and right of the center.

Center	Vertices	Endpoints of Minor Axis
$(-1,2)$	$(-1,2-4)$	$(-1-3,2)$
	$=(-1,-2)$	$=(-4,2)$
	$(-1,2+4)$	$(-1+3,2)$
	$=(-1,6)$	$=(2,2)$

17.
$$\frac{14^2}{25^2}+\frac{y^2}{15^2}=1$$
$$\frac{196}{625}+\frac{y^2}{225}=1$$
$$5625\left(\frac{196}{625}+\frac{y^2}{225}\right)=5625(1)$$
$$9(196)+25y^2=5625$$
$$1764+25y^2=5625$$
$$25y^2=3861$$
$$y^2=\frac{3861}{25}$$
$$y=\sqrt{\frac{3861}{25}}\approx12.43$$

The height of the archway 14 feet from the center is approximately 12.43 feet. Since the truck is 12 feet high, the truck will clear the archway.

18.
$$\frac{x^2}{16}-y^2=1$$
$$\frac{x^2}{16}-\frac{y^2}{1}=1$$

The vertices are $(-4,0)$ and $(4,0)$.

Construct a rectangle using –4 and 4 on the x–axis, and –1 and 1 on the y–axis. Draw extended diagonals to obtain the asymptotes.

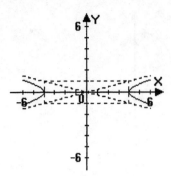

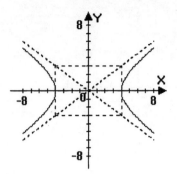

19. $\dfrac{y^2}{16} - x^2 = 1$

$\dfrac{y^2}{16} - \dfrac{x^2}{1} = 1$

The vertices are $(0,-4)$ and $(0,4)$.

Construct a rectangle using -1 and 1 on the x–axis, and -4 and 4 on the y–axis. Draw extended diagonals to obtain the asymptotes.

21. $4y^2 - x^2 = 16$

$\dfrac{4y^2}{16} - \dfrac{x^2}{16} = \dfrac{16}{16}$

$\dfrac{y^2}{4} - \dfrac{x^2}{16} = 1$

The vertices are $(0,-4)$ and $(0,4)$.

Construct a rectangle using -2 and 2 on the x–axis, and -4 and 4 on the y–axis. Draw diagonals to obtain the asymptotes.

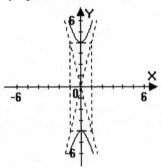

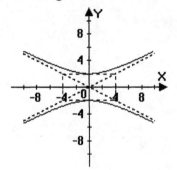

20. $9x^2 - 16y^2 = 144$

$\dfrac{9x^2}{144} - \dfrac{16y^2}{144} = \dfrac{144}{144}$

$\dfrac{x^2}{16} - \dfrac{y^2}{9} = 1$

The vertices are $(-4,0)$ and $(4,0)$.

Construct a rectangle using -4 and 4 on the x–axis, and -3 and 3 on the y–axis. Draw extended diagonals to obtain the asymptotes.

22. The vertex of the parabola is $(-4,3)$. The axis of symmetry is $y = 3$. The x–intercept is 5. The y–intercepts are 1 and 5.

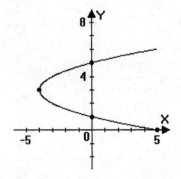

23. The vertex of the parabola is $(2,-3)$. The axis of symmetry is $y=-3$. The x–intercept is -16. The y–intercepts are -4 and -2.

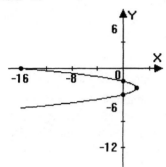

24. Vertex: $-\dfrac{b}{2a}=-\dfrac{-8}{2(1)}=-\dfrac{-8}{2}=4$

$x=4^2-8(4)+12=16-32+12$

$\quad =16-32+12=-4$

The vertex of the parabola is $(-4,4)$.

Axis of symmetry: $y=4$

The x–intercept is 12. The y–intercepts are 2 and 6.

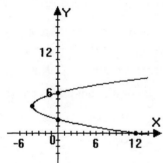

25. Vertex: $-\dfrac{b}{2a}=-\dfrac{-4}{2(-1)}=-\dfrac{-4}{-2}=-2$

$x=-(-2)^2-4(-2)+6=-4+8+6=10$

The vertex of the parabola is $(10,-2)$.

The axis of symmetry is $y=-2$. The x–intercept is 6. The y–intercepts are $-2\pm\sqrt{10}$.

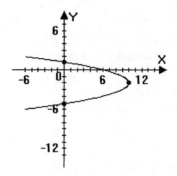

26. $x+8y=y^2+10$

Since only one variable is squared, the graph of the equation is a parabola.

27. $16x^2=32-y^2$

$16x^2+y^2=32$

Because x^2 and y^2 have different positive coefficients, the equation's graph is an ellipse.

28. $x^2=25+25y^2$

$x^2-25y^2=25$

Because x^2 and y^2 have opposite signs, the equation's graph is a hyperbola.

29. $x^2=4-y^2$

$x^2+y^2=4$

Because x^2 and y^2 have the same positive coefficient, the equation's graph is a circle.

30. $36y^2=576+16x^2$

$36y^2-16x^2=576$

Because x^2 and y^2 have opposite signs, the equation's graph is a hyperbola.

31. $\dfrac{(x+3)^2}{9}+\dfrac{(y-4)^2}{25}=1$

Because x^2 and y^2 have different positive coefficients, the equation's graph is an ellipse.

32. $y = x^2 + 6x + 9$

Since only one variable is squared, the graph of the equation is a parabola.

33. $5x^2 + 5y^2 = 180$

Because x^2 and y^2 have the same positive coefficient, the equation's graph is a circle.

$x^2 + y^2 = 36$

The center is $(0, 0)$ and the radius is 6 units.

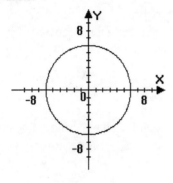

34. $4x^2 + 9y^2 = 36$

Because x^2 and y^2 have different positive coefficients, the equation's graph is an ellipse.

$$\frac{4x^2}{36} + \frac{9y^2}{36} = \frac{36}{36}$$

$$\frac{x^2}{9} + \frac{y^2}{4} = 1$$

The vertices are $(-3,0)$ and $(3,0)$. The endpoints of the minor axis are $(0,-2)$ and $(0,2)$.

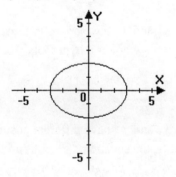

35. $4x^2 - 9y^2 = 36$

Because x^2 and y^2 have opposite signs, the equation's graph is a hyperbola.

$$\frac{4x^2}{36} - \frac{9y^2}{36} = \frac{36}{36}$$

$$\frac{x^2}{9} - \frac{y^2}{4} = 1$$

The vertices are $(-3,0)$ and $(3,0)$.

Construct a rectangle using -3 and 3 on the x–axis, and -2 and 2 on the y–axis. Draw diagonals to obtain the asymptotes.

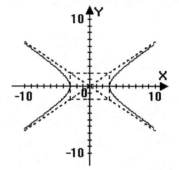

36. $\dfrac{x^2}{25} + \dfrac{y^2}{1} = 1$

Because x^2 and y^2 have different positive coefficients, the equation's graph is an ellipse. The vertices are $(-5,0)$ and $(5,0)$.

The endpoints of the minor axis are $(0,-1)$ and $(0,1)$.

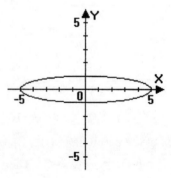

37. $x + 3 = -y^2 + 2y$

   $x = -y^2 + 2y - 3$

Since only one variable is squared, the graph of the equation is a parabola.

Vertex: $-\dfrac{b}{2a} = -\dfrac{2}{2(-1)} = -\dfrac{2}{-2} = 1$

$x = -1^2 + 2(1) - 3 = -1 + 2 - 3 = -2$

The vertex of the parabola is $(-2, 1)$.

The x–intercept is -3. There are no y–intercepts.

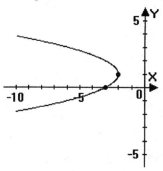

38. $y - 3 = x^2 - 2x$
$\quad\quad y = x^2 - 2x + 3$

Since only one variable is squared, the graph of the equation is a parabola.
Vertex:

$-\dfrac{b}{2a} = -\dfrac{-2}{2(1)} = -\dfrac{-2}{2} = 1$

$y = 1^2 - 2(1) + 3 = 1 - 2 + 3 = 2$

The vertex of the parabola is $(1, 2)$. The y–intercept is 3. There are no x–intercepts.

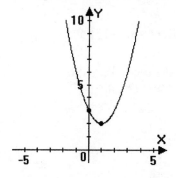

39. Because x^2 and y^2 have different positive coefficients, the equation's graph is an

ellipse. The center of the ellipse is $(-2, 5)$. The vertices lie 4 units to the left and right of the center. The endpoints of the minor axis lie two units above and below the center.

Center	Vertices	Endpoints of Minor Axis
$(-2, 5)$	$(-2-4, 5)$ $= (-6, 5)$	$(-2, 5-2)$ $= (-2, 3)$
	$(-2+4, 5)$ $= (2, 5)$	$(-2, 5+2)$ $= (-2, 7)$

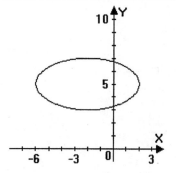

40. Because x^2 and y^2 have the same positive coefficient, the equation's graph is a circle. The center is $(3, -2)$ and the radius is 2 units.

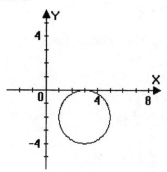

41. $\quad\quad\quad x^2 + y^2 + 6x - 2y + 6 = 0$

$\left(x^2 + 6x \quad\right) + \left(y^2 - 2y \quad\right) = -6$

$\left(x^2 + 6x + 9\right) + \left(y^2 - 2y + 1\right) = -6 + 9 + 1$

$\quad\quad (x+3)^2 + (y-1)^2 = 4$

The center is $(-3, 1)$ and the radius is 2 units.

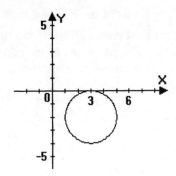

The solutions are $(1,0)$ and $(4,3)$.

44. Solve the second equation for y.
$$x+y=1$$
$$y=-x+1$$
Substitute $-x+1$ for y in the first equation.
$$-x+1=x^2+2x+1$$
$$0=x^2+3x$$
$$0=x(x+3)$$
$$x=0 \quad \text{and} \quad x+3=0$$
$$x=-3$$
Back-substitute -3 and 0 for x to find y.
$$y=-x+1 \quad \text{and} \quad y=-x+1$$
$$y=-0+1 \qquad\qquad y=-(-3)+1$$
$$y=1 \qquad\qquad y=3+1=4$$
The solutions are $(-3,4)$ and $(0,1)$.

45. Solve the second equation for y.
$$x+y=0$$
$$y=-x$$
Substitute $-x$ for y in the first equation.
$$x^2+(-x)^2=2$$
$$x^2+x^2=2$$
$$2x^2=2$$
$$x^2=1$$
$$x=\pm 1$$
Back-substitute -1 and 1 for x to find y.
$$y=-(-1) \quad \text{and} \quad y=-1$$
$$y=1$$
The solutions are $(-1,1)$ and $(1,-1)$.

46. Multiple the second equation by -1 and add to the first equation.
$$2x^2+y^2=24$$
$$\underline{-x^2-y^2=-15}$$
$$x^2=9$$
$$x=\pm 3$$
Back-substitute -3 and 3 for x to find y.

42. a.
$$3=a(6)^2$$
$$3=a(36)$$
$$a=\frac{3}{36}=\frac{1}{12}$$
$$y=\frac{1}{12}x^2$$

b.
$$a=\frac{1}{4p}$$
$$\frac{1}{12}=\frac{1}{4p}$$
$$4p=12$$
$$p=3$$
The light source should be placed at the point (0, 3). This is the point 3 inches above the vertex.

43. Solve the second equation for y.
$$x-y=1$$
$$-y=-x+1$$
$$y=x-1$$
Substitute $x-1$ for y in the first equation.
$$5(x-1)=x^2-1$$
$$5x-5=x^2-1$$
$$0=x^2-5x+4$$
$$0=(x-4)(x-1)$$
$$x-4=0 \quad \text{and} \quad x-1=0$$
$$x=4 \qquad\qquad x=1$$
Back-substitute 1 and 4 for x to find y.
$$y=x-1 \quad \text{and} \quad y=x-1$$
$$y=4-1 \qquad\qquad y=1-1$$
$$y=3 \qquad\qquad y=0$$

$$(\pm 3)^2 + y^2 = 15$$
$$9 + y^2 = 15$$
$$y^2 = 6$$
$$y = \pm\sqrt{6}$$

The solutions are $\left(-3,-\sqrt{6}\right)$, $\left(-3,\sqrt{6}\right)$, $\left(3,-\sqrt{6}\right)$ and $\left(3,\sqrt{6}\right)$.

47. Solve the second equation for y.
$$y - x = 0$$
$$y = x$$

Substitute x for y in the first equation and solve for x.
$$x(x) - 4 = 0$$
$$x^2 - 4 = 0$$
$$(x+2)(x-2) = 0$$
$$x + 2 = 0 \quad \text{and} \quad x - 2 = 0$$
$$x = -2 \qquad\qquad x = 2$$

Back-substitute –2 and 2 for x to find y.
$$y = x \quad \text{and} \quad y = x$$
$$y = -2 \qquad\qquad y = 2$$

The solutions are $(-2,-2)$ and $(2,2)$.

48. Solve the second equation for x.
$$x - 2y + 3 = 0$$
$$x = 2y - 3$$

Substitute $2y - 3$ for x in the first equation and solve for y.
$$y^2 = 4(2y-3)$$
$$y^2 = 8y - 12$$
$$y^2 - 8y + 12 = 0$$
$$(y-6)(y-2) = 0$$
$$y - 6 = 0 \quad \text{and} \quad y - 2 = 0$$
$$y = 6 \qquad\qquad y = 2$$

Back-substitute 2 and 6 for y to find x.
$$x = 2(6) - 3 = 12 - 3 = 9$$
$$x = 2(2) - 3 = 4 - 3 = 1$$

The solutions are $(1,2)$ and $(9,6)$.

49. Substitute $x + 2$ for y in the first equation and solve for x.
$$x^2 + (x+2)^2 = 10$$
$$x^2 + x^2 + 4x + 4 = 10$$
$$2x^2 + 4x + 4 = 10$$
$$2x^2 + 4x - 6 = 0$$
$$x^2 + 2x - 3 = 0$$
$$(x+3)(x-1) = 0$$
$$x + 3 = 0 \quad \text{and} \quad x - 1 = 0$$
$$x = -3 \qquad\qquad x = 1$$

Back-substitute –3 and 1 for x to find y.
$$y = -3 + 2 = -1$$
$$y = 1 + 2 = 3$$

The solutions are $(-3,-1)$ and $(1,3)$.

50. Substitute $2x + 1$ for y in the first equation and solve for x.
$$x(2x+1) = 1$$
$$2x^2 + x = 1$$
$$2x^2 + x - 1 = 0$$
$$(2x-1)(x+1) = 0$$
$$2x - 1 = 0 \quad \text{and} \quad x + 1 = 0$$
$$2x = 1 \qquad\qquad x = -1$$
$$x = \frac{1}{2}$$

Back-substitute –1 and $\frac{1}{2}$ for x to find y.
$$y = 2\left(\frac{1}{2}\right) + 1 = 1 + 1 = 2$$
$$y = 2(-1) + 1 = -2 + 1 = -1$$

The solutions are $(-1,-1)$ and $\left(\frac{1}{2}, 2\right)$.

51. Solve for y in the first equation.
$$x + y + 1 = 0$$
$$y = -x - 1$$

Substitute $-x - 1$ for y in the second equation and solve for x.

$$x^2 + (-x-1)^2 + 6(-x-1) - x = -5$$
$$x^2 + x^2 + 2x + 1 - 6x - 6 - x = -5$$
$$2x^2 - 5x - 5 = -5$$
$$2x^2 - 5x = 0$$
$$x(2x-5) = 0$$
$$x = 0 \quad \text{and} \quad 2x - 5 = 0$$
$$2x = 5$$
$$x = \frac{5}{2}$$

Back-substitute 0 and $\frac{5}{2}$ for x to find y.

$$y = -0 - 1 = -1$$
$$y = -\frac{5}{2} - 1 = -\frac{7}{2}$$

The solutions are $(0,-1)$ and $\left(\frac{5}{2}, -\frac{7}{2}\right)$.

52. Solve for x^2 in the second equation.
$$x^2 - y = 7$$
$$x^2 = y + 7$$

Substitute $y + 7$ for x^2 in the first equation and solve for y.
$$(y+7) + y^2 = 13$$
$$y^2 + y + 7 = 13$$
$$y^2 + y - 6 = 0$$
$$(y+3)(y-2) = 0$$
$$y + 3 = 0 \quad \text{and} \quad y - 2 = 0$$
$$y = -3 \qquad\qquad y = 2$$

Back-substitute -3 and 2 for y to find x.
$$x^2 = -3 + 7 \quad \text{and} \quad x^2 = 2 + 7$$
$$x^2 = 4 \qquad\qquad x^2 = 9$$
$$x = \pm 2 \qquad\qquad x = \pm 3$$

The solutions are $(-3,2),(-2,-3),\ (2,-3)$ and $(3,2)$.

53. Multiply the first equation by 4 and the second equation by 3.

$$8x^2 + 12y^2 = 84$$
$$\underline{9x^2 - 12y^2 = 69}$$
$$17x^2 = 153$$
$$x^2 = 9$$
$$x = \pm 3$$

Back-substitute ± 3 for x to find y.
$$2(\pm 3)^2 + 3y^2 = 21$$
$$2(9) + 3y^2 = 21$$
$$18 + 3y^2 = 21$$
$$3y^2 = 3$$
$$y^2 = 1$$
$$y = \pm 1$$

The solutions are $(-3,-1),(-3,1),$ $(3,-1)$ and $(3,1)$.

54. Let $x =$ the length of the rectangle
Let $y =$ the width of the rectangle
$$2x + 2y = 26$$
$$xy = 40$$

Solve the first equation for y.
$$2x + 2y = 26$$
$$x + y = 13$$
$$y = 13 - x$$

Substitute $13 - x$ for y in the second equation.
$$x(13 - x) = 40$$
$$13x - x^2 = 40$$
$$0 = x^2 - 13x + 40$$
$$0 = (x-8)(x-5)$$
$$x - 8 = 0 \quad \text{and} \quad x - 5 = 0$$
$$x = 8 \qquad\qquad x = 5$$

Back-substitute 5 and 8 for x to find y.
$$y = 13 - 8 = 5$$
$$y = 13 - 5 = 8$$

The solutions are the same. The dimensions are 8 meters by 5 meters.

55. $2x + y = 8$
$$xy = 6$$
Solve the first equation for y.

$2x + y = 8$

$\quad y = -2x + 8$

Substitute $-2x + 8$ for y in the second equation.

$x(-2x+8) = 6$

$-2x^2 + 8x = 6$

$-2x^2 + 8x - 6 = 0$

$x^2 - 4x + 3 = 0$

$(x-3)(x-1) = 0$

$x - 3 = 0 \quad$ and $\quad x - 1 = 0$

$\quad x = 3 \qquad\qquad x = 1$

Back-substitute 1 and 3 for x to find y.

$y = -2(3) + 8 = -6 + 8 = 2$

$y = -2(1) + 8 = -2 + 8 = 6$

The solutions are the points $(1,6)$ and $(3,2)$.

56. $x^2 + y^2 = 2900$

$x + (x+y) + y + y + (x-y) + x = 240$

$x + x + y + y + y + x - y + x = 240$

$\qquad\qquad\qquad 4x + 2y = 240$

The system of two variables in two equations is as follows.

$x^2 + y^2 = 2900$

$4x + 2y = 240$

Solve the second equation for y.

$4x + 2y = 240$

$\quad 2y = -4x + 240$

$\quad y = -2x + 120$

Substitute $-2x + 120$ for y to find x.

$\quad x^2 + (-2x+120)^2 = 2900$

$x^2 + 4x^2 - 480x + 14400 = 2900$

$\quad 5x^2 - 480x + 11500 = 0$

$\quad x^2 - 96x + 2300 = 0$

$\quad (x-50)(x-46) = 0$

$x - 50 = 0 \quad$ and $\quad x - 46 = 0$

$\quad x = 50 \qquad\qquad x = 46$

Back-substitute 46 and 50 for x to find y.

$y = -2(50) + 120 = -100 + 120 = 20$

$y = -2(46) + 120 = -92 + 120 = 28$

The solutions are $x = 50$ feet and $y = 20$ feet or $x = 46$ feet and $y = 28$ feet.

Chapter 13 Test

1.
$$d = \sqrt{(2-(-1))^2 + (-3-5)^2} = \sqrt{(3)^2 + (-8)^2}$$
$$= \sqrt{9+64} = \sqrt{73} \approx 8.54$$

2.
$$M = \left(\frac{-5+12}{2}, \frac{-2+(-6)}{2}\right) = \left(\frac{7}{2}, \frac{-8}{2}\right) = \left(\frac{7}{2}, -4\right)$$

3.
$$(x-3)^2 + (y-(-2))^2 = 5^2$$
$$(x-3)^2 + (y+2)^2 = 25$$

4.
$$(x-5)^2 + (y+3)^2 = 49$$
$$(x-5)^2 + (y-(-3))^2 = 7^2$$
The center is $(5,-3)$ and the radius is 7 units.

5.
$$x^2 + y^2 + 4x - 6y - 3 = 0$$
$$(x^2 + 4x \quad) + (y^2 - 6y \quad) = 3$$
$$(x^2 + 4x + 4) + (y^2 - 6y + 9) = 3 + 4 + 9$$
$$(x+2)^2 + (y-3)^2 = 16$$
$$(x-(-2))^2 + (y-3)^2 = 4^2$$
The center is $(-2,3)$ and the radius is 4 units.

6.
$$x = -2(y+3)^2 + 7$$
$$x = -2(y-(-3))^2 + 7$$
The vertex of the parabola is $(7,-3)$.

7. Vertex:
$$-\frac{b}{2a} = -\frac{10}{2(1)} = -\frac{10}{2} = -5$$

$x = (-5)^2 + 10(-5) + 23 = 25 - 50 + 23$

$\quad = 25 - 50 + 23 = -2$

The vertex of the parabola is $(-2, -5)$.

8. Because x^2 and y^2 have opposite signs, the equation's graph is a hyperbola. The vertices are $(-2, 0)$ and $(2, 0)$. Construct a rectangle using -2 and 2 on the x–axis, and -3 and 3 on the y–axis. Draw extended diagonals to obtain the asymptotes.

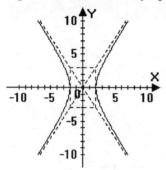

9. $4x^2 + 9y^2 = 36$

Because x^2 and y^2 have different positive coefficients, the equation's graph is an ellipse.

$$\frac{4x^2}{36} + \frac{9y^2}{36} = \frac{36}{36}$$

$$\frac{x^2}{9} + \frac{y^2}{4} = 1$$

The vertices are $(-3, 0)$ and $(3, 0)$. The endpoints of the minor axis are $(0, -2)$ and $(0, 2)$.

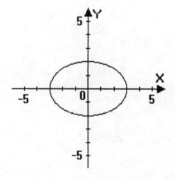

10. $x = (y+1)^2 - 4$

Since only one variable is squared, the graph of the equation is a parabola. The vertex of the parabola is $(4, -1)$. The x–intercept is 0. The y–intercepts are -3 and -1.

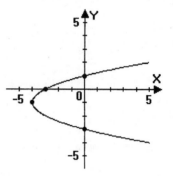

11. $16x^2 + y^2 = 16$

Because x^2 and y^2 have different positive coefficients, the equation's graph is an ellipse.

$$\frac{16x^2}{16} + \frac{y^2}{16} = \frac{16}{16}$$

$$\frac{x^2}{1} + \frac{y^2}{16} = 1$$

The vertices are $(0, -4)$ and $(0, 4)$. The endpoints of the minor axis are $(-1, 0)$ and $(1, 0)$.

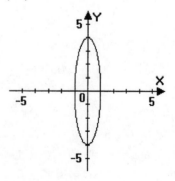

12. $\qquad 25y^2 = 9x^2 + 225$

$\quad 25y^2 - 9x^2 = 225$

Because x^2 and y^2 have opposite signs, the equation's graph is a hyperbola.

$$\frac{25y^2}{225} - \frac{9x^2}{225} = \frac{225}{225}$$

$$\frac{y^2}{9} - \frac{x^2}{25} = 1$$

The vertices are $(0,-3)$ and $(0,3)$.

Construct a rectangle using -5 and 5 on the x–axis, and -3 and 3 on the y–axis. Draw diagonals to obtain the asymptotes.

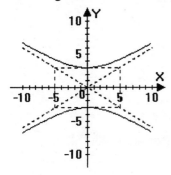

13. $x = -y^2 + 6y$

Since only one variable is squared, the graph of the equation is a parabola. Vertex:

$$-\frac{b}{2a} = -\frac{6}{2(-1)} = -\frac{6}{-2} = 3$$

$$x = -3^2 + 6(3) = -9 + 18 = 9$$

The vertex of the parabola is $(9,3)$. The x–intercept is 0. The y–intercepts are 0 and 6.

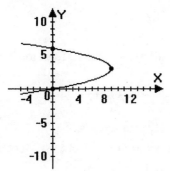

14. $$\frac{(x-2)^2}{16} + \frac{(y+3)^2}{9} = 1$$

Because x^2 and y^2 have different positive coefficients, the equation's graph is an ellipse. The center of the ellipse is $(2,-3)$.

The vertices lie 4 units to the left and right of the center. The endpoints of the minor axis lie 3 units above and below the center.

Center	Vertices	Endpoints of Minor Axis
$(2,-3)$	$(2-4,-3)$ $= (-2,-3)$	$(2,-3-3)$ $= (2,-6)$
	$(2+4,-3)$ $= (6,-3)$	$(2,-3+3)$ $= (2,0)$

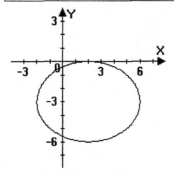

15. $(x+1)^2 + (y+2)^2 = 9$

Because x^2 and y^2 have the same positive coefficient, the equation's graph is a circle. The center of the circle is $(-1,-2)$ and the radius is 3.

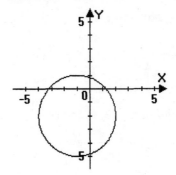

16.
$$\frac{x^2}{4} + \frac{y^2}{4} = 1$$

$$4\left(\frac{x^2}{4} + \frac{y^2}{4}\right) = 4(1)$$

$$x^2 + y^2 = 4$$

Because x^2 and y^2 have the same positive coefficient, the equation's graph is a circle. The center of the circle is $(0,0)$ and the radius is 2.

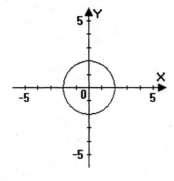

17. Solve the second equation for y.
$$x + y = 1$$
$$y = -x + 1$$
Substitute $-x + 1$ for y to find x.
$$x^2 + (-x + 1)^2 = 25$$
$$x^2 + x^2 - 2x + 1 = 25$$
$$2x^2 - 2x + 1 = 25$$
$$2x^2 - 2x - 24 = 0$$
$$x^2 - x - 12 = 0$$
$$(x - 4)(x + 3) = 0$$
$$x - 4 = 0 \quad \text{and} \quad x + 3 = 0$$
$$x = 4 \qquad\qquad x = -3$$
Back-substitute -3 and 4 for x to find y.
$$y = -4 + 1 = -3$$
$$y = -(-3) + 1 = 3 + 1 = 4$$
The solutions are $(-3,4)$ and $(4,-3)$.

18. Multiply the first equation by 2 and the second equation by 5.
$$4x^2 - 10y^2 = -4$$
$$\underline{15x^2 + 10y^2 = 175}$$
$$19x^2 = 171$$
$$x^2 = 9$$
$$x = \pm 3$$
In this case, we can back-substitute 9 for x^2 to find y.
$$x^2 = 9$$
$$2x^2 - 5y^2 = -2$$
$$2(9) - 5y^2 = -2$$
$$18 - 5y^2 = -2$$
$$-5y^2 = -20$$
$$y^2 = 4$$
$$y = \pm 2$$
The solutions are $(-3,-2),(-3,2),$
$(3,-2)$ and $(3,2)$.

19. Solve the first equation for y.
$$2x + y = 39$$
$$y = 39 - 2x$$
Substitute $39 - 2x$ for y to find x.
$$x(39 - 2x) = 180$$
$$39x - 2x^2 = 180$$
$$0 = 2x^2 - 39x + 180$$
$$0 = (2x - 15)(x - 12)$$
$$2x - 15 = 0 \quad \text{and} \quad x - 12 = 0$$
$$2x = 15 \qquad\qquad x = 12$$
$$x = \frac{15}{2}$$
Back-substitute $\frac{15}{2}$ and 12 for x to find y.
$$y = 39 - 2\left(\frac{15}{2}\right) = 39 - 15 = 24$$
$$y = 39 - 2(12) = 39 - 24 = 15$$
The dimensions are 15 feet by 12 feet or 24 feet by $\frac{15}{2}$ = 7.5 feet.

20. Let x = the length of the rectangle
Let y = the width of the rectangle

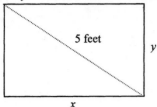

$x^2 + y^2 = 25$
$2x + 2y = 14$
Solve the second equation for y.
$2x + 2y = 14$
$2y = 14 - 2x$
$y = 7 - x$
Substitute $7 - x$ for y to find x.

$$x^2 + (7-x)^2 = 25$$
$$x^2 + 49 - 14x + x^2 = 25$$
$$2x^2 - 14x + 49 = 25$$
$$2x^2 - 14x + 24 = 0$$
$$x^2 - 7x + 12 = 0$$
$$(x-4)(x-3) = 0$$
$x - 4 = 0$ and $x - 3 = 0$
$x = 4$ $x = 3$
Back-substitute 3 and 4 for x to find y.
$x = 4$ and $x = 3$

$y = 7 - x$ $y = 7 - x$
$y = 7 - 4$ $y = 7 - 3$
$y = 3$ $y = 4$

The dimensions are 4 feet by 3 feet.

Cumulative Review Exercises
Chapters 1–13

1. $3x + 7 > 4$ or $6 - x < 1$
$3x > -3$ $ -x < -5$
$x > -1$ $ x > 5$

The solution set is $\{x | x > -1\}$ or $(-1, \infty)$.
 -1   5

2. $x(2x-7) = 4$
$2x^2 - 7x = 4$
$2x^2 - 7x - 4 = 0$
$(2x+1)(x-4) = 0$
$2x + 1 = 0$ and $x - 4 = 0$
$2x = -1$ $ x = 4$

$x = -\dfrac{1}{2}$

3.
$$\frac{5}{x-3} = 1 + \frac{30}{x^2 - 9}$$
$$\frac{5}{x-3} = 1 + \frac{30}{(x+3)(x-3)}$$
$$(x+3)(x-3)\left(\frac{5}{x-3}\right) = (x+3)(x-3)\left(1 + \frac{30}{(x+3)(x-3)}\right)$$

$$(x+3)(5)=(x+3)(x-3)+30$$
$$5x+15=x^2-9+30$$
$$15=x^2-5x+21$$
$$0=x^2-5x+6$$
$$0=(x-3)(x-2)$$

$x-3=0$ and $x-2=0$

$\cancel{x=3}$ $x=2$

Disregard 3 because it would make the denominator zero. The solution is 2.

4. $3x^2+8x+5<0$
$$3x^2+8x+5=0$$
$$(3x+5)(x+1)=0$$

$3x+5=0$ or $x+1=0$

$3x=-5$ $x=-1$

$x=-\dfrac{5}{3}$

Test Interval	Test Number	Test	Conclusion
$\left(-\infty,-\dfrac{5}{3}\right)$	-2	$3(-2)^2+8(-2)+5<0$ false	$\left(-\infty,-\dfrac{5}{3}\right)$ does not belong to the solution set.
$\left(-\dfrac{5}{3},-1\right)$	$-\dfrac{4}{3}$	$3\left(-\dfrac{4}{3}\right)^2+8\left(-\dfrac{4}{3}\right)+5<0$ true	$\left(-\dfrac{5}{3},-1\right)$ belongs to the solution set.
$(-1,\infty)$	0	$3(0)^2+8(0)+5<0$ false	$(-1,\infty)$ does not belong to the solution set.

The solution set is $\left(-\dfrac{5}{3},-1\right)$ or $\left\{x\left|-\dfrac{5}{3}<x<-1\right.\right\}$.

-5/3   -1

5. $3^{2x-1}=81$
$3^{2x-1}=3^4$
$2x-1=4$
$2x=5$
$x=\dfrac{5}{2}$

6. $30e^{0.7x}=240$
$e^{0.7x}=80$
$\ln e^{0.7x}=\ln 8$
$0.7x=\ln 8$
$x=\dfrac{\ln 8}{0.7}=\dfrac{2.08}{0.7}\approx2.97$

7. Multiply the second equation by 2 and add to the first equation.

$3x^2+4y^2=39$
$\underline{10x^2-4y^2=-26}$
$13x^2=13$
$x^2=1$
$x=\pm1$

In this case, we can back-substitute 9 for x^2 to find y.
$3(1)+4y^2=39$
$3+4y^2=39$
$4y^2=36$
$y^2=9$
$y=\pm3$

The solutions are $(-1,-3)$, $(-1,3)$, $(1,-3)$ and $(1,3)$.

8.
The y–intercept is 4 and the slope is $-\dfrac{2}{3}$.

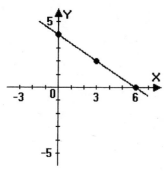

9. $3x - y > 6$

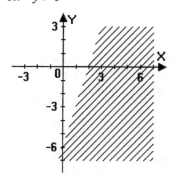

10. $x^2 + y^2 + 4x - 6y + 9 = 0$

Because x^2 and y^2 have the same positive coefficient, the equation's graph is a circle.

$(x^2 + 4x \quad) + (y^2 - 6y \quad) = -9$

$(x^2 + 4x + 4) + (y^2 - 6y + 9) = -9 + 4 + 9$

$(x + 2)^2 + (y - 3)^2 = 4$

The center of the circle is $(-2, 3)$ and the radius is 2.

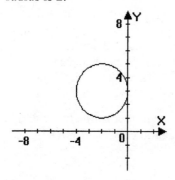

11. $9x^2 - 4y^2 = 36$

Because x^2 and y^2 have opposite signs, the equation's graph is a hyperbola.

$\dfrac{9x^2}{36} - \dfrac{4y^2}{36} = \dfrac{36}{36}$

$\dfrac{x^2}{4} - \dfrac{y^2}{9} = 1$

The vertices are $(-2, 0)$ and $(2, 0)$.

Construct a rectangle using –2 and 2 on the x–axis, and –3 and 3 on the y–axis. Draw extended diagonals to obtain the asymptotes.

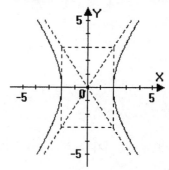

12.
$-2(3^2 - 12)^3 - 45 \div 9 - 3$

$= -2(9 - 12)^3 - 45 \div 9 - 3$

$= -2(-3)^3 - 45 \div 9 - 3$

$= -2(-27) - 45 \div 9 - 3$

$= 54 - 5 - 3 = 46$

13.

$$
\begin{array}{r}
x^2 - 5x - 1 \\
3x - 4 \overline{)3x^3 - 19x^2 + 17x + 4} \\
\underline{3x^3 - 4x^2} \\
-15x^2 + 17x \\
\underline{-15x^2 + 20x} \\
-3x + 4 \\
\underline{-3x + 4} \\
0
\end{array}
$$

$\dfrac{3x^3 - 19x^2 + 17x + 4}{3x - 4} = x^2 - 5x - 1$

14. $\sqrt[3]{4x^2y^5}\cdot\sqrt[3]{4xy^2}=\sqrt[3]{4x^2y^5\,4xy^2}$

$=\sqrt[3]{16x^3y^7}=\sqrt[3]{8\cdot2x^3y^6y}=2xy^2\sqrt[3]{2y}$

15. $(2+3i)(4-i)$

$=8-2i+12i-3i^2=8+10i-3(-1)$

$=8+10i+3=11+10i$

16. $12x^3-36x^2+27x=3x(4x^2-12x+9)$

$=3x(2x-3)^2$

17. $x^3-2x^2-9x+18=x^2(x-2)-9(x-2)$

$=(x-2)(x^2-9)$

$=(x-2)(x+3)(x-3)$

18. $6-3x\geq0$

$-3x\geq-6$

$x\leq2$

The domain of $f=\{x|x\leq2\}$ or $(-\infty,2]$.

19.

$\dfrac{1-\sqrt{x}}{1+\sqrt{x}}=\dfrac{1-\sqrt{x}}{1+\sqrt{x}}\cdot\dfrac{1-\sqrt{x}}{1-\sqrt{x}}=\dfrac{\left(1-\sqrt{x}\right)^2}{1^2+\left(\sqrt{x}\right)^2}$

$=\dfrac{\left(1-\sqrt{x}\right)^2}{1+x}$ or $\dfrac{1-2\sqrt{x}+x}{1+x}$

20. $\dfrac{1}{3}\ln x+7\ln y=\ln x^{\frac{1}{3}}+\ln y^7=\ln x^{\frac{1}{3}}y^7$

21.

$\begin{array}{r|rrrr} 2 & 3 & -5 & 2 & -1 \\ & & 6 & 2 & 8 \\ \hline & 3 & 1 & 4 & 7 \end{array}$

$(3x^3-5x^2+2x-1)\div(x-2)$

$=3x^2+x+4+\dfrac{7}{x-2}$

22. $x=-2\sqrt{3}$ and $x=2\sqrt{3}$

$x+2\sqrt{3}=0$ $x-2\sqrt{3}=0$

$(x+2\sqrt{3})(x-2\sqrt{3})=0$

$x^2-(2\sqrt{3})^2=0$

$x^2-4\cdot3=0$

$x^2-12=0$

23. Let $x=$ the rate of the slower car

	r	$\bullet$ t	$=$ d
Fast	$x+10$	2	$2(x+10)$
Slow	x	2	$2x$

$2(x+10)+2x=180$

$2x+20+2x=180$

$4x+20=180$

$4x=160$

$x=40$

The rate of the slower car is 40 miles per hour and the rate of the faster car is $40+10=50$ miles per hour.

24. Let $x=$ the number of miles driven in a day

$C_R=39+0.16x$

$C_A=25+0.24x$

$39+0.16x=25+0.24x$

$39=25+0.08x$

$14=0.08x$

$x=\dfrac{14}{0.08}=175$

The cost is the same when renting from either company when 175 miles are driven in a day.

$C_R=39+0.16(175)=39+28=67$

When 175 miles are driven, the cost is $67.

25. Let $x=$ the number of apples

Let $y=$ the number of bananas

$3x+2y=354$

$2x+3y=381$

Multiply the first equation by -3 and the second equation by 2 and solve by addition.

$$-9x - 6y = -1062$$
$$\underline{4x + 6y = 762}$$
$$-5x = -300$$
$$x = 60$$

Back-substitute 60 for x to find y.

$$3(60) + 2y = 354$$
$$180 + 2y = 354$$
$$2y = 174$$
$$y = 87$$

There are 60 calories in an apple and 87 calories in a banana.

Chapter 14

Sequences, Series, and Probability

Sequences and Summation Notation

14.1 CHECK POINTS

CHECK POINT 1

a. $a_1 = 2(1) + 5 = 2 + 5 = 7$ $\qquad$ $a_3 = 2(3) + 5 = 6 + 5 = 11$

$a_2 = 2(2) + 5 = 4 + 5 = 9$ $\qquad$ $a_4 = 2(4) + 5 = 8 + 5 = 13$

b.

$$a_1 = \frac{(-1)^1}{2^1 + 1} = \frac{-1}{2+1} = -\frac{1}{3} \qquad a_3 = \frac{(-1)^3}{2^3 + 1} = \frac{-1}{8+1} = -\frac{1}{9}$$

$$a_2 = \frac{(-1)^2}{2^2 + 1} = \frac{1}{4+1} = \frac{1}{5} \qquad a_4 = \frac{(-1)^4}{2^4 + 1} = \frac{1}{16+1} = \frac{1}{17}$$

CHECK POINT 2

$$a_1 = \frac{20}{(1+1)!} = \frac{20}{2!} = \frac{20}{2 \cdot 1} = 10 \qquad a_3 = \frac{20}{(3+1)!} = \frac{20}{4!} = \frac{20}{4 \cdot 3 \cdot 2 \cdot 1} = \frac{5}{6}$$

$$a_2 = \frac{20}{(2+1)!} = \frac{20}{3!} = \frac{20}{3 \cdot 2 \cdot 1} = \frac{10}{3} \qquad a_4 = \frac{20}{(4+1)!} = \frac{20}{5!} = \frac{20}{5 \cdot 4 \cdot 3 \cdot 2 \cdot 1} = \frac{1}{6}$$

CHECK POINT 3

a. $\displaystyle\sum_{i=1}^{6} 2i^2 = 2(1)^2 + 2(2)^2 + 2(3)^2 + 2(4)^2 + 2(5)^2 + 2(6)^2 = 2(1) + 2(4) + 2(9) + 2(16) + 2(25) + 2(36)$

$$= 2 + 8 + 18 + 32 + 50 + 72 = 182$$

b. $\displaystyle\sum_{k=3}^{5} (2^k - 3) = (2^3 - 3) + (2^4 - 3) + (2^5 - 3) = (8-3) + (16-3) + (32-3) = 5 + 13 + 29 = 47$

c. $\displaystyle\sum_{i=1}^{5} 4 = 4 + 4 + 4 + 4 + 4 = 20$

CHECK POINT 4

a. $1^2 + 2^2 + 3^2 + \ldots + 9^2 = \displaystyle\sum_{i=1}^{9} i^2$

b. $1 + \dfrac{1}{2} + \dfrac{1}{4} + \dfrac{1}{8} + \ldots + \dfrac{1}{2^{n-1}} = \displaystyle\sum_{i=1}^{n} \dfrac{1}{2^{n-1}}$

EXERCISE SET 14.1

1. $a_1 = 3(1) + 2 = 3 + 2 = 5$

$a_2 = 3(2) + 2 = 6 + 2 = 8$

$a_3 = 3(3) + 2 = 9 + 2 = 11$

$a_4 = 3(4) + 2 = 12 + 2 = 14$

3.
$$a_1 = 3^1 = 3$$
$$a_2 = 3^2 = 9$$
$$a_3 = 3^3 = 27$$
$$a_4 = 3^4 = 81$$

5.
$$a_1 = (-3)^1 = -3$$
$$a_2 = (-3)^2 = 9$$
$$a_3 = (-3)^3 = -27$$
$$a_4 = (-3)^4 = 81$$

7.
$$a_1 = (-1)^1 (1+3) = -1(4) = -4$$
$$a_2 = (-1)^2 (2+3) = 1(5) = 5$$
$$a_3 = (-1)^3 (3+3) = -1(6) = -6$$
$$a_4 = (-1)^4 (4+3) = 1(7) = 7$$

9.
$$a_1 = \frac{2(1)}{1+4} = \frac{2}{5}$$
$$a_2 = \frac{2(2)}{2+4} = \frac{4}{6} = \frac{2}{3}$$
$$a_3 = \frac{2(3)}{3+4} = \frac{6}{7}$$
$$a_4 = \frac{2(4)}{4+4} = \frac{8}{8} = 1$$

11.
$$a_1 = \frac{(-1)^{1+1}}{2^1 - 1} = \frac{(-1)^2}{2-1} = \frac{1}{1} = 1$$
$$a_2 = \frac{(-1)^{2+1}}{2^2 - 1} = \frac{(-1)^3}{4-1} = \frac{-1}{3} = -\frac{1}{3}$$
$$a_3 = \frac{(-1)^{3+1}}{2^3 - 1} = \frac{(-1)^4}{8-1} = \frac{1}{7}$$
$$a_4 = \frac{(-1)^{4+1}}{2^4 - 1} = \frac{(-1)^5}{16-1} = \frac{-1}{15} = -\frac{1}{15}$$

13.
$$a_1 = \frac{1^2}{1!} = \frac{1}{1} = 1$$
$$a_2 = \frac{2^2}{2!} = \frac{4}{2 \cdot 1} = \frac{4}{2} = 2$$
$$a_3 = \frac{3^2}{3!} = \frac{9}{3 \cdot 2 \cdot 1} = \frac{3}{2}$$
$$a_4 = \frac{4^2}{4!} = \frac{16}{4 \cdot 3 \cdot 2 \cdot 1} = \frac{2}{3}$$

15.
$$a_1 = 2(1+1)! = 2(2)! = 2(2 \cdot 1) = 2(2) = 4$$
$$a_2 = 2(2+1)! = 2(3)! = 2(3 \cdot 2 \cdot 1) = 2(6) = 12$$
$$a_3 = 2(3+1)! = 2(4)!$$
$$= 2(4 \cdot 3 \cdot 2 \cdot 1) = 2(24) = 48$$
$$a_4 = 2(4+1)! = 2(5)!$$
$$= 2(5 \cdot 4 \cdot 3 \cdot 2 \cdot 1) = 2(120) = 240$$

17.
$$\sum_{i=1}^{6} 5i = 5(1) + 5(2) + 5(3) + 5(4) + 5(5) + 5(6) = 5 + 10 + 15 + 20 + 25 + 30 = 105$$

19.
$$\sum_{i=1}^{4} 2i^2 = 2(1)^2 + 2(2)^2 + 2(3)^2 + 2(4)^2 = 2(1) + 2(4) + 2(9) + 2(16) = 2 + 8 + 18 + 32 = 60$$

21.
$$\sum_{k=1}^{5} k(k+4) = 1(1+4) + 2(2+4) + 3(3+4) + 4(4+4) + 5(5+4)$$
$$= 1(5) + 2(6) + 3(7) + 4(8) + 5(9) = 5 + 12 + 21 + 32 + 45 = 115$$

23.
$$\sum_{i=1}^{4} \left(-\frac{1}{2}\right)^i = \left(-\frac{1}{2}\right)^1 + \left(-\frac{1}{2}\right)^2 + \left(-\frac{1}{2}\right)^3 + \left(-\frac{1}{2}\right)^4 = -\frac{1}{2} + \frac{1}{4} + \left(-\frac{1}{8}\right) + \frac{1}{16}$$

$$= -\frac{1}{2}\cdot\frac{8}{8}+\frac{1}{4}\cdot\frac{4}{4}+\left(-\frac{1}{8}\right)\frac{2}{2}+\frac{1}{16}=-\frac{8}{16}+\frac{4}{16}-\frac{2}{16}+\frac{1}{16}=\frac{-8+4-2+1}{16}=-\frac{5}{16}$$

25.
$$\sum_{i=5}^{9}11 = 11+11+11+11+11 = 55$$

27.
$$\sum_{i=0}^{4}\frac{(-1)^i}{i!}=\frac{(-1)^0}{0!}+\frac{(-1)^1}{1!}+\frac{(-1)^2}{2!}+\frac{(-1)^3}{3!}+\frac{(-1)^4}{4!}=\frac{1}{1}+\frac{-1}{1}+\frac{1}{2\cdot 1}+\frac{-1}{3\cdot 2\cdot 1}+\frac{1}{4\cdot 3\cdot 2\cdot 1}$$
$$=1-1+\frac{1}{2}-\frac{1}{6}+\frac{1}{24}=\frac{1}{2}\cdot\frac{12}{12}-\frac{1}{6}\cdot\frac{4}{4}+\frac{1}{24}=\frac{12}{24}-\frac{4}{24}+\frac{1}{24}=\frac{12-4+1}{24}=\frac{9}{24}=\frac{3}{8}$$

29.
$$\sum_{i=1}^{5}\frac{i!}{(i-1)!}=\frac{1!}{(1-1)!}+\frac{2!}{(2-1)!}+\frac{3!}{(3-1)!}+\frac{4!}{(4-1)!}+\frac{5!}{(5-1)!}=\frac{1!}{0!}+\frac{2!}{1!}+\frac{3!}{2!}+\frac{4!}{3!}+\frac{5!}{4!}$$
$$=\frac{1}{1}+\frac{2\cdot\cancel{1!}}{\cancel{1!}}+\frac{3\cdot\cancel{2!}}{\cancel{2!}}+\frac{4\cdot\cancel{3!}}{\cancel{3!}}+\frac{5\cdot\cancel{4!}}{\cancel{4!}}=1+2+3+4+5=15$$

31.
$$1^2+2^2+3^2+...+15^2=\sum_{i=1}^{15}i^2$$

33.
$$2+2^2+2^3+...+2^{11}=\sum_{i=1}^{11}2^i$$

35.
$$1+2+3+...+30=\sum_{i=1}^{30}i$$

37.
$$\frac{1}{2}+\frac{2}{3}+\frac{3}{4}+...+\frac{14}{14+1}=\sum_{i=1}^{14}\frac{i}{i+1}$$

39.
$$4+\frac{4^2}{2}+\frac{4^3}{3}+...+\frac{4^n}{n}=\sum_{i=1}^{n}\frac{4^i}{i}$$

41.
$$1+3+5+...+(2n-1)=\sum_{i=1}^{n}(2i-1)$$

43.
$$5+7+9+11+...+31=\sum_{k=2}^{15}(2k+1)$$

45.
$$a+ar+ar^2+...+ar^{12}=\sum_{k=0}^{12}ar^k$$

47.
$$a+(a+d)+(a+2d)+...+a(a+nd)=\sum_{k=0}^{n}(a+kd)$$

49. a.
$$\sum_{i=1}^{9}a_i=333.3+407.5+495.4+662.1+722.9+778.0+753.1+847.0+938.9=5939.1 \text{ This}$$
means from 1991 to 1999, a total of 5939.1 million CDs were sold.

b.
$$\frac{1}{9}\sum_{i=1}^{9}a_i=\frac{1}{9}(5939.1)=659.9$$
This means that from 1991 to 1999, an average of 659.9 million CDs sold each year.

51. $a_1=0.16(1)^2-1.04(1)+7.39=0.16(1)-1.04+7.39=0.16-1.04+7.39=6.51$

$$a_2 = 0.16(2)^2 - 1.04(2) + 7.39 = 0.16(4) - 2.08 + 7.39 = 0.64 - 2.08 + 7.39 = 5.95$$

$$a_3 = 0.16(3)^2 - 1.04(3) + 7.39 = 0.16(9) - 3.12 + 7.39 = 1.44 - 3.12 + 7.39 = 5.71$$

$$a_4 = 0.16(4)^2 - 1.04(4) + 7.39 = 0.16(16) - 4.16 + 7.39 = 2.56 - 4.16 + 7.39 = 5.79$$

$$a_5 = 0.16(5)^2 - 1.04(5) + 7.39 = 0.16(25) - 5.20 + 7.39 = 4.00 - 5.20 + 7.39 = 6.19$$

$$\sum_{i=1}^{5} a_i = a_1 + a_2 + a_3 + a_4 + a_5 = 6.51 + 5.95 + 5.71 + 5.79 + 6.19 = 30.15$$

From 1991 to 1995, Americans spent $30.15 billion on recreational boating.

53.

$$a_{20} = 6000\left(1 + \frac{0.06}{4}\right)^{20} = 6000(1 + 0.015)^{20} = 6000(1.015)^{20} = 8081.13$$

The balance in the account after 5 years if $8081.13.

For Exercises 51-59, answers may vary.

61.

Statement **c.** is true. $\displaystyle\sum_{i=1}^{4} 3i + \sum_{i=1}^{4} 4i = \sum_{i=1}^{4} 7i$

$$\sum_{i=1}^{4} 3i + \sum_{i=1}^{4} 4i = (3 \cdot 1 + 3 \cdot 2 + 3 \cdot 3 + 3 \cdot 4) + (4 \cdot 1 + 4 \cdot 2 + 4 \cdot 3 + 4 \cdot 4) = 3(1 + 2 + 3 + 4) + 4(1 + 2 + 3 + 4)$$

$$= (1 + 2 + 3 + 4)(3 + 4) = (1 + 2 + 3 + 4)(7) = 7(1 + 2 + 3 + 4)$$

$$\sum_{i=1}^{4} 7i = 7 \cdot 1 + 7 \cdot 2 + 7 \cdot 3 + 7 \cdot 4 = 7(1 + 2 + 3 + 4)$$

Statement **a.** is false. $\displaystyle\sum_{i=1}^{2}(-1)^i 2^i = (-1)^1 2^1 + (-1)^2 2^2 = -1(2) + 1(4) = -2 + 4 = 2$

Statement **b.** is false. $\displaystyle\sum_{i=1}^{2} a_i b_i \ne \sum_{i=1}^{2} a_i \sum_{i=1}^{2} b_i$

$$\sum_{i=1}^{2} a_i b_i = a_1 b_1 + a_2 b_2$$

$$\sum_{i=1}^{2} a_i \sum_{i=1}^{2} b_i = (a_1 + a_2)(b_1 + b_2) = a_1 b_1 + a_1 b_2 + a_2 b_1 + a_2 b_2$$

Statement **d.** is false. $\displaystyle\sum_{i=0}^{6}(-1)^i (i+1)^2 \ne \sum_{j=1}^{7}(-1)^j j^2$

$$\sum_{i=0}^{6}(-1)^i (i+1)^2$$

$$= (-1)^0 (0+1)^2 + (-1)^1 (1+1)^2 + (-1)^2 (2+1)^2 + (-1)^3 (3+1)^2 + (-1)^4 (4+1)^2 + (-1)^5 (5+1)^2 + (-1)^6 (6+1)^2$$

$$= 1(1)^2 - 1(2)^2 + 1(3)^2 - 1(4)^2 + 1(5)^2 - 1(6)^2 + 1(7)^2 = 1(1) - 1(4) + 1(9) - 1(16) + 1(25) - 1(36) + 1(49)$$

$$= 1 - 4 + 9 - 16 + 25 - 36 + 49 = 28$$

$$\sum_{j=1}^{7}(-1)^{j} j^{2} = (-1)^{1} 1^{2} + (-1)^{2} 2^{2} + (-1)^{3} 3^{2} + (-1)^{4} 4^{2} + (-1)^{5} 5^{2} + (-1)^{6} 6^{2} + (-1)^{7} 7^{2}$$

$$= -1(1) + 1(4) - 1(9) + 1(16) - 1(25) + 1(36) - 1(49) = -1 + 4 - 9 + 16 - 25 + 36 - 49 = -28$$

63.

$$\sum_{i=2}^{4} 2i \log x = 2(2)\log x + 2(3)\log x + 2(4)\log x = 4\log x + 6\log x + 8\log x = \log x^{4} + \log x^{6} + \log x^{8}$$

$$= \log\left(x^{4} \cdot x^{6} \cdot x^{8}\right) = \log x^{18}$$

65. $\dfrac{600!}{599!} = \dfrac{600 \cdot \cancel{599!}}{\cancel{599!}} = 600$

67. Answers will vary. For example, consider Exercise 17.

$$\sum_{i=1}^{6} 5i$$

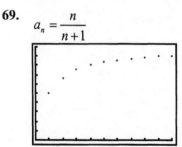

```
sum(seq(5I,I,1,6
))
             105
```

This is the same result obtained in Exercise 17.

69. $a_{n} = \dfrac{n}{n+1}$

As n increases, a_{n} increases.

71. $a_{n} = \dfrac{2n^{2} + 5n - 7}{n^{3}}$

As n increases, a_{n} decreases.

Review Exercises

73. $\sqrt[3]{40x^{4}y^{7}} = \sqrt[3]{8 \cdot 5x^{3}xy^{6}y} = 2xy^{2}\sqrt[3]{5xy}$

74. $27x^{3} - 8 = (3x - 2)(9x^{2} + 6x + 4)$

75.

$$\frac{6}{x} + \frac{6}{x+2} = \frac{5}{2}$$

$$2x(x+2)\left(\frac{6}{x} + \frac{6}{x+2}\right) = 2x(x+2)\left(\frac{5}{2}\right)$$

$$2(x+2)(6) + 2x(6) = x(x+2)(5)$$

$$12(x+2) + 12x = 5x(x+2)$$

$$12x + 24 + 12x = 5x^{2} + 10x$$

$$24x + 24 = 5x^{2} + 10x$$

$$0 = 5x^{2} - 14x - 24$$

$$0 = (5x + 6)(x - 4)$$

$$5x + 6 = 0 \quad \text{or} \quad x - 4 = 0$$

$$5x = -6 \qquad\qquad x = 4$$

$$x = -\frac{6}{5}$$

Arithmetic Sequences

14.2 CHECK POINTS

CHECK POINT 1

$a_{1} = 100$

$a_{2} = 100 - 30 = 70$

$a_{3} = 70 - 30 = 40$

$a_{4} = 40 - 30 = 10$

$a_5 = 10 - 30 = -20$

$a_6 = -20 - 30 = -50$

CHECK POINT 2

$a_9 = 6 + (9-1)(-5) = 6 + (8)(-5)$

$\quad = 6 - 40 = -34$

CHECK POINT 3

a. $a_n = 12808 + (n-1)2350$

$\quad = 12808 + 2350n - 2350$

$\quad = 2350n + 10,458$

b. $2010 - 1983 = 27$

$a_{27} = 2350(27) + 10,458$

$\quad = 63,450 + 10,458 = 73,908$

U.S. travelers will spend $73,908 million in other countries by 2010.

CHECK POINT 4

$a_{15} = a_1 + (n-1)d = 3 + (15-1)3$

$\quad = 3 + (14)3 = 45$

$S_{15} = \dfrac{15}{2}(3+45) = \dfrac{15}{2}(48) = 15(24) = 360$

CHECK POINT 5

$\displaystyle\sum_{i=1}^{30}(6i-11) = 6(1) - 11 + 6(2) - 11 + 6(3)$

$\quad -11 + \ldots + 6(30) - 11$

$= 6 - 11 + 12 - 11 + 18 - 11 + \ldots + 180 - 11$

$= -5 + 1 + 7 + \ldots + 169$

$S_{30} = \dfrac{30}{2}(-5 + 169) = 15(164) = 2460$

$\displaystyle\sum_{i=1}^{30}(6i-11) = 2460$

CHECK POINT 6

$a_{10} = 1800(10) + 49730$

$\quad = 18000 + 49730 = 67730$

$S_{10} = \dfrac{10}{2}(51530 + 67730) = 5(119260)$

$\quad = 596300$

It would cost $596,300 for nursing home care for a ten-year period beginning in 2001.

EXERCISE SET 14.2

1. Since $6 - 2 = 4$, $d = 4$.

3. Since $-2 - (-7) = 5$, $d = 5$.

5. Since $711 - 714 = -3$, $d = -3$.

7. $a_1 = 200$

$a_2 = 200 + 20 = 220$

$a_3 = 220 + 20 = 240$

$a_4 = 240 + 20 = 260$

$a_5 = 260 + 20 = 280$

$a_6 = 280 + 20 = 300$

9. $a_1 = -7$

$a_2 = -7 + 4 = -3$

$a_3 = -3 + 4 = 1$

$a_4 = 1 + 4 = 5$

$a_5 = 5 + 4 = 9$

$a_6 = 9 + 4 = 13$

11. $a_1 = 300$

$a_2 = 300 - 90 = 210$

$a_3 = 210 - 90 = 120$

$a_4 = 120 - 90 = 30$

$a_5 = 30 - 90 = -60$

$a_6 = -60 - 90 = -150$

13. $a_1 = \dfrac{5}{2}$

$a_2 = \dfrac{5}{2} - \dfrac{1}{2} = \dfrac{4}{2} = 2$

$a_3 = \dfrac{4}{2} - \dfrac{1}{2} = \dfrac{3}{2}$

$$a_4 = \frac{3}{2} - \frac{1}{2} = \frac{2}{2} = 1$$

$$a_5 = 1 - \frac{1}{2} = \frac{1}{2}$$

$$a_6 = \frac{1}{2} - \frac{1}{2} = 0$$

15. $a_1 = -0.4$

$a_2 = -0.4 - 1.6 = -2$

$a_3 = -2 - 1.6 = -3.6$

$a_4 = -3.6 - 1.6 = -5.2$

$a_5 = -5.2 - 1.6 = -6.8$

$a_6 = -6.8 - 1.6 = -8.4$

17. $a_6 = 13 + (6-1)4 = 13 + (5)4$

$\quad = 13 + 20 = 33$

19. $a_{50} = 7 + (50-1)5 = 7 + (49)5$

$\quad = 7 + 245 = 252$

21. $a_{200} = -40 + (200-1)5 = -40 + (199)5$

$\quad = -40 + 995 = 955$

23. $a_{60} = 35 + (60-1)(-3) = 35 + (59)(-3)$

$\quad = 35 + (-177) = -142$

25. $a_n = 1 + (n-1)4 = 1 + 4n - 4 = 4n - 3$

$a_{20} = 4(20) - 3 = 80 - 3 = 77$

27. $a_n = 7 + (n-1)(-4) = 7 - 4n + 4 = 11 - 4n$

$a_{20} = 11 - 4(20) = 11 - 80 = -69$

29. $a_n = -20 + (n-1)(-4)$

$\quad = -20 - 4n + 4 = -4n - 16$

$a_{20} = -4(20) - 16 = -80 - 16 = -96$

31. $a_n = -\frac{1}{3} + (n-1)\left(\frac{1}{3}\right)$

$\quad = -\frac{1}{3} + \frac{1}{3}n - \frac{1}{3} = \frac{1}{3}n - \frac{2}{3}$

$a_{20} = \frac{1}{3}(20) - \frac{2}{3} = \frac{20}{3} - \frac{2}{3} = \frac{18}{3} = 6$

33. $a_n = 4 + (n-1)(-0.3)$

$\quad = 4 - 0.3n + 0.3 = 4.3 - 0.3n$

$a_{20} = 4.3 - 0.3(20) = 4.3 - 6 = -1.7$

35. $a_{20} = 4 + (20-1)6 = 4 + (19)6$

$\quad = 4 + 114 = 118$

$S_{20} = \frac{20}{2}(4 + 118) = 10(122) = 1220$

37. $a_{50} = -10 + (50-1)4 = -10 + (49)4$

$\quad = -10 + 196 = 186$

$S_{50} = \frac{50}{2}(-10 + 186) = 25(176) = 4400$

39. $a_{100} = 1 + (100-1)1 = 1 + (99)1$

$\quad = 1 + 99 = 100$

$S_{100} = \frac{100}{2}(1 + 100) = 50(101) = 5050$

41. $a_{60} = 2 + (60-1)2 = 2 + (59)2$

$\quad = 2 + 118 = 120$

$S_{60} = \frac{60}{2}(2 + 120) = 30(122) = 3660$

43. Since there are 12 even integers between 21 and 45, find a_{12}.

$a_{12} = 22 + (12-1)2 = 22 + (11)2$

$\quad = 22 + 22 = 44$

$S_{12} = \frac{12}{2}(22 + 44) = 6(66) = 396$

45.
$$\sum_{i=1}^{17}(5i+3)=\big(5(1)+3\big)+\big(5(2)+3\big)+\big(5(3)+3\big)+...+\big(5(17)+3\big)$$

$$=(5+3)+(10+3)+(15+3)+...+(85+3)=8+13+18+...+88$$

$$S_{17}=\frac{17}{2}(8+88)=\frac{17}{2}(96)=17(48)=816$$

47.
$$\sum_{i=1}^{30}(-3i+5)=\big(-3(1)+5\big)+\big(-3(2)+5\big)+\big(-3(3)+5\big)+...+\big(-3(30)+5\big)$$

$$=(-3+5)+(-6+5)+(-9+5)+...+(-90+5)=2+(-1)+(-4)+...+(-85)$$

$$S_{30}=\frac{30}{2}\big(2+(-85)\big)=15(-83)=-1245$$

49.
$$\sum_{i=1}^{100}4i=4(1)+4(2)+4(3)+...+4(100)=4+8+12+...+400$$

$$S_{100}=\frac{100}{2}(4+400)=50(404)=20,200$$

51. a.
$$a_n=126,424+(n-1)(1265)$$
$$=126,424+1265n-1265$$
$$=1265n+125159$$

b.
$$a_{16}=1265(16)+125159$$
$$=20240+125159=145399$$
There will be 145,399 thousand, or 145,399,000 employees in the United States in 2005.

53. Company A
$$a_n=24000+(n-1)1600$$
$$=24000+1600n-1600$$
$$=1600n+22400$$
$$a_{10}=1600(10)+22400$$
$$=16000+22400=38400$$

Company B
$$a_n=28000+(n-1)1000$$
$$=28000+1000n-1000$$
$$=1000n+27000$$
$$a_{10}=1000(10)+27000$$
$$=10000+27000=37000$$

Company A will pay $1400 more in year 10.

55. a.
$$a_n=3.78+(n-1)0.576$$
$$=3.78+0.576n-0.576$$
$$=0.576n+3.204$$

b.
$$a_{41}=0.576(41)+3.204$$
$$=23.616+3.204=26.82$$
$$S_{40}=\frac{41}{2}(3.78+26.82)$$
$$=20.5(30.6)=627.3$$

The total amount of solid waste recovered from 1960 to 2000 is 627.3 million tons.

57.
$$a_{10}=33000+(10-1)2500$$
$$=33000+(9)2500$$
$$=33000+22500=55500$$
$$S_{10}=\frac{10}{2}(33000+55500)$$
$$=5(88500)=442500$$
The total salary over a ten-year period is $442,500.

59. $a_{26} = 30 + (26-1)2 = 30 + (25)2$

   $= 30 + 50 = 80$

   $S_{26} = \dfrac{26}{2}(30 + 80) = 13(110) = 1430$

There are 1430 seats in the theater.

For Exercises 61-65, answers may vary.

67. $a_1 = 21700 \quad d = 23172 - 21700 = 1472$
   Find n.

   $314628 = 21700 + (n-1)1472$

   $292928 = (n-1)1472$

   $\dfrac{292928}{1472} = \dfrac{(n-1)1472}{1472}$

   $199 = n - 1$

   $200 = n$

$314,628$ is the 200th term of the sequence.

69. $1 + 3 + 5 + \ldots + (2n-1)$

   $S_n = \dfrac{n}{2}(a_1 + a_n) = \dfrac{n}{2}(1 + (2n-1))$

   $= \dfrac{n}{2}(1 + 2n - 1) = \dfrac{n}{2}(2n)$

   $= n(n) = n^2$

71.   Answers will vary. For example, consider
Exercise 45.

   $\displaystyle\sum_{i=1}^{17}(5i+3)$

   ```
   sum(seq(5I+3,I,1
   ,17))
                 816
   ```

This is the same result obtained in
Exercise 45.

Review Exercises

72. $\log(x^2 - 5) - \log(x+5) = 3$

   $\log\left(\dfrac{x^2-5}{x+5}\right) = 3$

   $\dfrac{x^2-5}{x+5} = 10^3$

   $\dfrac{x^2-5}{x+5} = 1000$

   $x^2 - 5 = 1000(x+5)$

   $x^2 - 5 = 1000x + 5000$

   $x^2 - 1000x - 5005 = 0$

   $a = 1 \quad b = -1000 \quad c = -5005$

   $x = \dfrac{-(-1000) \pm \sqrt{(-1000)^2 - 4(1)(-5005)}}{2(1)} = \dfrac{1000 \pm \sqrt{1000000 + 20020}}{2}$

   $= \dfrac{1000 \pm \sqrt{1020020}}{2} = \dfrac{1000 \pm \sqrt{4 \cdot 255005}}{2} = \dfrac{1000 \pm 2\sqrt{255005}}{2} = 500 \pm \sqrt{255005}$

We disregard $500 - \sqrt{255005}$ because we cannot take the log of a negative number. The solution
is $500 + \sqrt{255005}$ or approximately 1005 and the solution set is $\left\{500 + \sqrt{255005}\right\}$.

73. $x^2 + 3x \le 10$

Solve the related quadratic equation.

$x^2 + 3x - 10 = 0$

$(x+5)(x-2) = 0$

$x + 5 = 0 \quad$ or $\quad x - 2 = 0$

$x = -5 \qquad\qquad x = 2$

The boundary points are -5 and 2.

Test Interval	Test Number	Test	Conclusion
$(-\infty, -5]$	-6	$(-6)^2 + 3(-6) \le 10$ $18 \le 10$, false	$(-\infty, -5]$ does not belong to the solution set.
$[-5, 2]$	0	$0^2 + 3(0) \le 10$ $0 \le 10$, true	$[-5, 2]$ belongs to the solution set.
$[2, \infty)$	3	$3^2 + 3(3) \le 10$ $18 \le 10$, false	$[2, \infty)$ does not belong to the solution set.

The solution set is $[-5, 2]$ or $\{x | -5 \le x \le 2\}$.

-5   2

74. $\dfrac{x^2 + 7x + 12}{x^2 - 16} = \dfrac{(x+3)(x+4)}{(x+4)(x-4)} = \dfrac{x+3}{x-4}$

Geometric Sequences and Series

14.3 CHECK POINTS

CHECK POINT 1

The first term is 12. The second term is

$12 \cdot \dfrac{1}{2} = 6$. The third term is $6 \cdot \dfrac{1}{2} = 3$. The

fourth term is $3 \cdot \dfrac{1}{2} = \dfrac{3}{2}$. The fifth term is

$\dfrac{3}{2} \cdot \dfrac{1}{2} = \dfrac{3}{4}$. The sixth term is $\dfrac{3}{4} \cdot \dfrac{1}{2} = \dfrac{3}{8}$.

CHECK POINT 2

$a_7 = 5(-3)^{7-1} = 5(-3)^6 = 5(729)$

$\quad = 5(729)3645$

CHECK POINT 3

$a_n = a_1 r^{n-1} = 3(2)^{n-1}$

$a_8 = 3(2)^{8-1} = 3(2)^7 = 3(128) = 384$

CHECK POINT 4

$S_n = \dfrac{2\left(1 - (-3)^n\right)}{1 - (-3)} = \dfrac{2\left(1 - (-3)^n\right)}{4} = \dfrac{1 - (-3)^n}{2}$

$S_9 = \dfrac{1 - (-3)^9}{2} = \dfrac{1 - (-19683)}{2}$

$\quad = \dfrac{19684}{2} = 9842$

CHECK POINT 5

$S_n = \dfrac{a_1\left(1 - r^n\right)}{1 - r} = \dfrac{6\left(1 - 3^n\right)}{1 - 3}$

$\quad = \dfrac{6\left(1 - 3^n\right)}{-2} = -3\left(1 - 3^n\right)$

$S_8 = -3\left(1 - 3^8\right) = -3\left(1 - 6561\right)$

$\quad = -3(-6560) = -3(-6560) = 19680$

CHECK POINT 6

We have $a_1 = 30,000$. We also know that over the next 29 years, the salary will increase by 6% each year. The first year, the salary is \$30,000. The second year, the salary is \$30,000 + 0.06(\$30,000) or 1.06(\$30,000). Extending this, we find that $r = 1.06$.

$$S_{30} = \frac{30000\left(1-(1.06)^{30}\right)}{1-1.06}$$

$$= \frac{30000(1-5.74349)}{-0.06}$$

$$= \frac{30000(-4.74349)}{-0.06}$$

$$= \frac{-142304.7}{-0.06} = 2,371,745$$

The total lifetime salary over the 30 years is $2,371,745.

CHECK POINT 7

$$A = P\frac{\left(1+\dfrac{r}{n}\right)^{nt}-1}{\dfrac{r}{n}} = 3000\frac{\left(1+\dfrac{0.10}{1}\right)^{1\cdot 40}-1}{\dfrac{.10}{1}}$$

$$= 3000\frac{(1.10)^{40}-1}{0.10} = 1,327,777.67$$

After 40 years, the value of the IRA is approximately $1,327,777.67.

CHECK POINT 8

$$r = \frac{a_2}{a_1} = \frac{2}{3}$$

$$S = \frac{a_1}{1-r} = \frac{3}{1-\dfrac{2}{3}} = \frac{3}{\dfrac{1}{3}} = 3\div\frac{1}{3} = 3\cdot\frac{3}{1} = 9$$

CHECK POINT 9

$$0.\overline{9} = 0.9999.... = \frac{9}{10}+\frac{9}{100}+\frac{9}{1000}+\frac{9}{10000}+...$$

$$0.\overline{9} = \frac{a_1}{1-r} = \frac{\dfrac{9}{10}}{1-\dfrac{1}{10}} = \frac{\dfrac{9}{10}}{\dfrac{9}{10}} = 1$$

CHECK POINT 10

The common ratio is 80% or 0.8.
We assume that each person will spend
$0.8\cdot 1000 = 800$.

$$S = \frac{a_1}{1-r} = \frac{800}{1-0.8} = \frac{800}{0.2} = 4000$$

EXERCISE SET 14.3

1.
$$r = \frac{a_2}{a_1} = \frac{15}{5} = 3$$

3.
$$r = \frac{a_2}{a_1} = \frac{30}{-15} = -2$$

5.
$$r = \frac{a_2}{a_1} = \frac{\dfrac{9}{2}}{3} = \frac{9}{2}\div 3 = \frac{9}{2}\cdot\frac{1}{3} = \frac{3}{2}$$

7.
$$r = \frac{a_2}{a_1} = \frac{-0.4}{4} = -0.1$$

9. The first term is 2. The second term is $2\cdot 3 = 6$. The third term is $6\cdot 3 = 18$. The fourth term is $18\cdot 3 = 54$. The fifth term is $54\cdot 3 = 162$.

11. The first term is 20. The second term is $20\cdot\dfrac{1}{2} = 10$. The third term is $10\cdot\dfrac{1}{2} = 5$. The fourth term is $5\cdot\dfrac{1}{2} = \dfrac{5}{2}$. The fifth term is $\dfrac{5}{2}\cdot\dfrac{1}{2} = \dfrac{5}{4}$.

13. The first term is –4.
The second term is $-4(-10) = 40$. The third term is $40(-10) = -400$. The fourth term is $-400(-10) = 4000$.
The fifth term is $4000(-10) = -40,000$.

15. The first term is $-\dfrac{1}{4}$. The second term is $-\dfrac{1}{4}(-2) = \dfrac{1}{2}$. The third term is $\dfrac{1}{2}(-2) = -1$. The fourth term is $-1(-2) = 2$. The fifth term is $2(-2) = -4$.

17. $a_8 = 6(2)^{8-1} = 6(2)^7 = 6(128) = 768$

19. $a_{12} = 5(-2)^{12-1} = 5(-2)^{11}$
$= 5(-2048) = -10240$

21. $a_6 = 6400\left(-\dfrac{1}{2}\right)^{6-1} = 6400\left(-\dfrac{1}{2}\right)^5 = -200$

23. $a_8 = 1,000,000(0.1)^{8-1} = 1,000,000(0.1)^7$
$= 1,000,000(0.0000001) = 0.1$

25. $r = \dfrac{a_2}{a_1} = \dfrac{12}{3} = 4$
$a_n = a_1 r^{n-1} = 3(4)^{n-1}$
$a_7 = 3(4)^{7-1} = 3(4)^6 = 3(4096) = 12,288$

27. $r = \dfrac{a_2}{a_1} = \dfrac{6}{18} = \dfrac{1}{3}$
$a_n = a_1 r^{n-1} = 18\left(\dfrac{1}{3}\right)^{n-1}$
$a_7 = 18\left(\dfrac{1}{3}\right)^{7-1} = 18\left(\dfrac{1}{3}\right)^6 = 18\left(\dfrac{1}{729}\right)$
$= \dfrac{18}{729} = \dfrac{2}{81}$

29. $r = \dfrac{a_2}{a_1} = \dfrac{-3}{1.5} = -2$
$a_n = a_1 r^{n-1} = 1.5(-2)^{n-1}$
$a_7 = 1.5(-2)^{7-1} = 1.5(-2)^6 = 1.5(64) = 96$

31. $r = \dfrac{a_2}{a_1} = \dfrac{-0.004}{0.0004} = -10$
$a_n = a_1 r^{n-1} = 0.0004(-10)^{n-1}$
$a_7 = 0.0004(-10)^{7-1} = 0.0004(-10)^6$
$= 0.0004(1000000) = 400$

33. $r = \dfrac{a_2}{a_1} = \dfrac{6}{2} = 3$
$S_{12} = \dfrac{2(1-3^{12})}{1-3} = \dfrac{2(1-531441)}{-2}$
$= \dfrac{2(-531440)}{-2} = \dfrac{-1,062,880}{-2} = 531,441$

35. $r = \dfrac{a_2}{a_1} = \dfrac{-6}{3} = -2$
$S_{11} = \dfrac{a_1(1-r^n)}{1-r} = \dfrac{3(1-(-2)^{11})}{1-(-2)}$
$= \dfrac{\cancel{3}(1-(-2048))}{\cancel{3}} = 2049$

37. $r = \dfrac{a_2}{a_1} = \dfrac{3}{-\dfrac{3}{2}} = 3 \div \left(-\dfrac{3}{2}\right) = 3 \cdot \left(-\dfrac{2}{3}\right) = -2$
$S_{14} = \dfrac{a_1(1-r^n)}{1-r} = \dfrac{-\dfrac{3}{2}(1-(-2)^{14})}{1-(-2)}$
$= \dfrac{-\dfrac{3}{2}(1-(-16384))}{3} = \dfrac{-\dfrac{3}{2}(16385)}{3}$
$= -\dfrac{3}{2}(16385) \div 3 = -\dfrac{49155}{2} \cdot \dfrac{1}{3} = -\dfrac{16385}{2}$

39. $\displaystyle\sum_{i=1}^{8} 3^i = \dfrac{3(1-3^8)}{1-3} = \dfrac{3(1-6561)}{-2}$
$= \dfrac{3(-6560)}{-2} = \dfrac{-19680}{-2} = 9840$

41. $\displaystyle\sum_{i=1}^{10} 5 \cdot 2^i = \dfrac{10(1-2^{10})}{1-2} = \dfrac{10(1-1024)}{-1}$
$= \dfrac{10(-1023)}{-1} = 10,230$

43.

$$\sum_{i=1}^{6}\left(\frac{1}{2}\right)^{i+1} = \frac{\frac{1}{4}\left(1-\left(\frac{1}{2}\right)^{6}\right)}{1-\frac{1}{2}} = \frac{\frac{1}{4}\left(1-\frac{1}{64}\right)}{\frac{1}{2}}$$

$$= \frac{\frac{1}{4}\left(\frac{64}{64}-\frac{1}{64}\right)}{\frac{1}{2}} = \frac{\frac{1}{4}\left(\frac{63}{64}\right)}{\frac{1}{2}}$$

$$= \frac{1}{4}\left(\frac{63}{64}\right) \div \frac{1}{2} = \frac{1}{4}\left(\frac{63}{64}\right) \cdot \frac{2}{1} = \frac{63}{128}$$

45.

$$r = \frac{a_2}{a_1} = \frac{\frac{1}{3}}{1} = \frac{1}{3}$$

$$S = \frac{a_1}{1-r} = \frac{1}{1-\frac{1}{3}} = \frac{1}{\frac{2}{3}} = 1 \div \frac{2}{3} = 1 \cdot \frac{3}{2} = \frac{3}{2}$$

47.

$$r = \frac{a_2}{a_1} = \frac{\frac{3}{4}}{3} = \frac{3}{4} \div 3 = \frac{3}{4} \cdot \frac{1}{3} = \frac{1}{4}$$

$$S = \frac{a_1}{1-r} = \frac{3}{1-\frac{1}{4}} = \frac{3}{\frac{3}{4}} = 3 \div \frac{3}{4} = 3 \cdot \frac{4}{3} = \frac{12}{3} = 4$$

49.

$$r = \frac{a_2}{a_1} = \frac{-\frac{1}{2}}{1} = -\frac{1}{2}$$

$$S = \frac{a_1}{1-r} = \frac{1}{1-\left(-\frac{1}{2}\right)} = \frac{1}{\frac{3}{2}} = 1 \div \frac{3}{2} = 1 \cdot \frac{2}{3} = \frac{2}{3}$$

51. $r = -0.3$

$$a_1 = 26(-0.3)^{1-1} = 26(-0.3)^{0} = 26(1) = 26$$

$$S = \frac{26}{1-(-0.3)} = \frac{26}{1.3} = 20$$

53.

$$0.\overline{5} = \frac{a_1}{1-r} = \frac{\frac{5}{10}}{1-\frac{1}{10}} = \frac{\frac{5}{10}}{\frac{9}{10}} = \frac{5}{10} \div \frac{9}{10} = \frac{5}{10} \cdot \frac{10}{9} = \frac{5}{9}$$

55.

$$0.\overline{47} = \frac{a_1}{1-r} = \frac{\frac{47}{100}}{1-\frac{1}{100}} = \frac{\frac{47}{100}}{\frac{99}{100}}$$

$$= \frac{47}{100} \div \frac{99}{100} = \frac{47}{100} \cdot \frac{100}{99} = \frac{47}{99}$$

57.

$$0.\overline{257} = \frac{a_1}{1-r} = \frac{\frac{257}{1000}}{1-\frac{1}{1000}} = \frac{\frac{257}{1000}}{\frac{999}{1000}}$$

$$= \frac{257}{1000} \div \frac{999}{1000} = \frac{257}{1000} \cdot \frac{1000}{999} = \frac{257}{999}$$

59. The sequence is arithmetic with common difference $d = 5$.

61. The sequence is geometric with common ratio $r = 2$.

63. The sequence is neither arithmetic nor geometric.

65.

$$r = \frac{a_2}{a_1} = \frac{2}{1} = 2$$

$$a_{15} = 1(2)^{15-1} = (2)^{14} = 16384$$

On the fifteenth day, you will put aside $16,384 for savings.

67. $r = 1.04$

$$a_7 = 3,000,000(1.04)^{7-1} = 3,000,000(1.04)^{6}$$

$$= 3,000,000(1.265319) = 3,795,957$$

The athlete's salary for year 7 will be $3,795,957.

69. a.

$$r_{95 \text{ to } 96} = \frac{21.36}{20.60} = 1.03689 \approx 1.04$$

$$r_{96 \text{ to } 97} = \frac{22.19}{21.36} = 1.03886 \approx 1.04$$

$$r_{97 \text{ to } 98} = \frac{23.02}{22.19} = 1.0374 \approx 1.04$$

b. $a_n = a_1 r^{n-1} = 20.60(1.04)^{n-1}$

c. $2005 - 1994 = 11$

$a_{11} = 20.60(1.04)^{11-1} = 20.60(1.04)^{10}$

$= 30.493$

The population of Iraq will be 30.493 million in 2005.

71. $r = \dfrac{a_2}{a_1} = \dfrac{2}{1} = 2$

$S_{15} = \dfrac{a_1(1-r^n)}{1-r} = \dfrac{1(1-(2)^{15})}{1-2}$

$= \dfrac{(1-32768)}{-1} = \dfrac{(-32767)}{-1} = 32767$

Your savings will be $32767 over the 15 days.

73. $r = 1.05$

$S_{20} = \dfrac{a_1(1-r^n)}{1-r} = \dfrac{24000(1-(1.05)^{20})}{1-1.05}$

$= \dfrac{24000(1-2.6533)}{-0.05}$

$= \dfrac{24000(-1.6533)}{-0.05} = 793583$

The total lifetime salary over the 20 years is $793,583.

75. $r = 0.9$

$S_{10} = \dfrac{a_1(1-r^n)}{1-r} = \dfrac{20(1-(0.9)^{10})}{1-0.9}$

$= \dfrac{20(1-0.348678)}{0.1} = \dfrac{20(0.651322)}{0.1}$

$= 130.264$

After 10 swings, the pendulum covers a distance of approximately 130 inches.

77. $A = P\dfrac{\left(1+\dfrac{r}{n}\right)^{nt}-1}{\dfrac{r}{n}} = 2500\dfrac{\left(1+\dfrac{0.09}{1}\right)^{1(40)}-1}{\dfrac{0.09}{1}}$

$= 2500\dfrac{(1+0.09)^{40}-1}{0.09} = 2500\dfrac{(1.09)^{40}-1}{0.09}$

$= 2500\dfrac{31.4094-1}{0.09} = 2500\dfrac{30.4094}{0.09} = 844706$

After 40 years, the value of the IRA will be $844,706.

79. $A = P\dfrac{\left(1+\dfrac{r}{n}\right)^{nt}-1}{\dfrac{r}{n}} = 600\dfrac{\left(1+\dfrac{0.08}{4}\right)^{4(18)}-1}{\dfrac{0.08}{4}}$

$= 600\dfrac{(1+0.02)^{72}-1}{0.02} = 600\dfrac{(1.02)^{72}-1}{0.02}$

$= 600\dfrac{4.16114-1}{0.02} = 600\dfrac{3.16114}{0.02} = 94834.2$

The value of the TSA after 18 years will be $94834.20.

81. $r = 60\% = 0.6$

$a_1 = 6(.6) = 3.6$

$S = \dfrac{3.6}{1-0.6} = \dfrac{3.6}{0.4} = 9$

The total economic impact of the factory will be $9 million per year.

83. $r = \dfrac{1}{4}$

$S = \dfrac{\dfrac{1}{4}}{1-\dfrac{1}{4}} = \dfrac{\dfrac{1}{4}}{\dfrac{3}{4}} = \dfrac{1}{4}\div\dfrac{3}{4} = \dfrac{1}{4}\cdot\dfrac{4}{3} = \dfrac{1}{3}$

Eventually $\dfrac{1}{3}$ of the largest square will be shaded.

For Exercises 85-91, answers may vary.

93. Statement **d.** is true. The common ratio is $0.5 = \dfrac{1}{2}$.

Statement **a.** is false. The sequence is not geometric. The fourth term would have to be $24\cdot 4 = 96$ for the sequence to be geometric.

Statement **b.** is false. We do not need to know the terms between $\dfrac{1}{8}$ and $\dfrac{1}{512}$, but we do need to know how many terms there are between $\dfrac{1}{8}$ and $\dfrac{1}{512}$.

Statement **c.** is false. The sum of the sequence is $\dfrac{10}{1-\left(-\dfrac{1}{2}\right)}$.

95.

$$1{,}000{,}000 = P\dfrac{\left(1+\dfrac{0.10}{12}\right)^{12(30)}-1}{\dfrac{0.10}{12}}$$

$$1{,}000{,}000 = P\dfrac{\left(1+\dfrac{1}{120}\right)^{360}-1}{\dfrac{1}{120}}$$

$$1{,}000{,}000 = P\dfrac{\left(1\dfrac{1}{120}\right)^{360}-1}{\dfrac{1}{120}}$$

$$1{,}000{,}000 = P\dfrac{19.8374-1}{\dfrac{1}{120}}$$

$$\dfrac{1}{120}(1{,}000{,}000) = \dfrac{1}{120}\left(P\dfrac{18.8374}{\dfrac{1}{120}}\right)$$

$$\dfrac{25000}{3} = 18.8374P$$

$$\dfrac{25000}{3(18.8374)} = P$$

$$442.382 = P$$

You should deposit approximately $442.38 per month.

97. Answers will vary. For example, consider Exercise 40.

$$\sum_{i=1}^{6} 4^i$$

sum(seq(4^I,I,1,6))

                                5460

This matches the result obtained in Exercise 40.

99.

$$f(x)=\dfrac{4\left[1-(0.6)^x\right]}{1-0.6}$$

$$S = \dfrac{4}{1-0.6} = \dfrac{4}{0.4} = 10$$

The sum of the series and the asymptote of the function are both 10.

Review Exercises

100.
$$\sqrt{28}-3\sqrt{7}+\sqrt{63} = \sqrt{4\cdot7}-3\sqrt{7}+\sqrt{9\cdot7}$$
$$= 2\sqrt{7}-3\sqrt{7}+3\sqrt{7}=2\sqrt{7}$$

101.
$$2x^2 = 4-x$$
$$2x^2+x-4 = 0$$
$$a=2 \quad b=1 \quad c=-4$$
$$x = \dfrac{-1\pm\sqrt{1^2-4(2)(-4)}}{2(2)} = \dfrac{-1\pm\sqrt{1+32}}{4}$$
$$= \dfrac{-1\pm\sqrt{33}}{4}$$

103.
$$\dfrac{6}{\sqrt{3}-\sqrt{5}} = \dfrac{6}{\sqrt{3}-\sqrt{5}}\cdot\dfrac{\sqrt{3}+\sqrt{5}}{\sqrt{3}+\sqrt{5}}$$
$$= \dfrac{6\left(\sqrt{3}+\sqrt{5}\right)}{3-5} = \dfrac{6\left(\sqrt{3}+\sqrt{5}\right)}{-2}$$
$$= -3\left(\sqrt{3}+\sqrt{5}\right)$$

The Binomial Theorem

14.4 CHECK POINTS

CHECK POINT 1

a. $\dbinom{6}{3} = \dfrac{6!}{3!(6-3)!} = \dfrac{6!}{3!3!} = \dfrac{6\cdot5\cdot4\cdot\cancel{3!}}{\cancel{3!}\,3\cdot2\cdot1} = 20$

b. $\dbinom{6}{0} = \dfrac{6!}{0!(6-0)!} = \dfrac{\cancel{6!}}{0!\,\cancel{6!}} = \dfrac{1}{1} = 1$

c. $\dbinom{8}{2} = \dfrac{8!}{2!(8-2)!} = \dfrac{8!}{2!6!} = \dfrac{8\cdot7\cdot\cancel{6!}}{2\cdot1\cdot\cancel{6!}} = 28$

d. $\dbinom{3}{3} = \dfrac{3!}{3!(3-3)!} = \dfrac{\cancel{3!}}{\cancel{3!}\,0!} = \dfrac{1}{1}$

CHECK POINT 2

Applying the Binomial Theorem to $(x+1)^4$, we have $a = x$, $b = 1$, and $n = 4$.

$$(x+1)^4 = \binom{4}{0}x^4 + \binom{4}{1}x^3 + \binom{4}{2}x^2 + \binom{4}{3}x + \binom{4}{4}$$

$$= \frac{4!}{0!(4-0)!}x^4 + \frac{4!}{1!(4-1)!}x^3 + \frac{4!}{2!(4-2)!}x^2 + \frac{4!}{3!(4-3)!}x + \frac{4!}{4!(4-4)!}$$

$$= \frac{\cancel{4!}}{0!\,\cancel{4!}}x^4 + \frac{4!}{1!3!}x^3 + \frac{4!}{2!2!}x^2 + \frac{4!}{3!1!}x + \frac{\cancel{4!}}{\cancel{4!}\,0!} = 1x^4 + \frac{4\cdot\cancel{3!}}{1\cdot\cancel{3!}}x^3 + \frac{4\cdot3\cdot\cancel{2!}}{2\cdot1\cdot\cancel{2!}}x^2 + \frac{4\cdot\cancel{3!}}{\cancel{3!}\cdot1}x + 1$$

$$= x^4 + 4x^3 + 6x^2 + 4x + 1$$

CHECK POINT 3

Applying the Binomial Theorem to $(2x - y)^5$, we have $a = 2x$, $b = -y$, and $n = 5$.

$$(x-2y)^5$$

$$= \binom{5}{0}x^5 + \binom{5}{1}x^4(-2y) + \binom{5}{2}x^3(-2y)^2 + \binom{5}{3}x^2(-2y)^3 + \binom{5}{4}x(-2y)^4 + \binom{5}{5}(-2y)^5$$

$$= \frac{\cancel{5!}}{0!\,\cancel{5!}}x^5 - \frac{5!}{1!(5-1)!}16x^4y + \frac{5!}{2!(5-2)!}8x^3y^2 - \frac{5!}{3!(5-3)!}4x^2y^3 + \frac{5!}{4!(5-4)!}2xy^4 - \frac{5!}{5!(5-5)!}32y^5$$

$$= 1x^5 - \frac{5\cdot\cancel{4!}}{1\cdot\cancel{4!}}2x^4y + \frac{5\cdot4\cdot\cancel{3!}}{2\cdot1\cdot\cancel{3!}}4x^3y^2 - \frac{5\cdot4\cdot\cancel{3!}}{\cancel{3!}\,2\cdot1}8x^2y^3 + \frac{5\cdot\cancel{4!}}{\cancel{4!}\cdot1}16xy^4 - \frac{\cancel{5!}}{\cancel{5!}\,0!}32y^5$$

$$= x^5 - 5(2x^4y) + 10(4x^3y^2) - 10(8x^2y^3) + 5(16xy^4) - 1(32y^5)$$

$$= x^5 - 10x^4y + 40x^3y^2 - 80x^2y^3 + 80xy^4 - 32y^5$$

CHECK POINT 4

Applying the Binomial Theorem to find the fifth term of $(2x + y)^9$, we have $a = 2x$, $b = y$, and $n = 9$.

$$\binom{n}{r-1}a^{n-r+1}b^{r-1} = \binom{9}{5-1}(2x)^{9-5+1}y^{5-1} = \binom{9}{4}(2x)^5 y^4 = \frac{9!}{4!(9-4)!}(2x)^5 y^4$$

$$= \frac{9\cdot8\cdot7\cdot6\cdot\cancel{5!}}{4\cdot3\cdot2\cdot1\cdot\cancel{5!}}32x^5y^4 = \frac{9\cdot8\cdot7\cdot6}{4\cdot3\cdot2\cdot1}32x^5y^4 = 126(32x^5y^4) = 4032x^5y^4$$

EXERCISE SET 14.4

1. $\displaystyle \binom{8}{3} = \frac{8!}{3!(8-3)!} = \frac{8!}{3!5!} = \frac{8 \cdot 7 \cdot \cancel{6} \cdot \cancel{5!}}{\cancel{3} \cancel{2} \cdot 1 \cdot \cancel{5!}} = 56$

3. $\displaystyle \binom{12}{1} = \frac{12!}{1!(12-1)!} = \frac{12 \cdot \cancel{11!}}{1 \cdot \cancel{11!}} = 12$

5. $\displaystyle \binom{6}{6} = \frac{\cancel{6!}}{\cancel{6!}(6-6)!} = \frac{1}{0!} = \frac{1}{1} = 1$

7. $\displaystyle \binom{100}{2} = \frac{100!}{2!(100-2)!} = \frac{100 \cdot 99 \cdot \cancel{98!}}{2 \cdot 1 \cdot \cancel{98!}} = 4950$

9. Applying the Binomial Theorem to $(x+2)^3$, we have $a = x$, $b = 2$, and $n = 3$.

$$(x+2)^3 = \binom{3}{0}x^3 + \binom{3}{1}x^2(2) + \binom{3}{2}x(2)^2 + \binom{3}{3}2^3$$

$$= \frac{3!}{0!(3-0)!}x^3 + \frac{3!}{1!(3-1)!}2x^2 + \frac{3!}{2!(3-2)!}4x + \frac{3!}{3!(3-3)!}8$$

$$= \frac{\cancel{3!}}{1 \cdot \cancel{3!}}x^3 + \frac{3 \cdot \cancel{2!}}{1 \cdot \cancel{2!}}2x^2 + \frac{3 \cdot \cancel{2!}}{\cancel{2!}1!}4x + \frac{\cancel{3!}}{\cancel{3!}0!}8 = x^3 + 3(2x^2) + 3(4x) + 1(8) = x^3 + 6x^2 + 12x + 8$$

11. Applying the Binomial Theorem to $(3x+y)^3$, we have $a = 3x$, $b = y$, and $n = 3$.

$$(3x+y)^3 = \binom{3}{0}(3x)^3 + \binom{3}{1}(3x)^2 y + \binom{3}{2}(3x)y^2 + \binom{3}{3}y^3$$

$$= \frac{3!}{0!(3-0)!}27x^3 + \frac{3!}{1!(3-1)!}9x^2 y + \frac{3!}{2!(3-2)!}3xy^2 + \frac{3!}{3!(3-3)!}y^3$$

$$= \frac{\cancel{3!}}{1 \cdot \cancel{3!}}27x^3 + \frac{3 \cdot \cancel{2!}}{1 \cdot \cancel{2!}}9x^2 y + \frac{3 \cdot \cancel{2!}}{\cancel{2!}1!}3xy^2 + \frac{\cancel{3!}}{\cancel{3!}0!}y^3 = 27x^3 + 3(9x^2 y) + 3(3xy^2) + 1(y^3)$$

$$= 27x^3 + 27x^2 y + 9xy^2 + y^3$$

13. Applying the Binomial Theorem to $(5x-1)^3$, we have $a = 5x$, $b = -1$, and $n = 3$.

$$(5x-1)^3 = \binom{3}{0}(5x)^3 + \binom{3}{1}(5x)^2(-1) + \binom{3}{2}(5x)(-1)^2 + \binom{3}{3}(-1)^3$$

$$= \frac{3!}{0!(3-0)!}125x^3 - \frac{3!}{1!(3-1)!}25x^2 + \frac{3!}{2!(3-2)!}5x(1) - \frac{3!}{3!(3-3)!}$$

$$= \frac{\cancel{3!}}{1 \cdot \cancel{3!}} 125x^3 - \frac{3 \cdot \cancel{2!}}{1 \cdot \cancel{2!}} 25x^2 + \frac{3 \cdot \cancel{2!}}{\cancel{2!}1!} 5x - \frac{\cancel{3!}}{\cancel{3!}0!} = 125x^3 - 3\left(25x^2\right) + 3(5x) - 1 = 125x^3 - 75x^2 + 15x - 1$$

15. Applying the Binomial Theorem to $(2x+1)^4$, we have $a = 2x$, $b = 1$, and $n = 4$.

$$(2x+1)^4 = \binom{4}{0}(2x)^4 + \binom{4}{1}(2x)^3 + \binom{4}{2}(2x)^2 + \binom{4}{3}2x + \binom{4}{4}$$

$$= \frac{4!}{0!(4-0)!}16x^4 + \frac{4!}{1!(4-1)!}8x^3 \cdot 1 + \frac{4!}{2!(4-2)!}4x^2 \cdot 1^2 + \frac{4!}{3!(4-3)!}2x \cdot 1^3 + \frac{4!}{4!(4-4)!} \cdot 1^4$$

$$= \frac{\cancel{4!}}{0! \cancel{4!}}16x^4 + \frac{4!}{1!3!}8x^3 \cdot 1 + \frac{4!}{2!2!}4x^2 \cdot 1 + \frac{4!}{3!1!}2x \cdot 1 + \frac{\cancel{4!}}{\cancel{4!}0!} \cdot 1$$

$$= 1\left(16x^4\right) + \frac{4 \cdot \cancel{3!}}{1 \cdot \cancel{3!}}8x^3 + \frac{4 \cdot 3 \cdot \cancel{2!}}{2 \cdot 1 \cdot \cancel{2!}}4x^2 + \frac{4 \cdot \cancel{3!}}{\cancel{3!} \cdot 1}2x + 1 = 16x^4 + 4\left(8x^3\right) + 6\left(4x^2\right) + 4(2x) + 1$$

$$= 16x^4 + 32x^3 + 24x^2 + 8x + 1$$

17. Applying the Binomial Theorem to $\left(x^2 + 2y\right)^4$, we have $a = x^2$, $b = 2y$, and $n = 4$.

$$\left(x^2 + 2y\right)^4 = \binom{4}{0}\left(x^2\right)^4 + \binom{4}{1}\left(x^2\right)^3(2y) + \binom{4}{2}\left(x^2\right)^2(2y)^2 + \binom{4}{3}x^2(2y)^3 + \binom{4}{4}(2y)^4$$

$$= \frac{4!}{0!(4-0)!}x^8 + \frac{4!}{1!(4-1)!}2x^6y + \frac{4!}{2!(4-2)!}4x^4y^2 + \frac{4!}{3!(4-3)!}8x^2y^3 + \frac{4!}{4!(4-4)!}16y^4$$

$$= \frac{\cancel{4!}}{0! \cancel{4!}}x^8 + \frac{4!}{1!3!}2x^6y + \frac{4!}{2!2!}4x^4y^2 + \frac{4!}{3!1!}8x^2y^3 + \frac{\cancel{4!}}{\cancel{4!}0!}16y^4$$

$$= 1\left(x^8\right) + \frac{4 \cdot \cancel{3!}}{1 \cdot \cancel{3!}}2x^6y + \frac{4 \cdot 3 \cdot \cancel{2!}}{2 \cdot 1 \cdot \cancel{2!}}4x^4y^2 + \frac{4 \cdot \cancel{3!}}{\cancel{3!} \cdot 1}8x^2y^3 + 16y^4$$

$$= x^8 + 4\left(2x^6y\right) + 6\left(4x^4y^2\right) + 4\left(8x^2y^3\right) + 16y^4 = x^8 + 8x^6y + 24x^4y^2 + 32x^2y^3 + 16y^4$$

19. Applying the Binomial Theorem to $(y-3)^4$, we have $a = y$, $b = -3$, and $n = 4$.

$$(y-3)^4 = \binom{4}{0}y^4 + \binom{4}{1}y^3(-3) + \binom{4}{2}y^2(-3)^2 + \binom{4}{3}y(-3)^3 + \binom{4}{4}(-3)^4$$

$$= \frac{4!}{0!(4-0)!}y^4 - \frac{4!}{1!(4-1)!}3y^3 + \frac{4!}{2!(4-2)!}9y^2 - \frac{4!}{3!(4-3)!}27y + \frac{4!}{4!(4-4)!}81$$

$$= \frac{\cancel{4!}}{0! \cancel{4!}}y^4 - \frac{4!}{1!3!}3y^3 + \frac{4!}{2!2!}9y^2 - \frac{4!}{3!1!}27y + \frac{\cancel{4!}}{\cancel{4!}0!}81$$

$$= 1\left(y^4\right) - \frac{4 \cdot \cancel{3!}}{1 \cdot \cancel{3!}}3y^3 + \frac{4 \cdot 3 \cdot \cancel{2!}}{2 \cdot 1 \cdot \cancel{2!}}9y^2 - \frac{4 \cdot \cancel{3!}}{\cancel{3!} \cdot 1}27y + 81$$

$$= y^4 - 4\left(3y^3\right) + 6\left(9y^2\right) - 4(27y) + 81 = y^4 - 12y^3 + 54y^2 - 108y + 81$$

21. Applying the Binomial Theorem to $\left(2x^3-1\right)^4$, we have $a=2x^3,\ b=-1,\ $ and $n=4.$

$$\left(2x^3-1\right)^4=\binom{4}{0}\left(2x^3\right)^4+\binom{4}{1}\left(2x^3\right)^3(-1)+\binom{4}{2}\left(2x^3\right)^2(-1)^2+\binom{4}{3}\left(2x^3\right)(-1)^3+\binom{4}{4}(-1)^4$$

$$=\frac{4!}{0!(4-0)!}16x^{12}-\frac{4!}{1!(4-1)!}8x^9+\frac{4!}{2!(4-2)!}4x^6-\frac{4!}{3!(4-3)!}2x^3+\frac{4!}{4!(4-4)!}$$

$$=\frac{\cancel{4!}}{0!\,\cancel{4!}}16x^{12}-\frac{4!}{1!3!}8x^9+\frac{4!}{2!2!}4x^6-\frac{4!}{3!1!}2x^3+\frac{\cancel{4!}}{\cancel{4!}0!}=1\left(16x^{12}\right)-\frac{4\cdot\cancel{3!}}{1\cdot\cancel{3!}}8x^9+\frac{4\cdot3\cdot\cancel{2!}}{2\cdot1\cdot\cancel{2!}}4x^6-\frac{4\cdot\cancel{3!}}{\cancel{3!}\cdot1}2x^3+1$$

$$=16x^{12}-4\left(8x^9\right)+6\left(4x^6\right)-4\left(2x^3\right)+1=16x^{12}-32x^9+24x^6-8x^3+1$$

23. Applying the Binomial Theorem to $(c+2)^5$, we have $a=c,\ b=2,\ $ and $n=5.$

$$(c+2)^5=\binom{5}{0}c^5+\binom{5}{1}c^4(2)+\binom{5}{2}c^3(2)^2+\binom{5}{3}c^2(2)^3+\binom{5}{4}c(2)^4+\binom{5}{5}2^5$$

$$=\frac{\cancel{5!}}{0!\,\cancel{5!}}c^5+\frac{5!}{1!(5-1)!}2c^4+\frac{5!}{2!(5-2)!}4c^3+\frac{5!}{3!(5-3)!}8c^2+\frac{5!}{4!(5-4)!}16c+\frac{5!}{5!(5-5)!}32$$

$$=1c^5+\frac{5\cdot\cancel{4!}}{1\cdot\cancel{4!}}2c^4+\frac{5\cdot4\cdot\cancel{3!}}{2\cdot1\cdot\cancel{3!}}4c^3+\frac{5\cdot4\cdot\cancel{3!}}{\cancel{3!}2\cdot1}8c^2+\frac{5\cdot\cancel{4!}}{\cancel{4!}\cdot1}16c+\frac{\cancel{5!}}{\cancel{5!}0!}32$$

$$=c^5+5\left(2c^4\right)+10\left(4c^3\right)+10\left(8c^2\right)+5(16c)+1(32)=c^5+10c^4+40c^3+80c^2+80c+32$$

25. Applying the Binomial Theorem to $(x-1)^5$, we have $a=x,\ b=-1,\ $ and $n=5.$

$$(x-1)^5=\binom{5}{0}x^5+\binom{5}{1}x^4(-1)+\binom{5}{2}x^3(-1)^2+\binom{5}{3}x^2(-1)^3+\binom{5}{4}x(-1)^4+\binom{5}{5}(-1)^5$$

$$=\frac{\cancel{5!}}{0!\,\cancel{5!}}x^5-\frac{5!}{1!(5-1)!}x^4+\frac{5!}{2!(5-2)!}x^3-\frac{5!}{3!(5-3)!}x^2+\frac{5!}{4!(5-4)!}x-\frac{5!}{5!(5-5)!}$$

$$=1x^5-\frac{5\cdot\cancel{4!}}{1\cdot\cancel{4!}}x^4+\frac{5\cdot4\cdot\cancel{3!}}{2\cdot1\cdot\cancel{3!}}x^3-\frac{5\cdot4\cdot\cancel{3!}}{\cancel{3!}2\cdot1}x^2+\frac{5\cdot\cancel{4!}}{\cancel{4!}\cdot1}x-\frac{\cancel{5!}}{\cancel{5!}0!}=x^5-5x^4+10x^3-10x^2+5x-1$$

27. Applying the Binomial Theorem to $(x-2y)^5$, we have $a=x,\ b=-2y,\ $ and $n=5.$

$$(x-2y)^5=\binom{5}{0}x^5+\binom{5}{1}x^4(-2y)+\binom{5}{2}x^3(-2y)^2+\binom{5}{3}x^2(-2y)^3+\binom{5}{4}x(-2y)^4+\binom{5}{5}(-2y)^5$$

$$=\frac{\cancel{5!}}{0!\,\cancel{5!}}x^5-\frac{5!}{1!(5-1)!}2x^4y+\frac{5!}{2!(5-2)!}4x^3y^2-\frac{5!}{3!(5-3)!}8x^2y^3+\frac{5!}{4!(5-4)!}16xy^4-\frac{5!}{5!(5-5)!}32y^5$$

$$=1x^5-\frac{5\cdot\cancel{4!}}{1\cdot\cancel{4!}}2x^4y+\frac{5\cdot4\cdot\cancel{3!}}{2\cdot1\cdot\cancel{3!}}4x^3y^2-\frac{5\cdot4\cdot\cancel{3!}}{\cancel{3!}2\cdot1}8x^2y^3+\frac{5\cdot\cancel{4!}}{\cancel{4!}\cdot1}16xy^4-\frac{\cancel{5!}}{\cancel{5!}0!}32y^5$$

$$=x^5-5\left(2x^4y\right)+10\left(4x^3y^2\right)-10\left(8x^2y^3\right)+5\left(16xy^4\right)-1\left(32y^5\right)$$

$$=x^5-10x^4y+40x^3y^2-80x^2y^3+80xy^4-32y^5$$

29. Applying the Binomial Theorem to $(2a+b)^6$, we have $a = 2a$, $b = b$, and $n = 6$.

$(2a+b)^6$

$$= \binom{6}{0}(2a)^6 + \binom{6}{1}(2a)^5 b + \binom{6}{2}(2a)^4 b^2 + \binom{6}{3}(2a)^3 b^3 + \binom{6}{4}(2a)^2 b^4 + \binom{6}{5}2ab^5 + \binom{6}{6}b^6$$

$$= \frac{6!}{0!(6-0)!}64a^6 + \frac{6!}{1!(6-1)!}32a^5 b + \frac{6!}{2!(6-2)!}16a^4 b^2 + \frac{6!}{3!(6-3)!}8a^3 b^3$$

$$+ \frac{6!}{4!(6-4)!}4a^2 b^4 + \frac{6!}{5!(6-5)!}2ab^5 + \frac{6!}{6!(6-6)!}b^6$$

$$= \frac{\cancel{6!}}{1\cancel{6!}}64a^6 + \frac{6\cdot\cancel{5!}}{1\cdot\cancel{5!}}32a^5 b + \frac{6\cdot5\cdot\cancel{4!}}{2\cdot1\cdot\cancel{4!}}16a^4 b^2 + \frac{\cancel{6}\cdot5\cdot4\cdot\cancel{3!}}{\cancel{3}\cancel{2}\cdot1\cdot\cancel{3!}}8a^3 b^3 + \frac{6\cdot5\cdot\cancel{4!}}{\cancel{4!}2\cdot1}4a^2 b^4 + \frac{6\cdot\cancel{5!}}{\cancel{5!}1}2ab^5 + \frac{\cancel{6!}}{\cancel{6!}\cdot1}b^6$$

$$= 64a^6 + 6(32a^5 b) + 15(16a^4 b^2) + 20(8a^3 b^3) + 15(4a^2 b^4) + 6(2ab^5) + 1b^6$$

$$= 64a^6 + 192a^5 b + 240a^4 b^2 + 160a^3 b^3 + 60a^2 b^4 + 12ab^5 + b^6$$

31.

1st Term $\binom{n}{r-1}a^{n-r+1}b^{r-1} = \binom{8}{1-1}x^{8-1+1}2^{1-1} = \binom{8}{0}x^8 2^0 = \frac{8!}{0!(8-0)!}x^8 \cdot 1 = \frac{\cancel{8!}}{0!\cancel{8!}}x^8 = x^8$

2nd Term $\binom{n}{r-1}a^{n-r+1}b^{r-1} = \binom{8}{2-1}x^{8-2+1}2^{2-1} = \binom{8}{1}x^7 2^1 = \frac{8!}{1!(8-1)!}2x^7 = \frac{8\cdot\cancel{7!}}{1\cdot\cancel{7!}}2x^7 = 8\cdot2x^7 = 16x^7$

3rd Term $\binom{n}{r-1}a^{n-r+1}b^{r-1} = \binom{8}{3-1}x^{8-3+1}2^{3-1} = \binom{8}{2}x^6 2^2 = \frac{8!}{2!(8-2)!}4x^6 = \frac{8\cdot7\cdot\cancel{6!}}{2\cdot1\cdot\cancel{6!}}4x^6 = 28\cdot4x^6 = 112x^6$

33.

1st Term $\binom{n}{r-1}a^{n-r+1}b^{r-1} = \binom{10}{1-1}x^{10-1+1}(-2y)^{1-1} = \binom{10}{0}x^{10}(-2y)^0 = \frac{10!}{0!(10-0)!}x^{10} \cdot 1 = \frac{\cancel{10!}}{0!\cancel{10!}}x^{10} = x^{10}$

2nd Term $\binom{n}{r-1}a^{n-r+1}b^{r-1} = \binom{10}{2-1}x^{10-2+1}(-2y)^{2-1} = \binom{10}{1}x^9(-2y)^1 = -\frac{10!}{1!(10-1)!}2x^9 y$

$$= -\frac{10\cdot\cancel{9!}}{1\cdot\cancel{9!}}2x^9 y = -10\cdot2x^9 y = -20x^9 y$$

3rd Term $\binom{n}{r-1}a^{n-r+1}b^{r-1} = \binom{10}{3-1}x^{10-3+1}(-2y)^{3-1} = \binom{10}{2}x^8(-2y)^2 = \frac{10!}{2!(10-2)!}4x^8 y^2$

$$= \frac{10\cdot9\cdot\cancel{8!}}{2\cdot1\cdot\cancel{8!}}4x^8 y^2 = 45\cdot4x^8 y^2 = 180x^8 y^2$$

35.

1st Term $\binom{n}{r-1}a^{n-r+1}b^{r-1} = \binom{16}{1-1}(x^2)^{16-1+1}(1)^{1-1} = \binom{16}{0}(x^2)^{16}1^0 = \frac{16!}{0!(16-0)!}x^{32} \cdot 1 = \frac{\cancel{16!}}{0!\cancel{16!}}x^{32} = x^{32}$

2nd Term $\binom{n}{r-1}a^{n-r+1}b^{r-1} = \binom{16}{2-1}(x^2)^{16-2+1}(1)^{2-1} = \binom{16}{1}(x^2)^{15}1^1 = \frac{16!}{1!(16-1)!}x^{30} \cdot 1 = \frac{16\cdot\cancel{15!}}{1\cdot\cancel{15!}}x^{30} = 16x^{30}$

3rd Term $\binom{n}{r-1}a^{n-r+1}b^{r-1} = \binom{16}{3-1}\left(x^2\right)^{16-3+1}\left(1\right)^{3-1} = \binom{16}{2}\left(x^2\right)^{14}1^2 = \dfrac{16!}{2!(16-2)!}x^{28}\cdot 1 = \dfrac{16\cdot 15\cdot \cancel{14!}}{2\cdot 1\cdot \cancel{14!}}x^{28} = 120x^{28}$

37. 1st Term

$\binom{n}{r-1}a^{n-r+1}b^{r-1} = \binom{20}{1-1}\left(y^3\right)^{20-1+1}\left(-1\right)^{1-1} = \binom{20}{0}\left(y^3\right)^{20}\left(-1\right)^0 = \dfrac{20!}{0!(20-0)!}y^{60}\cdot 1 = \dfrac{\cancel{20!}}{0!\,\cancel{20!}}y^{60} = x^{60}$

2nd Term

$\binom{n}{r-1}a^{n-r+1}b^{r-1} = \binom{20}{2-1}\left(y^3\right)^{20-2+1}\left(-1\right)^{2-1} = \binom{20}{1}\left(y^3\right)^{19}\left(-1\right)^1 = \dfrac{20!}{1!(20-1)!}y^{57}\cdot(-1) = -\dfrac{20\cdot \cancel{19!}}{1\cdot \cancel{19!}}y^{57} = -20y^{57}$

3rd Term

$\binom{n}{r-1}a^{n-r+1}b^{r-1} = \binom{20}{3-1}\left(y^3\right)^{20-3+1}\left(-1\right)^{3-1} = \binom{20}{2}\left(y^3\right)^{18}\left(-1\right)^2 = \dfrac{20!}{2!(20-2)!}y^{54}\cdot 1 = \dfrac{20\cdot 19\cdot \cancel{18!}}{2\cdot 1\cdot \cancel{18!}}y^{54} = 190y^{54}$

39. 3rd Term

$\binom{n}{r-1}a^{n-r+1}b^{r-1} = \binom{6}{3-1}\left(2x\right)^{6-3+1}y^{3-1} = \binom{6}{2}\left(2x\right)^4 y^2 = \dfrac{6!}{2!(6-2)!}16x^4y^2 = \dfrac{6\cdot 5\cdot \cancel{4!}}{2\cdot 1\cdot \cancel{4!}}16x^4y^2$

$= 15\left(16x^4y^2\right) = 240x^4y^2$

41. 5th Term

$\binom{n}{r-1}a^{n-r+1}b^{r-1} = \binom{9}{5-1}x^{9-5+1}\left(-1\right)^{5-1} = \binom{9}{4}x^5\left(-1\right)^4 = \dfrac{9!}{4!(9-4)!}x^5\cdot 1 = \dfrac{9\cdot 8\cdot 7\cdot \cancel{6}\cdot \cancel{5!}}{4\cdot \cancel{3}\cancel{2}\cdot 1\cdot \cancel{5!}}x^5 = 126x^5$

43. 6th Term

$\binom{n}{r-1}a^{n-r+1}b^{r-1} = \binom{8}{6-1}\left(x^2\right)^{8-6+1}\left(y^3\right)^{6-1} = \binom{8}{5}\left(x^2\right)^3\left(y^3\right)^5 = \dfrac{8!}{5!(8-5)!}x^6y^{15} = \dfrac{8\cdot 7\cdot \cancel{6}\cdot \cancel{5!}}{\cancel{5!}\cdot \cancel{3}\cancel{2}\cdot 1}x^6y^{15} = 56x^6y^{15}$

45. 4th Term

$\binom{n}{r-1}a^{n-r+1}b^{r-1} = \binom{9}{4-1}x^{9-4+1}\left(-\dfrac{1}{2}\right)^{4-1} = \binom{9}{3}x^6\left(-\dfrac{1}{2}\right)^3 = -\dfrac{9!}{3!(9-3)!}\cdot \dfrac{1}{8}x^6 = -\dfrac{9\cdot \cancel{8}\cdot 7\cdot \cancel{6!}}{3\cdot 2\cdot 1\cdot \cancel{6!}}\cdot \dfrac{1}{\cancel{8}}x^6 = -\dfrac{21}{2}x^6$

47. $g(t) = f(t+10) = 0.002(t+10)^3 - 0.9(t+10)^2 + 1.27(t+10) + 6.76$

Use the Binomial Theorem to expand $(t+10)^3$. (The Binomial Theorem could be used to expand $(t+10)^2$ also, but it can be multiplied more efficiently using the foil method.)

$(t+10)^3$

$= \binom{3}{0}t^3 + \binom{3}{1}t^2(10) + \binom{3}{2}t(10)^2 + \binom{3}{3}10^3 = \dfrac{3!}{0!(3-0)!}t^3 + \dfrac{3!}{1!(3-1)!}10t^2 + \dfrac{3!}{2!(3-2)!}100t + \dfrac{3!}{3!(3-3)!}1000$

$= \dfrac{\cancel{3!}}{1\cdot \cancel{3!}}t^3 + \dfrac{3\cdot \cancel{2!}}{1\cdot \cancel{2!}}10t^2 + \dfrac{3\cdot \cancel{2!}}{\cancel{2!}1!}100t + \dfrac{\cancel{3!}}{\cancel{3!}0!}1000 = t^3 + 3\left(10t^2\right) + 3(100t) + 1(1000) = t^3 + 30t^2 + 300t + 1000$

Now substitute the expanded expression.

$$g(t) = f(t+10) = 0.002(t+10)^3 - 0.9(t+10)^2 + 1.27(t+10) + 6.76$$
$$= 0.002(t^3 + 30t^2 + 300t + 1000) - 0.9(t^2 + 20t + 100) + 1.27(t+10) + 6.76$$
$$= 0.002t^3 + 0.06t^2 + 0.6t + 2 - 0.9t^2 - 18t - 90 + 1.27t + 12.7 + 6.76$$
$$= 0.002t^3 + 0.06t^2 - 0.9t^2 + 0.6t - 18t + 1.27t + 2 - 90 + 12.7 + 6.76$$
$$= 0.002t^3 - 0.84t^2 - 16.13t - 6854$$

For Exercises 49-57, answers may vary.

59. Rewrite $(x^2 + x + 1)^3$ as $(x^2 + (x+1))^3$

$$(x^2 + (x+1))^3 = \binom{3}{0}(x^2)^3 + \binom{3}{1}(x^2)^2(x+1) + \binom{3}{2}(x^2)(x+1)^2 + \binom{3}{3}(x+1)^3$$

$$= \frac{3!}{0!(3-0)!}x^6 + \frac{3!}{1!(3-1)!}x^4(x+1) + \frac{3!}{2!(3-2)!}x^2(x^2 + 2x + 1) + \frac{3!}{3!(3-3)!}(x^3 + 3x^2 + 3x + 1)$$

$$= \frac{3!}{1 \cdot 3!}x^6 + \frac{3 \cdot 2!}{1 \cdot 2!}(x^5 + x^4) + \frac{3 \cdot 2!}{2!1!}(x^4 + 2x^3 + x^2) + \frac{3!}{3!0!}(x^3 + 3x^2 + 3x + 1)$$

$$= x^6 + 3(x^5 + x^4) + 3(x^4 + 2x^3 + x^2) + 1(x^3 + 3x^2 + 3x + 1)$$

$$= x^6 + 3x^5 + 3x^4 + 3x^4 + 6x^3 + 3x^2 + x^3 + 3x^2 + 3x + 1 = x^6 + 3x^5 + 6x^4 + 7x^3 + 6x^2 + 3x + 1$$

61. For example, consider Exercise 2. $\binom{7}{2}$

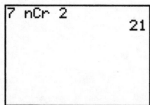

This is the same result obtained in Exercise 2.

63.
$$f_1(x) = (x+1)^4 \qquad\qquad f_2(x) = x^4$$
$$f_3(x) = x^4 + 4x^3 \qquad\qquad f_4(x) = x^4 + 4x^3 + 6x^2$$
$$f_5(x) = x^4 + 4x^3 + 6x^2 + 4x \qquad f_6(x) = x^4 + 4x^3 + 6x^2 + 4x + 1$$

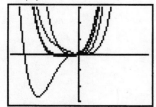

Graphs f_1 and f_6 are the same. This means that the functions are equivalent. Graphs f_2 through f_5 are increasingly similar to the graphs of f_1 and f_6.

65.

$$(x-2)^4 = \binom{4}{0}x^4 + \binom{4}{1}x^3(-2) + \binom{4}{2}x^2(-2)^2 + \binom{4}{3}x(-2)^3 + \binom{4}{4}(-2)^4$$

$$= \frac{4!}{0!(4-0)!}x^4 - \frac{4!}{1!(4-1)!}2x^3 + \frac{4!}{2!(4-2)!}4x^2 - \frac{4!}{3!(4-3)!}8x + \frac{4!}{4!(4-4)!}16$$

$$= \frac{\cancel{4!}}{0!\cancel{4!}}x^4 - \frac{4!}{1!3!}2x^3 + \frac{4!}{2!2!}4x^2 - \frac{4!}{3!1!}8x + \frac{\cancel{4!}}{\cancel{4!}0!}16 = 1(x^4) - \frac{4\cdot\cancel{3!}}{1\cdot\cancel{3!}}2x^3 + \frac{4\cdot3\cdot\cancel{2!}}{2\cdot1\cdot\cancel{2!}}4x^2 - \frac{4\cdot\cancel{3!}}{\cancel{3!}\cdot1}8x + 16$$

$$= x^4 - 4(2x^3) + 6(4x^2) - 4(8x) + 16 = x^4 - 8x^3 + 24x^2 - 32x + 16$$

Graph using the method from Exercises 59 and 60.

$$f_1(x) = (x-2)^4 \qquad\qquad f_2(x) = x^4$$
$$f_3(x) = x^4 - 8x^3 \qquad\qquad f_4(x) = x^4 - 8x^3 + 24x^2$$
$$f_5(x) = x^4 - 8x^3 + 24x^2 - 32x \quad f_6(x) = x^4 - 8x^3 + 24x^2 - 32x + 16$$

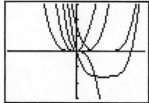

Graphs f_1 and f_6 are the same. This means that the functions are equivalent. Graphs f_2 through f_5 are increasingly similar to the graphs of f_1 and f_6.

67. Answers will vary. For example, consider Exercise 10.

$$(4x-1)^3$$

```
F1 ▼  F2 ▼  F3 ▼  F4 ▼  F5    F6
▼ ▲ Algebra Calc Other PrgmIO Clear a-z…




■ expand((4·x - 1)³)
                    64·x³ - 48·x² + 12·x - 1
expand((4x-1)^3)
MAIN       RAD AUTO        3D   1/99
```

This is the same result obtained in Exercise 10.

Review Exercises

68. $f(a+1) = (a+1)^2 + 2(a+1) + 3 = a^2 + 2a + 1 + 2a + 2 + 3 = a^2 + 4a + 6$

69. $f(g(x)) = f(2x-3) = (2x-3)^2 + 5(2x-3) = 4x^2 - 12x + 9 + 10x - 15 = 4x^2 - 2x - 6$

$g(f(x)) = g(x^2 + 5x) = 2(x^2 + 5x) - 3 = 2x^2 + 10x - 3$

70.

$$\frac{x}{x+3} - \frac{x+1}{2x^2 - 2x - 24} = \frac{x}{x+3} - \frac{x+1}{2(x^2 - x - 12)}$$

$$= \frac{x}{x+3} - \frac{x+1}{2(x-4)(x+3)}$$

$$= \frac{x}{x+3} \cdot \frac{2(x-4)}{2(x-4)} - \frac{x+1}{2(x-4)(x+3)}$$

$$= \frac{2x(x-4)}{2(x-4)(x+3)} - \frac{x+1}{2(x-4)(x+3)}$$

$$= \frac{2x(x-4) - (x+1)}{2(x-4)(x+3)} = \frac{2x^2 - 8x - x - 1}{2(x-4)(x+3)}$$

$$= \frac{2x^2 - 9x - 1}{2(x-4)(x+3)}$$

Counting Principles, Permutations, and Combinations

14.5 CHECK POINTS

CHECK POINT 1
size $\cdot$ crust $\cdot$ toppings $= 3 \cdot 4 \cdot 6 = 72$
72 different one-topping pizzas can be ordered.

CHECK POINT 2
$3 \cdot 3 \cdot 3 \cdot 3 \cdot 3 \cdot 3 = 3^6 = 729$
There are 729 ways to answer the questions.

CHECK POINT 3
$26 \cdot 26 \cdot 10 \cdot 10 \cdot 10 = 676,000$
676,000 different license plates can be manufactured.

CHECK POINT 4
$$_7P_4 = \frac{7!}{(7-4)!} = \frac{7!}{3!} = \frac{7 \cdot 6 \cdot 5 \cdot 4 \cdot 3!}{3!}$$
$$= 7 \cdot 6 \cdot 5 \cdot 4 = 840$$
There are 840 different ways to elect a president, vice-president, secretary, and treasurer.

CHECK POINT 5
$$_6P_6 = \frac{6!}{(6-6)!} = \frac{6!}{0!}$$
$$= \frac{6 \cdot 5 \cdot 4 \cdot 3 \cdot 2 \cdot 1}{1} = 720$$
There are 720 ways to line up the books.

CHECK POINT 6
a. Because order does not make a difference, this is a problem involving combinations.

b. Because order makes a difference, this is a problem involving permutations.

CHECK POINT 7
$$_{10}C_4 = \frac{10!}{(10-4)!4!} = \frac{10!}{6!4!}$$
$$= \frac{10 \cdot 9 \cdot 8 \cdot 7 \cdot \cancel{6!}}{\cancel{6!} \cdot 4 \cdot 3 \cdot 2 \cdot 1} = 210$$
There are 210 ways to select the physicians to attend the conference.

CHECK POINT 8
$$_{16}C_4 = \frac{16!}{(16-4)!4!} = \frac{16!}{12!4!}$$
$$= \frac{16 \cdot 15 \cdot 14 \cdot 13 \cdot \cancel{12!}}{\cancel{12!} \cdot 4 \cdot 3 \cdot 2 \cdot 1} = 1820$$
There are 1820 different 4-card hands.

EXERCISE SET 14.5

1.
$$_9P_4 = \frac{9!}{(9-4)!} = \frac{9!}{5!} = \frac{9 \cdot 8 \cdot 7 \cdot 6 \cdot 5!}{5!}$$
$$= 9 \cdot 8 \cdot 7 \cdot 6 = 3024$$

3.
$$_8P_5 = \frac{8!}{(8-5)!} = \frac{8!}{3!} = \frac{8 \cdot 7 \cdot 6 \cdot 5 \cdot 4 \cdot 3!}{3!}$$
$$= 8 \cdot 7 \cdot 6 \cdot 5 \cdot 4 = 6720$$

5.
$$_6P_6 = \frac{6!}{(6-6)!} = \frac{6!}{0!} = \frac{6 \cdot 5 \cdot 4 \cdot 3 \cdot 2 \cdot 1}{1} = 720$$

7.
$$_8P_0 = \frac{8!}{(8-0)!} = \frac{8!}{8!} = 1$$

9. $\displaystyle {}_9C_5 = \frac{9!}{(9-5)!\,5!} = \frac{9!}{4!\,5!} = 126$

11. $\displaystyle {}_{11}C_4 = \frac{11!}{(11-4)!\,4!} = \frac{11!}{7!\,4!} = 330$

13. $\displaystyle {}_7C_7 = \frac{7!}{(7-7)!\,7!} = \frac{7!}{0!\,7!} = 1$

15. $\displaystyle {}_5C_0 = \frac{5!}{(5-0)!\,0!} = \frac{5!}{5!\,0!} = 1$

17. Since order does not matter, combinations are involved.

19. Since order matters, permutations are involved.

21. $9 \cdot 3 = 27$
There are 27 ways you can order the car.

23. $2 \cdot 4 \cdot 5 = 40$
There are 40 ways to order a drink.

25. $3 \cdot 3 \cdot 3 \cdot 3 \cdot 3 = 3^5 = 243$
There are 243 ways to answer the questions.

27. $8 \cdot 2 \cdot 9 = 144$
There were 144 area codes possible.

29. $5 \cdot 4 \cdot 3 \cdot 2 \cdot 1 \cdot 1 = 120$
There are 120 ways to schedule the appearances.

31. $1 \cdot 3 \cdot 2 \cdot 1 \cdot 1 = 6$
6 five-sentence paragraphs can be formed.

33. $\displaystyle {}_{10}P_3 = \frac{10!}{(10-3)!} = \frac{10!}{7!} = \frac{10 \cdot 9 \cdot 8 \cdot \cancel{7!}}{\cancel{7!}} = 720$
There are 720 ways to fill the offices.

35. $\displaystyle {}_{13}P_7 = \frac{13!}{(13-7)!} = \frac{13!}{6!}$

$\displaystyle = \frac{13 \cdot 12 \cdot 11 \cdot 10 \cdot 9 \cdot 8 \cdot 7 \cdot \cancel{6!}}{\cancel{6!}} = 8,648,640$
There are 8,648,640 ways to program for the segment.

37. $\displaystyle {}_6P_3 = \frac{6!}{(6-3)!} = \frac{6!}{3!} = \frac{6 \cdot 5 \cdot 4 \cdot \cancel{3!}}{\cancel{3!}} = 120$
There are 120 ways the first three finishers can come in.

39. $\displaystyle {}_9P_5 = \frac{9!}{(9-5)!} = \frac{9!}{4!} = \frac{9 \cdot 8 \cdot 7 \cdot 6 \cdot 5 \cdot \cancel{4!}}{\cancel{4!}} = 15,120$
There are 15,120 possible line-ups.

41. $\displaystyle {}_6C_3 = \frac{6!}{(6-3)!\,3!} = \frac{6!}{3!\,3!} = 20$
There are 20 ways to select the three city commissioners.

43. $\displaystyle {}_{12}C_4 = \frac{12!}{(12-4)!\,4!} = \frac{12!}{8!\,4!} = 495$
There are 495 different collections of 4 books.

45. $\displaystyle {}_{17}C_8 = \frac{17!}{(17-8)!\,8!} = \frac{17!}{9!\,8!} = 24,310$
There are 24,310 different groups of 8 children.

47. $\displaystyle {}_{49}C_6 = \frac{49!}{(49-6)!\,6!} = \frac{49!}{43!\,6!} = 13,983,816$
13,983,816 selections are possible.

49. $\displaystyle {}_6P_4 = \frac{6!}{(6-4)!} = \frac{6!}{2!} = \frac{6 \cdot 5 \cdot 4 \cdot 3 \cdot \cancel{2!}}{\cancel{2!}} = 360$
There are 360 ways the first four finishers can come in.

51. $\displaystyle {}_{13}C_6 = \frac{13!}{(13-6)!\,6!} = \frac{13!}{7!\,6!} = 1716$
There are 1716 ways to select 6 people.

53. $_{20}C_3 = \dfrac{20!}{(20-3)!3!} = \dfrac{20!}{17!3!} = 1140$

There are 1140 ways to select 3 members.

55. $_7P_4 = \dfrac{7!}{(7-4)!} = \dfrac{7!}{3!} = 840$

840 four-letter passwords can be formed.

57. $_{15}P_3 = \dfrac{15!}{(15-3)!} = \dfrac{15!}{12!} = 2730$

2730 different cones can be created.

For Exercises 59-65, answers may vary.

67. Statement **c.** is true.

$_7P_3 = 3!,\ _7C_3 = \cancel{3!}\,\dfrac{7!}{(7-3)!\cancel{3!}} = _7P_3$

Statement **a.** is false. Since order does not matter, the number of ways to choose four questions out of ten is $_{10}C_4$.

Statement **b.** is false. If $r > 1$, $_nP_r$ is greater than $_nC_r$.

Statement **d.** is false. Since order matters, the number of ways to pick a winner and first runner-up is $_{20}P_2$.

69. $2 \cdot 6 \cdot 6 \cdot 2 = 144$

144 four-digit odd numbers less than 6000 can be formed.

71. For example, consider Exercise 1.

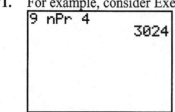

This is the same result obtained in Exercise 1.

Review Exercises

73. $(f \circ g)(x) = f(g(x)) = f(4x-1)$
$= (4x-1)^2 + 2(4x-1) - 5$

$= 16x^2 - 8x + 1 + 8x - 2 - 5 = 16x^2 - 6$

74. $|2x-5| > 3$

$2x - 5 < -3 \quad$ or $\quad 2x - 5 > 3$

$2x < 2 \qquad\qquad 2x > 8$

$x < 1 \qquad\qquad x > 4$

$\{x | x < 1 \text{ or } x > 4\}$ or $(-\infty, 1) \cup (4, \infty)$.

75. $x^2 + y^2 - 2x + 4y - 4 = 0$

$x^2 - 2x + y^2 + 4y = 4$

$(x^2 - 2x + 1) + (y^2 + 4y + 4) = 4 + 1 + 4$

$(x-1)^2 + (y+2)^2 = 9$

The center of the circle is $(1, -2)$ and the radius is 3 units.

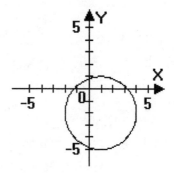

Probability

14.6 CHECK POINTS

CHECK POINT 1

$P(E) = \dfrac{\text{number who sleep 7 hours}}{\text{total number}}$

$= \dfrac{82.5}{275} = \dfrac{3}{10} = 0.3$

The probability of selecting an American who gets seven hours sleep on a typical night is $\dfrac{3}{10}$ or 0.3.

CHECK POINT 2

$S = \{1, 2, 3, 4, 5, 6\}$

$E = \{5, 6\}$

$$P(E) = \frac{n(E)}{n(S)} = \frac{2}{6} = \frac{1}{3}$$

CHECK POINT 3

Since there are 36 possible rolls of two dice, $n(S) = 36$.

$E = \{(1,4),(2,3)(3,2),(4,1)\}$

$n(E) = 4$

$$P(E) = \frac{n(E)}{n(S)} = \frac{4}{36} = \frac{1}{9}$$

CHECK POINT 4

There are 4 kings in a deck of 52 cards.

$$P(E) = \frac{n(E)}{n(S)} = \frac{4}{52} = \frac{1}{13}$$

CHECK POINT 5

$$_{30}C_5 = \frac{30!}{(30-5)!5!} = \frac{30!}{25!5!} = 142,506$$

$$P(E) = \frac{n(E)}{n(S)} = \frac{1}{142,506}$$

The probability of winning the prize is $\frac{1}{142,506}$ or approximately 0.00000702.

CHECK POINT 6

$$P(E) = \frac{n(E)}{n(S)} = \frac{142,505}{142,506} \approx 0.999993$$

The chances of not winning the lottery are $\frac{142,505}{142,506}$ or approximately 0.999993.

CHECK POINT 7

$$P(4 \text{ or } 5) = P(4) + P(5) = \frac{1}{6} + \frac{1}{6} = \frac{2}{6} = \frac{1}{3}$$

CHECK POINT 8

$P(\text{odd or} < 5)$

$= P(\text{odd}) + P(<5) - P(\text{odd and} < 5)$

$= \frac{4}{8} + \frac{4}{8} - \frac{2}{8} = \frac{6}{8} = \frac{3}{4}$

CHECK POINT 9

Let pf = picking fleas

Let sw = screeching wildly

$P(\text{pf or sw})$

$= P(\text{pf}) + P(\text{sw}) - P(\text{pf and sw})$

$= \frac{18}{25} + \frac{16}{25} - \frac{10}{25} = \frac{24}{25}$

CHECK POINT 10

$P(\text{green and green})$

$= P(\text{green}) \cdot P(\text{green})$

$= \frac{2}{38} \cdot \frac{2}{38} = \frac{4}{1444} = \frac{1}{361} \approx 0.00277$

CHECK POINT 11

$$P(4 \text{ boys in a row}) = \frac{1}{2} \cdot \frac{1}{2} \cdot \frac{1}{2} \cdot \frac{1}{2} = \frac{1}{16}$$

EXERCISE SET 14.6

1. $$P(2) = \frac{29,780,000}{70,241,000} = \frac{29,780}{70,241} \approx 0.424$$

3. $$P(\text{Africa}) = \frac{761}{5926} \approx 0.128$$

5. $$P(4) = \frac{1}{6}$$

7. $$P(\text{odd}) = \frac{3}{6} = \frac{1}{2}$$

9. $$P(>4) = \frac{2}{6} = \frac{1}{3}$$

11. $$P(\text{queen}) = \frac{4}{52} = \frac{1}{13}$$

13. $$P(\text{picture card}) = \frac{12}{52} = \frac{3}{13}$$

15. $$P(\text{HH}) = \frac{1}{4}$$

17.

$$P(\text{at least 1 male}) = \frac{7}{8}$$

19. Since there are 36 possible rolls of two dice, $n(S) = 36$.

$$E = \{(1,3),(2,2)(3,1)\}$$
$$n(E) = 3$$

$$P(E) = \frac{n(E)}{n(S)} = \frac{3}{36} = \frac{1}{12}$$

21.

$$_{51}C_6 = \frac{51!}{(51-6)!6!} = \frac{51!}{45!6!} = 18,009,460$$

$$P(E) = \frac{n(E)}{n(S)} = \frac{1}{18,009,460}$$

The probability of winning the prize with one lottery ticket is $\dfrac{1}{18,009,460}$ or approximately 0.0000000555.

$$P(E) = \frac{n(E)}{n(S)} = \frac{100}{18,009,460} = \frac{1}{900,473}$$

The probability of winning the prize with 100 lottery tickets is $\dfrac{1}{900,473}$ or approximately 0.00000555.

23. a.

$$_{52}C_5 = \frac{52!}{(52-5)!5!} = \frac{52!}{47!5!} = 2,598,960$$

There are 2,598,960 possible five-card poker hands.

b.

$$_{13}C_5 = \frac{13!}{(13-5)!5!} = \frac{13!}{8!5!} = 1287$$

There are 1287 possible five-card diamond flushes.

c.

$$P(\text{diamond flush}) = \frac{1287}{2,598,960}$$

$$= \frac{33}{66,640} \approx 0.000495$$

The probability of being dealt a diamond flush is $\dfrac{33}{66,640}$ or approximately 0.000495.

25.

$$P(\text{not under 5})$$
$$= \frac{274,634 - 18,987}{274,634} = \frac{255,647}{274,634} \approx 0.931$$

27.

$$P(\text{not } 25-34)$$
$$= \frac{274,634 - 37,233}{274,634} = \frac{237,401}{274,634} \approx 0.864$$

29.

$$P(14-17 \text{ or } 18-24)$$
$$= P(14-17) + P(18-24)$$
$$= \frac{15,752}{274,634} + \frac{26,258}{274,634} = \frac{52,985}{274,634} \approx 0.153$$

31.

$$P(2 \text{ or } 3) = P(2) + P(3)$$
$$= \frac{4}{52} + \frac{4}{52} = \frac{8}{52} = \frac{2}{13}$$

33.

$$P(\text{even or } < 5)$$
$$= P(\text{even}) + P(<5) - P(\text{even and} < 5)$$
$$= \frac{3}{6} + \frac{4}{6} - \frac{2}{6} = \frac{5}{6}$$

35.

$$P(7 \text{ or red}) = P(7) + P(\text{red}) - P(7 \text{ and red})$$
$$= \frac{4}{52} + \frac{26}{52} - \frac{2}{52} = \frac{28}{52} = \frac{7}{13}$$

37.

$$P(\text{odd or } < 6)$$
$$= P(\text{odd}) + P(<6) - P(\text{odd and} < 6)$$
$$= \frac{4}{8} + \frac{5}{8} - \frac{3}{8} = \frac{6}{8} = \frac{3}{4}$$

39.

$$P(\text{prof or male})$$
$$= P(\text{prof}) + P(\text{male}) - P(\text{prof and male})$$
$$= \frac{19}{40} + \frac{22}{40} - \frac{8}{40} = \frac{33}{40}$$

41.

$$P(2 \text{ and } 3) = P(2) \cdot P(3) = \frac{1}{6} \cdot \frac{1}{6} = \frac{1}{36}$$

43.

$$P(\text{even and} > 2) = P(\text{even}) \cdot P(>2)$$
$$= \frac{3}{6} \cdot \frac{4}{6} = \frac{12}{36} = \frac{1}{3}$$

45.

$$P(6 \text{ heads}) = \frac{1}{2} \cdot \frac{1}{2} \cdot \frac{1}{2} \cdot \frac{1}{2} \cdot \frac{1}{2} \cdot \frac{1}{2} = \frac{1}{64}$$

47. **a.** $P(\text{Hit 2 years in a row})$

$$= \frac{1}{16} \cdot \frac{1}{16} = \frac{1}{256}$$

      b. $P(\text{Hit 3 years in a row})$

$$= \frac{1}{16} \cdot \frac{1}{16} \cdot \frac{1}{16} = \frac{1}{4096}$$

      c. If the probability of getting hit by a hurricane is $\frac{1}{16}$, the probability of not getting hit by a hurricane is $\frac{15}{16}$.

$P(\text{Not hit 10 years in a row})$

$$= \left(\frac{15}{16}\right)^{10} \approx 0.524$$

      d. $P(\text{Hit at least once in next 10})$

$$= 1 - \left(\frac{15}{16}\right)^{10} \approx 1 - 0.524 = 0.476$$

For Exercises 49-59, answers may vary.

Review Exercises

61.

$$4x^2 + 25y^2 = 100$$

$$\frac{4}{100}x^2 + \frac{25}{100}y^2 = \frac{100}{100}$$

$$\frac{1}{25}x^2 + \frac{1}{4}y^2 = 1$$

62. $\log_2(x+5) + \log_2(x-1) = 4$

$$\log_2(x+5)(x-1) = 4$$

$$(x+5)(x-1) = 2^4$$

$$x^2 + 4x - 5 = 16$$

$$x^2 + 4x - 21 = 0$$

$$(x+7)(x-3) = 0$$

$$x+7 = 0 \quad \text{or} \quad x-3 = 0$$

$$x = -7 \qquad\qquad x = 3$$

We disregard –7 because it results in taking the logarithm of a negative number. The solution is 3.

63. $\left(x^3 + 5x^2 + 3x - 10\right) \div (x+2)$

$$\underline{-2|}\quad 1 \quad 5 \quad\;\; 3 \quad -10$$
$$\qquad\qquad -2 \;\; -6 \quad\;\; 6$$
$$\overline{\qquad 1 \quad 3 \;\; -3 \quad -4}$$

$$\left(x^3 + 5x^2 + 3x - 10\right) \div (x+2)$$

$$= x^2 + 3x - 3 - \frac{4}{x+2}$$

Chapter 14 Review Exercises

1. $a_1 = 7(1) - 4 = 7 - 4 = 3$ $a_3 = 7(3) - 4 = 21 - 4 = 17$

     $a_2 = 7(2) - 4 = 14 - 4 = 10$ $a_4 = 7(4) - 4 = 28 - 4 = 24$

2. $a_1 = (-1)^1 \dfrac{1+2}{1+1} = -\dfrac{3}{2}$ $a_2 = (-1)^2 \dfrac{2+2}{2+1} = \dfrac{4}{3}$

$$a_3 = (-1)^3 \frac{3+2}{3+1} = -\frac{5}{4} \qquad a_4 = (-1)^4 \frac{4+2}{4+1} = \frac{6}{5}$$

3.
$$a_1 = \frac{1}{(1-1)!} = \frac{1}{0!} = \frac{1}{1} = 1 \qquad a_3 = \frac{1}{(3-1)!} = \frac{1}{2!} = \frac{1}{2 \cdot 1} = \frac{1}{2}$$
$$a_2 = \frac{1}{(2-1)!} = \frac{1}{1!} = \frac{1}{1} = 1 \qquad a_4 = \frac{1}{(4-1)!} = \frac{1}{3!} = \frac{1}{3 \cdot 2 \cdot 1} = \frac{1}{6}$$

4.
$$a_1 = \frac{(-1)^{1+1}}{2^1} = \frac{(-1)^2}{2} = \frac{1}{2} \qquad a_3 = \frac{(-1)^{3+1}}{2^3} = \frac{(-1)^4}{8} = \frac{1}{8}$$
$$a_2 = \frac{(-1)^{2+1}}{2^2} = \frac{(-1)^3}{4} = -\frac{1}{4} \qquad a_4 = \frac{(-1)^{4+1}}{2^4} = \frac{(-1)^5}{16} = -\frac{1}{16}$$

5.
$$\sum_{i=1}^{5}(2i^2 - 3) = (2(1)^2 - 3) + (2(2)^2 - 3) + (2(3)^2 - 3) + (2(4)^2 - 3) + (2(5)^2 - 3) + (2(6)^2 - 3)$$
$$= (2(1) - 3) + (2(4) - 3) + (2(9) - 3) + (2(16) - 3) + (2(25) - 3)$$
$$= (2 - 3) + (8 - 3) + (18 - 3) + (32 - 3) + (50 - 3) = -1 + 5 + 15 + 29 + 47 = 95$$

6.
$$\sum_{i=0}^{4}(-1)^{i+1} i! = (-1)^{0+1} 0! + (-1)^{1+1} 1! + (-1)^{2+1} 2! + (-1)^{3+1} 3! + (-1)^{4+1} 4!$$
$$= (-1)^1 1 + (-1)^2 1 + (-1)^3 2 \cdot 1 + (-1)^4 3 \cdot 2 \cdot 1 + (-1)^5 4 \cdot 3 \cdot 2 \cdot 1 = -1 + 1 - 2 + 6 - 24 = -20$$

7.
$$\frac{1}{3} + \frac{2}{4} + \frac{3}{5} + \ldots + \frac{15}{17} = \sum_{i=1}^{15} \frac{i}{i+2}$$

8.
$$4^3 + 5^3 + 6^3 + \ldots + 13^3 = \sum_{i=4}^{13} i^3$$

9.
$$a_1 = 7 \qquad a_2 = 7 + 4 = 11$$
$$a_3 = 11 + 4 = 15 \qquad a_4 = 15 + 4 = 19$$
$$a_5 = 19 + 4 = 23 \qquad a_6 = 23 + 4 = 27$$

10.
$$a_1 = -4 \qquad a_2 = -4 - 5 = -9$$
$$a_3 = -9 - 5 = -14 \qquad a_4 = -14 - 5 = -19$$
$$a_5 = -19 - 5 = -24 \qquad a_6 = -24 - 5 = -29$$

11.
$$a_1 = \frac{3}{2} \qquad a_2 = \frac{3}{2} - \frac{1}{2} = \frac{2}{2} = 1$$
$$a_3 = 1 - \frac{1}{2} = \frac{1}{2} \qquad a_4 = \frac{1}{2} - \frac{1}{2} = 0$$
$$a_5 = 0 - \frac{1}{2} = -\frac{1}{2}$$
$$a_6 = -\frac{1}{2} - \frac{1}{2} = -\frac{2}{2} = -1$$

12.
$$a_6 = 5 + (6-1)3 = 5 + (5)3$$
$$= 5 + 15 = 20$$

13.
$$a_{12} = -8 + (12-1)(-2) = -8 + 11(-2)$$
$$= -8 + (-22) = -30$$

14.
$$a_{14} = 14 + (14-1)(-4) = 14 + 13(-4)$$
$$= 14 + (-52) = -38$$

15.
$$d = -3 - (-7) = 4$$
$$a_n = -7 + (n-1)4 = -7 + 4n - 4 = 4n - 11$$
$$a_{20} = 4(20) - 11 = 80 - 11 = 69$$

16. $a_n = 200 + (n-1)(-20)$
$\quad\quad = 200 - 20n + 20 = 220 - 20n$
$a_{20} = 220 - 20(20) = 220 - 400 = -180$

17. $a_n = -12 + (n-1)\left(-\dfrac{1}{2}\right) = -12 - \dfrac{1}{2}n + \dfrac{1}{2}$
$\quad\quad = -\dfrac{24}{2} - \dfrac{1}{2}n + \dfrac{1}{2} = -\dfrac{1}{2}n - \dfrac{23}{2}$
$a_{20} = -\dfrac{1}{2}(20) - \dfrac{23}{2} = -\dfrac{20}{2} - \dfrac{23}{2} = -\dfrac{43}{2}$

18. $d = 8 - 15 = -7$
$\quad a_n = 15 + (n-1)(-7) = 15 - 7n + 7$
$\quad\quad = 22 - 7n$
$a_{20} = 22 - 7(20) = 22 - 140 = -118$

19. $d = 12 - 5 = 7$
$\quad a_{22} = 5 + (22 - 1)7 = 5 + (21)7$
$\quad\quad = 5 + 147 = 152$
$\quad S_{22} = \dfrac{22}{2}(5 + 152) = 11(157) = 1727$

20. $d = -3 - (-6) = 3$
$\quad a_{15} = -6 + (15 - 1)3 = -6 + (14)3 = 36$
$\quad S_{15} = \dfrac{15}{2}(-6 + 36) = \dfrac{15}{2}(30) = 225$

21. We are given that $a_1 = 300$.
$\quad S_{100} = \dfrac{100}{2}(3 + 300) = 50(303) = 15150$

22. $\displaystyle\sum_{i=1}^{16}(3i + 2) = (3(1)+2) + (3(2)+2) + (3(3)+2) + \dots + (3(16)+2)$
$\quad\quad\quad = (3+2)+(6+2)+(9+2)+\dots+(48+2) = 5+8+11+\dots+50$
$S_{16} = \dfrac{16}{2}(5 + 50) = 8(55) = 440$

23. $\displaystyle\sum_{i=1}^{25}(-2i + 6) = (-2(1)+6) + (-2(2)+6) + (-2(3)+6) + \dots + (-2(25)+6)$
$\quad\quad\quad = (-2+6)+(-4+6)+(-6+6)+\dots+(-50+6) = 4+2+0+\dots+(-44)$
$S_{25} = \dfrac{25}{2}(4 + (-44)) = \dfrac{25}{2}(-40) = -500$

24. $\displaystyle\sum_{i=1}^{30}(-5i) = (-5(1)) + (-5(2)) + (-5(3)) + \dots + (-5(30)) = -5 + (-10) + (-15) + \dots + (-150)$
$S_{30} = \dfrac{30}{2}(-5 + (-150)) = 15(-155) = -2325$

25. **a.** $a_n = 1043.04 + (n-1)(-0.4118) = 1043.04 - 0.4118n + 0.4118 = 1043.4518 - 0.4118n$
$\quad$ **b.** $a_{100} = 1043.4518 - 0.4118(100) = 1043.4518 - 41.18 = 1002.2718$

26. $a_{10} = 31500 + (10 - 1)2300 = 31500 + (9)2300 = 31500 + 20700 = 52200$
$\quad S_{10} = \dfrac{10}{2}(31500 + 52200) = 5(83700) = 418500$

The total salary over a ten-year period is \$418,500.

27. $a_{35} = 25 + (35-1)1 = 25 + (34)1$
$= 25 + 34 = 59$
$S_{35} = \dfrac{35}{2}(25+59) = \dfrac{35}{2}(84) = 1470$

There are 1470 seats in the theater.

28. The first term is 3. The second term is $3 \cdot 2 = 6$. The third term is $6 \cdot 2 = 12$. The fourth term is $12 \cdot 2 = 24$. The fifth term is $24 \cdot 2 = 48$.

29. The first term is $\dfrac{1}{2}$. The second term is $\dfrac{1}{2} \cdot \dfrac{1}{2} = \dfrac{1}{4}$. The third term is $\dfrac{1}{4} \cdot \dfrac{1}{2} = \dfrac{1}{8}$. The fourth term is $\dfrac{1}{8} \cdot \dfrac{1}{2} = \dfrac{1}{16}$. The fifth term is $\dfrac{1}{16} \cdot \dfrac{1}{2} = \dfrac{1}{32}$.

30. The first term is 16. The second term is $16 \cdot -\dfrac{1}{4} = -4$. The third term is $-4 \cdot -\dfrac{1}{4} = 1$. The fourth term is $1 \cdot -\dfrac{1}{4} = -\dfrac{1}{4}$. The fifth term is $-\dfrac{1}{4} \cdot -\dfrac{1}{4} = \dfrac{1}{16}$.

31. The first term is -5. The second term is $-5 \cdot -1 = 5$. The third term is $5 \cdot -1 = -5$. The fourth term is $-5 \cdot -1 = 5$. The fifth term is $5 \cdot -1 = -5$.

32. $a_7 = 2(3)^{7-1} = 2(3)^6 = 2(729) = 1458$

33. $a_6 = 16\left(\dfrac{1}{2}\right)^{6-1} = 16\left(\dfrac{1}{2}\right)^5 = 16\left(\dfrac{1}{32}\right) = \dfrac{1}{2}$

34. $a_5 = -3(2)^{5-1} = -3(2)^4 = -3(16) = -48$

35. $a_n = a_1 r^{n-1} = 1(2)^{n-1}$
$a_8 = 1(2)^{8-1} = 1(2)^7 = 1(128) = 128$

36. $a_n = a_1 r^{n-1} = 100\left(\dfrac{1}{10}\right)^{n-1}$
$a_8 = 100\left(\dfrac{1}{10}\right)^{8-1} = 100\left(\dfrac{1}{10}\right)^7$
$= 100\left(\dfrac{1}{10000000}\right) = \dfrac{1}{100000}$

37. $d = \dfrac{-4}{12} = -\dfrac{1}{3}$
$a_n = a_1 r^{n-1} = 12\left(-\dfrac{1}{3}\right)^{n-1}$
$a_8 = 12\left(-\dfrac{1}{3}\right)^{8-1} = 12\left(-\dfrac{1}{3}\right)^7$
$= 12\left(-\dfrac{1}{2187}\right) = -\dfrac{12}{2187} = -\dfrac{4}{729}$

38. $r = \dfrac{a_2}{a_1} = \dfrac{-15}{5} = -3$
$S_{15} = \dfrac{5\left(1-(-3)^{15}\right)}{1-(-3)}$
$= \dfrac{5\left(1-(-14348907)\right)}{4}$
$= \dfrac{5(14348908)}{4} = \dfrac{71744540}{4} = 17{,}936{,}135$

39. $r = \dfrac{a_2}{a_1} = \dfrac{4}{8} = \dfrac{1}{2}$
$S_7 = \dfrac{8\left(1-\left(\dfrac{1}{2}\right)^7\right)}{1-\dfrac{1}{2}} = \dfrac{8\left(1-\dfrac{1}{128}\right)}{\dfrac{1}{2}}$
$= \dfrac{8\left(\dfrac{128}{128}-\dfrac{1}{128}\right)}{\dfrac{1}{2}} = \dfrac{8\left(\dfrac{127}{128}\right)}{\dfrac{1}{2}}$
$= \dfrac{8}{1}\left(\dfrac{127}{128}\right) \div \dfrac{1}{2} = \dfrac{8}{1}\left(\dfrac{127}{128}\right) \cdot \dfrac{2}{1}$

$$= \frac{2032}{128} = \frac{127}{8} = 15.875$$

40.
$$\sum_{i=1}^{6} 5^i = \frac{5(1-5^6)}{1-5} = \frac{5(1-15625)}{-4}$$
$$= \frac{5(-15624)}{-4} = 5(3906) = 19,530$$

41.
$$\sum_{i=1}^{7} 3(-2)^i = \frac{-6(1-(-2)^7)}{1-(-2)} = \frac{-6(1-(-128))}{3}$$
$$= \frac{-6(129)}{3} = -2(129) = -258$$

42.
$$\sum_{i=1}^{5} 2\left(\frac{1}{4}\right)^{i-1} = \frac{2\left(1-\left(\frac{1}{4}\right)^5\right)}{1-\frac{1}{4}}$$
$$= \frac{2\left(1-\frac{1}{1024}\right)}{\frac{3}{4}} = \frac{2\left(\frac{1024}{1024}-\frac{1}{1024}\right)}{\frac{3}{4}}$$
$$= \frac{2\left(\frac{1023}{1024}\right)}{\frac{3}{4}} = \frac{\frac{2046}{1024}}{\frac{3}{4}} = \frac{2046}{1024} \div \frac{3}{4}$$
$$= \frac{2046}{1024} \cdot \frac{4}{3} = \frac{682}{256} = \frac{341}{128}$$

43.
$$r = \frac{a_2}{a_1} = \frac{3}{9} = \frac{1}{3}$$
$$S = \frac{9}{1-\frac{1}{3}} = \frac{9}{\frac{2}{3}} = 9 \div \frac{2}{3} = 9 \cdot \frac{3}{2} = \frac{27}{2}$$

44.
$$r = \frac{a_2}{a_1} = \frac{-1}{2} = -\frac{1}{2}$$
$$S = \frac{2}{1-\left(-\frac{1}{2}\right)} = \frac{2}{\frac{3}{2}} = 2 \div \frac{3}{2} = 2 \cdot \frac{2}{3} = \frac{4}{3}$$

45.
$$r = \frac{a_2}{a_1} = \frac{4}{-6} = -\frac{2}{3}$$

$$S = \frac{-6}{1-\left(-\frac{2}{3}\right)} = \frac{-6}{\frac{5}{3}} = -6 \div \frac{5}{3}$$
$$= -6 \cdot \frac{3}{5} = -\frac{18}{5}$$

46.
$$\sum_{i=1}^{\infty} 5(0.8)^i = \frac{4}{1-0.8} = \frac{4}{0.2} = 20$$

47.
$$0.\overline{6} = \frac{a_1}{1-r} = \frac{\frac{6}{10}}{1-\frac{1}{10}} = \frac{\frac{6}{10}}{\frac{9}{10}} = \frac{6}{10} \cdot \frac{10}{9} = \frac{2}{3}$$

48.
$$0.\overline{47} = \frac{a_1}{1-r} = \frac{\frac{47}{100}}{1-\frac{1}{100}} = \frac{\frac{47}{100}}{\frac{99}{100}}$$
$$= \frac{47}{100} \div \frac{99}{100} = \frac{47}{100} \cdot \frac{100}{99} = \frac{47}{99}$$

49. $r = 1.06$
$$a_n = a_1 r^{n-1} = 32000(1.06)^{n-1}$$
$$a_6 = 32000(1.06)^{6-1} = 32000(1.06)^5$$
$$= 32000(1.338226) = 42823.22$$

The salary in the sixth year is approximately \$42,823.22.

$$S_6 = \frac{a_1(1-r^n)}{1-r} = \frac{32000(1-(1.06)^6)}{1-1.06}$$
$$= \frac{32000(1-1.418519)}{-0.06}$$
$$= \frac{32000(-0.418519)}{-0.06} = 223210.13$$

The total salary over the six years is approximately \$223,210.13.

50.
$$A = P\frac{\left(1+\frac{r}{n}\right)^{nt}-1}{\frac{r}{n}} = 200 \cdot \frac{\left(1+\frac{0.10}{12}\right)^{12(18)}-1}{\frac{0.10}{12}}$$

$$= 200 \cdot \frac{\left(1 + \frac{1}{120}\right)^{216} - 1}{\frac{1}{120}} = 200 \cdot \frac{\left(\frac{121}{120}\right)^{216} - 1}{\frac{1}{120}}$$

$$= 200 \cdot \frac{6.0047 - 1}{\frac{1}{120}} = 200 \cdot \frac{5.0047}{\frac{1}{120}}$$

$$= 120112.80$$

After 18 years, the value of the account will be approximately $120,112.80.

51. $r = 70\% = 0.7$

$a_1 = 4(.7) = 2.8$

$$S = \frac{2.8}{1 - 0.7} = \frac{2.8}{0.3} = 9.\overline{3}$$

The total spending in the town will be approximately $9.3 million each year.

52. $\dbinom{11}{8} = \frac{11!}{8!(11-8)!} = \frac{11 \cdot 10 \cdot 9 \cdot \cancel{8!}}{\cancel{8!} \cdot 3 \cdot 2 \cdot 1} = 165$

53. $\dbinom{90}{2} = \frac{90!}{2!(90-2)!} = \frac{90 \cdot 89 \cdot \cancel{88!}}{2 \cdot 1 \cdot \cancel{88!}} = 4005$

54. Applying the Binomial Theorem to $(2x+1)^3$, we have $a = 2x$, $b = 1$, and $n = 3$.

$$(2x+1)^3 = \binom{3}{0}(2x)^3 + \binom{3}{1}(2x)^2 \cdot 1 + \binom{3}{2}(2x) \cdot 1^2 + \binom{3}{3}1^3$$

$$= \frac{3!}{0!(3-0)!}8x^3 + \frac{3!}{1!(3-1)!}4x^2 \cdot 1 + \frac{3!}{2!(3-2)!}2x \cdot 1 + \frac{3!}{3!(3-3)!}1$$

$$= \frac{\cancel{3!}}{1 \cdot \cancel{3!}}8x^3 + \frac{3 \cdot \cancel{2!}}{1 \cdot \cancel{2!}}4x^2 + \frac{3 \cdot \cancel{2!}}{\cancel{2!}1!}2x + \frac{\cancel{3!}}{\cancel{3!}0!} = 8x^3 + 3(4x^2) + 3(2x) + 1$$

$$= 8x^3 + 12x^2 + 6x + 1$$

55. Applying the Binomial Theorem to $(x^2 - 1)^4$, we have $a = x^2$, $b = -1$, and $n = 4$.

$$(x^2-1)^4 = \binom{4}{0}(x^2)^4 + \binom{4}{1}(x^2)^3(-1) + \binom{4}{2}(x^2)^2(-1)^2 + \binom{4}{3}x^2(-1)^3 + \binom{4}{4}(-1)^4$$

$$= \frac{4!}{0!(4-0)!}x^8 - \frac{4!}{1!(4-1)!}x^6 + \frac{4!}{2!(4-2)!}x^4 - \frac{4!}{3!(4-3)!}x^2 + \frac{4!}{4!(4-4)!}1$$

$$= \frac{\cancel{4!}}{0!\cancel{4!}}x^8 - \frac{4!}{1!3!}x^6 + \frac{4!}{2!2!}x^4 - \frac{4!}{3!1!}x^2 + \frac{\cancel{4!}}{\cancel{4!}0!}$$

$$= 1(x^8) - \frac{4 \cdot \cancel{3!}}{1 \cdot \cancel{3!}}x^6 + \frac{4 \cdot 3 \cdot \cancel{2!}}{2 \cdot 1 \cdot \cancel{2!}}x^4 - \frac{4 \cdot \cancel{3!}}{\cancel{3!} \cdot 1}x^2 + 1 = x^8 - 4x^6 + 6x^4 - 4x^2 + 1$$

56. Applying the Binomial Theorem to $(x+2y)^5$, we have $a = x$, $b = 2y$, and $n = 5$.

$$(x+2y)^5 = \binom{5}{0}x^5 + \binom{5}{1}x^4(2y) + \binom{5}{2}x^3(2y)^2 + \binom{5}{3}x^2(2y)^3 + \binom{5}{4}x(2y)^4 + \binom{5}{5}(2y)^5$$

$$= \frac{\cancel{5!}}{0!\cancel{5!}}x^5 + \frac{5!}{1!(5-1)!}2x^4y + \frac{5!}{2!(5-2)!}4x^3y^2 + \frac{5!}{3!(5-3)!}8x^2y^3 + \frac{5!}{4!(5-4)!}16xy^4 + \frac{5!}{5!(5-5)!}32y$$

$$= 1x^5 + \frac{5 \cdot \cancel{4!}}{1 \cdot \cancel{4!}}2x^4y + \frac{5 \cdot 4 \cdot \cancel{3!}}{2 \cdot 1 \cdot \cancel{3!}}4x^3y^2 + \frac{5 \cdot 4 \cdot \cancel{3!}}{\cancel{3!}2 \cdot 1}8x^2y^3 + \frac{5 \cdot \cancel{4!}}{\cancel{4!} \cdot 1}16xy^4 + \frac{\cancel{5!}}{\cancel{5!}0!}32y^5$$

$$= x^5 + 5\left(2x^4 y\right) + 10\left(4x^3 y^2\right) + 10\left(8x^2 y^3\right) + 5\left(16xy^4\right) + 1\left(32y^5\right)$$
$$= x^5 + 10x^4 y + 40x^3 y^2 + 80x^2 y^3 + 80xy^4 + 32y^5$$

57.   Applying the Binomial Theorem to $\left(x - 2\right)^6$, we have $a = x$, $b = -2$, and $n = 6$.

$$\left(x-2\right)^6 = \binom{6}{0}x^6 + \binom{6}{1}x^5\left(-2\right) + \binom{6}{2}x^4\left(-2\right)^2 + \binom{6}{3}x^3\left(-2\right)^3 + \binom{6}{4}x^2\left(-2\right)^4 + \binom{6}{5}x\left(-2\right)^5 + \binom{6}{6}\left(-2\right)^6$$

$$= \frac{6!}{0!(6-0)!}x^6 + \frac{6!}{1!(6-1)!}x^5\left(-2\right) + \frac{6!}{2!(6-2)!}x^4\left(-2\right)^2 + \frac{6!}{3!(6-3)!}x^3\left(-2\right)^3$$

$$\qquad + \frac{6!}{4!(6-4)!}x^2\left(-2\right)^4 + \frac{6!}{5!(6-5)!}x\left(-2\right)^5 + \frac{6!}{6!(6-6)!}\left(-2\right)^6$$

$$= \frac{\cancel{6!}}{1\cancel{6!}}x^6 - \frac{6\cdot\cancel{5!}}{1\cdot\cancel{5!}}2x^5 + \frac{6\cdot 5\cdot\cancel{4!}}{2\cdot 1\cdot\cancel{4!}}4x^4 - \frac{6\cdot 5\cdot 4\cdot\cancel{3!}}{3\cdot 2\cdot 1\cdot\cancel{3!}}8x^3 + \frac{6\cdot 5\cdot\cancel{4!}}{\cancel{4!}2\cdot 1}16x^2 - \frac{6\cdot\cancel{5!}}{\cancel{5!}1}32x + \frac{\cancel{6!}}{\cancel{6!}\cdot 1}64$$

$$= x^6 - 6\left(2x^5\right) + 15\left(4x^4\right) - 20\left(8x^3\right) + 15\left(16x^2\right) - 6\left(32x\right) + 1\cdot 64$$

$$= x^6 - 12x^5 + 60x^4 - 160x^3 + 240x^2 - 192x + 64$$

58.   1st Term

$$\binom{n}{r-1}a^{n-r+1}b^{r-1} = \binom{8}{1-1}\left(x^2\right)^{8-1+1}3^{1-1} = \binom{8}{0}\left(x^2\right)^8 3^0 = \frac{8!}{0!(8-0)!}x^{16}\cdot 1 = \frac{\cancel{8!}}{0!\cancel{8!}}x^{16} = x^{16}$$

2nd Term

$$\binom{n}{r-1}a^{n-r+1}b^{r-1} = \binom{8}{2-1}\left(x^2\right)^{8-2+1}3^{2-1} = \binom{8}{1}\left(x^2\right)^7 3^1 = \frac{8!}{1!(8-1)!}3x^{14} = \frac{8\cdot\cancel{7!}}{1\cdot\cancel{7!}}3x^{14} = 8\cdot 3x^{14} = 24x^{14}$$

3rd Term

$$\binom{n}{r-1}a^{n-r+1}b^{r-1} = \binom{8}{3-1}\left(x^2\right)^{8-3+1}3^{3-1} = \binom{8}{2}\left(x^2\right)^6 3^2 = \frac{8!}{2!(8-2)!}9x^{12} = \frac{8\cdot 7\cdot\cancel{6!}}{2\cdot 1\cdot\cancel{6!}}9x^{12} = 28\cdot 9x^{12} = 252x^{12}$$

59.   1st Term

$$\binom{n}{r-1}a^{n-r+1}b^{r-1} = \binom{9}{1-1}x^{9-1+1}\left(-3\right)^{1-1} = \binom{9}{0}x^9\left(-3\right)^0 = \frac{9!}{0!(9-0)!}x^9\cdot 1 = \frac{\cancel{9!}}{0!\cancel{9!}}x^9 = x^9$$

2nd Term

$$\binom{n}{r-1}a^{n-r+1}b^{r-1} = \binom{9}{2-1}x^{9-2+1}\left(-3\right)^{2-1} = \binom{9}{1}x^8\left(-3\right)^1 = -\frac{9!}{1!(9-1)!}3x^8 = -\frac{9\cdot\cancel{8!}}{1\cdot\cancel{8!}}3x^8 = -9\cdot 3x^8 = -27x^8$$

3rd Term

$$\binom{n}{r-1}a^{n-r+1}b^{r-1} = \binom{9}{3-1}x^{9-3+1}\left(-3\right)^{3-1} = \binom{9}{2}x^7\left(-3\right)^2 = \frac{9!}{2!(9-2)!}9x^7 = \frac{9\cdot 8\cdot\cancel{7!}}{2\cdot 1\cdot\cancel{7!}}9x^7 = 36\cdot 9x^7 = 324x^7$$

60.   4th Term

$$\binom{n}{r-1}a^{n-r+1}b^{r-1} = \binom{5}{4-1}x^{5-4+1}\left(2\right)^{4-1} = \binom{5}{3}x^2\left(2\right)^3 = \frac{5!}{3!(5-3)!}8x^2 = \frac{5!}{3!2!}8x^2 = \frac{5\cdot 4\cdot\cancel{3!}}{\cancel{3!}\cdot 2\cdot 1}8x^2 = \left(10\right)8x^2 = 80x^2$$

61.

$$\text{5th Term } \binom{n}{r-1}a^{n-r+1}b^{r-1} = \binom{6}{5-1}(2x)^{6-5+1}(-3)^{5-1} = \binom{6}{4}(2x)^2(-3)^4 = \frac{6!}{4!(6-4)!}4x^2(81)$$

$$= \frac{6!}{4!2!}324x^2 = \frac{6 \cdot 5 \cdot \cancel{4!}}{\cancel{4!} \cdot 2 \cdot 1}324x^2 = (15)324x^2 = 4860x^2$$

62.

$$_8P_3 = \frac{8!}{(8-3)!} = \frac{8!}{5!} = \frac{8 \cdot 7 \cdot 6 \cdot 5!}{5!}$$
$$= 8 \cdot 7 \cdot 6 = 336$$

63.

$$_9P_5 = \frac{9!}{(9-5)!} = \frac{9!}{4!} = \frac{9 \cdot 8 \cdot 7 \cdot 6 \cdot 5 \cdot 4!}{4!}$$
$$= 9 \cdot 8 \cdot 7 \cdot 6 \cdot 5 = 15,120$$

64.

$$_8C_3 = \frac{8!}{(8-3)!3!} = \frac{8!}{5!3!} = \frac{8 \cdot 7 \cdot 6 \cdot \cancel{5!}}{\cancel{5!}3 \cdot 2 \cdot 1} = 56$$

65.

$$_{13}C_{11} = \frac{13!}{(13-11)!11!} = \frac{13!}{2!11!}$$
$$= \frac{13 \cdot 12 \cdot \cancel{11!}}{2 \cdot 1 \cdot \cancel{11!}} = 78$$

66. $4 \cdot 5 = 20$

You have 20 choices with this brand of pen.

67. $3 \cdot 3 \cdot 3 \cdot 3 \cdot 3 = 3^5 = 243$

There are 243 possibilities.

68.

$$_{15}P_4 = \frac{15!}{(15-4)!} = \frac{15!}{11!} = \frac{15 \cdot 14 \cdot 13 \cdot 12 \cdot \cancel{11!}}{\cancel{11!}}$$
$$= 15 \cdot 14 \cdot 13 \cdot 12 = 32,760$$

There are 32,760 ways to fill the offices.

69.

$$_{20}C_4 = \frac{20!}{(20-4)!4!} = \frac{20!}{16!4!}$$
$$= \frac{20 \cdot 19 \cdot 18 \cdot 17 \cdot \cancel{16!}}{\cancel{16!} \cdot 4 \cdot 3 \cdot 2 \cdot 1} = 4845$$

There are 4845 ways to select four actors

70.

$$_{20}C_3 = \frac{20!}{(20-3)!3!} = \frac{20!}{17!3!}$$

$$= \frac{20 \cdot 19 \cdot 18 \cdot \cancel{17!}}{\cancel{17!} \cdot 3 \cdot 2 \cdot 1} = 1140$$

There are 1140 ways to select three CDs.

71.

$$_{20}P_4 = \frac{20!}{(20-4)!} = \frac{20!}{16!}$$

$$= \frac{20 \cdot 19 \cdot 18 \cdot 17 \cdot \cancel{16!}}{\cancel{16!}} = 116,280$$

There are 116,280 ways to cast the actors for the roles.

72.

$$_5P_5 = \frac{5!}{(5-5)!} = \frac{5!}{0!} = \frac{5 \cdot 4 \cdot 3 \cdot 2 \cdot 1}{1} = 120$$

There are 120 ways to line up the planes.

73.

$$P(\text{Hispanic}) = \frac{9,630,188}{31,878,234} \approx 0.302$$

74.

$$P(\text{Hispanic}) = \frac{5,503,372}{19,128,261} \approx 0.288$$

75.

$$P(<5) = \frac{4}{6} = \frac{2}{3}$$

76.

$$P(<3 \text{ or } >4) = P(<3) + P(>4)$$
$$= \frac{2}{6} + \frac{2}{6} = \frac{4}{6} = \frac{2}{3}$$

77.

$$P(\text{ace or king}) = P(\text{ace}) + P(\text{king})$$
$$= \frac{4}{52} + \frac{4}{52} = \frac{8}{52} = \frac{2}{13}$$

78.

$$P(\text{queen or red})$$
$$= P(\text{q}) + P(\text{r}) - P(\text{q and r})$$
$$= \frac{4}{52} + \frac{26}{52} - \frac{2}{52} = \frac{28}{52} = \frac{7}{13}$$

79. $P(\text{queen or red})$
$$= P(q) + P(r) - P(q \text{ and } r)$$
$$= \frac{4}{52} + \frac{26}{52} - \frac{2}{52} = \frac{28}{52} = \frac{7}{13}$$

80. $P(\text{red or} > 3)$
$$= P(\text{red}) + P(>3) - P(\text{red and} > 3)$$
$$= \frac{3}{6} + \frac{3}{6} - \frac{1}{6} = \frac{5}{6}$$

81. a. $_{20}C_5 = \dfrac{20!}{(20-5)!5!} = \dfrac{20!}{15!5!}$
$$= 15,504$$
$$P(E) = \frac{n(E)}{n(S)} = \frac{1}{15,504}$$
The probability of winning the prize with one lottery ticket is $\dfrac{1}{18,009,460}$ or approximately 0.0000645.

b. $P(E) = \dfrac{n(E)}{n(S)} = \dfrac{100}{15,504} = \dfrac{25}{3876}$
The probability of winning the prize with 100 lottery tickets is $\dfrac{25}{3876}$ or approximately 0.00645.

82. $P(\text{black or male})$
$$= P(b) + P(m) - P(b \text{ and } m)$$
$$= \frac{70}{200} + \frac{140}{200} - \frac{50}{200} = \frac{160}{200} = \frac{4}{5}$$

83. $P(\text{female or white})$
$$= P(f) + P(w) - P(f \text{ and } w)$$
$$= \frac{60}{200} + \frac{130}{200} - \frac{40}{200} = \frac{150}{200} = \frac{3}{4}$$

84. $\dfrac{1}{2} \cdot \dfrac{1}{2} \cdot \dfrac{1}{2} \cdot \dfrac{1}{2} \cdot \dfrac{1}{2} = \dfrac{1}{32}$

85. a. $P(\text{flood 2 years in a row})$
$$= 0.2 \cdot 0.2 = 0.04$$
b. $P(\text{flood 3 years in a row})$
$$= 0.2 \cdot 0.2 \cdot 0.2 = 0.008$$

c. If the probability of a flood in any given year is 0.2, the probability of not having a flood in a given year is $1 - 0.2 = 0.8$.
$P(\text{no flood 4 years in a row})$
$$= 0.8 \cdot 0.8 \cdot 0.8 \cdot 0.8 = 0.4096$$

Chapter 14 Test

1.
$$a_1 = \frac{(-1)^{1+1}}{1^2} = \frac{(-1)^2}{1} = \frac{1}{1} = 1$$
$$a_2 = \frac{(-1)^{2+1}}{2^2} = \frac{(-1)^3}{4} = \frac{-1}{4} = -\frac{1}{4}$$
$$a_3 = \frac{(-1)^{3+1}}{3^2} = \frac{(-1)^4}{9} = \frac{1}{9}$$
$$a_4 = \frac{(-1)^{4+1}}{4^2} = \frac{(-1)^5}{16} = \frac{-1}{16} = -\frac{1}{16}$$
$$a_5 = \frac{(-1)^{5+1}}{5^2} = \frac{(-1)^6}{25} = \frac{1}{25}$$

2.
$$\sum_{i=1}^{5}(i^2 + 10)$$
$$= (1^2 + 10) + (2^2 + 10) + (3^2 + 10)$$
$$+ (4^2 + 10) + (5^2 + 10)$$
$$= (1 + 10) + (4 + 10) + (9 + 10)$$
$$+ (16 + 10) + (25 + 10)$$
$$= 11 + 14 + 19 + 26 + 35 = 105$$

3. $\dfrac{2}{3} + \dfrac{3}{4} + \dfrac{4}{5} + ... + \dfrac{21}{22} = \displaystyle\sum_{i=2}^{21} \dfrac{i}{i+1}$

4. $d = 9 - 4 = 5$
$$a_n = 4 + (n-1)5 = 4 + 5n - 5 = 5n - 1$$
$$a_{12} = 5(12) - 1 = 60 - 1 = 59$$

5. $d = \dfrac{a_2}{a_1} = \dfrac{4}{16} = \dfrac{1}{4}$
$$a_n = a_1 r^{n-1} = 16\left(\frac{1}{4}\right)^{n-1}$$

$$a_{12} = 16\left(\frac{1}{4}\right)^{12-1} = 16\left(\frac{1}{4}\right)^{11} = 16\left(\frac{1}{4194304}\right)$$

$$= \frac{16}{4194304} = \frac{1}{262144}$$

$$= \frac{-2(32769)}{3} = -21,846$$

6.
$$d = -14 - (-7) = -7$$
$$a_{10} = -7 + (10-1)(-7) = -7 + (9)(-7)$$
$$= -7 + (-63) = -70$$
$$S_{10} = \frac{10}{2}(-7 + (-70)) = 5(-77) = -385$$

10. $r = \frac{1}{2}$

$$S = \frac{4}{1 - \frac{1}{2}} = \frac{4}{\frac{1}{2}} = 4 \div \frac{1}{2} = 4 \cdot \frac{2}{1} = 8$$

7.
$$\sum_{i=1}^{30}(3i - 4)$$
$$= (3(1) - 4) + (3(2) - 4) + (3(3) - 4)$$
$$+ \ldots + (3(20) - 4)$$
$$= (3 - 4) + (6 - 4) + (9 - 4) + \ldots + (60 - 4)$$
$$= -1 + 2 + 5 + \ldots + 56$$
$$S_{20} = \frac{20}{2}(-1 + 56) = 10(55) = 550$$

11.
$$0.\overline{73} = \frac{a_1}{1 - r} = \frac{\frac{73}{100}}{1 - \frac{1}{100}} = \frac{\frac{73}{100}}{\frac{99}{100}}$$
$$= \frac{73}{100} \div \frac{99}{100} = \frac{73}{100} \cdot \frac{100}{99} = \frac{73}{99}$$

12. $r = 1.04$
$$S_8 = \frac{a_1(1 - r^n)}{1 - r} = \frac{30000\left(1 - (1.04)^8\right)}{1 - 1.04}$$
$$= \frac{30000(1 - 1.368569)}{-0.04} = \frac{30000(-0.368569)}{-0.04}$$
$$= 276,426.75$$

The total salary over the eight years is approximately \$276,426.75

8.
$$r = \frac{a_2}{a_1} = \frac{-14}{7} = -2$$
$$S_{10} = \frac{7\left(1 - (-2)^{10}\right)}{1 - (-2)} = \frac{7(1 - 1024)}{3}$$
$$= \frac{7(-1023)}{3} = -2387$$

13.
$$\binom{9}{2} = \frac{9!}{2!(9-2)!} = \frac{9!}{2!7!} = \frac{9 \cdot 8 \cdot \cancel{7!}}{2 \cdot 1 \cdot \cancel{7!}} = 36$$

9.
$$\sum_{i=1}^{15}(-2)^i = \frac{-2\left(1 - (-2)^{15}\right)}{1 - (-2)} = \frac{-2(1 - (-32768))}{3}$$

14. Applying the Binomial Theorem to $\left(x^2 - 1\right)^5$, we have $a = x^2$, $b = -1$, and $n = 5$.

$$\left(x^2 - 1\right)^5$$
$$= \binom{5}{0}(x^2)^5 + \binom{5}{1}(x^2)^4(-1) + \binom{5}{2}(x^2)^3(-1)^2 + \binom{5}{3}(x^2)^2(-1)^3 + \binom{5}{4}(x^2)(-1)^4 + \binom{5}{5}(-1)^5$$
$$= \frac{5!}{0!5!}x^{10} - \frac{5!}{1!(5-1)!}x^8 + \frac{5!}{2!(5-2)!}x^6 - \frac{5!}{3!(5-3)!}x^4 + \frac{5!}{4!(5-4)!}x^2 - \frac{5!}{5!(5-5)!}$$
$$= 1x^{10} - \frac{5 \cdot \cancel{4!}}{1 \cdot \cancel{4!}}x^8 + \frac{5 \cdot 4 \cdot \cancel{3!}}{2 \cdot 1 \cdot \cancel{3!}}x^6 - \frac{5 \cdot 4 \cdot \cancel{3!}}{\cancel{3!}2 \cdot 1}x^4 + \frac{5 \cdot \cancel{4!}}{\cancel{4!} \cdot 1}x^2 - \frac{\cancel{5!}}{\cancel{5!}0!}$$
$$= x^{10} - 5x^8 + 10x^6 - 10x^4 + 5x^2 - 1$$

15. 1st Term

$$\binom{n}{r-1}a^{n-r+1}b^{r-1} = \binom{8}{1-1}x^{8-1+1}\left(y^2\right)^{1-1} = \binom{8}{0}x^8\left(y^2\right)^0 = \frac{8!}{0!(8-0)!}x^8 \cdot 1 = \frac{8!}{0!\,8!}x^8 = x^8$$

2nd Term

$$\binom{n}{r-1}a^{n-r+1}b^{r-1} = \binom{8}{2-1}x^{8-2+1}\left(y^2\right)^{2-1} = \binom{8}{1}x^7\left(y^2\right)^1 = \frac{8!}{1!(8-1)!}x^7y^2 = \frac{8 \cdot 7!}{1 \cdot 7!}x^7y^2 = 8x^7y^2$$

3rd Term

$$\binom{n}{r-1}a^{n-r+1}b^{r-1} = \binom{8}{3-1}x^{8-3+1}\left(y^2\right)^{3-1} = \binom{8}{2}x^6\left(y^2\right)^2 = \frac{8!}{2!(8-2)!}x^6y^4 = \frac{8 \cdot 7 \cdot 6!}{2 \cdot 1 \cdot 6!}x^6y^4 = 28x^6y^4$$

16. $${}_{11}P_3 = \frac{11!}{(11-3)!} = \frac{11!}{8!} = \frac{11 \cdot 10 \cdot 9 \cdot 8!}{8!} = 990$$

There are 990 ways to fill the three positions.

17. $${}_{10}C_4 = \frac{10!}{(10-4)!4!} = \frac{10!}{6!4!} = 210$$

There are 210 different sets of four books.

18. $$10 \cdot 10 \cdot 10 \cdot 10 = 10,000$$
10,000 can be formed.

19. Answers may vary.

20. $${}_{15}C_6 = \frac{15!}{(15-6)!6!} = \frac{15!}{9!6!} = 5005$$

$$P(E) = \frac{n(E)}{n(S)} = \frac{50}{5005} = \frac{10}{1001}$$

The probability of winning the prize with 50 lottery tickets is $\dfrac{10}{1001}$ or approximately 0.00999.

21. $P(\text{black or picture})$
$= P(\text{b}) + P(\text{p}) - P(\text{b and p})$
$$= \frac{26}{52} + \frac{12}{52} - \frac{6}{52} = \frac{32}{52} = \frac{8}{13}$$

22. $P(\text{freshmen or female})$
$= P(\text{fresh}) + P(\text{fem}) - P(\text{fresh and fem})$
$$= \frac{25}{50} + \frac{20}{50} - \frac{15}{50} = \frac{30}{50} = \frac{3}{5}$$

23. $$\frac{1}{4} \cdot \frac{1}{4} \cdot \frac{1}{4} \cdot \frac{1}{4} = \frac{1}{256}$$

The probability of answering all questions correct is $\dfrac{1}{256}$.

24. $$P(\text{red}) \cdot P(\text{blue}) = \frac{2}{8} \cdot \frac{2}{8} = \frac{4}{16} = \frac{1}{4}$$

Cumulative Review Exercises
Chapters 1–14

1. $9(x-1) = 1 + 3(x-2)$
$9x - 9 = 1 + 3x - 6$
$9x - 9 = 3x - 5$
$6x - 9 = -5$
$6x = 4$
$$x = \frac{4}{6} = \frac{2}{3}$$

2. Solve the second equation for x.
$x - 2y = -9$
$\quad x = 2y - 9$
Substitute $2y - 9$ for x in the first equation and solve for y.
$3(2y - 9) + 4y = -7$
$\quad 6y - 27 + 4y = -7$
$\quad\quad 10y - 27 = -7$
$\quad\quad\quad 10y = 20$
$\quad\quad\quad\quad y = 2$
Back-substitute 2 for y to find x.
$x = 2(2) - 9 = 4 - 9 = -5$

The solution is $(-5, 2)$.

3. Multiply the second equation by 3 and add to the first equation.

$$x - y + 3z = -9$$
$$6x + 9y - 3z = 48$$
$$\overline{\qquad 7x + 8y = 39}$$

Multiply the second equation by –1 and add to the third equation.

$$-2x - 3y + z = -16$$
$$5x + 2y - z = 15$$
$$\overline{\qquad 3x - y = -1}$$

We now have a system of two equations in two variables.

$$7x + 8y = 39$$
$$3x - y = -1$$

Multiply the second equation by 8 and add to the first equation.

$$7x + 8y = 39$$
$$24x - 8y = -8$$
$$\overline{\qquad 31x = 31}$$
$$x = 1$$

Back-substitute 1 for x to find y.

$$7(1) + 8y = 39$$
$$7 + 8y = 39$$
$$8y = 32$$
$$y = 4$$

Back-substitute 1 for x and 4 for y to find z.

$$1 - 4 + 3z = -9$$
$$-3 + 3z = -9$$
$$3z = -6$$
$$z = -2$$

The solution is $(1, 4, -2)$.

4.
$$7x + 18 \le 9x - 2$$
$$-2x + 18 \le -2$$
$$-2x \le -20$$
$$x \ge 10$$

The solution set is $\{x \mid x \ge 10\}$ or $[10, \infty)$.

5.
$$4x - 3 < 13 \quad \text{and} \quad -3x - 4 \ge 8$$
$$4x < 16 \qquad\qquad -3x \ge 12$$
$$x < 4 \qquad\qquad\quad x \le -4$$

The solution set is $\{x \mid x \le -4\}$ or $(-\infty, -4]$.

6.
$$2x + 4 > 8 \quad \text{or} \quad x - 7 \le 3$$
$$2x > 4 \qquad\qquad x \le 10$$
$$x > 2$$

The solution set is $\mathbb{R}$, $(-\infty, \infty)$ or $\{x \mid x \text{ is a real number}\}$.

7.
$$|2x - 1| < 5$$
$$-5 < 2x - 1 < 5$$
$$-4 < 2x < 6$$
$$-2 < x < 3$$

The solution set is $\{x \mid -2 < x < 3\}$ or $(-2, 3)$.

8.
$$\left| \frac{2}{3}x - 4 \right| = 2$$

$$\frac{2}{3}x - 4 = 2 \quad \text{or} \quad \frac{2}{3}x - 4 = -2$$

$$\frac{2}{3}x = 6 \qquad\qquad \frac{2}{3}x = 2$$

$$x = \frac{3}{2} \cdot 6 \qquad\qquad x = \frac{3}{2} \cdot 2$$

$$x = 9 \qquad\qquad\quad x = 3$$

9.
$$\frac{4}{x - 3} - \frac{6}{x + 3} = \frac{24}{x^2 - 9}$$

$$\frac{4}{x - 3} - \frac{6}{x + 3} = \frac{24}{(x - 3)(x + 3)}$$

Multiply both sides of the equation by $(x - 3)(x + 3)$.

$$4(x + 3) - 6(x - 3) = 24$$
$$4x + 12 - 6x + 18 = 24$$
$$-2x + 30 = 24$$
$$-2x = -6$$
$$x = 3$$

Since 3 would make one or more of the denominators in the original equation zero, we disregard it and conclude that there is no solution. The solution set is $\varnothing$ or $\{\ \ \}$.

10. $\sqrt{x+4}-\sqrt{x-3}=1$

$\sqrt{x+4}=1+\sqrt{x-3}$

$x+4=\left(1+\sqrt{x-3}\right)^2$

$x+4=1+2\sqrt{x-3}+x-3$

$x+4=2\sqrt{x-3}+x-2$

$6=2\sqrt{x-3}$

$3=\sqrt{x-3}$

$3^2=x-3$

$9=x-3$

$12=x$

11. $2x^2=5-4x$

$2x^2+4x-5=0$

$a=2 \quad b=4 \quad c=-5$

$x=\dfrac{-4\pm\sqrt{4^2-4(2)(-5)}}{2(2)}=\dfrac{-4\pm\sqrt{16+40}}{4}$

$=\dfrac{-4\pm\sqrt{56}}{4}=\dfrac{-4\pm2\sqrt{14}}{4}$

$=\dfrac{2\left(-2\pm\sqrt{14}\right)}{4}=\dfrac{-2\pm\sqrt{14}}{2}$

12. Let $t=x^{\frac{1}{3}}$

$x^{\frac{2}{3}}-5x^{\frac{1}{3}}+6=0$

$\left(x^{\frac{1}{3}}\right)^2-5x^{\frac{1}{3}}+6=0$

$t^2-5t+6=0$

$(t-3)(t-2)=0$

$t-3=0 \quad \text{or} \quad t-2=0$

$t=3 \qquad\qquad t=2$

$x^{\frac{1}{3}}=3 \qquad\qquad x^{\frac{1}{3}}=2$

$x=3^3 \qquad\qquad x=2^3$

$x=27 \qquad\qquad x=8$

13. $2x^2+x-6\le0$

Solve the related quadratic equation.

$2x^2+x-6=0$

$(2x-3)(x+2)=0$

$2x-3=0 \quad \text{or} \quad x+2=0$

$2x=3 \qquad\qquad x=-2$

$x=\dfrac{3}{2}$

Test Interval	Test Number	Test	Conclusion
$(-\infty,-2]$	-3	$2(-3)^2+(-3)-6\le0 \quad$ false	$(-\infty,-2]$ does not belong to the solution set.
$\left[-2,\dfrac{3}{2}\right]$	0	$2(0)^2+0-6\le0 \quad$ true	$\left[-2,\dfrac{3}{2}\right]$ belongs to the solution set.
$\left[\dfrac{3}{2},\infty\right)$	2	$2(2)^2+2-6\le0 \quad$ false	$\left[\dfrac{3}{2},\infty\right)$ does not belong to the solution set.

The solution set is $\left[-2,\dfrac{3}{2}\right]$ or $\left\{x\middle|-2\le x\le\dfrac{3}{2}\right\}$.

14. $\log_8 x + \log_8 (x+2) = 1$

$\qquad \log_8 (x(x+2)) = 1$

$\qquad\qquad x(x+2) = 8^1$

$\qquad\qquad x^2 + 2x = 8$

$\qquad\qquad x^2 + 2x - 8 = 0$

$\qquad\qquad (x+4)(x-2) = 0$

$x+4 = 0 \quad$ or $\quad x-2 = 0$

$\cancel{x = -4} \qquad\qquad x = 2$

Since we cannot take the logarithm of a negative number, we disregard –4 and conclude that the solution is 2.

15. $5^{2x+3} = 125$

$\qquad 5^{2x+3} = 5^3$

$\qquad 2x+3 = 3$

$\qquad\quad 2x = 0$

$\qquad\quad x = 0$

16. Multiply the first equation by –3 and the second equation by 2 and solve by addition.

$\qquad -6x^2 + 9y^2 = -15$

$\qquad \underline{6x^2 + 8y^2 = \quad 32}$

$\qquad\qquad 17y^2 = 17$

$\qquad\qquad y^2 = 1$

$\qquad\qquad y = \pm 1$

Back-substitute ± 1 for y to find x.

$2x^2 - 3(\pm 1)^2 = 5$

$\qquad 2x^2 - 3(1) = 5$

$\qquad 2x^2 - 3 = 5$

$\qquad\quad 2x^2 = 8$

$\qquad\quad x^2 = 4$

$\qquad\quad x = \pm 2$

The solutions are $(-2,-1), (-2,1),$ $(2,-1)$ and $(2,1)$.

17. Solve the second equation for x.

$\qquad x - y = 6$

$\qquad\quad x = y + 6$

Substitute $y+6$ for x.

$2(y+6)^2 - y^2 = -8$

$2(y^2 + 12x + 36) - y^2 = -8$

$2y^2 + 24x + 72 - y^2 = -8$

$\qquad y^2 + 24x + 80 = 0$

$\qquad (y+20)(y+4) = 0$

$y+20 = 0 \quad$ or $\quad y+4 = 0$

$\qquad y = -20 \qquad\qquad y = -4$

Back-substitute –4 and –20 for y to find x.

$x = -20 + 6 \quad$ or $\quad x = -4 + 6$

$x = -14 \qquad\qquad x = 2$

The solutions are $(-14,-20)$ and $(2,-4)$.

18. $x - 3y = 6$

$\qquad -3y = -x + 6$

$\qquad y = \dfrac{1}{3}x - 2$

slope $= \dfrac{1}{3} \qquad y$–intercept $= -2$

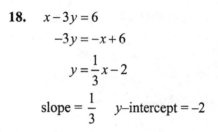

19. $f(x) = \dfrac{1}{2}x - 1$

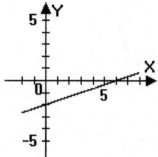

20. $3x - 2y > -6$

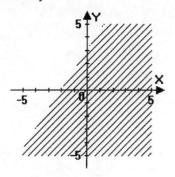

21. $f(x) = -2(x-3)^2 + 2$

The parabola opens downward. The vertex of the parabola is $(3,2)$. The axis of symmetry is $x = 3$. The y–intercept is -16. The x–intercepts are 2 and 4.

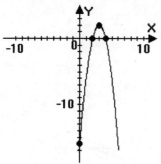

22. $\dfrac{x^2}{16} + \dfrac{y^2}{4} = 1$

The equation's graph is an ellipse. The vertices are $(-4,0)$ and $(4,0)$. The endpoints of the minor axis are $(0,-2)$ and $(0,2)$.

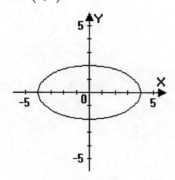

23. $y = \log_2 x$

x	y
1	0
2	1
3	1.5849625
4	2
5	2.3219281

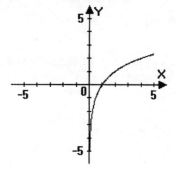

24. $x^2 - y^2 = 9$

$\dfrac{x^2}{9} - \dfrac{y^2}{9} = 1$

The vertices are $(-3,0)$ and $(3,0)$.
Construct a rectangle using -3 and 3 on the x–axis, and -3 and 3 on the y–axis. Draw extended diagonals to obtain the asymptotes.

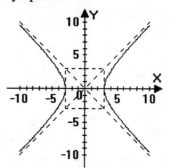

25. $4[2x - 6(x-y)] = 4[2x - 6x - 6y]$
$$= 4[-4x - 6y] = -16x - 24y$$

26. $(-5x^3 y^2)(4x^4 y^{-6}) = -5(4)x^3 x^4 y^2 y^{-6}$
$$= -20x^7 y^{-4} = \dfrac{-20x^7}{y^4}$$

27. $\left(8x^2 - 9xy - 11y^2\right) - \left(7x^2 - 4xy + 5y^2\right)$
$= 8x^2 - 9xy - 11y^2 - 7x^2 + 4xy - 5y^2$
$= x^2 - 5xy - 16y^2$

28. $(3x - 1)(2x + 5) = 6x^2 + 15x - 2x - 5$
$= 6x^2 + 13x - 5$

29. $\left(3x^2 - 4y\right)^2 = 9x^4 - 24x^2y + 16y^2$

30. $\dfrac{3x}{x+5} - \dfrac{2}{x^2 + 7x + 10}$
$= \dfrac{3x}{x+5} - \dfrac{2}{(x+2)(x+5)}$
$= \dfrac{3x}{x+5} \cdot \dfrac{(x+2)}{(x+2)} - \dfrac{2}{(x+5)(x+2)}$
$= \dfrac{3x(x+2) - 2}{(x+5)(x+2)} = \dfrac{3x^2 + 6x - 2}{(x+5)(x+2)}$

31. $\dfrac{1 - \dfrac{9}{x^2}}{1 + \dfrac{3}{x}} = \dfrac{1 - \dfrac{9}{x^2}}{1 + \dfrac{3}{x}} \cdot \dfrac{x^2}{x^2} = \dfrac{x^2 - 9}{x^2 + 3x}$
$= \dfrac{(x+3)(x-3)}{x(x+3)} = \dfrac{x-3}{x}$

32. $\dfrac{x^2 - 6x + 8}{3x + 9} \div \dfrac{x^2 - 4}{x + 3}$
$= \dfrac{x^2 - 6x + 8}{3x + 9} \cdot \dfrac{x + 3}{x^2 - 4}$
$= \dfrac{(x-4)(x-2)}{3(x+3)} \cdot \dfrac{x+3}{(x+2)(x-2)}$
$= \dfrac{x-4}{3(x+2)} = \dfrac{x-4}{3x+6}$

33. $\sqrt{5xy} \cdot \sqrt{10x^2 y} = \sqrt{50x^3 y^2}$
$= \sqrt{25 \cdot 2x^2 xy^2}$
$= 5xy\sqrt{2x}$

34. $4\sqrt{72} - 3\sqrt{50} = 4\sqrt{36 \cdot 2} - 3\sqrt{25 \cdot 2}$
$= 4 \cdot 6\sqrt{2} - 3 \cdot 5\sqrt{2}$
$= 24\sqrt{2} - 15\sqrt{2} = 9\sqrt{2}$

35. $(5 + 3i)(7 - 3i) = 35 - 15i + 21i - 9i^2$
$= 35 + 6i - 9(-1)$
$= 35 + 6i + 9 = 44 + 6i$

36. $81x^4 - 1 = \left(9x^2 + 1\right)\left(9x^2 - 1\right)$
$= \left(9x^2 + 1\right)(3x + 1)(3x - 1)$

37. $24x^3 - 22x^2 + 4x = 2x\left(12x^2 - 11x + 2\right)$
$= 2x(4x - 1)(3x - 2)$

38. $x^3 + 27y^3 = (x + 3y)\left(x^2 - 3xy + 9y^2\right)$

39. $(f - g)(x) = f(x) - g(x)$
$= \left(x^2 + 3x - 15\right) - (x - 2)$
$= x^2 + 3x - 15 - x + 2$
$= x^2 + 2x - 13$
$(f - g)(5) = 5^2 + 2(5) - 13$
$= 25 + 10 - 13 = 22$

40. $\left(\dfrac{f}{g}\right)(x) = \dfrac{f(x)}{g(x)} = \dfrac{x^2 + 3x - 15}{x - 2}$
$= \dfrac{(x+5)\cancel{(x-2)}}{\cancel{x-2}} = x + 5$

Domain of $\dfrac{f}{g}$ must exclude all numbers that will make the denominator of the function zero. Domain of $\dfrac{f}{g}$ is $\{x \mid x \text{ is a real number and } x \neq 2\}$.

41. $f(g(x)) = f(x - 2)$
$= (x - 2)^2 + 3(x - 2) - 15$
$= x^2 - 4x + 4 + 3x - 6 - 15$
$= x^2 - x - 17$

706

42.
$$g\big(f(x)\big) = f\big(x^2 + 3x - 15\big)$$
$$= \big(x^2 + 3x - 15\big) - 2$$
$$= x^2 + 3x - 15 - 2$$
$$= x^2 + 3x - 17$$

43.
$$f(x) = 7x - 3$$
$$y = 7x - 3$$
Interchange x and y.
$$x = 7y - 3$$
$$x + 3 = 7y$$
$$\frac{x+3}{7} = y$$
$$f^{-1}(x) = \frac{x+3}{7}$$

44.
$$d = \sqrt{\big(6-(-3)\big)^2 + \big(-1-(-4)\big)^2}$$
$$= \sqrt{9^2 + 3^2} = \sqrt{81+9} = \sqrt{90}$$
$$= \sqrt{9 \cdot 10} = 3\sqrt{10}$$

45.

$$
\begin{array}{r|rrrr}
-2 & 3 & -1 & 4 & 8 \\
   &   & -6 & 14 & -36 \\
\hline
   & 3 & -7 & 18 & -28
\end{array}
$$

$$\big(3x^3 - x^2 + 4x + 8\big) \div (x+2)$$
$$= 3x^2 - 7x + 18 - \frac{28}{x+2}$$

46.
$$A = \frac{5r+2}{t}$$
$$At = 5r + 2$$
$$t = \frac{5r+2}{A}$$

47.
$$3x + y = 9$$
$$y = -3x + 9$$
Since the lines are parallel, the slope is -3.
$$y - 5 = -3\big(x - (-2)\big)$$
$$y - 5 = -3(x+2)$$
$$y - 5 = -3x - 6$$
$$y = -3x - 1$$

48.
$$\begin{vmatrix} -2 & -4 \\ 5 & 7 \end{vmatrix} = -2(7) - 5(-4)$$
$$= -14 + 20 = 6$$

49.
$$2\ln x - \frac{1}{2}\ln y = \ln x^2 - \ln y^{\frac{1}{2}} = \ln \frac{x^2}{y^{\frac{1}{2}}} = \ln \frac{x^2}{\sqrt{y}}$$

50.
$$\sum_{i=2}^{5} \big(i^3 - 4\big)$$
$$= \big(2^3 - 4\big) + \big(3^3 - 4\big) + \big(4^3 - 4\big) + \big(5^3 - 4\big)$$
$$= (8-4) + (27-4) + (64-4) + (125-4)$$
$$= 4 + 23 + 60 + 121 = 208$$

51.
$$d = 6 - 2 = 4$$
$$a_{30} = 2 + (30-1)4 = 2 + (29)4$$
$$= 2 + 116 = 118$$
$$S_{30} = \frac{30}{2}(2 + 118) = 15(120) = 1800$$

52.
$$0.\overline{6} = \frac{a_1}{1-r} = \frac{\frac{3}{10}}{1 - \frac{1}{10}} = \frac{\frac{3}{10}}{\frac{9}{10}} = \frac{3}{10} \cdot \frac{10}{9} = \frac{1}{3}$$

53.
$$\big(2x - y^3\big)^4 = \binom{4}{0}(2x)^4 + \binom{4}{1}(2x)^3\big(-y^3\big) + \binom{4}{2}(2x)^2\big(-y^3\big)^2 + \binom{4}{3}2x\big(-y^3\big)^3 + \binom{4}{4}\big(-y^3\big)^4$$

$$= \frac{4!}{0!(4-0)!}16x^4 - \frac{4!}{1!(4-1)!}8x^3y^3 + \frac{4!}{2!(4-2)!}4x^2y^6 - \frac{4!}{3!(4-3)!}2xy^9 + \frac{4!}{4!(4-4)!}y^{12}$$

$$= \frac{\cancel{4!}}{0!\,\cancel{4!}}16x^4 - \frac{4!}{1!3!}8x^3y^3 + \frac{4!}{2!2!}4x^2y^6 - \frac{4!}{3!1!}2xy^9 + \frac{\cancel{4!}}{\cancel{4!}0!}y^{12}$$

$$= 1\big(16x^4\big) - \frac{4 \cdot \cancel{3!}}{1 \cdot \cancel{3!}}8x^3y^3 + \frac{4 \cdot 3 \cdot \cancel{2!}}{2 \cdot 1 \cdot \cancel{2!}}4x^2y^6 - \frac{4 \cdot \cancel{3!}}{\cancel{3!} \cdot 1}2xy^9 + y^{12}$$

$$= 16x^4 - 4\big(8x^3y^3\big) + 6\big(4x^2y^6\big) - 4\big(2xy^9\big) + y^{12} = 16x^4 - 32x^3y^3 + 24x^2y^6 - 8xy^9 + y^{12}$$

54. $f(x) = \dfrac{x-2}{x^2-3x+2} = \dfrac{x-2}{(x-2)(x-1)}$

The domain of f is $\{x \mid x$ is a real number and $x \neq 1$ and $x \neq 2\}$.

55. $f(x) = \ln(2x-8)$

$2x-8 > 0$

$\quad 2x > 8$

$\quad\quad x > 4$

The domain of f is $\{x \mid x$ is a real number and $x > 4\}$.

56. Let x = the original price of the computer

$x - 0.30x = 434$

$\quad 0.70x = 434$

$\quad\quad x = \dfrac{434}{0.70}$

$\quad\quad x = 620$

The original price of the computer is $620.

57. Let x = the width of the rectangle

$3x + 1$ = the length of the rectangle

$x(3x+1) = 52$

$3x^2 + x = 52$

$3x^2 + x - 52 = 0$

$(3x+13)(x-4) = 0$

$3x + 13 = 0 \quad$ or $\quad x - 4 = 0$

$3x = -13 \quad\quad\quad\quad x = 4$

$x = \cancel{-\dfrac{13}{3}}$

We disregard $-\dfrac{13}{3}$ because we cannot have a negative length measurement. The width is 4 yards and the length is $3x + 1 = 3(4) + 1 = 12 + 1 = 13$ yards. The rectangle's dimensions are 4 yards by 13 yards.

58. Let x = the amount invested at 12%

Let y = the amount invested at 14%

$x + y = 4000$

$0.12x + 0.14y = 508$

Solve for y in the first equation.

$x + y = 4000$

$\quad y = 4000 - x$

Substitute $4000 - x$ for y in the second equation and solve for x.

$0.12x + 0.14(4000 - x) = 508$

$0.12x + 560 - 0.14x = 508$

$560 - 0.02x = 508$

$-0.02x = -52$

$x = 2600$

Back-substitute 2600 for x to find y.

$y = 4000 - x = 4000 - 2600 = 1400$

$2600 was invested at 12% and $1400 was invested at 14%.

59. $\quad\quad A = Pe^{rt}$

$18000 = 6000e^{r(10)}$

$\quad\quad 3 = e^{10r}$

$\quad \ln 3 = \ln e^{10r}$

$1.0986 = 10r$

$0.110 \approx r$

An interest rate of approximately 11% is required.

60. $i = \dfrac{k}{R}$

Use $R = 22$ and $i = 5$ to find k.

$5 = \dfrac{k}{22}$

$110 = k$

The equation becomes $i = \dfrac{110}{R}$.

$i = \dfrac{110}{10} = 11$

When the resistance is 10 ohms, 11 amperes of current is needed.